MW00605311

BIG IDEAS MATH 8®

VIRGINIA EDITION

Ron Larson
Laurie Boswell

Erie, Pennsylvania
BigIdeasLearning.com

Big Ideas Learning, LLC
1762 Norcross Road
Erie, PA 16510-3838
USA

For product information and customer support, contact Big Ideas Learning at **1-877-552-7766** or visit us at ***BigIdeasLearning.com***.

Printed in the U.S.A.

ISBN 13: 978-1-60840-171-0
ISBN 10: 1-60840-171-5

3 4 5 6 7 8 9 10 WEB 14 13 12 11

AUTHORS

Ron Larson is a professor of mathematics at Penn State Erie, The Behrend College, where he has taught since receiving his Ph.D. in mathematics from the University of Colorado in 1970. Dr. Larson is well known as the lead author of a comprehensive program for mathematics that spans middle school, high school, and college courses. His high school and Advanced Placement books are published by Holt McDougal. Ron's numerous professional activities keep him in constant touch with the needs of students, teachers, and supervisors. Ron and Laurie Boswell began writing together in 1992. Since that time, they have authored over two dozen textbooks. In their collaboration, Ron is primarily responsible for the pupil edition and Laurie is primarily responsible for the teaching edition of the text.

Laurie Boswell is the Head of School and a mathematics teacher at the Riverside School in Lyndonville, Vermont. Dr. Boswell received her Ed.D. from the University of Vermont in 2010. She is a recipient of the Presidential Award for Excellence in Mathematics Teaching. Laurie has taught math to students at all levels, elementary through college. In addition, Laurie was a Tandy Technology Scholar, and served on the NCTM Board of Directors from 2002 to 2005. She currently serves on the board of NCSM, and is a popular national speaker. Along with Ron, Laurie has co-authored numerous math programs.

ABOUT THE BOOK

This book is brand new! It is not a revision of a previously published book.

When the NCTM released its new *Curriculum Focal Points* for mathematics for grades 6–8, we were delighted. The traditional mile-wide and inch-deep programs that have been followed for years have clearly not worked. Middle school students need something new . . . fewer topics with deeper coverage.

- **DEEPER** Each section is designed for 2–3 day coverage.
- **DYNAMIC** Each section begins with a full class period of active learning.
- **DOABLE** Each section is accompanied by full student and teacher support.
- **DAZZLING** How else can we say this? This book puts the dazzle back in math!

Ron Larson   Laurie Boswell

TEACHER REVIEWERS

- Gail Englert
  Math Department Chairperson
  Norfolk Public Schools
  Norfolk, VA

- J. Patrick Lintner
  Mathematics Supervisor
  Harrisonburg City Public Schools
  Harrisonburg, VA

- Jamie Rosati Perkins
  Middle School Mathematics Coach
  Henrico County Public Schools
  Richmond, VA

- Dianne Schoonover
  Secondary Math Teacher Specialist
  Hampton City Schools
  Hampton, VA

- Bill Setzer
  Retired Mathematics Supervisor
  Roanoke County Schools
  Salem, VA

- Beth Swain
  Mathematics Coordinator
  Salem City Schools
  Salem, VA

- Denise Walston
  Mathematics Coordinator
  Norfolk Public Schools
  Norfolk, VA

STUDENT REVIEWERS

- Ashley Benovic
- Vanessa Bowser
- Sara Chinsky
- Kaitlyn Grimm
- Lakota Noble
- Norhan Omar
- Jack Puckett
- Abby Quinn
- Victoria Royal
- Madeline Su
- Lance Williams

CONSULTANTS

Patsy Davis
Educational Consultant
Knoxville, Tennessee

Bob Fulenwider
Mathematics Consultant
Bakersfield, California

Deb Johnson
Differentiated Instruction Consultant
Missoula, Montana

Mark Johnson
Mathematics Assessment Consultant
Raymond, New Hampshire

Ryan Keating
Special Education Advisor
Gilbert, Arizona

Michael McDowell
Project-Based Instruction Specialist
Scottsdale, Arizona

Sean McKeighan
Interdisciplinary Advisor
Midland, Texas

Bonnie Spence
Differentiated Instruction Consultant
Missoula, Montana

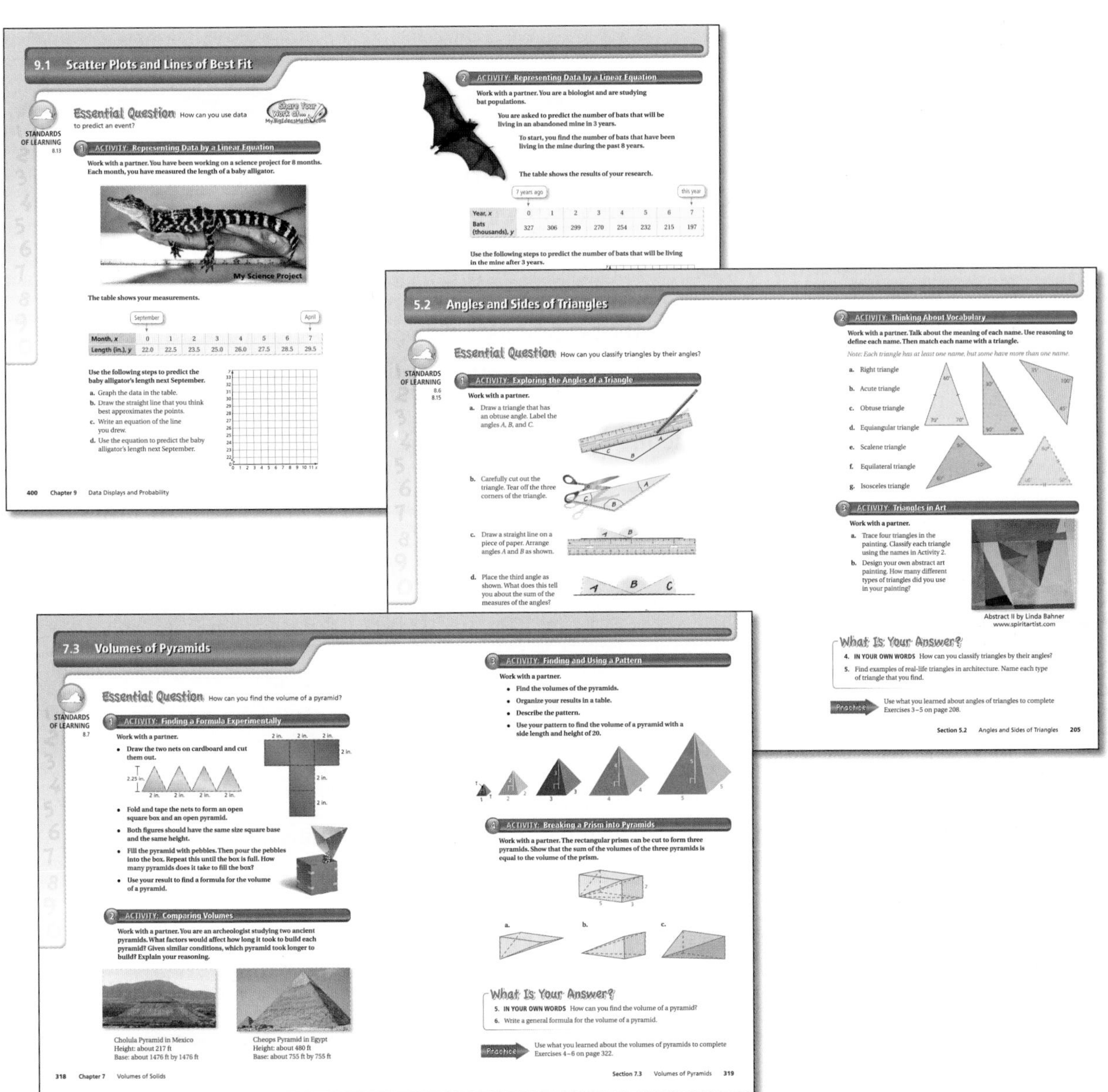

Virginia Standards of Learning for Grade 8

Chapter Coverage for Content Strands

1 2 3 4 5 6 7 8 9 10

Strand Number and Number Sense

Focus: Relationships within the Real Number System

Standards of Learning

8.1 The student will **(a)** simplify numerical expressions involving positive exponents, using rational numbers, order of operations, and properties of operations with real numbers; and **(b)** compare and order decimals, fractions, percents, and numbers written in scientific notation.

8.2 The student will describe orally and in writing the relationships between the subsets of the real number system.

Strand Computation and Estimation

Focus: Practical Applications of Operations with Rational Numbers

Standards of Learning

8.3 The student will **(a)** solve practical problems involving rational numbers, percents, ratios, and proportions; and **(b)** determine the percent increase or decrease for a given situation.

8.4 The student will apply the order of operations to evaluate algebraic expressions for given replacement values of the variables.

8.5 The student will **(a)** determine whether a given number is a perfect square; and **(b)** find the two consecutive whole numbers between which a square root lies.

Strand Measurement

Focus: Problem Solving

Standards of Learning

8.6 The student will **(a)** verify by measuring and describe the relationships among vertical angles, adjacent angles, supplementary angles, and complementary angles; and **(b)** measure angles of less than 360°.

8.7 The student will **(a)** investigate and solve practical problems involving volume and surface area of prisms, cylinders, cones, and pyramids; and **(b)** describe how changing one measured attribute of a figure affects the volume and surface area.

1 2 3 4 5 6 7 8 9 10

Strand Geometry

Focus: Problem Solving with 2- and 3-Dimensional Figures

Standards of Learning

8.8 The student will **(a)** apply transformations to plane figures; and **(b)** identify applications of transformations.

8.9 The student will construct a three-dimensional model, given the top or bottom, side, and front views.

8.10 The student will **(a)** verify the Pythagorean Theorem; and **(b)** apply the Pythagorean Theorem.

8.11 The student will solve practical area and perimeter problems involving composite plane figures.

1 2 3 4 5 6 7 8 9 10

Strand Probability and Statistics

Focus: Statistical Analysis of Graphs and Problem Situations

Standards of Learning

8.12 The student will determine the probability of independent and dependent events with and without replacement.

8.13 The student will **(a)** make comparisons, predictions, and inferences, using information displayed in graphs; and **(b)** construct and analyze scatterplots.

1 2 3 4 5 6 7 8 9 10

Strand Patterns, Functions, and Algebra

Focus: Linear Relationships

Standards of Learning

8.14 The student will make connections between any two representations (tables, graphs, words, and rules) of a given relationship.

8.15 The student will **(a)** solve multistep linear equations in one variable with the variable on one and two sides of the equation; **(b)** solve two-step linear inequalities and graph the results on a number line; and **(c)** identify properties of operations used to solve an equation.

8.16 The student will graph a linear equation in two variables.

8.17 The student will identify the domain, range, independent variable, or dependent variable in a given situation.

Solving Equations and Inequalities

"I love my math book. It has so many interesting examples and homework problems. I have always liked math, but I didn't know how it could be used. Now I have lots of ideas."

Graphing and Writing Linear Equations

"I like starting each new lesson with a partner activity. I just moved to this school and the activities helped me make friends."

Functions

"I like having the book on the Internet. The online tutorials help me with my homework when I get stuck on a problem."

4

Percents

"I love the cartoons. They are funny and they help me remember the math. I want to be a cartoonist some day."

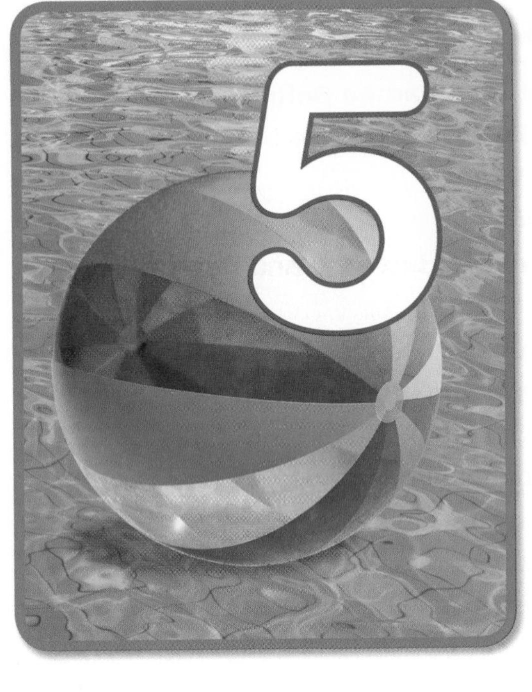
5

Angles and Polygons

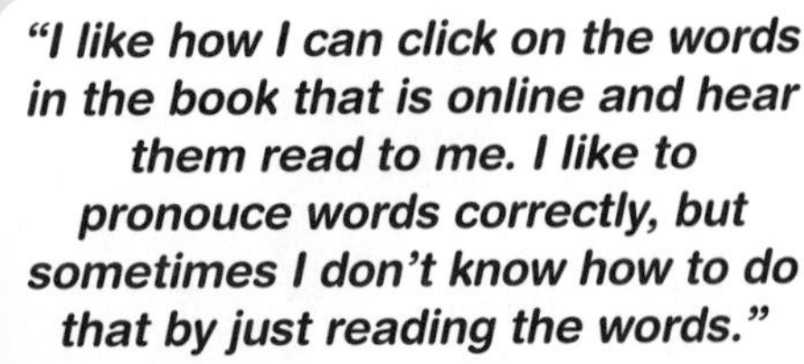
"I like how I can click on the words in the book that is online and hear them read to me. I like to pronouce words correctly, but sometimes I don't know how to do that by just reading the words."

Surface Areas of Solids

"I really liked the projects at the end of the book. The history project on ancient Egypt was my favorite. Someday I would like to visit Egypt and go to the pyramids."

Volumes of Solids

"I like how the glossary in the book is part of the index. When I couldn't remember how a vocabulary word was defined, I could go to the index and find where the word was defined in the book."

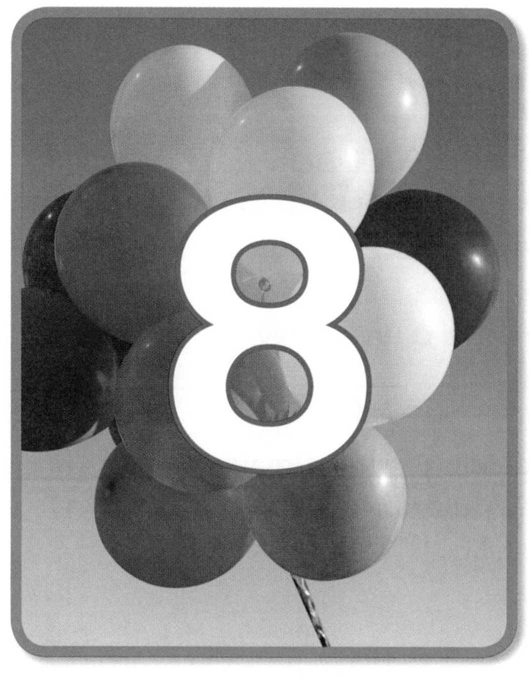

Square Roots and the Pythagorean Theorem

"I like the practice tests in the book. I get really nervous on tests. So, having a practice test to work on at home helped me to chill out when the real test came."

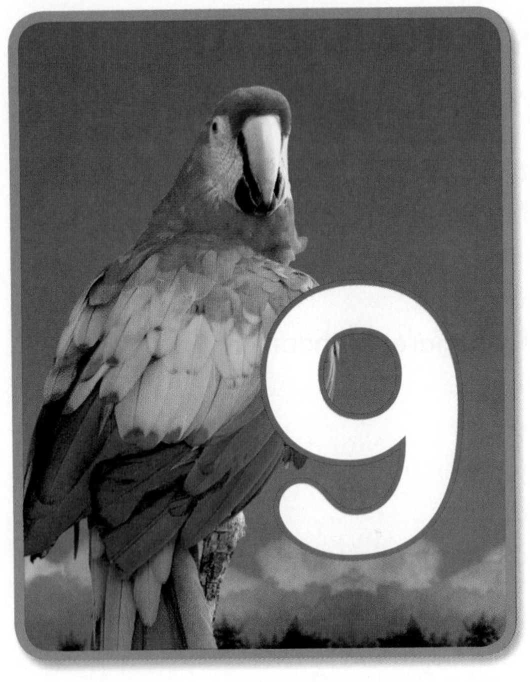

Data Displays and Probability

"I like the review at the beginning of each chapter. This book has examples to help me remember things from last year. I don't like it when the review is just a list of questions."

"I like the workbook (Record and Practice Journal). It saved me a lot of work to not have to copy all the questions and graphs."

Exponents and Scientific Notation

Appendix A: My Big Ideas Projects

How to Use Your Math Book

- Read the **Essential Question** in the activity.

  Work with a partner to decide **What Is Your Answer?**

  Now you are ready to do the **Practice** problems.

- Find the **Key Vocabulary** words, **highlighted in yellow**.

  Read their definitions. Study the concepts in each **Key Idea**.
  If you forget a definition, you can look it up online in the

  Multi-Language Glossary at BigIdeasMath.com.

- After you study each **EXAMPLE**, do the exercises in the **On Your Own**.

  Now You're Ready to do the exercises that correspond to the example.

  As you study, look for a 

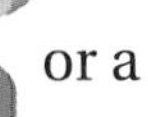 or a **Common Error** .

- The exercises are divided into 3 parts.

   Vocabulary and Concept Check

   Practice and Problem Solving

   Fair Game Review

  If an exercise has a 1 next to it, look back at Example 1 for help with that exercise.

  More help is available at 
.

- To help study for your test, use the following.

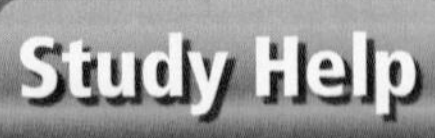

Chapter Review **Chapter Test**

SCAVENGER HUNT

Use this *Scavenger Hunt* to find where things are in **Chapter 1**.

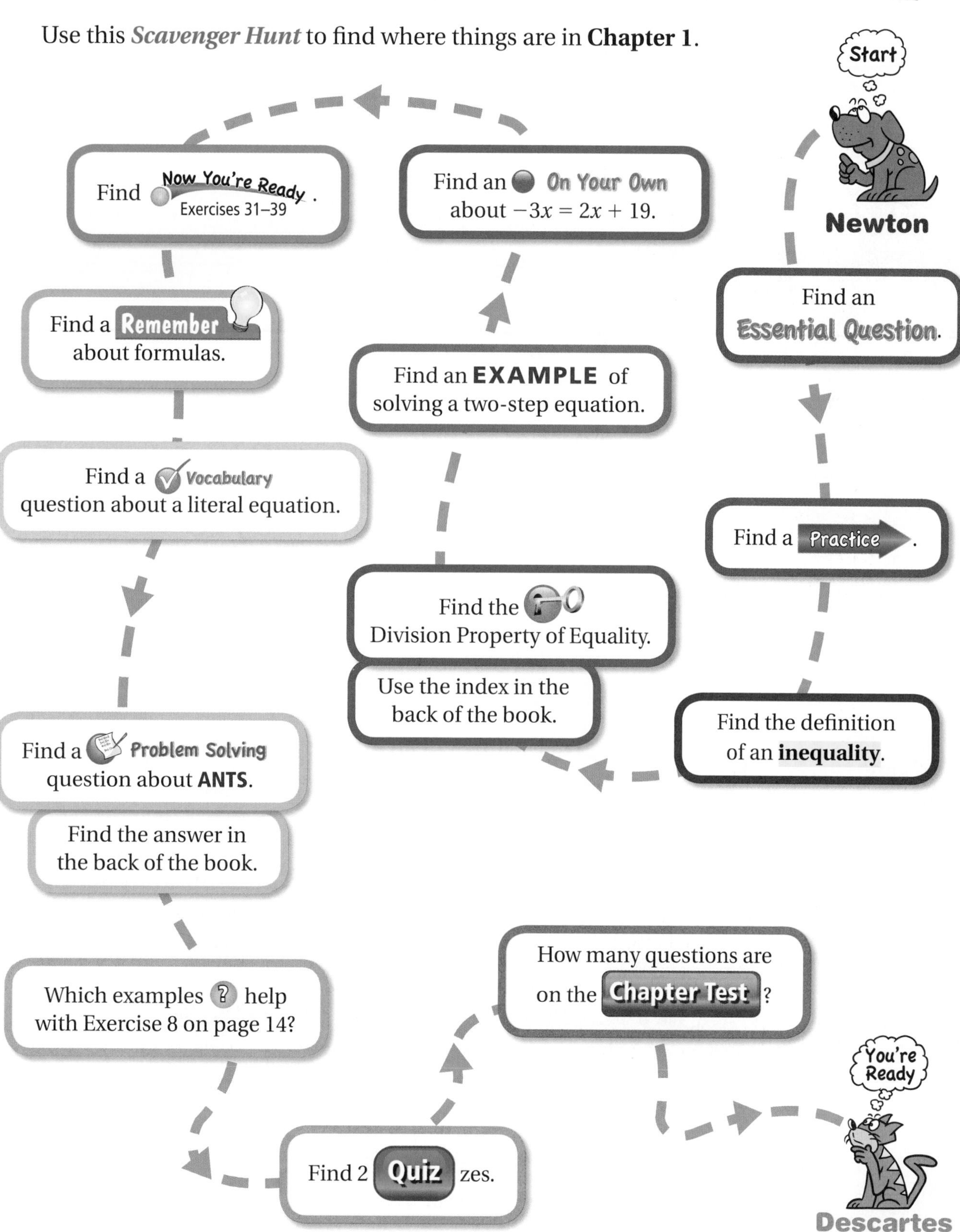

Start
Newton
Find an Essential Question.
Find a Practice.
Find the definition of an **inequality**.
Find the Division Property of Equality.
Use the index in the back of the book.
Find an EXAMPLE of solving a two-step equation.
Find an On Your Own about $-3x = 2x + 19$.
Find Now You're Ready Exercises 31–39.
Find a Remember about formulas.
Find a Vocabulary question about a literal equation.
Find a Problem Solving question about **ANTS**.
Find the answer in the back of the book.
Which examples help with Exercise 8 on page 14?
Find 2 Quizzes.
How many questions are on the Chapter Test?
You're Ready
Descartes

1 Solving Equations and Inequalities

< ≤
That's easy. One just means I am happy.
The other means that I have a piece of spaghetti stuck between my fangs.

"Here is a math quiz, Descartes. Tell me about these symbols."

YOU
FLUFFY
<

"Just think of the Addition Property of Inequality in this way. If Fluffy has more cat treats than you have ..."

YOU
FLUF
<
This guy really knows how to hurt a cat, doesn't he?

"... and you each get 2 more cat treats, then Fluffy will STILL have more cat treats than you have!"

What You Learned Before

"Some people remember which is bigger by thinking that < is the mouth of a hungry alligator who is trying to eat the LARGER number."

Simplifying Algebraic Expressions

Example 1 **Simplify $10b + 13 - 6b + 4$.**

$10b + 13 - 6b + 4 = 10b - 6b + 13 + 4$	Commutative Property of Addition
$= (10 - 6)b + 13 + 4$	Distributive Property
$= 4b + 17$	Simplify.

Example 2 **Simplify $5(x + 4) + 2x$.**

$5(x + 4) + 2x = 5(x) + 5(4) + 2x$	Distributive Property
$= 5x + 20 + 2x$	Multiply.
$= 5x + 2x + 20$	Commutative Property of Addition
$= (5 + 2)x + 20$	Distributive Property
$= 7x + 20$	Add coefficients.

Try It Yourself

Simplify the expression.

1. $9m - 7m + 2m$ **2.** $3g - 9 + 11g - 21$ **3.** $6(3 - y)$

4. $12(a - 4)$ **5.** $22.5 + 7(n - 3.4)$ **6.** $15k + 8(11 - k)$

Writing Reciprocals

Example 3 **Write the reciprocal of the number.**

	Original Number	*Fraction*	*Reciprocal*	*Check*
a.	$\frac{2}{3}$	$\frac{2}{3}$	$\frac{3}{2}$	$\frac{2}{3} \times \frac{3}{2} = 1$
b.	6	$\frac{6}{1}$	$\frac{1}{6}$	$\frac{6}{1} \times \frac{1}{6} = 1$
c.	$-\frac{5}{7}$	$-\frac{5}{7}$	$-\frac{7}{5}$	$-\frac{5}{7} \times \left(-\frac{7}{5}\right) = 1$

Try It Yourself

Write the reciprocal of the number.

7. $\frac{3}{7}$ **8.** 4 **9.** $\frac{11}{21}$ **10.** $-\frac{4}{13}$

1.1 Solving Simple Equations

STANDARDS OF LEARNING
8.15

Essential Question How can you use inductive reasoning to discover rules in mathematics? How can you test a rule?

1 ACTIVITY: Sum of the Angles of a Triangle

Work with a partner. Copy the triangles. Use a protractor to measure the angles of each triangle. Copy and complete the table to organize your results.

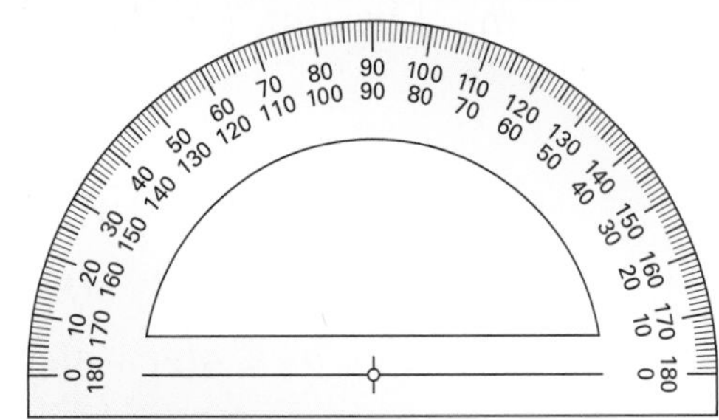

a.

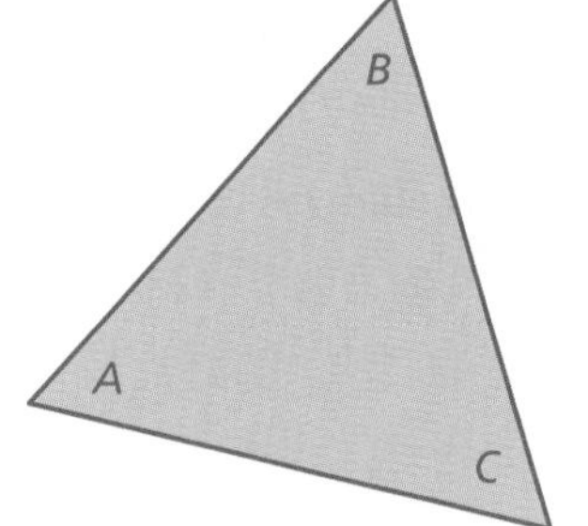

b.

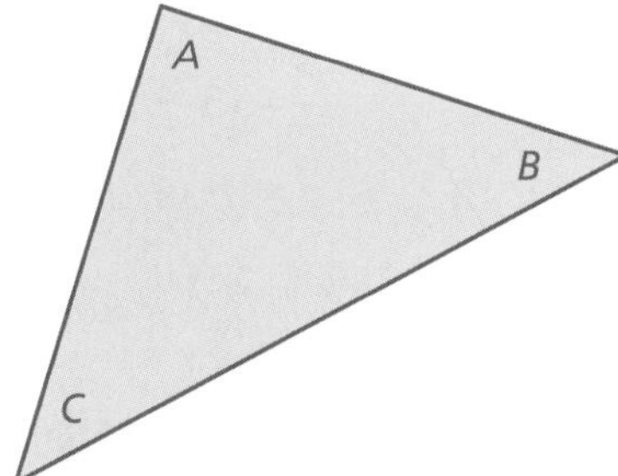

c.

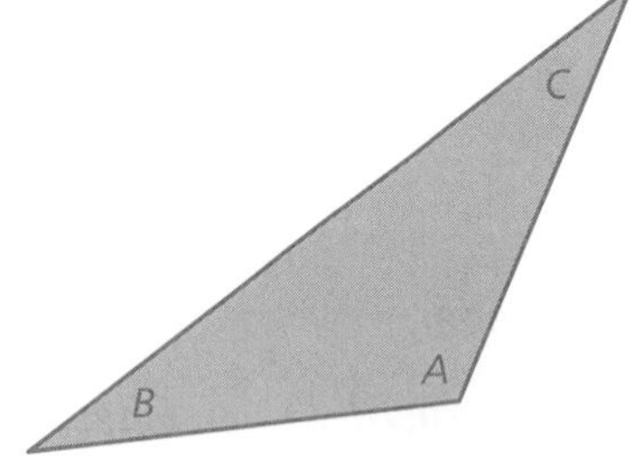

d.

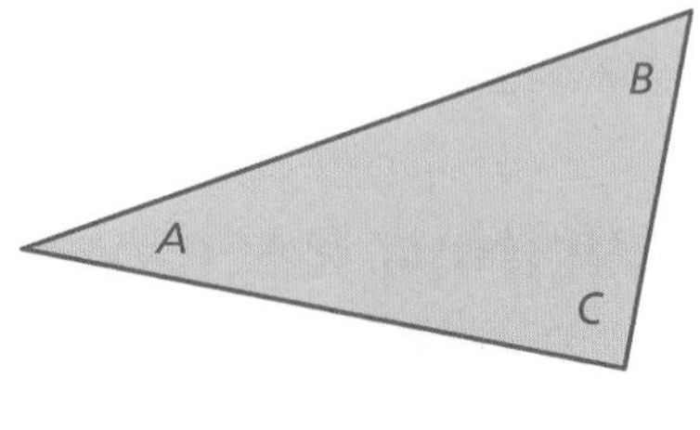

Triangle	Angle A (degrees)	Angle B (degrees)	Angle C (degrees)	$A + B + C$
a.				
b.				
c.				
d.				

2 ACTIVITY: Writing a Rule

Work with a partner. Use inductive reasoning to write and test a rule.

a. Use the completed table in Activity 1 to write a rule about the sum of the angle measures of a triangle.

b. **TEST YOUR RULE** Draw four triangles that are different from those in Activity 1. Measure the angles of each triangle. Organize your results in a table. Find the sum of the angle measures of each triangle.

3 ACTIVITY: Applying Your Rule

Work with a partner. Use the rule you wrote in Activity 2 to write an equation for each triangle. Then, solve the equation to find the value of *x*. Use a protractor to check the reasonableness of your answer.

a.

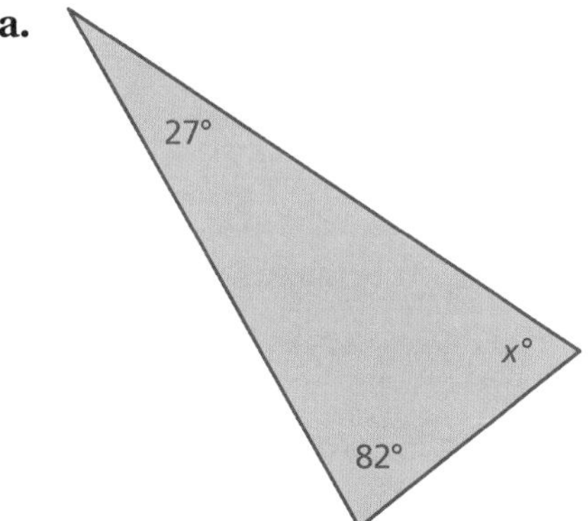

b.

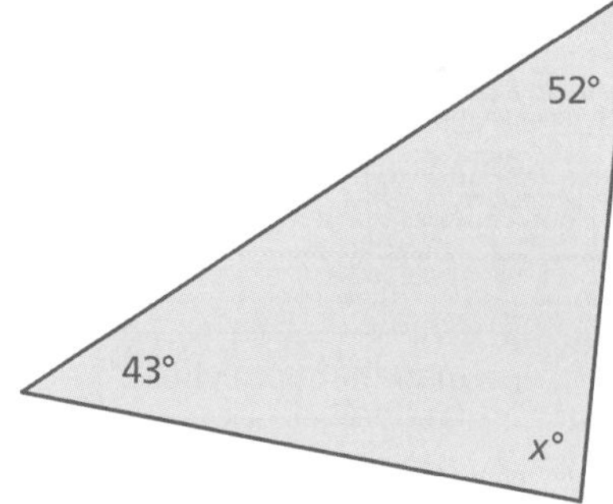

c.

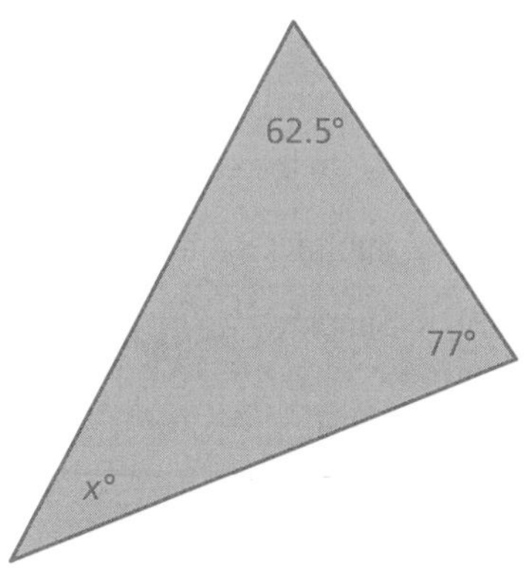

d.

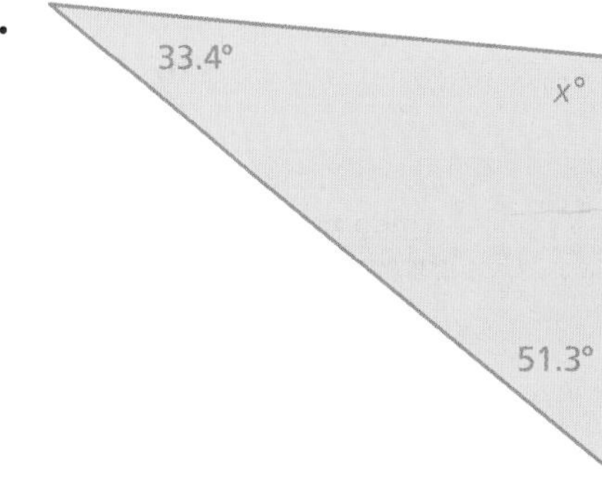

What Is Your Answer?

4. **IN YOUR OWN WORDS** How can you use inductive reasoning to discover rules in mathematics? How can you test a rule? How can you use a rule to solve problems in mathematics?

Practice Use what you learned about solving simple equations to complete Exercises 4–6 on page 7.

1.1 Lesson

Addition and subtraction are inverse operations.

Key Ideas

Addition Property of Equality

Words Adding the same number to each side of an equation produces an equivalent equation.

Algebra If $a = b$, then $a + c = b + c$.

Subtraction Property of Equality

Words Subtracting the same number from each side of an equation produces an equivalent equation.

Algebra If $a = b$, then $a - c = b - c$.

EXAMPLE 1 Solving Equations Using Addition or Subtraction

a. Solve $x - 7 = -6$.

	$x - 7 = -6$	Write the equation.
Undo the subtraction. →	$\underline{+7} \quad \underline{+7}$	Add 7 to each side.
	$x = 1$	Simplify.

The solution is $x = 1$.

Check

$x - 7 = -6$

$1 - 7 \stackrel{?}{=} -6$

$-6 = -6$ ✓

b. Solve $y + 3.4 = 0.5$.

	$y + 3.4 = 0.5$	Write the equation.
Undo the addition. →	$\underline{-3.4} \quad \underline{-3.4}$	Subtract 3.4 from each side.
	$y = -2.9$	Simplify.

The solution is $y = -2.9$.

Check

$y + 3.4 = 0.5$

$-2.9 + 3.4 \stackrel{?}{=} 0.5$

$0.5 = 0.5$ ✓

c. Solve $h + 2\pi = 3\pi$.

	$h + 2\pi = 3\pi$	Write the equation.
Undo the addition. →	$\underline{-2\pi} \quad \underline{-2\pi}$	Subtract 2π from each side.
	$h = \pi$	Simplify.

The solution is $h = \pi$.

On Your Own

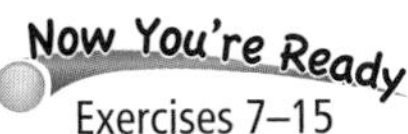

Now You're Ready
Exercises 7–15

Solve the equation. Check your solution.

1. $b + 2 = -5$ **2.** $g - 1.7 = -0.9$ **3.** $-3 = k + 3$

4. $r - \pi = \pi$ **5.** $t - \frac{1}{4} = -\frac{3}{4}$ **6.** $5.6 + z = -8$

Key Ideas

Remember

Multiplication and division are inverse operations.

Multiplication Property of Equality

Words Multiplying each side of an equation by the same number produces an equivalent equation.

Algebra If $a = b$, then $a \cdot c = b \cdot c$.

Division Property of Equality

Words Dividing each side of an equation by the same number produces an equivalent equation.

Algebra If $a = b$, then $a \div c = b \div c$, $c \neq 0$.

EXAMPLE 2 Solving Equations Using Multiplication or Division

a. Solve $-\frac{3}{4}n = -2$.

$-\frac{3}{4}n = -2$ Write the equation.

Use the reciprocal. → $-\frac{4}{3} \cdot \left(-\frac{3}{4}n\right) = -\frac{4}{3} \cdot (-2)$ Multiply each side by $-\frac{4}{3}$, the reciprocal of $-\frac{3}{4}$.

$n = \frac{8}{3}$ Simplify.

∴ The solution is $n = \frac{8}{3}$.

b. Solve $\pi x = 3\pi$.

$\pi x = 3\pi$ Write the equation.

Undo the multiplication. → $\frac{\pi x}{\pi} = \frac{3\pi}{\pi}$ Divide each side by π.

$x = 3$ Simplify.

∴ The solution is $x = 3$.

Check

$\pi x = 3\pi$

$\pi(3) \stackrel{?}{=} 3\pi$

$3\pi = 3\pi$ ✓

On Your Own

Now You're Ready
Exercises 18–26

Solve the equation. Check your solution.

7. $\frac{y}{4} = -7$ **8.** $6\pi = \pi x$ **9.** $0.09w = 1.8$

EXAMPLE 3 Standardized Test Practice

What value of k makes the equation $k + 4 \div 0.2 = 5$ true?

Ⓐ -15 Ⓑ -5 Ⓒ -3 Ⓓ 1.5

$k + 4 \div 0.2 = 5$ Write the equation.

$k + 20 = 5$ Divide 4 by 0.2.

$\underline{-20} \quad \underline{-20}$ Subtract 20 from each side.

$k = -15$ Simplify.

∴ The correct answer is Ⓐ.

EXAMPLE 4 Real-Life Application

The melting point of bromine is −7°C.

The *melting point* of a solid is the temperature at which the solid becomes a liquid. The melting point of bromine is $\frac{1}{30}$ of the melting point of nitrogen. Write and solve an equation to find the melting point of nitrogen.

Words The melting point of bromine is $\frac{1}{30}$ of the melting point of nitrogen.

Variable Let n be the melting point of nitrogen.

Equation $-7 = \frac{1}{30} \cdot n$

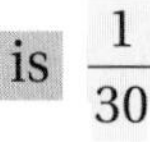

$-7 = \frac{1}{30}n$ Write the equation.

$30 \cdot (-7) = 30 \cdot \left(\frac{1}{30}n\right)$ Multiply each side by 30.

$-210 = n$ Simplify.

∴ The melting point of nitrogen is −210°C.

On Your Own

10. Solve $p - 8 \div \frac{1}{2} = -3$.

11. Solve $q + |-10| = 2$.

12. The melting point of mercury is about $\frac{1}{4}$ of the melting point of krypton. The melting point of mercury is −39°C. Write and solve an equation to find the melting point of krypton.

1.1 Exercises

Vocabulary and Concept Check

1. **VOCABULARY** Which of the operations $+$, $-$, $\times$, and $\div$ are inverses of each other?
2. **VOCABULARY** Are the equations $3x = -9$ and $4x = -12$ equivalent? Explain.
3. **WHICH ONE DOESN'T BELONG?** Which equation does *not* belong with the other three? Explain your reasoning.

$x - 2 = 4$ $\quad$ $x - 3 = 6$ $\quad$ $x - 5 = 1$ $\quad$ $x - 6 = 0$

Practice and Problem Solving

Find the value of x. Use a protractor to check the reasonableness of your answer.

4. 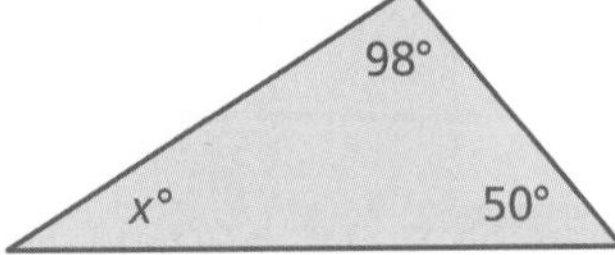

5. 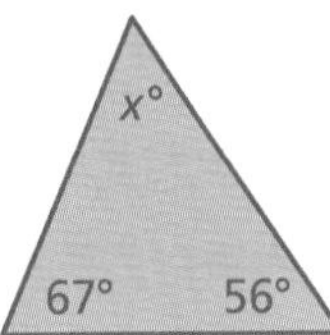

6. 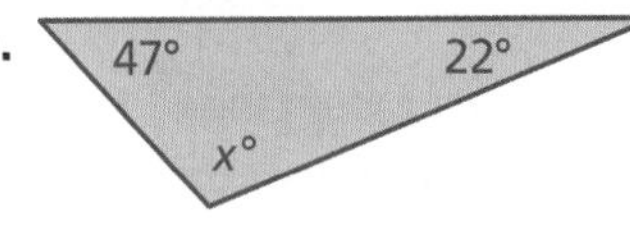

Solve the equation. Check your solution.

(1) 7. $x + 12 = 7$ 8. $g - 16 = 8$ 9. $-9 + p = 12$

10. $0.7 + y = -1.34$ 11. $x - 8\pi = \pi$ 12. $4\pi = w - 6\pi$

13. $\frac{5}{6} = \frac{1}{3} + d$ 14. $\frac{3}{8} = r + \frac{2}{3}$ 15. $n - 1.4 = -6.3$

16. **CONCERT** A discounted concert ticket is \$14.50 less than the original price p. You pay \$53 for a discounted ticket. Write and solve an equation to find the original price.

17. **BOWLING** Your friend's final bowling score is 105. Your final bowling score is 14 pins less than your friend's final score.

a. Write and solve an equation to find your final score.

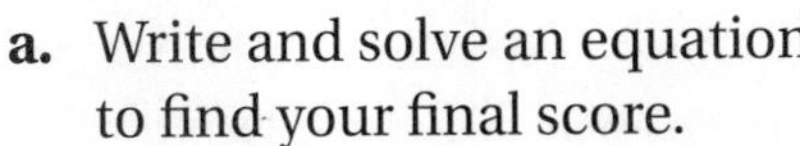

b. Your friend made a spare in the tenth frame. Did you? Explain.

9	10	FINAL SCORE
8 – 89	7 / 6 105	105
6 3 82	9	?

Solve the equation. Check your solution.

2 18. $7x = 35$

19. $4 = -0.8n$

20. $6 = -\frac{w}{8}$

21. $\frac{m}{\pi} = 7.3$

22. $-4.3g = 25.8$

23. $\frac{3}{2} = \frac{9}{10}k$

24. $-7.8x = -1.56$

25. $-2 = \frac{6}{7}p$

26. $3\pi d = 12\pi$

27. **ERROR ANALYSIS** Describe and correct the error in solving the equation.

✗
$-1.5 + k = 8.2$
$k = 8.2 + (-1.5)$
$k = 6.7$

28. **TENNIS** A gym teacher orders 42 tennis balls. Each package contains 3 tennis balls. Which of the following equations represents the number x of packages?

$x + 3 = 42$ $3x = 42$ $\frac{x}{3} = 42$ $x = \frac{3}{42}$

In Exercises 29–32, write and solve an equation to answer the question.

29. **PARK** You clean a community park for 6.5 hours. You earn \$42.25. How much do you earn per hour?

30. **SPACE SHUTTLE** A space shuttle is scheduled to launch from Kennedy Space Center in 3.75 hours. What time is it now?

Launch Time
11:20 A.M.

31. **BANKING** After earning interest, the balance of an account is \$420. The new balance is $\frac{7}{6}$ of the original balance. How much interest was earned?

Tallest Coasters at Cedar Point	
Roller Coaster	**Height (feet)**
Top Thrill Dragster	420
Millennium Force	310
Magnum XL-200	205
Mantis	?

32. **ROLLER COASTER** Cedar Point amusement park has some of the tallest roller coasters in the United States. The Mantis is 165 feet shorter than the Millennium Force. What is the height of the Mantis?

Solve the equation. Check your solution.

3 **33.** $-3 = h + 8 \div 2$

34. $12 = w - |-7|$

35. $q + |6.4| = 9.6$

36. $d - 2.8 \div 0.2 = -14$

37. $\frac{8}{9} = x + \frac{1}{3}(7)$

38. $p - \frac{1}{4} \cdot 3 = -\frac{5}{6}$

39. CRITICAL THINKING Is the solution of $-2x = -15$ *greater than* or *less than* -15? Explain.

40. OPEN-ENDED Write a subtraction equation and a division equation that each has a solution of -2.

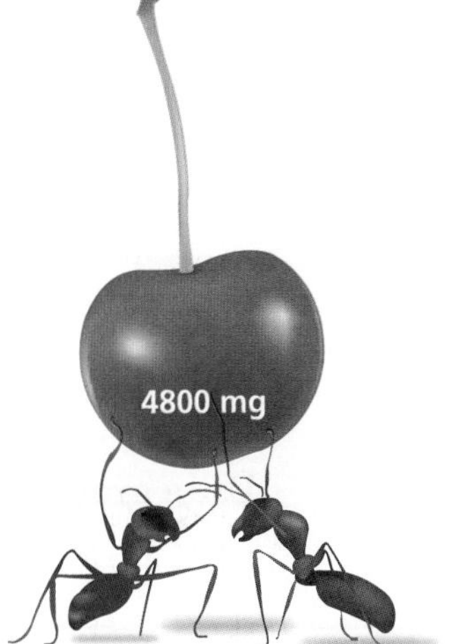

41. ANTS Some ant species can carry 50 times their body weight. It takes 32 ants to carry the cherry. About how much does each ant weigh?

42. PICTURES One-fourth of the girls and one-eighth of the boys in an eighth grade retake their school pictures. The photographer retakes pictures for 16 girls and 7 boys. How many students are in the eighth grade?

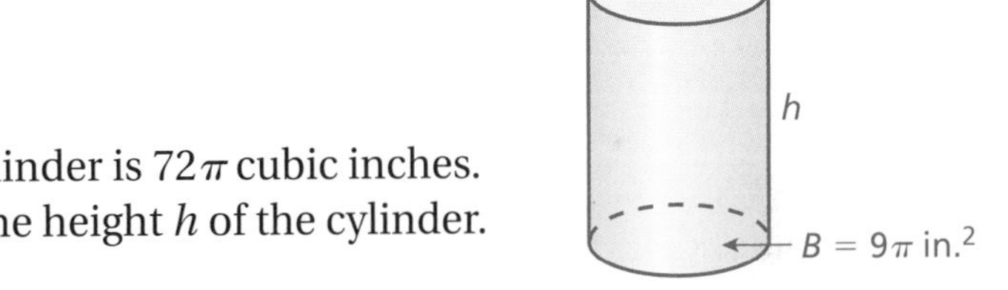

43. VOLUME The volume V of the cylinder is 72π cubic inches. Use the formula $V = Bh$ to find the height h of the cylinder.

h

$B = 9\pi$ in.^{2}

44. Critical Thinking A neighbor pays you and two friends \$90 to paint her garage. The money is divided three ways in the ratio 2 : 3 : 5.

a. How much is each share?

b. What is one possible reason the money is not divided evenly?

Fair Game Review What you learned in previous grades & lessons

Simplify the expression. *(Skills Review Handbook)*

45. $2(x - 2) + 5x$

46. $0.4b - 3.2 + 1.2b$

47. $\frac{1}{4}g + 6g - \frac{2}{3}$

48. MULTIPLE CHOICE The temperature at 4 P.M. was -12 °C. By 11 P.M. the temperature had dropped 14 degrees. What was the temperature at 11 P.M.? *(Skills Review Handbook)*

(A) -26 °C (B) -2 °C (C) 2 °C (D) 26 °C

1.2 Solving Multi-Step Equations

STANDARDS OF LEARNING

8.15

Essential Question How can you solve a multi-step equation? How can you check the reasonableness of your solution?

1 ACTIVITY: Solving for the Angles of a Triangle

Work with a partner. Write an equation for each triangle. Solve the equation to find the value of the variable. Then find the angle measures of each triangle. Use a protractor to check the reasonableness of your answer.

a.

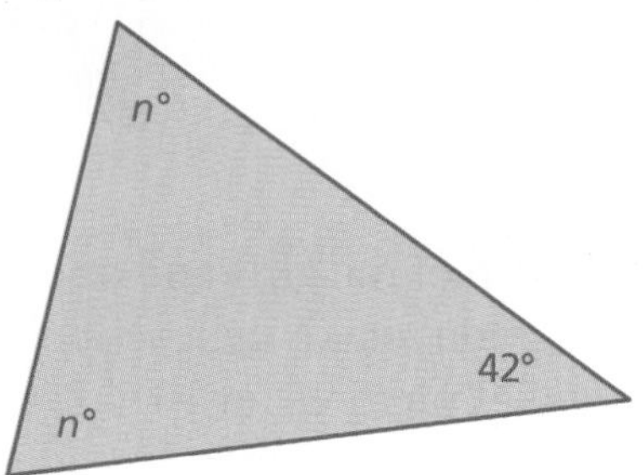

b.

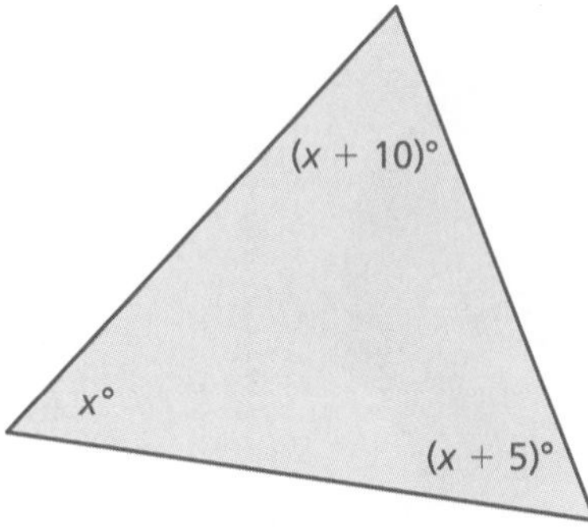

c.

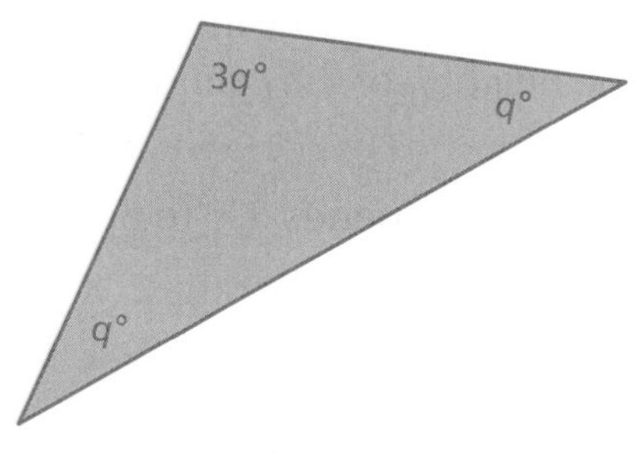

d.

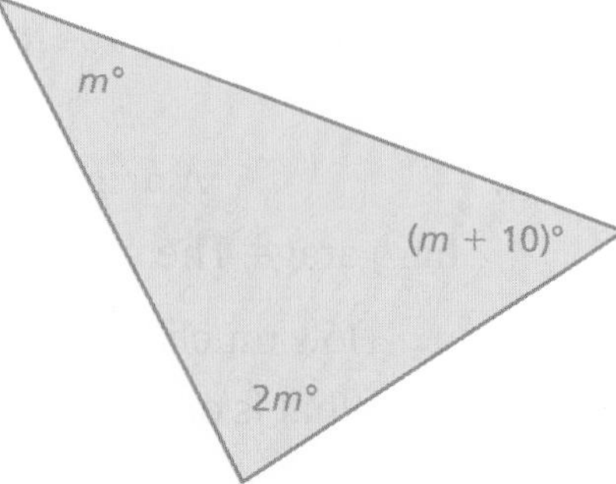

e.

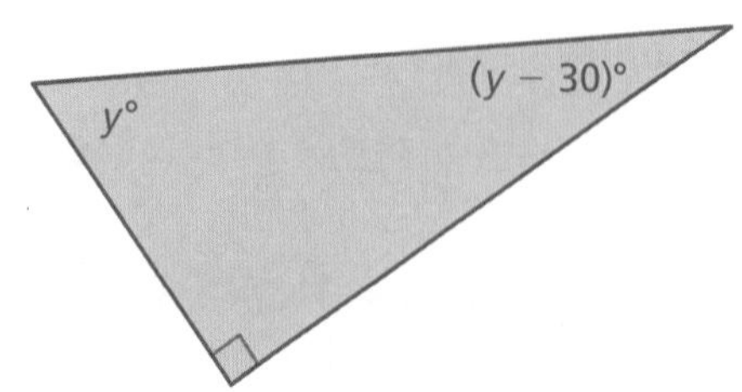

f.

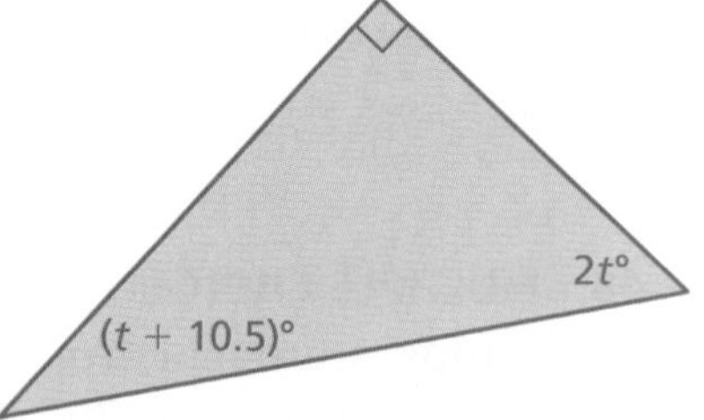

2 ACTIVITY: Problem-Solving Strategy

Work with a partner.

The six triangles form a rectangle.

Find the angle measures of each triangle. Use a protractor to check the reasonableness of your answers.

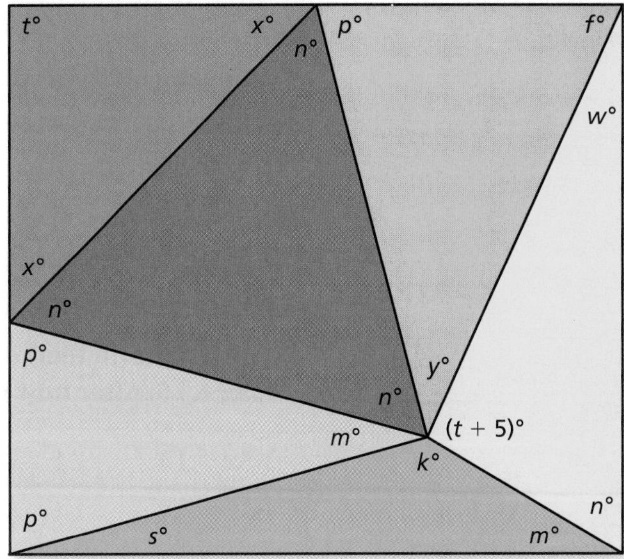

3 ACTIVITY: Puzzle

Work with a partner. A survey asked 200 people to name their favorite weekday. The results are shown in the circle graph.

a. How many degrees are in each part of the circle graph?

b. What percent of the people chose each day?

c. How many people chose each day?

d. Organize your results in a table.

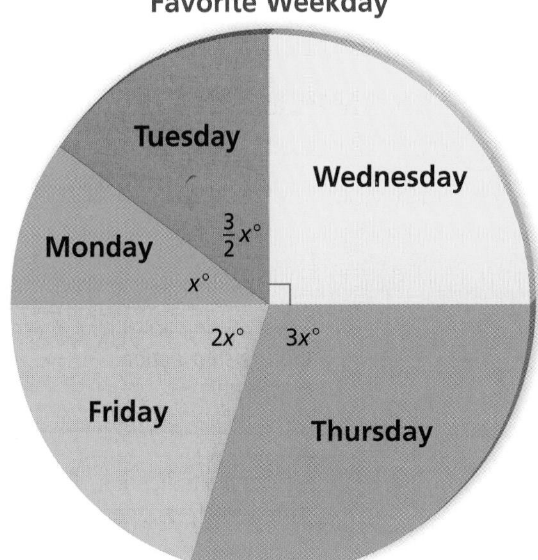

What Is Your Answer?

4. **IN YOUR OWN WORDS** How can you solve a multi-step equation? How can you check the reasonableness of your solution?

Practice Use what you learned about solving multi-step equations to complete Exercises 3–5 on page 14.

1.2 Lesson

Solving Multi-Step Equations

To solve multi-step equations, use inverse operations to isolate the variable.

EXAMPLE 1 Solving a Two-Step Equation

The height (in feet) of a tree after x years is $1.5x + 15$. After how many years is the tree 24 feet tall?

	$1.5x + 15 = 24$	Write an equation.
Undo the addition. →	$\underline{-15} \quad \underline{-15}$	Subtract 15 from each side.
	$1.5x = 9$	Simplify.
Undo the multiplication. →	$\dfrac{1.5x}{1.5} = \dfrac{9}{1.5}$	Divide each side by 1.5.
	$x = 6$	Simplify.

∴ The tree is 24 feet tall after 6 years.

EXAMPLE 2 Combining Like Terms to Solve an Equation

Solve $8x - 6x - 25 = -35$.

	$8x - 6x - 25 = -35$	Write the equation.
	$2x - 25 = -35$	Combine like terms.
Undo the subtraction. →	$\underline{+25} \quad \underline{+25}$	Add 25 to each side.
	$2x = -10$	Simplify.
Undo the multiplication. →	$\dfrac{2x}{2} = \dfrac{-10}{2}$	Divide each side by 2.
	$x = -5$	Simplify.

∴ The solution is $x = -5$.

On Your Own

Now You're Ready
Exercises 6–9

Solve the equation. Check your solution.

1. $-3z + 1 = 7$
2. $\frac{1}{2}x - 9 = -25$
3. $-4n - 8n + 17 = 23$

EXAMPLE 3 Using the Distributive Property to Solve an Equation

Solve $2(1 - 5x) + 4 = -8$.

$2(1 - 5x) + 4 = -8$	Write the equation.
$2(1) - 2(5x) + 4 = -8$	Use Distributive Property.
$2 - 10x + 4 = -8$	Multiply.
$-10x + 6 = -8$	Combine like terms.
$\underline{-6} \quad \underline{-6}$	Subtract 6 from each side.
$-10x = -14$	Simplify.
$\dfrac{-10x}{-10} = \dfrac{-14}{-10}$	Divide each side by −10.
$x = 1.4$	Simplify.

Study Tip

Here is another way to solve the equation in Example 3.

$2(1 - 5x) + 4 = -8$

$2(1 - 5x) = -12$

$1 - 5x = -6$

$-5x = -7$

$x = 1.4$

EXAMPLE 4 Real-Life Application

Use the table to find the number of miles x you need to run on Friday so that the mean number of miles run per day is 1.5.

Day	Miles
Monday	2
Tuesday	0
Wednesday	1.5
Thursday	0
Friday	x

Write an equation using the definition of mean.

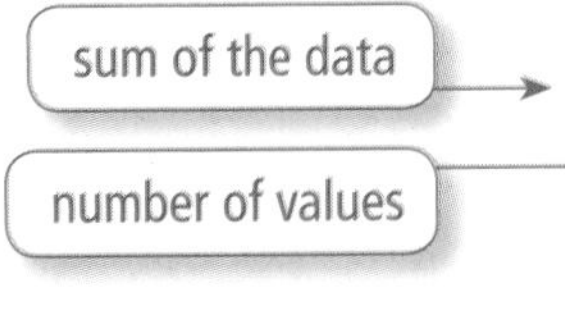

sum of the data / number of values →	$\dfrac{2 + 0 + 1.5 + 0 + x}{5} = 1.5$	Write the equation.
	$\dfrac{3.5 + x}{5} = 1.5$	Combine like terms.
Undo the division. →	$5 \cdot \dfrac{3.5 + x}{5} = 5 \cdot 1.5$	Multiply each side by 5.
	$3.5 + x = 7.5$	Simplify.
Undo the addition. →	$\underline{-3.5} \quad \underline{-3.5}$	Subtract 3.5 from each side.
	$x = 4$	Simplify.

∴ You need to run 4 miles on Friday.

On Your Own

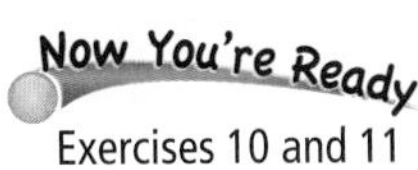

Exercises 10 and 11

Solve the equation. Check your solution.

4. $-3(x + 2) + 5x = -9$
5. $5 + 1.5(2d - 1) = 0.5$
6. You scored 88, 92, and 87 on three tests. Write and solve an equation to find the score you need on the fourth test so that your mean test score is 90.

1.2 Exercises

Vocabulary and Concept Check

1. **WRITING** Write the word sentence as an equation. Then solve.

   2 more than 3 times a number is 17.

2. **OPEN-ENDED** Explain how to solve the equation $2(4x - 11) + 9 = 19$.

Practice and Problem Solving

Find the value of the variable. Then find the angle measures of the polygon. Use a protractor to check the reasonableness of your answer.

3. 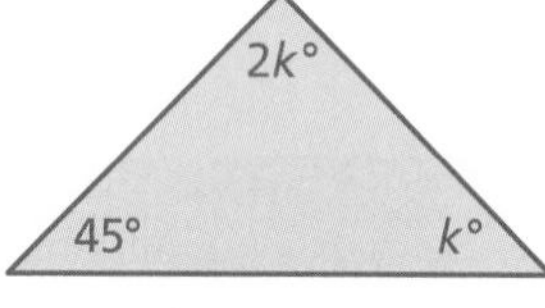

Sum of angle measures: 180°

4. 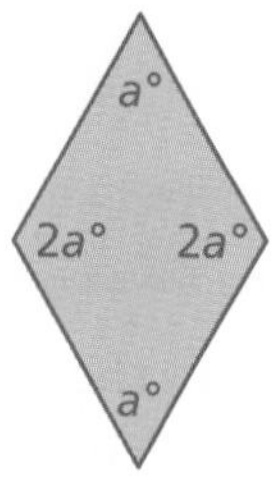

Sum of angle measures: 360°

5. 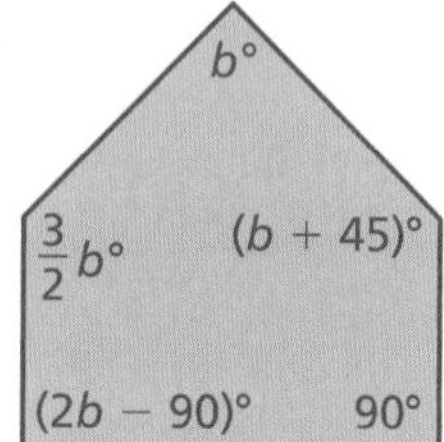

Sum of angle measures: 540°

Solve the equation. Check your solution.

①② 6. $10x + 2 = 32$

7. $19 - 4c = 17$

8. $1.1x + 1.2x - 5.4 = -10$

9. $\frac{2}{3}h - \frac{1}{3}h + 11 = 8$

③ 10. $6(5 - 8v) + 12 = -54$

11. $21(2 - x) + 12x = 44$

12. **ERROR ANALYSIS** Describe and correct the error in solving the equation.

   ✗
   $$-2(7 - y) + 4 = -4$$
   $$-14 - 2y + 4 = -4$$
   $$-10 - 2y = -4$$
   $$-2y = 6$$
   $$y = -3$$

13. **WATCHES** The cost (in dollars) of making n watches is represented by $C = 15n + 85$. How many watches are made when the cost is $385?

14. **HOUSE** The height of the house is 26 feet. What is the height x of each story?

In Exercises 15–17, write and solve an equation to answer the question.

15. **POSTCARD** The area of the postcard is 24 square inches. What is the width b of the message (in inches)?

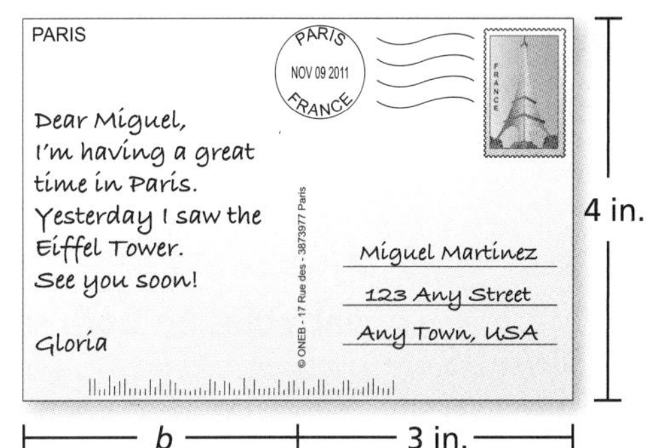

16. **BREAKFAST** You order two servings of pancakes and a fruit cup. The cost of the fruit cup is \$1.50. You leave a 15% tip. Your total bill is \$11.50. How much does one serving of pancakes cost?

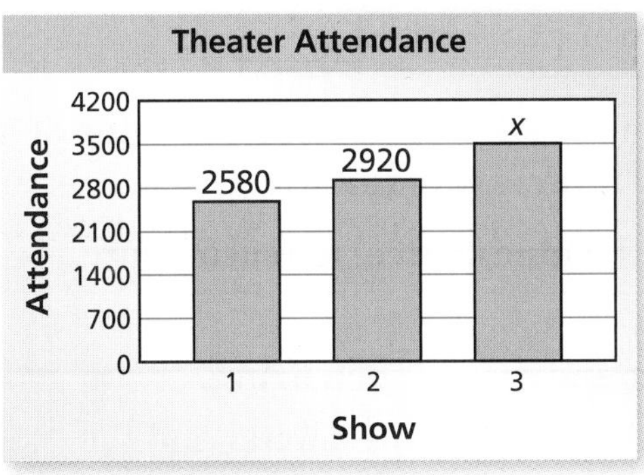

17. **THEATER** How many people must attend the third show so that the average attendance for the three shows is 3000?

18. **DIVING** Olympic divers are scored by an international panel of judges. The highest and lowest scores are dropped. The total of the remaining scores is multiplied by the degree of difficulty of the dive. This product is multiplied by 0.6 to determine the final score.

   a. A diver's final score is 77.7. What is the degree of difficulty of the dive?

Judge	Russia	China	Mexico	Germany	Italy	Japan	Brazil
Score	7.5	8.0	6.5	8.5	7.0	7.5	7.0

   b. Critical Thinking The degree of difficulty of a dive is 4.0. The diver's final score is 97.2. Judges award half or whole points from 0 to 10. What scores could the judges have given the diver?

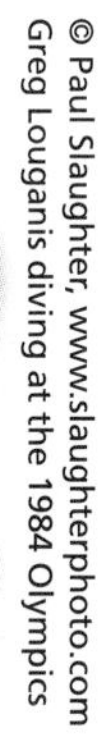
© Paul Slaughter, www.slaughterphoto.com
Greg Louganis diving at the 1984 Olympics

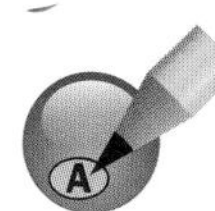

Fair Game Review What you learned in previous grades & lessons

Let $a = 3$ and $b = -2$. Copy and complete the statement using <, >, or =.
(Skills Review Handbook)

19. $-5a$ ☐ 4 20. 5 ☐ $b + 7$ 21. $a - 4$ ☐ $10b + 8$

22. **MULTIPLE CHOICE** What value of x makes the equation $x + 5 = 2x$ true? *(Skills Review Handbook)*

Ⓐ -1 Ⓑ 0 Ⓒ 3 Ⓓ 5

1.3 Solving Equations with Variables on Both Sides

STANDARDS OF LEARNING 8.15

Essential Question How can you solve an equation that has variables on both sides?

1 ACTIVITY: Perimeter and Area

Work with a partner. Each figure has the unusual property that the value of its perimeter (in feet) is equal to the value of its area (in square feet).

- **Write an equation (value of perimeter = value of area) for each figure.**
- **Solve each equation for x.**
- **Use the value of x to find the perimeter and area of each figure.**
- **Check your solution by comparing the value of the perimeter and the value of the area of each figure.**

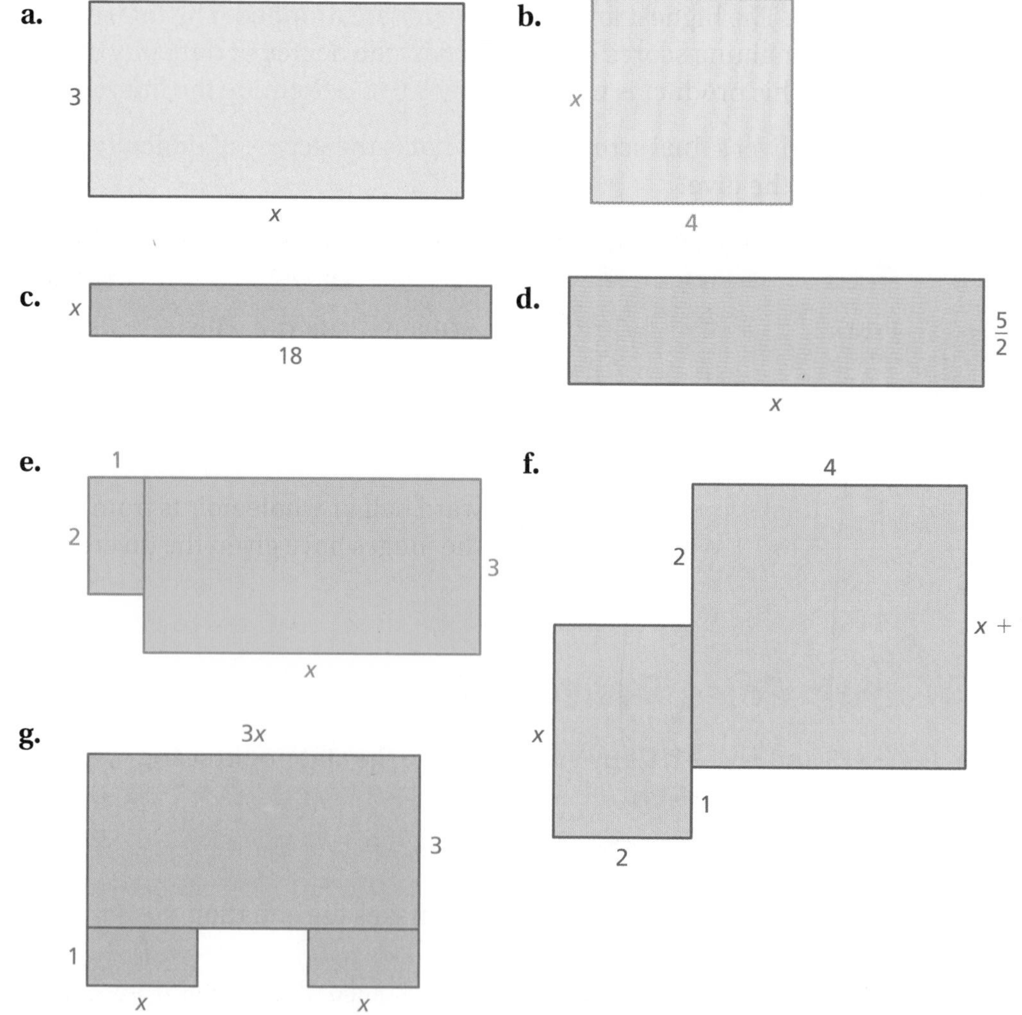

2 ACTIVITY: Surface Area and Volume

Work with a partner. Each solid has the unusual property that the value of its surface area (in square inches) is equal to the value of its volume (in cubic inches).

- **Write an equation (value of surface area = value of volume) for each figure.**
- **Solve each equation for x.**
- **Use the value of x to find the surface area and volume of each figure.**
- **Check your solution by comparing the value of the surface area and the value of the volume of each figure.**

a.

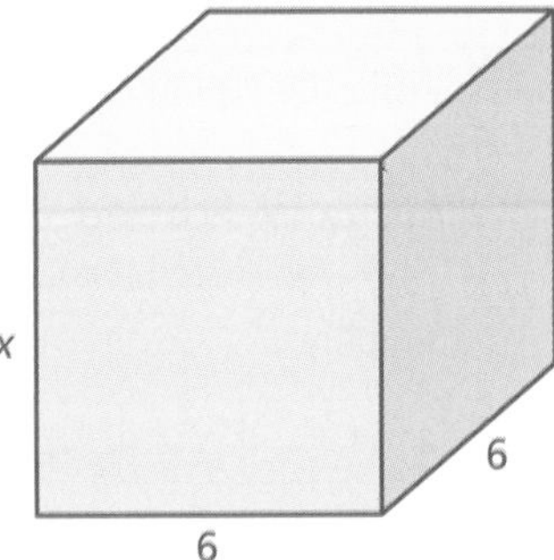

b.

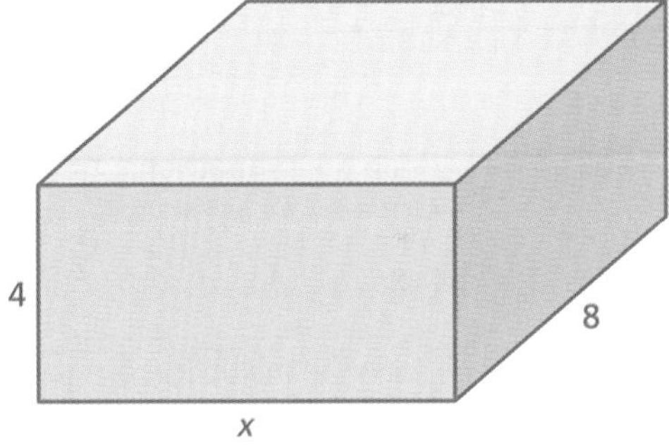

3 ACTIVITY: Puzzle

Work with a partner. The two triangles are similar. The perimeter of the larger triangle is 150% of the perimeter of the smaller triangle. Find the dimensions of each triangle.

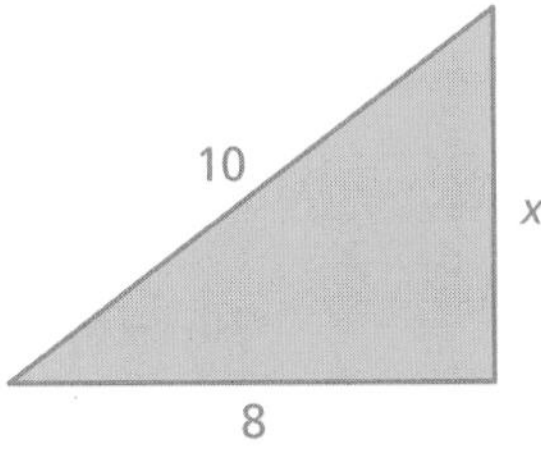

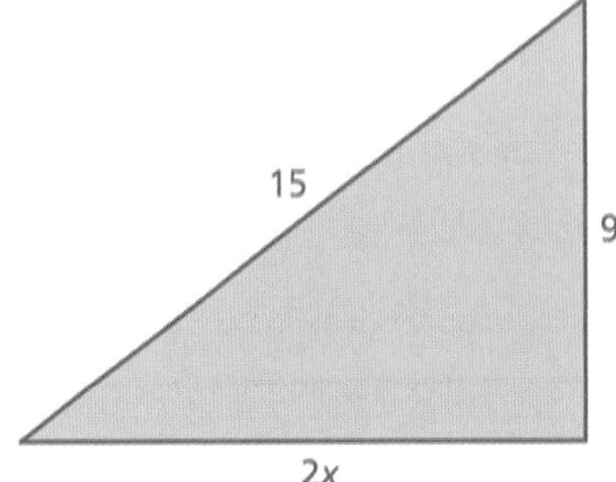

What Is Your Answer?

4. **IN YOUR OWN WORDS** How can you solve an equation that has variables on both sides? Write an equation that has variables on both sides. Solve the equation.

Practice Use what you learned about solving equations with variables on both sides to complete Exercises 3–5 on page 20.

Solving Equations with Variables on Both Sides

To solve equations with variables on both sides, collect the variable terms on one side and the constant terms on the other side.

EXAMPLE 1 Solving an Equation with Variables on Both Sides

Solve $15 - 2x = -7x$. Check your solution.

	$15 - 2x = -7x$	Write the equation.
Undo the subtraction. →	$+ 2x \quad + 2x$	Add $2x$ to each side.
	$15 = -5x$	Simplify.
Undo the multiplication. →	$\dfrac{15}{-5} = \dfrac{-5x}{-5}$	Divide each side by -5.
	$-3 = x$	Simplify.

Check

$15 - 2x = -7x$

$15 - 2(-3) \stackrel{?}{=} -7(-3)$

$21 = 21$ ✓

The solution is $x = -3$.

EXAMPLE 2 Using the Distributive Property to Solve an Equation

Solve $-2(x - 5) = 6\left(2 - \frac{1}{2}x\right)$.

	$-2(x - 5) = 6\left(2 - \frac{1}{2}x\right)$	Write the equation.
	$-2x + 10 = 12 - 3x$	Use Distributive Property.
Undo the subtraction. →	$+ 3x \qquad + 3x$	Add $3x$ to each side.
	$x + 10 = 12$	Simplify.
Undo the addition. →	$- 10 \quad - 10$	Subtract 10 from each side.
	$x = 2$	Simplify.

The solution is $x = 2$.

On Your Own

Exercises 6–14

Solve the equation. Check your solution.

1. $-3x = 2x + 19$
2. $2.5y + 6 = 4.5y - 1$
3. $6(4 - z) = 2z$

EXAMPLE 3 Standardized Test Practice

The circles are identical. What is the area of each circle?

Ⓐ 2 Ⓑ 4 Ⓒ 16π Ⓓ 64π

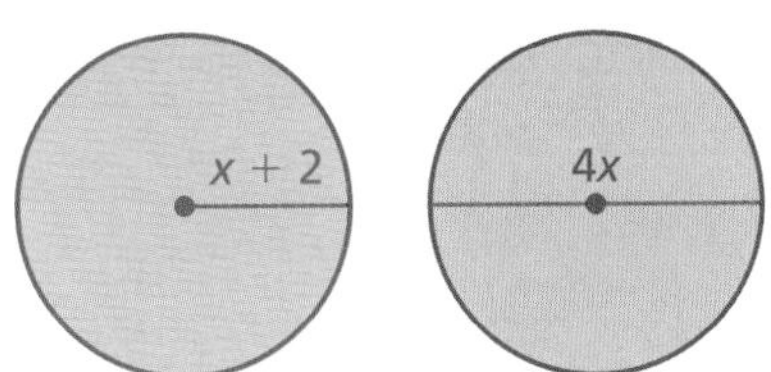

The circles are identical, so the radius of each circle is the same.

$x + 2 = 2x$	Write an equation. The radius of the purple circle is $2x$.
$-x \quad -x$	Subtract x from each side.
$2 = x$	Simplify.

∴ The area of each circle is $\pi r^2 = \pi(4)^2 = 16\pi$. So, the correct answer is Ⓒ.

EXAMPLE 4 Real-Life Application

A boat travels x miles per hour upstream on the Mississippi River. On the return trip, the boat travels 2 miles per hour faster. How far does the boat travel upstream?

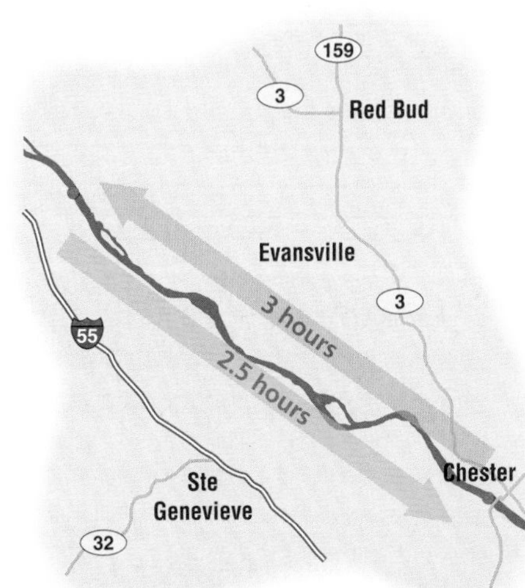

The speed of the boat on the return trip is $(x + 2)$ miles per hour.

Distance upstream = Distance of return trip

$3x = 2.5(x + 2)$	Write an equation.
$3x = 2.5x + 5$	Use Distributive Property.
$-2.5x \quad -2.5x$	Subtract $2.5x$ from each side.
$0.5x = 5$	Simplify.
$\frac{0.5x}{0.5} = \frac{5}{0.5}$	Divide each side by 0.5.
$x = 10$	Simplify.

∴ The boat travels 10 miles per hour for 3 hours upstream. So, it travels 30 miles upstream.

On Your Own

4. **WHAT IF?** In Example 3, the diameter of the purple circle is $3x$. What is the area of each circle?

5. A boat travels x miles per hour from one island to another island in 2.5 hours. The boat travels 5 miles per hour faster on the return trip of 2 hours. What is the distance between the islands?

1.3 Exercises

Vocabulary and Concept Check

1. **WRITING** Is $x = 3$ a solution of the equation $3x - 5 = 4x - 9$? Explain.
2. **OPEN-ENDED** Write an equation that has variables on both sides and has a solution of -3.

Practice and Problem Solving

The value of the figure's surface area is equal to the value of the figure's volume. Find the value of *x*.

3. 

4. 

5. 

Solve the equation. Check your solution.

① ② 6. $m - 4 = 2m$

7. $3k - 1 = 7k + 2$

8. $6.7x = 5.2x + 12.3$

9. $-24 - \frac{1}{8}p = \frac{3}{8}p$

10. $12(2w - 3) = 6w$

11. $2(n - 3) = 4n + 1$

12. $2(4z - 1) = 3(z + 2)$

13. $0.1x = 0.2(x + 2)$

14. $\frac{1}{6}d + \frac{2}{3} = \frac{1}{4}(d - 2)$

15. **ERROR ANALYSIS** Describe and correct the error in solving the equation.

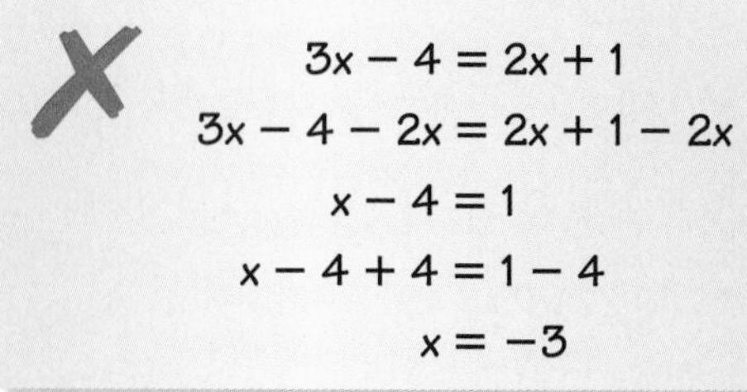

16. **TRAIL MIX** The equation $4.05p + 14.40 = 4.50(p + 3)$ represents the number p of pounds of peanuts you need to make trail mix. How many pounds of peanuts do you need for the trail mix?

17. **CARS** Write and solve an equation to find the number of miles you must drive to have the same cost for each of the car rentals.

$15 plus $0.50 per mile

$25 plus $0.25 per mile

A polygon is *regular* if each of its sides has the same length. Find the perimeter of the regular polygon.

18.

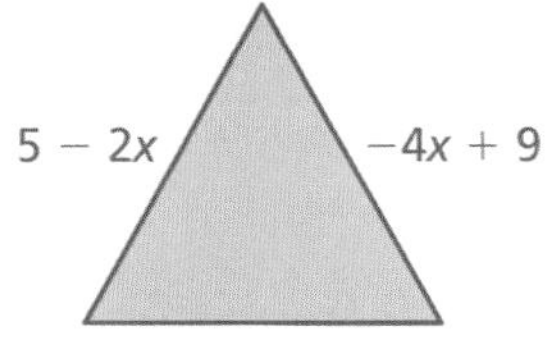

19.

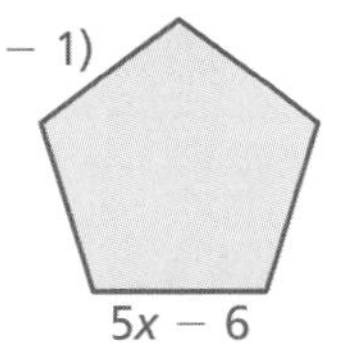

20. $\frac{4}{3}x - \frac{1}{3}$; $x + 7$

21. POSTAGE The cost of mailing a DVD in an envelope by express mail is equal to the cost of mailing a DVD in a box by priority mail. What is the weight of the DVD with its packing material? Round your answer to the nearest hundredth.

	Packing Material	Priority Mail	Express Mail
Box	\$2.25	\$2.50 per lb	\$8.50 per lb
Envelope	\$1.10	\$2.50 per lb	\$8.50 per lb

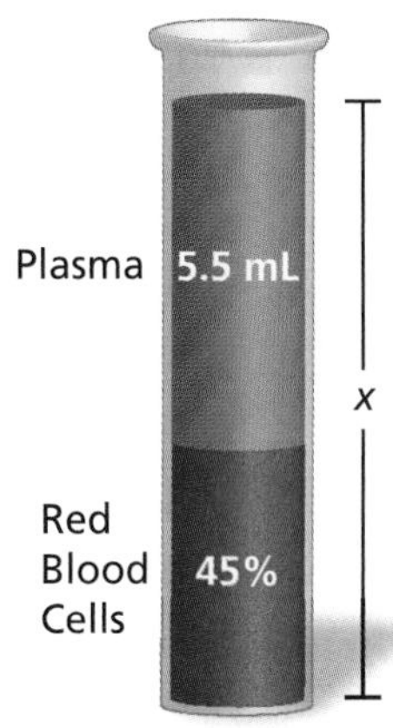

22. REASONING Would you solve the equation $0.25x + 7 = \frac{1}{3}x - 8$ using fractions or decimals? Explain.

23. BLOOD SAMPLE The amount of red blood cells in a blood sample is equal to the total amount in the sample minus the amount of plasma. What is the total amount x of blood drawn?

24. NUTRITION One serving of oatmeal provides 16% of the fiber you need daily. You must get the remaining 21 grams of fiber from other sources. How many grams of fiber should you consume daily?

25. Geometry The perimeter of the square is equal to the perimeter of the triangle. What are the side lengths of each figure?

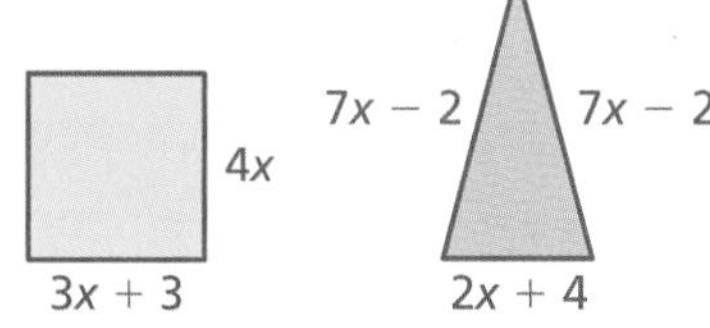

Fair Game Review What you learned in previous grades & lessons

Find the volume of the figure. Use 3.14 for π. *(Skills Review Handbook)*

26.

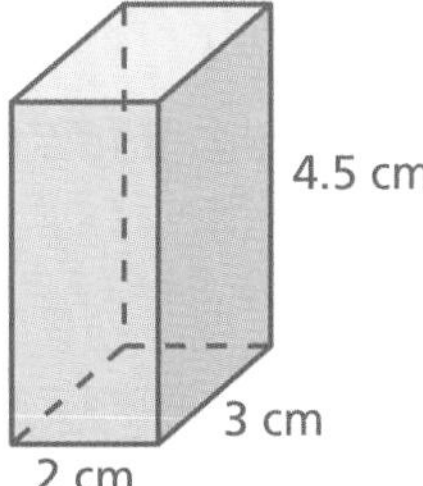

27.

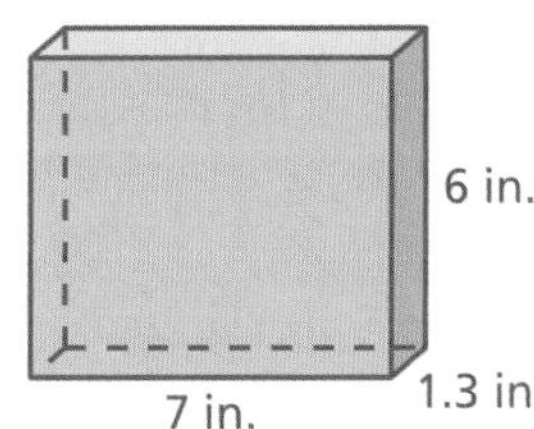

28.

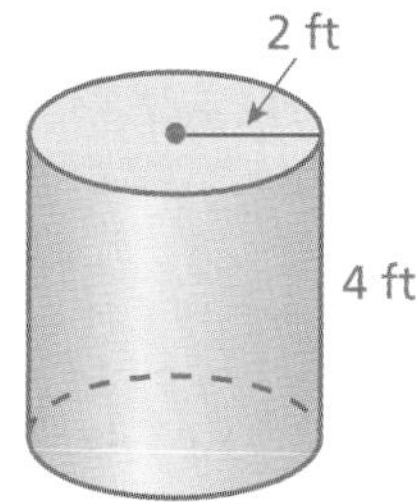

29. MULTIPLE CHOICE A car travels 480 miles on 15 gallons of gasoline. How many miles does the car travel per gallon? *(Skills Review Handbook)*

Ⓐ 28 mi/gal Ⓑ 30 mi/gal Ⓒ 32 mi/gal Ⓓ 35 mi/gal

1.4 Rewriting Equations and Formulas

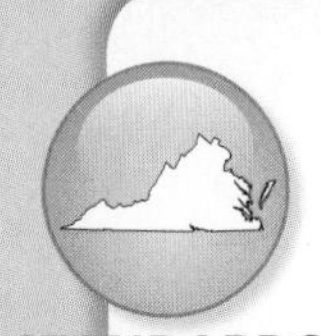

STANDARDS OF LEARNING
8.15

Essential Question How can you use a formula for one measurement to write a formula for a different measurement?

1 ACTIVITY: Using Perimeter and Area Formulas

Work with a partner.

a.
- Write a formula for the perimeter P of a rectangle.
- Solve the formula for w.
- Use the new formula to find the width of the rectangle.

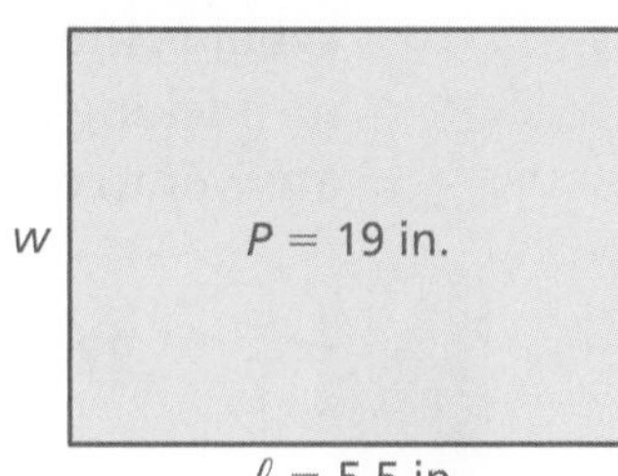

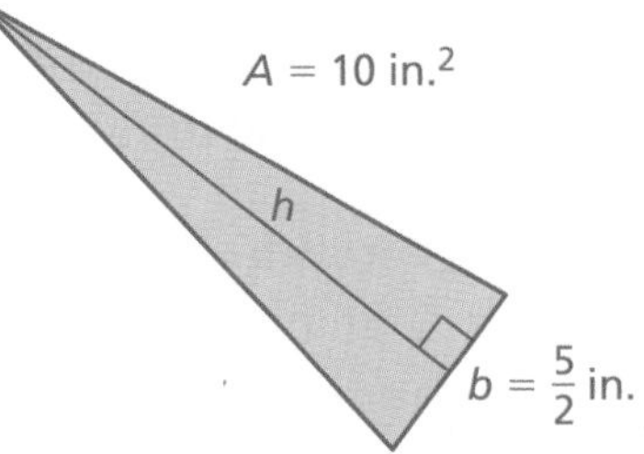

b.
- Write a formula for the area A of a triangle.
- Solve the formula for h.
- Use the new formula to find the height of the triangle.

c.
- Write a formula for the circumference C of a circle.
- Solve the formula for r.
- Use the new formula to find the radius of the circle.

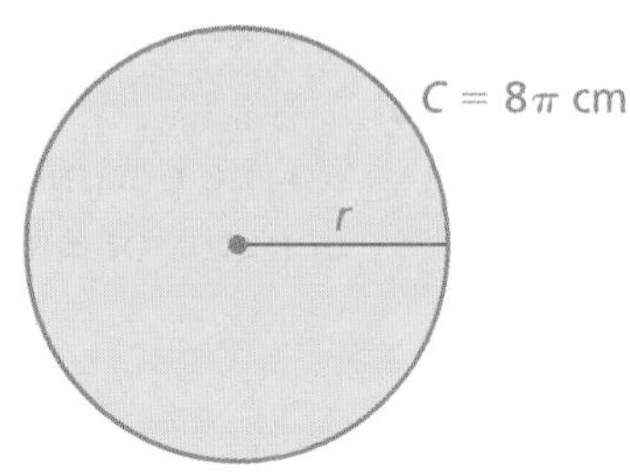

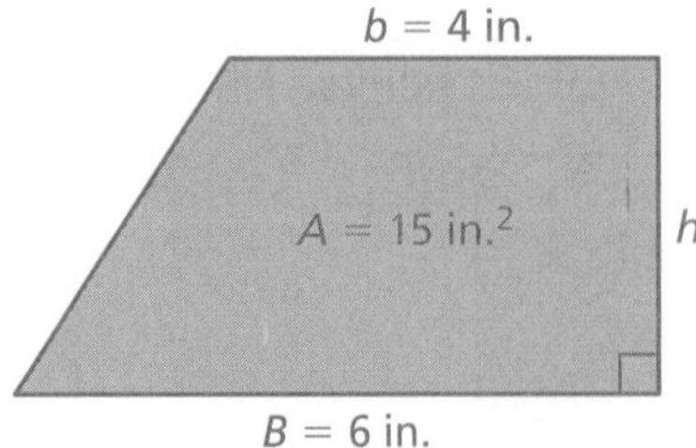

d.
- Write a formula for the area A of a trapezoid.
- Solve the formula for h.
- Use the new formula to find the height of the trapezoid.

e.
- Write a formula for the area A of a parallelogram.
- Solve the formula for h.
- Use the new formula to find the height of the parallelogram.

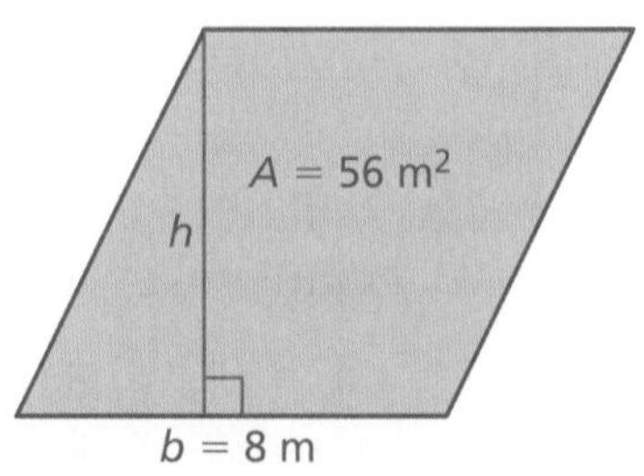

2 ACTIVITY: Using Volume Formulas

Work with a partner.

a.
- Write a formula for the volume V of a prism.
- Solve the formula for h.
- Use the new formula to find the height of the prism.

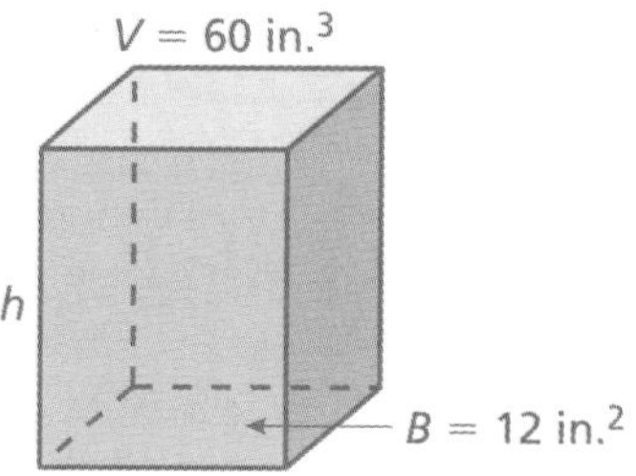

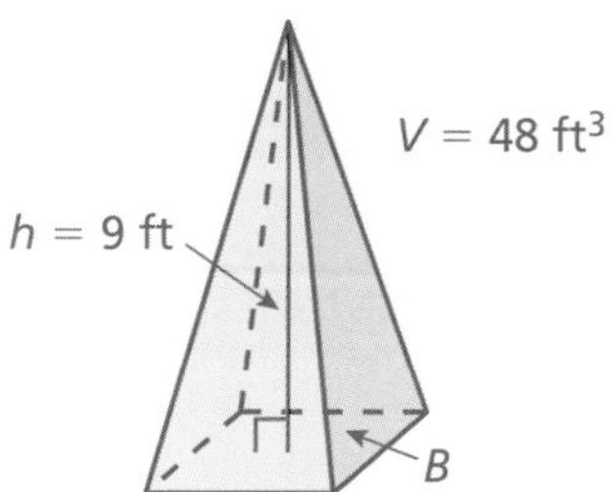

b.
- The formula for the volume V of a pyramid is $V = \frac{1}{3}Bh$.
- Solve the formula for B.
- Use the new formula to find the area of the base of the pyramid.

c.
- Write a formula for the volume V of a cylinder.
- Solve the formula for B.
- Use the new formula to find the area of the base of the cylinder.

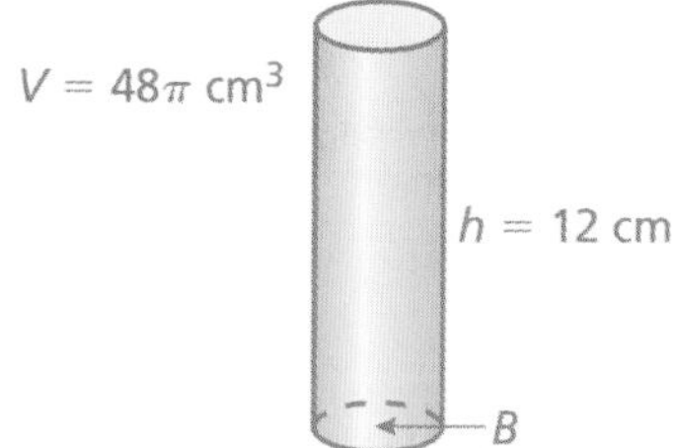

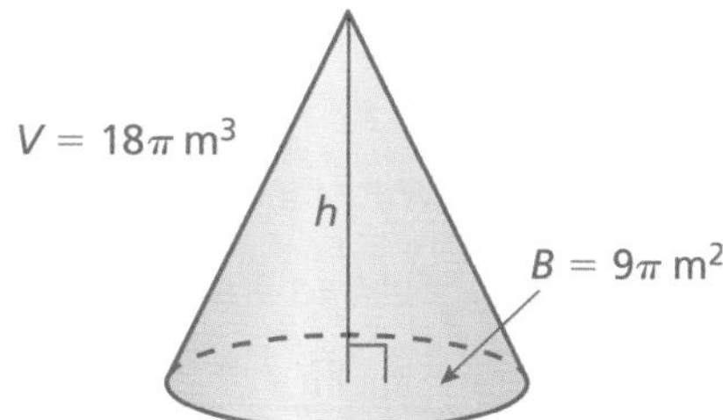

d.
- The formula for the volume V of a cone is $V = \frac{1}{3}Bh$.
- Solve the formula for h.
- Use the new formula to find the height of the cone.

What Is Your Answer?

3. **IN YOUR OWN WORDS** How can you use a formula for one measurement to write a formula for a different measurement? Give an example that is different from the examples on these two pages.

Use what you learned about rewriting equations and formulas to complete Exercises 3 and 4 on page 26.

1.4 Lesson

Key Vocabulary
literal equation, *p. 24*

An equation that has two or more variables is called a **literal equation**. To rewrite a literal equation, solve for one variable in terms of the other variable(s).

EXAMPLE 1 Rewriting an Equation

Solve the equation $2y + 5x = 6$ for y.

	$2y + 5x = 6$	Write the equation.
Undo the addition.	$2y + 5x - 5x = 6 - 5x$	Subtract $5x$ from each side.
	$2y = 6 - 5x$	Simplify.
Undo the multiplication.	$\frac{2y}{2} = \frac{6 - 5x}{2}$	Divide each side by 2.
	$y = 3 - \frac{5}{2}x$	Simplify.

On Your Own

Now You're Ready
Exercises 5–10

Solve the equation for y.

1. $5y - x = 10$
2. $4x - 4y = 1$
3. $12 = 6x + 3y$

EXAMPLE 2 Rewriting a Formula

Remember

A *formula* shows how one variable is related to one or more other variables. A formula is a type of literal equation.

The formula for the surface area S of a cone is $S = \pi r^2 + \pi r\ell$. Solve the formula for the slant height ℓ.

$S = \pi r^2 + \pi r\ell$	Write the formula.
$S - \pi r^2 = \pi r^2 - \pi r^2 + \pi r\ell$	Subtract πr^2 from each side.
$S - \pi r^2 = \pi r\ell$	Simplify.
$\frac{S - \pi r^2}{\pi r} = \frac{\pi r\ell}{\pi r}$	Divide each side by πr.
$\frac{S - \pi r^2}{\pi r} = \ell$	Simplify.

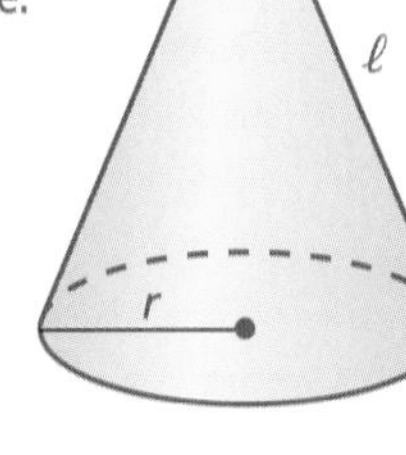

On Your Own

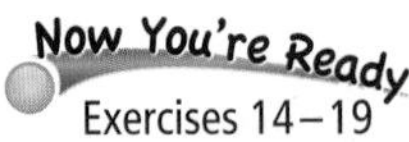

Now You're Ready
Exercises 14–19

Solve the formula for the red variable.

4. Area of rectangle: $A = bh$
5. Simple interest: $I = Prt$
6. Surface area of cylinder: $S = 2\pi r^2 + 2\pi rh$

Multi-Language Glossary at BigIdeasMath.com.

Key Idea

Temperature Conversion

A formula for converting from degrees Fahrenheit F to degrees Celsius C is

$$C = \frac{5}{9}(F - 32).$$

EXAMPLE 3 Rewriting the Temperature Formula

Solve the temperature formula for F.

	$C = \frac{5}{9}(F - 32)$	Write the temperature formula.
Use the reciprocal. →	$\frac{9}{5} \cdot C = \frac{9}{5} \cdot \frac{5}{9}(F - 32)$	Multiply each side by $\frac{9}{5}$, the reciprocal of $\frac{5}{9}$.
	$\frac{9}{5}C = F - 32$	Simplify.
Undo the subtraction. →	$\frac{9}{5}C + 32 = F - 32 + 32$	Add 32 to each side.
	$\frac{9}{5}C + 32 = F$	Simplify.

∴ The rewritten formula is $F = \frac{9}{5}C + 32$.

EXAMPLE 4 Real-Life Application

Lightning
30,000°C

Which has the greater temperature?

Convert the Celsius temperature of lightning to Fahrenheit.

$F = \frac{9}{5}C + 32$	Write the rewritten formula from Example 3.
$= \frac{9}{5}(30{,}000) + 32$	Substitute 30,000 for C.
$= 54{,}032$	Simplify.

∴ Because 54,032 °F is greater than 11,000 °F, lightning has the greater temperature.

On Your Own

7. Room temperature is considered to be 70 °F. Suppose the temperature is 23 °C. Is this greater than or less than room temperature?

1.4 Exercises

Vocabulary and Concept Check

1. **VOCABULARY** Is $-2x = \frac{3}{8}$ a literal equation? Explain.

2. **DIFFERENT WORDS, SAME QUESTION** Which is different? Find "both" answers.

Solve $4x - 2y = 6$ for y.	Solve $6 = 4x - 2y$ for y.
Solve $4x - 2y = 6$ for y in terms of x.	Solve $4x - 2y = 6$ for x in terms of y.

Practice and Problem Solving

3. a. Write a formula for the area A of a triangle.
   b. Solve the formula for b.
   c. Use the new formula to find the base of the triangle.

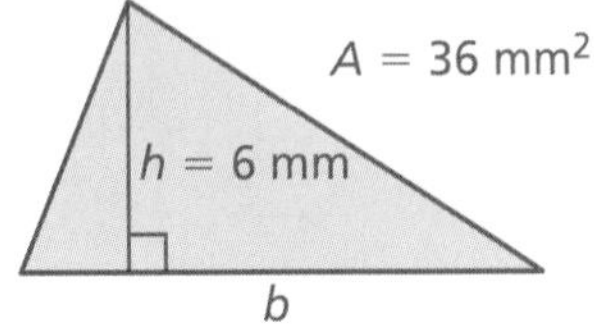

4. a. Write a formula for the lateral surface area S of a cylinder.
   b. Solve the formula for h.
   c. Use the new formula to find the height of the cylinder.

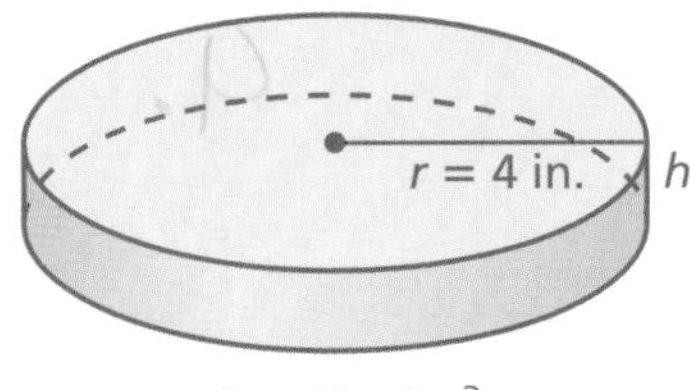

Solve the equation for y.

1 5. $\frac{1}{3}x + y = 4$

6. $3x + \frac{1}{5}y = 7$

7. $6 = 4x + 9y$

8. $\pi = 7x - 2y$

9. $4.2x - 1.4y = 2.1$

10. $6y - 1.5x = 8$

11. **ERROR ANALYSIS** Describe and correct the error in rewriting the equation.

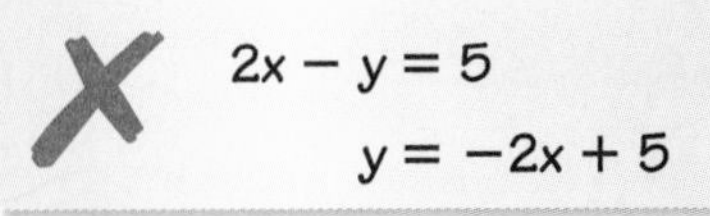

12. **TEMPERATURE** The formula $K = C + 273.15$ converts temperatures from Celsius C to Kelvin K.
    a. Solve the formula for C.
    b. Convert 300 K to Celsius.

13. **INTEREST** The formula for simple interest is $I = Prt$.
    a. Solve the formula for t.
    b. Use the new formula to find the value of t in the table.

I	\$75
P	\$500
r	5%
t	

Solve the formula for the red variable.

2 **14.** $d = rt$ **15.** $e = mc^2$ **16.** $R - C = P$

17. $A = \frac{1}{2}\pi w^2 + 2\ell w$ **18.** $B = 3\frac{V}{h}$ **19.** $g = \frac{1}{6}(w + 40)$

20. WRITING Why is it useful to rewrite a formula in terms of another variable?

21. TEMPERATURE The formula $K = \frac{5}{9}(F - 32) + 273.15$ converts temperatures from Fahrenheit F to Kelvin K.

- **a.** Solve the formula for F.
- **b.** The freezing point of water is 273.15 Kelvin. What is this temperature in Fahrenheit?
- **c.** The temperature of dry ice is −78.5 °C. Which is colder, dry ice or liquid nitrogen?

Navy Pier Ferris Wheel

22. FERRIS WHEEL The Navy Pier Ferris Wheel in Chicago has a circumference that is 56% of the circumference of the first Ferris wheel built in 1893.

- **a.** What is the radius of the Navy Pier Ferris Wheel?
- **b.** What was the radius of the first Ferris wheel?
- **c.** The first Ferris wheel took 9 minutes to make a complete revolution. How fast was the wheel moving?

23. Geometry The formula for the volume of a sphere is $V = \frac{4}{3}\pi r^3$. Solve the formula for r^3. Use guess, check, and revise to find the radius of the sphere.

Fair Game Review What you learned in previous grades & lessons

Multiply. *(Skills Review Handbook)*

24. $5 \times \frac{3}{4}$ **25.** $2.4 \times \frac{8}{3}$ **26.** $\frac{1}{4} \times \frac{3}{2} \times \frac{8}{9}$ **27.** $25 \times \frac{3}{5} \times \frac{1}{12}$

28. MULTIPLE CHOICE Which of the following is not equivalent to $\frac{3}{4}$? *(Skills Review Handbook)*

Ⓐ 0.75 Ⓑ 3:4 Ⓒ 75% Ⓓ 4:3

1 Study Help

You can use a **Y chart** to compare two topics. List differences in the branches and similarities in the base of the Y. Here is an example of a Y chart that compares solving simple equations to solving multi-step equations.

Solving Simple Equations

- You can solve the equation in one step.

Solving Multi-Step Equations

- You must use more than one step to solve the equation.
- Undo the operations in the reverse order of the order of operations.

Both

- As necessary, use the Addition, Subtraction, Multiplication, and Division Properties of Equality to solve for the variable.
- The variable can end up on either side of the equation.
- It is always a good idea to check your solution.

On Your Own

Make a Y chart to help you study and compare these topics.

1. solving equations with the variable on one side and solving equations with variables on both sides
2. solving multi-step equations and solving equations with variables on both sides
3. solving multi-step equations and rewriting literal equations

After you complete this chapter, make Y charts for the following topics.

4. solving one-step inequalities and solving two-step inequalities
5. solving equations and solving inequalities

"I made a Y chart to compare and contrast yours and Fluffy's characteristics."

1.1–1.4 Quiz

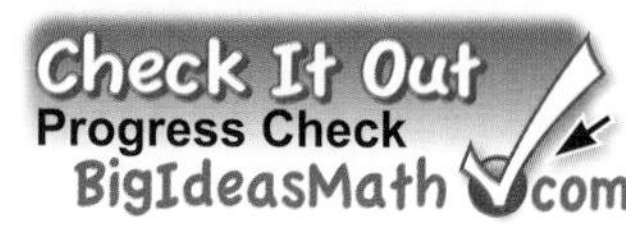

Solve the equation. Check your solution. *(Section 1.1)*

1. $-\frac{1}{2} = y - 1$

2. $-3\pi + w = 2\pi$

3. $1.2m = 0.6$

Find the value of *x*. Then find the angle measures of the polygon. *(Section 1.2)*

4.

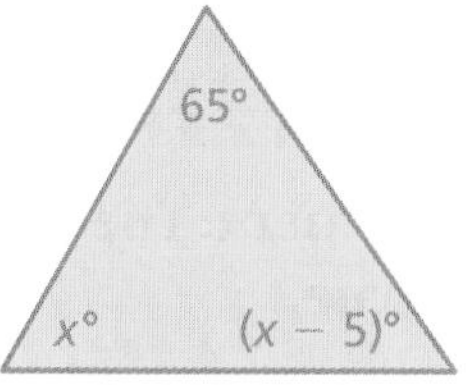

Sum of angle measures: 180°

5.

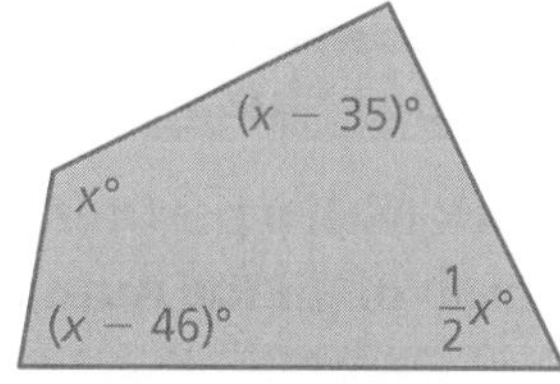

Sum of angle measures: 360°

Solve the equation. Check your solution. *(Section 1.3)*

6. $2(x + 4) = -5x + 1$

7. $\frac{1}{2}s = 4s - 21$

Solve the formula for the red variable. *(Section 1.4)*

8. Volume of a cylinder: $V = \pi r^2 h$

9. Area of a trapezoid: $A = \frac{1}{2}h(b + B)$

10. INTEREST The formula for simple interest I is $I = Prt$. Solve the formula for the interest rate r. What is the interest rate r if the principal P is \$1500, the time t is 2 years, and the interest earned I is \$900? *(Section 1.4)*

11. PASTURE A 455-foot fence encloses a pasture. What is the length of each side of the pasture? *(Section 1.2)*

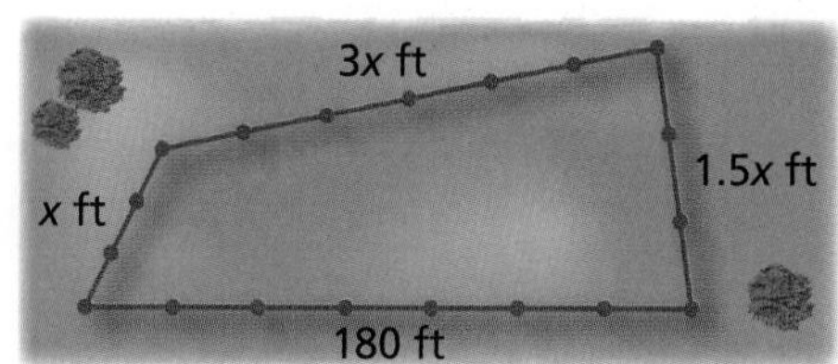

12. POSTERS A machine prints 230 movie posters each hour. Write and solve an equation to find the number of hours it takes the machine to print 1265 posters. *(Section 1.1)*

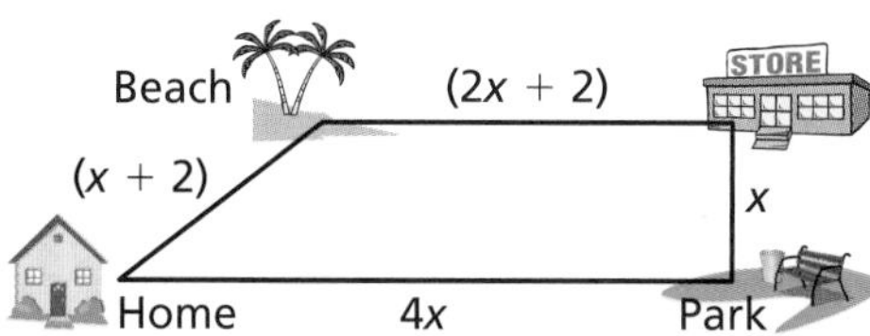

13. ROUTES From your home, the route to the store that passes the beach is 2 miles shorter than the route to the store that passes the park. What is the length of each route? *(Section 1.3)*

1.5 Writing and Graphing Inequalities

STANDARDS OF LEARNING
8.15

Essential Question How can you use an inequality to describe a real-life statement?

1 ACTIVITY: Writing and Graphing Inequalities

Work with a partner. Write an inequality for the statement. Then sketch the graph of all the numbers that make the inequality true.

a. **Statement:** The temperature t in Minot, North Dakota has never been below -36°F.

Inequality:

Graph:

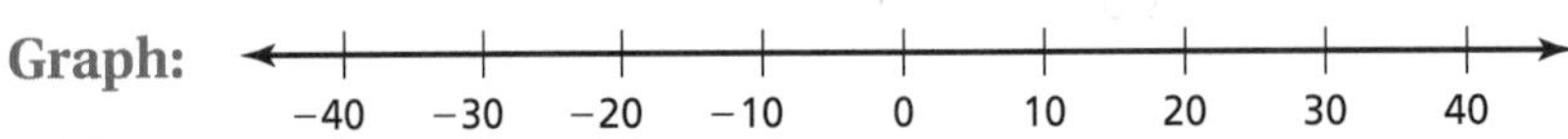

TIMM'S HILL
WISCONSIN'S HIGHEST
NATURAL POINT
ELEV. 1951.5 FT

b. **Statement:** The elevation e in Wisconsin is at most 1951.5 feet above sea level.

Inequality:

Graph:

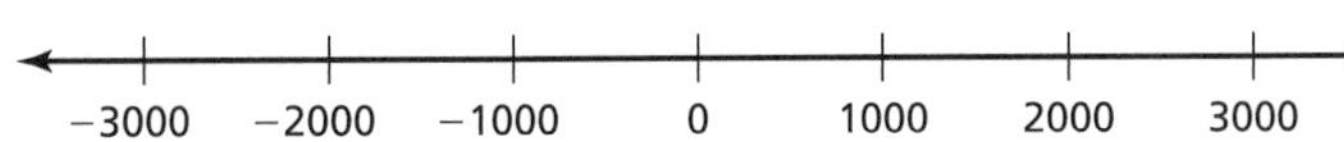

2 ACTIVITY: Writing and Graphing Inequalities

Work with a partner. Write an inequality for the graph. Then, in words, describe all the values of x that make the inequality true.

a.

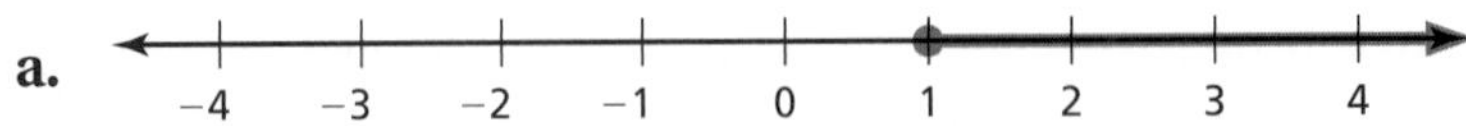

b.

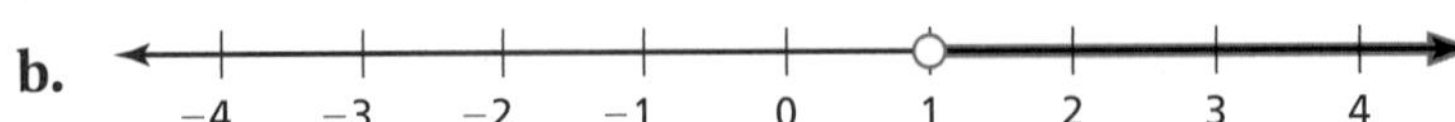

c.

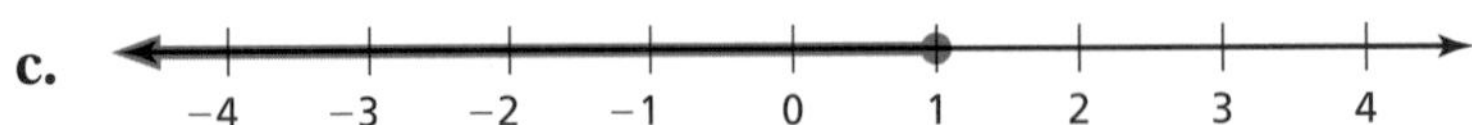

d.

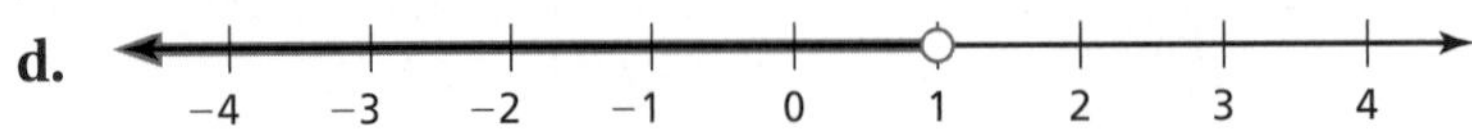

3 ACTIVITY: Triangle Inequality

Work with a partner. Use 8 to 10 pieces of spaghetti.

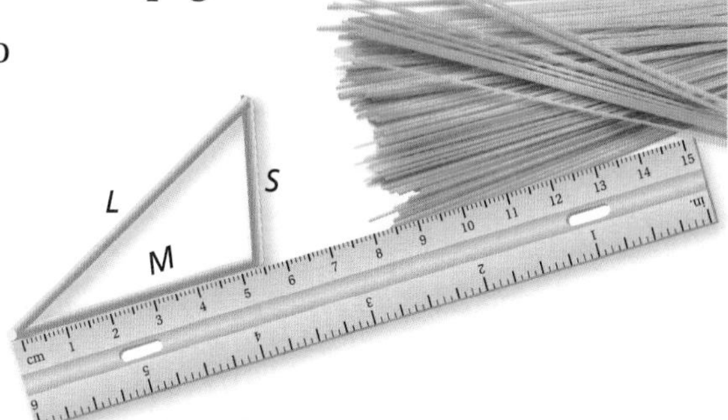

- Break one piece of spaghetti into three parts that can be used to form a triangle.
- Form a triangle and use a centimeter ruler to measure each side. Round the side lengths to the nearest tenth.
- Record the side lengths in a table.

Side Lengths That Form a Triangle			
Small	Medium	Large	$S + M$

- Repeat the process with two other pieces of spaghetti.
- Repeat the experiment by breaking pieces of spaghetti into three pieces that *do not* form a triangle. Record the lengths in a table.

Side Lengths That Do Not Form a Triangle			
Small	Medium	Large	$S + M$

- **INDUCTIVE REASONING** Write a rule that uses an inequality to compare the lengths of three sides of a triangle.
- Use your rule to decide whether the following triangles are possible. Explain.

a.

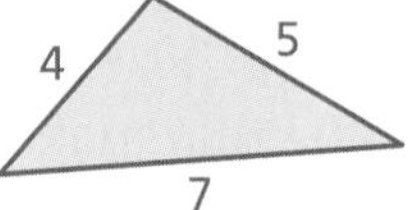

b.

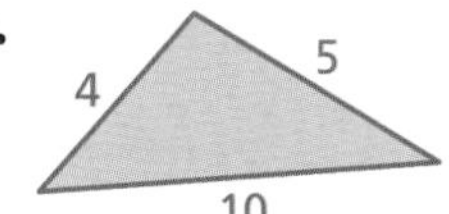

c.

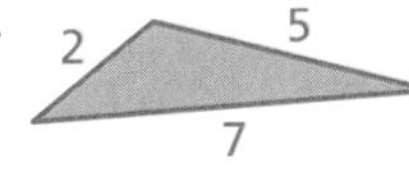

What Is Your Answer?

4. **IN YOUR OWN WORDS** How can you use an inequality to describe a real-life statement? Give two examples of real-life statements that can be represented by inequalities.

Practice Use what you learned about writing and graphing inequalities to complete Exercises 4 and 5 on page 34.

1.5 Lesson

Key Vocabulary
inequality, *p. 32*
solution of an inequality, *p. 32*
solution set, *p. 32*
graph of an inequality, *p. 33*

An **inequality** is a mathematical sentence that compares expressions. It contains the symbols $<$, $>$, $\leq$, or $\geq$. To write an inequality, look for the following phrases to determine where to place the inequality symbol.

Inequality Symbols

Symbol	$<$	$>$	$\leq$	$\geq$
Key Phrases	• is less than • is fewer than	• is greater than • is more than	• is less than or equal to • is at most • is no more than	• is greater than or equal to • is at least • is no less than

EXAMPLE 1 Writing an Inequality

A number w minus 3.5 is less than or equal to -2. Write this sentence as an inequality.

A number w minus 3.5 is less than or equal to -2.

$w - 3.5$ $\quad\leq\quad$ -2

∴ An inequality is $w - 3.5 \leq -2$.

On Your Own

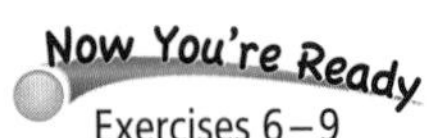

Exercises 6–9

Write the word sentence as an inequality.

1. A number b is fewer than 30.4.
2. Twice a number k is at least $-\frac{7}{10}$.

A **solution of an inequality** is a value that makes the inequality true. An inequality can have more than one solution. The set of all solutions of an inequality is called the **solution set**.

Reading

The symbol $\ngeq$ means "is not greater than or equal to."

Value of x	$x + 5 \geq -2$	Is the inequality true?
-6	$-6 + 5 \overset{?}{\geq} -2$ $-1 \geq -2$ ✓	yes
-7	$-7 + 5 \overset{?}{\geq} -2$ $-2 \geq -2$ ✓	yes
-8	$-8 + 5 \overset{?}{\geq} -2$ $-3 \ngeq -2$ ✗	no

Multi-Language Glossary at BigIdeasMath.com.

EXAMPLE 2 Checking Solutions

Tell whether −4 is a solution of the inequality.

a. $x + 8 < -3$

$x + 8 < -3$	Write the inequality.	$-4.5x > -21$
$-4 + 8 \stackrel{?}{<} -3$	Substitute −4 for *x*.	$-4.5(-4) \stackrel{?}{>} -21$
$4 \not< -3$ ✗	Simplify.	$18 > -21$ ✓

b. $-4.5x > -21$

4 is *not* less than −3.

So, −4 is *not* a solution of the inequality.

18 is greater than −21.

So, −4 is a solution of the inequality.

On Your Own

Now You're Ready
Exercises 11–16

Tell whether −6 is a solution of the inequality.

3. $c + 4 < -1$ **4.** $5 - m \le 10$ **5.** $21 \div x \ge -3.5$

The **graph of an inequality** shows all of the solutions of the inequality on a number line. An open circle ○ is used when a number is *not* a solution. A closed circle ● is used when a number is a solution. An arrow to the left or right shows that the graph continues in that direction.

EXAMPLE 3 Graphing an Inequality

Graph $y \le -3$.

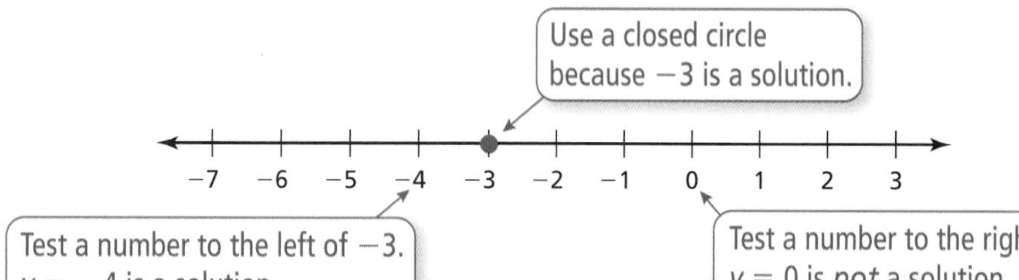
Use a closed circle because −3 is a solution.
−7 −6 −5 −4 −3 −2 −1 0 1 2 3
Test a number to the left of −3. y = −4 is a solution.
Test a number to the right of −3. y = 0 is *not* a solution.

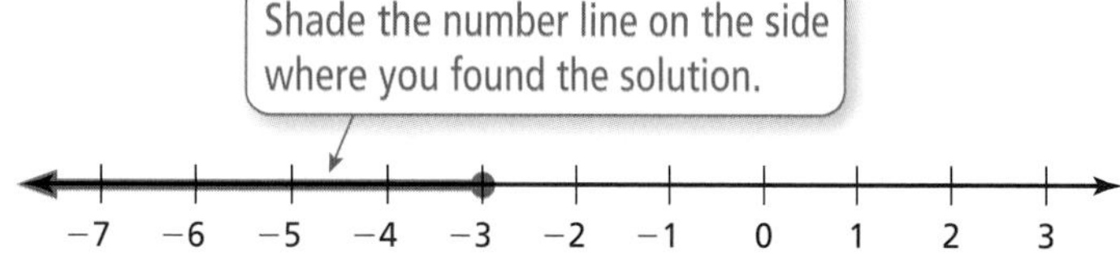
Shade the number line on the side where you found the solution.
−7 −6 −5 −4 −3 −2 −1 0 1 2 3

On Your Own

Now You're Ready
Exercises 17–20

Graph the inequality on a number line.

6. $b > -8$ **7.** $g \le 1.4$ **8.** $r < -\frac{1}{2}$ **9.** $\frac{5}{2} \le v$

1.5 Exercises

Vocabulary and Concept Check

1. **VOCABULARY** Would an open circle or a closed circle be used in the graph of the inequality $k < 250$? Explain.
2. **DIFFERENT WORDS, SAME QUESTION** Which is different? Write "both" inequalities.

w is greater than or equal to -7.	w is no less than -7.
w is no more than -7.	w is at least -7.

3. **REASONING** Do $x \geq -9$ and $-9 \geq x$ represent the same inequality? Explain.

Practice and Problem Solving

Write an inequality for the graph. Then, in words, describe all the values of x that make the inequality true.

4. −3 0 3 6 9 12 15 18

5. 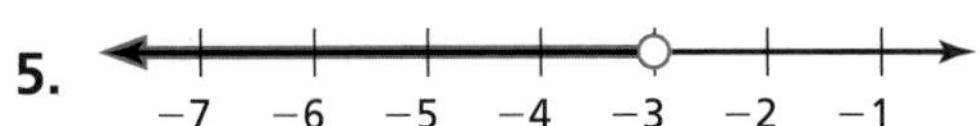

Write the word sentence as an inequality.

1 6. A number x is no less than -4.

7. A number y added to 5.2 is less than 23.

8. A number b multiplied by -5 is at most $-\frac{3}{4}$.

9. A number k minus 8.3 is greater than 48.

10. **ERROR ANALYSIS** Describe and correct the error in writing the word sentence as an inequality.

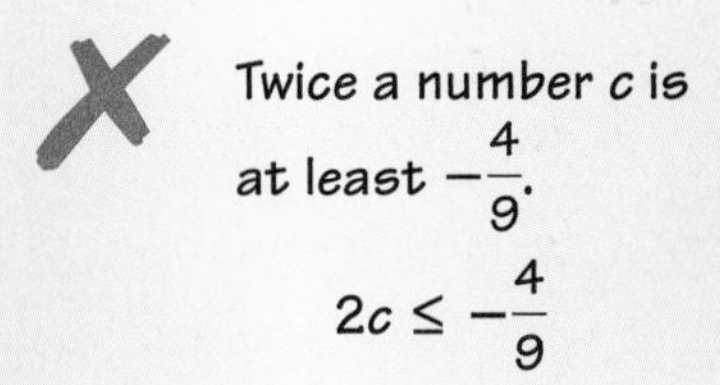

Twice a number c is at least $-\frac{4}{9}$.
$2c \leq -\frac{4}{9}$

Tell whether the given value is a solution of the inequality.

2 11. $s + 6 \leq 12;\ s = 4$

12. $15n > -3;\ n = -2$

13. $a - 2.5 \leq 1.6;\ a = 4.1$

14. $-3.3q > -13;\ q = 4.6$

15. $\frac{4}{5}h \geq -4;\ h = -15$

16. $\frac{1}{12} - p < \frac{1}{3};\ p = \frac{1}{6}$

Graph the inequality on a number line.

3 17. $g \geq -6$

18. $q > 1.25$

19. $z < 11\frac{1}{4}$

20. $w \leq -2\frac{1}{3}$

21. **DRIVING** When you are driving with a learner's license, a licensed driver who is 21 years of age or older must be with you. Write an inequality that represents this situation.

Tell whether the given value is a solution of the inequality.

22. $3p > 5 + p;\ p = 4$

23. $\frac{y}{2} \geq y - 11;\ y = 18$

24. VIDEO GAME RATINGS Each rating is matched with the inequality that represents the recommended ages of players. Your friend is old enough to play "E 10+" games. Is your friend old enough to play "T" games? Explain.

$x \geq 3$

$x \geq 6$

$x \geq 10$

$x \geq 13$

$x \geq 17$

The ESRB rating icons are registered trademarks of the Entertainment Software Association.

25. SCUBA DIVING Three requirements for a scuba diving training course are shown.

a. Write and graph three inequalities that represent the requirements.

b. You can swim 10 lengths of a 25-yard pool. Do you satisfy the swimming requirement of the course? Explain.

26. LUGGAGE On an airplane, the maximum sum of the length, width, and height of a carry-on bag is 45 inches. Find three different sets of dimensions that are reasonable for a carry-on bag.

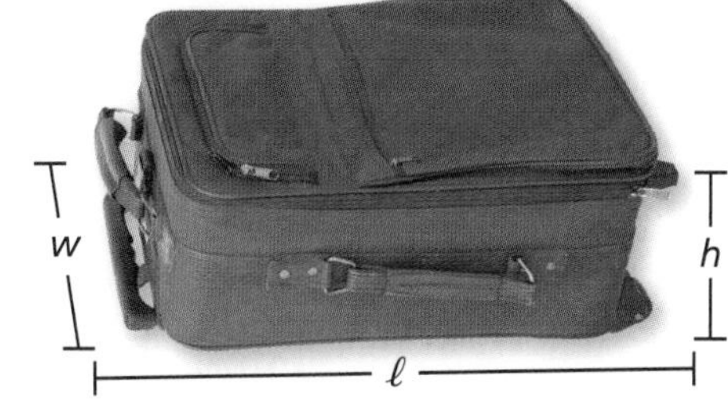

27. Critical Thinking A number m is less than another number n. The number n is less than or equal to a third number p.

a. Write two inequalities representing these relationships.

b. Describe the relationship between m and p.

c. Can m be equal to p? Explain.

Fair Game Review What you learned in previous grades & lessons

Solve the equation. Check your solution. *(Section 1.1)*

28. $r - 12 = 3$

29. $4.2 + p = 2.5$

30. $n - 3\pi = 7\pi$

31. MULTIPLE CHOICE Which expression has a value less than 1? *(Skills Review Handbook)*

Ⓐ $\frac{1}{2^{-2}}$ Ⓑ 2^{-2} Ⓒ 2^0 Ⓓ 2^2

1.6 Solving One-Step Inequalities

STANDARDS OF LEARNING
8.15

Essential Question How can you use addition or subtraction to solve an inequality?

1 ACTIVITY: Quarterback Passing Efficiency

Work with a partner. The National Collegiate Athletic Association (NCAA) uses the following formula to rank the passing efficiency *P* of quarterbacks.

$$P = \frac{8.4Y + 100C + 330T - 200N}{A}$$

Y = total length of all completed passes (in Yards)

C = Completed passes

T = passes resulting in a Touchdown

N = iNtercepted passes

A = Attempted passes

M = incoMplete passes

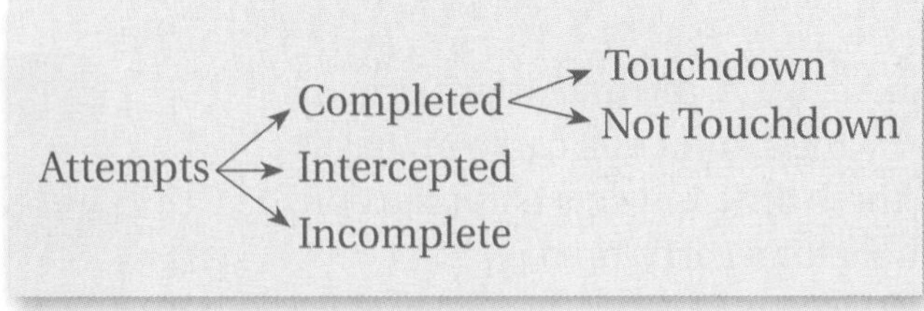

Which of the following equations or inequalities are true relationships among the variables? Explain your reasoning.

a. $C + N < A$ **b.** $C + N \le A$ **c.** $T < C$ **d.** $T \le C$

e. $N < A$ **f.** $A > T$ **g.** $A - C \ge M$ **h.** $A = C + N + M$

2 ACTIVITY: Quarterback Passing Efficiency

Work with a partner. Which of the following quarterbacks has a passing efficiency rating that satisfies the inequality $P > 100$? Show your work.

Player	Attempts	Completions	Yards	Touchdowns	Interceptions
A	149	88	1065	7	9
B	400	205	2000	10	3
C	426	244	3105	30	9
D	188	89	1167	6	15

3 ACTIVITY: Finding Solutions of Inequalities

Work with a partner. Use the passing efficiency formula to create a passing record that makes the inequality true. Then describe the values of *P* that make the inequality true.

a. $P < 0$

Attempts	Completions	Yards	Touchdowns	Interceptions

b. $P + 100 \geq 250$

Attempts	Completions	Yards	Touchdowns	Interceptions

c. $180 < P - 50$

Attempts	Completions	Yards	Touchdowns	Interceptions

d. $P + 30 \geq 120$

Attempts	Completions	Yards	Touchdowns	Interceptions

e. $P - 250 > -80$

Attempts	Completions	Yards	Touchdowns	Interceptions

What Is Your Answer?

4. Write a rule that describes how to solve inequalities like those in Activity 3. Then use your rule to solve each of the inequalities in Activity 3.

5. **IN YOUR OWN WORDS** How can you use addition or subtraction to solve an inequality?

6. How is solving the inequality $x + 3 < 4$ similar to solving the equation $x + 3 = 4$? How is it different?

Practice Use what you learned about solving inequalities using addition or subtraction to complete Exercises 5–7 on page 41.

1.6 Lesson

Study Tip

You can solve inequalities in much the same way you solve equations. Use inverse operations to get the variable by itself.

Addition Property of Inequality

Words If you add the same number to each side of an inequality, the inequality remains true.

Algebra If $a < b$, then $a + c < b + c$.

Subtraction Property of Inequality

Words If you subtract the same number from each side of an inequality, the inequality remains true.

Algebra If $a < b$, then $a - c < b - c$.

These properties are true for $<$, $>$, $\leq$, and $\geq$.

EXAMPLE 1 Solving Inequalities Using Addition or Subtraction

a. Solve $x - 5 < -3$. Graph the solution.

	$x - 5 < -3$	Write the inequality.
Undo the subtraction. →	$\underline{+5} \quad \underline{+5}$	Add 5 to each side.
	$x < 2$	Simplify.

The solution is $x < 2$.

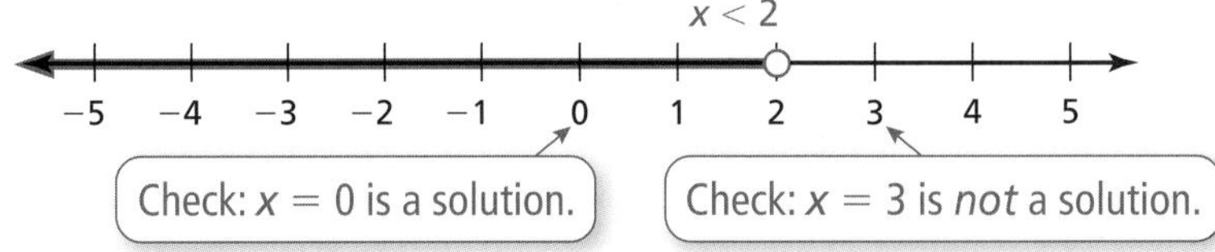

Reading

The inequality $-8.3 \leq x$ is the same as $x \geq -8.3$.

b. Solve $-3.5 \leq 4.8 + x$.

	$-3.5 \leq \quad 4.8 + x$	Write the inequality.
Undo the addition. →	$\underline{-4.8} \quad \underline{-4.8}$	Subtract 4.8 from each side.
	$-8.3 \leq x$	Simplify.

The solution is $x \geq -8.3$.

On Your Own

Now You're Ready
Exercises 8–16

Solve the inequality. Graph the solution.

1. $n + 7 \geq -4$
2. $r - 1.2 > -0.5$
3. $\frac{3}{5} \geq z + \frac{2}{5}$

Multiplication and Division Properties of Inequality (Case 1)

Words If you multiply or divide each side of an inequality by the same *positive* number, the inequality remains true.

Algebra If $a < b$, then $a \cdot c < b \cdot c$ for a positive number c.

If $a < b$, then $\frac{a}{c} < \frac{b}{c}$ for a positive number c.

EXAMPLE 2 Solving Inequalities Using Multiplication or Division

a. Solve $\frac{x}{10} \le -2$. Graph the solution.

$\frac{x}{10} \le -2$ Write the inequality.

Undo the division. → $10 \cdot \frac{x}{10} \le 10 \cdot (-2)$ Multiply each side by 10.

$x \le -20$ Simplify.

The solution is $x \le -20$.

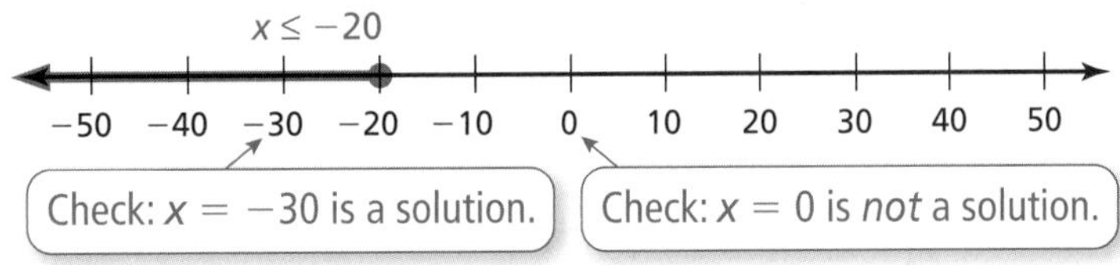
x ≤ −20
−50 −40 −30 −20 −10 0 10 20 30 40 50
Check: x = −30 is a solution.
Check: x = 0 is *not* a solution.

b. Solve $2.5x > 11.25$. Graph the solution.

$2.5x > 11.25$ Write the inequality.

Undo the multiplication. → $\frac{2.5x}{2.5} > \frac{11.25}{2.5}$ Divide each side by 2.5.

$x > 4.5$ Simplify.

The solution is $x > 4.5$.

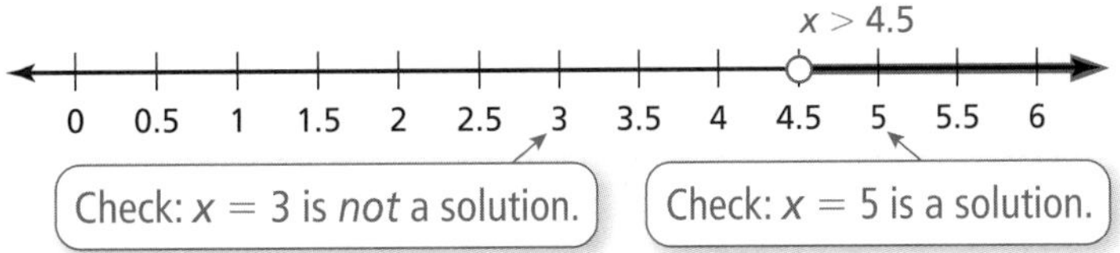
x > 4.5
0 0.5 1 1.5 2 2.5 3 3.5 4 4.5 5 5.5 6
Check: x = 3 is *not* a solution.
Check: x = 5 is a solution.

On Your Own

Now You're Ready
Exercises 21–29

Solve the inequality. Graph the solution.

4. $\frac{b}{8} \ge -5$
5. $-0.4 > \frac{g}{15}$
6. $63 < 9q$
7. $1.6u > -19.2$

Common Error

A negative sign in an inequality does not necessarily mean you must reverse the inequality symbol.

Only reverse the inequality symbol when you multiply or divide both sides by a negative number.

Key Idea

Multiplication and Division Properties of Inequality (Case 2)

Words If you multiply or divide each side of an inequality by the same *negative* number, the direction of the inequality symbol must be reversed for the inequality to remain true.

Algebra If $a < b$, then $a \cdot c > b \cdot c$ for a negative number c.

If $a < b$, then $\frac{a}{c} > \frac{b}{c}$ for a negative number c.

EXAMPLE 3 Solving Inequalities Using Multiplication or Division

a. Solve $\frac{y}{-4} > 6$. Graph the solution.

$\frac{y}{-4} > 6$ Write the inequality.

Undo the division. → $-4 \cdot \frac{y}{-4} < -4 \cdot 6$ Multiply each side by -4. Reverse the inequality symbol.

$y < -24$ Simplify.

The solution is $y < -24$.

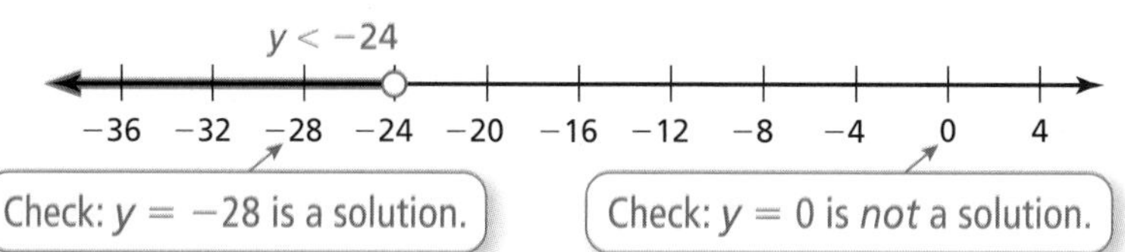

b. Solve $-21 \geq -1.4y$.

$-21 \geq -1.4y$ Write the inequality.

Undo the multiplication. → $\frac{-21}{-1.4} \leq \frac{-1.4y}{-1.4}$ Divide each side by -1.4. Reverse the inequality symbol.

$15 \leq y$ Simplify.

The solution is $y \geq 15$.

On Your Own

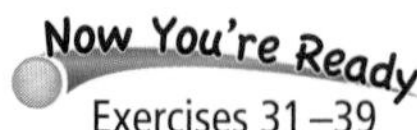

Now You're Ready
Exercises 31–39

Solve the inequality. Graph the solution.

8. $7 > \frac{j}{-1.5}$

9. $\frac{a}{-3} \leq -2$

10. $-2s < 24$

11. $-3.1z \geq 62$

1.6 Exercises

Vocabulary and Concept Check

1. **REASONING** How are inequalities and equations the same? different?
2. **WRITING** Explain how solving $3m < -9$ is different from solving $-3m < 9$.
3. **OPEN-ENDED** Write an inequality that is solved using the Subtraction Property of Inequality.
4. **WHICH ONE DOESN'T BELONG?** Which inequality does *not* belong with the other three? Explain your reasoning.

$2n \geq 10$	$10 \leq 2n$	$-2n \leq -10$	$10 \geq -2n$

Practice and Problem Solving

Use the formula in Activity 1 to create a passing record that makes the inequality true.

5. $P \geq 180$
6. $P + 40 < 110$
7. $280 \leq P - 20$

Solve the inequality. Graph the solution.

1 8. $g + 8 > 5$
9. $m - 6 < 4$
10. $-10 \leq x - 3$
11. $k - 2.9 \geq 1.5$
12. $3.6 \leq w + 5.8$
13. $c - \frac{1}{4} > -\frac{3}{4}$
14. $b + \frac{2}{3} \geq -\frac{1}{2}$
15. $m - 4.7 < -12.3$
16. $6 \geq x + \frac{2}{5}$

17. **ERROR ANALYSIS** Describe and correct the error in solving the inequality.

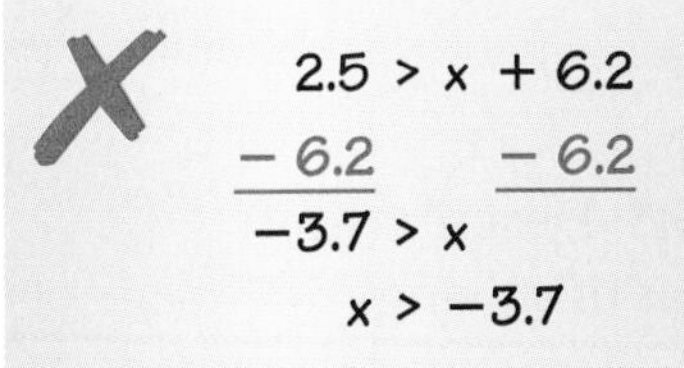

18. **WATER** A dog's water container holds at most 20 quarts.

    a. Which inequality shows how much water w your dog has drunk? Solve the inequality.

$w + 16 \geq 20$	$w + 16 \leq 20$

    b. Interpret the solution to part (a).

Write and solve an inequality that represents the value of x.

19. The base is less than or equal to the height.

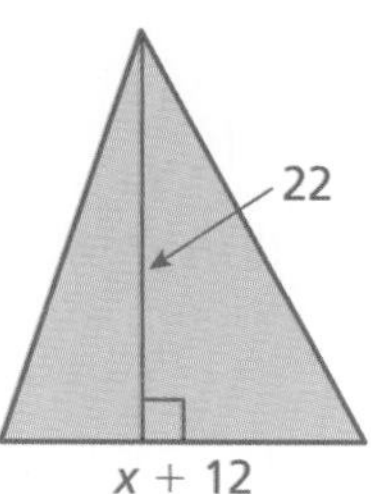

20. The height is greater than the base.

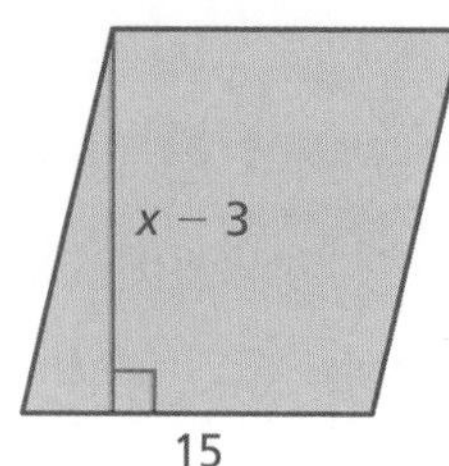

Solve the inequality. Graph the solution.

2 **21.** $6m > -54$

22. $\frac{z}{6} < 8$

23. $\frac{v}{2} \le -15$

24. $51 \le 17c$

25. $\frac{7}{10}x < -\frac{3}{5}$

26. $-12.4 \ge \frac{h}{5}$

27. $\frac{g}{5.1} > -4$

28. $28.8 < 3.2d$

29. $9.8b \ge -29.4$

30. ERROR ANALYSIS Describe and correct the error in solving the inequality.

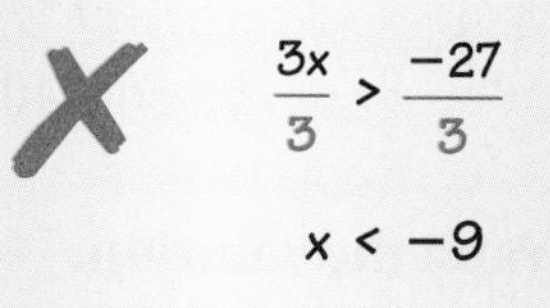

$$\frac{3x}{3} > \frac{-27}{3}$$

$$x < -9$$

Solve the inequality. Graph the solution.

3 **31.** $\frac{n}{-4} < 5$

32. $0 \ge \frac{w}{-8}$

33. $6 > b \div (-3)$

34. $-3p > 72$

35. $-27 \le -5.4a$

36. $\frac{u}{-1.8} < -2.5$

37. $-0.5d \ge -3.4$

38. $\frac{h}{-8} > \frac{3}{4}$

39. $21.6 \le -7.2x$

40. ERROR ANALYSIS Describe and correct the error in solving the inequality.

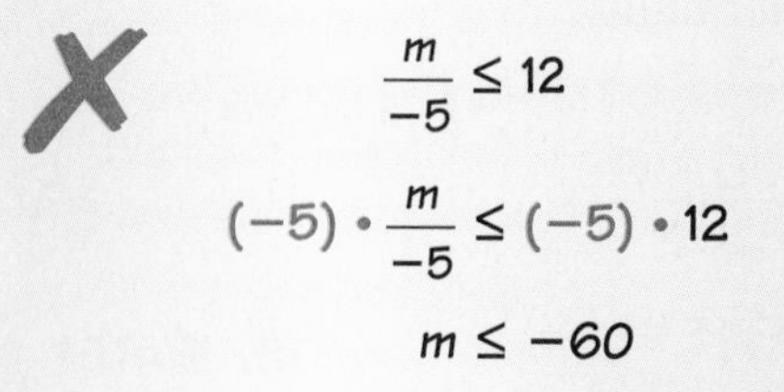

$$\frac{m}{-5} \le 12$$

$$(-5) \cdot \frac{m}{-5} \le (-5) \cdot 12$$

$$m \le -60$$

41. FUNDRAISER You are selling sandwiches as a fundraiser. Your goal is to raise at least $225.

a. Write and solve an inequality to determine how many sandwiches you must sell to meet your goal.

b. How does your answer to part (a) change when the price decreases? increases?

Write and solve an inequality that represents the value of x.

42. Area $< 30 \text{ m}^2$

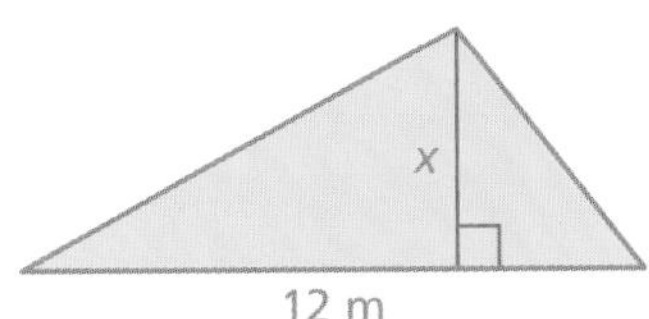

43. Area $\geq 108 \text{ mm}^2$

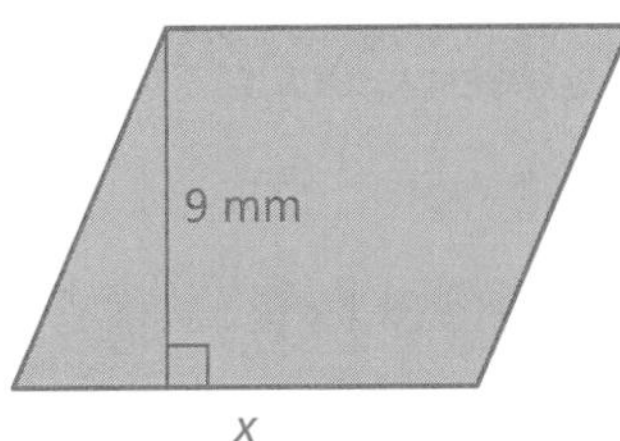

REASONING Determine whether the statement is *always, sometimes,* or *never* true. Explain your reasoning.

44. If k is greater than 0, then $kx > 0$.

45. If k is greater than 0 and x is greater than 0, then $kx > 0$.

46. If k is less than 0, then $kx < 0$.

47. If k is less than 0 and x is greater than 0, then $kx > 0$.

48. BOWLING You can rent bowling shoes each time you bowl or you can buy a new pair for $48. Write and solve an inequality to determine when it is less expensive to buy new bowling shoes than to rent.

49. LAUNDROMAT A dryer at a laundromat will run for 10 minutes on one quarter. To dry your clothes, you need to run the dryer for at least 50 minutes. How much will it cost to dry your clothes?

Let $a > b$ and $x > y$. Tell whether the statement is *always* true. Explain your reasoning.

50. $a + x > b + y$

51. $a - x > b - y$

52. $ax > by$

53. $\frac{a}{x} > \frac{y}{b}$

Fair Game Review What you learned in previous grades & lessons

Solve the equation. Check your solution. *(Section 1.2)*

54. $29 = 17 - 2x$

55. $\frac{3}{4}m - \frac{1}{4}m - 6 = \frac{1}{2}$

56. $3(2.5 - k) - k = 14.5$

57. MULTIPLE CHOICE The inside diameter of the cooler is 1 foot. About how many gallons of water does the cooler contain? ($1 \text{ ft}^3 \approx 7.5$ gal) *(Skills Review Handbook)*

Ⓐ 1 gal

Ⓑ 8 gal

Ⓒ 12 gal

Ⓓ 18 gal

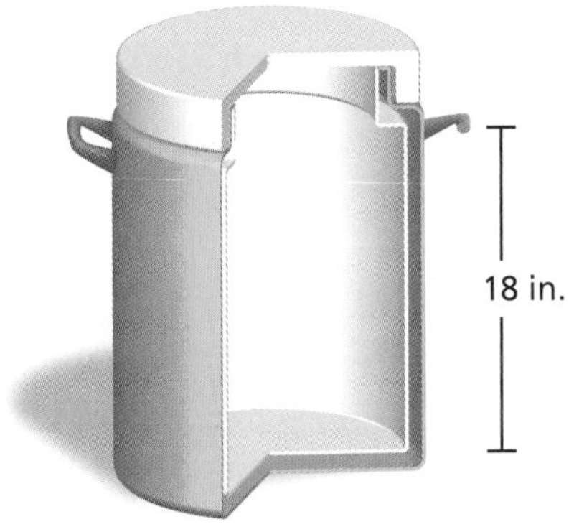

1.7 Solving Two-Step Inequalities

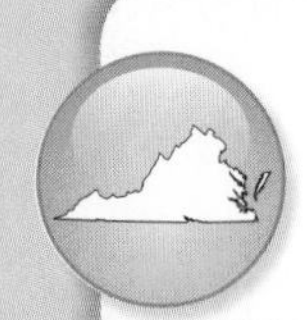

STANDARDS OF LEARNING
8.15

Essential Question
How can you solve a two-step inequality?

1 ACTIVITY: Matching Inequalities

Work with a partner. Match the inequality with its graph.

a. $3x + 2 < 11$ **b.** $3x - 4 \leq 5$ **c.** $\frac{x}{2} - 1 \geq 0$

d. $9 < 2x + 3$ **e.** $5 \leq 4x - 7$ **f.** $\frac{x}{2} + 6 < 8$

A. −8 −6 −4 −2 0 2 4 6 8

B. −8 −6 −4 −2 0 2 4 6 8

C. −8 −6 −4 −2 0 2 4 6 8

D. −8 −6 −4 −2 0 2 4 6 8

E. −8 −6 −4 −2 0 2 4 6 8

F. −8 −6 −4 −2 0 2 4 6 8

2 ACTIVITY: Writing an Inequality

Work with a partner. One of your favorite stores is having a 75% off sale. You have \$20. You want to buy a pair of jeans.

a. Which of the following represents your ability to buy the jeans with \$20?

$0.25x < 20$	$0.25x \leq 20$
$0.25x > 20$	$0.25x \geq 20$

b. What does x represent? Graph the possible values of x on a number line.

c. Can you afford a pair of jeans that originally costs \$100? Explain.

3 ACTIVITY: Spaceman Game

$x + 13 \geq 90$
$x - 2 \geq 5$
$39 < 3x$
$65 < x + 10$
$2x \geq 22$
$x + 5 > 24$
$33 \leq x - 5$
$3x > 126$
$6 < x - 2$
$x + 2 \geq 3$
$x + 30 \geq 84$
$35 \leq x + 6$
$32 \leq x - 29$
$7x > 441$
$110 < x + 32$
$180 \leq 4x$
$x - 52 \geq 32$
$x - 9 > 21$
$2x \geq 178$
$4 < x + 1$
$x - 24 > 34$
$58 < x - 28$
$134 < 2x$
$\frac{x}{2} \geq 45$
$17 < \frac{x}{3}$
$\frac{x}{3} \geq 5$
$8 \leq \frac{x}{2}$
$\frac{x}{4} \geq 12$
$\frac{x}{5} > 14$
$37 \leq \frac{x}{2}$

Play with a partner.

- Player 1: Start the game by finding the inequality from the list that has a solution of $x \geq 1$. This allows you to destroy Asteroids 1, 2, and 3.
- Player 2: Asteroid 3 is destroyed. Find the inequality from the list that has a solution of $x > 3$ or $x \geq 4$. This allows you to destroy Asteroid 4, an alien, and Asteroid 6.
- You can only destroy asteroids and aliens in a straight line.
- Each asteroid is worth 1 point. Each alien is worth 2 points.
- Take turns until someone reaches the end of the maze. The player with the most points wins.
- If an incorrect inequality is chosen, the player loses that turn.

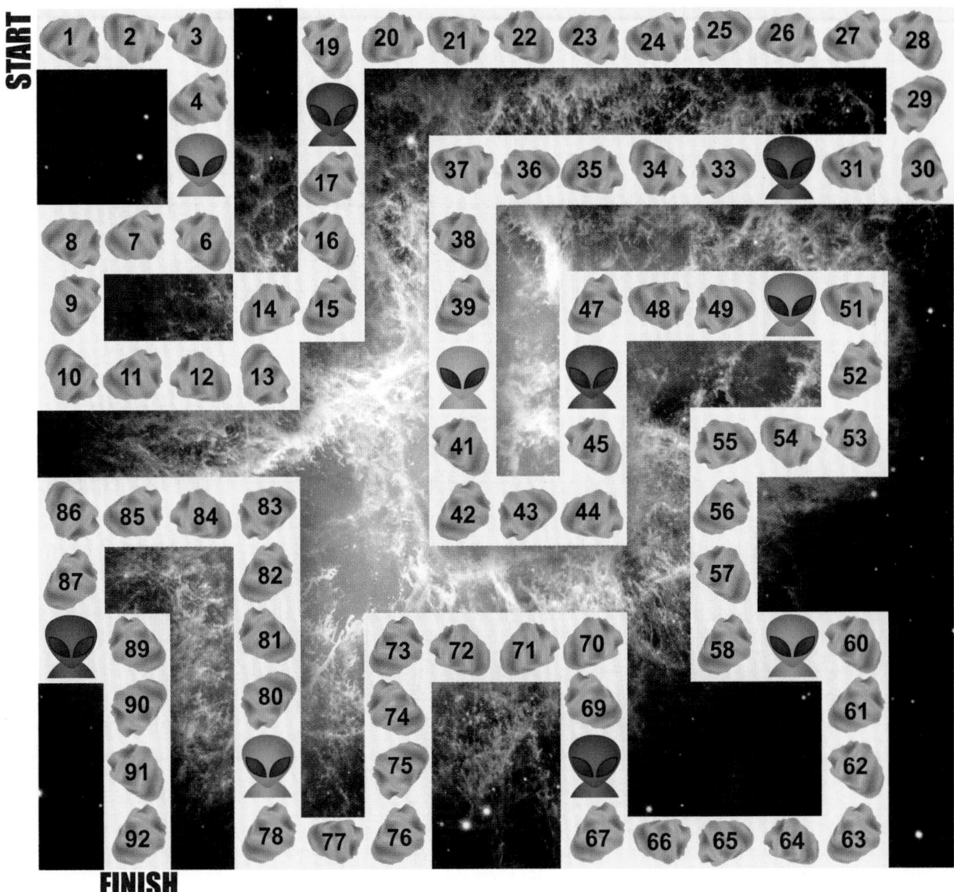

What Is Your Answer?

4. IN YOUR OWN WORDS How can you solve a two-step inequality?

Practice Use what you learned about solving two-step inequalities to complete Exercises 3 and 4 on page 48.

1.7 Lesson

You can solve two-step inequalities in much the same way you solve two-step equations.

EXAMPLE 1 Solving Two-Step Inequalities

a. Solve $5x - 4 \geq 11$. Graph the solution.

	$5x - 4 \geq 11$	Write the inequality.
Step 1: Undo the subtraction. →	$+4 \quad +4$	Add 4 to each side.
	$5x \geq 15$	Simplify.
Step 2: Undo the multiplication. →	$\frac{5x}{5} \geq \frac{15}{5}$	Divide each side by 5.
	$x \geq 3$	Simplify.

∴ The solution is $x \geq 3$.

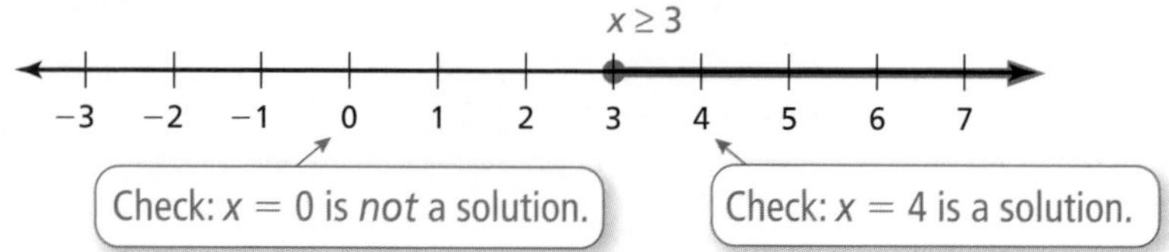

b. Solve $\frac{y}{-6} + 7 < 9$. Graph the solution.

	$\frac{y}{-6} + 7 < 9$	Write the inequality.
Step 1: Undo the addition. →	$-7 \quad -7$	Subtract 7 from each side.
	$\frac{y}{-6} < 2$	Simplify.
Step 2: Undo the division. →	$-6 \cdot \frac{y}{-6} > -6 \cdot 2$	Multiply each side by −6. Reverse the inequality symbol.
	$y > -12$	Simplify.

∴ The solution is $y > -12$.

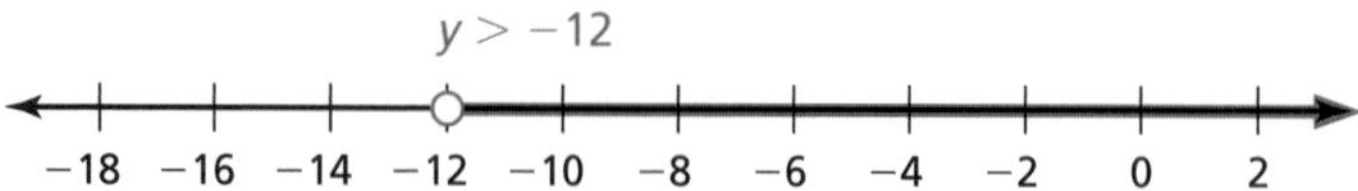

On Your Own

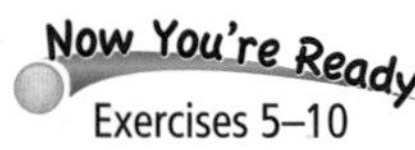

Solve the inequality. Graph the solution.

1. $4b - 1 < 7$
2. $8 + 9c \geq -28$
3. $\frac{n}{-2} + 11 > 12$

EXAMPLE 2 Standardized Test Practice

Which graph represents the solution of $-7(x + 3) \le 28$?

Ⓐ 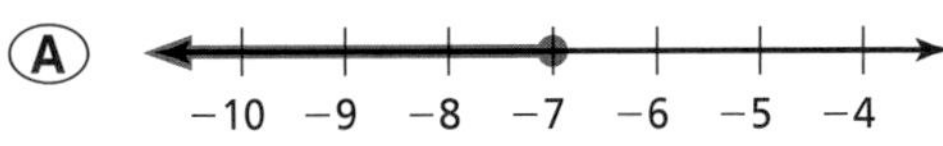

Ⓑ 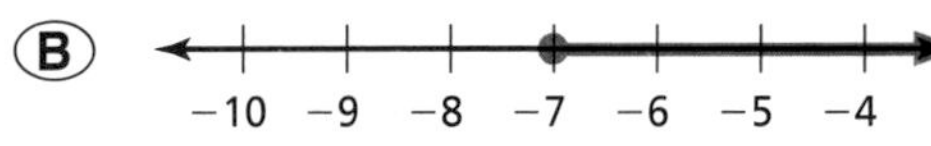

Ⓒ 4 5 6 7 8 9 10

Ⓓ 

	$-7(x + 3) \le 28$	Write the inequality.
	$-7x - 21 \le 28$	Use Distributive Property.
Step 1: Undo the subtraction. →	$+21 \quad +21$	Add 21 to each side.
	$-7x \le 49$	Simplify.
Step 2: Undo the multiplication. →	$\dfrac{-7x}{-7} \ge \dfrac{49}{-7}$	Divide each side by −7. Reverse the inequality symbol.
	$x \ge -7$	Simplify.

∴ The correct answer is Ⓑ.

EXAMPLE 3 Real-Life Application

Trivia Challenge
Your Scores
95 Round 1: Very impressive!
91 Round 2: Good job!
77 Round 3: You can do better!
89 Round 4: Nice work!

You need a mean score of at least 90 to advance to the next round of the trivia game. What score do you need on the fifth game to advance?

Use the definition of mean to write and solve an inequality. Let x be the score on the fifth game.

The phrase "at least" means greater than or equal to.

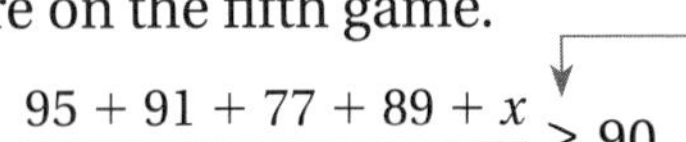

$$\frac{95 + 91 + 77 + 89 + x}{5} \ge 90$$

$\dfrac{352 + x}{5} \ge 90$	Simplify.
$5 \cdot \dfrac{352 + x}{5} \ge 5 \cdot 90$	Multiply each side by 5.
$352 + x \ge 450$	Simplify.
$-352 \quad -352$	Subtract 352 from each side.
$x \ge 98$	Simplify.

∴ You need at least 98 points to advance to the next round.

Remember

The mean in Example 3 is equal to the sum of the game scores divided by the number of games.

On Your Own

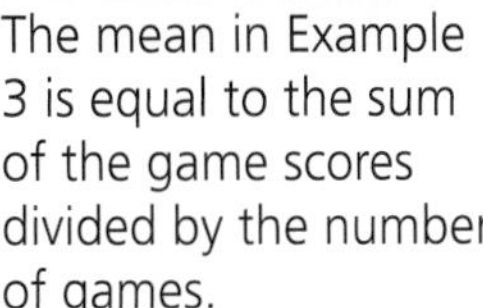

Solve the inequality. Graph the solution.

4. $2(k - 5) < 6$
5. $-4(n - 10) < 32$
6. $-3 \le 0.5(8 + y)$
7. **WHAT IF?** In Example 3, you need a mean score of at least 88 to advance to the next round of the trivia game. What score do you need on the fifth game to advance?

1.7 Exercises

Vocabulary and Concept Check

1. **WRITING** Compare and contrast solving two-step inequalities and solving two-step equations.

2. **OPEN-ENDED** Describe how to solve the inequality $3(a + 5) < 9$.

Practice and Problem Solving

Match the inequality with its graph.

3. $\frac{t}{3} - 1 \geq -3$

A. −9 −8 −7 −6 −5 −4 −3 −2

B. −9 −8 −7 −6 −5 −4 −3 −2

C. −9 −8 −7 −6 −5 −4 −3 −2

4. $5x + 7 \leq 32$

A. 2 3 4 5 6 7 8 9

B. 2 3 4 5 6 7 8 9

C. 2 3 4 5 6 7 8 9

Solve the inequality. Graph the solution.

① 5. $7b + 4 \geq 11$

6. $2v - 4 < 8$

7. $1 - \frac{m}{3} \leq 6$

8. $\frac{4}{5} < 3w - \frac{11}{5}$

9. $1.8 < 0.5 - 1.3p$

10. $-2.4r + 9.6 \geq 4.8$

11. **ERROR ANALYSIS** Describe and correct the error in solving the inequality.

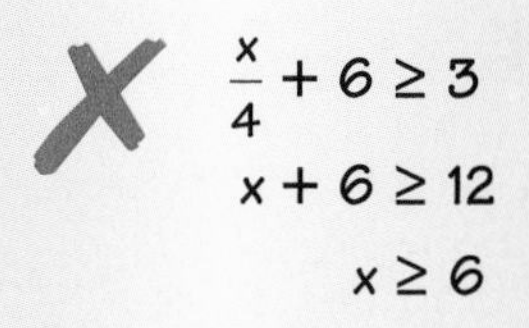

$\frac{x}{4} + 6 \geq 3$

$x + 6 \geq 12$

$x \geq 6$

Solve the inequality. Graph the solution.

② 12. $6(g + 2) \leq 18$

13. $2(y - 5) \leq 16$

14. $-10 \geq \frac{5}{3}(h - 3)$

15. $-\frac{1}{3}(u + 2) > 5$

16. $2.7 > 0.9(n - 1.7)$

17. $10 > -2.5(z - 3.1)$

Anytown Savings and Loan
Your current balance is
$320.00
The minimum balance is $100.00.
Would you like to make another transaction?
Yes No

18. **ATM** Write and solve an inequality that represents the number of $20 bills you can withdraw from the account without going below the minimum balance.

Solve the inequality. Graph the solution.

19. $5x - 2x + 7 \leq 15 + 10$

20. $7b - 12b + 1.4 > 8.4 - 22$

21. **TYPING** One line of text on a page uses about $\frac{3}{16}$ of an inch. There are 1-inch margins at the top and bottom of a page. Write and solve an inequality to find the number of lines that can be typed on a page that is 11 inches long.

22. **WOODWORKING** A woodworker builds a cabinet in 20 hours. The cabinet is sold at a store for \$500. Write and solve an inequality that represents the hourly wage the store can pay the woodworker and still make a profit of at least \$100.

23. **KILLER WHALES** A killer whale has eaten 75 pounds of fish today. It needs to eat at least 140 pounds of fish each day.

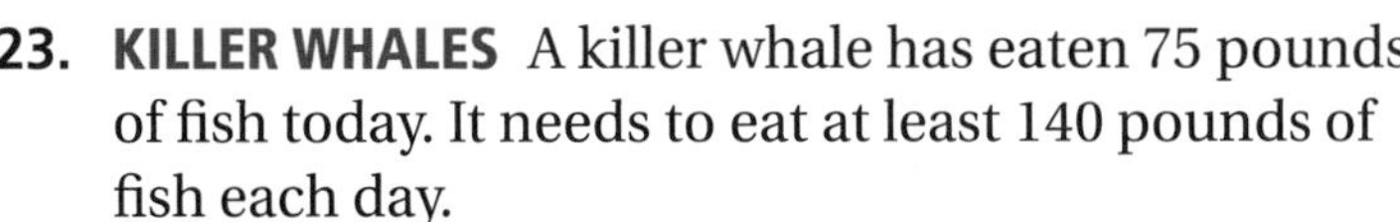

a. A bucket holds 15 pounds of fish. Write and solve an inequality to represent how many more buckets of fish the whale needs to eat.

b. Should the whale be given *four* or *five* more buckets of fish? Explain.

24. **DRIVE-IN** A drive-in movie theater charges \$3.50 per car. The drive-in has already admitted 100 cars. Write and solve an inequality to find how many more cars the drive-in needs to admit to earn at least \$500.

25. Challenge For what values of r will the area of the shaded region be greater than or equal to 12?

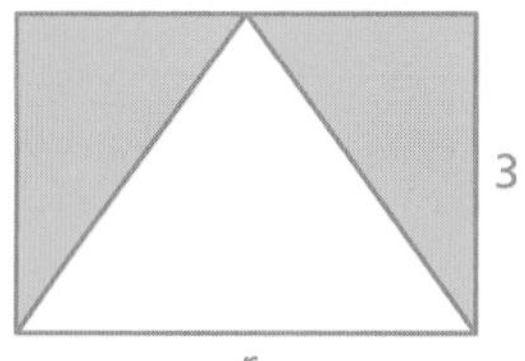

Fair Game Review What you learned in previous grades & lessons

Find the area of the circle. *(Skills Review Handbook)*

26.

27.

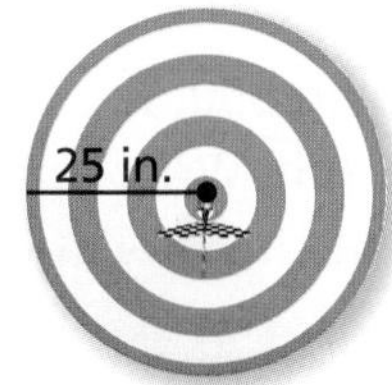

28.

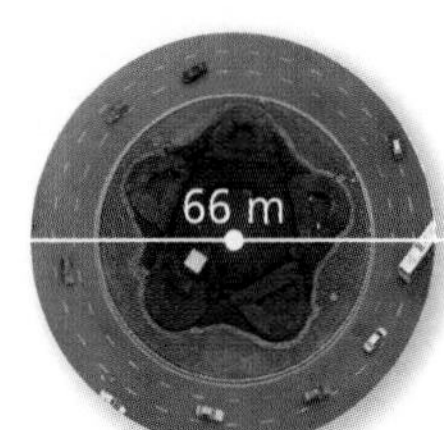

29. **MULTIPLE CHOICE** What is the volume of the cube? *(Skills Review Handbook)*

Ⓐ 8 ft^3 Ⓑ 16 ft^3

Ⓒ 24 ft^3 Ⓓ 32 ft^3

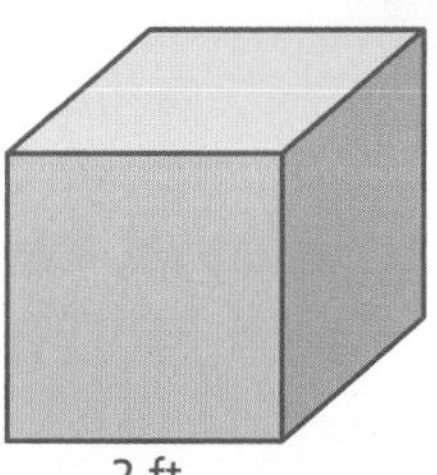

1.5–1.7 Quiz

Write the word sentence as an inequality. *(Section 1.5)*

1. A number x plus 1 is less than -13.

2. A number t minus 1.6 is at most 9.

Graph the inequality on a number line. *(Section 1.5)*

3. $x > -10$

4. $y \leq \frac{3}{5}$

5. $w < 6.8$

Solve the inequality. *(Section 1.6)*

6. $x - 2 < 4$

7. $g + 14 \geq 30$

8. $-2m > 14$

Solve the inequality. Graph the solution. *(Section 1.7)*

9. $2m + 1 \geq 7$

10. $\frac{n}{6} - 8 \leq 2$

11. $2 - \frac{j}{5} > 7$

12. $\frac{5}{4} > -3w - \frac{7}{4}$

13. MP3 PLAYER Your MP3 player can store up to 160 gigabytes of media. You transfer 8.5 gigabytes of media to the MP3 player. Write and solve an inequality that represents the amount of memory available on the MP3 player. *(Section 1.6)*

14. LIFEGUARD Three requirements for a lifeguard training course are shown. *(Section 1.5)*

a. Write and graph three inequalities that represent the requirements.

b. You can swim 350 feet. Do you satisfy the swimming requirement of the course? Explain.

LIFEGUARDS NEEDED
Take Our Training Course NOW!!!
Lifeguard Training Requirements
- Swim at least 100 yards
- Tread water for at least 5 minutes
- Swim 10 yards or more underwater without taking a breath

15. BOOKS You have a gift card worth \$50. You want to buy several paperback books that cost \$6 each. Write and solve an inequality to find the number of books you can buy and still have at least \$20 on the gift card. *(Section 1.7)*

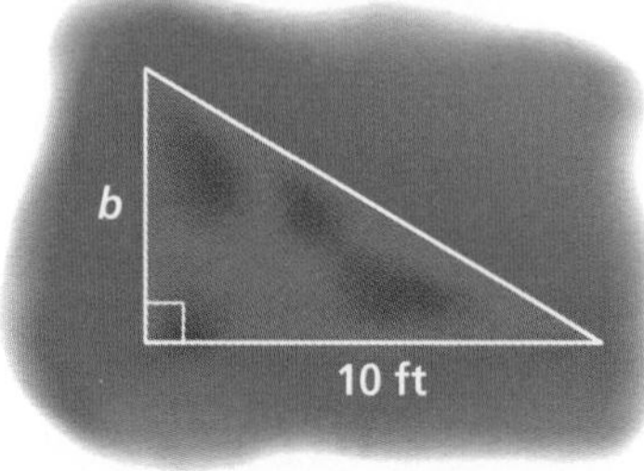

16. GARDEN The area of the triangular garden must be less than 35 square feet. Write and solve an inequality that represents the value of b. *(Section 1.6)*

1 Chapter Review

Check It Out
Vocabulary Help
BigIdeasMath.com

Review Key Vocabulary

literal equation, *p. 24*
inequality, *p. 32*
solution of an inequality, *p. 32*
solution set, *p. 32*
graph of an inequality, *p. 33*

Review Examples and Exercises

1.1 Solving Simple Equations *(pp. 2–9)*

The *boiling point* of a liquid is the temperature at which the liquid becomes a gas. The boiling point of mercury is about $\frac{41}{200}$ of the boiling point of lead. Write and solve an equation to find the boiling point of lead.

Let x be the boiling point of lead.

$$\frac{41}{200}x = 357$$ Write the equation.

$$\frac{200}{41} \cdot \left(\frac{41}{200}x\right) = \frac{200}{41} \cdot 357$$ Multiply each side by $\frac{200}{41}$.

$$x \approx 1741$$ Simplify.

∴ The boiling point of lead is about 1741°C.

Exercises

Solve the equation. Check your solution.

1. $y + 8 = -11$
2. $3.2 = -0.4n$
3. $-\frac{t}{4} = -3\pi$

1.2 Solving Multi-Step Equations *(pp. 10–15)*

Solve $-14x + 28 + 6x = -44$.

$$-14x + 28 + 6x = -44$$ Write the equation.

$$-8x + 28 = -44$$ Combine like terms.

Step 1: Undo the addition. → $$-28 \quad -28$$ Subtract 28 from each side.

$$-8x = -72$$ Simplify.

Step 2: Undo the multiplication. → $$\frac{-8x}{-8} = \frac{-72}{-8}$$ Divide each side by −8.

$$x = 9$$ Simplify.

∴ The solution is $x = 9$.

Exercises

Find the value of x. Then find the angle measures of the polygon.

4. 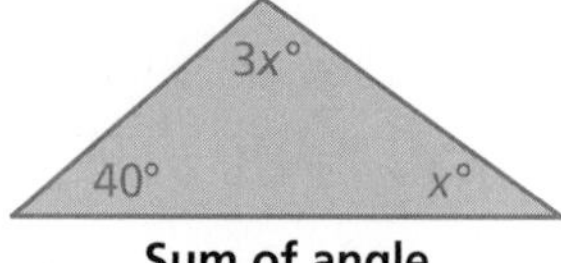

Sum of angle measures: 180°

5. 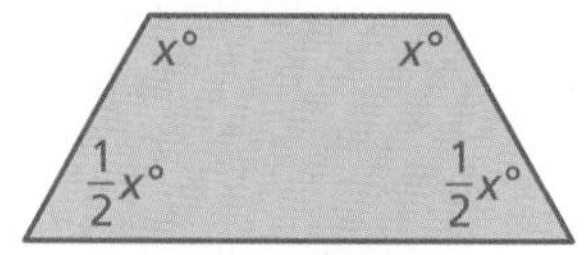

Sum of angle measures: 360°

6. 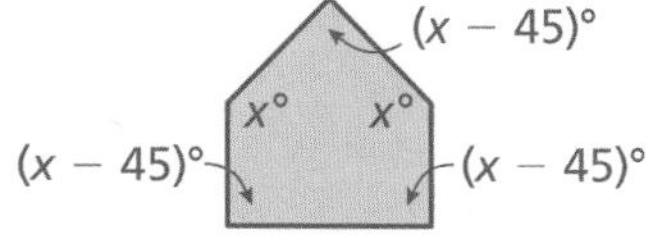

Sum of angle measures: 540°

1.3 Solving Equations with Variables on Both Sides (pp. 16–21)

Solve $3(x - 4) = -2(4 - x)$.

$3(x - 4) = -2(4 - x)$	Write the equation.
$3x - 12 = -8 + 2x$	Use Distributive Property.
$\underline{-\ 2x} \qquad \underline{-\ 2x}$	Subtract $2x$ from each side.
$x - 12 = -8$	Simplify.
$\underline{+\ 12} \qquad \underline{+\ 12}$	Add 12 to each side.
$x = 4$	Simplify.

Undo the addition.

Undo the subtraction.

∴ The solution is $x = 4$.

Exercises

Solve the equation. Check your solution.

7. $5m - 1 = 4m + 5$
8. $3(5p - 3) = 5(p - 1)$
9. $\frac{2}{5}n + \frac{1}{10} = \frac{1}{2}(n + 4)$

1.4 Rewriting Equations and Formulas (pp. 22–27)

The equation for a line in slope-intercept form is $y = mx + b$. Solve the equation for x.

$y = mx + b$	Write the equation.
$y - b = mx + b - b$	Subtract b from each side.
$y - b = mx$	Simplify.
$\frac{y - b}{m} = \frac{mx}{m}$	Divide each side by m.
$\frac{y - b}{m} = x$	Simplify.

∴ So, $x = \frac{y - b}{m}$.

Exercises

10. **a.** The formula $F = \frac{9}{5}(K - 273.15) + 32$ converts temperatures from Kelvin K to Fahrenheit F. Solve the formula for K.

b. Convert 240 °F to Kelvin K. Round your answer to the nearest hundredth.

11. **a.** Write the formula for the area A of a trapezoid.

b. Solve the formula for h.

c. Use the new formula to find the height h of the trapezoid.

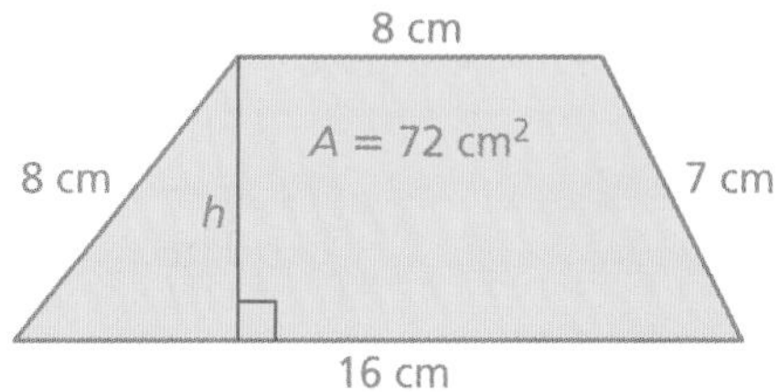

8 cm
A = 72 cm²
8 cm
h
7 cm
16 cm

1.5 Writing and Graphing Inequalities *(pp. 30–35)*

a. Four plus a number w is at least $-\frac{1}{2}$. Write this sentence as an inequality.

Four plus a number w | is at least | $-\frac{1}{2}$.

$4 + w \geq -\frac{1}{2}$

An inequality is $4 + w \geq -\frac{1}{2}$.

b. Graph $m > 4$.

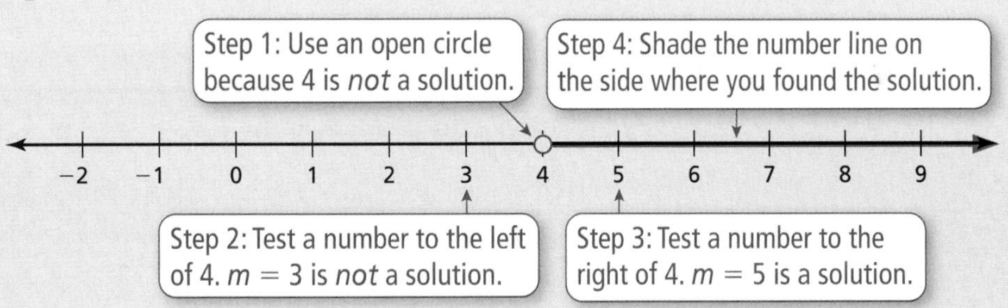

Step 1: Use an open circle because 4 is *not* a solution.
Step 4: Shade the number line on the side where you found the solution.
−2
−1
0
1
2
3
4
5
6
7
8
9
Step 2: Test a number to the left of 4. m = 3 is *not* a solution.
Step 3: Test a number to the right of 4. m = 5 is a solution.

Exercises

Write the word sentence as an inequality.

12. A number v is less than -2.

13. A number x minus $\frac{1}{4}$ is no more than $-\frac{3}{4}$.

Tell whether the given value is a solution of the inequality.

14. $10 - q < 3;\ q = 6$

15. $12 \div m \geq -4;\ m = -3$

Graph the inequality on a number line.

16. $p < 1.2$

17. $n > 10\frac{1}{4}$

1.6 Solving One-Step Inequalities (pp. 36–43)

a. Solve $x - 7 > -15$. Graph the solution.

Undo the subtraction.

$$x - 7 > -15$$ Write the inequality.

$$\underline{+7} \quad \underline{+7}$$ Add 7 to each side.

$$x > -8$$ Simplify.

The solution is $x > -8$.

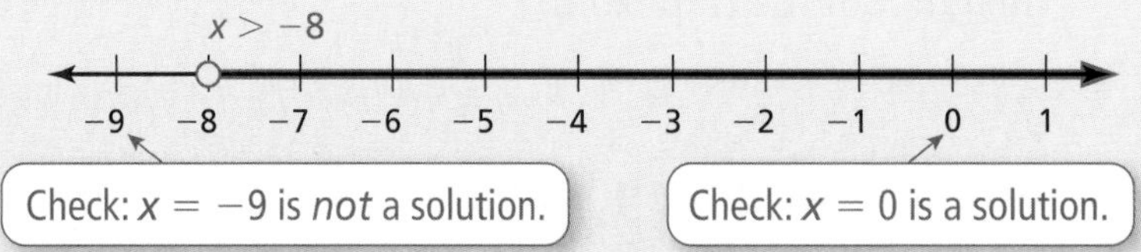
x > −8
−9 −8 −7 −6 −5 −4 −3 −2 −1 0 1
Check: x = −9 is not a solution.
Check: x = 0 is a solution.

b. Solve $\frac{x}{-2} \le -3$. Graph the solution.

$$\frac{x}{-2} \le -3$$ Write the inequality.

Undo the division.

$$-2 \cdot \frac{x}{-2} \ge -2 \cdot (-3)$$ Multiply each side by −2. Reverse the inequality symbol.

$$x \ge 6$$ Simplify.

The solution is $x \ge 6$.

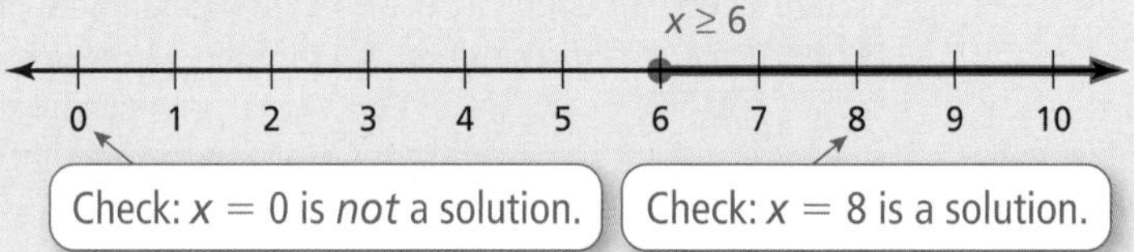
x ≥ 6
0 1 2 3 4 5 6 7 8 9 10
Check: x = 0 is not a solution.
Check: x = 8 is a solution.

Exercises

Solve the inequality. Graph the solution.

18. $c + 13 \ge -3.7$ **19.** $8 < \frac{j}{-2.1}$ **20.** $\frac{1}{3} \le \frac{2}{9}m$

21. PARTY You host a party. You can spend no more than \$100. Write and solve an inequality to find the number of guests you can invite to the party.

Cost per guest: \$7

1.7 Solving Two-Step Inequalities (pp. 44–49)

a. Solve $2x - 3 \leq -9$. Graph the solution.

	$2x - 3 \leq -9$	Write the inequality.
Step 1: Undo the subtraction.	$\underline{+3} \quad \underline{+3}$	Add 3 to each side.
	$2x \leq -6$	Simplify.
Step 2: Undo the multiplication.	$\frac{2x}{2} \leq \frac{-6}{2}$	Divide each side by 2.
	$x \leq -3$	Simplify.

The solution is $x \leq -3$.

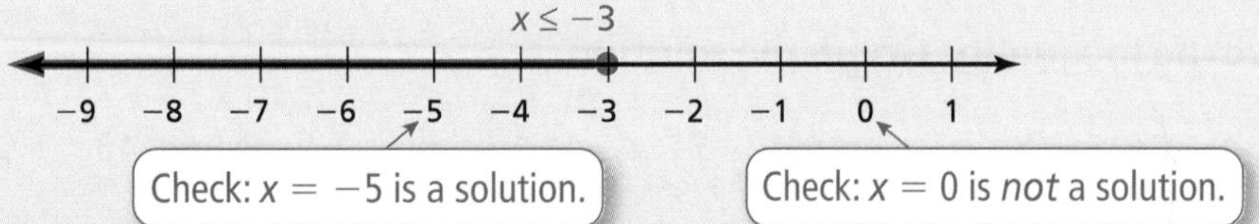

x ≤ −3
−9 −8 −7 −6 −5 −4 −3 −2 −1 0 1
Check: x = −5 is a solution.
Check: x = 0 is not a solution.

b. Solve $\frac{t}{-3} + 4 > 7$. Graph the solution.

	$\frac{t}{-3} + 4 > 7$	Write the inequality.
Step 1: Undo the addition.	$\underline{-4} \quad \underline{-4}$	Subtract 4 from each side.
	$\frac{t}{-3} > 3$	Simplify.
Step 2: Undo the division.	$-3 \cdot \frac{t}{-3} < -3 \cdot 3$	Multiply each side by −3. Reverse the inequality symbol.
	$t < -9$	Simplify.

The solution is $t < -9$.

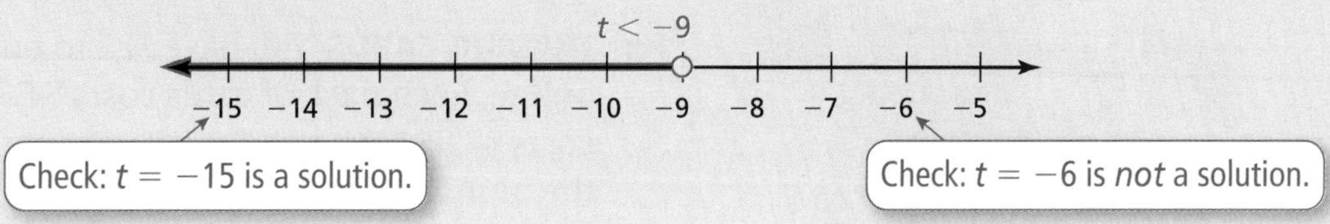

t < −9
−15 −14 −13 −12 −11 −10 −9 −8 −7 −6 −5
Check: t = −15 is a solution.
Check: t = −6 is not a solution.

Exercises

Solve the inequality. Graph the solution.

22. $4x + 3 < 11$ **23.** $\frac{z}{-4} - 3 \leq 1$ **24.** $-3w - 4 > 8$

25. $8(q + 2) < 40$ **26.** $-\frac{1}{2}(p + 4) \leq 18$ **27.** $1.5(k + 3.2) \geq 6.9$

Chapter Test

Solve the equation. Check your solution.

1. $4 + y = 9.5$
2. $x - 3\pi = 5\pi$
3. $3.8n - 13 = 1.4n + 5$

Solve the formula for the red variable.

4. Perimeter of a rectangle: $P = 2\ell + 2w$
5. Distance formula: $d = rt$

Write the word sentence as an inequality.

6. A number j plus 20.5 is greater than or equal to 50.
7. A number r multiplied by $\frac{1}{7}$ is less than -14.

Solve the inequality. Graph the solution.

8. $n - 3 > -3$
9. $x - \frac{7}{8} \leq \frac{9}{8}$
10. $-6b \geq -30$
11. $\frac{y}{-4} \geq 13$
12. $3v - 7 \geq -13.3$
13. $-5(t + 11) < -60$

14. **BASKETBALL** Your basketball team wins a game by 13 points. The opposing team scores 72 points. Write and solve an equation to find your team's score.

15. **JOBS** Your profit for mowing lawns this week is $24. You paid $40 for gas for the lawnmower. How many hours did you work this week?

16. **TRADING CARDS** You have $25 to buy trading cards online. Each pack of cards costs $4.50. Shipping costs $2.95. Write and solve an inequality to find the number of packs of trading cards you can buy.

17. **SCIENCE QUIZZES** The table shows your scores on four science quizzes. What score do you need on the fifth quiz to have a mean score of at least 80?

Quiz	1	2	3	4	5
Score (%)	76	87	73	72	?

1 Standardized Test Practice

Test-Taking Strategy
Solve Directly or Eliminate Choices

When a cat wakes up, it's grumpy for x hours, where $2x-5x=x-4$. What's x?
Ⓐ 0 Ⓑ 1 Ⓒ 2 Ⓓ -3

Don't talk to me until I've had my morning milk.

"You can eliminate A and D. Then, solve directly to determine that the correct answer is B."

1. Which value of x makes the equation true?

$$4x = 32$$

A. 8 **C.** 36

B. 28 **D.** 128

2. A taxi ride costs \$3 plus \$2 for each mile driven. When you rode in a taxi, the total cost was \$39. This can be modeled by the equation below, where m represents the number of miles driven.

$$2m + 3 = 39$$

How long was your taxi ride?

F. 72 mi **H.** 21 mi

G. 34 mi **I.** 18 mi

3. One fluid ounce (fl oz) contains 6 teaspoons. You add $\frac{1}{4}$ teaspoon of vanilla each time you make hot chocolate. How many times can you make hot chocolate using the bottle of vanilla shown?

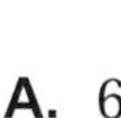

A. 6 **C.** 40

B. 24 **D.** 96

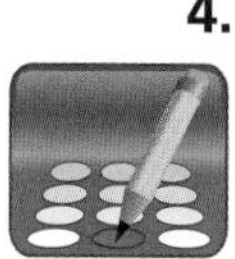

4. A bicyclist is riding at a speed of 900 feet per minute. How many yards does the bicyclist ride in 1 second?

5. The formula below relates distance, rate, and time.

$$d = rt$$

Solve this formula for t.

F. $t = dr$ **H.** $t = d - r$

G. $t = \frac{d}{r}$ **I.** $t = \frac{r}{d}$

6. What could be the first step to solve the equation shown below?

$$3x + 5 = 2(x + 7)$$

A. Combine $3x$ and 5.

B. Multiply x by 2 and 7 by 2.

C. Subtract x from $3x$.

D. Subtract 5 from 7.

7. You work as a sales representative. You earn \$400 per week plus 5% of your total sales for the week.

Part A Last week, you had total sales of \$5000. Find your total earnings. Show your work.

Part B One week, you earned \$1350. Let s represent your total sales that week. Write an equation that could be used to find s.

Part C Using your equation from Part B, find s. Show all steps clearly.

8. In ten years, Maria will be 39 years old. Let m represent Maria's age today. Which equation can be used to find m?

F. $m = 39 + 10$

G. $m - 10 = 39$

H. $m + 10 = 39$

I. $10m = 39$

9. Which value of y makes the equation below true?

$$3y + 8 = 7y + 11$$

A. -4.75

B. -0.75

C. 0.75

D. 4.75

10. The equation below is used to convert a Fahrenheit temperature F to its equivalent Celsius temperature C.

$$C = \frac{5}{9}(F - 32)$$

Which formula can be used to convert a Celsius temperature to its equivalent Fahrenheit temperature?

F. $F = \frac{5}{9}(C - 32)$

G. $F = \frac{9}{5}(C + 32)$

H. $F = \frac{9}{5}C + \frac{32}{5}$

I. $F = \frac{9}{5}C + 32$

11. You have already saved \$35 for a new cell phone. You need \$175 in all. You think you can save \$10 per week. At this rate, how many more weeks will you need to save money before you can buy the new cell phone?

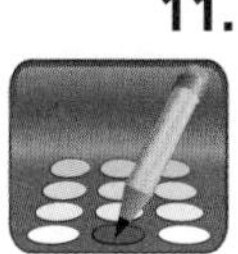

12. The cube shown below has edge lengths of 1 foot. What is the volume of the cube?

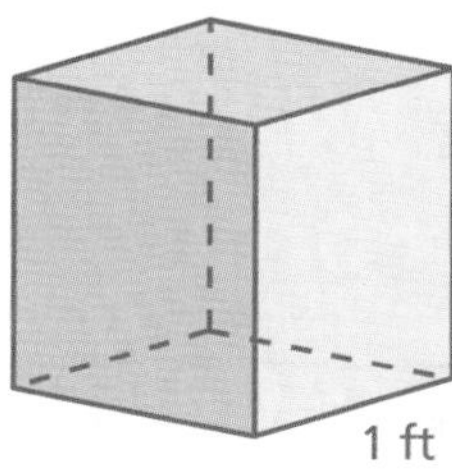

A. 12 in.^3

B. 36 in.^3

C. 144 in.^3

D. 1728 in.^3

13. Which value of x makes the equation below true?

$$6(x - 3) = 4x - 7$$

F. -5.5

G. -2

H. 1.1

I. 5.5

14. The drawing below shows equal weights on two sides of a balance scale.

What can you conclude from the drawing?

A. A mug weighs one-third as much as a trophy.

B. A mug weighs one-half as much as a trophy.

C. A mug weighs twice as much as a trophy.

D. A mug weighs three times as much as a trophy.

2 Graphing and Writing Linear Equations

"Okay Descartes, stand on the *y*-axis and try to intercept the pass when I throw."

"Here's an easy example of a line with a slope of 1."

"You eat one mouse treat the first day. Two treats the second day. And so on. Get it?"

What You Learned Before

"I estimate that we are on a slope of about −0.625. What do you think?"

Evaluating Expressions Using Order of Operations

Example 1 **Evaluate $2xy + 3(x + y)$ when $x = 4$ and $y = 7$.**

$2xy + 3(x + y) = 2(4)(7) + 3(4 + 7)$	Substitute 4 for x and 7 for y.
$= 8(7) + 3(4 + 7)$	Use order of operations.
$= 56 + 3(11)$	Simplify.
$= 56 + 33$	Multiply.
$= 89$	Add.

Try It Yourself

Evaluate the expression when $a = \frac{1}{4}$ and $b = 6$.

1. $-8ab$ **2.** $16a^2 - 4b$ **3.** $\frac{5b}{32a^2}$ **4.** $12a + (b - a - 4)$

Plotting Points

Example 2 **Write the ordered pair that corresponds to Point U.**

Point U is 3 units to the left of the origin and 4 units down. So, the x-coordinate is -3 and the y-coordinate is -4.

∴ The ordered pair $(-3, -4)$ corresponds to Point U.

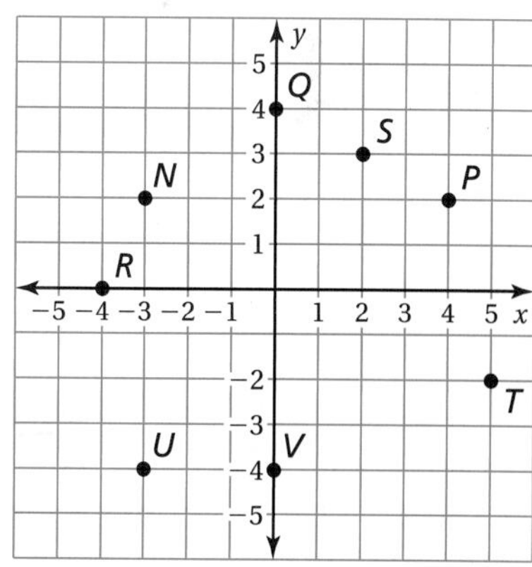

Example 3 **Which point is located at $(5, -2)$?**

Start at the origin. Move 5 units right and 2 units down.

∴ Point T is located at $(5, -2)$.

Try It Yourself

Use the graph to answer the question.

5. Write the ordered pair that corresponds to Point Q.

6. Write the ordered pair that corresponds to Point P.

7. Which point is located at $(-4, 0)$?

8. Which point is located in Quadrant II?

2.1 Graphing Linear Equations

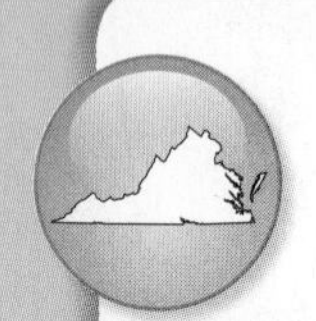

STANDARDS OF LEARNING
8.16

Essential Question How can you recognize a linear equation? How can you draw its graph?

1 ACTIVITY: Graphing a Linear Equation

Work with a partner.

a. Use the equation $y = \frac{1}{2}x + 1$ to complete the table. (Choose any two x-values and find the y-values.)

	Solution Points	
x		
$y = \frac{1}{2}x + 1$		

b. Write the two ordered pairs given by the table. These are called **solution points** of the equation.

c. Plot the two solution points. Draw a line *exactly* through the two points.

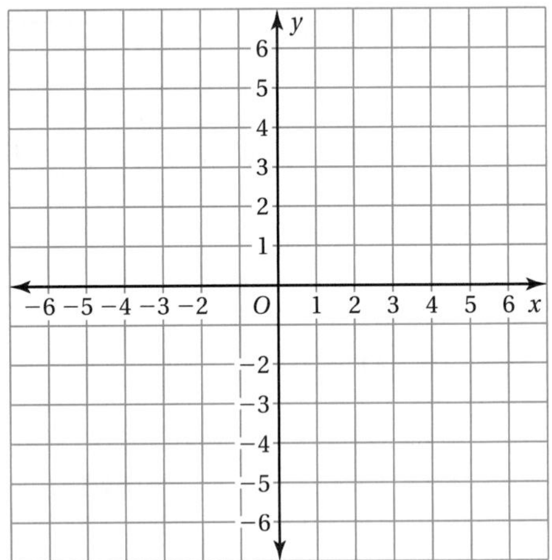

d. Find a different point on the line. Check that this point is a solution point of the equation $y = \frac{1}{2}x + 1$.

e. **GENERALIZE** Do you think it is true that *any* point on the line is a solution point of the equation $y = \frac{1}{2}x + 1$? Explain.

f. Choose five additional x-values for the table. (Choose positive and negative x-values.) Plot the five corresponding solution points. Does each point lie on the line?

	Solution Points				
x					
$y = \frac{1}{2}x + 1$					

g. **GENERALIZE** Do you think it is true that *any* solution point of the equation $y = \frac{1}{2}x + 1$ is a point on the line? Explain.

h. **THE MEANING OF A WORD** Why is $y = ax + b$ called a *linear equation*?

2 HISTORY: Analytic Geometry

René Descartes was a French philosopher, scientist, and mathematician.

René Descartes (1596–1650)

Up until the time of Descartes, *algebra* and *geometry* were separate fields of mathematics. Descartes's invention of the coordinate plane was of huge importance to mathematics. For the first time, people could "see" solutions of equations. No longer did people have to work with algebra from a purely symbolic point of view.

That's my name too.

Descartes's combination of geometry and algebra is called *analytic* (or algebraic) *geometry*. One of the main discoveries in analytic geometry is that all of the important types of graphs (lines, parabolas, circles, ellipses, and so on) can be represented by simple algebraic equations.

Within a few dozen years, other mathematicians were able to discover all of *calculus*, a field of mathematics that is of great value in business, science, and engineering.

In this book, you will study lines. In Algebra 1 and Algebra 2, you will study many other types of equations.

Line: $y = ax + b$

Parabola: $y = ax^2 + b$

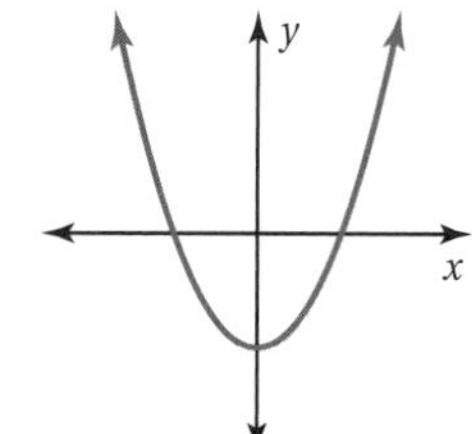

Circle: $x^2 + y^2 = r^2$

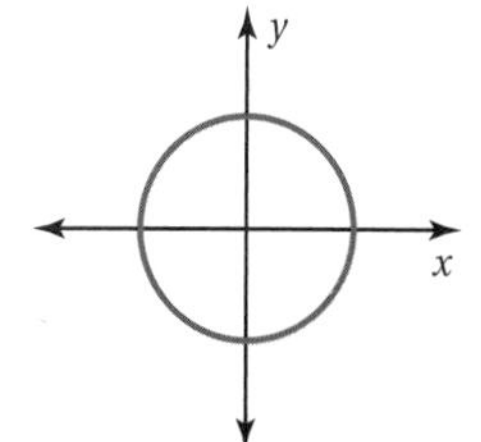

What Is Your Answer?

3. **IN YOUR OWN WORDS** How can you recognize a linear equation? How can you draw its graph? Write an equation that is linear. Write an equation that is *not* linear.

4. Are you a visual learner? Most people can learn mathematics more easily when they see "pictures" of the mathematics. Why do you think Descartes's invention was important to mathematics?

Practice Use what you learned about graphing linear equations to complete Exercises 3 and 4 on page 66.

2.1 Lesson

Key Vocabulary
linear equation, *p. 64*
solution of a linear equation, *p. 64*

Linear Equations

A **linear equation** is an equation whose graph is a line. The points on the line are **solutions** of the equation.

You can use a graph to show the solutions of a linear equation. The graph below is for the equation $y = x + 1$.

x	y	(x, y)
-1	0	$(-1, 0)$
0	1	$(0, 1)$
2	3	$(2, 3)$

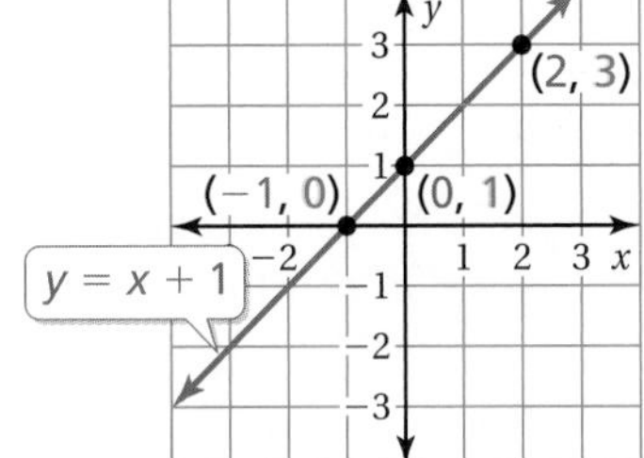

Remember

An ordered pair (x, y) is used to locate a point in a coordinate plane.

EXAMPLE 1 Graphing a Linear Equation

Graph $y = -2x + 1$.

Step 1: Make a table of values.

x	$y = -2x + 1$	y	(x, y)
-1	$y = -2(-1) + 1$	3	$(-1, 3)$
0	$y = -2(0) + 1$	1	$(0, 1)$
2	$y = -2(2) + 1$	-3	$(2, -3)$

Step 2: Plot the ordered pairs.

Step 3: Draw a line through the points.

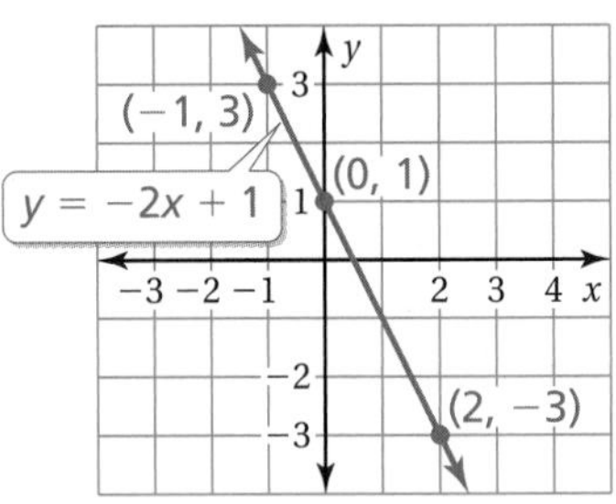

Key Idea

Graphing a Horizontal Line

The graph of $y = a$ is a horizontal line passing through $(0, a)$.

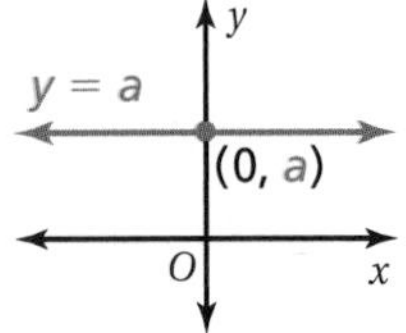

Multi-Language Glossary at BigIdeasMath.com.

EXAMPLE 2 Graphing a Horizontal Line

Graph $y = -3$.

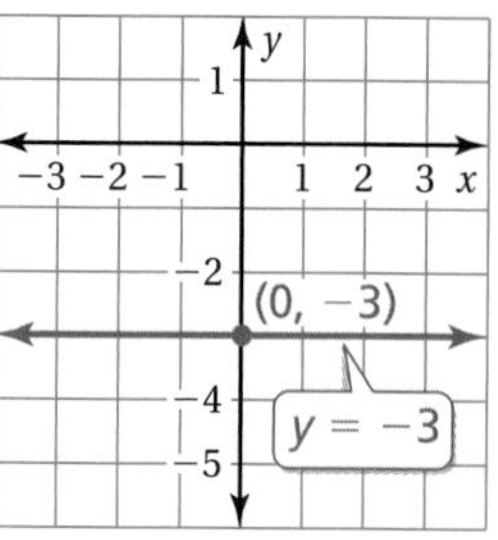

The graph of $y = -3$ is a horizontal line passing through $(0, -3)$.

Plot $(0, -3)$. Draw a horizontal line through the point.

On Your Own

Now You're Ready
Exercises 5–13

Graph the linear equation.

1. $y = 3x$
2. $y = -\frac{1}{2}x + 2$
3. $y = \pi$
4. $y = -1.5$

EXAMPLE 3 Real-Life Application

The wind speed y (in miles per hour) of a tropical storm is $y = 2x + 66$, where x is the number of hours after the storm enters the Gulf of Mexico.

a. Graph the equation.

b. When does the storm become a hurricane?

A tropical storm becomes a hurricane when wind speeds are at least 74 miles per hour.

a. Make a table of values.

x	$y = 2x + 66$	y	(x, y)
0	$y = 2(0) + 66$	66	(0, 66)
1	$y = 2(1) + 66$	68	(1, 68)
2	$y = 2(2) + 66$	70	(2, 70)
3	$y = 2(3) + 66$	72	(3, 72)

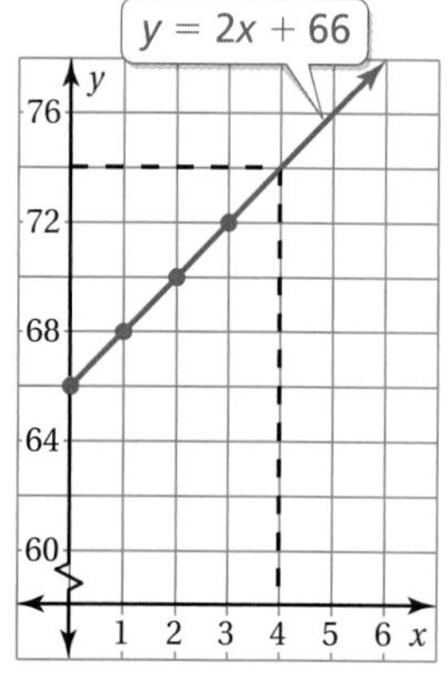

Plot the ordered pairs and draw a line through the points.

b. From the graph, you can see that $y = 74$ when $x = 4$.

So, the storm becomes a hurricane 4 hours after it enters the Gulf of Mexico.

On Your Own

5. **WHAT IF?** In Example 3, the wind speed of the storm is $y = 1.5x + 62$. When does the storm become a hurricane?

2.1 Exercises

Vocabulary and Concept Check

1. **VOCABULARY** What type of graph represents the solutions of the equation $y = 2x + 3$?

2. **WHICH ONE DOESN'T BELONG?** Which equation does *not* belong with the other three? Explain your reasoning.

$y = 0.5x - 0.2$ | $4x + 3 = y$ | $y = x^2 + 6$ | $\frac{3}{4}x + \frac{1}{3} = y$

Practice and Problem Solving

Copy and complete the table. Plot the two solution points and draw a line *exactly* through the two points. Find a different solution point on the line.

3.

x		
$y = 3x - 1$		

4.

x		
$y = \frac{1}{3}x + 2$		

Graph the linear equation.

5. $y = -5x$
6. $y = \frac{1}{4}x$
7. $y = 5$
8. $y = x - 3$
9. $y = -7x - 1$
10. $y = -\frac{x}{3} + 4$
11. $y = \frac{3}{4}x - \frac{1}{2}$
12. $y = -\frac{2}{3}$
13. $y = 6.75$

14. **ERROR ANALYSIS** Describe and correct the error in graphing the equation.

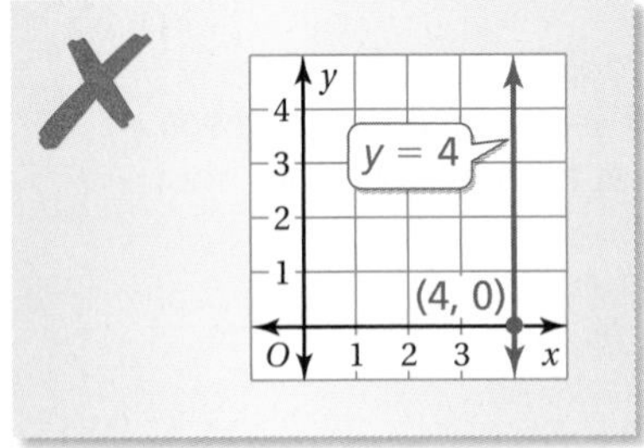

15. **MESSAGING** You sign up for an unlimited text messaging plan for your cell phone. The equation $y = 20$ represents the cost y (in dollars) for sending x text messages. Graph the equation.

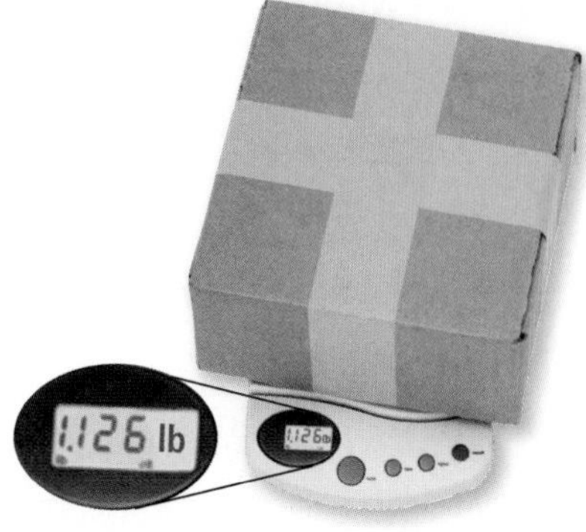

16. **MAIL** The equation $y = 2x + 3$ represents the cost y (in dollars) of mailing a package that weighs x pounds.

    a. Graph the equation.

    b. Use the graph to estimate how much it costs to mail the package.

    c. Use the equation to find exactly how much it costs to mail the package.

Solve for y. Then graph the equation.

17. $y - 3x = 1$

18. $5x + 2y = 4$

19. $-\frac{1}{3}y + 4x = 3$

20. $x + 0.5y = 1.5$

21. SAVINGS You have $100 in your savings account and plan to deposit $12.50 each month.

a. Write and graph a linear equation that represents the balance in your account.

b. How many months will it take you to save enough money to buy 10 acres of land on Mars?

22. CAMERA One second of video on your digital camera uses the same amount of memory as two pictures. Your camera can store 250 pictures.

a. Write and graph a linear equation that represents the number y of pictures your camera can store if you take x seconds of video.

b. How many pictures can your camera store after you take the video shown?

23. SEA LEVEL Along the U.S. Atlantic Coast, the sea level is rising about 2 millimeters per year.

a. Write and graph a linear equation that represents how much sea level rises over a period of time.

b. How many millimeters has sea level risen since you were born?

24. Geometry The sum S of the measures of the angles of a polygon is $S = (n - 2) \cdot 180$, where n is the number of sides of the polygon. Plot four points (n, S) that satisfy the equation. Do the points lie on a line? Explain your reasoning.

Fair Game Review What you learned in previous grades & lessons

Write the ordered pair corresponding to the point.
(Skills Review Handbook)

25. Point A

26. Point B

27. Point C

28. Point D

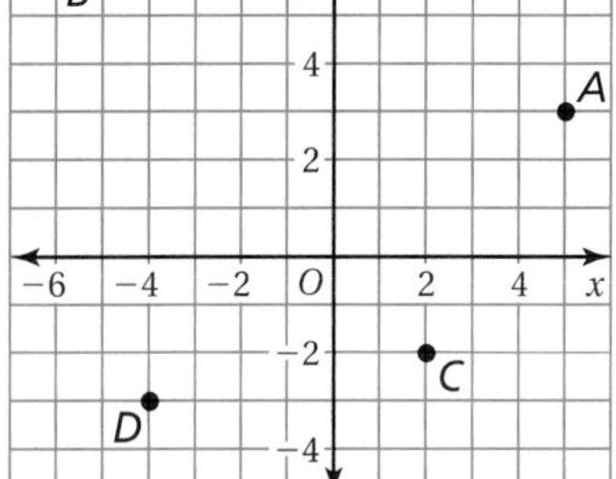

29. MULTIPLE CHOICE A debate team has 15 female members. The ratio of females to males is 3 : 2. How many males are on the debate team? *(Skills Review Handbook)*

Ⓐ 6 Ⓑ 10 Ⓒ 22 Ⓓ 25

2.2 Slope of a Line

STANDARDS OF LEARNING
8.3
8.16

Essential Question How can the slope of a line be used to describe the line?

Slope is the rate of change between any two points on a line. It is the measure of the *steepness* of the line.

To find the slope of a line, find the ratio of the change in y (vertical change) to the change in x (horizontal change).

$$\text{slope} = \frac{\text{change in } y}{\text{change in } x}$$

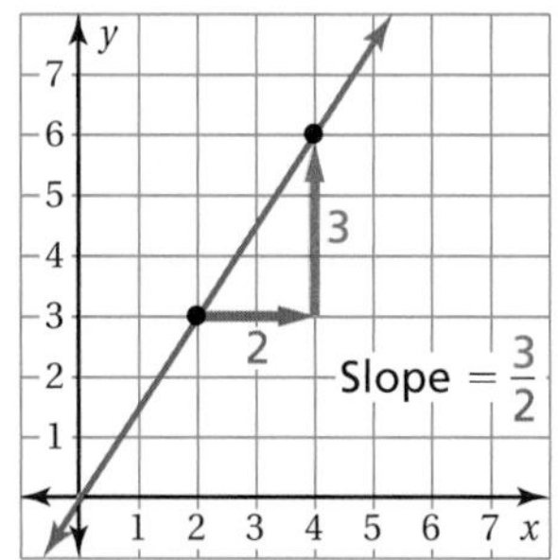

1 ACTIVITY: Finding the Slope of a Line

Work with a partner. Find the slope of each line using two methods.

Method 1: Use the two black points. •

Method 2: Use the two pink points. •

Do you get the same slope using each method?

a.

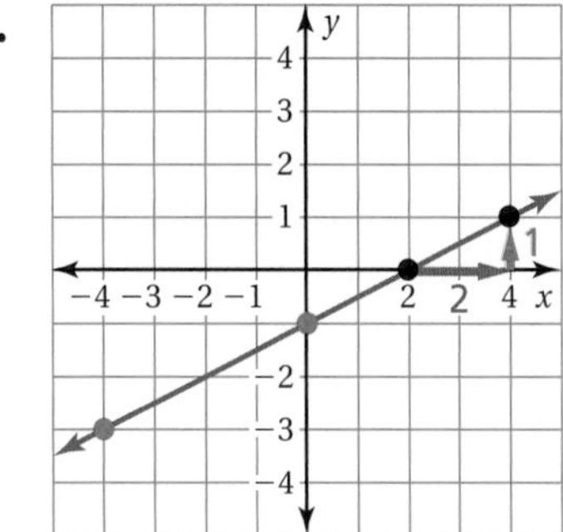

b.

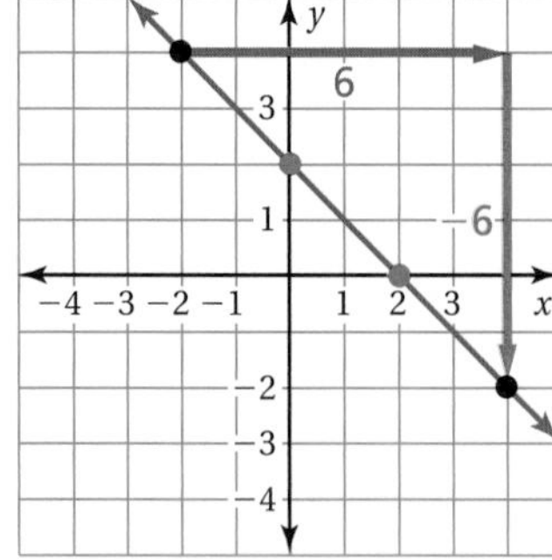

c.

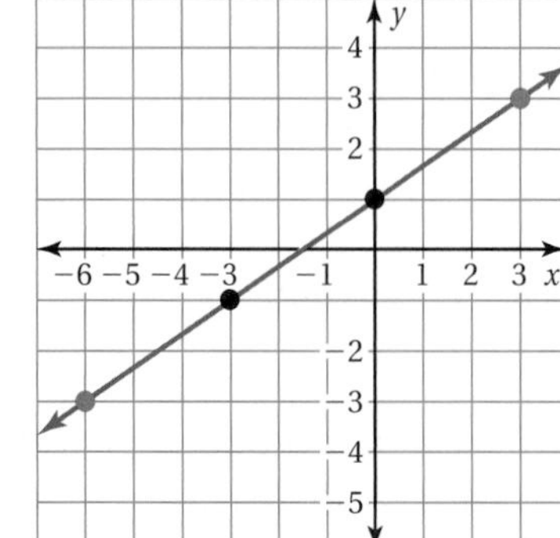

d.

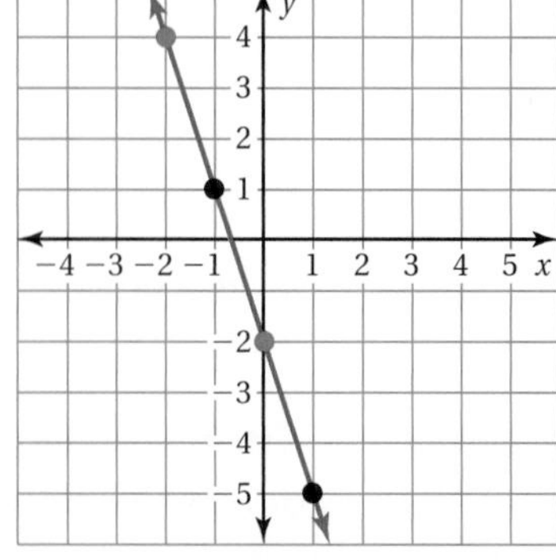

2 ACTIVITY: Drawing Lines with Given Slopes

Work with a partner.

- **Draw a line through the black point using the given slope.**
- **Draw a line through the pink point using the given slope.**
- **What do you notice about the two lines?**

a. Slope $= 2$

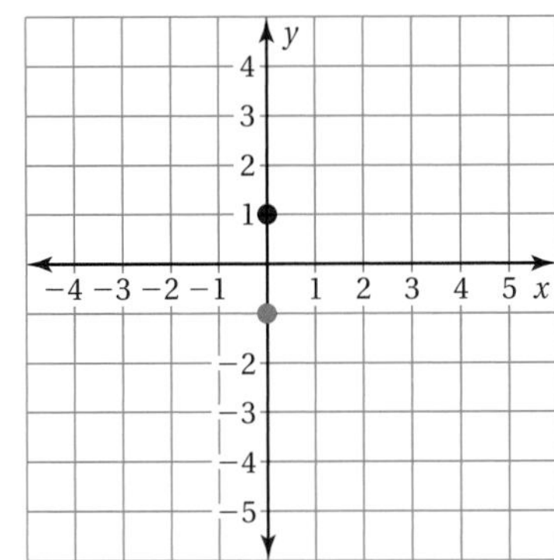

b. Slope $= -\frac{1}{2}$

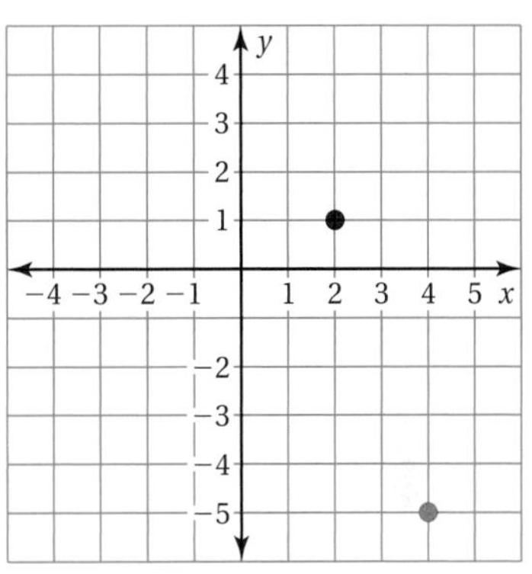

c. Slope $= \frac{3}{4}$

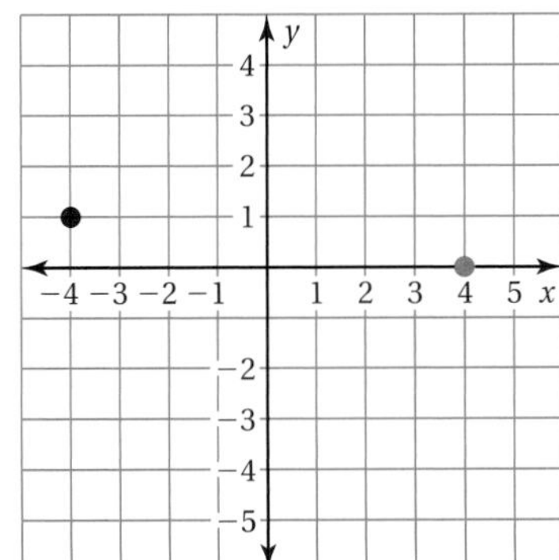

d. Slope $= -2$

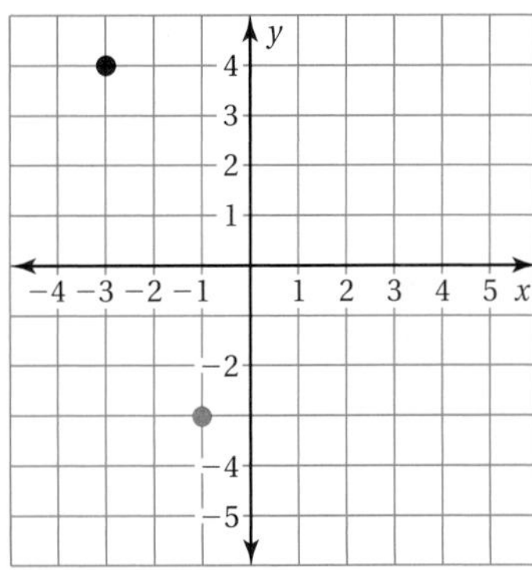

What Is Your Answer?

3. IN YOUR OWN WORDS How can the slope of a line be used to describe the line?

a. Draw three lines that have positive slopes.

b. Draw three lines that have negative slopes.

4. Line A has a slope of 1. Line B has a slope of 2. Compare the slopes of the lines. Illustrate your comparison.

5. Line C has a slope of -1. Line D has a slope of -2. Compare the slopes of the lines. Illustrate your comparison.

Practice Use what you learned about the slope of a line to complete Exercises 4–6 on page 73.

Key Vocabulary
slope, *p. 70*
rise, *p. 70*
run, *p. 70*

Key Idea

Slope

The **slope** of a line is a ratio of the change in y (the **rise**) to the change in x (the **run**) between any two points on the line.

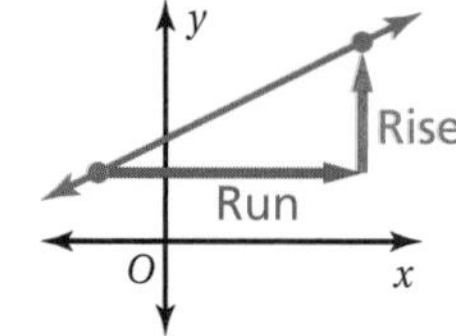

$$\text{slope} = \frac{\text{change in } y}{\text{change in } x} = \frac{\text{rise}}{\text{run}}$$

Positive slope

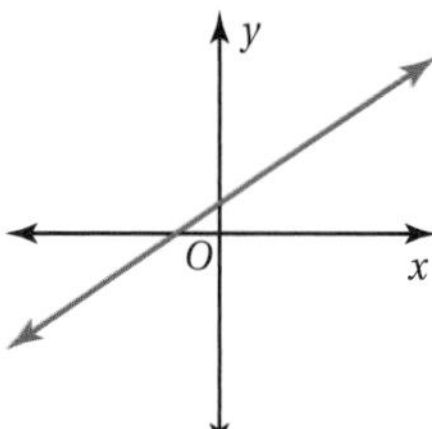

The line rises from left to right.

Negative slope

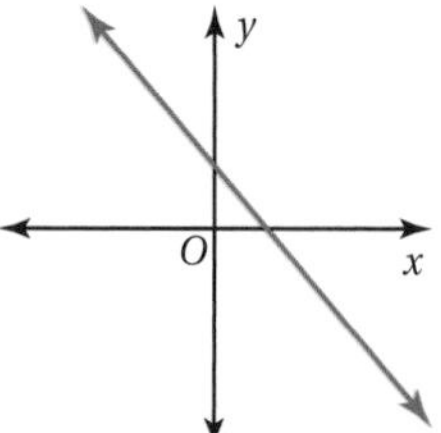

The line falls from left to right.

EXAMPLE  1 Finding the Slope of a Line

Tell whether the slope of the line is *positive* or *negative*. Then find the slope.

a.

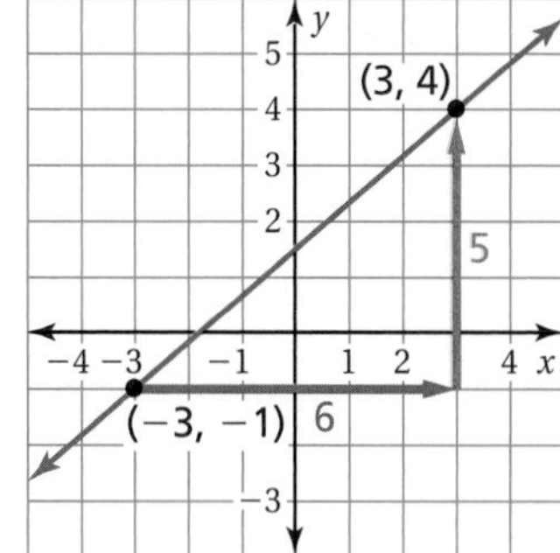

The line rises from left to right. So, the slope is positive.

$$\text{slope} = \frac{\text{rise}}{\text{run}}$$

$$= \frac{5}{6}$$

The slope is $\frac{5}{6}$.

b.

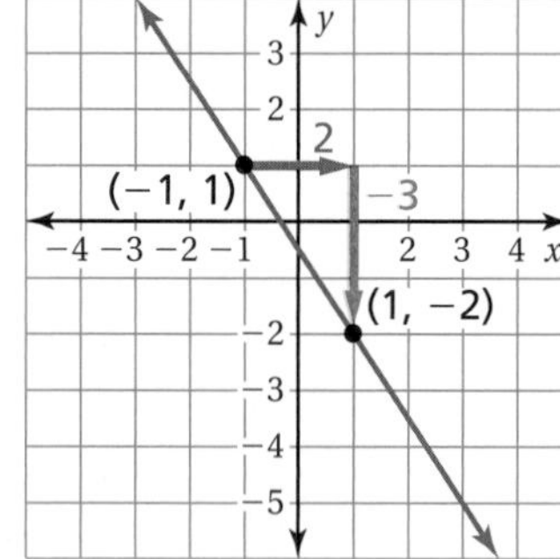

The line falls from left to right. So, the slope is negative.

$$\text{slope} = \frac{\text{rise}}{\text{run}}$$

$$= \frac{-3}{2}, \text{ or } -\frac{3}{2}$$

The slope is $-\frac{3}{2}$.

EXAMPLE 2 Finding the Slope of a Horizontal Line

Study Tip

The slope of a horizontal line is always 0.

Find the slope of the line.

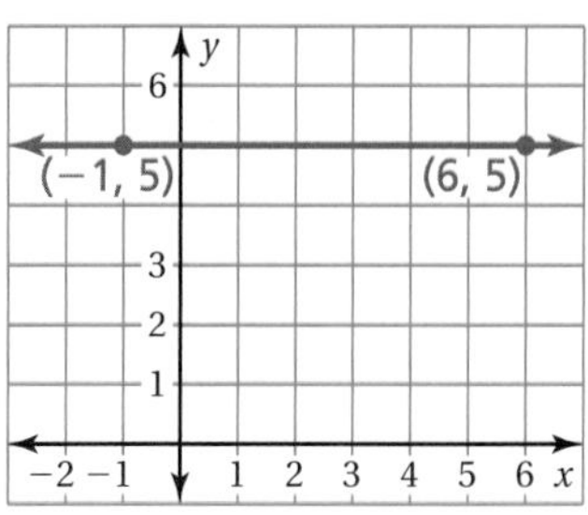

The line is not rising or falling. So, the rise is 0.

$$\text{slope} = \frac{\text{rise}}{\text{run}}$$

$$= \frac{0}{7}$$

∴ The slope is 0.

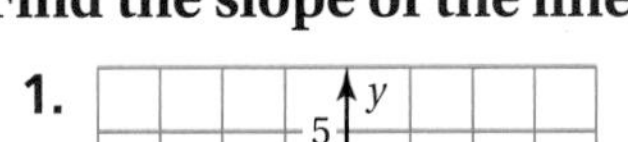

On Your Own

Now You're Ready Exercises 7–12

Find the slope of the line.

1. 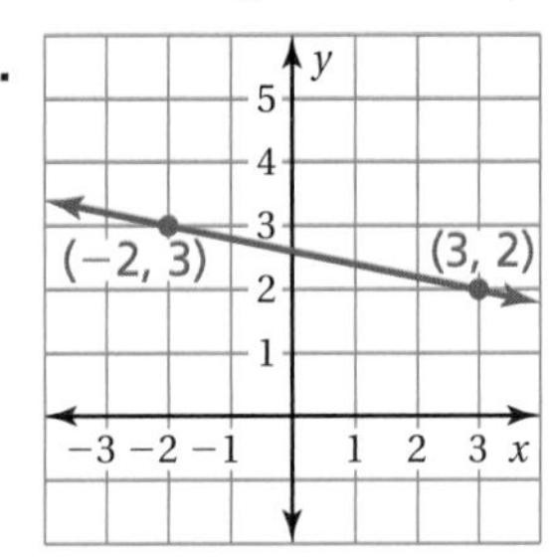

2. 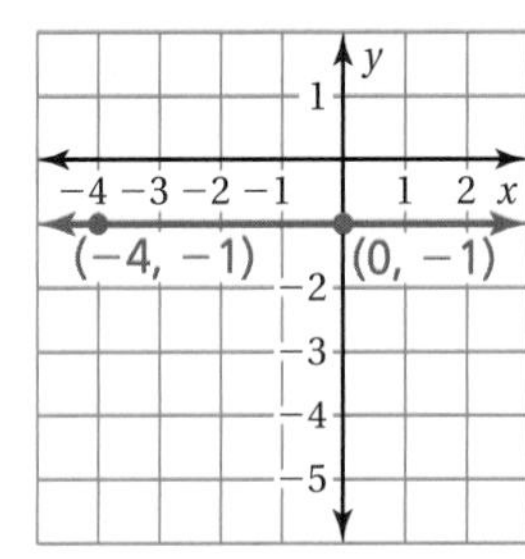

3. 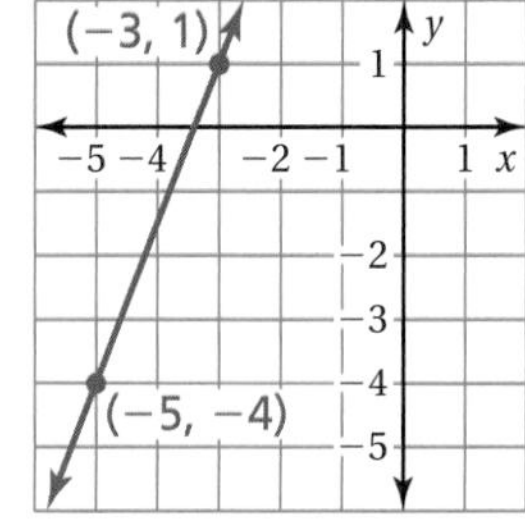

EXAMPLE 3 Finding Slope from a Table

The points in the table lie on a line. Find the slope of the line. Then draw its graph.

x	1	4	7	10
y	8	6	4	2

Choose any two points from the table. Then find the change in *y* and the change in *x*.

Use the points (1, 8) and (4, 6).

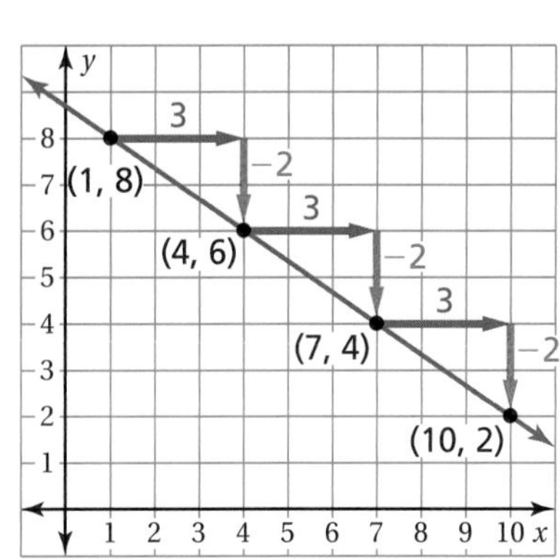

$$\text{slope} = \frac{\text{change in } y}{\text{change in } x}$$

$$= \frac{6 - 8}{4 - 1}$$

$$= \frac{-2}{3}$$

∴ The slope is $-\frac{2}{3}$.

On Your Own

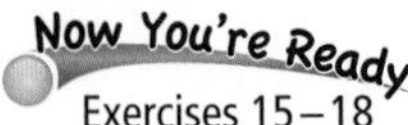

The points in the table lie on a line. Find the slope of the line. Then draw its graph.

4.

x	1	3	5	7
y	2	5	8	11

5.

x	−3	−2	−1	0
y	6	4	2	0

Key Idea

Parallel Lines and Slopes

Two lines in the same plane that do not intersect are parallel lines. Two lines with the same slope are parallel.

EXAMPLE 4 Finding Parallel Lines

Which two lines are parallel? Explain.

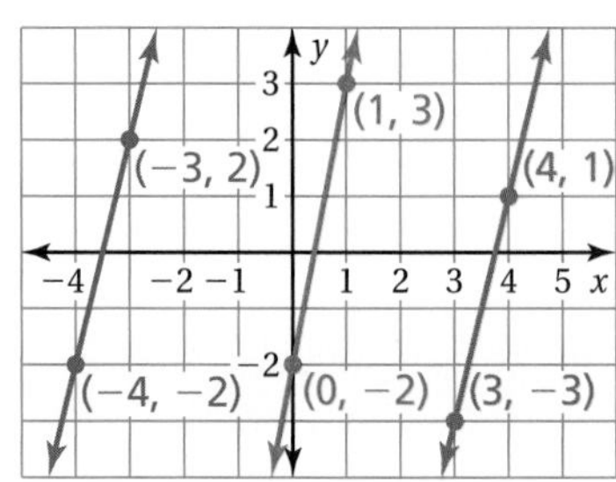

Find the slope of each line.

Blue Line	*Red Line*	*Green Line*
$\text{slope} = \dfrac{\text{rise}}{\text{run}}$	$\text{slope} = \dfrac{\text{rise}}{\text{run}}$	$\text{slope} = \dfrac{\text{rise}}{\text{run}}$
$= \dfrac{4}{1}$	$= \dfrac{5}{1}$	$= \dfrac{4}{1}$
$= 4$	$= 5$	$= 4$

The slope of the blue and green lines is 4. The slope of the red line is 5.

∴ The blue and green lines have the same slope, so they are parallel.

On Your Own

6. Which two lines are parallel? Explain.

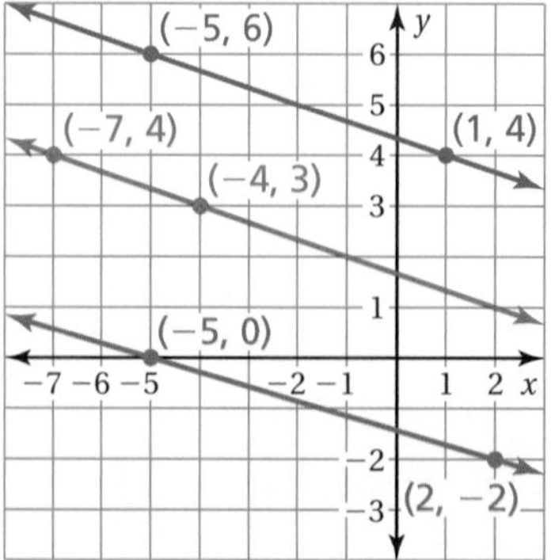

2.2 Exercises

Vocabulary and Concept Check

1. **CRITICAL THINKING** Refer to the graph.
   a. Which lines have positive slopes?
   b. Which line has the steepest slope?
   c. Are any two of the lines parallel? Explain.

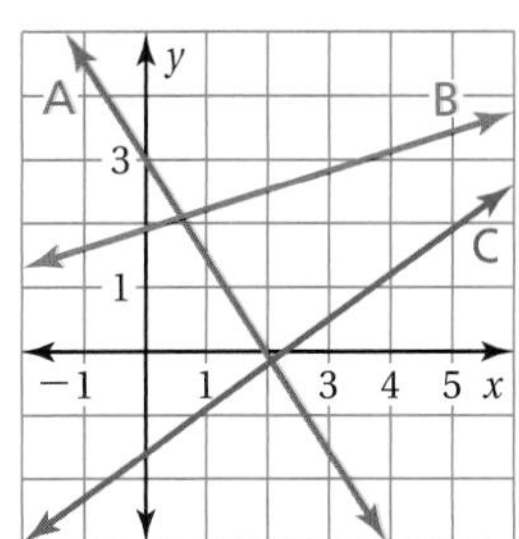

2. **OPEN-ENDED** Describe a real-life situation that involves slope.

3. **REASONING** The slope of a line is 0. What do you know about the line?

Practice and Problem Solving

Draw a line through each point using the given slope. What do you notice about the two lines?

4. Slope $= 1$

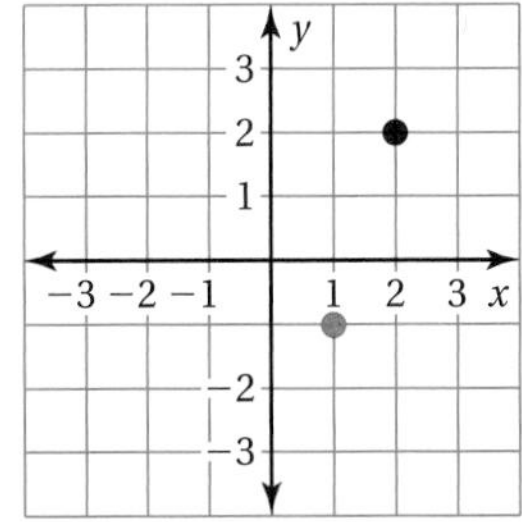

5. Slope $= -3$

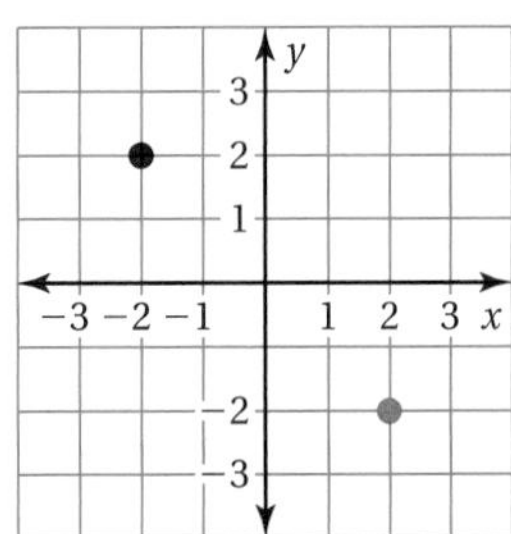

6. Slope $= \frac{1}{4}$

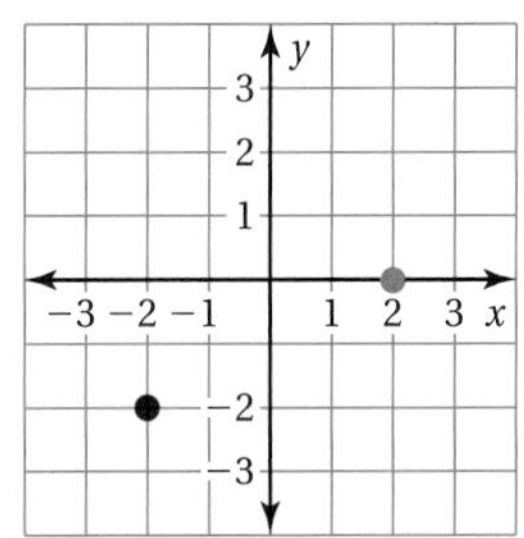

Find the slope of the line.

7.

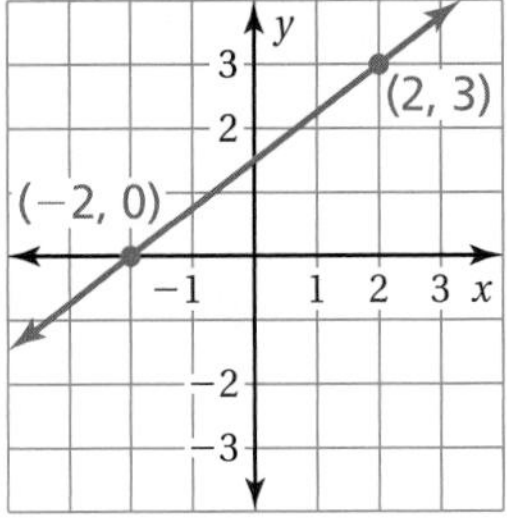

8.

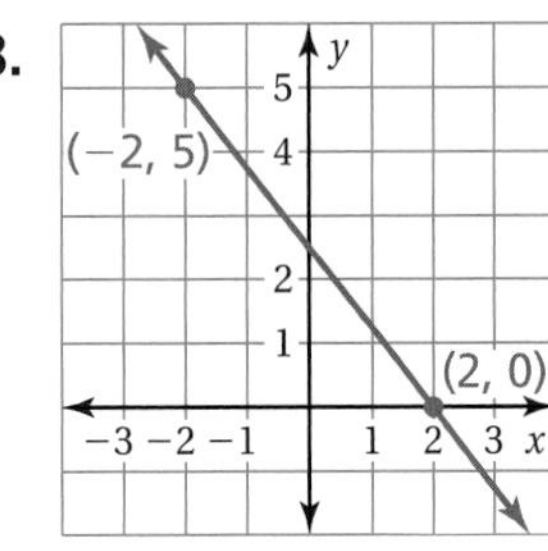

9.

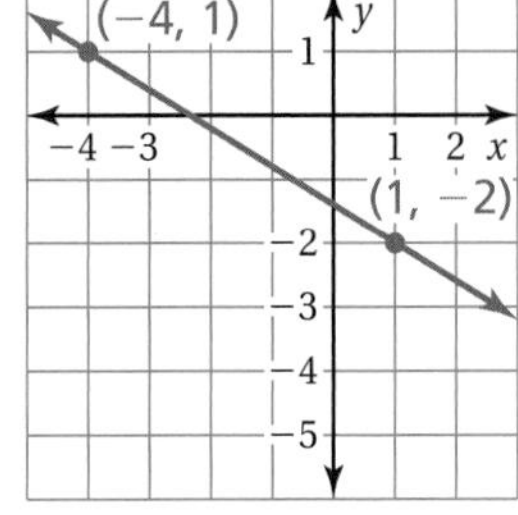

10.

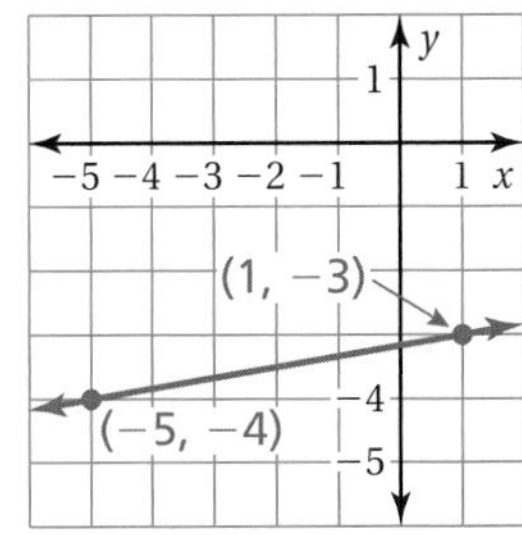

11.

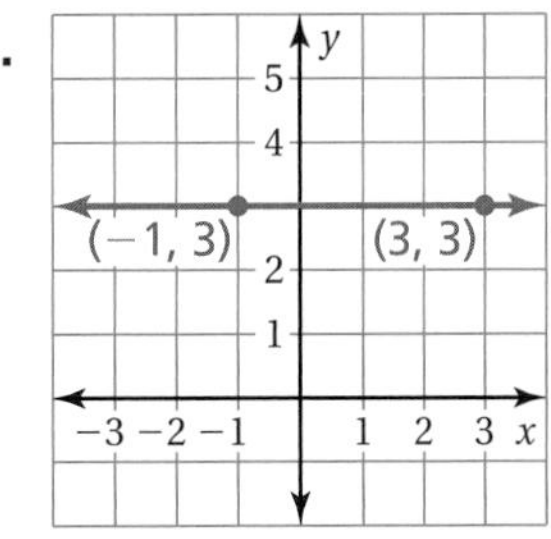

12.

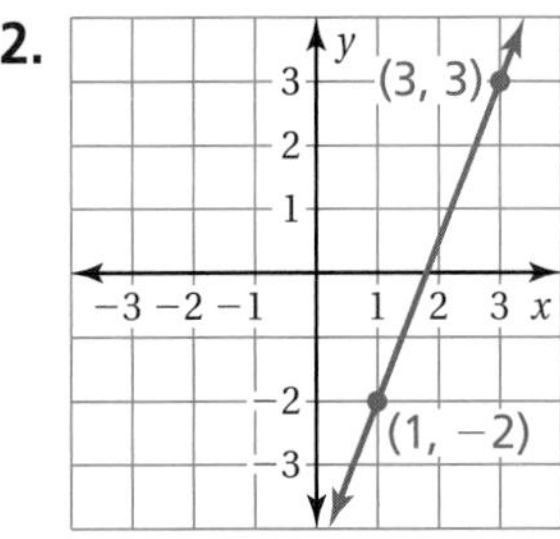

13. **ERROR ANALYSIS** Describe and correct the error in finding the slope of the line.

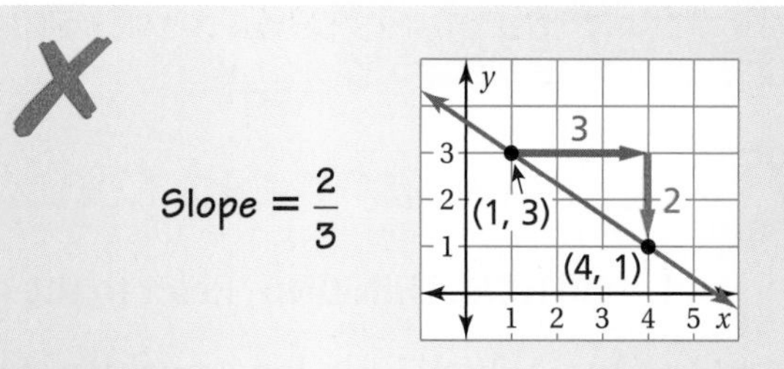

14. **CRITICAL THINKING** Is it more difficult to walk up the ramp or the hill? Explain.

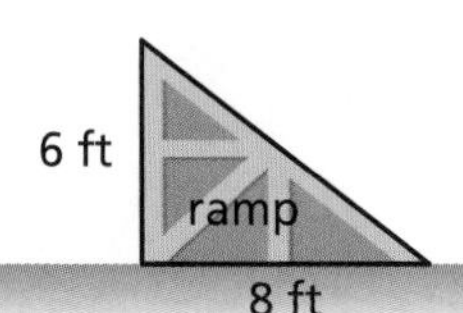

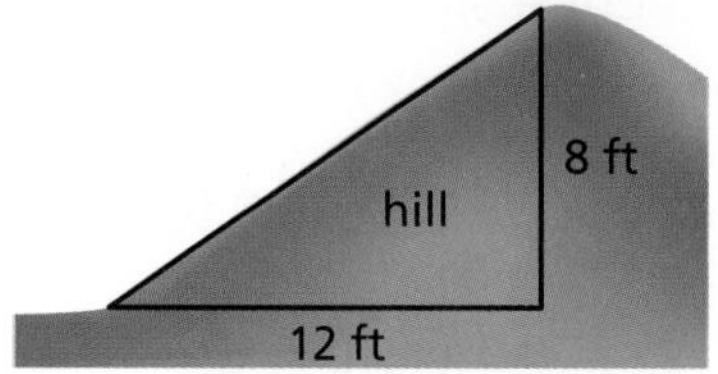

The points in the table lie on a line. Find the slope of the line. Then draw its graph.

③ 15.

x	1	3	5	7
y	2	10	18	26

16.

x	−3	2	7	12
y	0	2	4	6

17.

x	−6	−2	2	6
y	8	5	2	−1

18.

x	−8	−2	4	10
y	8	1	−6	−13

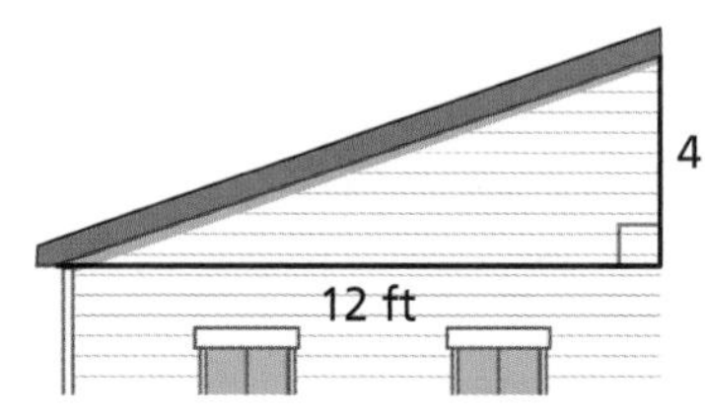

19. **PITCH** Carpenters refer to the slope of a roof as the *pitch* of the roof. Find the pitch of the roof.

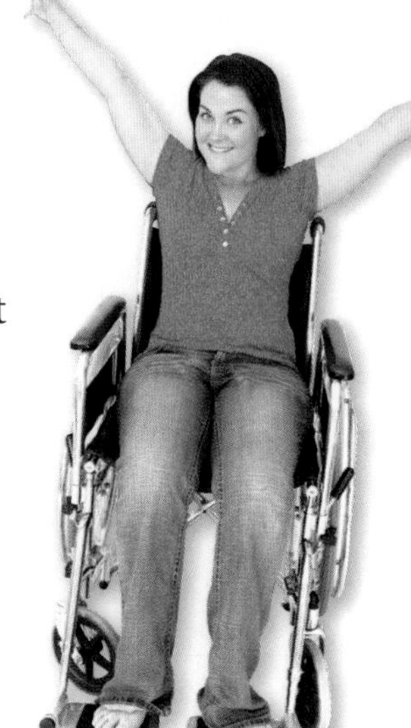

20. **PROJECT** The guidelines for a wheelchair ramp suggest that the ratio of the rise to the run be no greater than 1 : 12.

   a. Find a wheelchair ramp in your school or neighborhood. Measure its slope. Does the ramp follow the guidelines?

   b. Design a wheelchair ramp that provides access to a building with a front door that is 2.5 feet higher than the sidewalk. Illustrate your design.

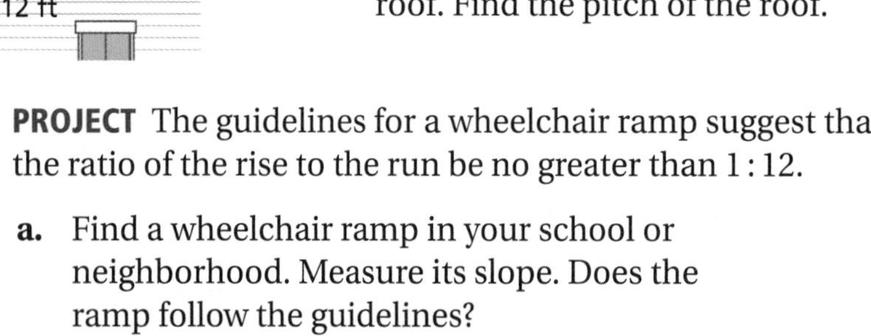

Which two lines are parallel? Explain.

④ 21.

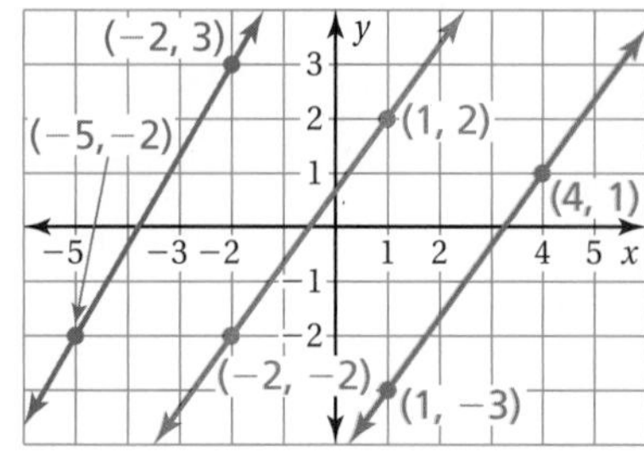

22.

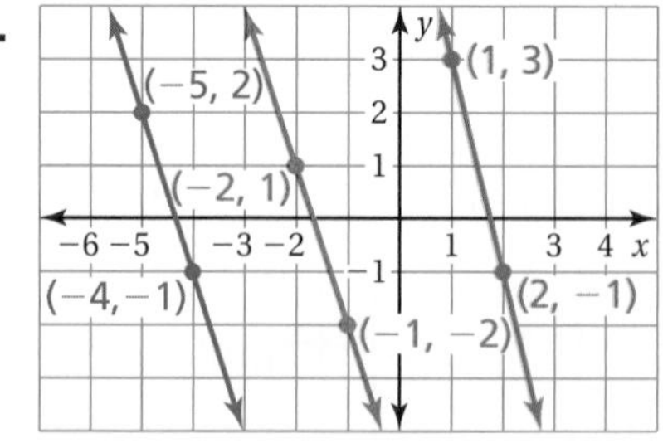

Tell whether the quadrilateral is a parallelogram. Explain.

23.

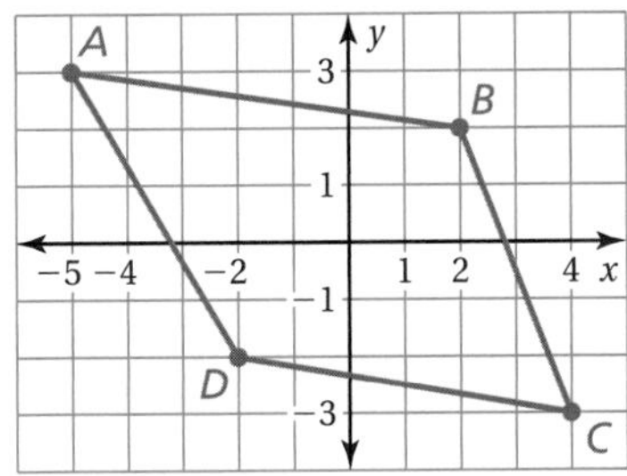

24.

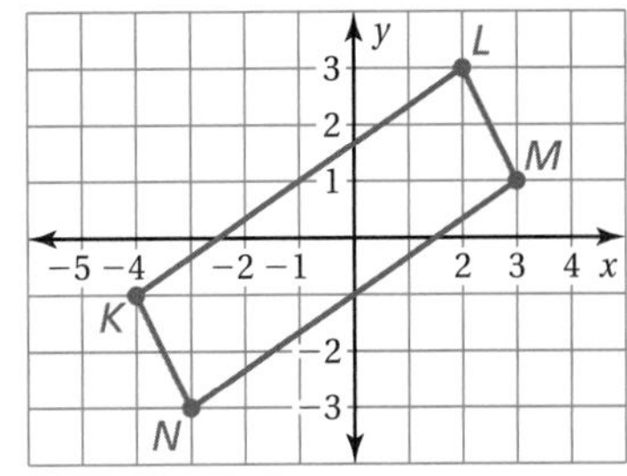

25. TURNPIKE TRAVEL The graph shows the cost of traveling by car on a turnpike.

- **a.** Find the slope of the line.
- **b.** Explain the meaning of the slope as a rate of change.

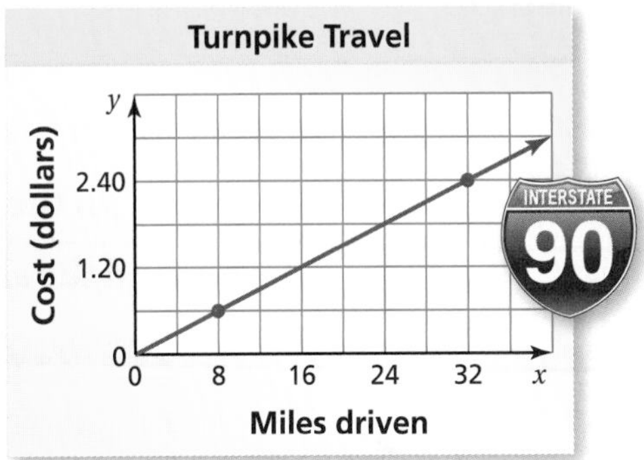

26. BOAT RAMP Which is steeper: the boat ramp or a road with a 12% grade? Explain. (*Note:* Road grade is the vertical increase divided by the horizontal distance.)

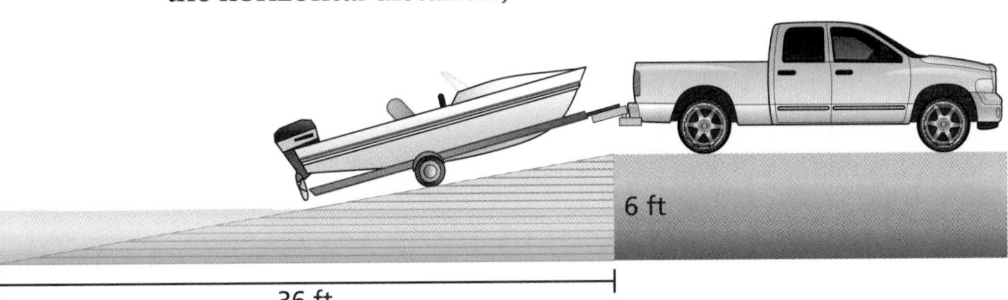

27. Critical Thinking The top and bottom of the slide are parallel to the ground.

- **a.** What is the slope of the main portion of the slide?
- **b.** How does the slope change if the bottom of the slide is only 12 inches above the ground? Is the slide steeper? Explain.

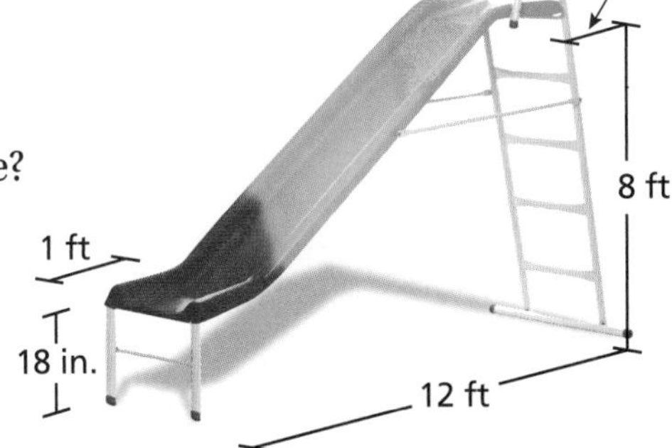

Fair Game Review What you learned in previous grades & lessons

Graph the linear equation. *(Section 2.1)*

28. $y = -\frac{1}{2}x$ **29.** $y = 3x - \frac{3}{4}$ **30.** $y = -\frac{x}{3} - \frac{3}{2}$

31. MULTIPLE CHOICE What is the prime factorization of 84? *(Skills Review Handbook)*

Ⓐ $2 \times 3 \times 7$ Ⓑ $2^2 \times 3 \times 7$ Ⓒ $2 \times 3^2 \times 7$ Ⓓ $2^2 \times 21$

2.3 Graphing Linear Equations in Slope-Intercept Form

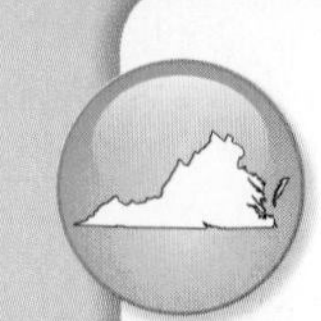

STANDARDS OF LEARNING
8.16

Essential Question How can you describe the graph of the equation $y = mx + b$?

1 ACTIVITY: Finding Slopes and y-Intercepts

Work with a partner.

- **Graph the equation.**
- **Find the slope of the line.**
- **Find the point where the line crosses the y-axis.**

a. $y = -\frac{1}{2}x + 1$

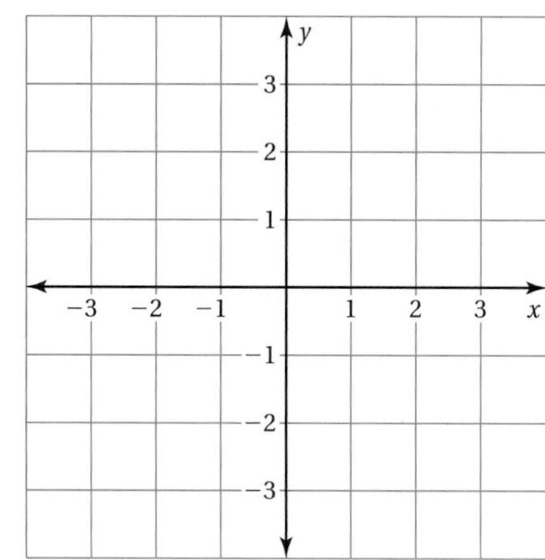

b. $y = -x + 2$

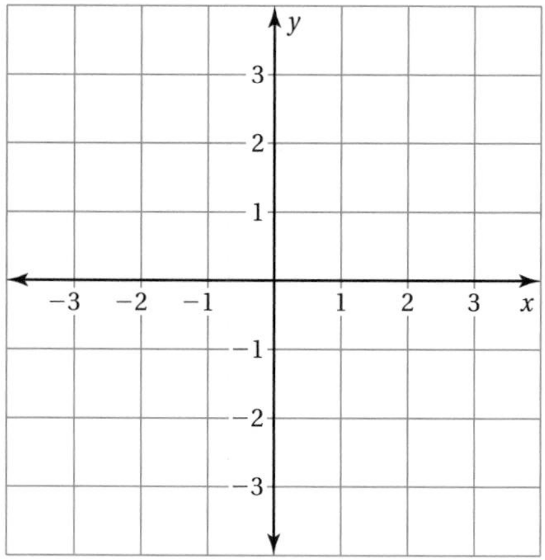

c. $y = -x - 2$

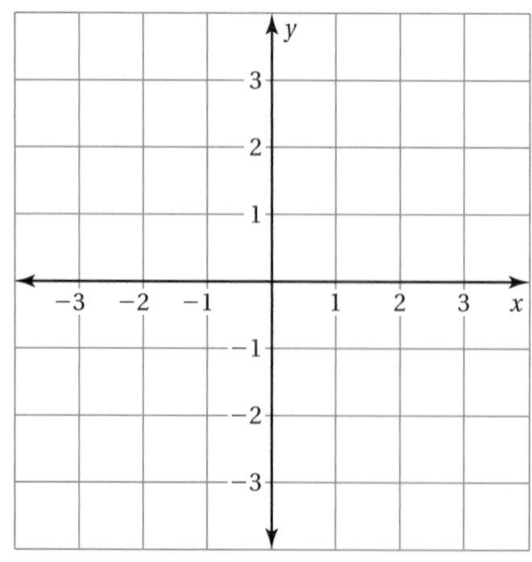

d. $y = \frac{1}{2}x + 1$

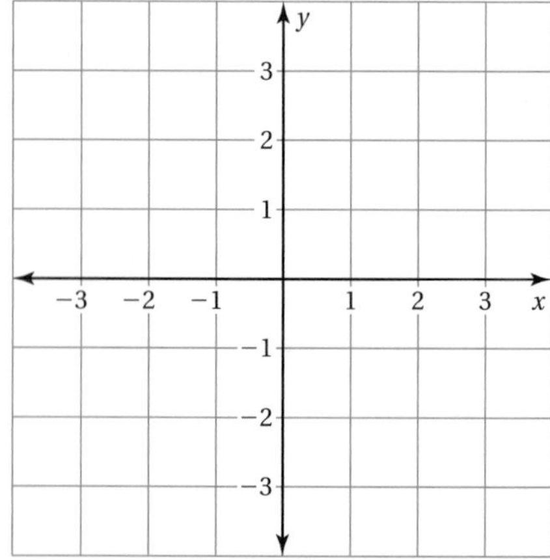

Inductive Reasoning

Work with a partner. Graph each equation. Then copy and complete the table.

	Equation	Description of Graph	Slope of Graph	Point of Intersection with y-axis
1a	**2.** $y = -\frac{1}{2}x + 1$	Line	$-\frac{1}{2}$	(0, 1)
1b	**3.** $y = -x + 2$			
1c	**4.** $y = -x - 2$			
1d	**5.** $y = \frac{1}{2}x + 1$			
	6. $y = x + 2$			
	7. $y = x - 2$			
	8. $y = \frac{1}{2}x - 1$			
	9. $y = -\frac{1}{2}x - 1$			
	10. $y = 3x + 2$			
	11. $y = 3x - 2$			
	12. $y = -2x + 3$			

What Is Your Answer?

13. **IN YOUR OWN WORDS** How can you describe the graph of the equation $y = mx + b$?

- **a.** How does the value of m affect the graph of the equation?
- **b.** How does the value of b affect the graph of the equation?
- **c.** Check your answers to parts (a) and (b) with three equations that are not in the table.

14. Why is $y = mx + b$ called the "slope-intercept" form of the equation of a line?

Practice Use what you learned about graphing linear equations in slope-intercept form to complete Exercises 4–6 on page 80.

Key Vocabulary
x-intercept, *p. 78*
y-intercept, *p. 78*
slope-intercept form, *p. 78*

Intercepts

The **x-intercept** of a line is the x-coordinate of the point where the line crosses the x-axis. It occurs when $y = 0$.

The **y-intercept** of a line is the y-coordinate of the point where the line crosses the y-axis. It occurs when $x = 0$.

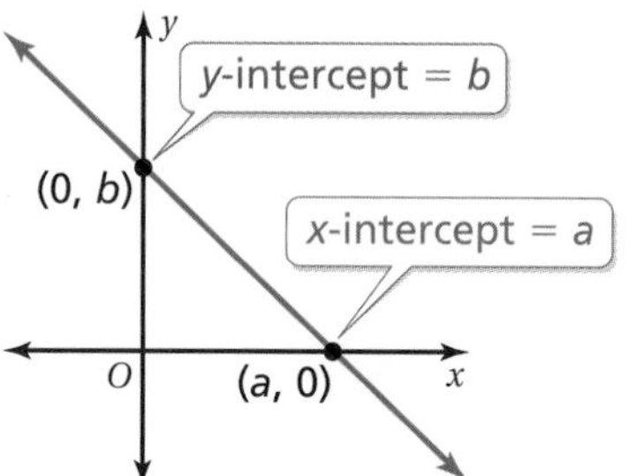

Slope-Intercept Form

Words An equation written in the form $y = mx + b$ is in **slope-intercept form**. The slope of the line is m and the y-intercept of the line is b.

Algebra $y = mx + b$

slope: m; y-intercept: b

EXAMPLE 1 Identifying Slopes and y-Intercepts

Find the slope and y-intercept of the graph of each linear equation.

a. $y = -4x - 2$

$y = -4x + (-2)$ Write in slope-intercept form.

The slope is -4 and the y-intercept is -2.

b. $y - 5 = \frac{3}{2}x$

$y = \frac{3}{2}x + 5$ Add 5 to each side.

The slope is $\frac{3}{2}$ and the y-intercept is 5.

On Your Own

Now You're Ready
Exercises 7–15

Find the slope and y-intercept of the graph of the linear equation.

1. $y = 3x - 7$

2. $y - 1 = -\frac{2}{3}x$

Multi-Language Glossary at BigIdeasMath.com.

EXAMPLE 2 Graphing a Linear Equation in Slope-Intercept Form

Graph $y = -3x + 3$. Identify the x-intercept.

Step 1: Find the slope and y-intercept.

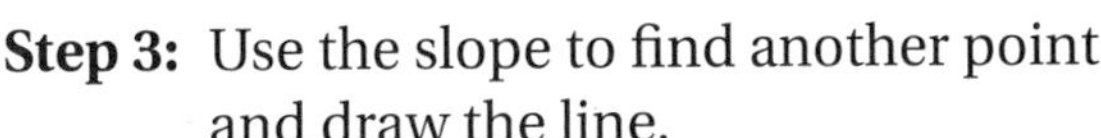

Step 2: The y-intercept is 3. So, plot (0, 3).

Step 3: Use the slope to find another point and draw the line.

$$\text{slope} = \frac{\text{rise}}{\text{run}} = \frac{-3}{1}$$

Plot the point that is 1 unit right and 3 units down from (0, 3). Draw a line through the two points.

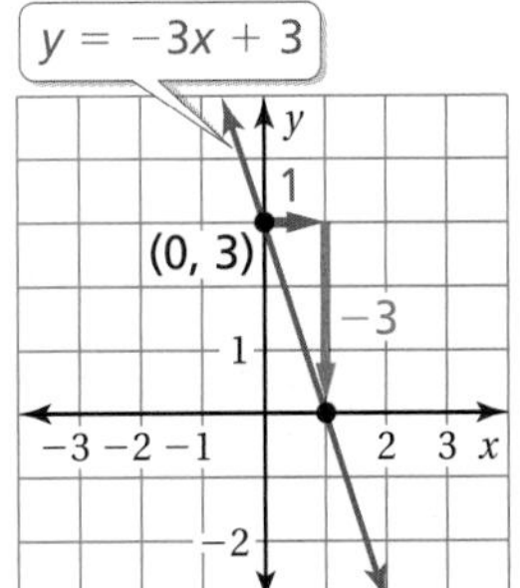

The line crosses the x-axis at (1, 0). So, the x-intercept is 1.

Study Tip

You can check the x-intercept by substituting $y = 0$ in the equation and solving for x.

$y = -3x + 3$

$0 = -3x + 3$

$-3 = -3x$

$1 = x$

EXAMPLE 3 Real-Life Application

The cost y (in dollars) of taking a taxi x miles is $y = 2.5x + 2$. (a) Graph the equation. (b) Interpret the y-intercept and slope.

a. The slope of the line is $2.5 = \frac{5}{2}$. Use the slope and y-intercept to graph the equation.

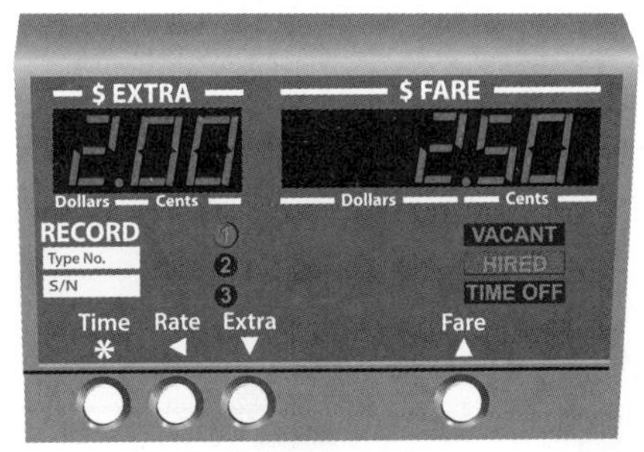

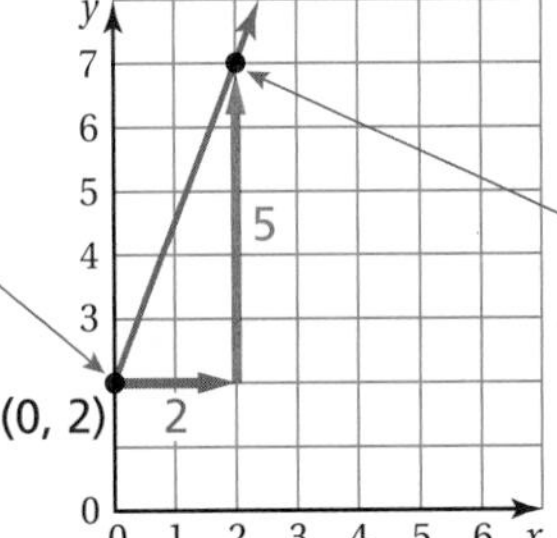

b. The slope is 2.5. So, the cost per mile is \$2.50. The y-intercept is 2. So, there is an initial fee of \$2 to take the taxi.

On Your Own

Now You're Ready
Exercises 18–23

Graph the linear equation. Identify the x-intercept.

3. $y = x - 4$

4. $y = -\frac{1}{2}x + 1$

5. In Example 3, the cost y (in dollars) of taking a different taxi x miles is $y = 2x + 1.5$. Interpret the y-intercept and slope.

2.3 Exercises

Vocabulary and Concept Check

1. **VOCABULARY** How can you find the x-intercept of the graph of $2x + 3y = 6$?
2. **CRITICAL THINKING** Is the equation $y = 3x$ in slope-intercept form? Explain.
3. **OPEN-ENDED** Describe a real-life situation that can be modeled by a linear equation. Write the equation. Interpret the y-intercept and slope.

Practice and Problem Solving

Match the equation with its graph. Identify the slope and y-intercept.

4. $y = 2x + 1$
5. $y = \frac{1}{3}x - 2$
6. $y = -\frac{2}{3}x + 1$

A. 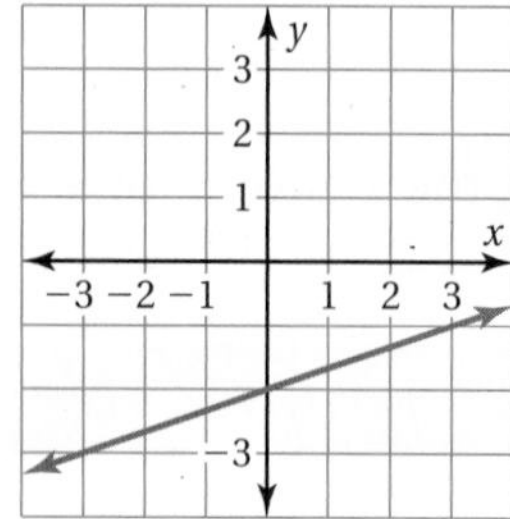

B. 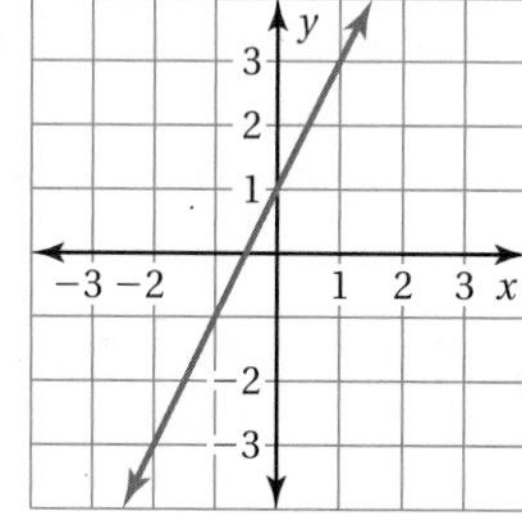

C. 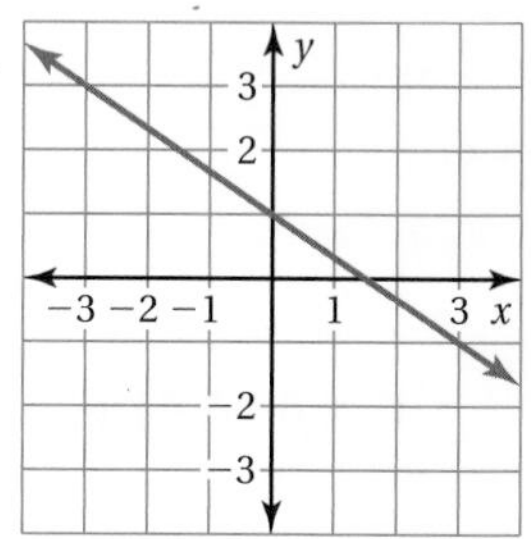

Find the slope and y-intercept of the graph of the linear equation.

7. $y = 4x - 5$
8. $y = -7x + 12$
9. $y = -\frac{4}{5}x - 2$
10. $y = 2.25x + 3$
11. $y + 1 = \frac{4}{3}x$
12. $y - 6 = \frac{3}{8}x$
13. $y - 3.5 = -2x$
14. $y + 5 = -\frac{1}{2}x$
15. $y = 1.5x + 11$

16. **ERROR ANALYSIS** Describe and correct the error in finding the slope and y-intercept of the graph of the linear equation.

$y = 4x - 3$

The slope is 4 and the y-intercept is 3.

17. **SKYDIVING** A skydiver parachutes to the ground. The height y (in feet) of the skydiver after x seconds is $y = -10x + 3000$.

   a. Graph the equation.

   b. Interpret the x-intercept and slope.

Graph the linear equation. Identify the x-intercept.

② **18.** $y = \frac{1}{5}x + 3$ **19.** $y = 6x - 7$ **20.** $y = -\frac{8}{3}x + 9$

21. $y = -1.4x - 1$ **22.** $y + 9 = -3x$ **23.** $y - 4 = -\frac{3}{5}x$

24. PHONES The cost y (in dollars) of making a long distance phone call for x minutes is $y = 0.25x + 2$.

a. Graph the equation.

b. Interpret the slope and y-intercept.

25. APPLES Write a linear equation that models the cost y of picking x pounds of apples. Graph the equation.

26. ELEVATOR The basement of a building is 40 feet below ground level. The elevator rises at a rate of 5 feet per second. You enter the elevator in the basement. Write an equation that represents the height y (in feet) of the elevator after x seconds. Graph the equation.

27. BONUS You work in an electronics store. You earn a fixed amount of $35 per day, plus a 15% bonus on the merchandise you sell. Write an equation that models the amount y (in dollars) you earn for selling x dollars of merchandise in one day. Graph the equation.

28. Critical Thinking Six friends create a website. The website earns money by selling banner ads. The site has five banner ads. It costs $120 a month to operate the website.

a. A banner ad earns $0.005 per click. Write a linear equation that represents the monthly income y (in dollars) for x clicks.

b. Draw a graph of the equation in part (a). On the graph, label the number of clicks needed for the friends to start making a profit.

What you learned in previous grades & lessons

Solve the equation for y. *(Section 1.4)*

29. $y - 2x = 3$ **30.** $4x + 5y = 13$ **31.** $2x - 3y = 6$ **32.** $7x + 4y = 8$

33. MULTIPLE CHOICE Which point is a solution of the equation $3x - 8y = 11$? *(Section 2.1)*

Ⓐ $(1, 1)$ Ⓑ $(1, -1)$ Ⓒ $(-1, 1)$ Ⓓ $(-1, -1)$

2.4 Graphing Linear Equations in Standard Form

STANDARDS OF LEARNING
8.16

Essential Question How can you describe the graph of the equation $ax + by = c$?

1 ACTIVITY: Using a Table to Plot Points

Work with a partner. You sold a total of $16 worth of tickets to a school concert. You lost track of how many of each type of ticket you sold.

$$\frac{\$4}{\text{Adult}} \cdot \text{Number of Adult Tickets} + \frac{\$2}{\text{Child}} \cdot \text{Number of Child Tickets} = \$16$$

a. Let x represent the number of adult tickets.
Let y represent the number of child tickets.
Write an equation that relates x and y.

b. Copy and complete the table showing the different combinations of tickets you might have sold.

Number of Adult Tickets, x					
Number of Child Tickets, y					

c. Plot the points from the table. Describe the pattern formed by the points.

d. If you remember how many adult tickets you sold, can you determine how many child tickets you sold? Explain your reasoning.

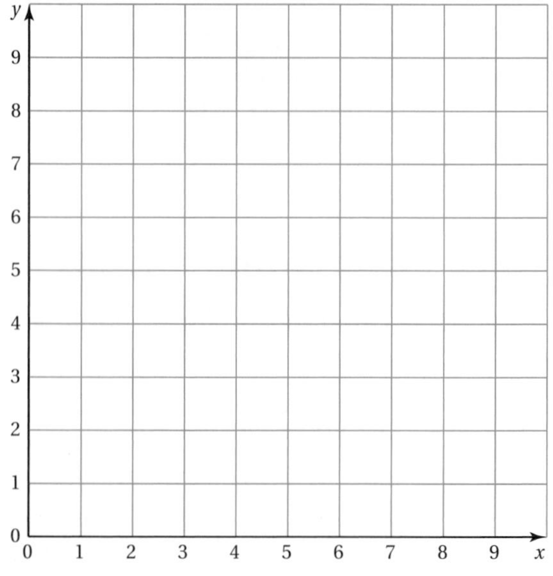

2 ACTIVITY: Rewriting an Equation

Work with a partner. You sold a total of $16 worth of cheese. You forgot how many pounds of each type of cheese you sold.

$\frac{\$4}{\text{lb}}$ • Pounds of Swiss + $\frac{\$2}{\text{lb}}$ • Pounds of Cheddar = $16

a. Let x represent the number of pounds of Swiss cheese.
Let y represent the number of pounds of Cheddar cheese.
Write an equation that relates x and y.

b. Write the equation in slope-intercept form. Then graph the equation.

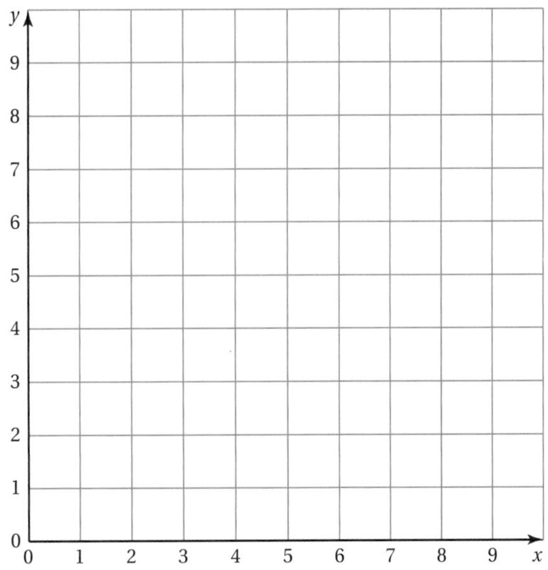

What Is Your Answer?

3. **IN YOUR OWN WORDS** How can you describe the graph of the equation $ax + by = c$?

4. Activities 1 and 2 show two different methods for graphing $ax + by = c$. Describe the two methods. Which method do you prefer? Explain.

5. Write a real-life problem that is similar to those shown in Activities 1 and 2.

Practice Use what you learned about graphing linear equations in standard form to complete Exercises 3 and 4 on page 86.

2.4 Lesson

Key Vocabulary
standard form, *p. 84*

Study Tip
Any linear equation can be written in standard form.

Key Idea

Standard Form of a Linear Equation

The **standard form** of a linear equation is

$$ax + by = c$$

where a and b are not both zero.

EXAMPLE 1 Graphing a Linear Equation in Standard Form

Graph $-2x + 3y = -6$.

Step 1: Write the equation in slope-intercept form.

$-2x + 3y = -6$	Write the equation.
$3y = 2x - 6$	Add $2x$ to each side.
$y = \frac{2}{3}x - 2$	Divide each side by 3.

Step 2: Use the slope and y-intercept to graph the equation.

$$y = \frac{2}{3}x + (-2)$$

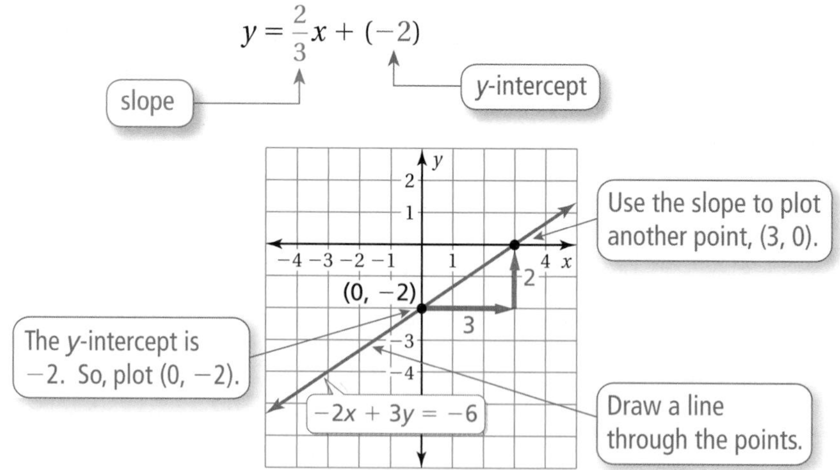

On Your Own

Now You're Ready
Exercises 5–10

Graph the linear equation.

1. $x + y = -2$
2. $-\frac{1}{2}x + 2y = 6$
3. $-\frac{2}{3}x + y = 0$
4. $2x + y = 5$

EXAMPLE 2 Graphing a Linear Equation in Standard Form

Graph $x + 3y = -3$ using intercepts.

Step 1: To find the x-intercept, substitute 0 for y.

$$x + 3y = -3$$
$$x + 3(0) = -3$$
$$x = -3$$

To find the y-intercept, substitute 0 for x.

$$x + 3y = -3$$
$$0 + 3y = -3$$
$$y = -1$$

Step 2: Graph the equation.

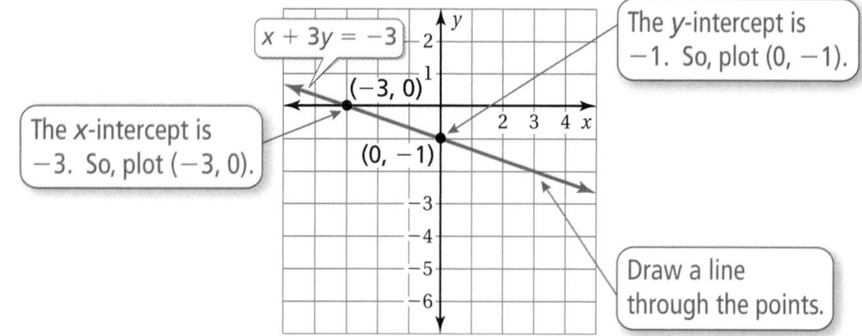

x + 3y = −3
The x-intercept is −3. So, plot (−3, 0).
(−3, 0)
(0, −1)
The y-intercept is −1. So, plot (0, −1).
Draw a line through the points.

EXAMPLE 3 Real-Life Application

You have \$6 to spend on apples and bananas. (a) Graph the equation $1.5x + 0.6y = 6$, where x is the number of pounds of apples and y is the number of pounds of bananas. (b) Interpret the intercepts.

a. Find the intercepts and graph the equation.

***x*-intercept**	***y*-intercept**
$1.5x + 0.6y = 6$	$1.5x + 0.6y = 6$
$1.5x + 0.6(0) = 6$	$1.5(0) + 0.6y = 6$
$x = 4$	$y = 10$

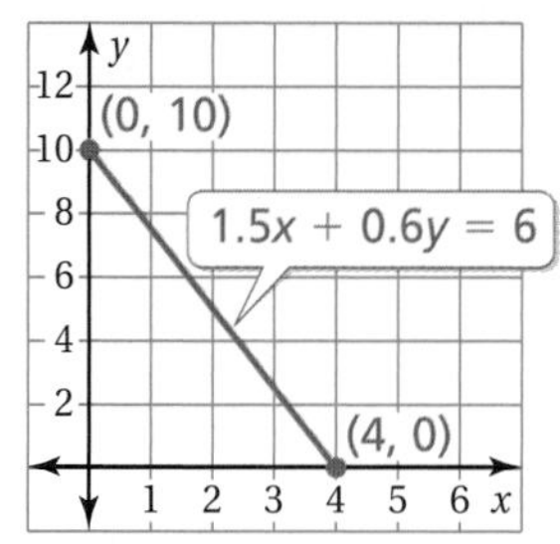

(0, 10)
1.5x + 0.6y = 6
(4, 0)

b. The x-intercept shows that you can buy 4 pounds of apples if you don't buy any bananas. The y-intercept shows that you can buy 10 pounds of bananas if you don't buy any apples.

On Your Own

Now You're Ready
Exercises 16–18

Graph the linear equation using intercepts.

5. $2x - y = 8$

6. $x + 3y = 6$

7. **WHAT IF?** In Example 3, you buy y pounds of oranges instead of bananas. Oranges cost \$1.20 per pound. Graph the equation $1.5x + 1.2y = 6$. Interpret the intercepts.

2.4 Exercises

Vocabulary and Concept Check

1. **VOCABULARY** Is the equation $y = -2x + 5$ in standard form? Explain.

2. **REASONING** Does the graph represent a linear equation? Explain.

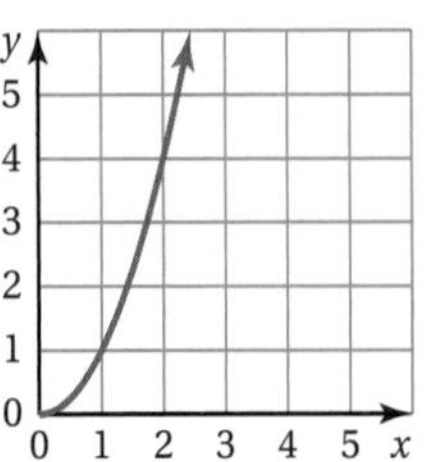

Practice and Problem Solving

Define two variables for the verbal model. Write an equation in slope-intercept form that relates the variables. Graph the equation.

3. $\dfrac{\$2.00}{\text{pound}}$ • Pounds of peaches + $\dfrac{\$1.50}{\text{pound}}$ • Pounds of apples = \$15

4. $\dfrac{16 \text{ miles}}{\text{hour}}$ • Hours biked + $\dfrac{2 \text{ miles}}{\text{hour}}$ • Hours walked = 32 miles

Write the linear equation in slope-intercept form.

1 5. $2x + y = 17$

6. $5x - y = \frac{1}{4}$

7. $-\frac{1}{2}x + y = 10$

Graph the linear equation.

8. $-18x + 9y = 72$

9. $16x - 4y = 2$

10. $\frac{1}{4}x + \frac{3}{4}y = 1$

Use the graph to find the *x*- and *y*-intercepts.

11. 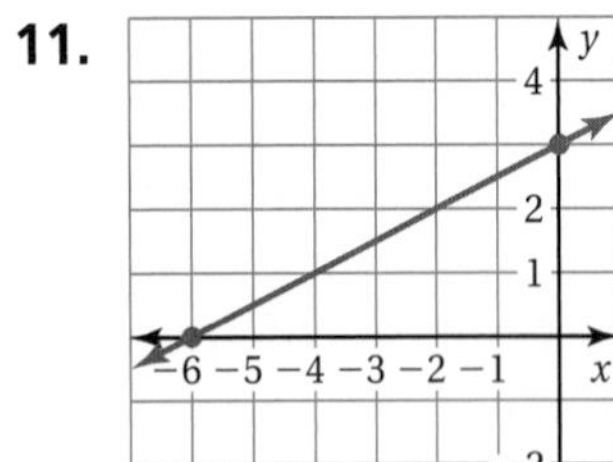

12. 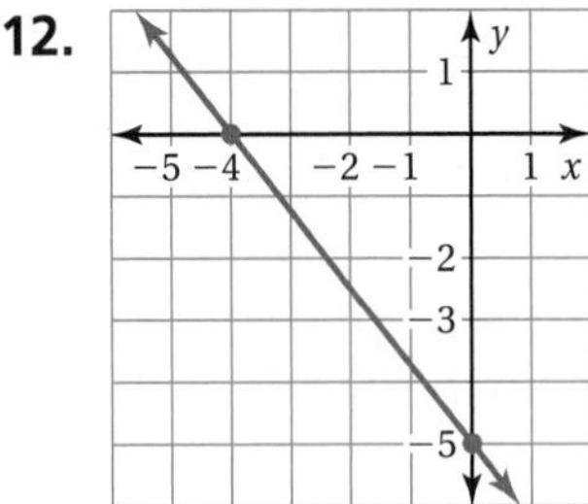

13. 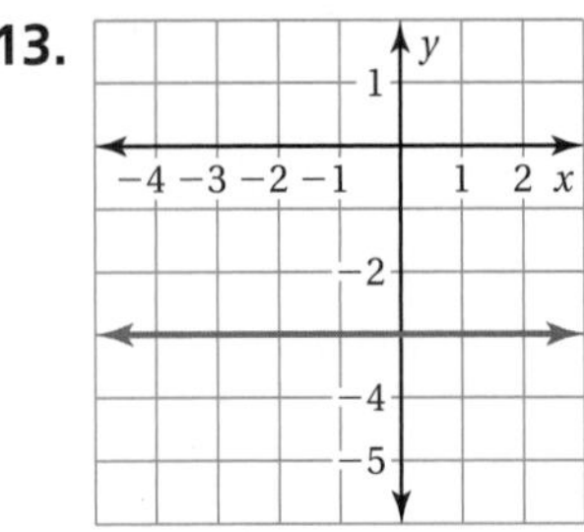

14. **ERROR ANALYSIS** Describe and correct the error in finding the x-intercept.

15. **BRACELET** A charm bracelet costs \$65, plus \$25 for each charm.

  a. Write an equation in standard form that represents the total cost of the bracelet.

  b. How much does the bracelet shown cost?

Graph the linear equation using intercepts.

2 **16.** $3x - 4y = -12$ **17.** $2x + y = 8$ **18.** $\frac{1}{3}x - \frac{1}{6}y = -\frac{2}{3}$

19. SHOPPING The amount of money you spend on x CDs and y DVDs is given by the equation $14x + 18y = 126$. Find the intercepts and graph the equation.

20. SCUBA Five friends go scuba diving. They rent a boat for x days and scuba gear for y days. The total spent is $1000.

a. Write an equation in standard form that represents the situation.

b. Graph the equation and interpret the intercepts.

21. WAGES You work at a restaurant as a host and a server. You earn $9.45 for each hour you work as a host and $7.65 for each hour you work as a server.

a. Write an equation in standard form that models your earnings.

b. Graph the equation.

Basic Information
Pay to the Order of: .... John Doe
# of hours worked as .... host: x
# of hours worked as .... server: y
Earnings for this pay .... period: $160.65

22. REASONING Does the graph of every linear equation have an x-intercept? Explain your reasoning. Include an example.

23. Critical Thinking For a house call, a veterinarian charges $70, plus $40 an hour.

a. Write an equation that represents the total fee y charged by the veterinarian for a visit lasting x hours.

b. Find the x-intercept. Will this point appear on the graph of the equation? Explain your reasoning.

c. Graph the equation.

Fair Game Review What you learned in previous grades & lessons

Copy and complete the table of values. *(Skills Review Handbook)*

24.

x	-2	-1	0	1	2
$2x + 5$					

25.

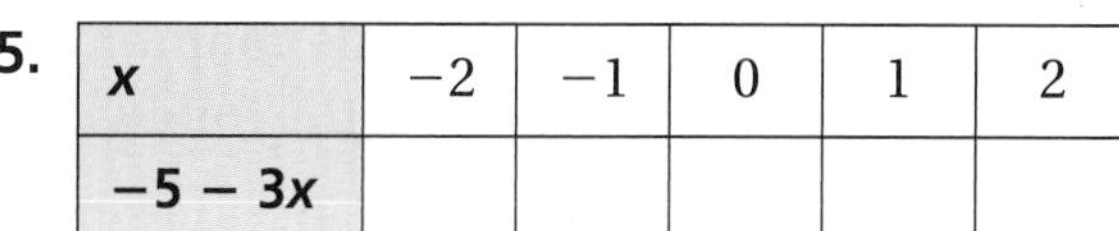

x	-2	-1	0	1	2
$-5 - 3x$					

26. MULTIPLE CHOICE Which value of x makes the equation $4x - 12 = 3x - 9$ true? *(Section 1.3)*

(A) -1 (B) 0 (C) 1 (D) 3

2 Study Help

You can use a **process diagram** to show the steps involved in a procedure. Here is an example of a process diagram for graphing a linear equation.

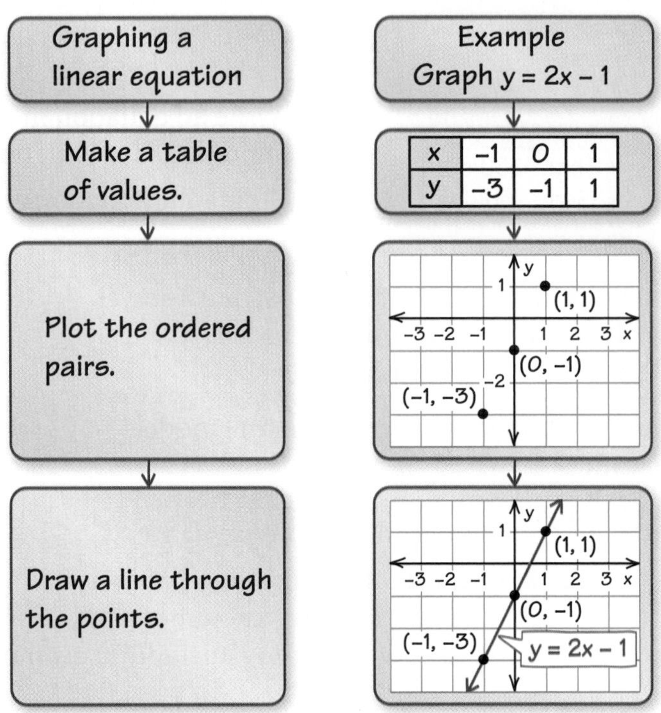

On Your Own

Make a process diagram with an example to help you study these topics.

1. finding the slope of a line
2. graphing a linear equation using
   a. slope and y-intercept
   b. x- and y-intercepts

After you complete this chapter, make process diagrams for the following topics.

3. writing equations in slope-intercept form
4. writing equations using a slope and a point
5. writing equations using two points

"Here is a process diagram with suggestions for what to do if a hyena knocks on your door."

2.1–2.4 Quiz

Check It Out
Progress Check
BigIdeasMath.com

Graph the linear equation using a table. *(Section 2.1)*

1. $y = -12x$
2. $y = -x + 8$
3. $y = \frac{x}{3} - 4$
4. $y = 3.5$

Find the slope of the line. *(Section 2.2)*

5. 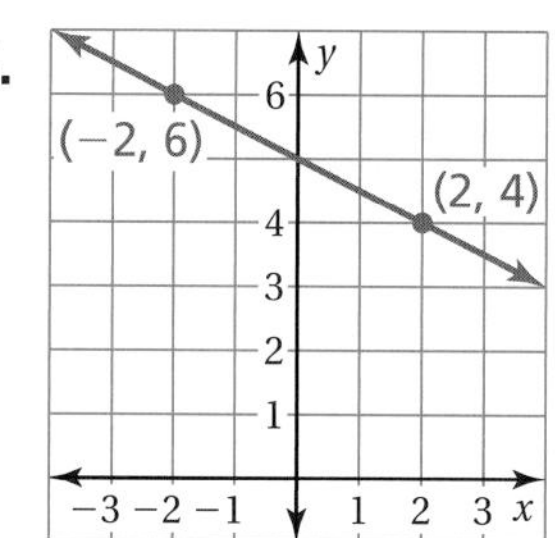

6. 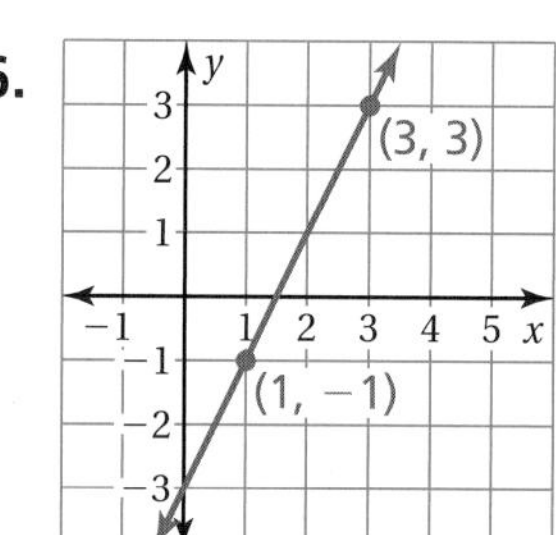

Find the slope and *y*-intercept of the graph of the equation. *(Section 2.3)*

7. $y = \frac{1}{4}x - 8$
8. $y = -x + 3$

Find the *x*- and *y*-intercepts of the graph of the equation. *(Section 2.4)*

9. $3x - 2y = 12$
10. $x + 5y = 15$

11. **BARBEQUE** The equation $3x + 2y = 30$ represents the amount of money your family spends on x pounds of beef and y pounds of chicken for a barbeque. Graph the equation and interpret the intercepts. *(Section 2.4)*

12. **BANKING** A bank charges \$3 each time you use an out-of-network ATM. At the beginning of the month, you have \$1500 in your bank account. You withdraw \$60 from your bank account each time you use an out-of-network ATM. Write and graph a linear equation that represents the balance in your account after you use an out-of-network ATM x times. *(Section 2.1)*

13. **STATE FAIR** Write a linear equation that models the cost y of one person going on x rides at the fair. Graph the equation. *(Section 2.3)*

14. **PAINTING** You used \$90 worth of paint for a school float. *(Section 2.4)*

    a. Graph the equation $18x + 15y = 90$, where x is the number of gallons of blue paint and y is the number of gallons of white paint.

    b. Interpret the intercepts.

2.5 Writing Equations in Slope-Intercept Form

STANDARDS OF LEARNING
8.16

Essential Question How can you write an equation of a line when you are given the slope and y-intercept of the line?

1 ACTIVITY: Writing Equations of Lines

Work with a partner.

- **Find the slope of each line.**
- **Find the y-intercept of each line.**
- **Write an equation for each line.**
- **What do the three lines have in common?**

a.

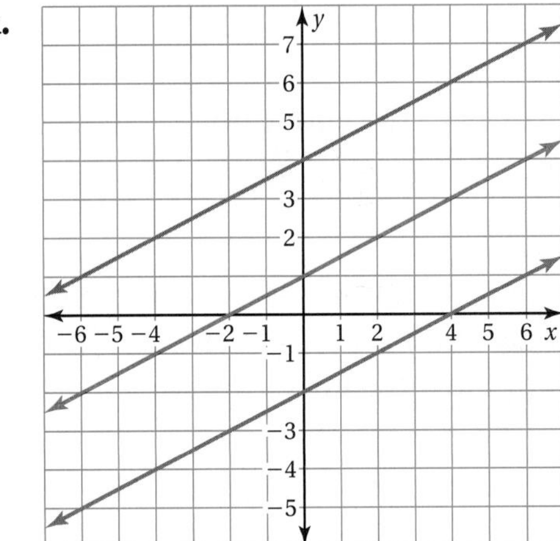

b.

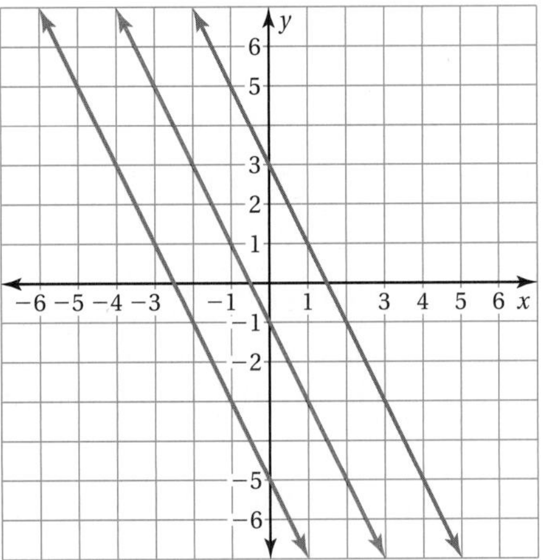

c.

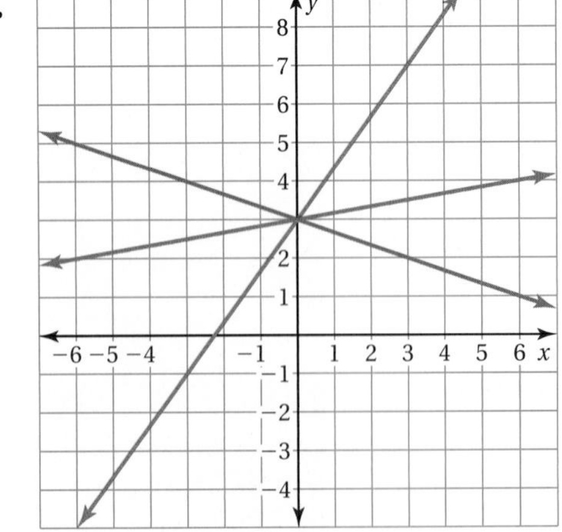

d.

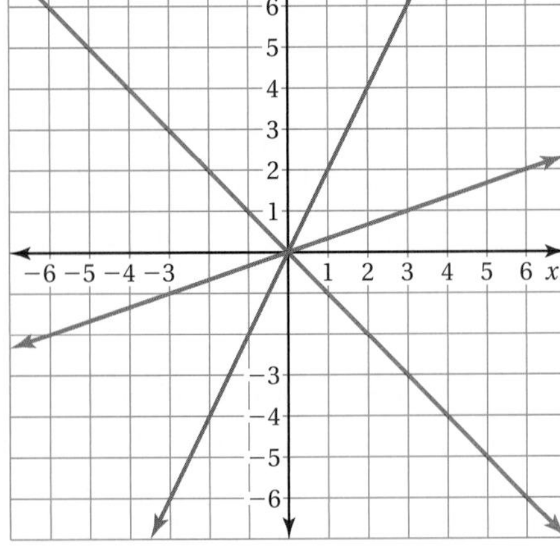

2 ACTIVITY: Describing a Parallelogram

Work with a partner.

- **Find the area of each parallelogram.**
- **Write an equation for each side of each parallelogram.**
- **What do you notice about the slopes of the opposite sides of each parallelogram?**

a.

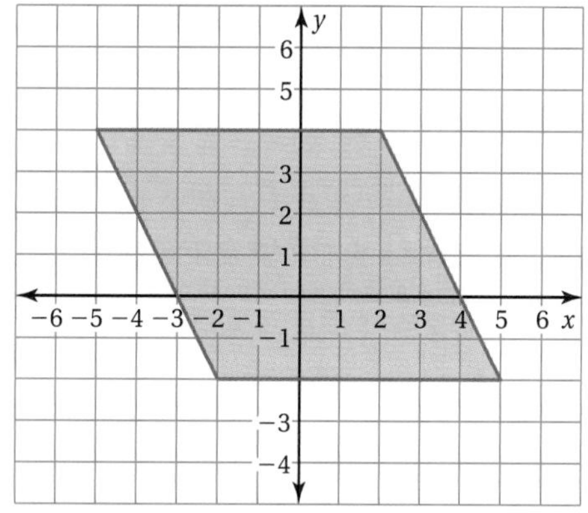

b.

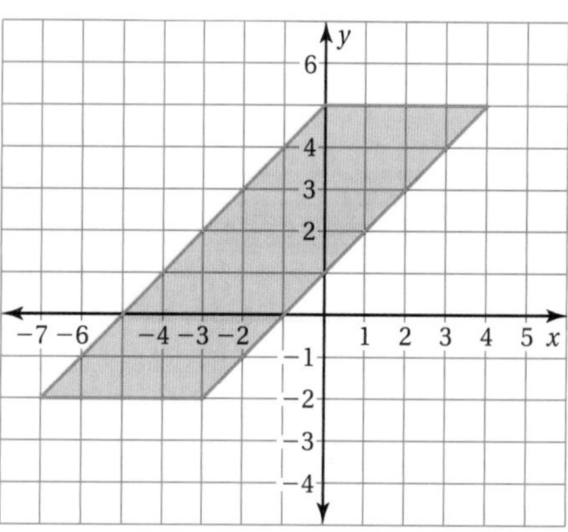

3 ACTIVITY: Interpreting the Slope and *y*-Intercept

Work with a partner. The graph shows a trip taken by a car where *t* is the time (in hours) and *y* is the distance (in miles) from Phoenix.

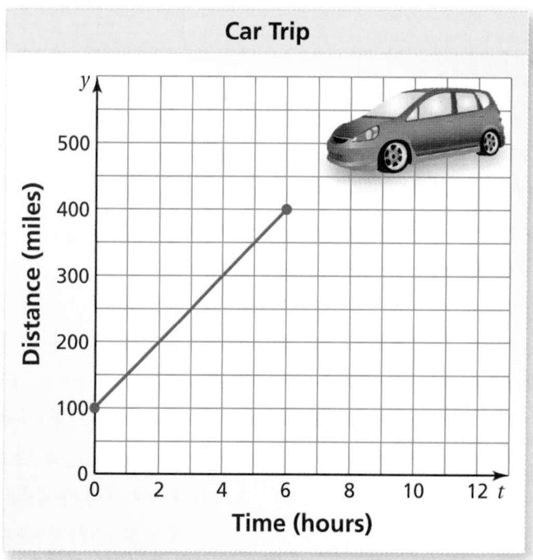

a. How far from Phoenix was the car at the beginning of the trip?

b. What was the car's speed?

c. How long did the trip last?

d. How far from Phoenix was the car at the end of the trip?

What Is Your Answer?

4. **IN YOUR OWN WORDS** How can you write an equation of a line when you are given the slope and *y*-intercept of the line? Give an example that is different from those in Activities 1, 2, and 3.

Practice Use what you learned about writing equations in slope-intercept form to complete Exercises 3 and 4 on page 94.

2.5 Lesson

EXAMPLE 1 Writing Equations in Slope-Intercept Form

Write an equation of the line in slope-intercept form.

a.

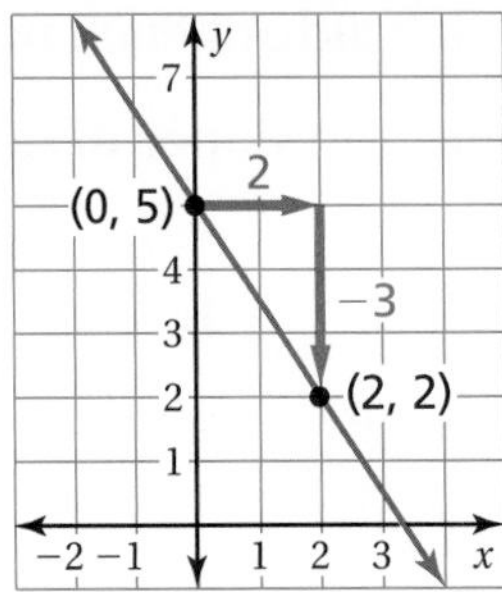

Find the slope and y-intercept.

$$\text{slope} = \frac{\text{rise}}{\text{run}} = \frac{-3}{2} = -\frac{3}{2}$$

Because the line crosses the y-axis at $(0, 5)$, the y-intercept is 5.

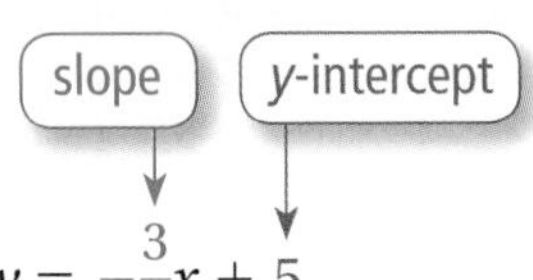

So, the equation is $y = -\frac{3}{2}x + 5$.

Study Tip

After writing an equation, check that the given points are solutions of the equation.

b.

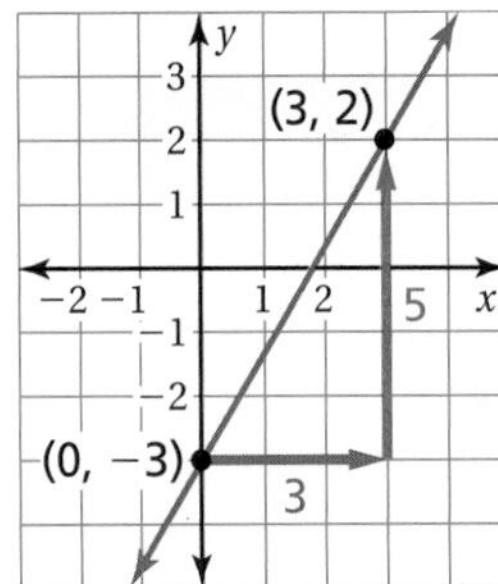

Find the slope and y-intercept.

$$\text{slope} = \frac{\text{rise}}{\text{run}} = \frac{5}{3}$$

Because the line crosses the y-axis at $(0, -3)$, the y-intercept is -3.

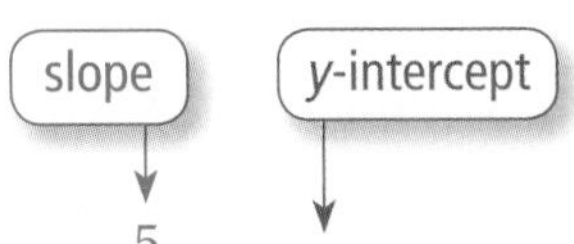

So, the equation is $y = \frac{5}{3}x + (-3)$, or $y = \frac{5}{3}x - 3$.

On Your Own

Now You're Ready
Exercises 5–10

Write an equation of the line in slope-intercept form.

1.

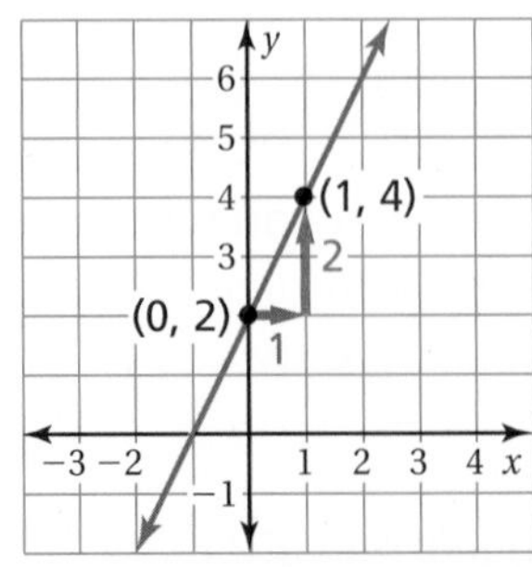

2.

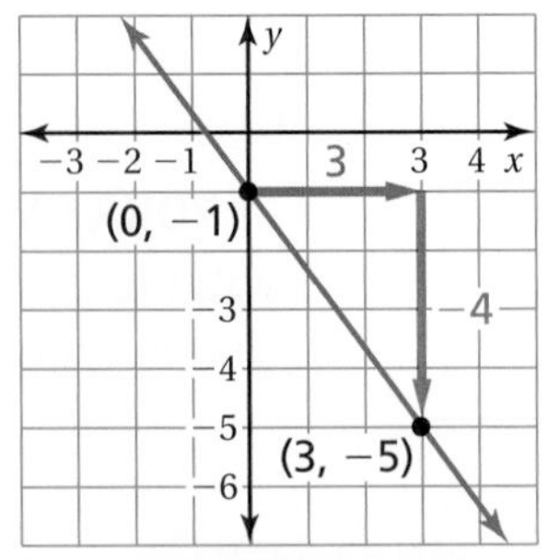

EXAMPLE 2 Standardized Test Practice

Which equation is shown in the graph?

Ⓐ $y = -4$ Ⓑ $y = -3$

Ⓒ $y = 0$ Ⓓ $y = -3x$

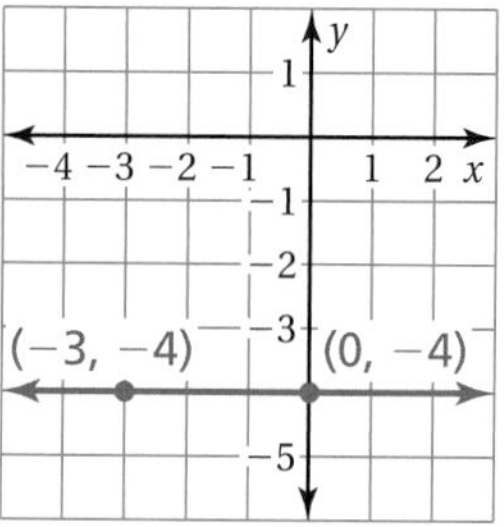

Remember

The graph of $y = a$ is a horizontal line that passes through $(0, a)$.

Find the slope and y-intercept.

The line is horizontal, so the rise is 0.

$$\text{slope} = \frac{\text{rise}}{\text{run}} = \frac{0}{3} = 0$$

Because the line crosses the y-axis at $(0, -4)$, the y-intercept is -4.

∴ So, the equation is $y = 0x + (-4)$, or $y = -4$. The correct answer is Ⓐ.

EXAMPLE 3 Real-Life Application

The graph shows the distance remaining to complete a tunnel. (a) Write an equation that represents the distance y (in feet) remaining after x months. (b) How much time does it take to complete the tunnel?

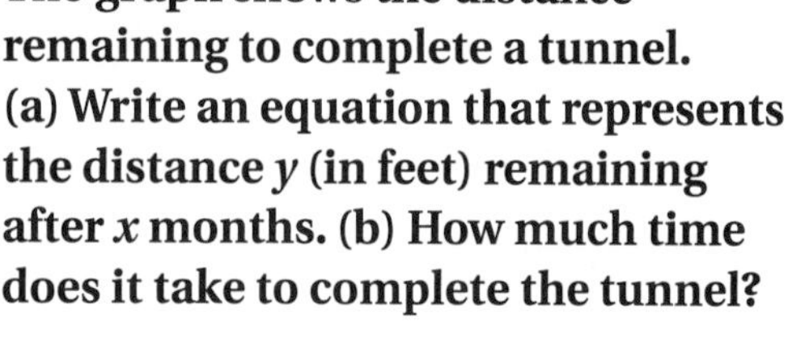

Engineers used tunnel boring machines like the ones shown above to dig an extension of the Metro Gold Line in Los Angeles. The new tunnels are 1.7 miles long and 21 feet wide.

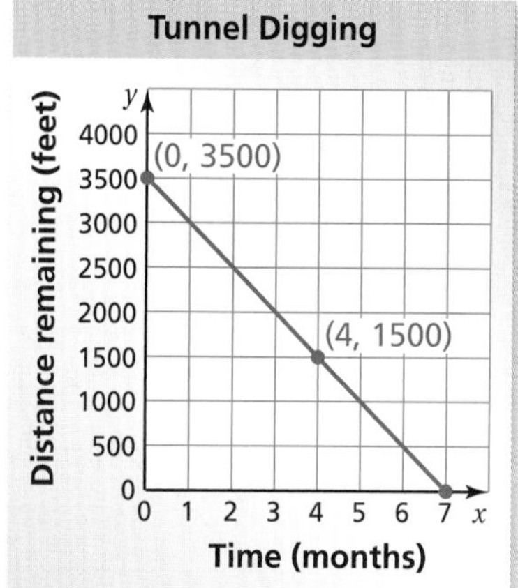

a. Find the slope and y-intercept.

$$\text{slope} = \frac{\text{rise}}{\text{run}} = \frac{-2000}{4} = -500$$

Because the line crosses the y-axis at $(0, 3500)$, the y-intercept is 3500.

∴ So, the equation is $y = -500x + 3500$.

b. The tunnel is complete when the distance remaining is 0 feet. So, find the value of x when $y = 0$.

$y = -500x + 3500$	Write the equation.
$0 = -500x + 3500$	Substitute 0 for y.
$-3500 = -500x$	Subtract 3500 from each side.
$7 = x$	Solve for x.

∴ It takes 7 months to complete the tunnel.

On Your Own

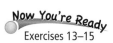

Now You're Ready Exercises 13–15

3. Write an equation of the line that passes through $(0, 5)$ and $(4, 5)$.

4. **WHAT IF?** In Example 3, the points are $(0, 3500)$ and $(5, 1500)$. How long does it take to complete the tunnel?

2.5 Exercises

Vocabulary and Concept Check

1. **WRITING** Explain how to find the slope of a line given the intercepts of the line.
2. **WRITING** Explain how to write an equation of a line using its graph.

Practice and Problem Solving

Write an equation for each side of the figure.

3. 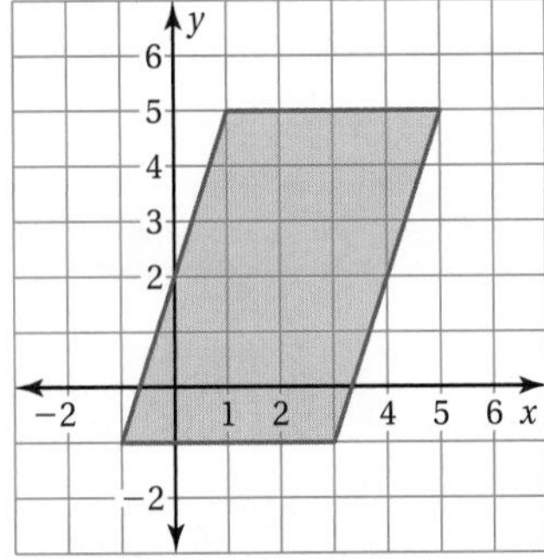

4. 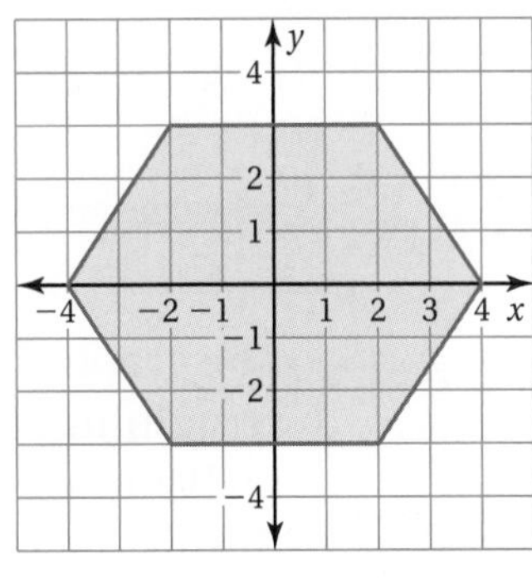

Write an equation of the line in slope-intercept form.

5. 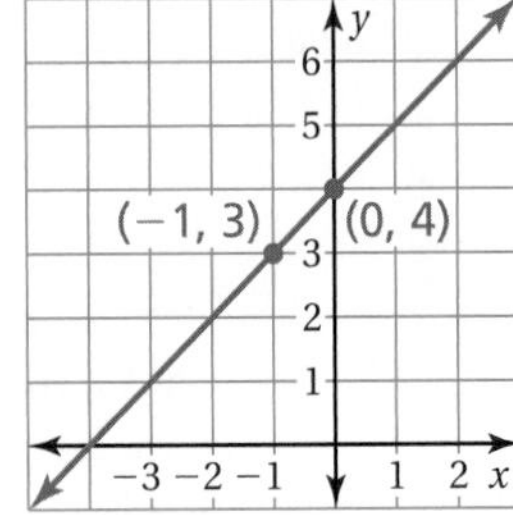

6. 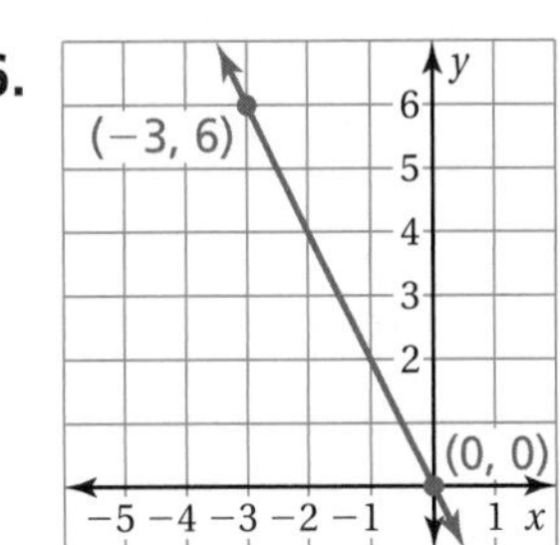

7. 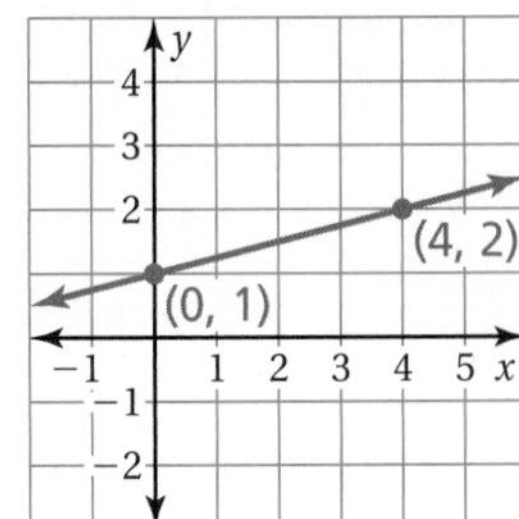

8. 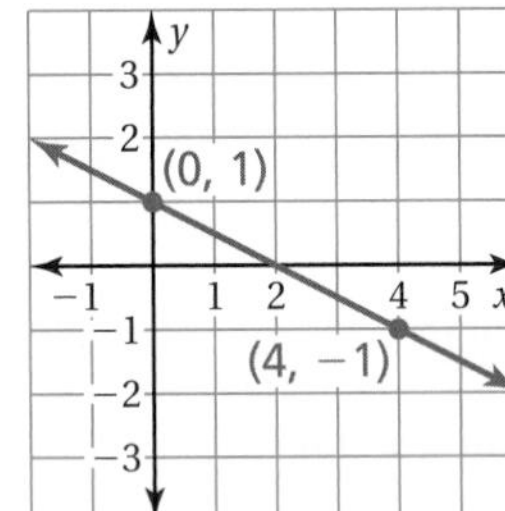

9. 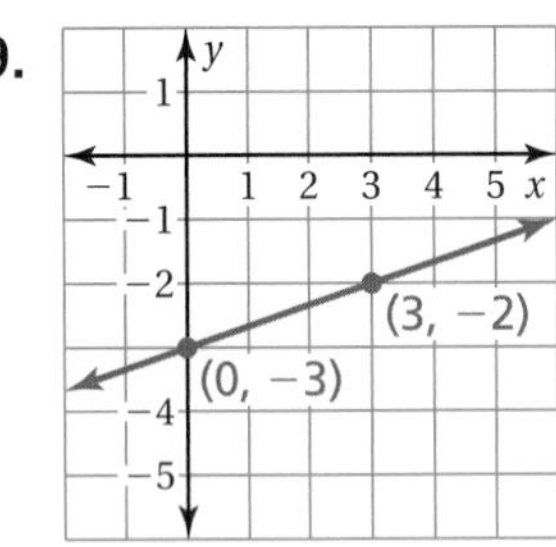

10. 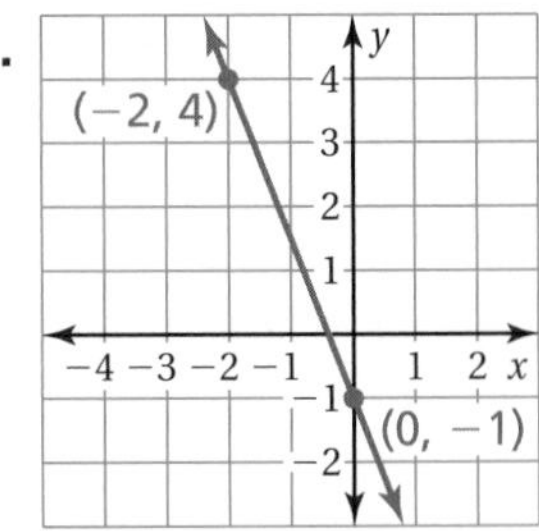

11. **ERROR ANALYSIS** Describe and correct the error in writing the equation of the line.

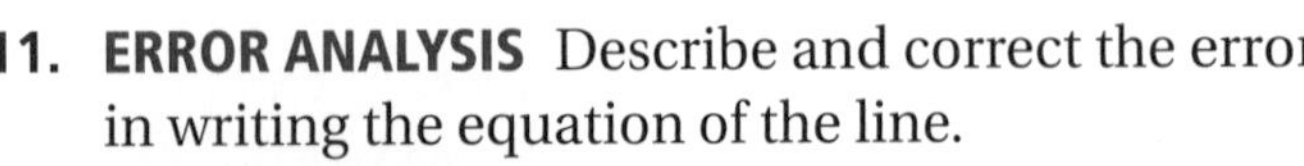

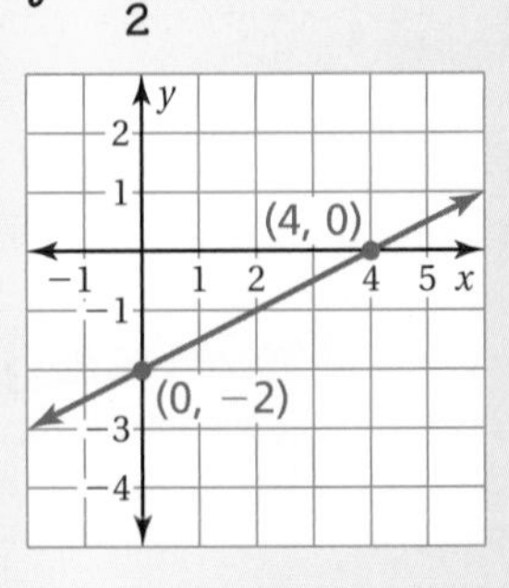

12. **BOA** A boa constrictor is 18 inches long at birth and grows 8 inches per year. Write an equation that represents the length y (in feet) of a boa constrictor that is x years old.

Write an equation of the line that passes through the points.

2 **13.** (2, 5), (0, 5) **14.** (−3, 0), (0, 0) **15.** (0, −2), (4, −2)

16. WALKATHON One of your friends gives you \$10 for a charity walkathon. Another friend gives you an amount per mile. After 5 miles, you have raised \$13.50 total. Write an equation that represents the amount y of money you have raised after x miles.

17. BRAKING TIME During each second of braking, an automobile slows by about 10 miles per hour.

a. Plot the points (0, 60) and (6, 0). What do the points represent?

b. Draw a line through the points. What does the line represent?

c. Write an equation of the line.

18. PAPER You have 500 sheets of notebook paper. After 1 week, you have 72% of the sheets left. You use the same number of sheets each week. Write an equation that represents the number y of pages remaining after x weeks.

19. Critical Thinking The palm tree on the left is 10 years old. The palm tree on the right is 8 years old. The trees grow at the same rate.

a. Estimate the height y (in feet) of each tree.

b. Plot the two points (x, y), where x is the age of each tree and y is the height of each tree.

c. What is the rate of growth of the trees?

d. Write an equation that represents the height of a palm tree in terms of its age.

Fair Game Review What you learned in previous grades & lessons

Plot the ordered pair in a coordinate plane. *(Skills Review Handbook)*

20. (1, 4) **21.** (−1, −2) **22.** (0, 1) **23.** (2, 7)

24. MULTIPLE CHOICE Which of the following statements is true? *(Section 2.3)*

Ⓐ The x-intercept is 5.

Ⓑ The x-intercept is −2.

Ⓒ The y-intercept is 5.

Ⓓ The y-intercept is −2.

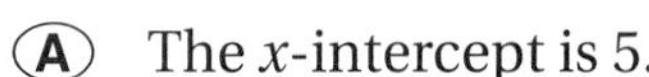

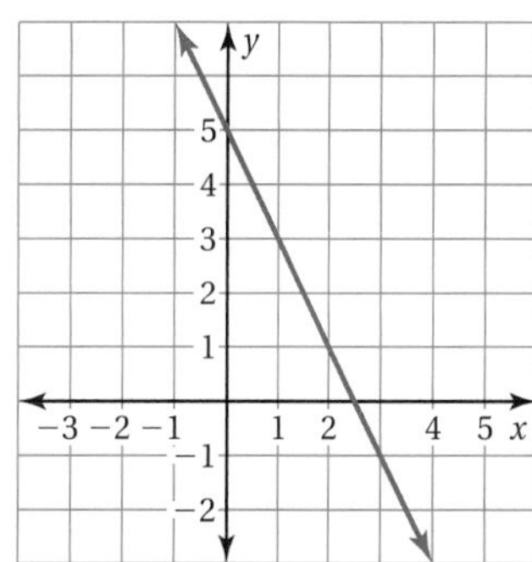

2.6 Writing Equations Using a Slope and a Point

STANDARDS OF LEARNING
8.16

Essential Question How can you write an equation of a line when you are given the slope and a point on the line?

1 ACTIVITY: Writing Equations of Lines

Work with a partner.

- **Sketch the line that has the given slope and passes through the given point.**
- **Find the *y*-intercept of the line.**
- **Write an equation of the line.**

a. $m = -2$

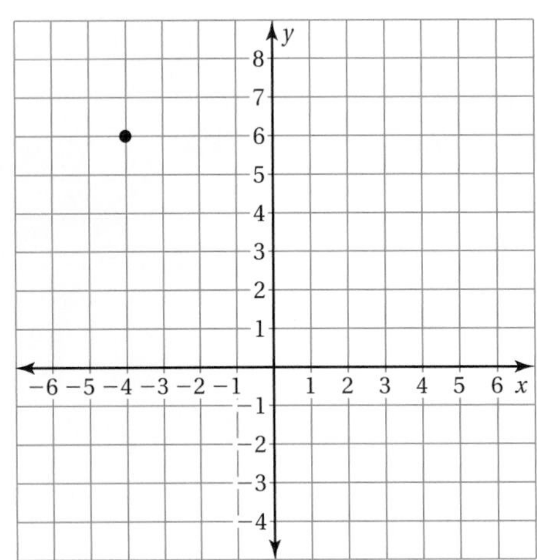

b. $m = \frac{1}{3}$

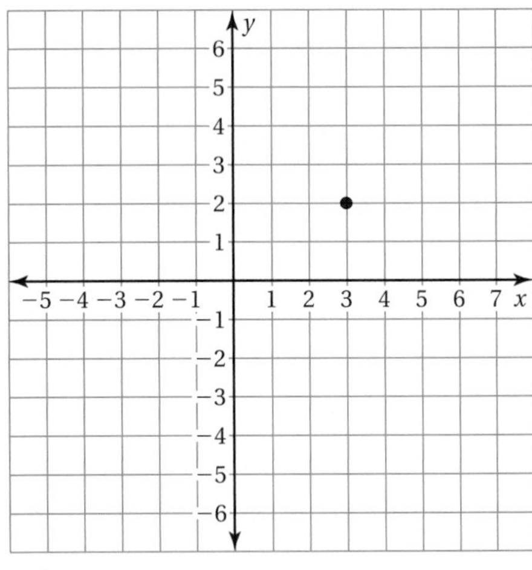

c. $m = -\frac{2}{3}$

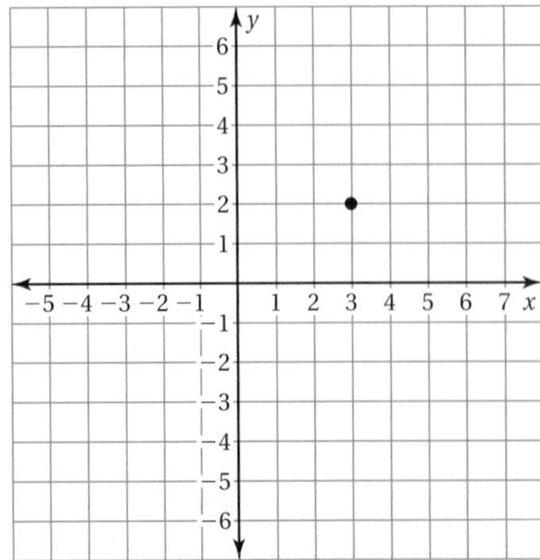

d. $m = \frac{5}{2}$

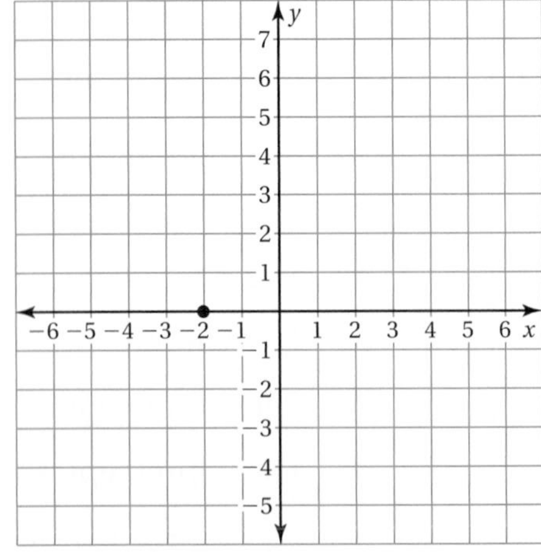

2 ACTIVITY: Writing Linear Equations

Work with a partner.

a. For 4 months, you have saved \$25 a month. You now have \$175 in your savings account.

- Draw a graph that shows the balance in your account after t months.
- Write an equation that represents the balance A after t months.

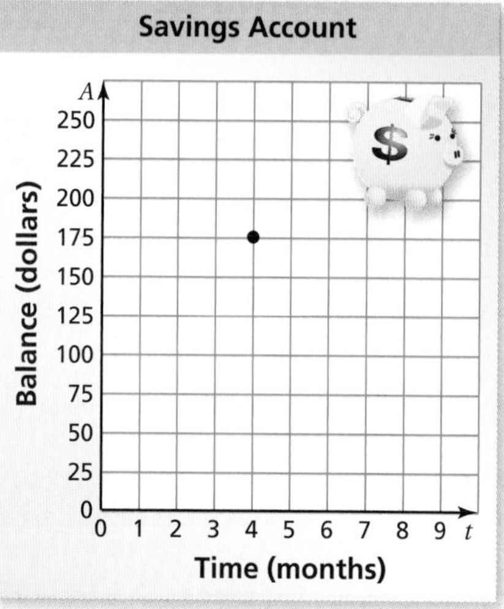

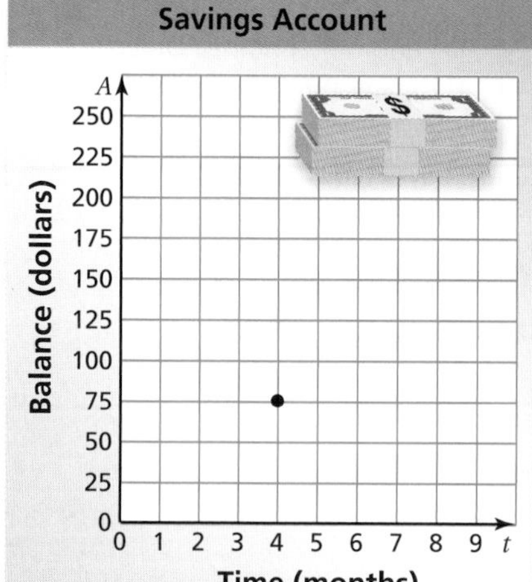

b. For 4 months, you have withdrawn \$25 a month from your savings account. Your account balance is now \$75.

- Draw a graph that shows the balance in your account after t months.
- Write an equation that represents the balance A after t months.

c. For 6 years, the population of a town has grown by 5000 people per year. The population is now 70,000.

- Draw a graph that shows the population after t years.
- Write an equation that represents the population P after t years.

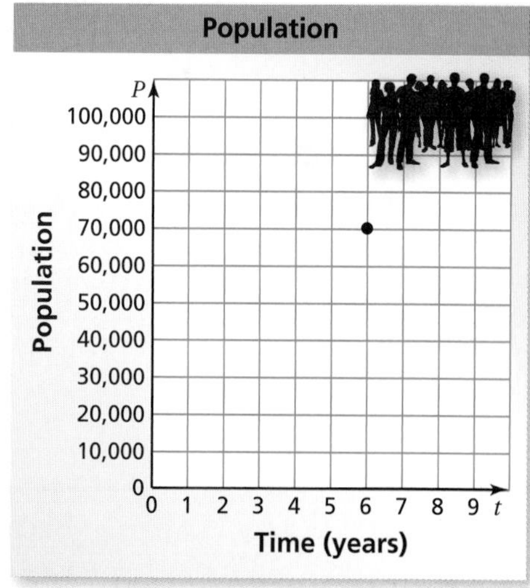

What Is Your Answer?

3. **IN YOUR OWN WORDS** How can you write an equation of a line when you are given the slope and a point on the line? Give an example that is different from those in Activities 1 and 2.

Practice Use what you learned about writing equations using a slope and a point to complete Exercises 3–5 on page 100.

2.6 Lesson

EXAMPLE 1 Writing Equations Using a Slope and a Point

Write an equation of the line with the given slope that passes through the given point.

a. $m = \frac{2}{3}$; $(-6, 1)$

Use a graph to find the y-intercept.

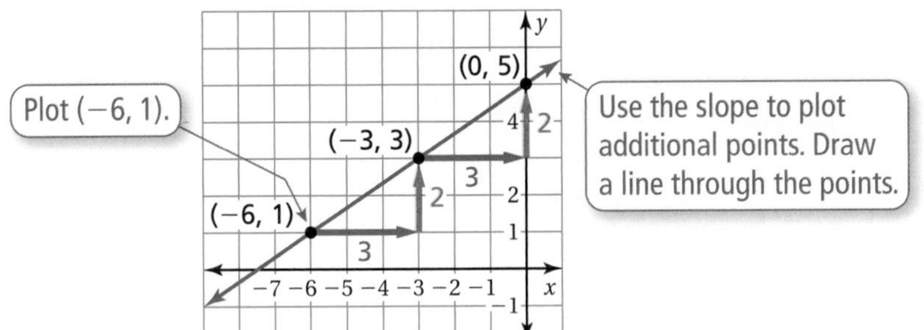

Because the line crosses the y-axis at $(0, 5)$, the y-intercept is 5.

So, the equation is $y = \frac{2}{3}x + 5$.

> **Check**
>
> Check that $(-6, 1)$ is a solution of the equation.
>
> $y = \frac{2}{3}x + 5$
>
> $1 \stackrel{?}{=} \frac{2}{3}(-6) + 5$
>
> $1 = 1$ ✓

b. $m = -3$; $(1, -4)$

Use a graph to find the y-intercept.

Plot (1, −4).

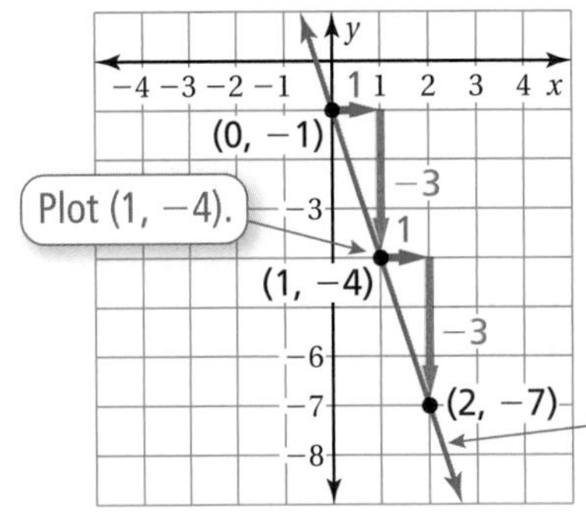

Use the slope to plot additional points. Draw a line through the points.

Because the line crosses the y-axis at $(0, -1)$, the y-intercept is -1.

So, the equation is $y = -3x + (-1)$, or $y = -3x - 1$.

> **Check**
>
> Check that $(1, -4)$ is a solution of the equation.
>
> $y = -3x - 1$
>
> $-4 \stackrel{?}{=} -3(1) - 1$
>
> $-4 = -4$ ✓

On Your Own

Now You're Ready
Exercises 6–11

Write an equation of the line with the given slope that passes through the given point.

1. $m = 1$; $(2, 0)$

2. $m = -\frac{1}{2}$; $(2, 3)$

EXAMPLE 2 Real-Life Application

10 feet per second

You finish parasailing and are being pulled back to the boat. After 2 seconds, you are 25 feet above the boat. (a) Write an equation that represents the height y (in feet) above the boat after x seconds. (b) At what height were you parasailing? (c) When do you reach the boat?

a. You are being pulled down at the rate of 10 feet per second. So, the slope is -10. You are 25 feet above the boat after 2 seconds. So, the line passes through (2, 25).

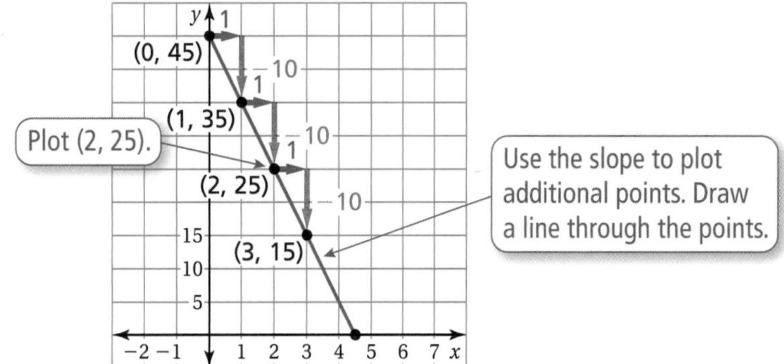
(0, 45)
(1, 35)
(2, 25)
(3, 15)
Plot (2, 25).
Use the slope to plot additional points. Draw a line through the points.

Because the line crosses the y-axis at (0, 45), the y-intercept is 45.

So, the equation is $y = -10x + 45$.

Check

Check that (2, 25) is a solution of the equation.

$y = -10x + 45$	Write the equation.
$25 \stackrel{?}{=} -10(2) + 45$	Substitute.
$25 = 25$ ✓	Simplify.

b. You start descending when $x = 0$. The y-intercept is 45. So, you were parasailing at a height of 45 feet.

c. You reach the boat when $y = 0$.

$y = -10x + 45$	Write the equation.
$0 = -10x + 45$	Substitute 0 for y.
$-45 = -10x$	Subtract 45 from each side.
$4.5 = x$	Solve for x.

You reach the boat after 4.5 seconds.

On Your Own

3. **WHAT IF?** In Example 2, you are 35 feet above the boat after 2 seconds. When do you reach the boat?

2.6 Exercises

Vocabulary and Concept Check

1. **WRITING** What information do you need to write an equation of a line?
2. **WRITING** Describe how to write an equation of a line using its slope and a point on the line.

Practice and Problem Solving

Write an equation of the line with the given slope that passes through the given point.

3. $m = \frac{1}{2}$

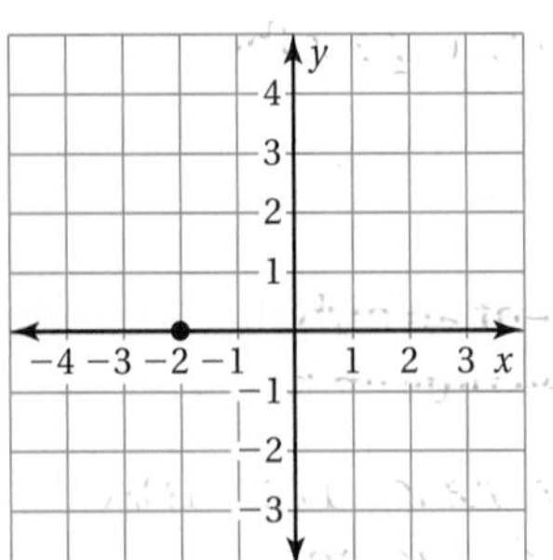

4. $m = -\frac{3}{4}$

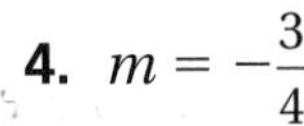

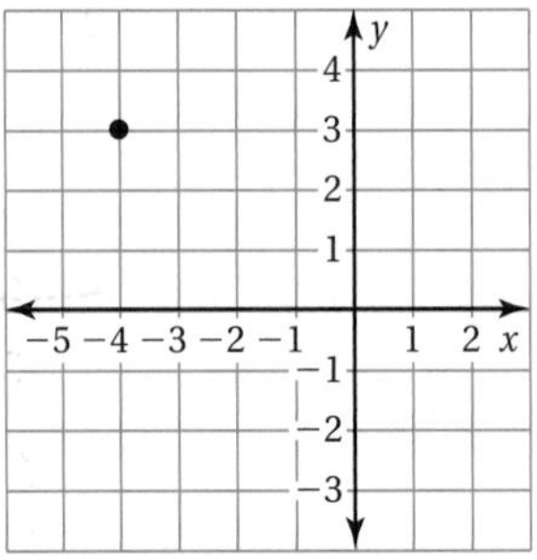

5. $m = -3$

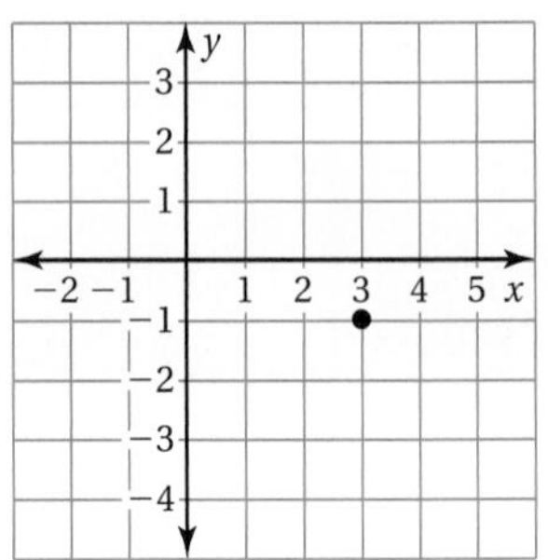

1 6. $m = -\frac{2}{3}$; (3, 0)

7. $m = \frac{3}{4}$; (4, 8)

8. $m = 4$; (1, −3)

9. $m = -\frac{1}{7}$; (7, −5)

10. $m = \frac{5}{3}$; (3, 3)

11. $m = -2$; (−1, −4)

12. **ERROR ANALYSIS** Describe and correct the error in writing an equation of the line with a slope of $\frac{1}{3}$ that passes through the point (6, 4).

   ✗ $y = \frac{1}{3}x + 4$

13. **CHEMISTRY** At 0°C, the volume of a gas is 22 liters. For each degree the temperature T (in degrees Celsius) increases, the volume V (in liters) of the gas increases by $\frac{2}{25}$. Write an equation that represents the volume of the gas in terms of the temperature.

14. CARS After it is purchased, the value of a new car decreases $4000 each year. After 3 years, the car is worth $18,000.

a. Write an equation that represents the value V (in dollars) of the car x years after it is purchased.

b. What was the original value of the car?

15. CRICKETS According to Dolbear's Law, you can predict the temperature T (in degrees Fahrenheit) by counting the number x of chirps made by a snowy tree cricket in 1 minute. For a rise in temperature of 0.25 degree, the cricket makes an additional chirp each minute.

a. A cricket chirps 40 times in 1 minute when the temperature is 50°F. Write an equation that represents the temperature in terms of the number of chirps in 1 minute.

b. You count 100 chirps in 1 minute. What is the temperature?

c. The temperature is 96 °F. How many chirps would you expect the cricket to make?

16. AIRBOATS You rent an airboat. The total cost includes a flat fee plus an hourly fee.

a. After 4 hours the total cost is $140. Write an equation that represents the total cost y after x hours.

b. Interpret the y-intercept.

17. Critical Thinking Bone mineral density is a measure of the strength of bones. The average bone mineral density of a female astronaut who has never been in space is 2.9 grams per square centimeter. For the first 3 years she spends in space, her bone density decreases by 0.03 gram per square centimeter per month.

a. Write an equation that represents the bone mineral density y of a female astronaut in terms of the number x of months she spends in space.

b. What is her bone mineral density after 2 years and 6 months in space?

c. Explain why the amount of time an astronaut can spend in space is limited.

Fair Game Review What you learned in previous grades & lessons

18. Plot the ordered pairs in the same coordinate plane. *(Skills Review Handbook)*

$(2, 5), (-3, -6), (0, 7), (-5, 0), (-8, 9)$

19. MULTIPLE CHOICE What is the y-intercept of the equation $5x - 2y = 28$? *(Section 2.4)*

Ⓐ $-\frac{5}{2}$ Ⓑ -14 Ⓒ $\frac{5}{2}$ Ⓓ 5.6

2.7 Writing Equations Using Two Points

STANDARDS OF LEARNING
8.16

Essential Question How can you write an equation of a line when you are given two points on the line?

1 ACTIVITY: Writing Equations of Lines

Work with a partner.

- **Sketch the line that passes through the given points.**
- **Find the slope and *y*-intercept of the line.**
- **Write an equation of the line.**

a. 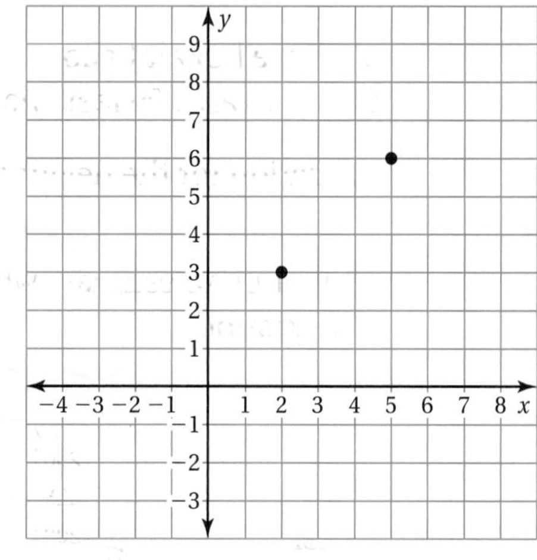

b. 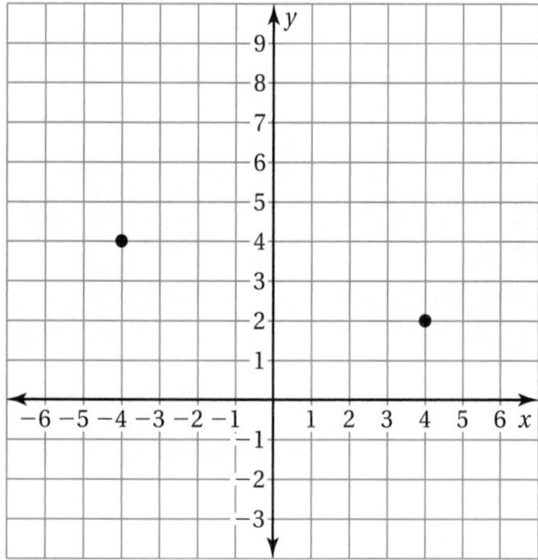

c. 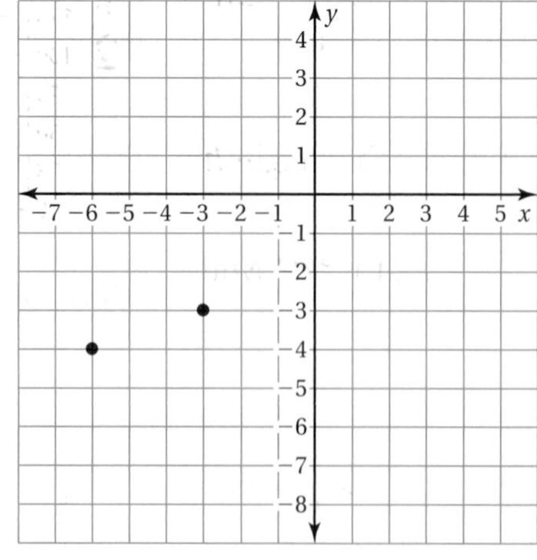

d. 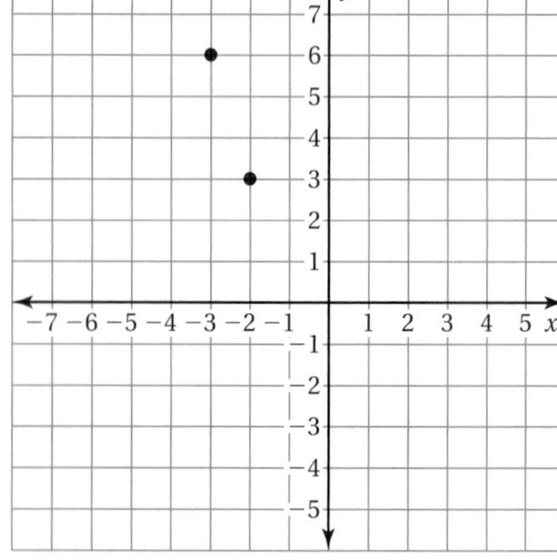

2 ACTIVITY: Writing and Using Linear Equations

Work with a partner.

a. You are rising in a hot air balloon. After 1 minute, you are 200 feet above the ground. After 4 minutes, you are 800 feet above the ground.

- Write an equation for the height h in terms of the time t.
- Use your equation to find the height of the balloon after 5 minutes.

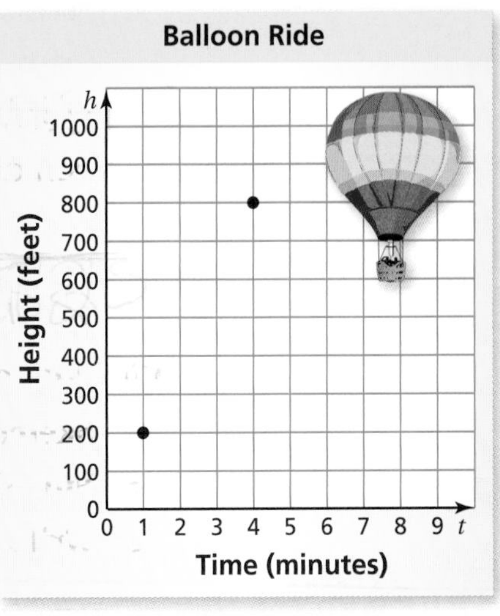

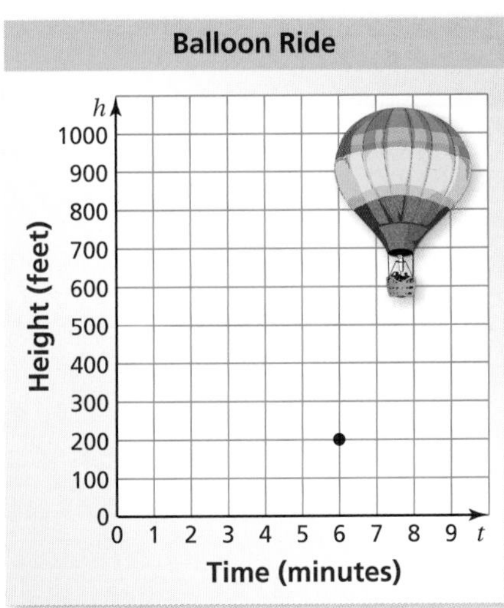

b. After 5 minutes, the hot air balloon starts to descend. After 6 minutes, you are 200 feet above the ground.

- Write an equation for the height h in terms of the time t.
- Use your equation to estimate when the balloon lands on the ground.

c. You are on a roller coaster. After 3 seconds, you are 190 feet above the ground and have reached maximum speed. One second later, you are 95 feet above the ground.

- Write an equation for the height h in terms of the time t.
- When will you reach ground level?

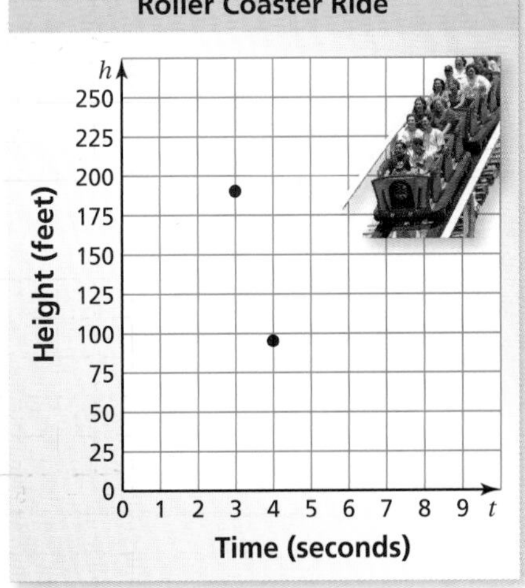

What Is Your Answer?

3. **IN YOUR OWN WORDS** How can you write an equation of a line when you are given two points on the line? Give an example that is different from those in Activities 1 and 2.

Practice Use what you learned about writing equations using two points to complete Exercises 3–5 on page 106.

2.7 Lesson

EXAMPLE 1 Writing Equations Using Two Points

Write an equation of the line that passes through the points.

a. $(-6, 6), (-3, 4)$

Use a graph to find the slope and y-intercept.

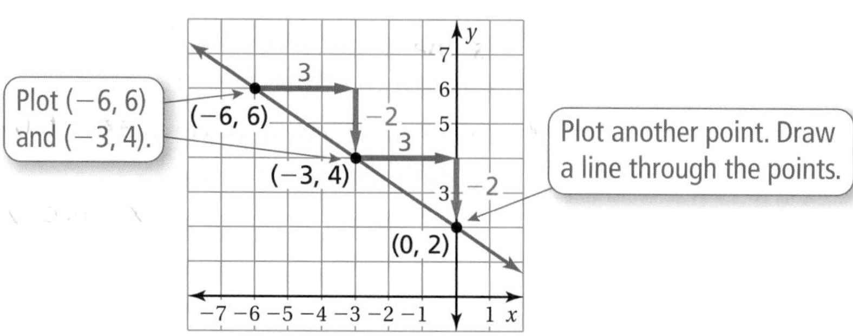

Study Tip

After writing an equation, check that the given points are solutions of the equation.

$$\text{slope} = \frac{\text{rise}}{\text{run}} = \frac{-2}{3} = -\frac{2}{3}$$

Because the line crosses the y-axis at $(0, 2)$, the y-intercept is 2.

∴ So, the equation is $y = -\frac{2}{3}x + 2$.

b. $(-2, -4), (1, -1)$

Use a graph to find the slope and y-intercept.

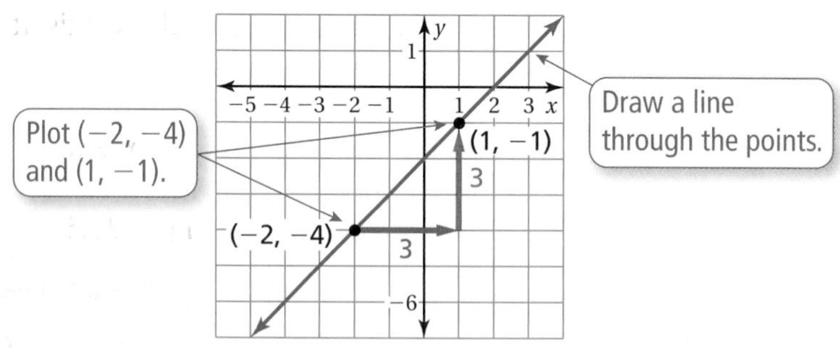

$$\text{slope} = \frac{\text{rise}}{\text{run}} = \frac{3}{3} = 1$$

Because the line crosses the y-axis at $(0, -2)$, the y-intercept is -2.

∴ So, the equation is $y = 1x + (-2)$, or $y = x - 2$.

On Your Own

Now You're Ready
Exercises 6–14

Write an equation of the line that passes through the points.

1. $(2, 3), (4, 4)$

2. $(-1, 2), (1, -4)$

EXAMPLE 2 Standardized Test Practice

The graph of which equation passes through (2, −1) and (4, −2)?

Ⓐ $y = -\frac{1}{2}x$ Ⓑ $y = \frac{1}{2}x$

Ⓒ $y = -2x$ Ⓓ $y = 2x$

Graph the line through the points. Find the slope and y-intercept.

$$\text{slope} = \frac{\text{rise}}{\text{run}} = \frac{-1}{2} = -\frac{1}{2}$$

Because the line crosses the y-axis at (0, 0), the y-intercept is 0.

∴ So, the equation is $y = -\frac{1}{2}x + 0$, or $y = -\frac{1}{2}x$.

The correct answer is Ⓐ.

EXAMPLE 3 Real-Life Application

22.5 oz

A 2-week old kitten weighs 9 ounces. Two weeks later, it weighs 15 ounces. (a) Write an equation to represent the weight y (in ounces) of the kitten x weeks after birth. (b) How old is the kitten in the photo?

a. The kitten weighs 9 ounces after 2 weeks and 15 ounces after 4 weeks. So, graph the line that passes through (2, 9) and (4, 15).

$$\text{slope} = \frac{\text{rise}}{\text{run}} = \frac{6}{2} = 3$$

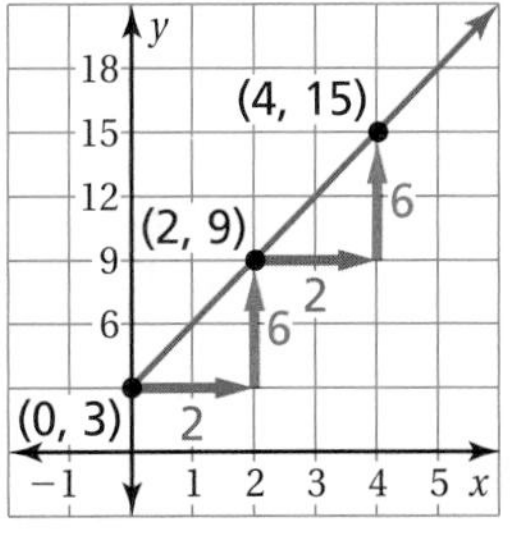

Because the line crosses the y-axis at (0, 3), the y-intercept is 3.

∴ So, the equation is $y = 3x + 3$.

b. Find the value of x when $y = 22.5$.

$y = 3x + 3$	Write the equation.
$22.5 = 3x + 3$	Substitute 22.5 for y.
$19.5 = 3x$	Subtract 3 from each side.
$6.5 = x$	Solve for x.

∴ The kitten in the photo is 6.5 weeks old.

On Your Own

3. The graph of which equation in Example 2 passes through (−2, 4) and (−1, 2)?

4. A 3-week old kitten weighs 12 ounces. Two weeks later, it weighs 18 ounces. How old is the kitten when it weighs 27 ounces?

2.7 Exercises

Vocabulary and Concept Check

1. **WRITING** Describe how to write an equation of a line using two points on the line.

2. **WHICH ONE DOESN'T BELONG?** Which pair of points does *not* belong with the other three? Explain your reasoning.

(0, 1), (2, 3)	(1, 2), (4, 5)	(2, 3), (5, 6)	(1, 2), (4, 6)

Practice and Problem Solving

Find the slope and *y*-intercept of the line that passes through the points. Then write an equation of the line.

3. 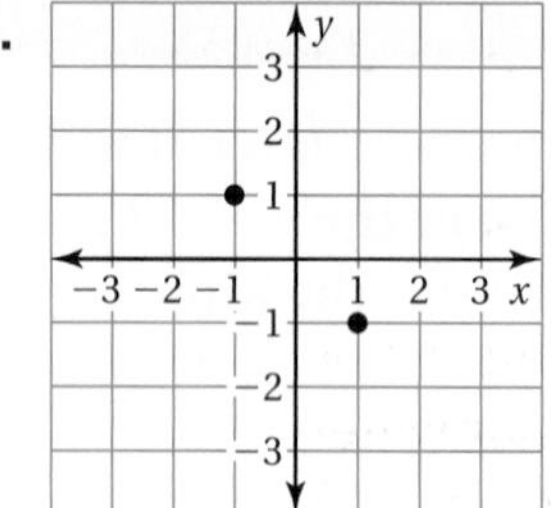

4. 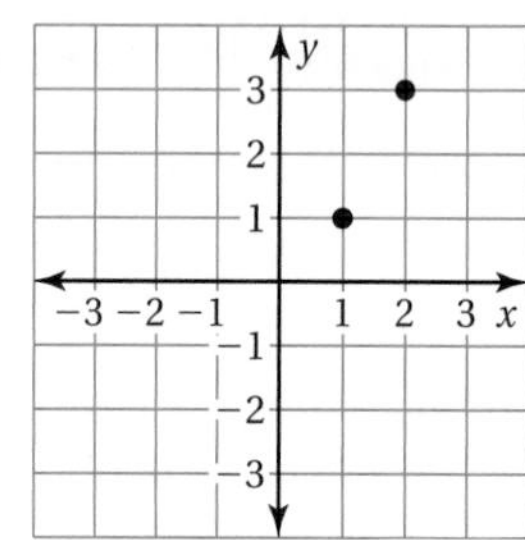

5. 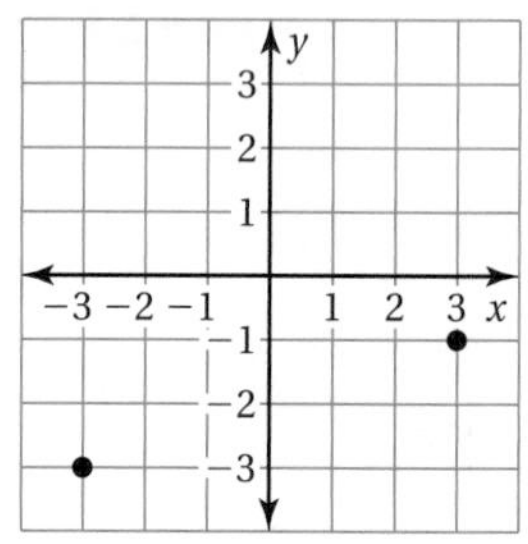

Write an equation of the line that passes through the points.

1 6. (−1, −1), (1, 5)
7. (2, 4), (3, 6)
8. (−2, 3), (2, 7)
9. (4, 1), (8, 2)
10. (−9, 5), (−3, 3)
11. (1, 2), (−2, −1)
12. (−5, 2), (5, −2)
13. (2, −7), (8, 2)
14. (1, −2), (3, −8)

15. **ERROR ANALYSIS** Describe and correct the error in finding the equation of the line that passes through (−1, −6) and (3, 2).

✗ slope $= \frac{\text{rise}}{\text{run}} = \frac{8}{4} = 2$

The *y*-intercept is (0, −4).

The equation is $y = -4x + 2$.

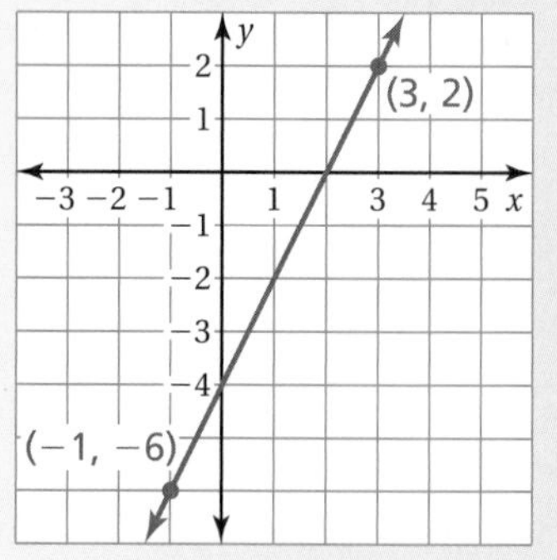

16. **JET SKI** It costs \$175 to rent a jet ski for 2 hours. It costs \$300 to rent a jet ski for 4 hours. Write an equation that represents the cost *y* (in dollars) of renting a jet ski for *x* hours.

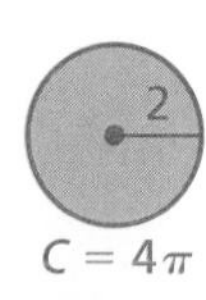

$C = 4\pi$

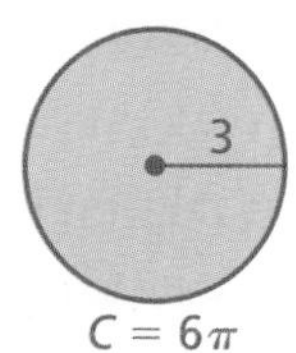

$C = 6\pi$

17. **CIRCUMFERENCE** Consider the circles shown.
    a. Plot the points $(2, 4\pi)$ and $(3, 6\pi)$.
    b. Write an equation of the line that passes through the two points. How does the equation relate to circles?

18. SOAP BOX DERBY The table shows the changes in elevation for a Soap Box Derby track.

Track Distance	Elevation
0 ft	48 ft
100 ft	38 ft
200 ft	28 ft
350 ft	18 ft
600 ft	8 ft
989 ft	0 ft

a. Draw a Soap Box Derby track in a coordinate plane.

b. Does each section of the track have the same slope? Explain.

c. Write an equation that represents the elevation y (in feet) of the track between 100 feet and 200 feet.

19. CAR VALUE The value of a car decreases at a constant rate. After 3 years, the value of the car is $15,000. After 2 more years the value of the car is $11,000.

a. Write an equation that represents the value y (in dollars) of the car after x years.

b. Graph the equation.

c. What is the y-intercept of the line? Interpret the y-intercept.

Leaning Tower of Pisa

20. WATERING CAN You water the plants in your classroom at a constant rate. After 5 seconds, your watering can contains 58 ounces of water. Fifteen seconds later, the can contains 28 ounces of water.

a. Write an equation that represents the amount y (in ounces) of water in the can after x seconds.

b. How much water was in the can when you started watering the plants?

c. When is the watering can empty?

21. Critical Thinking The Leaning Tower of Pisa in Italy was built between 1173 and 1350.

a. Write an equation for the yellow line.

b. The tower is 56 meters tall. How far off center is the top of the tower?

Fair Game Review What you learned in previous grades & lessons

Find the percent of the number. *(Skills Review Handbook)*

22. 15% of 300 **23.** 140% of 125 **24.** 6% of −75

25. MULTIPLE CHOICE What is the x-intercept of the equation $3x + 5y = 30$? *(Section 2.4)*

Ⓐ −10 Ⓑ −6 Ⓒ 6 Ⓓ 10

2.8 Solving Real-Life Problems

STANDARDS OF LEARNING
8.16

Essential Question How can you use a linear equation in two variables to model and solve a real-life problem?

1 EXAMPLE: Writing a Story

Write a story that uses the graph at the right.

- **In your story, interpret the slope of the line, the *y*-intercept, and the *x*-intercept.**
- **Make a table that shows data from the graph.**
- **Label the axes of the graph with units.**
- **Draw pictures for your story.**

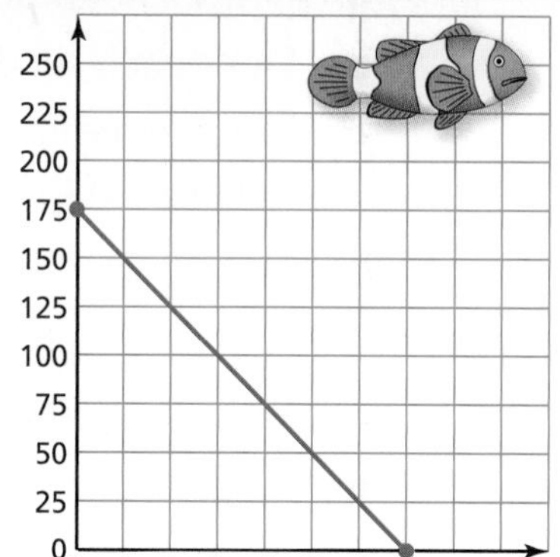

There are many possible stories. Here is one about a reef tank.

Tom works at an aquarium shop on Saturdays. One Saturday, when Tom gets to work, he is asked to clean a 175-gallon reef tank.

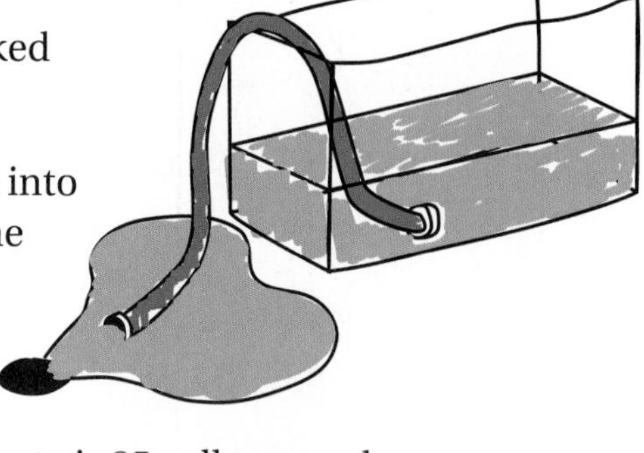

His first job is to drain the tank. He puts a hose into the tank and starts a siphon. Tom wonders if the tank will finish draining before he leaves work.

He measures the amount of water that is draining out and finds that 12.5 gallons drain out in 30 minutes. So, he figures that the rate is 25 gallons per hour. To see when the tank will be empty, Tom makes a table and draws a graph.

x-intercept: number of hours to empty the tank

x	0	1	2	3	4	5	6	7
y	175	150	125	100	75	50	25	0

y-intercept: amount of water in full tank

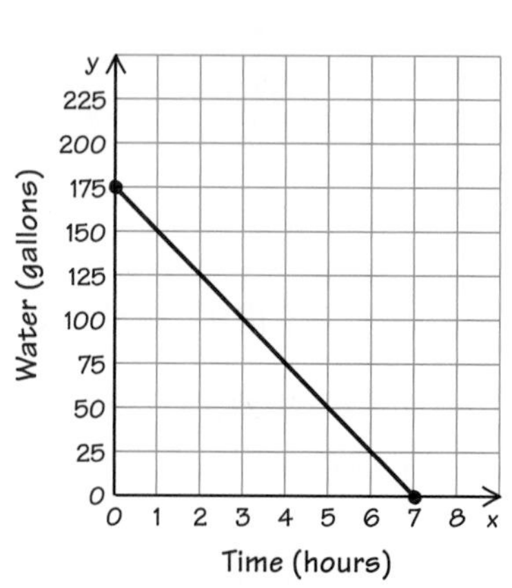

From the table and also from the graph, Tom sees that the tank will be empty after 7 hours. This will give him 1 hour to wash the tank before going home.

2 ACTIVITY: Writing a Story

Work with a partner. Write a story that uses the graph of a line.

- **In your story, interpret the slope of the line, the y-intercept, and the x-intercept.**
- **Make a table that shows data from the graph.**
- **Label the axes of the graph with units.**
- **Draw pictures for your story.**

3 ACTIVITY: Drawing Graphs

Work with a partner. Describe a real-life problem that has the given rate and intercepts. Draw a line that represents the problem.

a. Rate: -30 feet per second
y-intercept: 150 feet
x-intercept: 5 seconds

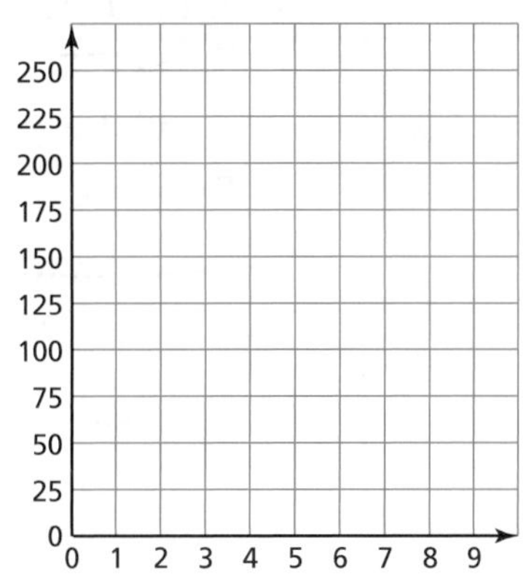

b. Rate: -25 dollars per month
y-intercept: \$200
x-intercept: 8 months

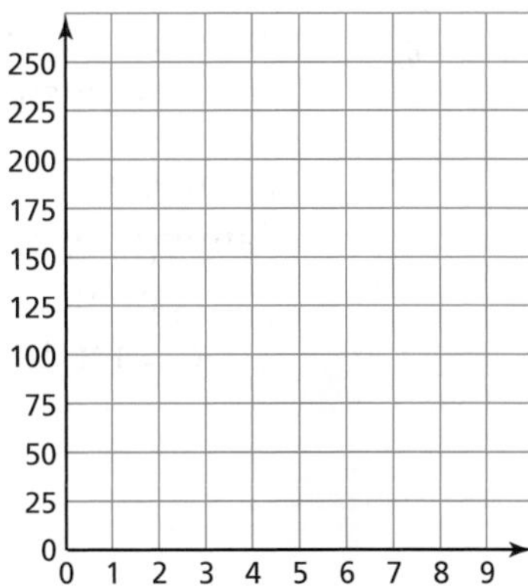

What Is Your Answer?

4. **IN YOUR OWN WORDS** How can you use a linear equation in two variables to model and solve a real-life problem? List three different rates that can be represented by slopes in real-life problems.

Practice Use what you learned about solving real-life problems to complete Exercises 4 and 5 on page 112.

EXAMPLE 1 **Real-Life Application**

The percent y (in decimal form) of battery power remaining x hours after you turn on a laptop computer is $y = -0.2x + 1$. (a) Graph the equation. (b) Interpret the x- and y-intercepts. (c) After how many hours is the battery power at 75%?

a. Use the slope and the y-intercept to graph the equation.

$$y = -0.2x + 1$$

slope: -0.2; y-intercept: 1

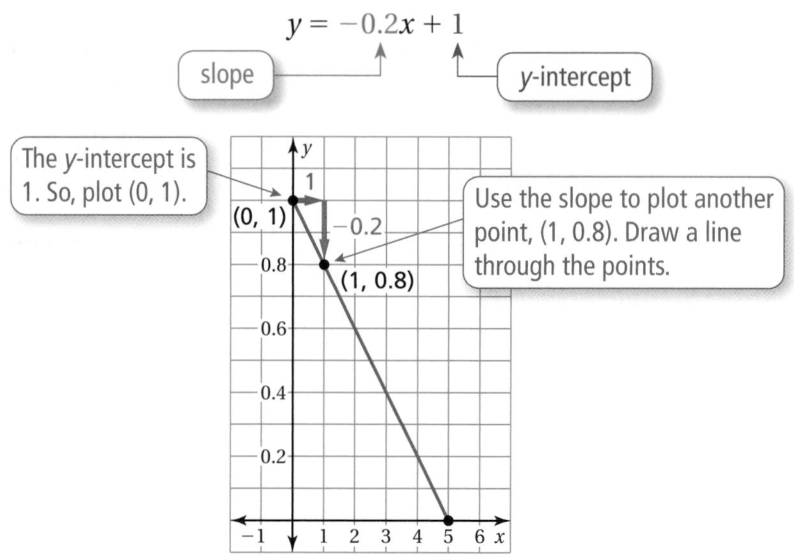

b. To find the x-intercept, substitute 0 for y in the equation.

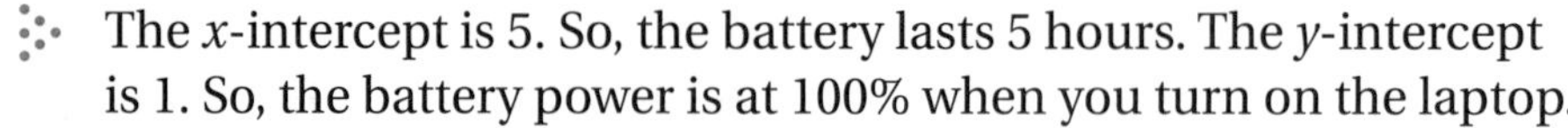

$y = -0.2x + 1$	Write the equation.
$0 = -0.2x + 1$	Substitute 0 for y.
$5 = x$	Solve for x.

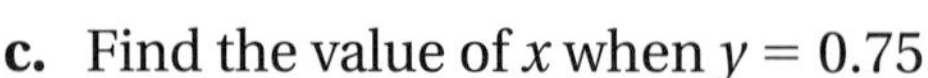

The x-intercept is 5. So, the battery lasts 5 hours. The y-intercept is 1. So, the battery power is at 100% when you turn on the laptop.

c. Find the value of x when $y = 0.75$.

$y = -0.2x + 1$	Write the equation.
$0.75 = -0.2x + 1$	Substitute 0.75 for y.
$1.25 = x$	Solve for x.

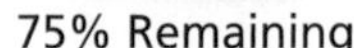

75% Remaining

The battery power is at 75% after 1.25 hours.

On Your Own

1. The amount y (in gallons) of gasoline remaining in a gas tank after driving x hours is $y = -2x + 12$. (a) Graph the equation. (b) Interpret the x- and y-intercepts. (c) After how many hours are there 5 gallons left?

EXAMPLE 2 Real-Life Application

The graph relates temperatures y (in degrees Fahrenheit) to temperatures x (in degrees Celsius). (a) Find the slope and y-intercept. (b) Write an equation of the line. (c) What is the mean temperature of Earth in degrees Fahrenheit?

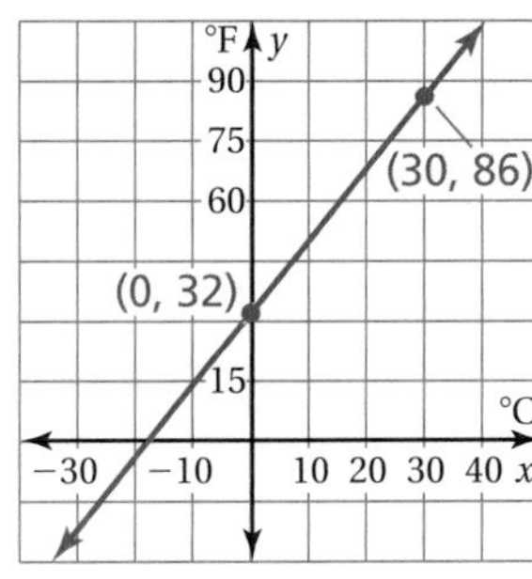

Mean Temperature:
15°C

a. slope $= \dfrac{\text{change in } y}{\text{change in } x} = \dfrac{54}{30} = \dfrac{9}{5}$

The line crosses the y-axis at (0, 32). So, the y-intercept is 32.

The slope is $\dfrac{9}{5}$ and the y-intercept is 32.

b. Use the slope and y-intercept to write an equation.

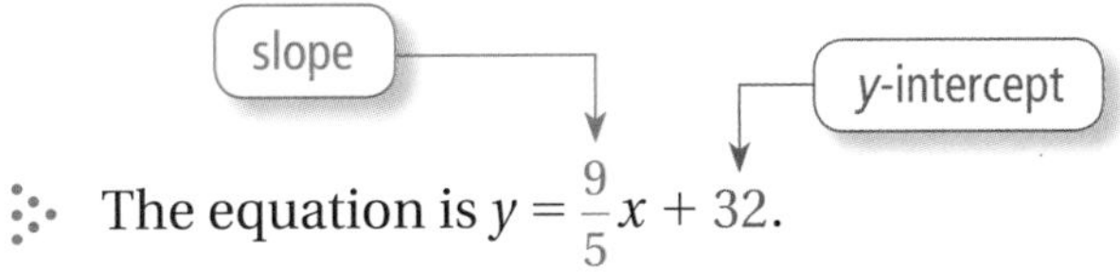

The equation is $y = \dfrac{9}{5}x + 32$.

c. In degrees Celsius, the mean temperature of Earth is 15°. To find the mean temperature in degrees Fahrenheit, find the value of y when $x = 15$.

$y = \dfrac{9}{5}x + 32$ Write the equation.

$= \dfrac{9}{5}(15) + 32$ Substitute 15 for x.

$= 59$ Simplify.

The mean temperature of Earth is 59°F.

On Your Own

Now You're Ready
Exercise 7

2. The graph shows the height y (in feet) of a flag x seconds after you start raising it up a flagpole.

a. Find and interpret the slope.

b. Write an equation of the line.

c. What is the height of the flag after 9 seconds?

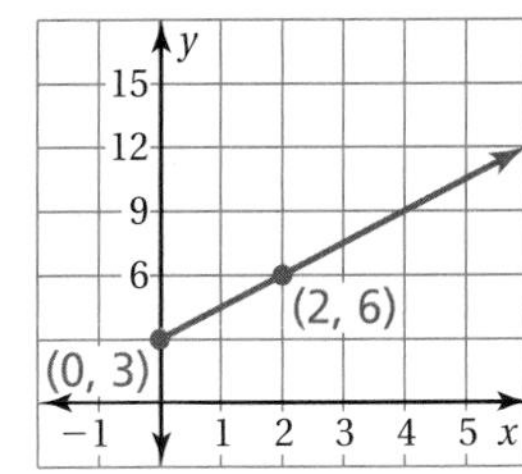

2.8 Exercises

Vocabulary and Concept Check

1. **REASONING** Explain how to find the slope, y-intercept, and x-intercept of the line shown.

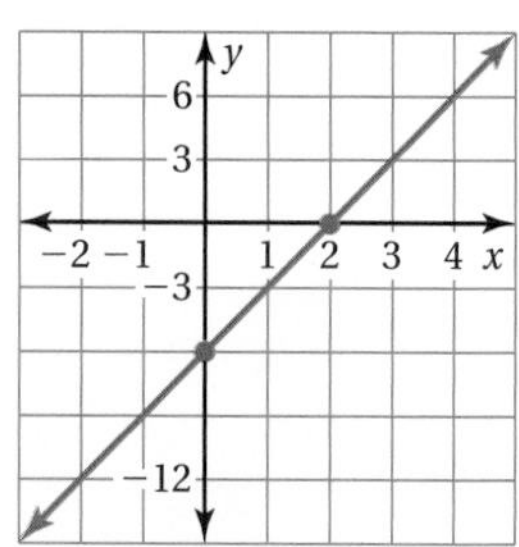

2. **OPEN-ENDED** Describe a real-life situation that uses a negative slope.

3. **REASONING** In a real-life situation, what does the slope of a line represent?

Practice and Problem Solving

Describe a real-life problem that has the given rate and intercepts. Draw a line that represents the problem.

4. Rate: −1.6 gallons per hour

   y-intercept: 16 gallons

   x-intercept: 10 hours

5. Rate: −45 pesos per week

   y-intercept: 180 pesos

   x-intercept: 4 weeks

1 6. **DOWNLOAD** You are downloading a song. The percent y (in decimal form) of megabytes remaining to download after x seconds is $y = -0.1x + 1$.

   a. Graph the equation.

   b. Interpret the x- and y-intercepts.

   c. After how many seconds is the download 50% complete?

2 7. **HIKING** The graph relates temperature y (in degrees Fahrenheit) to altitude x (in thousands of feet).

   a. Find the slope and y-intercept.

   b. Write an equation of the line.

   c. What is the temperature at sea level?

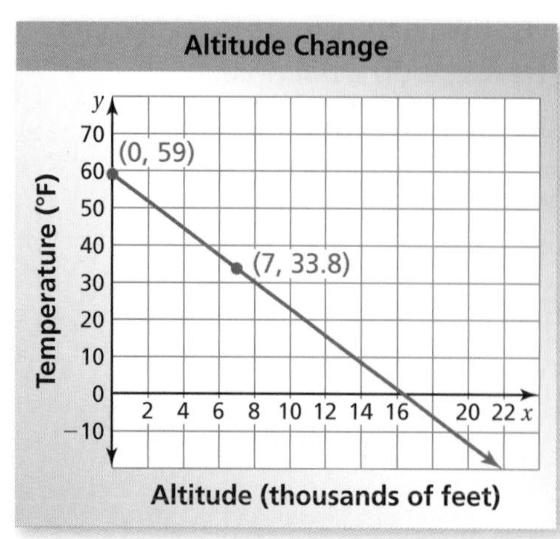

8. **TRAVEL** Your family is driving from Cincinnati to St. Louis. The graph relates your distance from St. Louis y (in miles) and travel time x (in hours).

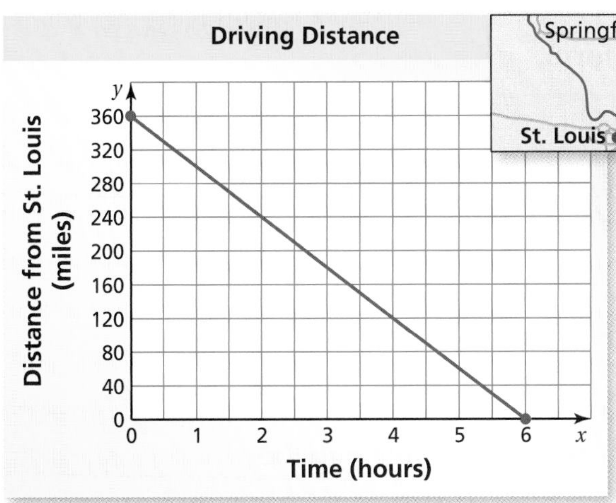

a. Interpret the x- and y-intercepts.

b. What is the slope? What does the slope represent in this situation?

c. Write an equation of the line. How would the graph and the equation change if you were able to travel in a straight line?

9. **PROJECT** Use a map or the Internet to find the latitude and longitude of your school to the nearest whole number. Then find the latitudes and longitudes of: Antananarivo, Madagascar; Denver, Colorado; Brasilia, Brazil; London, England; and Beijing, China.

a. Plot a point for each of the cities in the same coordinate plane. Let the positive y-axis represent north and the positive x-axis represent east.

b. Write an equation of the line that passes through Denver and Beijing.

c. In part (b), what geographic location does the y-intercept represent?

10. **Reasoning** A band is performing at an auditorium for a fee of \$1500. In addition to this fee, the band receives 30% of each \$20 ticket sold. The maximum capacity of the auditorium is 800 people.

a. Write an equation that represents the band's revenue R when x tickets are sold.

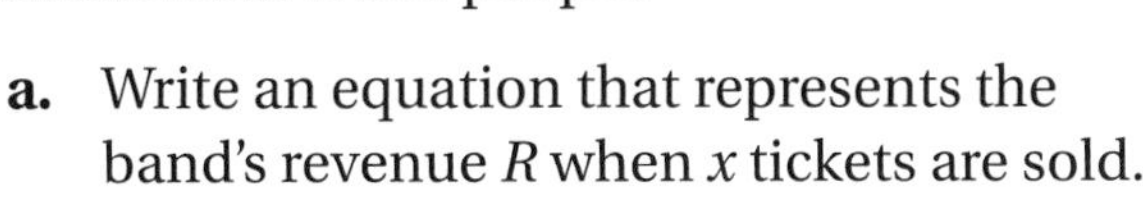

b. The band needs \$5000 for new equipment. How many tickets must be sold for the band to earn enough money to buy the new equipment?

Fair Game Review What you learned in previous grades & lessons

Solve the inequality. Graph the solution. *(Section 1.6)*

11. $1.5 \geq x + 2.8$

12. $k - \frac{1}{8} < -\frac{5}{8}$

13. $\frac{m}{1.8} \leq -4$

14. $25.6 > -3.2y$

15. **MULTIPLE CHOICE** Which equation is the slope-intercept form of $24x - 8y = 56$? *(Section 2.4)*

Ⓐ $y = -3x + 7$ Ⓑ $y = 3x - 7$ Ⓒ $y = -3x - 7$ Ⓓ $y = 3x + 7$

2.5–2.8 Quiz

Check It Out
Progress Check
BigIdeasMath.com

Write an equation of the line in slope-intercept form. *(Section 2.5)*

1.

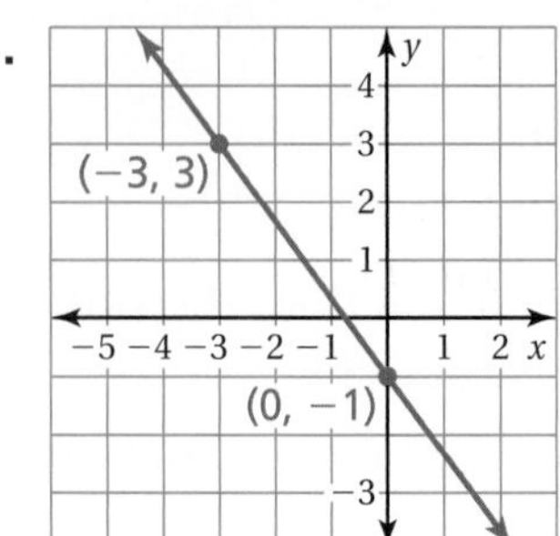

2.

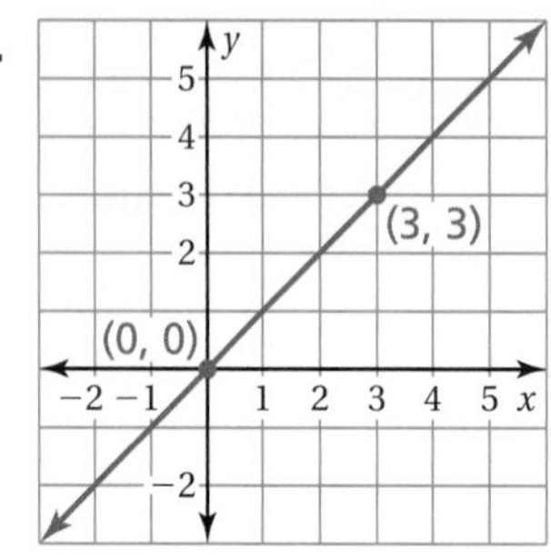

3.

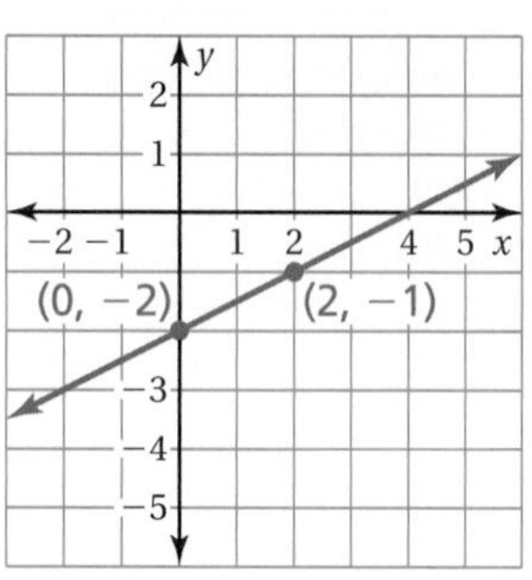

Write an equation of the line with the given slope that passes through the given point. *(Section 2.6)*

4. $m = 2;\ (1, 3)$

5. $m = -\frac{1}{8};\ (8, -5)$

Write an equation of the line that passes through the points. *(Section 2.7)*

6. $\left(0, -\frac{2}{3}\right), \left(-3, -\frac{2}{3}\right)$

7. $(4, 0), (0, 4)$

8. **FISH POND** You are draining a fish pond. The amount y (in liters) of water remaining after x hours is $y = -60x + 480$. (a) Graph the equation. (b) Interpret the x- and y-intercepts. *(Section 2.8)*

9. **CONSTRUCTION** A construction crew is extending a highway sound barrier that is 13 miles long. The crew builds $\frac{1}{2}$ mile per week. Write an equation for the length y (in miles) of the barrier after x weeks. *(Section 2.5)*

10. **STORAGE** You pay \$510 to rent a storage unit for 3 months. The total cost includes an initial deposit plus a monthly fee of \$160. *(Section 2.6)*

a. Write an equation that represents your total cost y (in dollars) after x months.

b. Interpret the y-intercept.

11. **CORN** After 3 weeks, a corn plant is 2 feet tall. After 9 weeks, the plant is 8 feet tall. Write an equation that represents the height y (in feet) of the corn plant after x weeks. *(Section 2.7)*

12. **WATER** A recreation department bought bottled water to sell at a fair. The graph shows the number y of bottles remaining after each hour x. *(Section 2.8)*

a. Find the slope and y-intercept.

b. Write an equation of the line.

c. The fair started at 10 A.M. When did the recreation department run out of bottled water?

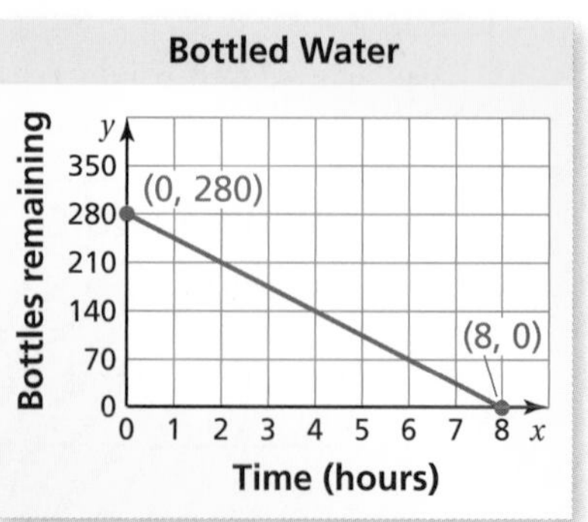

2 Chapter Review

Check It Out
Vocabulary Help
BigIdeasMath.com

Review Key Vocabulary

linear equation, *p. 64*
solution of a linear equation, *p. 64*
slope, *p. 70*
rise, *p. 70*
run, *p. 70*
x-intercept, *p. 78*
y-intercept, *p. 78*
slope-intercept form, *p. 78*
standard form, *p. 84*

Review Examples and Exercises

2.1 Graphing Linear Equations *(pp. 62–67)*

Graph $y = 3x - 1$.

Step 1: Make a table of values.

x	$y = 3x - 1$	y	(x, y)
-2	$y = 3(-2) - 1$	-7	$(-2, -7)$
-1	$y = 3(-1) - 1$	-4	$(-1, -4)$
0	$y = 3(0) - 1$	-1	$(0, -1)$
1	$y = 3(1) - 1$	2	$(1, 2)$

Step 2: Plot the ordered pairs.

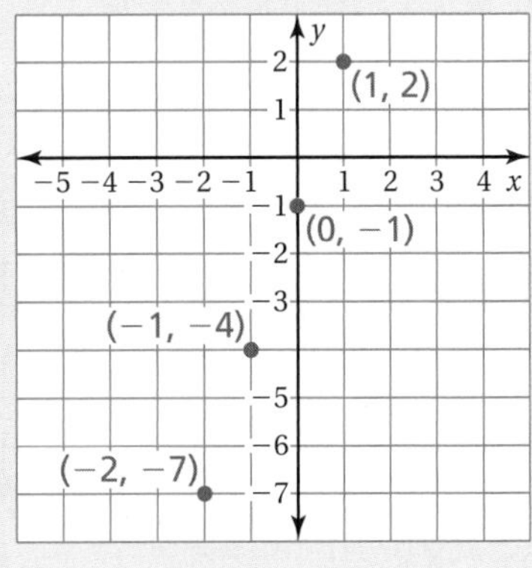

Step 3: Draw a line through the points.

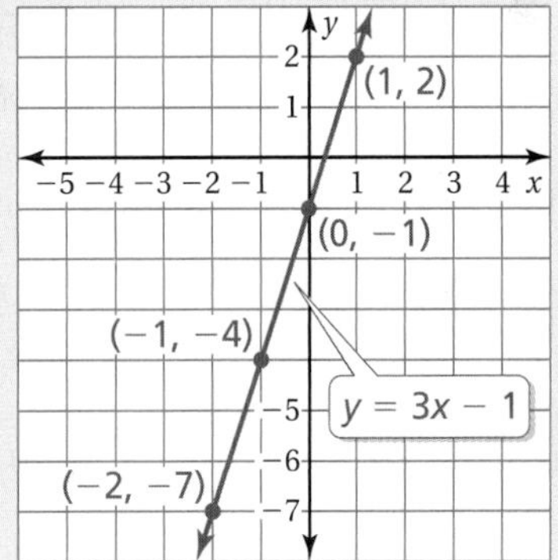

Exercises

Graph the linear equation.

1. $y = \frac{3}{5}x$
2. $y = -2$
3. $y = 9 - x$
4. $y = 1$
5. $y = \frac{2}{3}x + 2$
6. $y = 1 + x$

2.2 Slope of a Line (pp. 68–75)

Which two lines are parallel? Explain.

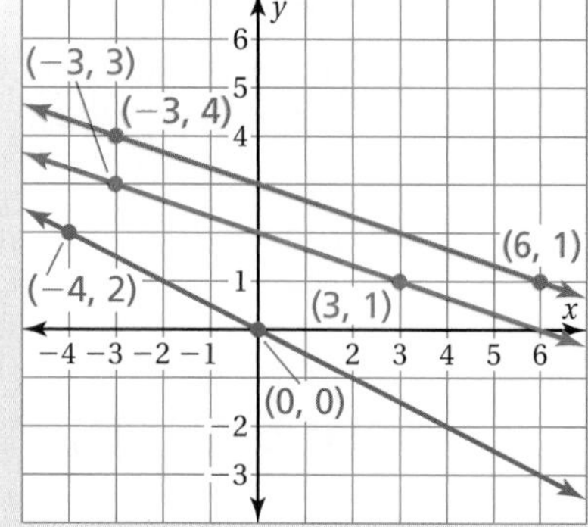

Find the slope of each line.

Red Line	*Blue Line*	*Green Line*
$\frac{-2}{6} = -\frac{1}{3}$	$\frac{-2}{4} = -\frac{1}{2}$	$\frac{-3}{9} = -\frac{1}{3}$

∴ The red and green lines have the same slope, so they are parallel.

Exercises

The points in the table lie on a line. Find the slope of the line. Then draw its graph.

7.

x	0	1	2	3
y	−1	0	1	2

8.

x	−2	0	2	4
y	3	4	5	6

2.3 Graphing Linear Equations in Slope-Intercept Form (pp. 76–81)

Graph $y = 0.5x - 3$. Identify the x-intercept.

Step 1: Find the slope and y-intercept.

$$y = 0.5x + (-3)$$

slope: 0.5; y-intercept: −3

Step 2: The y-intercept is −3. So, plot (0, −3).

Step 3: Use the slope to find another point and draw the line.

$$\text{slope} = \frac{\text{rise}}{\text{run}} = \frac{1}{2}$$

Plot the point that is 2 units right and 1 unit up from (0, −3). Draw a line through the two points.

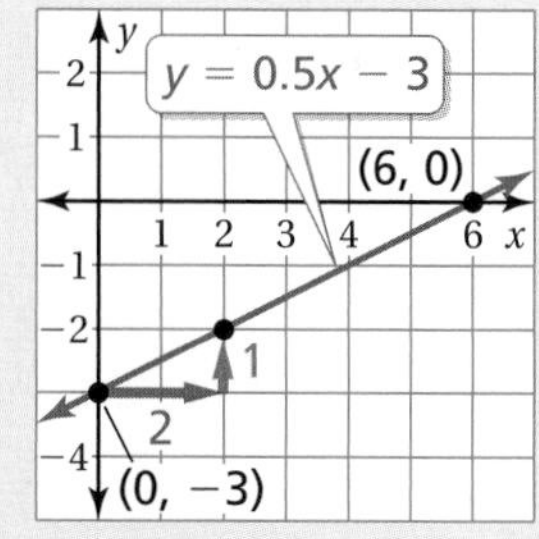

∴ The line crosses the x-axis at (6, 0). So, the x-intercept is 6.

Exercises

Graph the linear equation. Identify the x-intercept.

9. $y = 2x - 6$ **10.** $y = -4x + 8$ **11.** $y = -x - 8$

2.4 Graphing Linear Equations in Standard Form (pp. 82–87)

Graph $8x + 4y = 16$.

Step 1: Write the equation in slope-intercept form.

$8x + 4y = 16$	Write the equation.
$4y = -8x + 16$	Subtract $8x$ from each side.
$y = -2x + 4$	Divide each side by 4.

Step 2: Use the slope and y-intercept to plot two points.

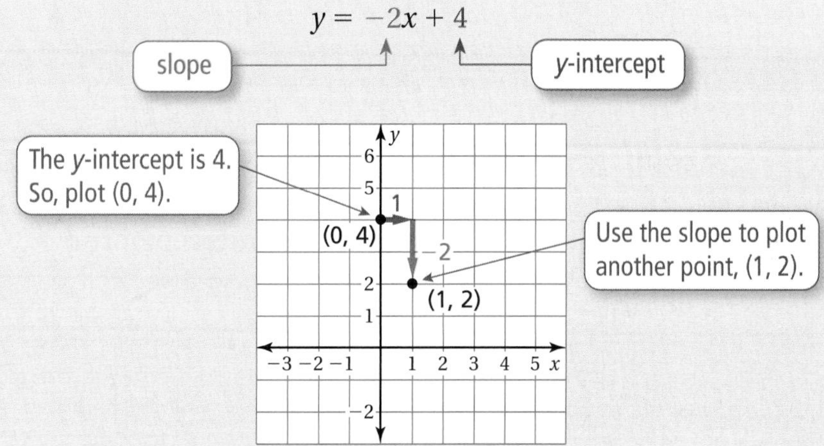

Step 3: Draw a line through the points.

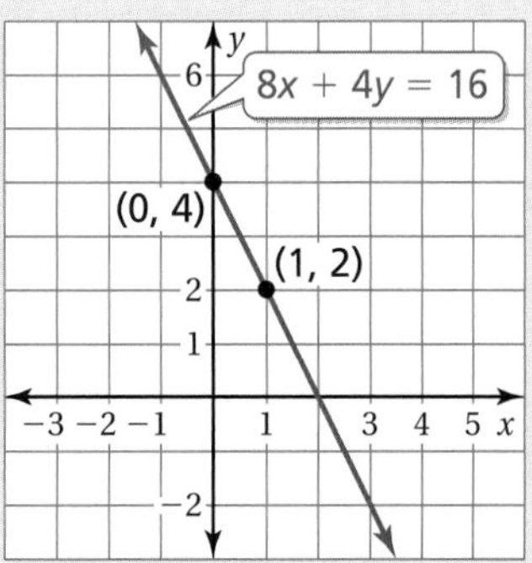

Exercises

Graph the linear equation.

12. $\frac{1}{4}x + y = 3$

13. $-4x + 2y = 8$

14. $x + 5y = 10$

15. $-\frac{1}{2}x + \frac{1}{8}y = \frac{3}{4}$

2.5 Writing Equations in Slope-Intercept Form (pp. 90–95)

Write an equation of the line in slope-intercept form.

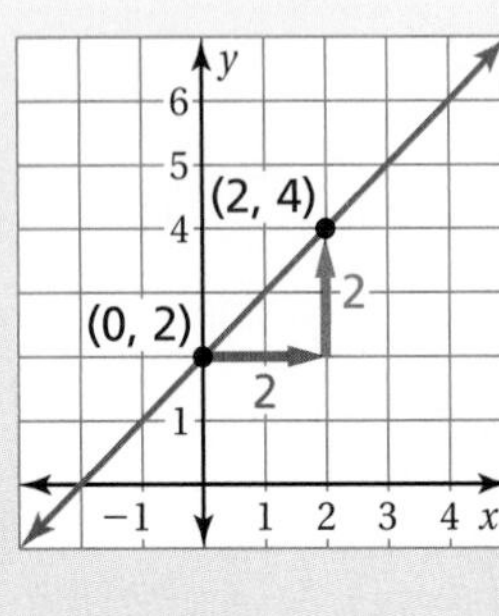

Find the slope and y-intercept.

$$\text{slope} = \frac{\text{rise}}{\text{run}} = \frac{2}{2} = 1$$

Because the line crosses the y-axis at (0, 2), the y-intercept is 2.

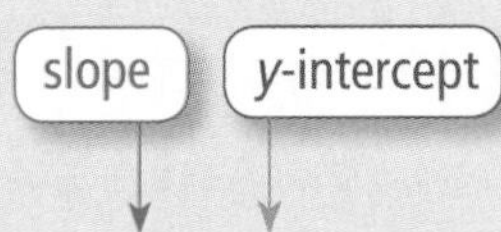

So, the equation is $y = 1x + 2$, or $y = x + 2$.

Exercises

Write an equation of the line in slope-intercept form.

16.

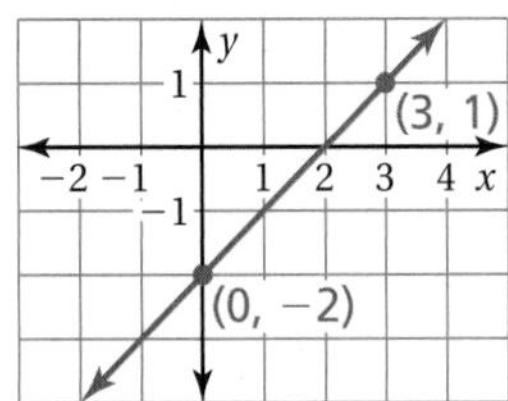

17.

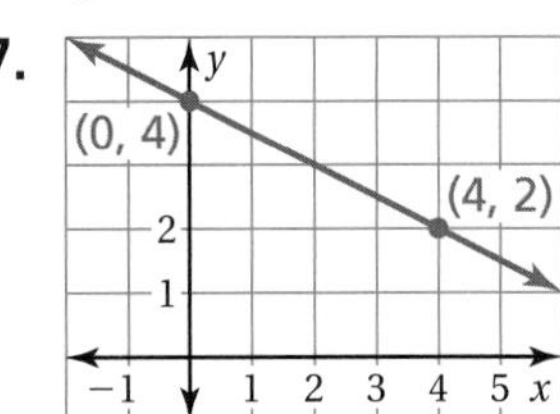

2.6 Writing Equations Using a Slope and a Point (pp. 96–101)

Write an equation of the line with a slope of $\frac{2}{3}$ that passes through the point $(-3, -1)$.

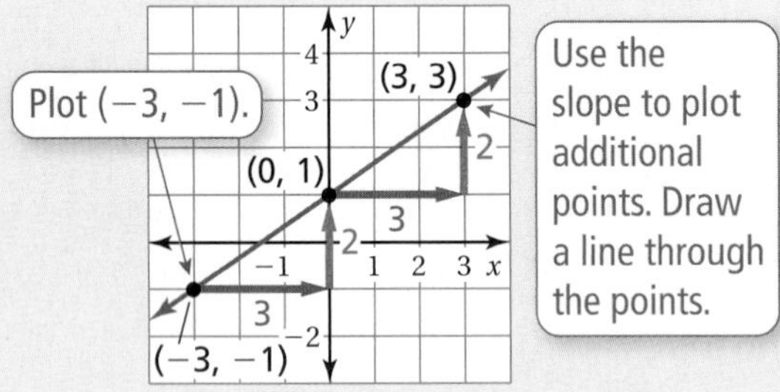

Use a graph to find the y-intercept.

Because the line crosses the y-axis at (0, 1), the y-intercept is 1.

So, the equation is $y = \frac{2}{3}x + 1$.

Exercises

Write an equation of the line with the given slope that passes through the given point.

18. $m = 3$; $(4, 4)$ **19.** $m = 2$; $(2, 6)$ **20.** $m = -0.5$; $(-4, 2)$

2.7 Writing Equations Using Two Points *(pp. 102–107)*

Write an equation of the line that passes through the points (2, 3) and (−2, −3).

Use a graph to find the slope and y-intercept.

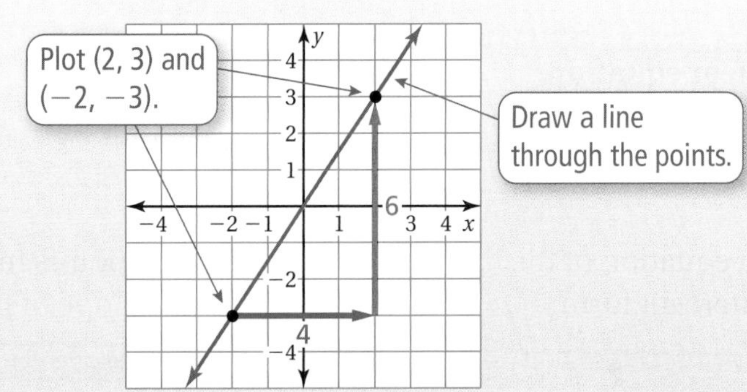

Plot (2, 3) and (−2, −3).
Draw a line through the points.
y
x
6
4

$$\text{slope} = \frac{\text{rise}}{\text{run}} = \frac{6}{4} = \frac{3}{2}$$

Because the line crosses the y-axis at (0, 0), the y-intercept is 0.

So, the equation is $y = \frac{3}{2}x + 0$, or $y = \frac{3}{2}x$.

Exercises

Write an equation of the line that passes through the points.

21. (−2, 0), (2, −4)

22. (−2, −2), (4, 1)

2.8 Solving Real-Life Problems *(pp. 108–113)*

The amount y (in dollars) of money you have left after playing x games at a carnival is $y = -0.75x + 10$. How much money do you have after playing eight games?

$y = -0.75x + 10$	Write the equation.
$= -0.75(8) + 10$	Substitute 8 for x.
$= 4$	Simplify.

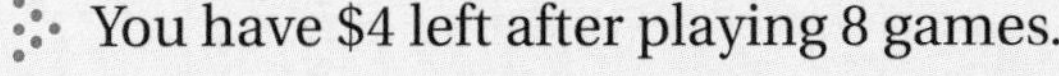

You have \$4 left after playing 8 games.

Exercises

23. HAY The amount y (in bales) of hay remaining after feeding cows for x days is $y = -3.5x + 105$. (a) Graph the equation. (b) Interpret the x- and y-intercepts. (c) How many bales are left after 10 days?

2 Chapter Test

Check It Out
Test Practice
BigIdeasMath.com

Find the slope and *y*-intercept of the graph of the linear equation.

1. $y = 6x - 5$

2. $y + 4.3 = 0.1x$

3. $-\frac{1}{2}x + 2y = 7$

Graph the linear equation.

4. $y = 2x + 4$

5. $y = -\frac{1}{2}x - 5$

6. $-3x + 6y = 12$

7. Write an equation of the line in slope-intercept form.

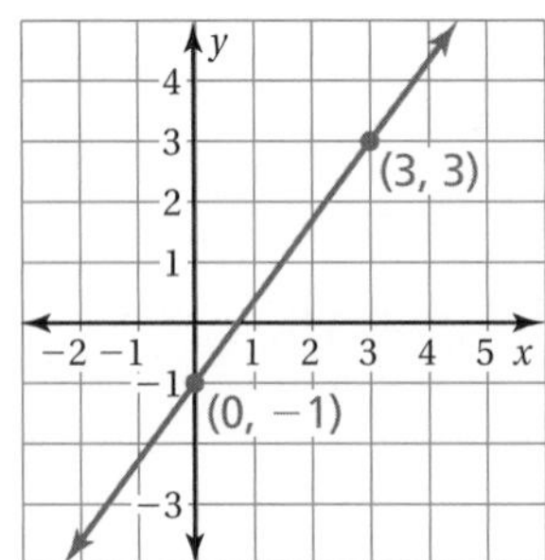

8. The points in the table lie on a line. Find the slope of the line. Then draw its graph.

x	*y*
−1	−4
0	−1
1	2
2	5

Write an equation of the line with the given slope that passes through the given point.

9. $m = -3;\ (-2, -2)$

10. $m = \frac{2}{3};\ (3, 3)$

Write an equation of the line that passes through the points.

11. $(-1, 5), (3, -3)$

12. $(-4, 1), (4, 3)$

13. $(-2, 5), (-1, 1)$

14. BRAILLE Because of its size and detail, Braille takes longer to read than text. A person reading Braille reads at 25% the rate of a person reading text. Write an equation that represents the average rate *y* of a Braille reader in terms of the average rate *x* of a text reader.

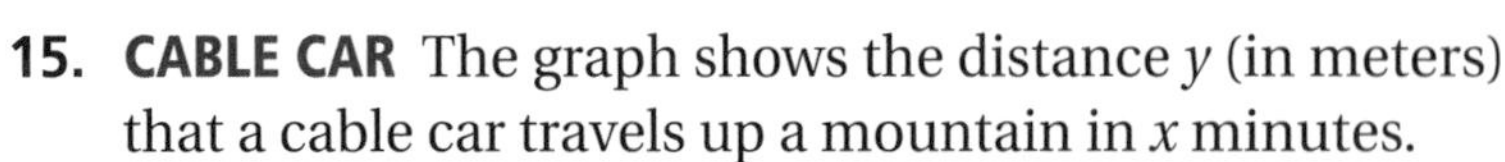

15. CABLE CAR The graph shows the distance *y* (in meters) that a cable car travels up a mountain in *x* minutes.

a. Find and interpret the slope.

b. Write an equation of the line.

c. How far does the cable car travel in 15 minutes?

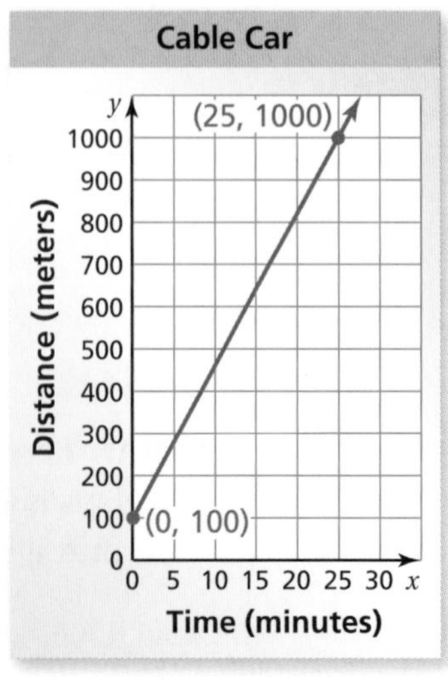

2 Standardized Test Practice

Test-Taking Strategy
Estimate the Answer

In x days, your owner vacuums $y = 107x$ hairs from the rug. How many in 3 days?
Ⓐ 201 Ⓑ 539 Ⓒ 321 Ⓓ 1,000,000

So, you prefer a hairless cat?

"Using estimation you can see that there are about 300 hairs. So, it's got to be C."

1. The graph below shows the value of United States dollars compared to Guatemalan quetzals.

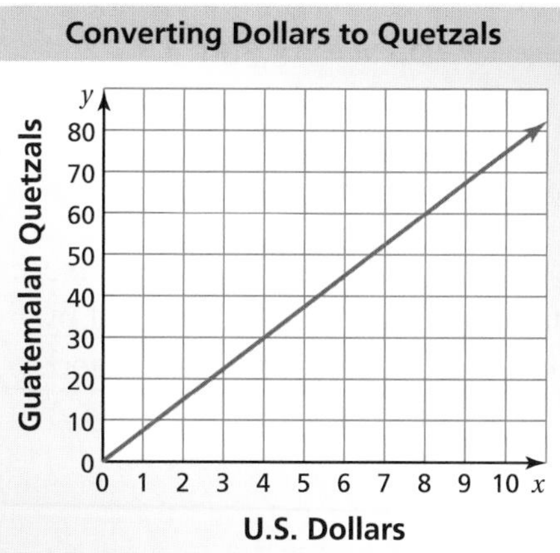

What is the value of 60 quetzals?

A. \$6 **C.** \$8

B. \$7 **D.** \$9

2. Which equation matches the line shown in the graph?

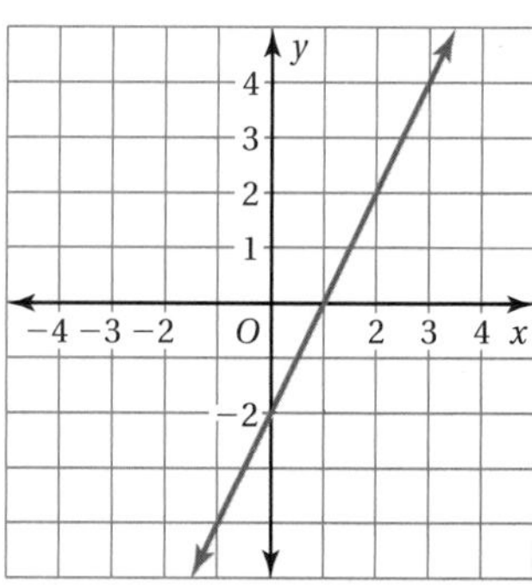

F. $y = 2x - 2$

G. $y = 2x + 1$

H. $y = x - 2$

I. $y = x + 1$

3. A faucet releases 6 quarts of water per minute. How many gallons of water will the faucet release in one hour?

A. 45 gal **C.** 360 gal

B. 90 gal **D.** 1440 gal

4. The equation $6x - 5y = 14$ is written in standard form. Which point lies on the graph of this equation?

F. $(-4, -1)$ **H.** $(-1, -4)$

G. $(-2, 4)$ **I.** $(4, -2)$

5. A car's value depreciates at a rate of \$2,500 per year. Three years after a car is purchased, its value is \$21,000. Which equation can be used to find v, its value in dollars, n years after it is purchased?

A. $v = 28{,}500 - 2{,}500n$

B. $v = 21{,}000 - 2{,}500n$

C. $v = 18{,}500 - 2{,}500n$

D. $v = 18{,}500 - n$

6. A cell phone plan costs \$10 per month plus \$0.10 for each minute used. Last month, you spent \$18.50 using this plan. This can be modeled by the equation below, where m represents the number of minutes used.

$$0.1m + 10 = 18.5$$

How many minutes did you use last month?

F. 8.4 min

G. 85 min

H. 185 min

I. 285 min

7. What is the slope of the line that passes through the points $(2, -2)$ and $(8, 1)$?

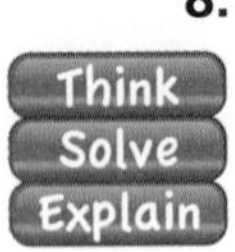

8. It costs \$40 to rent a car for one day. In addition, the rental agency charges you for each mile driven, as shown in the graph.

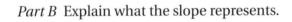

Part A Determine the slope of the line joining the points on the graph.

Part B Explain what the slope represents.

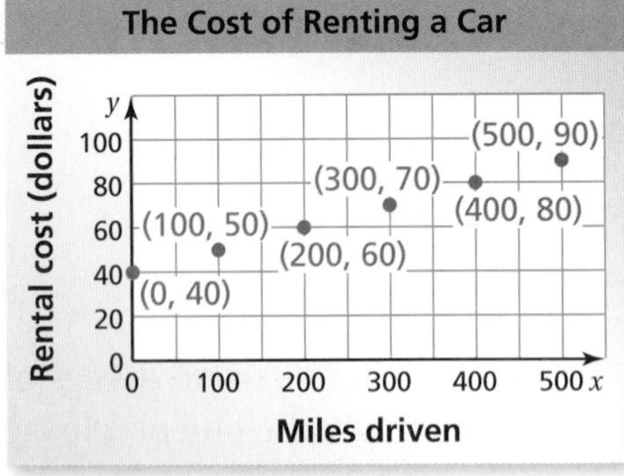

9. You bought a lead pencil for \$5 and three identical markers. You spent \$12.47 in all. Which equation could be used to find the price p of one marker?

A. $5 + p = 12.47$

B. $5 + 3p = 12.47$

C. $3(5 + p) = 12.47$

D. $3p = 12.47 + 5$

10. Which line has a slope of 0?

F. 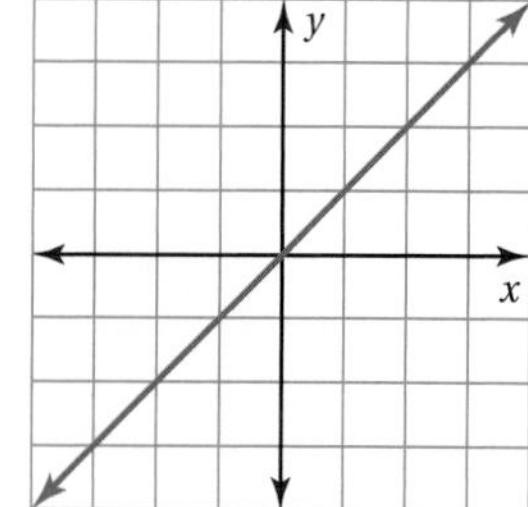

H. 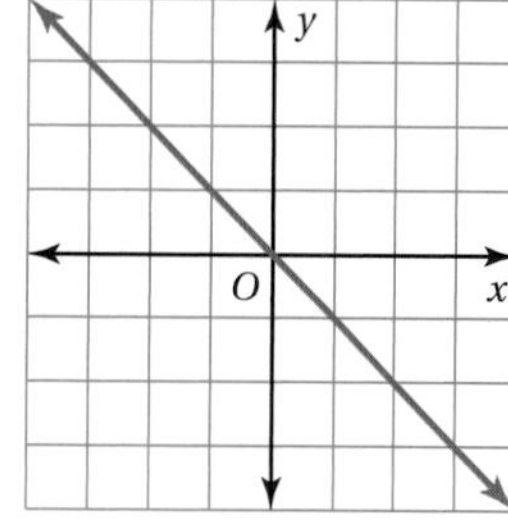

G. 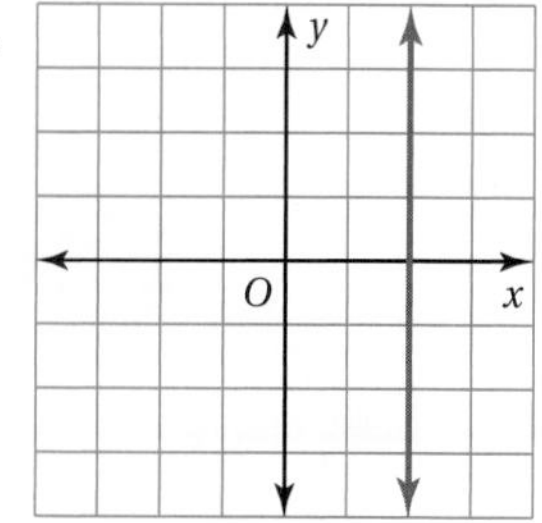

I. 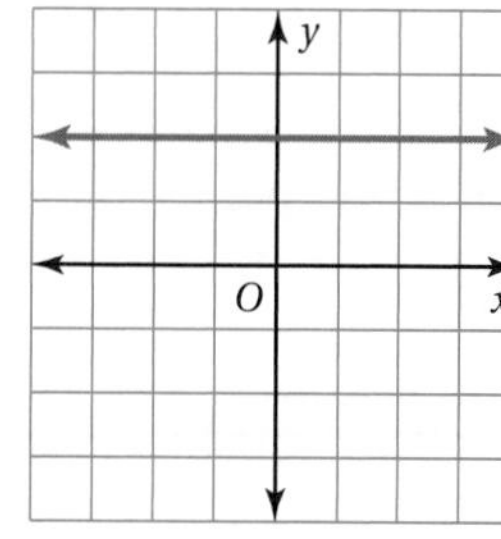

11. Solve the formula $K = 3M - 7$ for M.

A. $M = K + 7$

C. $M = \frac{K}{3} + 7$

B. $M = \frac{K + 7}{3}$

D. $M = \frac{K - 7}{3}$

12. The linear equation $5x + 2y = 10$ is written in standard form. What is the slope of the graph of this equation?

F. 5

H. -2.5

G. 2.5

I. -5

13. A package of breakfast cereal is labeled "750 g." This cereal is shipped in cartons that hold 24 packages. What is the total mass, in kilograms, of the breakfast cereal in 10 cartons?

14. A line has a slope of 4 and passes through the point (a, b). Which point must also lie on this line?

A. $(a, b + 4)$

C. $(a + 1, b + 4)$

B. $(2a, 8b)$

D. $(2a, 5b)$

3 Functions

"Here's how I remember that the range is the *y*-values."

"I draw a cabin on the *y*-axis. Then, I hum 'Home, Home on the range'."

"It is my treat-converter function machine. However many cat treats I input, the machine outputs TWICE that many dog biscuits. Isn't that cool?"

What You Learned Before

"Do you think the stripes in this shirt make me look too linear?"

STTRIIIKKKE three. You're out!

Recognizing Patterns

Describe the pattern of inputs and outputs.

Example 1

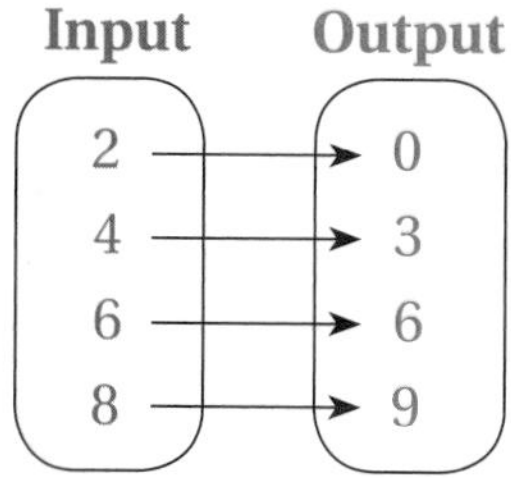

As the input increases by 2, the output increases by 3.

Example 2

Input, x	6	1	-4	-9	-14
Output, y	7	8	9	10	11

As the input x decreases by 5, the output y increases by 1.

Example 3 **Draw a mapping diagram for the graph. Then describe the pattern of inputs and outputs.**

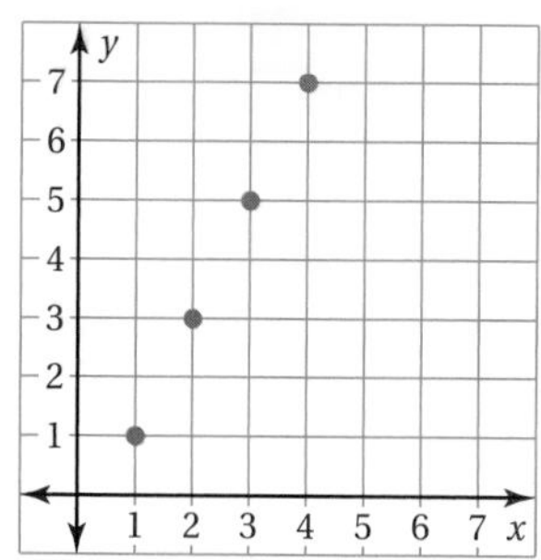

Input | Output
1 → 1
2 → 3
3 → 5
4 → 7

As the input increases by 1, the output increases by 2.

Try It Yourself

Describe the pattern of inputs x and outputs y.

1.

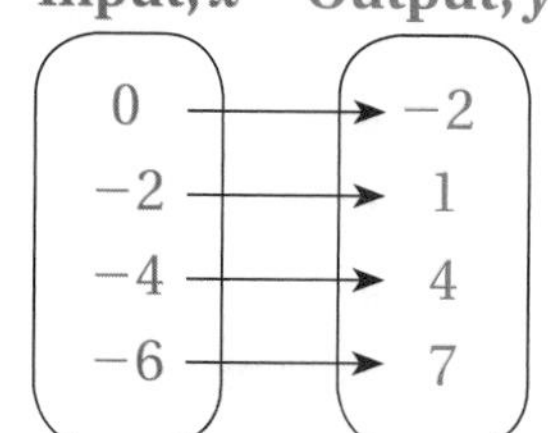

2.

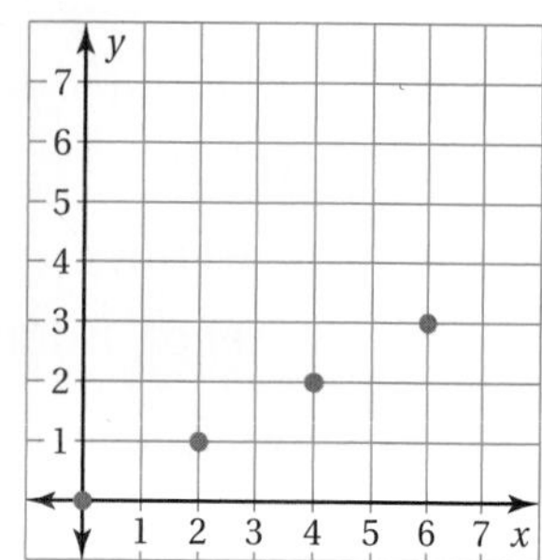

3.

Input, x	0	-1	-2	-3	-4
Output, y	7	3.5	0	-3.5	-7

3.1 Domain and Range of a Function

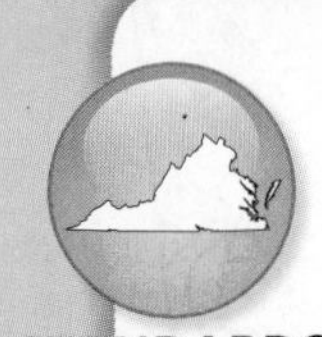

STANDARDS OF LEARNING
8.17

Essential Question How can you find the domain and range of a function?

1 ACTIVITY: The Domain and Range of a Function

Work with a partner. In Activity 1 in Section 2.4, you completed the table shown below. The table shows the number of adult and child tickets sold for a school concert.

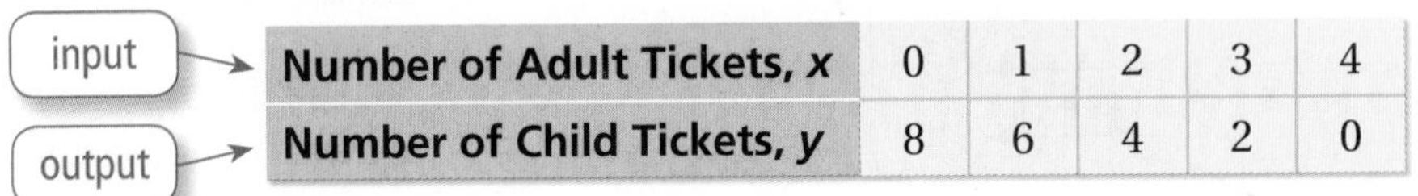

input →	Number of Adult Tickets, x	0	1	2	3	4
output →	Number of Child Tickets, y	8	6	4	2	0

The variables x and y are related by the linear equation $4x + 2y = 16$

a. Write the equation in *function form* by solving for y.

b. The **domain** of a function is the set of all input values. Find the domain of the function.

Domain = ______

Why is $x = 5$ not in the domain of the function?

Why is $x = \frac{1}{2}$ not in the domain of the function?

c. The **range** of a function is the set of all output values. Find the range of the function.

Range = ______

d. Functions can be described in many ways.

- by an equation
- by an input-output table
- in words
- by a graph
- as a set of ordered pairs

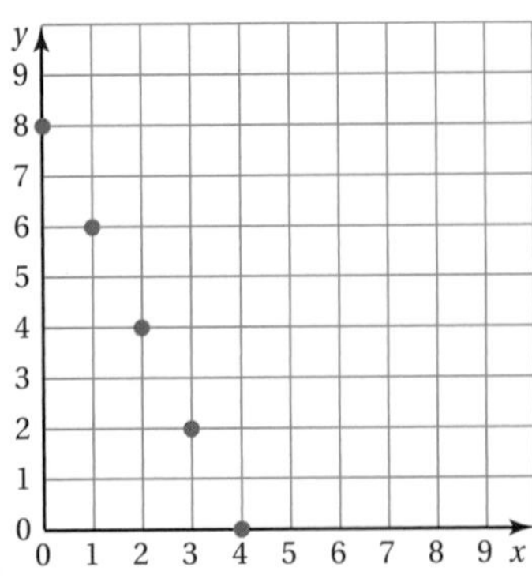

Use the graph to write the function as a set of ordered pairs.

(___ , ___), (___ , ___), (___ , ___),
(___ , ___), (___ , ___)

2 ACTIVITY: Finding Domains and Ranges

Work with a partner.

- **Copy and complete each input-output table.**
- **Find the domain and range of the function represented by the table.**

a. $y = -3x + 4$

x	−2	−1	0	1	2
y					

b. $y = \frac{1}{2}x - 6$

x	0	1	2	3	4
y					

c.

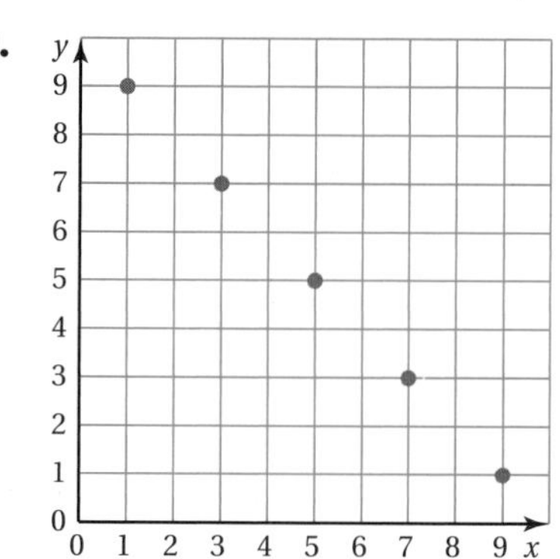

x					
y					

d.

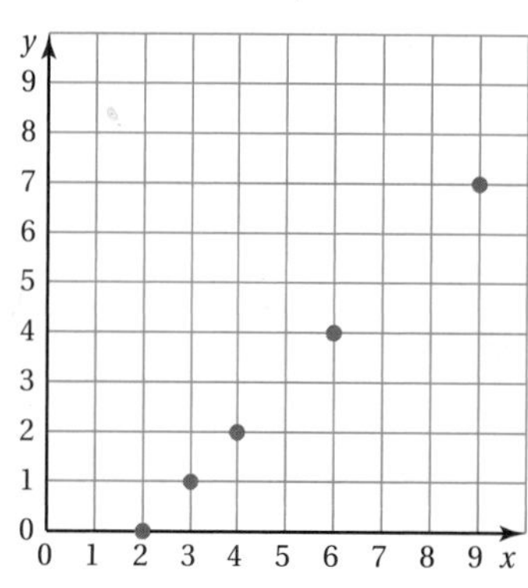

x					
y					

What Is Your Answer?

3. **IN YOUR OWN WORDS** How can you find the domain and range of a function?
4. **The following are general rules for finding a person's foot length.**

   To find the length *y* (in inches) of a woman's foot, divide her shoe size *x* by 3 and add 7.

   To find the length *y* (in inches) of a man's foot, divide his shoe size *x* by 3 and add 7.3.

   a. Write an equation for one of the statements.

   b. Make an input-output table for the function in part (a). Use shoe sizes $5\frac{1}{2}$ to 12.

   c. Label the domain and range of the function on the table.

Practice Use what you learned about the domain and range of a function to complete Exercise 3 on page 130.

3.1 Lesson

Key Vocabulary
function, *p. 128*
domain, *p. 128*
range, *p. 128*
independent variable, *p. 128*
dependent variable, *p. 128*

Key Idea

Functions

A **function** is a relationship that pairs each *input* with exactly one *output*. The **domain** is the set of all possible input values. The **range** is the set of all possible output values.

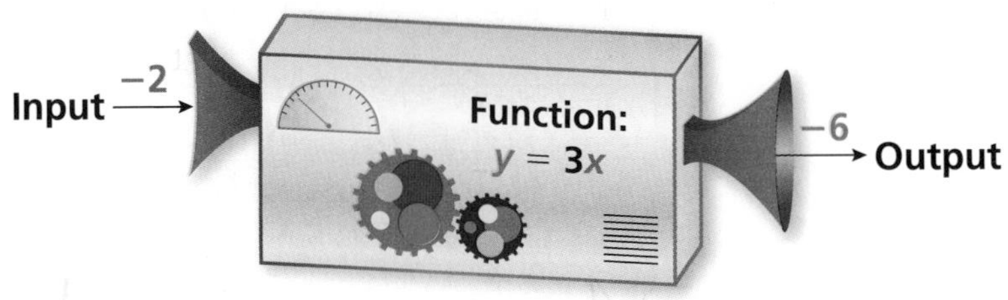

EXAMPLE 1 Finding Domain and Range from a Graph

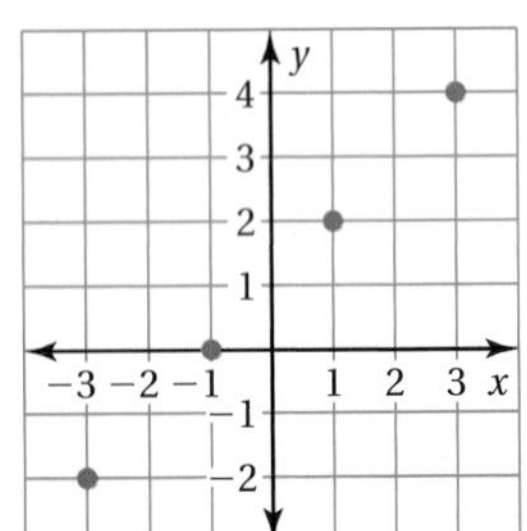

Find the domain and range of the function represented by the graph.

Write the ordered pairs. Identify the inputs and outputs.

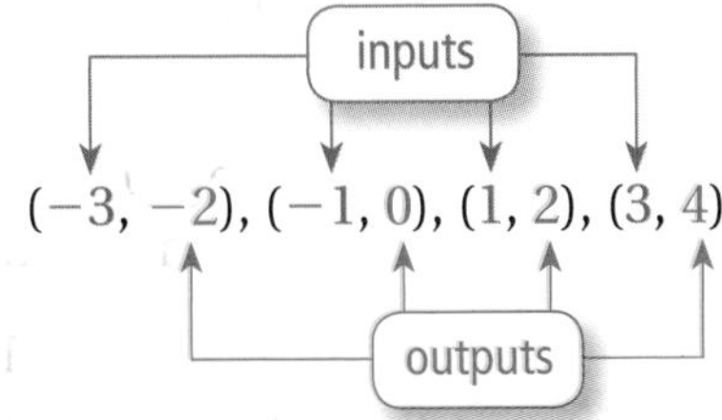

∴ The domain is -3, -1, 1, and 3. The range is -2, 0, 2, and 4.

On Your Own

Now You're Ready
Exercises 4–6

Find the domain and range of the function represented by the graph.

1. 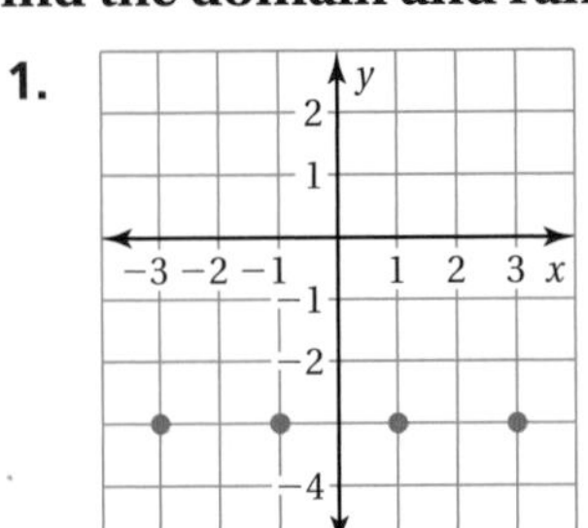

2. 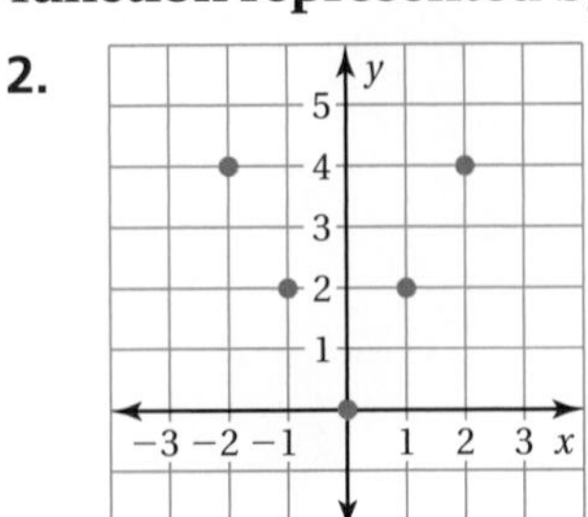

When an equation represents a function, the variable that represents input values is the **independent variable**. The variable that represents output values is the **dependent variable**. This variable *depends* on the value of the independent variable.

Multi-Language Glossary at BigIdeasMath.com.

EXAMPLE 2 Finding the Range of a Function

The domain of the function represented by $y = -2x + 8$ is $-2, 0, 2,$ and 4. What is the range of the function?

Make an input-output table.

Because x represents the input values, x is the independent variable.

Because y represents the output values, y is the dependent variable.

Input, x	$-2x + 8$	Output, y
−2	$-2(-2) + 8$	12
0	$-2(0) + 8$	8
2	$-2(2) + 8$	4
4	$-2(4) + 8$	0

∴ So, the range is 12, 8, 4, and 0.

EXAMPLE 3 Real-Life Application

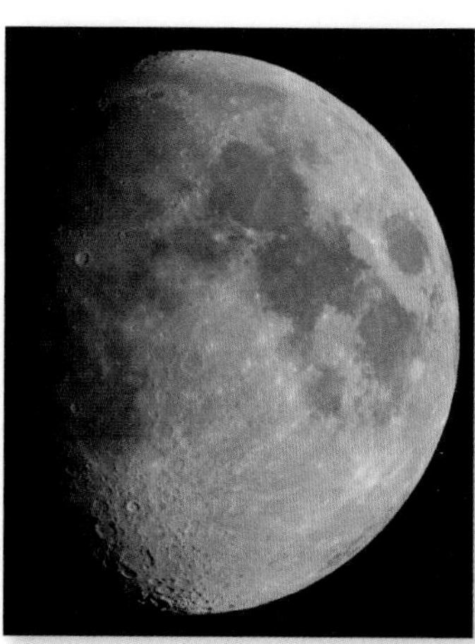

The table shows the percent y (in decimal form) of the moon that was visible at midnight x days after January 24, 2011. (a) Interpret the domain and range. (b) What percent of the moon was visible on January 26, 2011?

x	y
0	0.76
1	0.65
2	0.54
3	0.43
4	0.32

a. Zero days after January 24 is January 24. One day after January 24 is January 25. So, the domain of 0, 1, 2, 3, and 4 represents January 24, 25, 26, 27, and 28.

The range is 0.76, 0.65, 0.54, 0.43, and 0.32. These amounts are decreasing, so the moon was less visible each day.

b. January 26, 2011 corresponds to the input $x = 2$. When $x = 2$, $y = 0.54$. So, 0.54, or 54% of the moon was visible on January 26, 2011.

On Your Own

Exercises 9–11

Copy and complete the input-output table for the function. Then find the domain and range of the function represented by the table.

3. $y = 2x - 3$

x	−1	0	1	2
y				

4. $x + y = -3$

x	0	1	2	3
y				

5. The table shows the percent y (in decimal form) of the moon that was visible at midnight x days after December 17, 2012. (a) Interpret the domain and range. (b) What percent of the moon was visible on December 21, 2012?

x	0	1	2	3	4
y	0.2	0.3	0.4	0.5	0.6

3.1 Exercises

Check It Out
Help with Homework
BigIdeasMath.com

Vocabulary and Concept Check

1. **VOCABULARY** How are independent variables and dependent variables different?
2. **DIFFERENT WORDS, SAME QUESTION** Which is different? Find "both" answers.

Find the range of the function represented by the table.	Find the inputs of the function represented by the table.
Find the x-values of the function represented by (2, 7), (4, 5), and (6, −1).	Find the domain of the function represented by (2, 7), (4, 5), and (6, −1).

x	2	4	6
y	7	5	−1

Practice and Problem Solving

3. The number of earrings and headbands you can buy with \$24 is represented by the equation $8x + 4y = 24$. The table shows the number of earrings and headbands.

   a. Write the equation in function form.
   b. Find the domain and range.
   c. Why is $x = 6$ not in the domain of the function?

Earrings, x	0	1	2	3
Headbands, y	6	4	2	0

Find the domain and range of the function represented by the graph.

4. 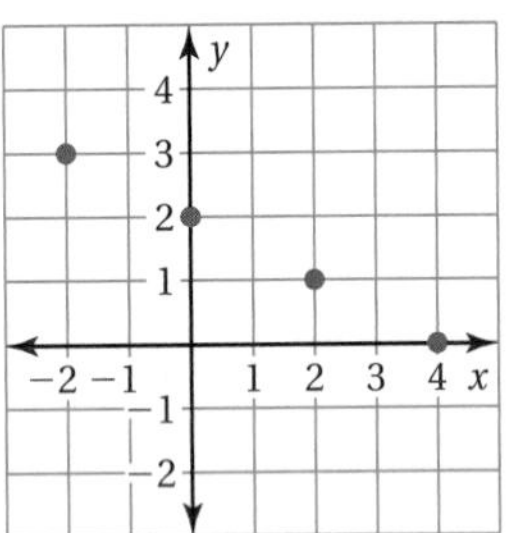

5. 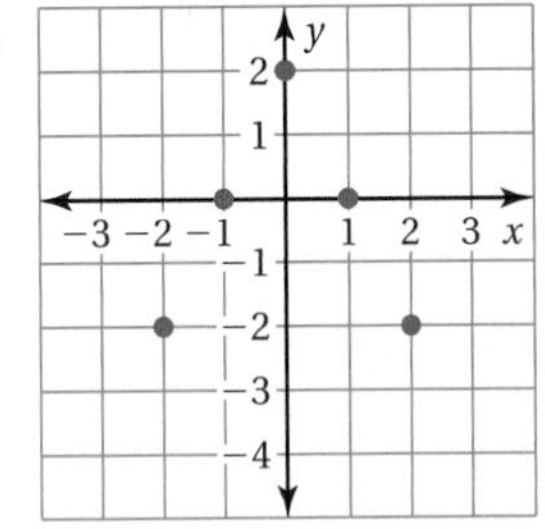

6. 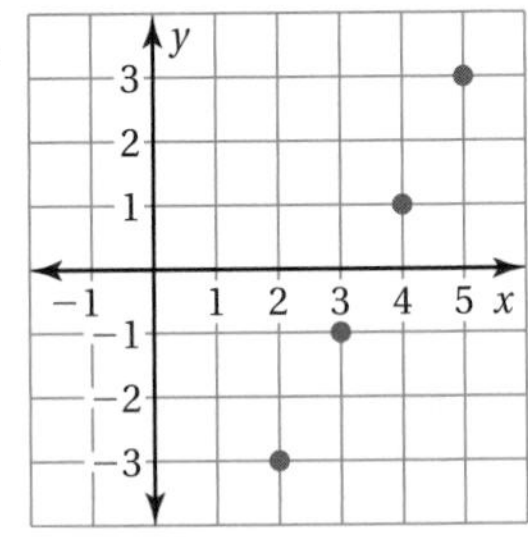

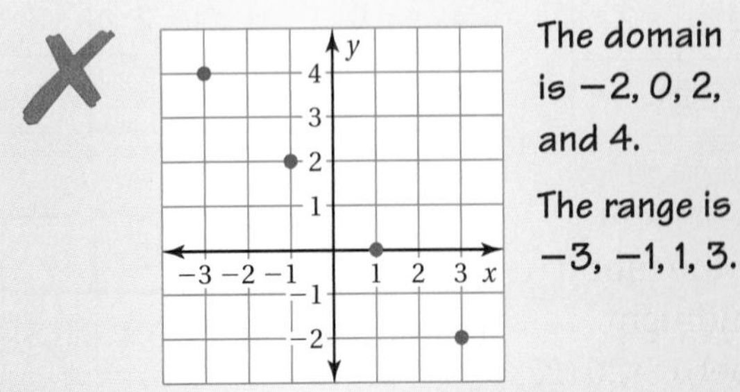
The domain is −2, 0, 2, and 4.
The range is −3, −1, 1, 3.

7. **ERROR ANALYSIS** Describe and correct the error in finding the domain and range of the function represented by the graph.

8. **REASONING** Find the domain and range of the function represented by the table.

Tickets, x	2	3	5	8
Cost, y	\$14	\$21	\$35	\$56

Copy and complete the input-output table for the function. Then find the domain and range of the function represented by the table.

2 **9.** $y = 6x + 2$

x	-1	0	1	2
y				

10. $y = -\frac{1}{4}x - 2$

x	0	4	8	12
y				

11. $y = 1.5x + 3$

x	-1	0	1	2
y				

12. VAULTING In the sport of vaulting, a vaulter performs a routine while on a moving horse. For each round x of competition, the vaulter receives a score y from 1 to 10.

a. Find the domain and range of the function represented by the table.

b. Interpret the domain and range.

c. What is the mean score of the vaulter?

x	y
1	6.856
2	7.923
3	8.135

13. MANATEE A manatee eats about 12% of its body weight each day.

a. Write an equation that represents the amount y (in pounds) of food a manatee eats each day for its weight x. Identify the independent variable and the dependent variable.

b. Create an input-output table for the equation in part (a). Use the inputs 150, 300, 450, 600, 750, and 900.

c. Find the domain and range of the function represented by the table.

d. The weights of three manatees are 300 pounds, 750 pounds, and 1050 pounds. What is the total amount of food that these three manatees eat in a day? in a week?

14. 

Describe the domain and range of the function.

a. $y = |x|$ **b.** $y = -|x|$ **c.** $y = |x| - 6$ **d.** $y = -|x| + 4$

Fair Game Review What you learned in previous grades & lessons

Graph the linear equation. *(Section 2.1)*

15. $y = 2x + 8$ **16.** $5x + 6y = 12$ **17.** $-x - 3y = 2$ **18.** $y = 7x - 5$

19. MULTIPLE CHOICE The minimum number of people needed for a group rate at an amusement park is 8. Which inequality represents the number of people needed to get the group rate? *(Section 1.5)*

Ⓐ $x \leq 8$ Ⓑ $x > 8$ Ⓒ $x < 8$ Ⓓ $x \geq 8$

3.2 Discrete and Continuous Domains

STANDARDS OF LEARNING
8.17

Essential Question How can you decide whether the domain of a function is discrete or continuous?

1 EXAMPLE: Discrete and Continuous Domains

In Activities 1 and 2 in Section 2.4, you studied two real-life problems represented by the same equation.

$$4x + 2y = 16 \quad \text{or} \quad y = -2x + 8$$

a. 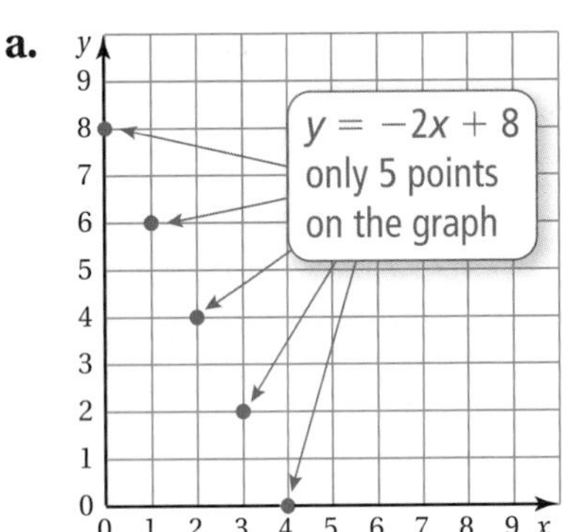

Domain (x-values): 0, 1, 2, 3, 4

Range (y-values): 8, 6, 4, 2, 0

The domain is **discrete** because it consists of only the numbers 0, 1, 2, 3, and 4.

b. 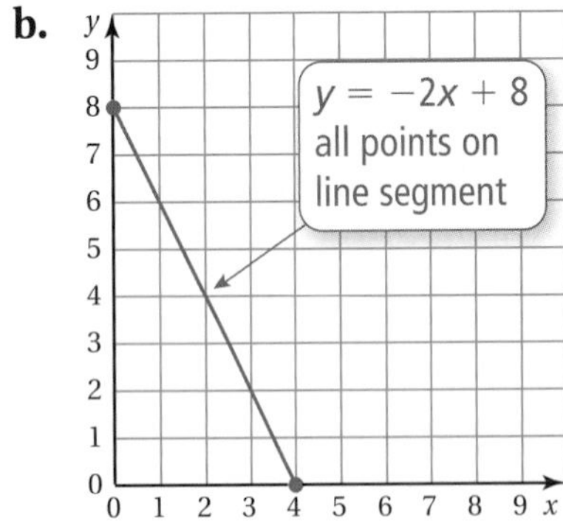

Domain (x-values): $x \geq 0$ and $x \leq 4$
(All numbers from 0 to 4)

Range (y-values): $y \geq 0$ and $y \leq 8$
(All numbers from 0 to 8)

The domain is **continuous** because it consists of all numbers from 0 to 4 on the number line.

2 ACTIVITY: Discrete and Continuous Domains

Work with a partner.

- **Write a function to represent each problem.**
- **Graph each function.**
- **Describe the domain and range of each function. Is the domain discrete or continuous?**

a. You are in charge of reserving hotel rooms for a youth soccer team. Each room costs \$69, plus \$6 tax, per night. You need each room for two nights. You need 10 to 16 rooms. Write a function for the total hotel cost.

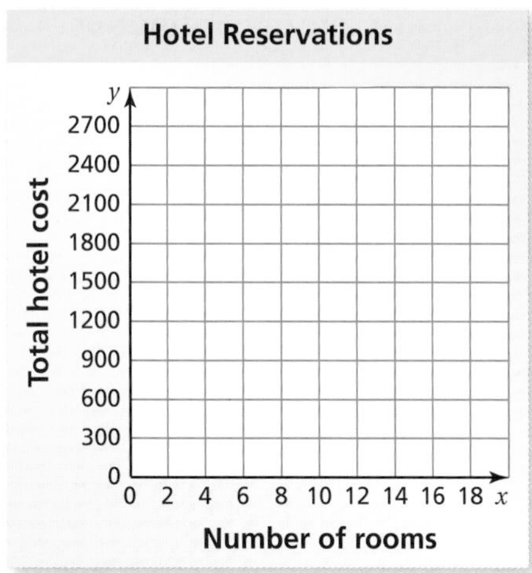

b. The airline you are using for the soccer trip needs an estimate of the total weight of the team's luggage. You determine that there will be 36 pieces of luggage and each piece will weigh from 25 to 45 pounds. Write a function for the total weight of the luggage.

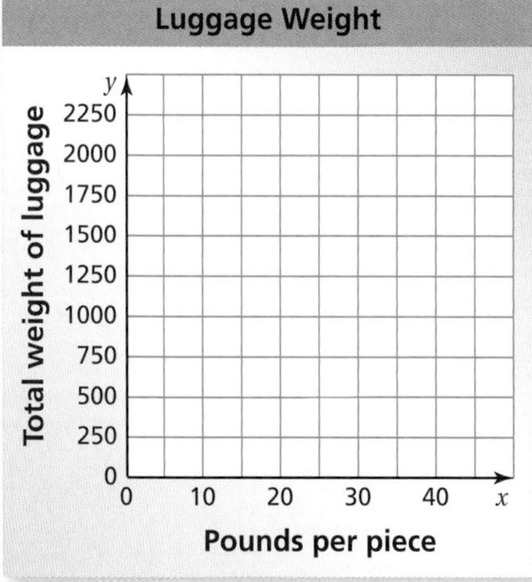

What Is Your Answer?

3. **IN YOUR OWN WORDS** How can you decide whether the domain of a function is discrete or continuous? Describe two real-life examples of functions: one with a discrete domain and one with a continuous domain.

Use what you learned about discrete and continuous domains to complete Exercises 3 and 4 on page 136.

Key Vocabulary
discrete domain, p. 134
continuous domain, p. 134

Discrete and Continuous Domains

A **discrete domain** is a set of input values that consists of only certain numbers in an interval.

Example: Integers from 1 to 5

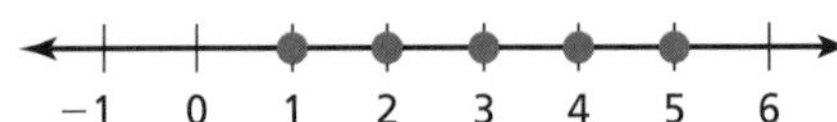

A **continuous domain** is a set of input values that consists of all numbers in an interval.

Example: All numbers from 1 to 5

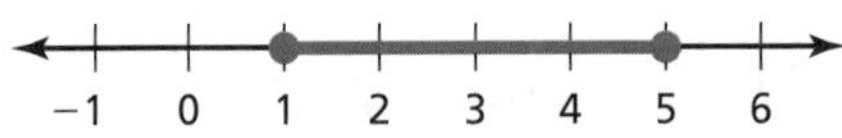

EXAMPLE 1 Graphing Discrete Data

The function $y = 15.95x$ represents the cost y (in dollars) of x tickets for a museum. Graph the function using a domain of 0, 1, 2, 3, and 4. Is the domain of the graph discrete or continuous? Explain.

Make an input-output table.

Input, x	$15.95x$	Output, y	Ordered Pair, (x, y)
0	15.95(0)	0	(0, 0)
1	15.95(1)	15.95	(1, 15.95)
2	15.95(2)	31.9	(2, 31.9)
3	15.95(3)	47.85	(3, 47.85)
4	15.95(4)	63.8	(4, 63.8)

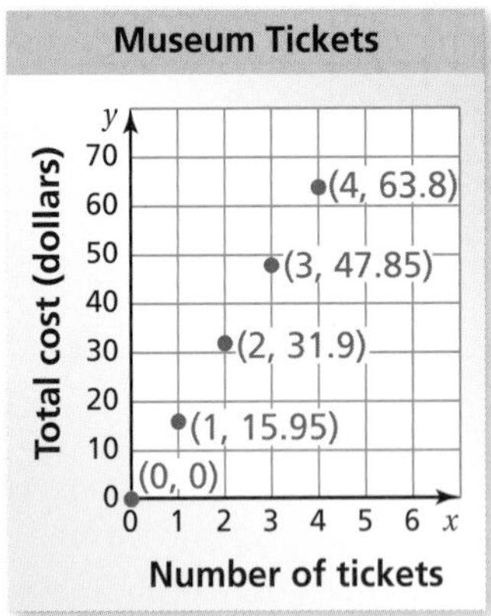

Plot the ordered pairs. Because you cannot buy part of a ticket, the graph consists of individual points.

So, the domain is discrete.

On Your Own

1. The function $m = 50 - 9d$ represents the amount of money m (in dollars) you have after buying d DVDs. Graph the function. Is the domain discrete or continuous? Explain.

Multi-Language Glossary at BigIdeasMath.com.

EXAMPLE 2 Graphing Continuous Data

A cereal bar contains 130 calories. The number *c* of calories consumed is a function of the number *b* of bars eaten. Graph the function. Is the domain of the graph discrete or continuous?

Make an input-output table.

Input, *b*	Output, *c*	Ordered Pair, (*b*, *c*)
0	0	(0, 0)
1	130	(1, 130)
2	260	(2, 260)
3	390	(3, 390)
4	520	(4, 520)

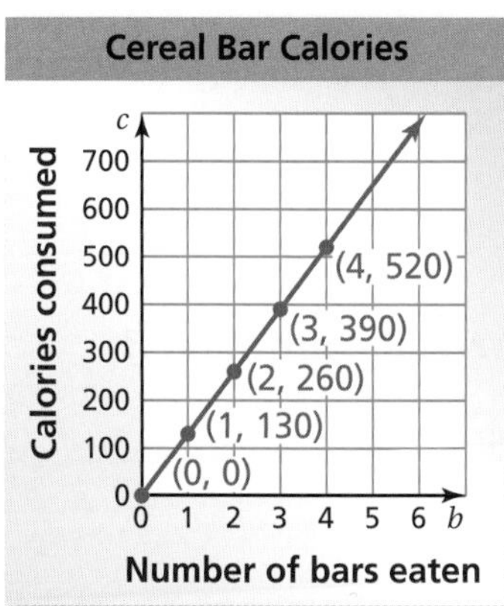

Plot the ordered pairs. Because you can eat part of a cereal bar, b can be any value greater than or equal to 0. Draw a line through the points.

So, the domain is continuous.

EXAMPLE 3 Standardized Test Practice

You conduct an experiment on the speed of sound waves in dry air at 86°F. You record your data in a table. Which of the following is true?

Input Time, *t* (seconds)	Output Distance, *d* (miles)
2	0.434
4	0.868
6	1.302
8	1.736
10	2.170

Ⓐ The domain is $t \geq 2$ and $t \leq 10$ and it is discrete.

Ⓑ The domain is $t \geq 2$ and $t \leq 10$ and it is continuous.

Ⓒ The domain is $d \geq 0.434$ and $d \leq 2.17$ and it is discrete.

Ⓓ The domain is $d \geq 0.434$ and $d \leq 2.17$ and it is continuous.

The domain is the set of possible input values, or the time t. The time t can be any value from 2 to 10. So, the domain is continuous.

The correct answer is Ⓑ.

On Your Own

2. A 20-gallon bathtub is draining at a rate of 2.5 gallons per minute. The number g of gallons remaining is a function of the number m of minutes. Graph the function. Is the domain discrete or continuous?

3. Are the data shown in the table discrete or continuous? Explain.

Number of Stories	1	2	3	4	5
Height of Building (feet)	12	24	36	48	60

3.2 Exercises

Vocabulary and Concept Check

1. **VOCABULARY** Explain how continuous domains and discrete domains are different.

2. **WRITING** Describe how you can use a graph to determine whether a domain is discrete or continuous.

Practice and Problem Solving

Describe the domain and range of the function. Is the domain discrete or continuous?

3. 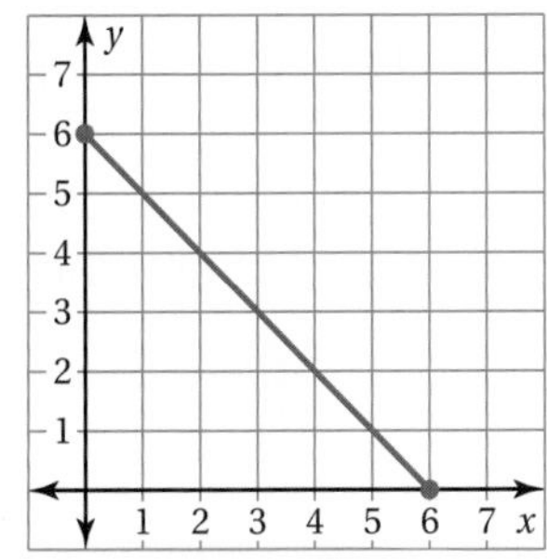

4. 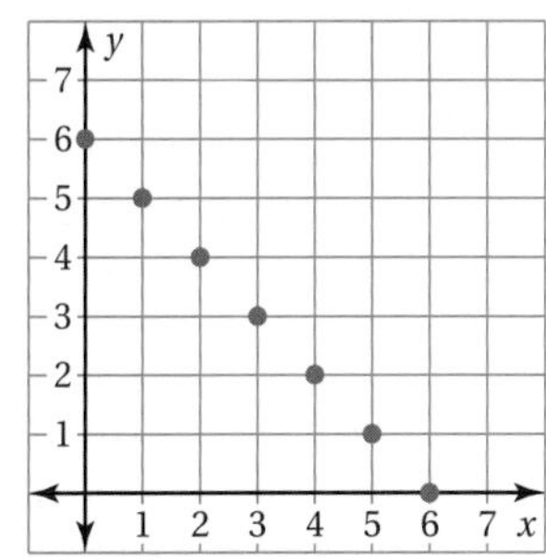

Graph the function. Is the domain of the graph discrete or continuous?

5.

Input Bags, x	Output Marbles, y
2	20
4	40
6	60

6.

Input Years, x	Output Height of a Tree, y (feet)
0	3
1	6
2	9

7.

Input Width, x (inches)	Output Volume, y (cubic inches)
5	50
10	100
15	150

8.

Input Hats, x	Output Cost, y (dollars)
0	0
1	8.45
2	16.9

9. **ERROR ANALYSIS** Describe and correct the error in classifying the domain.

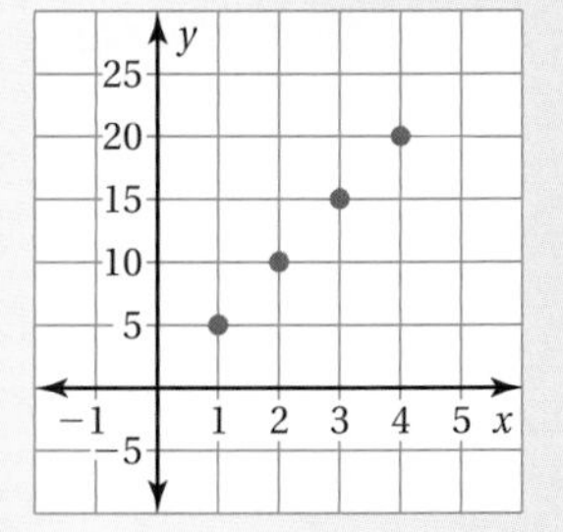

10. **YARN** The function $m = 40 - 8.5b$ represents the amount m of money (in dollars) that you have after buying b balls of yarn. Graph the function using a domain of 0, 1, 2, and 3. Is the domain discrete or continuous?

11. **REASONING** The input of one function is *length*. The input of another function is *number of shirts*. Which function has a continuous domain? Explain.

12. **DISTANCE** The function $y = 3.28x$ converts length from x meters to y feet. Graph the function. Is the domain discrete or continuous?

13. **AREA** The area A of the triangle is a function of the height h. Graph the function. Is the domain discrete or continuous?

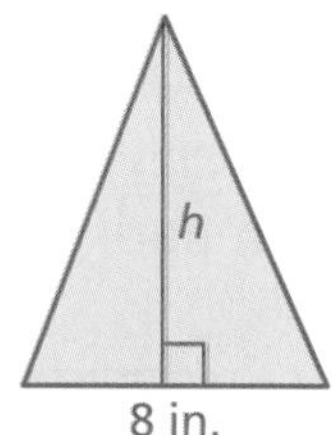

14. **PACKING** You are packing books into boxes. The box can hold at most 10 books. The function $y = 5.2x$ represents the weight y (in pounds) of x books.

    a. Is 52 in the range? Explain.

    b. Is 15 in the domain? Explain.

    c. Graph the function.

    d. Is the domain discrete or continuous?

15. Reasoning You want to fill a 2-foot shelf with framed pictures. There are x pictures in 4-inch frames and y pictures in 8-inch frames.

    a. Write a function for this situation.

    b. Graph the function.

    c. Is the domain discrete or continuous?

Fair Game Review What you learned in previous grades & lessons

Find the slope of the line. *(Section 2.2)*

16. 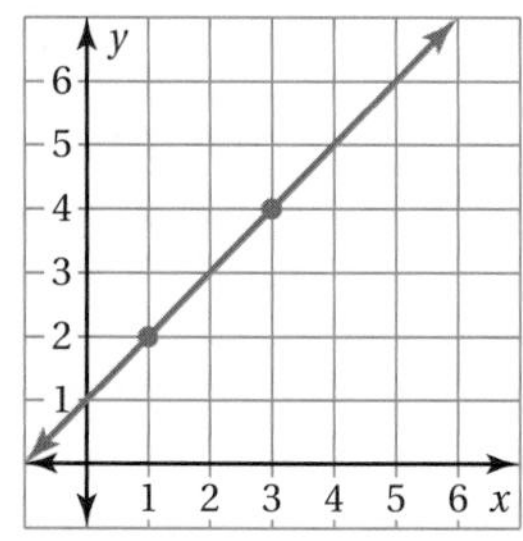

17. 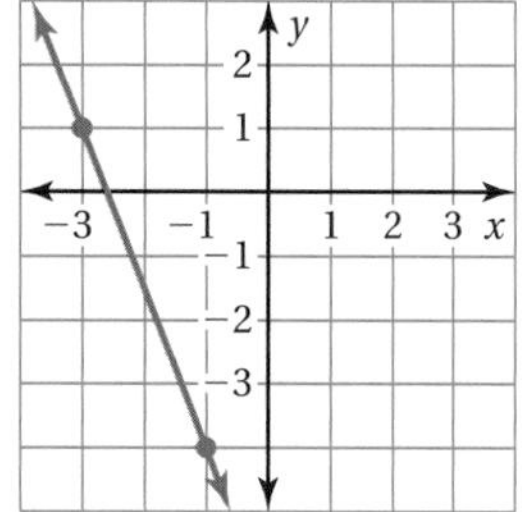

18. 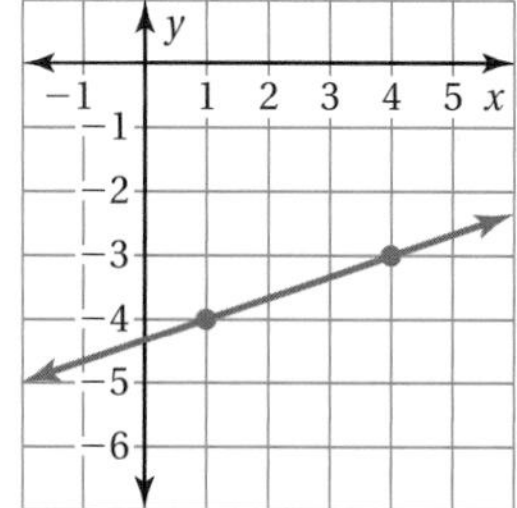

19. **MULTIPLE CHOICE** What is the y-intercept of the graph of the linear equation? *(Section 2.3)*

    Ⓐ -4 Ⓑ -2 Ⓒ 2 Ⓓ 4

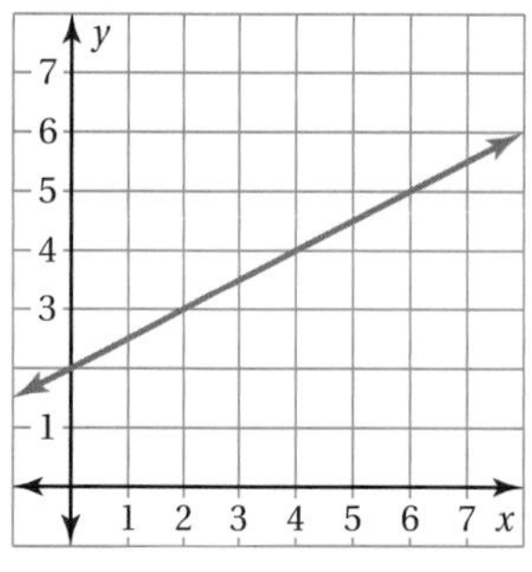

3 Study Help

You can use a **comparison chart** to compare two topics. Here is an example of a comparison chart for domain and range.

<table>
<tr><th></th><th>Domain</th><th>Range</th></tr>
<tr><td>Definition</td><td>the set of all possible input values</td><td>the set of all possible output values</td></tr>
<tr><td>Algebra
Example: $y = mx + b$</td><td>x-values</td><td>corresponding y-values</td></tr>
<tr><td>Ordered pairs
Example: (−4, 0), (−3, 1), (−2, 2), (−1, 3)</td><td>−4, −3, −2, −1</td><td>0, 1, 2, 3</td></tr>
<tr><td>Table
Example:<table><tr><td>x</td><td>−1</td><td>0</td><td>2</td><td>3</td></tr><tr><td>y</td><td>1</td><td>0</td><td>4</td><td>9</td></tr></table></td><td>−1, 0, 2, 3</td><td>0, 1, 4, 9</td></tr>
<tr><td>Graph
Example:</td><td>−3, −1, 2, 3</td><td>−1, 1, 2</td></tr>
</table>

On Your Own

Make a comparison chart to help you study and compare these topics.

1. discrete data and continuous data

After you complete this chapter, make comparison charts for the following topics.

2. linear functions with positive slopes and linear functions with negative slopes
3. linear functions and nonlinear functions

"Creating a comparison chart causes canines to crystalize concepts."

3.1–3.2 Quiz

Check It Out
Progress Check
BigIdeasMath.com

Find the domain and range of the function represented by the graph. *(Section 3.1)*

1. 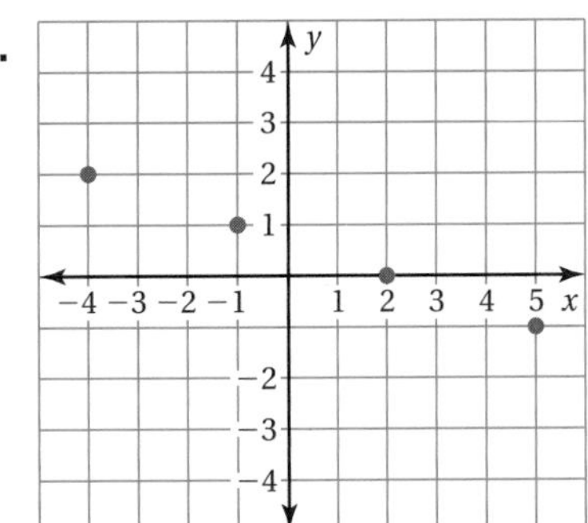

2. 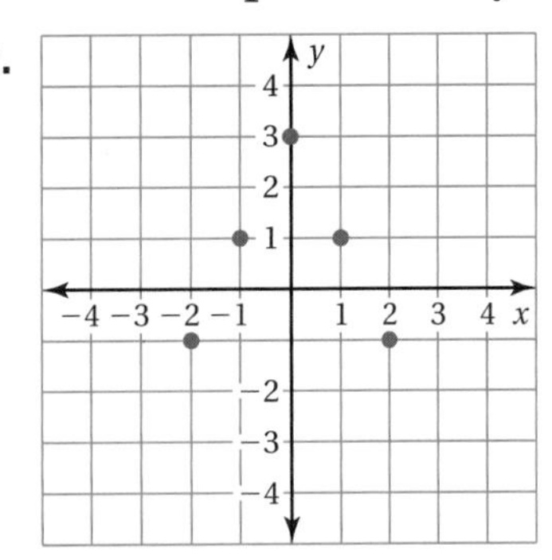

3. 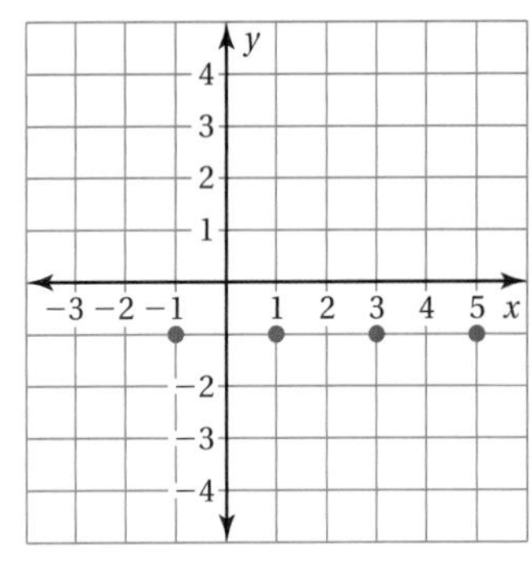

Copy and complete the input-output table for the function. Then find the domain and range of the function represented by the table. *(Section 3.1)*

4. $y = 5x - 6$

x	0	1	2	3
y				

5. $2x + y = 2$

x	−1	0	1	2
y				

Graph the function. Is the domain of the graph discrete or continuous? *(Section 3.2)*

6.

Rulers, x	Cost, y
0	0
1	1.5
2	3
3	4.5

7.

Gallons, x	Miles Remaining, y
0	300
1	265
2	230
3	195

8.

Minutes, x	0	10	20	30
Height, y	40	35	30	25

9.

Relay Teams, x	2	4	6	8
Athletes, y	8	16	24	32

10. **VIDEO GAME** The function $m = 30 - 3r$ represents the amount m (in dollars) of money you have after renting r video games. Graph the function using a domain of 0, 1, 2, 3, and 4. Is the domain of the graph discrete or continuous? *(Section 3.2)*

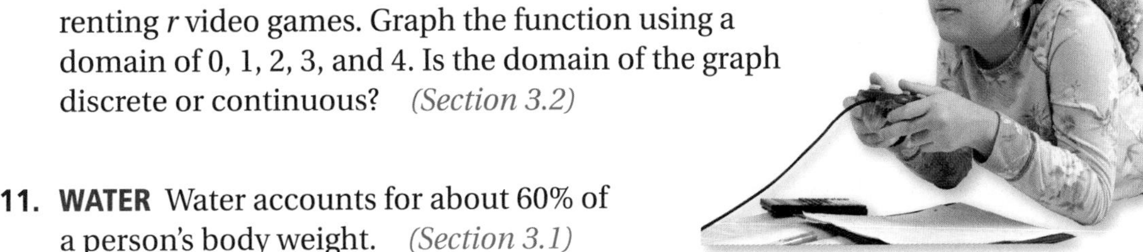

11. **WATER** Water accounts for about 60% of a person's body weight. *(Section 3.1)*

   a. Write an equation that represents the water weight y of a person who weighs x pounds. Identify the independent variable and the dependent variable.

   b. Make an input-output table for the function in part (a). Use the inputs 100, 120, 140, and 160.

3.3 Linear Function Patterns

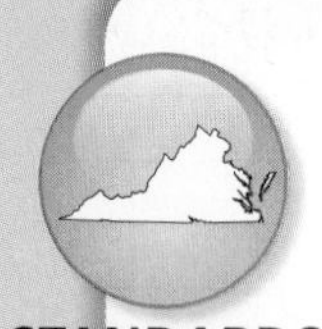

STANDARDS OF LEARNING
8.14

Essential Question How can you use a linear function to describe a linear pattern?

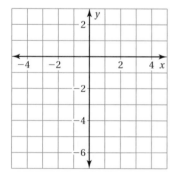

1 ACTIVITY: Finding Linear Patterns

Work with a partner.

- **Plot the points from the table in a coordinate plane.**
- **Write a linear equation for the function represented by the graph.**

a.

x	0	2	4	6	8
y	150	125	100	75	50

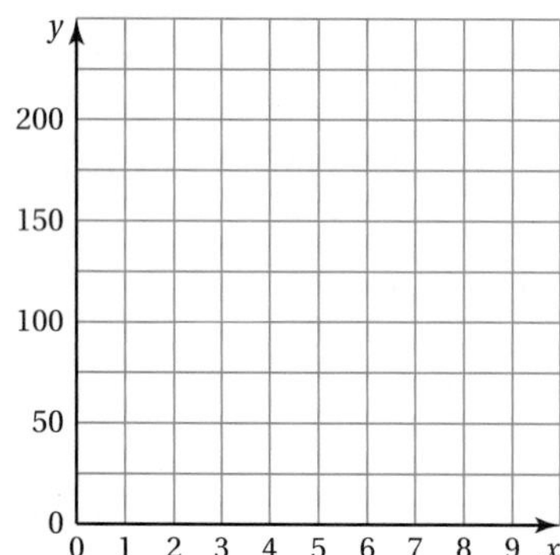

b.

x	4	6	8	10	12
y	15	20	25	30	35

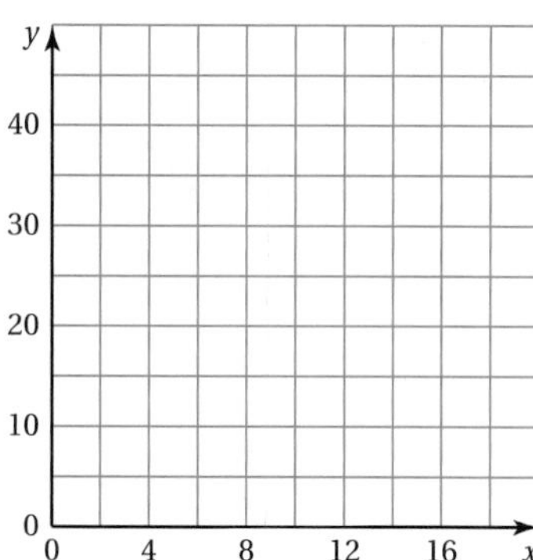

c.

x	−4	−2	0	2	4
y	4	6	8	10	12

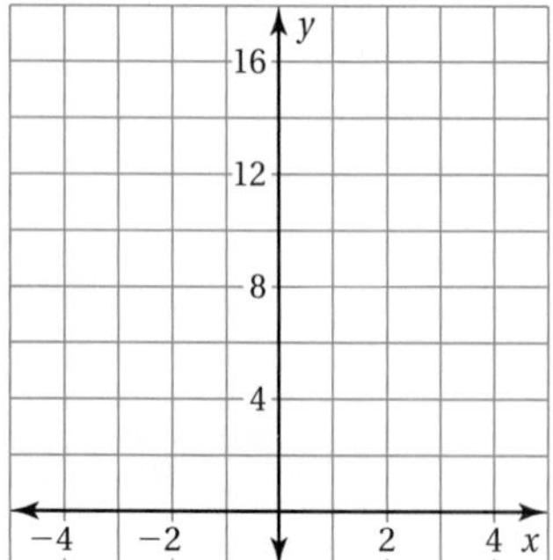

d.

x	−4	−2	0	2	4
y	1	0	−1	−2	−3

y
2
−4 −2 2 4 x
−2
−4
−6

2 ACTIVITY: Finding Linear Patterns

Work with a partner. The table shows a familiar linear pattern from geometry.

- **Write a linear function that relates y to x.**
- **What do the variables x and y represent?**
- **Graph the linear function.**

a.

x	1	2	3	4	5
y	2π	4π	6π	8π	10π

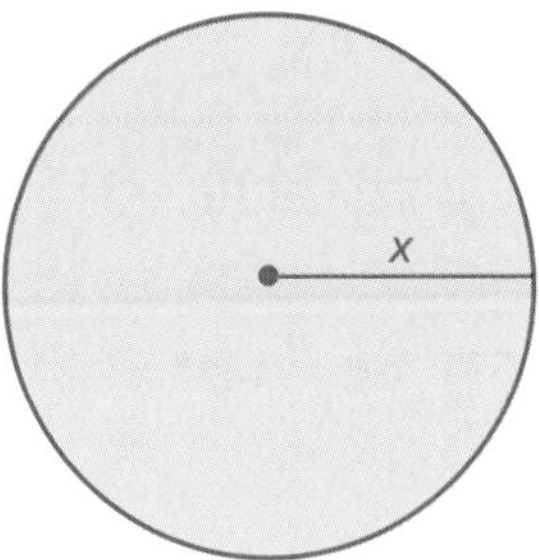

b.

x	1	2	3	4	5
y	10	12	14	16	18

c.

x	1	2	3	4	5
y	5	6	7	8	9

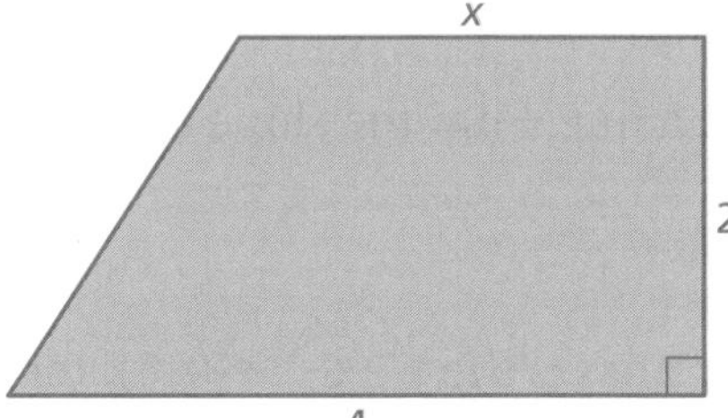

d.

x	1	2	3	4	5
y	28	40	52	64	76

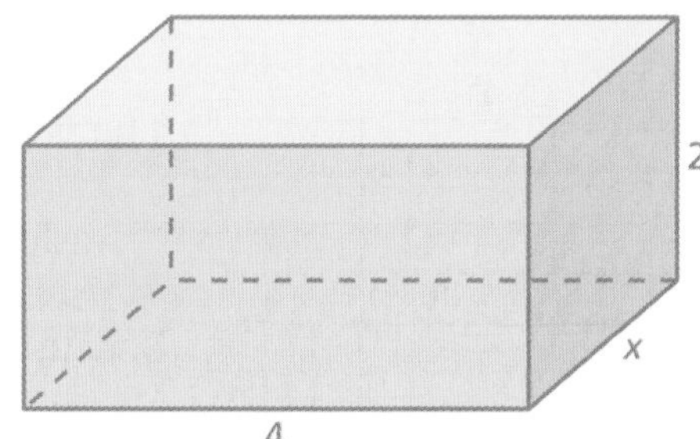

What Is Your Answer?

3. **IN YOUR OWN WORDS** How can you use a linear function to describe a linear pattern?
4. Describe the strategy you used to find the linear functions in Activities 1 and 2.

Practice Use what you learned about linear function patterns to complete Exercises 3 and 4 on page 144.

3.3 Lesson

Key Vocabulary
linear function, *p. 142*

A **linear function** is a function whose graph is a line.

EXAMPLE 1 Finding a Linear Function Using a Graph

Use the graph to write a linear function that relates y to x.

The points lie on a line. Find the slope and y-intercept of the line.

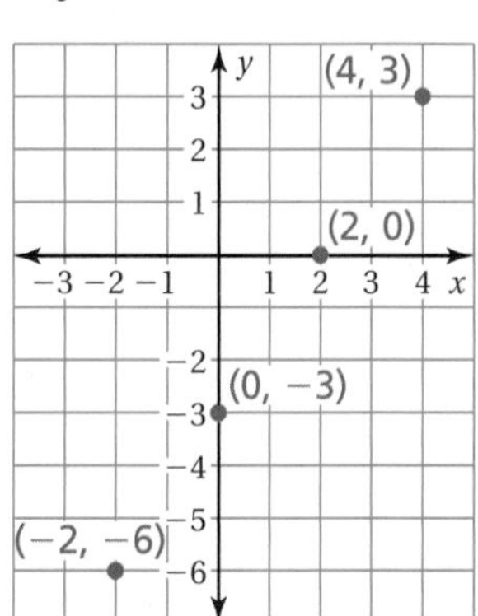

$$\text{slope} = \frac{\text{rise}}{\text{run}} = \frac{3}{2}$$

Because the line crosses the y-axis at $(0, -3)$, the y-intercept is -3.

So, the linear function is $y = \frac{3}{2}x - 3$.

EXAMPLE 2 Finding a Linear Function Using a Table

Use the table to write a linear function that relates y to x.

x	−3	−2	−1	0
y	9	7	5	3

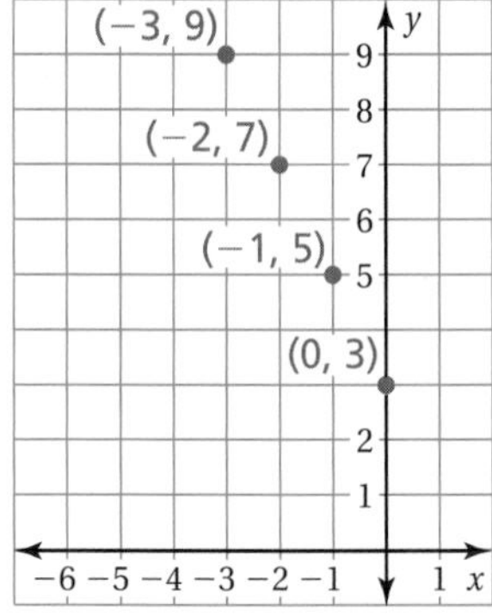

Plot the points in the table.

The points lie on a line. Find the slope and y-intercept of the line.

$$\text{slope} = \frac{\text{rise}}{\text{run}} = \frac{-2}{1} = -2$$

Because the line crosses the y-axis at $(0, 3)$, the y-intercept is 3.

So, the linear function is $y = -2x + 3$.

On Your Own

Now You're Ready
Exercises 5–10

Use the graph or table to write a linear function that relates y to x.

1.

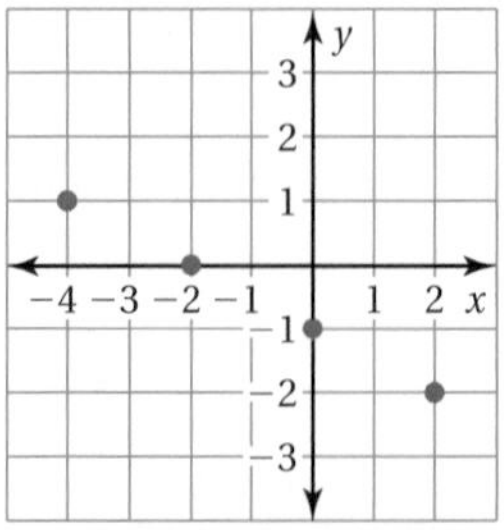

2.

x	−2	−1	0	1
y	2	2	2	2

Multi-Language Glossary at BigIdeasMath.com.

EXAMPLE 3 Real-Life Application

Hours Kayaking, x	Calories Burned, y
2	600
4	1200
6	1800
8	2400

Graph the data in the table. (a) Is the domain discrete or continuous? (b) Write a linear function that relates y to x. (c) How many calories do you burn in 4.5 hours?

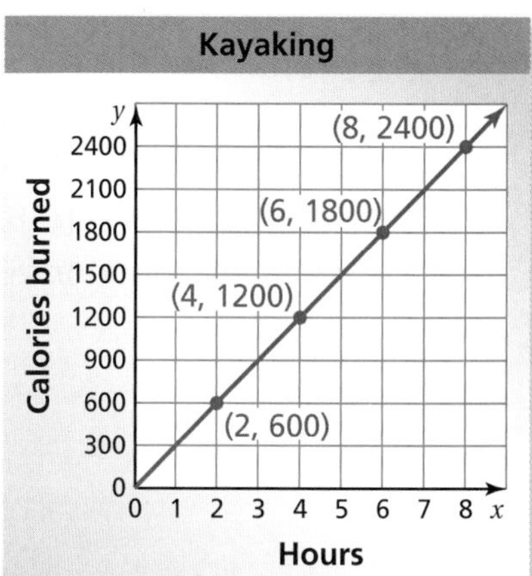

a. Plot the points. Time can represent any value greater than or equal to 0, so the domain is continuous. Draw a line through the points.

b. The slope is $\frac{600}{2} = 300$ and the y-intercept is 0.

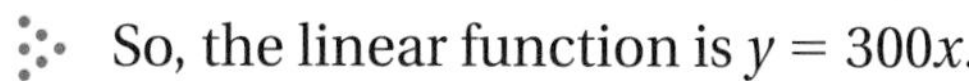

So, the linear function is $y = 300x$.

c. Find the value of y when $x = 4.5$.

$y = 300x$	Write the equation.
$= 300(4.5)$	Substitute 4.5 for x.
$= 1350$	Multiply.

You burn 1350 calories in 4.5 hours of kayaking.

On Your Own

Hours Rock Climbing, x	Calories Burned, y
3	1950
6	3900
9	5850
12	7800

3. Graph the data in the table.

a. Is the domain discrete or continuous?

b. Write a linear function that relates y to x.

c. How many calories do you burn in 5.5 hours?

Summary

Representing a Function

Words An output is 2 more than the input.

Equation $y = x + 2$

Input-Output Table

Input, x	−1	0	1	2
Output, y	1	2	3	4

Graph

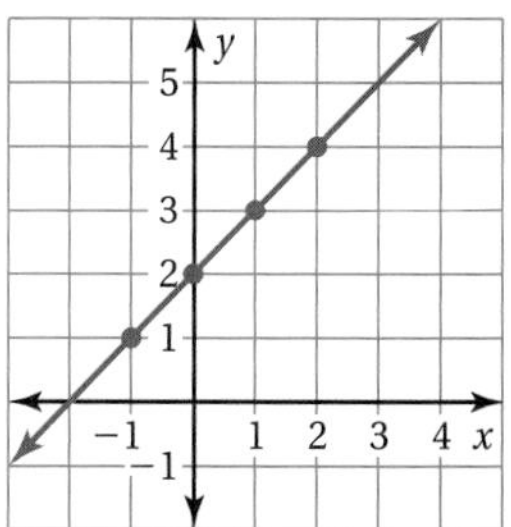

3.3 Exercises

Vocabulary and Concept Check

1. **VOCABULARY** Describe four ways to represent a function.
2. **VOCABULARY** Is the function represented by the graph a linear function? Explain.

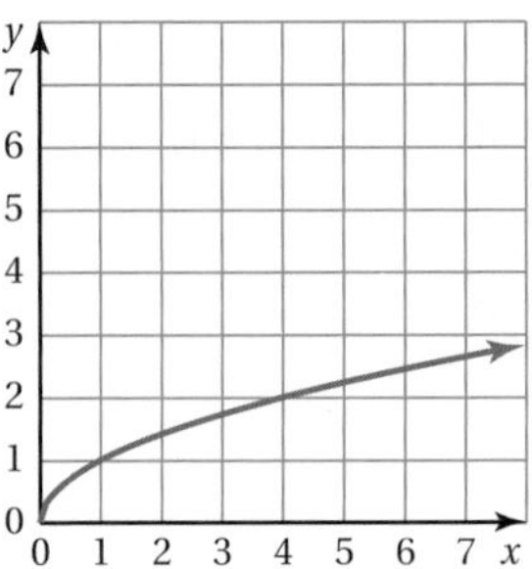

Practice and Problem Solving

The table shows a familiar linear pattern from geometry. Write a linear function that relates y to x. What do the variables x and y represent? Graph the linear function.

3.

x	1	2	3	4	5
y	π	2π	3π	4π	5π

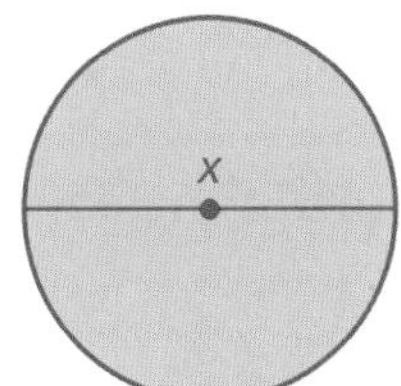

4.

x	1	2	3	4	5
y	2	4	6	8	10

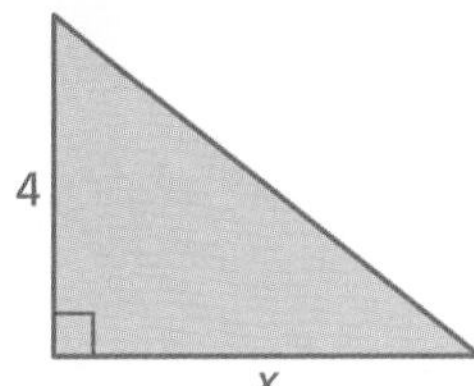

Use the graph or table to write a linear function that relates y to x.

5. 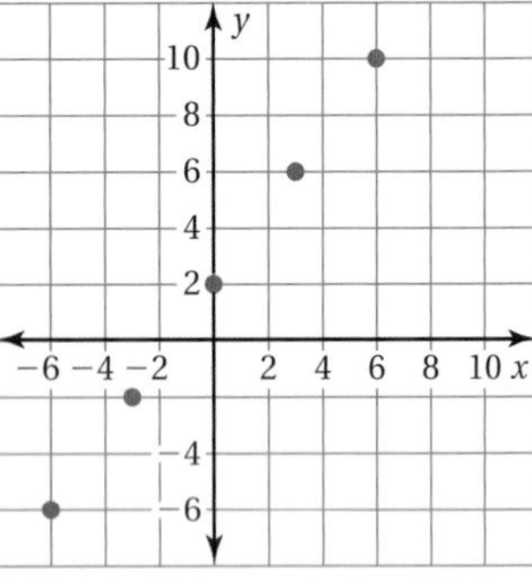

6. 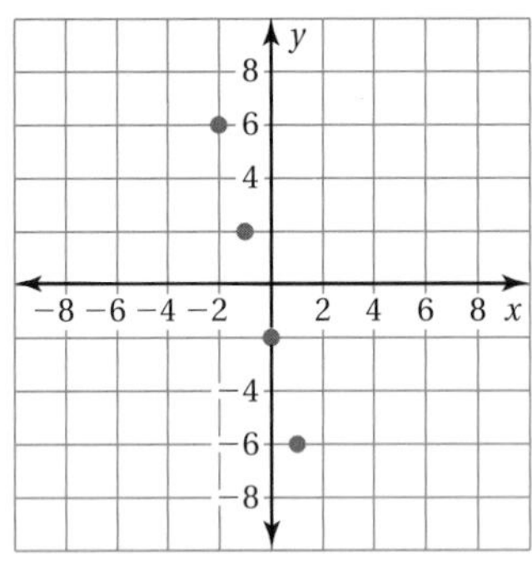

7. 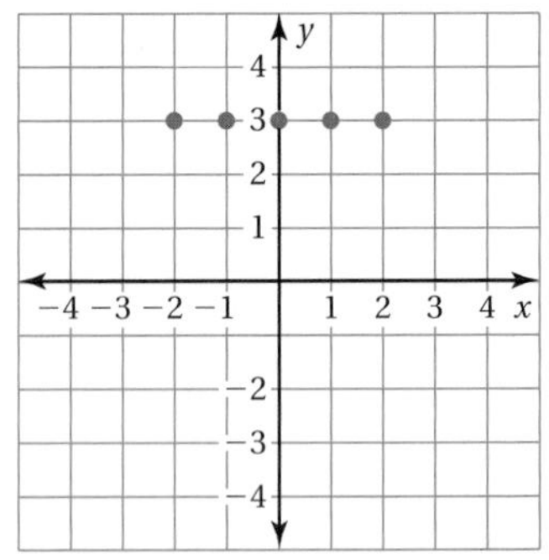

8.

x	−2	−1	0	1
y	−4	−2	0	2

9.

x	−8	−4	0	4
y	2	1	0	−1

10.

x	−3	0	3	6
y	3	5	7	9

11. **MOVIES** The table shows the cost y (in dollars) of renting x movies.

   a. Graph the data. Is the domain of the graph discrete or continuous?

   b. Write a linear function that relates y to x.

   c. How much does it cost to rent three movies?

Number of Movies, x	0	1	2	4
Cost, y	0	3	6	12

12. **BIKE JUMPS** A bunny hop is a bike trick in which the rider brings both tires off the ground without using a ramp. The table shows the height y (in inches) of a bunny hop on a bike that weighs x pounds.

Weight, x	19	21	23
Height, y	10.2	9.8	9.4

a. Graph the data. Then describe the pattern.
b. Write a linear function that relates the height of a bunny hop to the weight of the bike.
c. What is the height of a bunny hop on a bike that weighs 21.5 pounds?

Years of Education, x	Annual Salary, y
0	28
2	40
4	52
6	64
10	88

13. **SALARY** The table shows a person's annual salary y (in thousands of dollars) after x years of education beyond high school.

a. Graph the data.
b. Write a linear function that relates the person's annual salary to the number of years of education beyond high school.
c. What is the annual salary of the person after 8 years of education beyond high school?

14. Critical Thinking The Heat Index is calculated using the relative humidity and the temperature. For every 1 degree increase in the temperature from 94° F to 98° F at 75% relative humidity, the Heat Index rises 4° F.

a. On a summer day, the relative humidity is 75%, the temperature is 94° F, and the Heat Index is 122° F. Construct a table that relates the temperature t to the Heat Index H. Start the table at 94° F and end it at 98° F.
b. Write a linear function that represents this situation.
c. Estimate the Heat Index when the temperature is 100° F.

Fair Game Review What you learned in previous grades & lessons

Write an equation of the line that passes through the points. *(Section 2.7)*

15. (0, 0), (4, 4)
16. (−4, 9), (1, −1)
17. (−2, 1), (3, 1)

18. **MULTIPLE CHOICE** You buy a pair of gardening gloves for $2.25 and x packets of seeds for $0.88 each. Which equation represents the total cost y? *(Skills Review Handbook)*

Ⓐ $y = 0.88x - 2.25$
Ⓑ $y = 0.88x + 2.25$
Ⓒ $y = 2.25x - 0.88$
Ⓓ $y = 2.25x + 0.88$

3.4 Comparing Linear and Nonlinear Functions

STANDARDS OF LEARNING
8.13

Essential Question How can you recognize when a pattern in real life is linear or nonlinear?

1 ACTIVITY: Finding Patterns for Similar Figures

Work with a partner. Copy and complete each table for the sequence of similar rectangles. Graph the data in each table. Decide whether each pattern is linear or nonlinear.

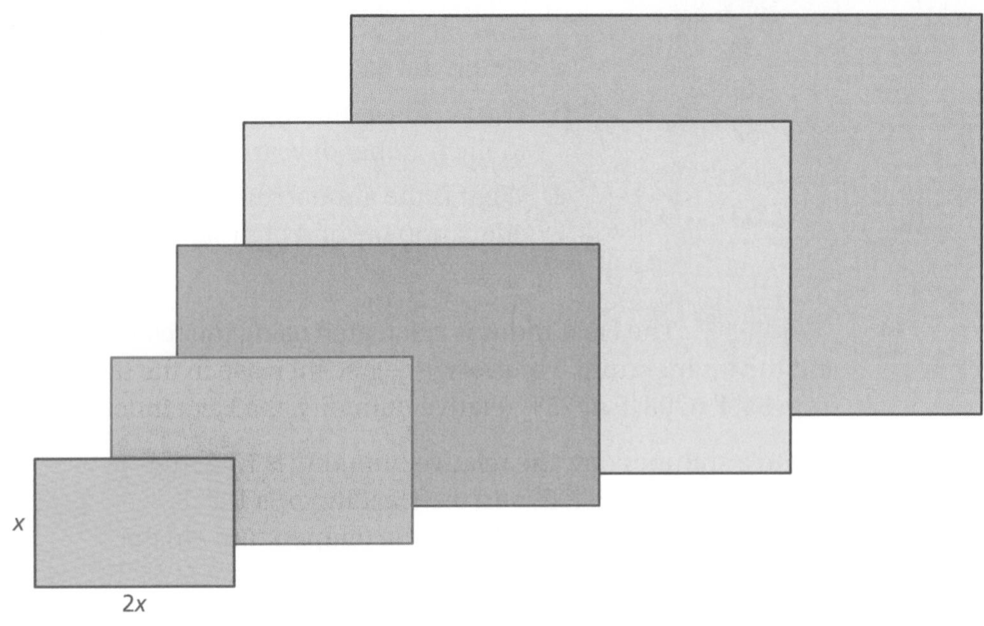

a. Perimeters of Similar Rectangles

x	1	2	3	4	5
P					

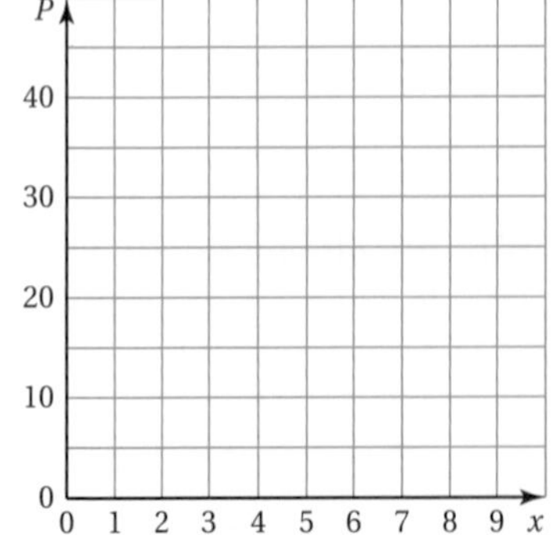

b. Areas of Similar Rectangles

x	1	2	3	4	5
A					

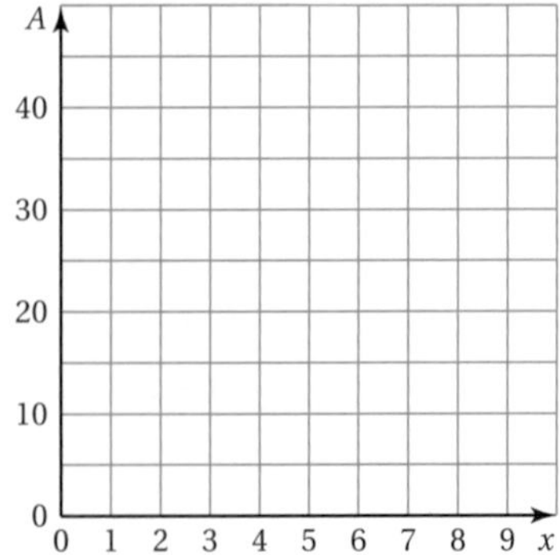

2 ACTIVITY: Comparing Linear and Nonlinear Functions

Work with a partner. Each table shows the height h (in feet) of a falling object at t seconds.

- **Graph the data in each table.**
- **Decide whether each graph is linear or nonlinear.**
- **Compare the two falling objects. Which one has an increasing speed?**

a. Falling parachute jumper

t	0	1	2	3	4
h	300	285	270	255	240

Parachute Jumper

Height (feet): h, 0, 60, 120, 180, 240

Time (seconds): 0 1 2 3 4 5 6 7 8 9 t

b. Falling bowling ball

t	0	1	2	3	4
h	300	284	236	156	44

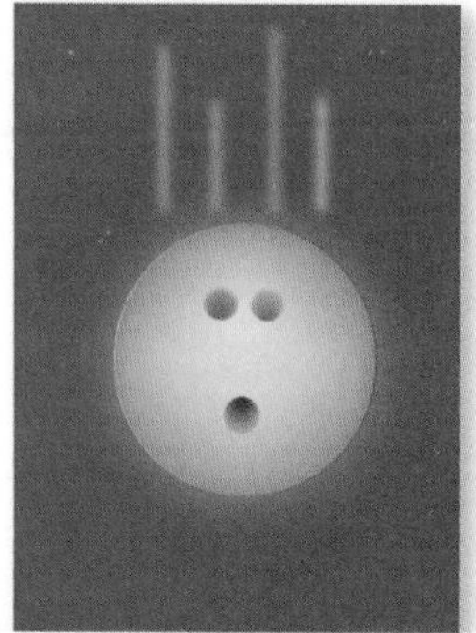

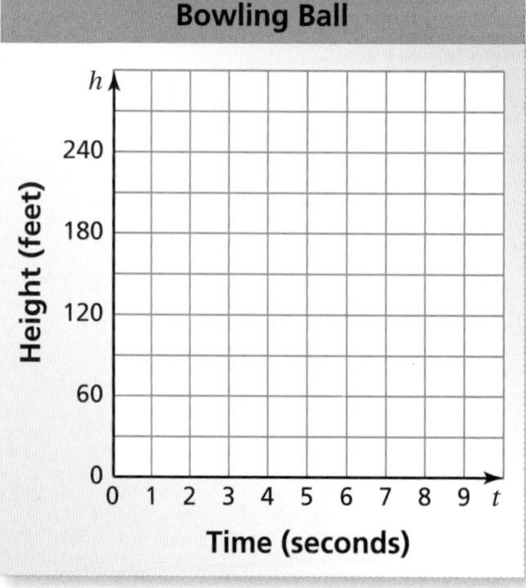

What Is Your Answer?

3. IN YOUR OWN WORDS How can you recognize when a pattern in real life is linear or nonlinear? Describe two real-life patterns: one that is linear and one that is nonlinear. Use patterns that are different from those described in Activities 1 and 2.

Practice Use what you learned about comparing linear and nonlinear functions to complete Exercises 3–6 on page 150.

3.4 Lesson

Key Vocabulary
nonlinear function, *p. 148*

The graph of a linear function shows a constant rate of change. A **nonlinear function** does not have a constant rate of change. So, its graph is *not* a line.

EXAMPLE 1 Identifying Functions from Tables

Does the table represent a *linear* or *nonlinear* function? Explain.

a.

+3 +3 +3

x	3	6	9	12
y	40	32	24	16

−8 −8 −8

As x increases by 3, y decreases by 8. The rate of change is constant. So, the function is linear.

b.

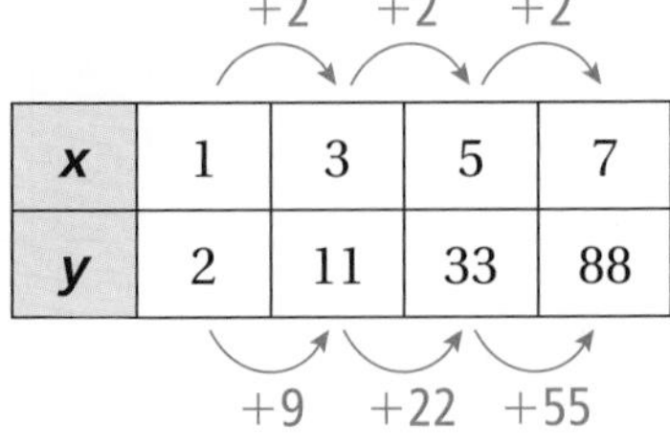

+2 +2 +2

x	1	3	5	7
y	2	11	33	88

+9 +22 +55

As x increases by 2, y increases by different amounts. The rate of change is *not* constant. So, the function is nonlinear.

EXAMPLE 2 Identifying Functions from Graphs

Does the graph represent a *linear* or *nonlinear* function? Explain.

a.

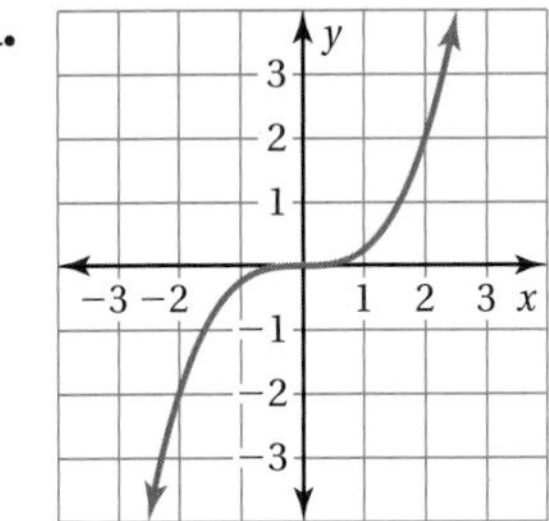

The graph is *not* a line.
So, the function is nonlinear.

b.

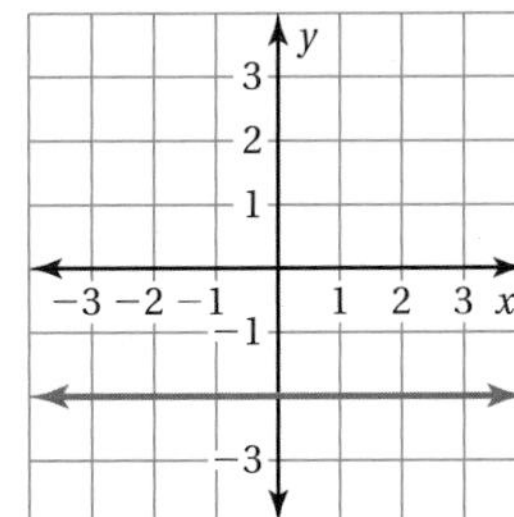

The graph is a line.
So, the function is linear.

On Your Own

Now You're Ready
Exercises 3–11

Does the table or graph represent a *linear* or *nonlinear* function? Explain.

1.

x	*y*
0	25
7	20
14	15
21	10

2.

x	*y*
2	8
4	4
6	0
8	−4

3.

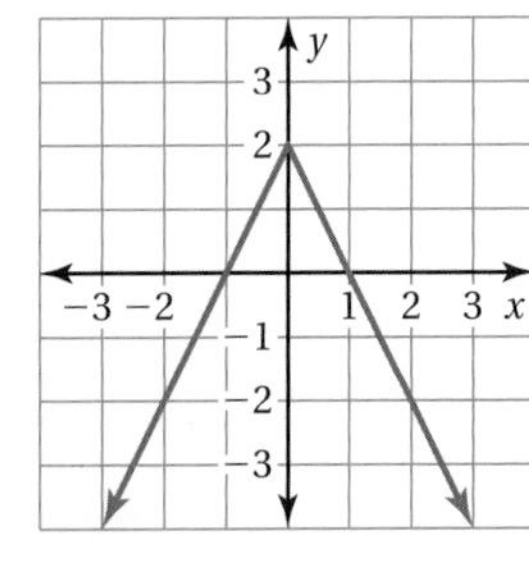

Multi-Language Glossary at BigIdeasMath.com.

EXAMPLE 3 Standardized Test Practice

Which equation represents a *nonlinear* function?

Ⓐ $y = 4.7$ Ⓑ $y = \pi x$

Ⓒ $y = \frac{4}{x}$ Ⓓ $y = 4(x - 1)$

The equations $y = 4.7$, $y = \pi x$, and $y = 4(x - 1)$ can be rewritten in slope-intercept form. So, they are linear functions.

The equation $y = \frac{4}{x}$ cannot be rewritten in slope-intercept form. So, it is a nonlinear function.

∴ The correct answer is Ⓒ.

EXAMPLE 4 Real-Life Application

Account A earns simple interest. Account B earns compound interest. The table shows the balances for 5 years. Graph the data and compare the graphs.

Year, t	Account A Balance	Account B Balance
0	$100	$100
1	$110	$110
2	$120	$121
3	$130	$133.10
4	$140	$146.41
5	$150	$161.05

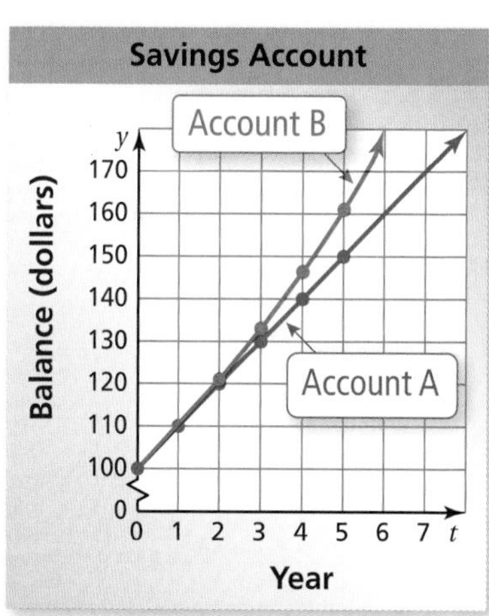

The balance of Account A has a constant rate of change of $10. So, the function representing the balance of Account A is linear.

The balance of Account B increases by different amounts each year. Because the rate of change is not constant, the function representing the balance of Account B is nonlinear.

On Your Own

Now You're Ready
Exercises 12–14

Does the equation represent a *linear* or *nonlinear* function? Explain.

4. $y = x + 5$ **5.** $y = \frac{4x}{3}$ **6.** $y = 1 - x^2$

3.4 Exercises

Vocabulary and Concept Check

1. **VOCABULARY** Describe how linear functions and nonlinear functions are different.
2. **WHICH ONE DOESN'T BELONG?** Which equation does *not* belong with the other three? Explain your reasoning.

$5y = 2x$ $\quad y = \frac{2}{5}x$ $\quad 10y = 4x$ $\quad 5xy = 2$

Practice and Problem Solving

Graph the data in the table. Decide whether the function is *linear* or *nonlinear*.

① **3.**

x	0	1	2	3
y	4	8	12	16

4.

x	1	2	3	4
y	1	2	6	24

5.

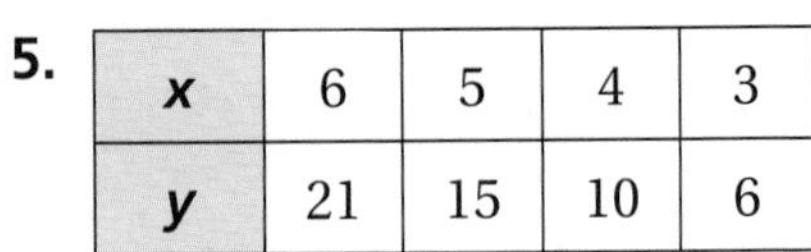

x	6	5	4	3
y	21	15	10	6

6.

x	−1	0	1	2
y	−7	−3	1	5

Does the table or graph represent a *linear* or *nonlinear* function? Explain.

② **7.**

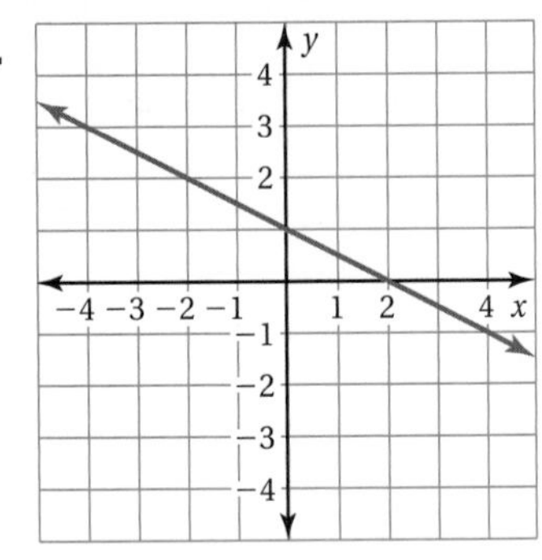

8.

9.

x	5	11	17	23
y	7	11	15	19

10.

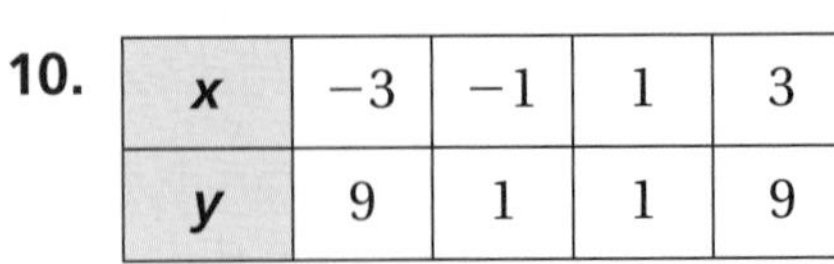

x	−3	−1	1	3
y	9	1	1	9

11. **VOLUME** The table shows the volume V (in cubic feet) of a cube with a side length of x feet. Does the table represent a linear or nonlinear function? Explain.

Side Length, x	1	2	3	4	5	6	7	8
Volume, V	1	8	27	64	125	216	343	512

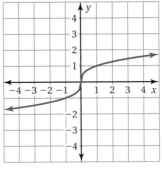

Does the equation represent a *linear* or *nonlinear* function? Explain.

3 **12.** $2x + 3y = 7$

13. $y + x = 4x + 5$

14. $y = \frac{8}{x^2}$

15. SUNFLOWER SEEDS The table shows the cost y (in dollars) of x pounds of sunflower seeds.

Pounds, x	Cost, y
2	2.80
3	?
4	5.60

a. What is the missing y-value that makes the table represent a linear function?

b. Write a linear function that represents the cost y of x pounds of seeds.

16. LIGHT The frequency y (in terahertz) of a light wave is a function of its wavelength x (in nanometers). Does the table represent a linear or nonlinear function? Explain.

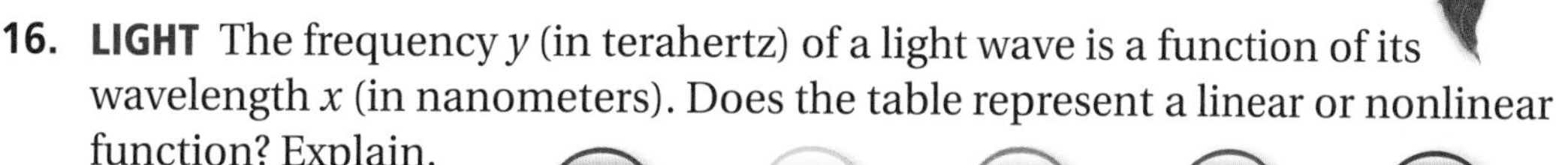

Color	Red	Yellow	Green	Blue	Violet
Wavelength, x	660	595	530	465	400
Frequency, y	454	504	566	645	749

17. LIGHTHOUSES The table shows the heights x (in feet) of four Florida lighthouses and the number y of steps in each. Does the table represent a linear or nonlinear function? Explain.

Lighthouse	Height, x	Steps, y
Ponce de Leon Inlet	175	213
St. Augustine	167	219
Cape Canaveral	145	179
Key West	86	98

18. PROJECT The wooden bars of a xylophone produce different musical notes when struck. The pitch of a note is determined by the length of the bar. Use the Internet or some other reference to decide whether the pitch of a note is a linear function of the length of the bar.

19. Geometry The radius of the base of a cylinder is 3 feet. Is the volume of the cylinder a linear or nonlinear function of the height of the cylinder? Explain.

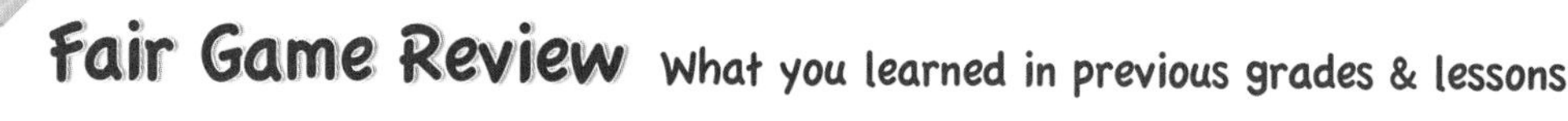

Fair Game Review What you learned in previous grades & lessons

Classify the angle as *acute, obtuse, right,* or *straight.* *(Skills Review Handbook)*

20.

21.

22.

23.

24. MULTIPLE CHOICE What is the value of x? *(Skills Review Handbook)*

Ⓐ 25 Ⓑ 35 Ⓒ 55 Ⓓ 125

125° 55° x° 125°

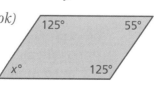

3.3–3.4 Quiz

Check It Out
Progress Check
BigIdeasMath.com

Use the graph or table to write a linear function that relates y to x. *(Section 3.3)*

1.

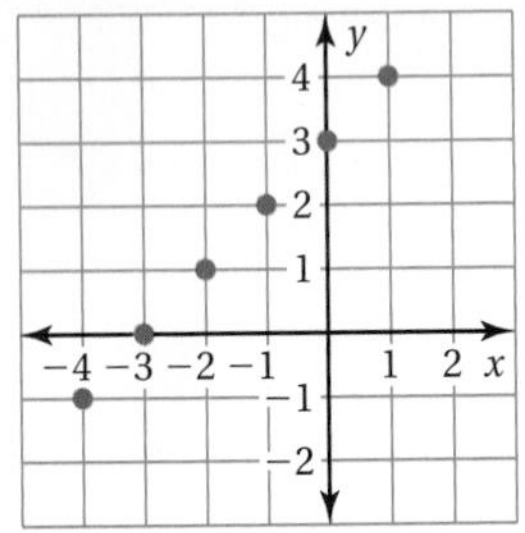

2.

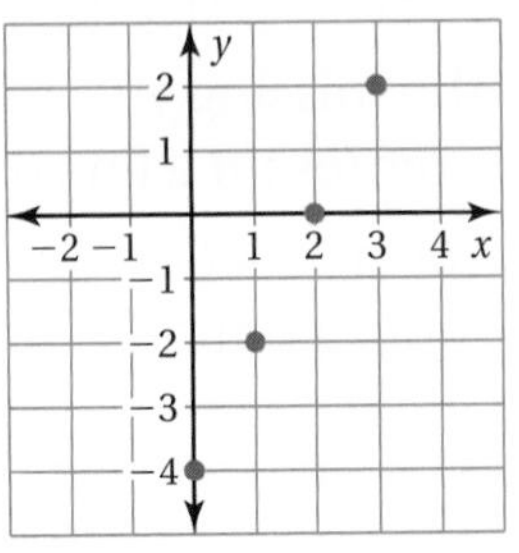

3.

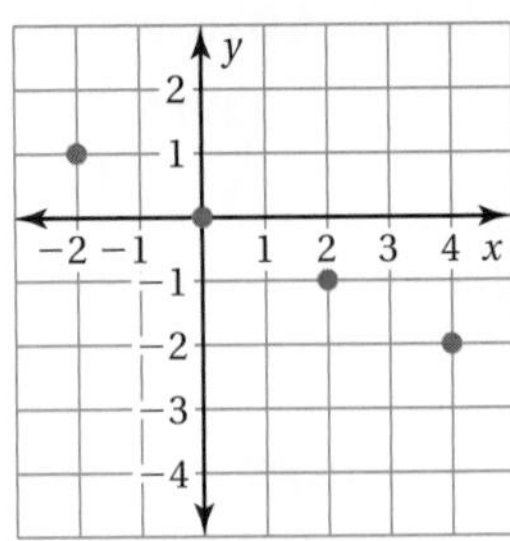

4.

x	0	1	2	3
y	2	1	0	−1

5.

x	−3	0	3	6
y	−3	−1	1	3

Does the table or graph represent a *linear* or *nonlinear* function? Explain. *(Section 3.4)*

6.

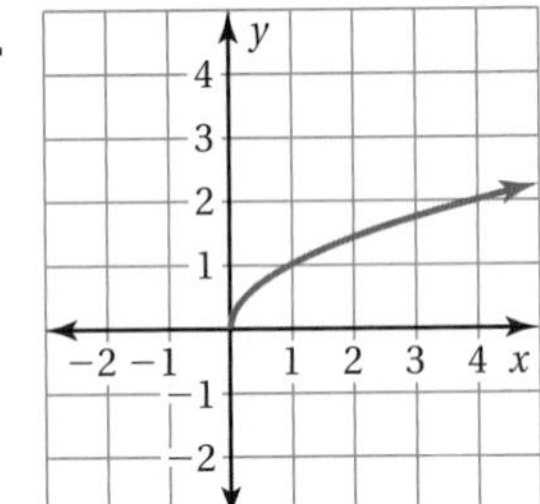

7.

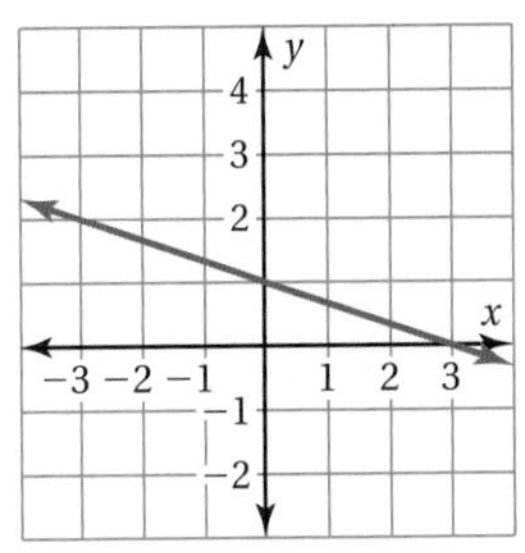

8.

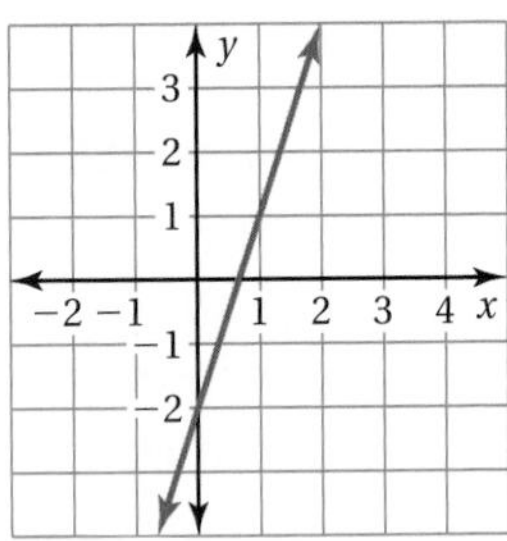

9.

x	y
0	0
2	−2
4	−4
6	−6

10.

x	y
1	−2
3	7
5	23
7	47

11.

x	y
0	3
3	0
6	3
9	6

12. ADVERTISING The table shows the revenue R (in millions of dollars) of a company when it spends A (in millions of dollars) on advertising. *(Section 3.3)*

Advertising, A	Revenue, R
0	2
2	6
4	10
6	14
8	18

a. Write a linear function that relates the revenue to the advertising cost.

b. What is the revenue of the company when it spends $10 million on advertising?

13. CHICKEN SALAD The equation $y = 7.9x$ represents the cost y (in dollars) of buying x pounds of chicken salad. Does this equation represent a linear or nonlinear function? Explain. *(Section 3.4)*

Check It Out
Vocabulary Help
BigIdeasMath.com

Review Key Vocabulary

function, *p. 128*
domain, *p. 128*
range, *p. 128*
independent variable, *p. 128*
dependent variable, *p. 128*
discrete domain, *p. 134*
continuous domain, *p. 134*
linear function, *p. 142*
nonlinear function, *p. 148*

Review Examples and Exercises

3.1 Domain and Range of a Function *(pp. 126–131)*

Find the domain and range of the function represented by the graph.

Write the ordered pairs. Identify the inputs and outputs.

inputs

$(-2, -3), (0, -1), (2, 1), (4, 3)$

outputs

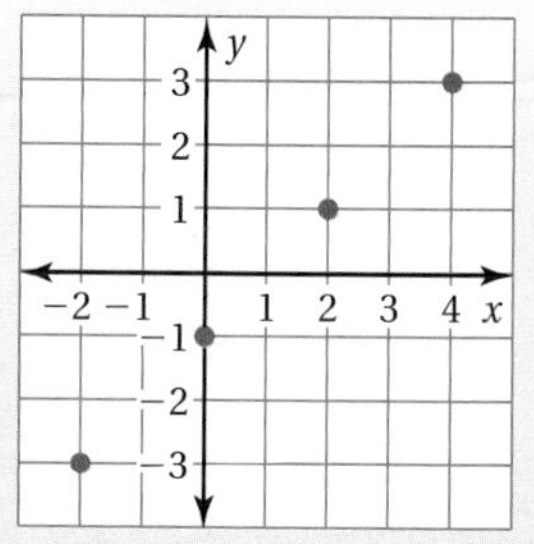

∴ The domain is -2, 0, 2, and 4. The range is -3, -1, 1, and 3.

Exercises

Find the domain and range of the function represented by the graph.

1.

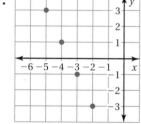

2.

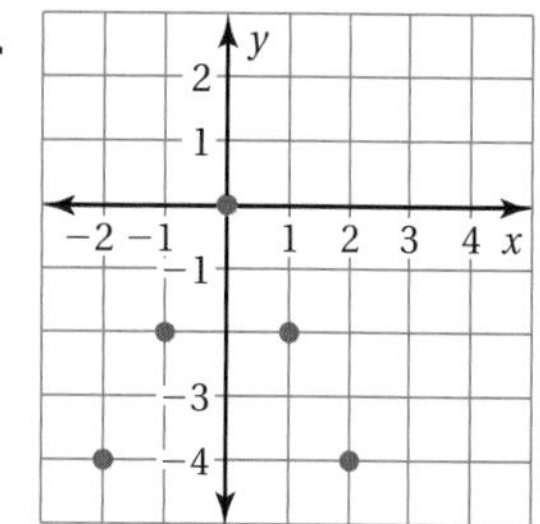

Copy and complete the input-output table for the function. Then find the domain and range of the function represented by the table.

3. $y = 3x - 1$

x	*y*
-1	
0	
1	
2	

4. $4x + y = 2$

x	*y*
0	
1	
2	
3	

3.2 Discrete and Continuous Domains (pp. 132–137)

The function $y = 19.5x$ represents the cost y (in dollars) of x yearbooks. Graph the function. Is the domain of the graph discrete or continuous?

Make an input-output table.

Input, x	$19.5x$	Output, y	Ordered Pair, (x, y)
0	19.5(0)	0	(0, 0)
1	19.5(1)	19.5	(1, 19.5)
2	19.5(2)	39	(2, 39)
3	19.5(3)	58.5	(3, 58.5)
4	19.5(4)	78	(4, 78)

Plot the ordered pairs.

Yearbooks

Cost (dollars) vs. Number of yearbooks: (0, 0), (1, 19.5), (2, 39), (3, 58.5), (4, 78)

Because you cannot buy part of a yearbook, the graph consists of individual points.

∴ So, the domain is discrete.

Exercises

Graph the function. Is the domain of the graph discrete or continuous?

5.

Hours, x	Miles, y
0	0
1	4
2	8
3	12
4	16

6.

Stamps, x	Cost, y
20	8.4
40	16.8
60	25.2
80	33.6
100	42

3.3 Linear Function Patterns (pp. 140–145)

Use the graph to write a linear function that relates y to x.

The points lie on a line. Find the slope and y-intercept of the line.

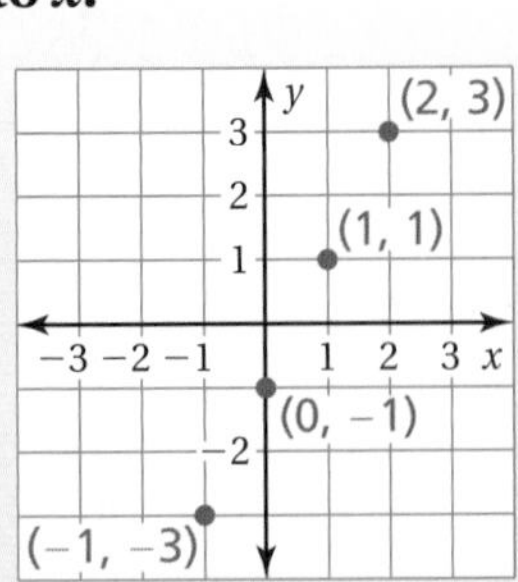

$$\text{slope} = \frac{\text{rise}}{\text{run}} = \frac{2}{1} = 2$$

Because the line crosses the y-axis at $(0, -1)$, the y-intercept is -1.

∴ So, the linear function is $y = 2x - 1$.

Exercises

Use the graph or table to write a linear function that relates *y* to *x*.

7.

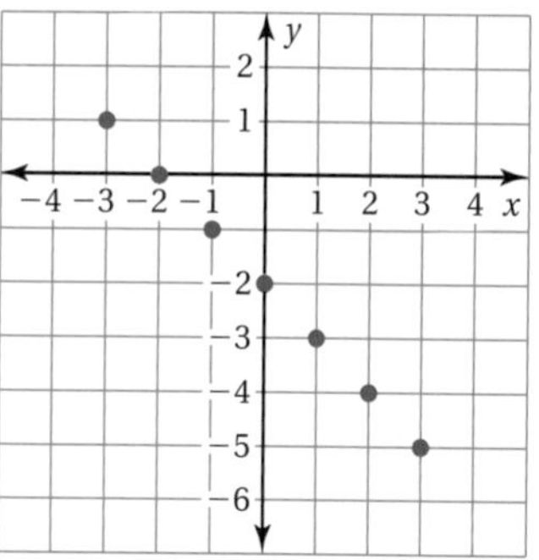

8.

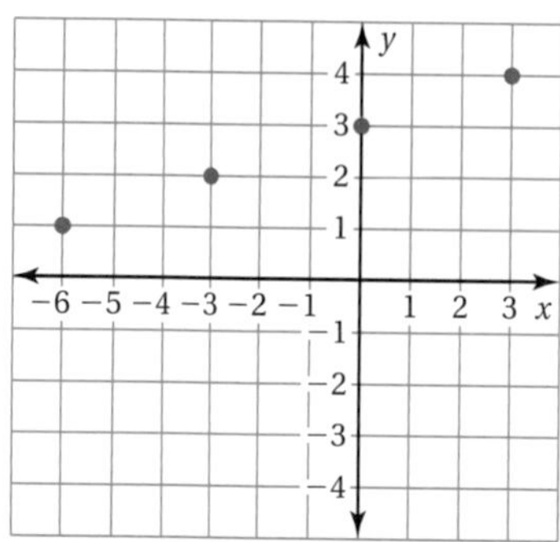

9.

x	−2	−1	0	1
y	−5	−2	1	4

10.

x	−2	0	2	4
y	−7	−7	−7	−7

3.4 Comparing Linear and Nonlinear Functions *(pp. 146–151)*

Does the table represent a *linear* or *nonlinear* function? Explain.

a.

x	0	2	4	6
y	0	1	4	9

(*x*: +2, +2, +2; *y*: +1, +3, +5)

As *x* increases by 2, *y* increases by different amounts. The rate of change is *not* constant. So, the function is nonlinear.

b.

x	*y*
0	50
5	40
10	30
15	20

(*x*: +5, +5, +5; *y*: −10, −10, −10)

As *x* increases by 5, *y* decreases by 10. The rate of change is constant. So, the function is linear.

Exercises

Does the table or graph represent a *linear* or *nonlinear* function? Explain.

11.

x	*y*
3	1
6	10
9	19
12	28

12.

x	*y*
1	3
3	1
5	1
7	3

13.

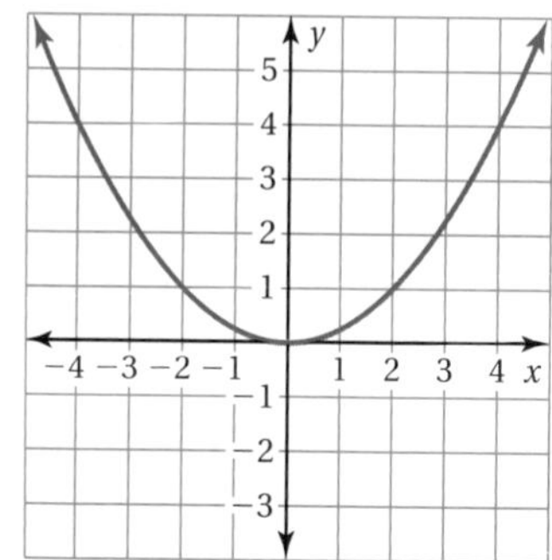

3 Chapter Test

Check It Out
Test Practice
BigIdeasMath.com

1. Find the domain and range of the function represented by the graph.

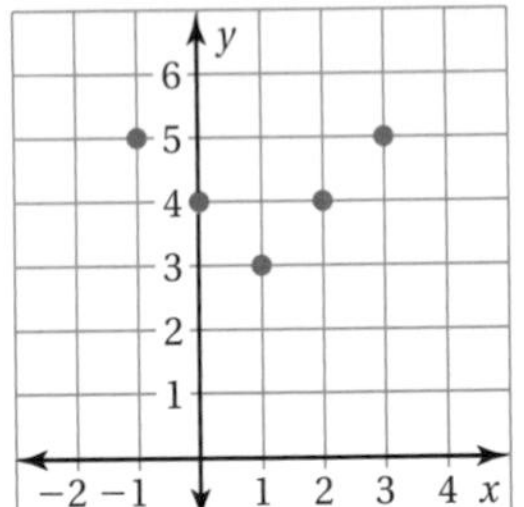

2. Copy and complete the input-output table for the function $y = 7x - 3$. Then find the domain and range of the function represented by the table.

x	-1	0	1	2
y				

Graph the function. Is the domain of the graph discrete or continuous?

3.

Hair Clips, x	Cost, y
0	0
1	1.5
2	3
3	4.5

4.

Minutes, x	Gallons, y
0	60
5	45
10	30
15	15

5. Write a linear function that relates y to x.

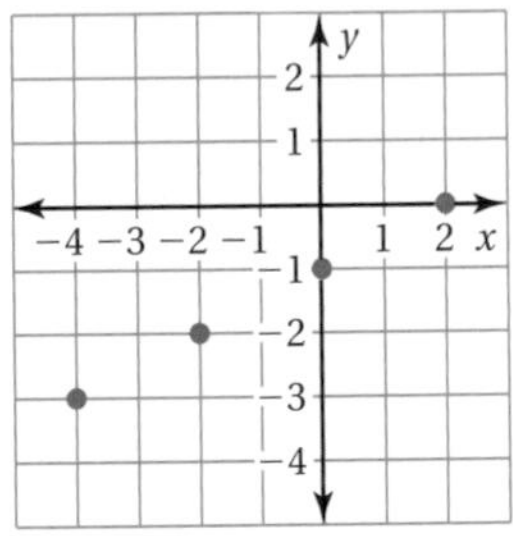

6. Does the table represent a *linear* or *nonlinear* function? Explain.

x	0	2	4	6
y	8	0	-8	-16

7. **SAVINGS** You save 15% of your monthly earnings x (in dollars).
   a. Write an equation that represents the amount y (in dollars) you save each month. Identify the independent variable and the dependent variable.
   b. Create an input-output table for the equation in part (a). Use the inputs 25, 30, 35, and 40.
   c. What is the total amount saved during those 4 months?

8. **FOOD DRIVE** You are putting cans of food into boxes for a food drive. One box holds 30 cans of food. Write a linear function that represents the number y of cans of food that will fit in x boxes.

9. **SURFACE AREA** The table shows the surface area S (in square inches) of a cube with a side length of x inches. Does the table represent a linear or nonlinear function? Explain.

Side Length, x	1	2	3	4
Surface Area, S	6	24	54	96

3 Standardized Test Practice

1. The domain of the function $y = 0.2x - 5$ is 5, 10, 15, 20. What is the range of this function?

   A. 20, 15, 10, 5 **C.** 4, 3, 2, 1

   B. 0, 5, 10, 15 **D.** −4, −3, −2, −1

Test-Taking Strategy
Work Backwards

For *x* cats, a litter box is changed $y=3x$ times per month. How many cats are there when $y=12$?
Ⓐ 1 Ⓑ 2 Ⓒ 3 Ⓓ 4

Share a litter box? Please!

KEEP OFF!

"Work backwards by trying 1, 2, 3, and 4. You will see that 3(4) = 12. So, D is correct."

2. A toy runs on a rechargeable battery. During use, the battery loses power at a constant rate. The percent *P* of total power left in the battery *x* hours after being fully charged can be found using the equation shown below. When will the battery be fully discharged?

$$P = -0.25x + 1$$

   F. After 4 hours of use

   G. After 1 hour of use

   H. After 0.75 hour of use

   I. After 0.25 hour of use

3. A limousine company charges a fixed cost for a limousine and an hourly rate for its driver. It costs \$500 to rent the limousine for 5 hours and \$800 to rent the limousine for 10 hours. What is the fixed cost, in dollars, to rent the limousine?

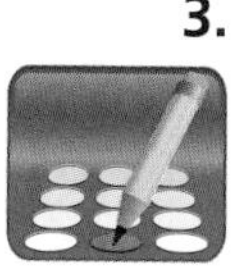

4. Which graph shows a nonlinear function?

A.

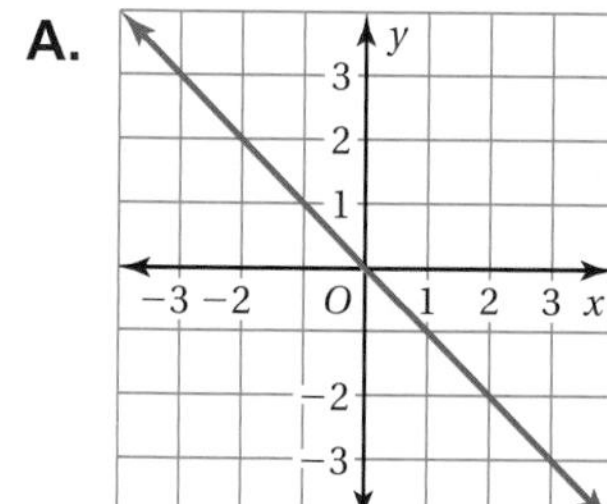

B.

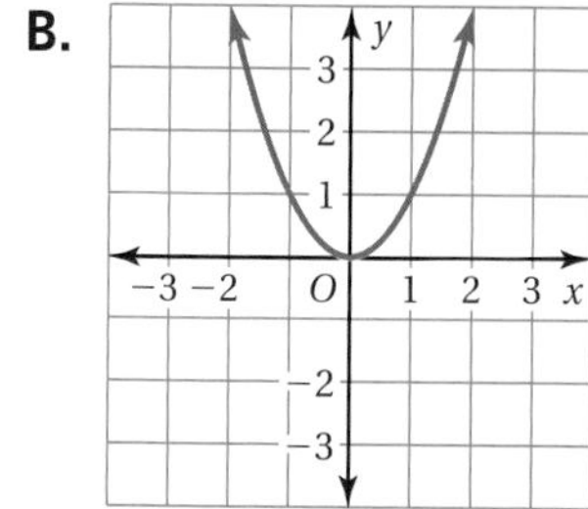

C.

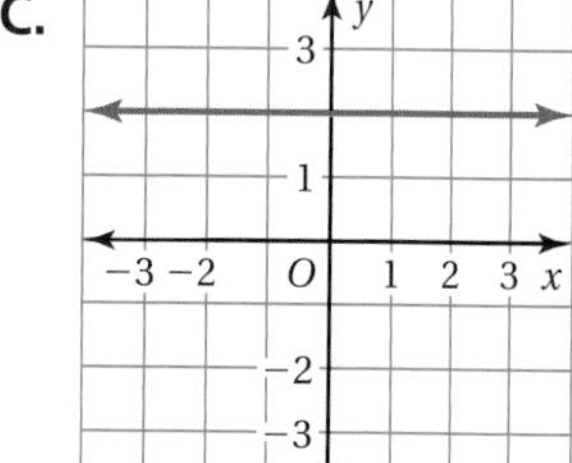

D.

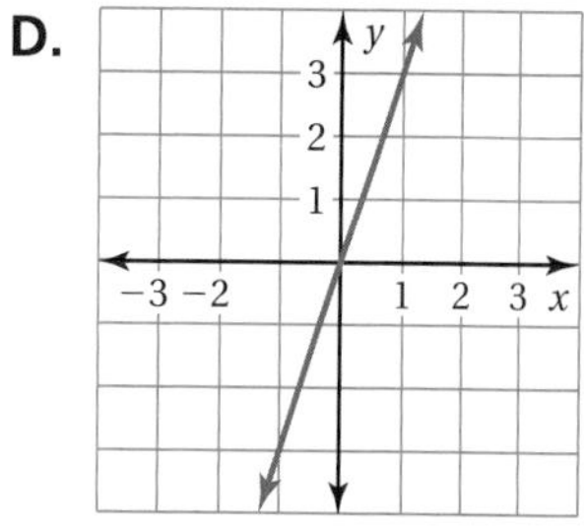

5. In many states, you must be at least 14 years old to operate a personal watercraft. Which inequality represents this situation?

F. $y > 14$

G. $y < 14$

H. $y \geq 14$

I. $y \leq 14$

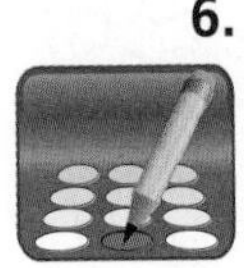

6. The temperature fell by the same number of degrees each hour over a six-hour period. How many degrees Fahrenheit did the temperature fall each hour?

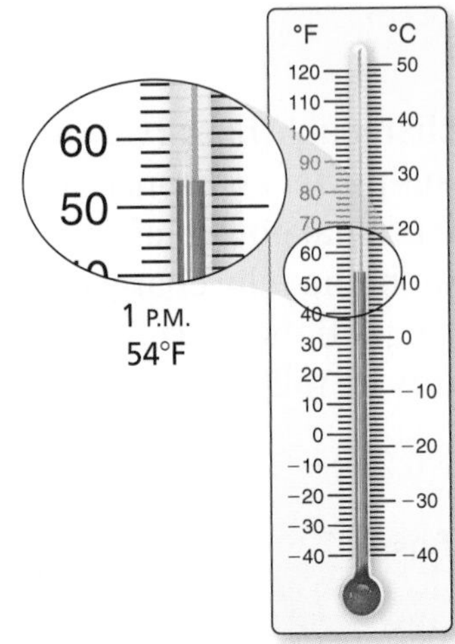

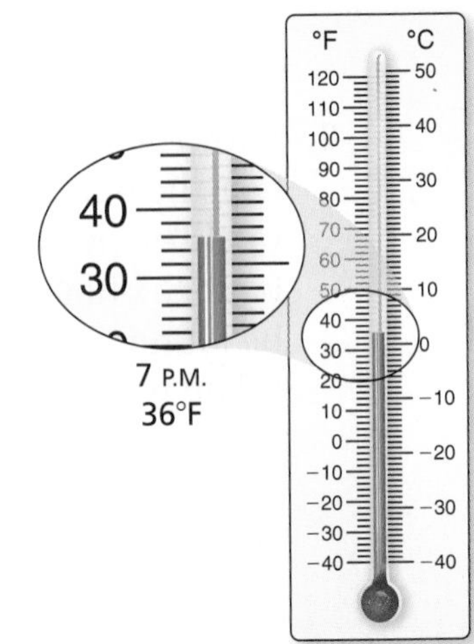

7. What is the domain of the function graphed in the coordinate plane below?

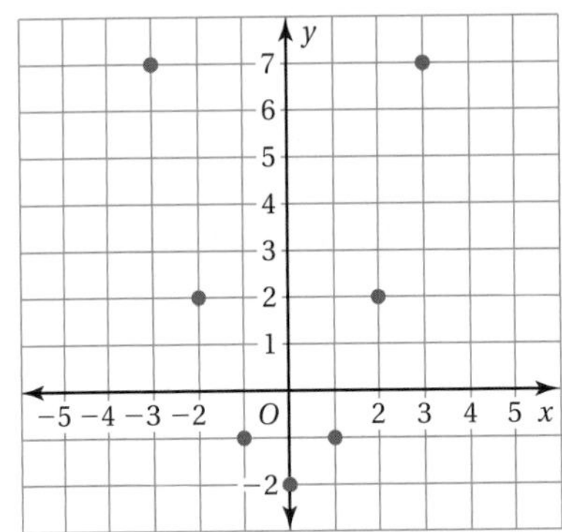

A. 0, 1, 2, 3

B. −2, −1, 2, 7

C. −3, −2, −1, 0, 1, 2, 3

D. −2, −1, 0, 1, 2, 3, 7

8. What value of w makes the equation below true?

$$\frac{w}{3} = 3(w - 1) - 1$$

F. $\frac{3}{2}$

G. $\frac{5}{4}$

H. $\frac{3}{4}$

I. $\frac{1}{2}$

9. What is the slope of the line shown in the graph below?

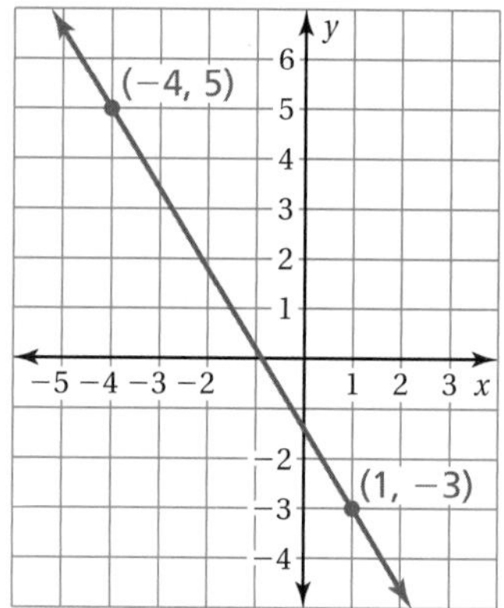

A. $-\frac{2}{5}$

B. $-\frac{2}{3}$

C. $-\frac{8}{5}$

D. $-\frac{8}{3}$

10. A line with slope of $\frac{1}{3}$ contains the point (6, 1). What is the equation of the line?

F. $y = \frac{1}{3}x$

G. $y = \frac{1}{3}x + 1$

H. $x - 3y = 3$

I. $x + 3y = 3$

11. **Think Solve Explain** The tables show how the perimeter and area of a square are related to its side length. Examine the data in the table.

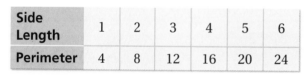

Side Length	1	2	3	4	5	6
Perimeter	4	8	12	16	20	24

Side Length	1	2	3	4	5	6
Area	1	4	9	16	25	36

Part A Does the first table show a linear function? Explain your reasoning.

Part B Does the second table show a linear function? Explain your reasoning.

12. A bottle of orange extract marked 25 mL costs \$2.49. What is the cost per liter?

A. \$2490.00 per L

B. \$99.60 per L

C. \$9.96 per L

D. \$0.00249 per L

4 Percents

"Here's my sales strategy. I buy each dog bone for $0.05."

"Then I mark each one up to $1. Then, I have a 75% off sale. Cool, huh?"

"Dear Vet: I have this strange feeling that I am wagging my tail 15% fewer times than I used to wag it."

"Oh look. He already answered me."

"Dear Newton, I only practice general vet work. I need to refer you to a dog tail specialist."

What You Learned Before

Favorite Pets
Cats 46%
Dogs 47%
Other
Other? What else is there?

"The fact that these two percents do not total 100 is a sad commentary on humans."

Writing Percents Using Models

What percent of the model is shaded?

Example 1

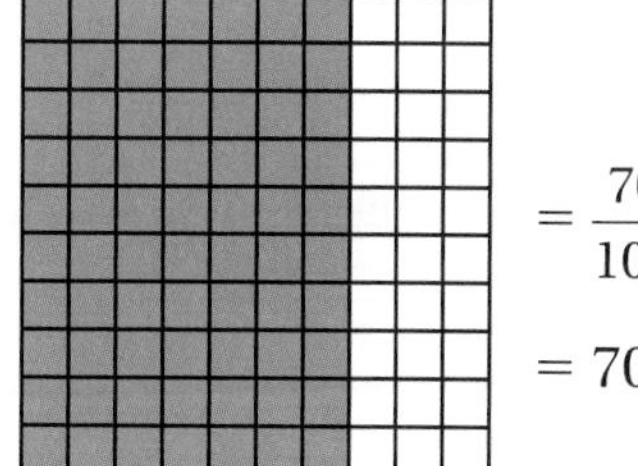

$= \dfrac{70}{100}$

$= 70\%$

Example 2

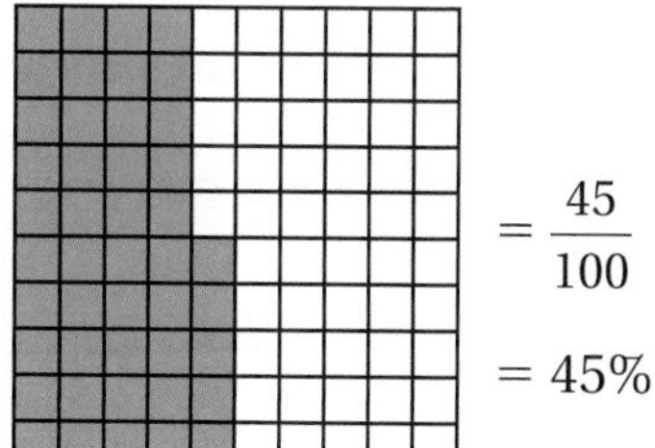

$= \dfrac{45}{100}$

$= 45\%$

Try It Yourself

What percent of the model is shaded?

1.

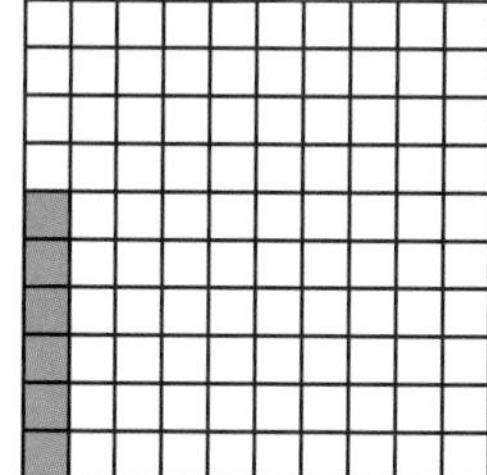

2.

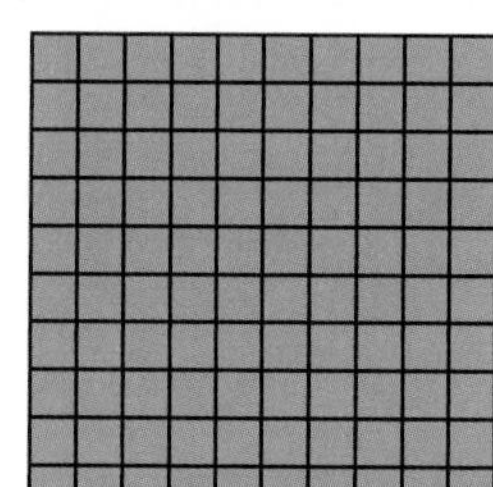

3.

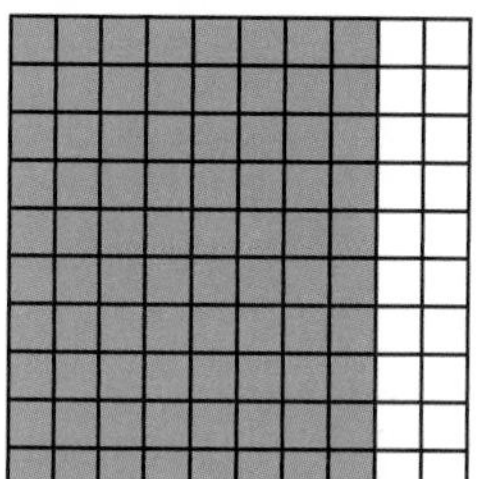

Writing Decimals, Percents, and Fractions

Example 3 **Write $\frac{3}{5}$ as a decimal.**

$$\frac{3}{5} = \frac{3 \cdot 2}{5 \cdot 2} = \frac{6}{10} = 0.6$$

Example 4 **Write $\frac{3}{5}$ as a percent.**

$$\frac{3}{5} = \frac{3 \cdot 20}{5 \cdot 20} = \frac{60}{100} = 60\%$$

Multiply to make the denominator 100.

Try It Yourself

Copy and complete the table.

	Percent	Decimal	Fraction
4.	35%		
5.		0.6	
6.			$\frac{13}{25}$

	Percent	Decimal	Fraction
7.	10%		
8.		0.85	
9.			$\frac{1}{5}$

4.1 The Percent Equation

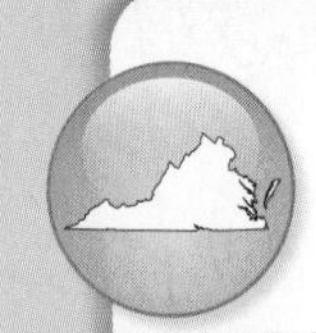

STANDARDS OF LEARNING 8.3

Essential Question How can you use models to estimate percent questions?

1 ACTIVITY: Estimating a Percent

Work with a partner. Estimate the locations of 50%, 75%, 40%, 6%, and 65% on the model. 50% is done for you.

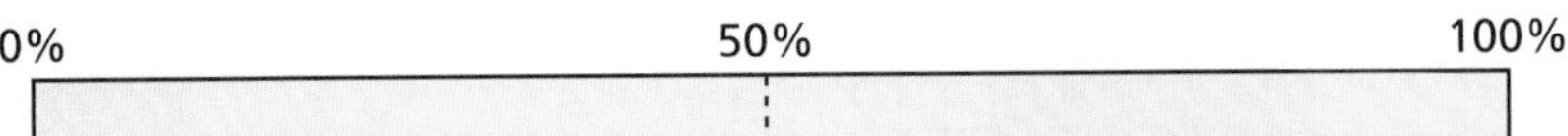

2 ACTIVITY: Estimating a Part of a Number

The statement "25% of 12 is 3" has three numbers. In real-life problems, any one of these numbers can be unknown.

Part → 3, Whole → 12

$$\frac{3}{12} = 0.25 = 25\%$$ ← Percent

Which number is missing?	Question	Type of Question
3	What is 25% of 12?	Find a part of a number.
25%	3 is what percent of 12?	Find a percent.
12	3 is 25% of what?	Find the whole.

Work with a partner. Estimate the answer to each question using a model.

a. Sample: What number is 50% of 30?

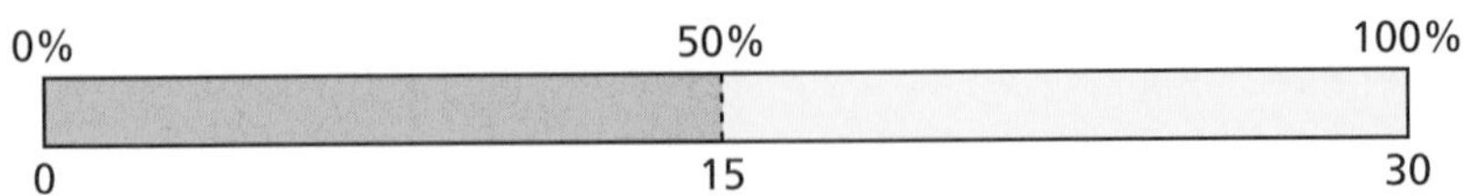

So, from the model, 15 is 50% of 30.

b. What number is 75% of 30?

c. What number is 40% of 30?

d. What number is 6% of 30?

e. What number is 65% of 30?

3 ACTIVITY: Estimating a Percent

Work with a partner. Estimate the answer to the question using a model.

a. Sample: 15 is what percent of 75?

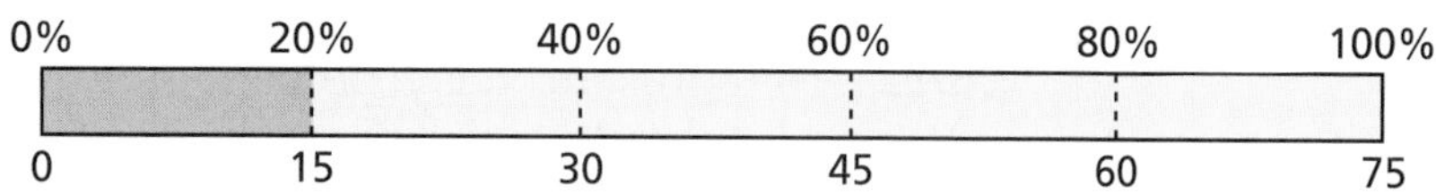

So, 15 is 20% of 75.

b. 5 is what percent of 20?

c. 18 is what percent of 40?

d. 50 is what percent of 80?

e. 75 is what percent of 50?

4 ACTIVITY: Estimating a Whole

Work with a partner. Estimate the answer to the question using a model.

a. Sample: 24 is $33\frac{1}{3}\%$ of what number?

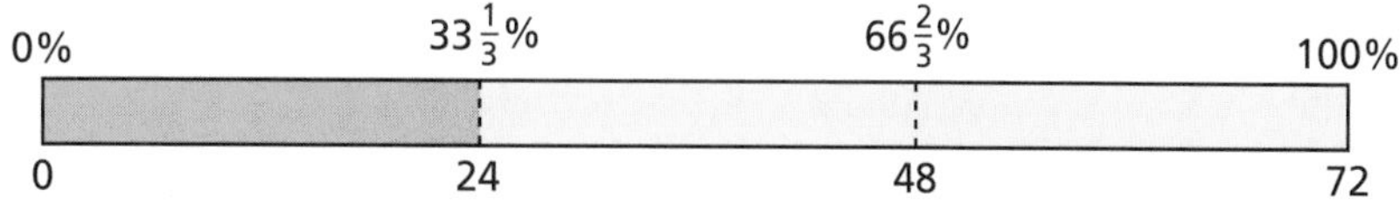

So, 24 is $33\frac{1}{3}\%$ of 72.

b. 13 is 25% of what number?

c. 110 is 20% of what number?

d. 75 is 75% of what number?

e. 81 is 45% of what number?

What Is Your Answer?

5. **IN YOUR OWN WORDS** How can you use models to estimate percent questions? Give examples to support your answer.

Practice Use what you learned about estimating percent questions to complete Exercises 4–9 on page 166.

4.1 Lesson

Key Vocabulary
percent, *p. 164*

A **percent** is a ratio whose denominator is 100. Here are two examples.

$$4\% = \frac{4}{100} = 0.04 \qquad 25\% = \frac{25}{100} = 0.25$$

Key Idea

The Percent Equation

Words To represent "a is p percent of w," use an equation.

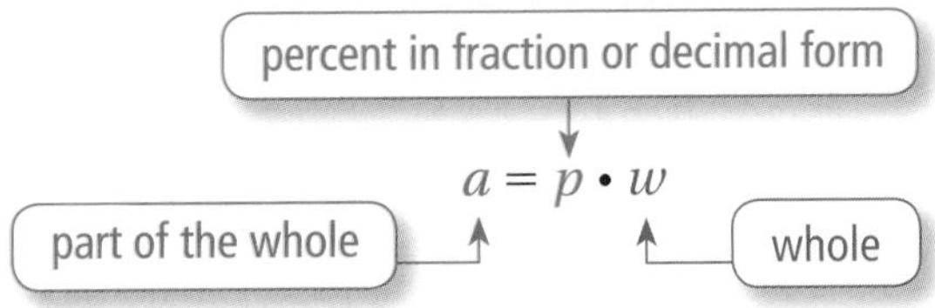

Numbers $15 = 0.5 \cdot 30$

EXAMPLE 1 Finding a Part of a Number

What number is 24% of 50?

Estimate

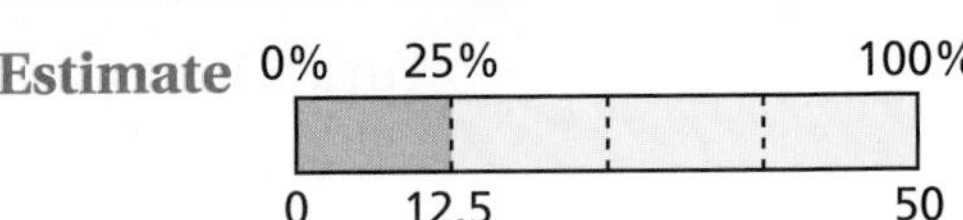

Common Error
Remember to convert a percent to a fraction or decimal before using the percent equation. For Example 1, write 24% as $\frac{24}{100}$.

$a = p \cdot w$	Write percent equation.
$= \frac{24}{100} \cdot 50$	Substitute $\frac{24}{100}$ for p and 50 for w.
$= 12$	Multiply.

So, 12 is 24% of 50.

Reasonable? $12 \approx 12.5$ ✓

EXAMPLE 2 Finding a Percent

9.5 is what percent of 25?

Estimate

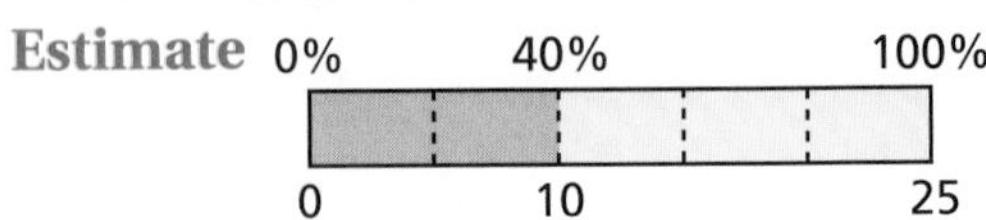

$a = p \cdot w$	Write percent equation.
$9.5 = p \cdot 25$	Substitute 9.5 for a and 25 for w.
$0.38 = p$	Divide each side by 25.

Because 0.38 equals 38%, 9.5 is 38% of 25.

Reasonable? $38\% \approx 40\%$ ✓

EXAMPLE 3 Finding a Whole

39 is 52% of what number?

Estimate 0% 50% 100%

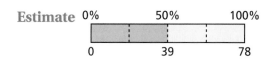

0 39 78

$a = p \cdot w$	Write percent equation.
$39 = 0.52 \cdot w$	Substitute 39 for *a* and 0.52 for *p*.
$75 = w$	Divide each side by 0.52.

So, 39 is 52% of 75.

Reasonable? $75 \approx 78$ 

On Your Own

Now You're Ready
Exercises 10–17

Write and solve an equation to answer the question.

1. What number is 10% of 20?
2. What number is 150% of 40?
3. 3 is what percent of 600?
4. 18 is what percent of 20?
5. 8 is 80% of what number?
6. 90 is 18% of what number?

EXAMPLE 4 Real-Life Application

8th Street Cafe

DATE: MAY04'10 05:45PM
TABLE: 29
SERVER: CHARITY

Food Total	**27.50**
Tax	**1.65**
Subtotal	**29.15**

TIP: ______________

TOTAL: ______________

Thank You

a. Find the percent of sales tax on the food total.

b. Find the amount of a 16% tip on the food total.

a. Answer the question: $1.65 is what percent of $27.50?

$a = p \cdot w$	Write percent equation.
$1.65 = p \cdot 27.50$	Substitute 1.65 for *a* and 27.50 for *w*.
$0.06 = p$	Divide each side by 27.50.

Because 0.06 equals 6%, the percent of sales tax is 6%.

b. Answer the question: What tip amount is 16% of $27.50?

$a = p \cdot w$	Write percent equation.
$= 0.16 \cdot 27.50$	Substitute 0.16 for *p* and 27.50 for *w*.
$= 4.40$	Multiply.

So, the amount of the tip is $4.40.

On Your Own

7. **WHAT IF?** In Example 4, find the amount of a 20% tip on the food total.

4.1 Exercises

Vocabulary and Concept Check

1. **VOCABULARY** Write the percent equation in words.
2. **REASONING** A number n is 150% of number m. Is n *greater than, less than,* or *equal to* m? Explain your reasoning.
3. **DIFFERENT WORDS, SAME QUESTION** Which is different? Find "both" answers.

What number is 20% of 55?	55 is 20% of what number?
20% of 55 is what number?	0.2 • 55 is what number?

Practice and Problem Solving

Estimate the answer to the question using a model.

4. What number is 24% of 80?
5. 15 is what percent of 40?
6. 15 is 30% of what number?
7. What number is 120% of 70?
8. 20 is what percent of 52?
9. 48 is 75% of what number?

Write and solve an equation to answer the question.

1 10. 20% of 150 is what number?
11. 45 is what percent of 60?
2 12. 35% of what number is 35?
3 13. 32% of 25 is what number?
14. 29 is what percent of 20?
15. 0.5% of what number is 12?
16. What percent of 300 is 51?
17. 120% of what number is 102?

ERROR ANALYSIS Describe and correct the error in using the percent equation.

18. What number is 35% of 20?

$$\begin{aligned} a &= p \cdot w \\ &= 35 \cdot 20 \\ &= 700 \end{aligned}$$

19. 30 is 60% of what number?

$$\begin{aligned} a &= p \cdot w \\ &= 0.6 \cdot 30 \\ &= 18 \end{aligned}$$

20. **BASEBALL** A pitcher throws 75 pitches. Of these, 72% were strikes. How many strikes did the pitcher throw?
21. **FUNDRAISING** Your school raised 125% of its fundraising goal. The school raised \$6750. What was the goal?
22. **SURFBOARD** The sales tax on a surfboard is \$12. What is the percent of sales tax?

SALE \$240

PUZZLE **There were w signers of the Declaration of Independence. The youngest was Edward Rutledge, who was x years old. The oldest was Benjamin Franklin, who was y years old.**

23. x is 25% of 104. What was Rutledge's age?

24. 7 is 10% of y. What was Franklin's age?

25. w is 80% of y. How many signers were there?

26. y is what percent of $(w + y - x)$?

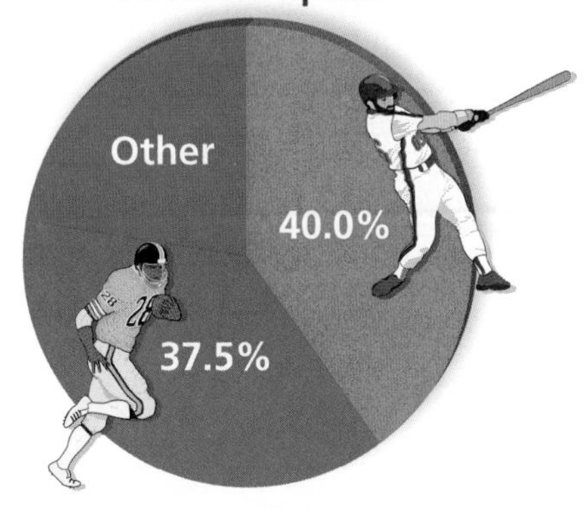

27. REASONING How can you tell whether the percent of a number will be *greater than*, *less than*, or *equal to* the number?

28. SURVEY In a survey, a group of students were asked their favorite sport. "Other" sports were chosen by 18 people.

a. How many students participated?

b. How many chose football?

29. WATER TANK Water tank A has a capacity of 550 gallons and is 66% full. Water tank B is 53% full. The ratio of the capacity of tank A to tank B is 11 : 15.

a. How much water is in tank A?

b. What is the capacity of tank B?

c. How much water is in tank B?

30. TRUE OR FALSE? Tell whether the statement is *true* or *false*. Explain your reasoning.

If W is 25% of Z, then $Z : W$ is 75 : 25.

31. Reasoning The table shows your test results for math class. What test score is needed on the last exam to earn 90% of the total points?

Test Score	Point Value
83%	100
91.6%	250
88%	150
?	300

Fair Game Review What you learned in previous grades & lessons

Simplify. Write as a decimal. *(Skills Review Handbook)*

32. $\frac{10-4}{10}$ **33.** $\frac{25-3}{25}$ **34.** $\frac{105-84}{84}$ **35.** $\frac{170-125}{125}$

36. MULTIPLE CHOICE There are 160 people in a grade. The ratio of boys to girls is 3 to 5. Which proportion can you use to find the number x of boys? *(Skills Review Handbook)*

Ⓐ $\frac{3}{8} = \frac{x}{160}$ Ⓑ $\frac{3}{5} = \frac{x}{160}$ Ⓒ $\frac{5}{8} = \frac{x}{160}$ Ⓓ $\frac{3}{5} = \frac{160}{x}$

4.2 Percents of Increase and Decrease

STANDARDS OF LEARNING
8.3

Essential Question What is a percent of decrease? What is a percent of increase?

1 ACTIVITY: Percent of Decrease

Each year in the Columbia River Basin, adult salmon swim up river to streams to lay eggs and hatch their young.

To go up the river, the adult salmon use fish ladders. But, to go down the river, the young salmon must pass through several dams.

There are electric turbines at each of the eight dams on the main stem of the Columbia and Snake Rivers. About 88% of the young salmon pass through these turbines unharmed.

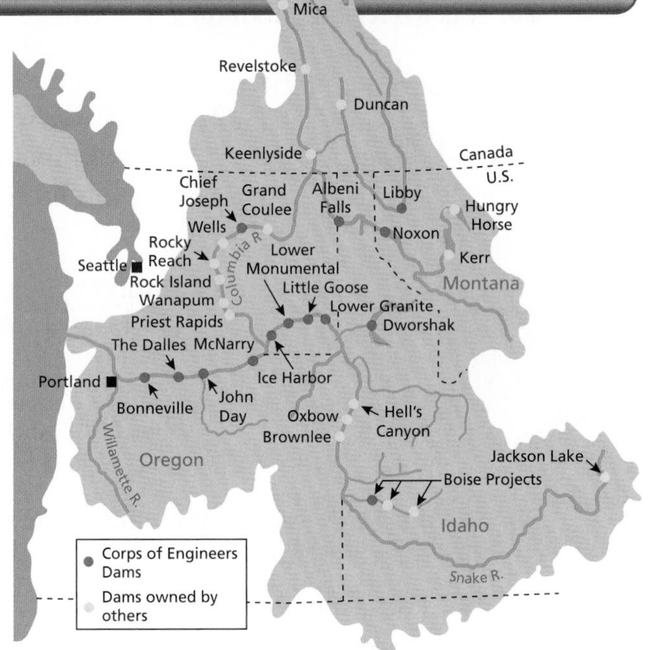

Copy and complete the table and the bar graph to show the number of young salmon that make it through the dams.

Dam	0	1	2	3	4	5	6	7	8
Salmon	1000	880	774						

88% of 1000 = 0.88 • 1000
= 880

88% of 880 = 0.88 • 880
= 774.4 ≈ 774

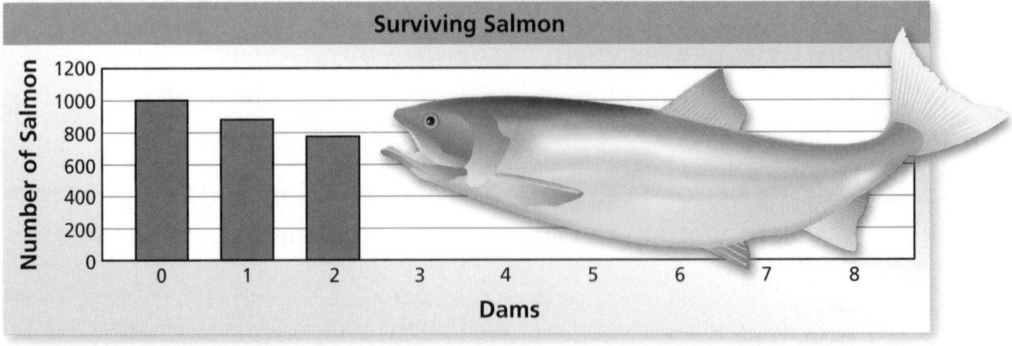

2 ACTIVITY: Percent of Increase

From 2000 to 2006, the population of Florida increased about 2% each year. Copy and complete the table and the bar graph using this pattern. Predict the population in 2015.

2006
Population
18,000,000

For 2007:

$$2\% \text{ of } 18{,}000{,}000 = 0.02 \cdot 18{,}000{,}000$$
$$= 360{,}000$$

$$18{,}000{,}000 + 360{,}000 = 18{,}360{,}000$$

(2006 Population) (Increase) (2007 Population)

Year	Population
2006	18,000,000
2007	18,360,000
2008	
2009	
2010	
2011	
2012	
2013	
2014	
2015	

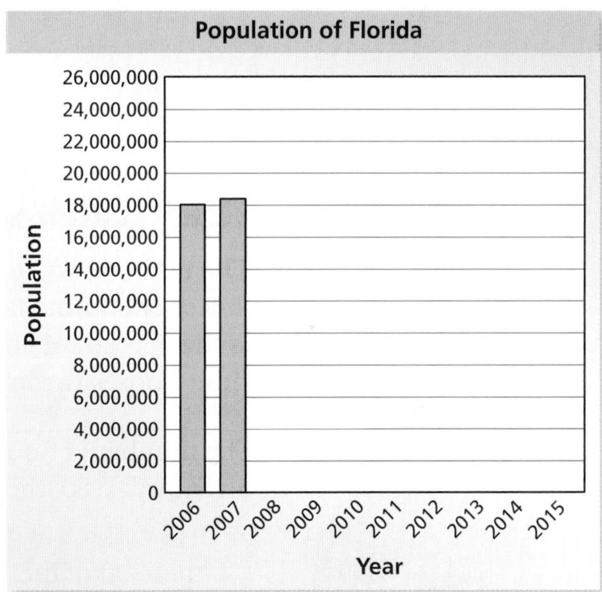

What Is Your Answer?

3. In Activity 1, by what percent does the number of young salmon decrease with each dam?
4. Describe real-life examples of a percent of decrease and a percent of increase.
5. **IN YOUR OWN WORDS** What is a percent of decrease? What is a percent of increase?

Practice Use what you learned about percent of increase and percent of decrease to complete Exercises 13–18 on page 172.

4.2 Lesson

Key Vocabulary
percent of change, *p. 170*
percent of increase, *p. 170*
percent of decrease, *p. 170*

A **percent of change** is the percent that a quantity changes from the original amount.

$$\text{percent of change} = \frac{\text{amount of change}}{\text{original amount}}$$

Percents of Increase and Decrease

When the original amount increases, the percent of change is called a **percent of increase**.

$$\text{percent of increase} = \frac{\text{new amount} - \text{original amount}}{\text{original amount}}$$

When the original amount decreases, the percent of change is called a **percent of decrease**.

$$\text{percent of decrease} = \frac{\text{original amount} - \text{new amount}}{\text{original amount}}$$

EXAMPLE 1 Finding a Percent of Increase

The table shows the number of hours you spent online last weekend. What is the percent of change in your online time from Saturday to Sunday?

Day	Hours Online
Saturday	2
Sunday	4.5

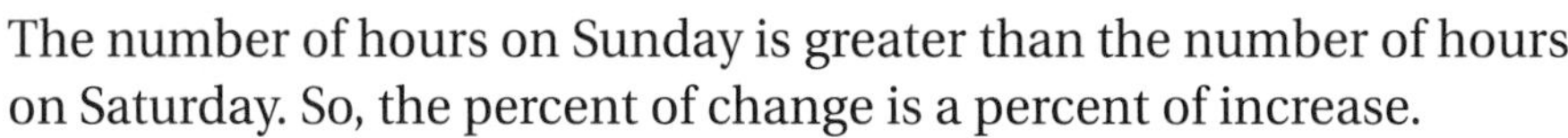

The number of hours on Sunday is greater than the number of hours on Saturday. So, the percent of change is a percent of increase.

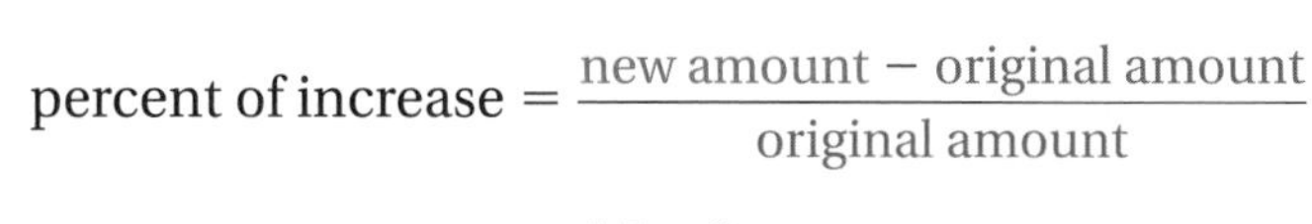

$$\text{percent of increase} = \frac{\text{new amount} - \text{original amount}}{\text{original amount}}$$

$$= \frac{4.5 - 2}{2} \qquad \text{Substitute.}$$

$$= \frac{2.5}{2} \qquad \text{Subtract.}$$

$$= 1.25, \text{ or } 125\% \qquad \text{Write as a percent.}$$

Your online time increased 125% from Saturday to Sunday.

On Your Own

Find the percent of change. Round to the nearest tenth of a percent, if necessary.

1. 10 inches to 25 inches
2. 57 people to 65 people

Multi-Language Glossary at BigIdeasMath.com.

EXAMPLE 2 Finding a Percent of Decrease

The bar graph shows a softball player's home run totals. What was the percent of change from 2007 to 2008?

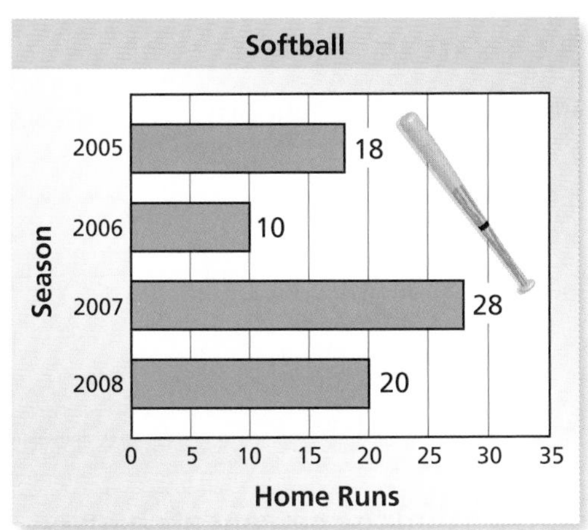

The number of home runs decreased from 2007 to 2008. So, the percent of change is a percent of decrease.

$$\text{percent of decrease} = \frac{\text{original amount} - \text{new amount}}{\text{original amount}}$$

$$= \frac{28 - 20}{28} \qquad \text{Substitute.}$$

$$= \frac{8}{28} \qquad \text{Subtract.}$$

$$\approx 0.286, \text{ or } 28.6\% \qquad \text{Write as a percent.}$$

The number of home runs decreased about 28.6%.

On Your Own

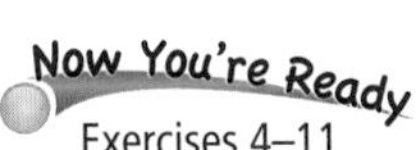

3. What was the percent of change from 2005 to 2006?

EXAMPLE 3 Standardized Test Practice

You have 250 songs on your MP3 player. You delete 20% of the songs. How many songs are left?

(A) 50 (B) 150 (C) 200 (D) 300

Find the amount of decrease.

$$20\% \text{ of } 250 = 0.2 \cdot 250 \qquad \text{Write as multiplication.}$$

$$= 50 \qquad \text{Multiply.}$$

The decrease is 50 songs. So, there are $250 - 50 = 200$ songs left.

The correct answer is (C).

On Your Own

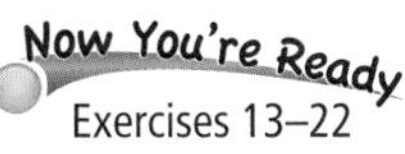

4. **WHAT IF?** After deleting the 50 songs in Example 3, you add 10% more songs. How many songs are on the MP3 player?

4.2 Exercises

Check It Out
Help with Homework
BigIdeasMath.com

Vocabulary and Concept Check

1. **VOCABULARY** How do you know whether a percent of change is a *percent of increase* or a *percent of decrease*?
2. **NUMBER SENSE** Without calculating, which has a greater percent of increase?
   - 5 bonus points on a 50-point exam
   - 5 bonus points on a 100-point exam
3. **WRITING** What does it mean to have a 100% decrease?

Practice and Problem Solving

Identify the percent of change as an *increase* or *decrease*. Then find the percent of change. Round to the nearest tenth of a percent, if necessary.

1 2 **4.** 12 inches to 36 inches

5. 75 people to 25 people

6. 50 pounds to 35 pounds

7. 24 songs to 78 songs

8. 10 gallons to 24 gallons

9. 72 paper clips to 63 paper clips

10. 16 centimeters to 44.2 centimeters

11. 68 miles to 42.5 miles

12. ERROR ANALYSIS Describe and correct the error in finding the percent increase from 18 to 26.

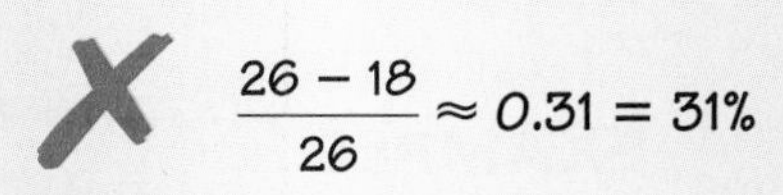
$\frac{26 - 18}{26} \approx 0.31 = 31\%$

Find the new amount.

3 **13.** 8 meters increased by 25%

14. 15 liters increased by 60%

15. 50 points decreased by 26%

16. 25 penalties decreased by 32%

17. 68 students increased by 125%

18. 1000 grams decreased by 94%

19. 62 kilograms decreased by 32%

20. 124 ounces decreased by 67%

21. ERROR ANALYSIS Describe and correct the error in using the percent of change to find a new amount.

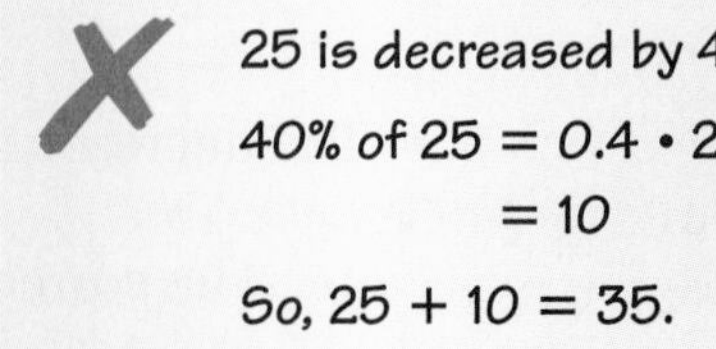
25 is decreased by 40%.
40% of 25 = 0.4 • 25
= 10
So, 25 + 10 = 35.

22. VIDEO GAME Last week, you finished Level 2 of a video game in 32 minutes. Today, you finish Level 2 in 28 minutes. What is your percent of change?

Identify the percent of change as an *increase* or *decrease*. Then find the percent of change. Round to the nearest tenth of a percent, if necessary.

23. $\frac{1}{4}$ to $\frac{1}{2}$ **24.** $\frac{4}{5}$ to $\frac{3}{5}$ **25.** $\frac{3}{8}$ to $\frac{7}{8}$ **26.** $\frac{5}{4}$ to $\frac{3}{8}$

27. CRITICAL THINKING Explain why a change from 20 to 40 is a 100% increase, but a change from 40 to 20 is a 50% decrease.

28. POPULATION The table shows population data for a community.

Year	Population
2000	118,000
2006	138,000

a. What is the percent of change from 2000 to 2006?

b. Use this percent of change to predict the population in 2012.

29. GEOMETRY Suppose the length and width of the sandbox are doubled.

a. Find the percent of change in the perimeter.

b. Find the percent of change in the area.

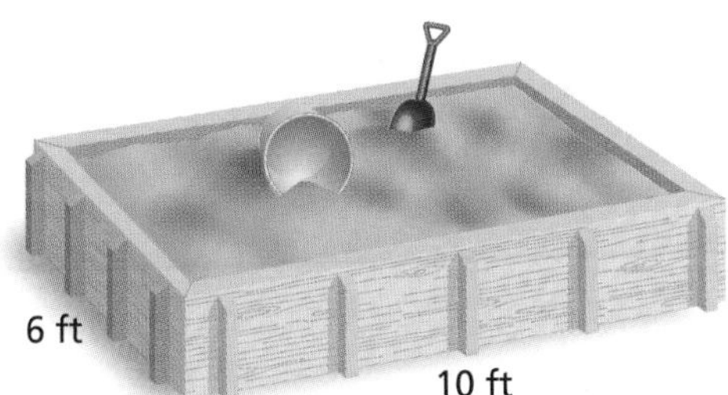

30. RUNNING Find the percent of change in the time to run a mile from June to September.

31. CRITICAL THINKING A number increases by 10% and then decreases by 10%. Will the result be *greater than*, *less than*, or *equal to* the original number? Explain.

32. DONATIONS Donations to an annual fundraiser are 15% greater this year than last year. Last year, donations were 10% greater than the year before. The amount raised this year is \$10,120. How much was raised 2 years ago?

33. Reasoning Forty students are in the science club. Of those, 45% are girls. This percent increases to 56% after new girls join the club. How many new girls join?

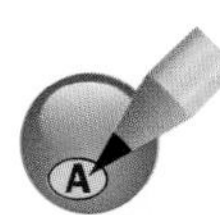

Fair Game Review What you learned in previous grades & lessons

Write and solve an equation to answer the question. *(Section 4.1)*

34. What number is 25% of 64? **35.** 39.2 is what percent of 112?

36. 5 is 5% of what number? **37.** 18 is 32% of what number?

38. MULTIPLE CHOICE The graph of which equation passes through $(-2, 3)$ and $(1, -3)$? *(Section 2.7)*

Ⓐ $y = -2x - 1$ Ⓑ $y = -\frac{1}{2}x - 1$ Ⓒ $y = \frac{1}{2}x - 1$ Ⓓ $y = 2x + 1$

4 Study Help

You can use a **summary triangle** to explain a concept. Here is an example of a summary triangle for finding a percent of a number.

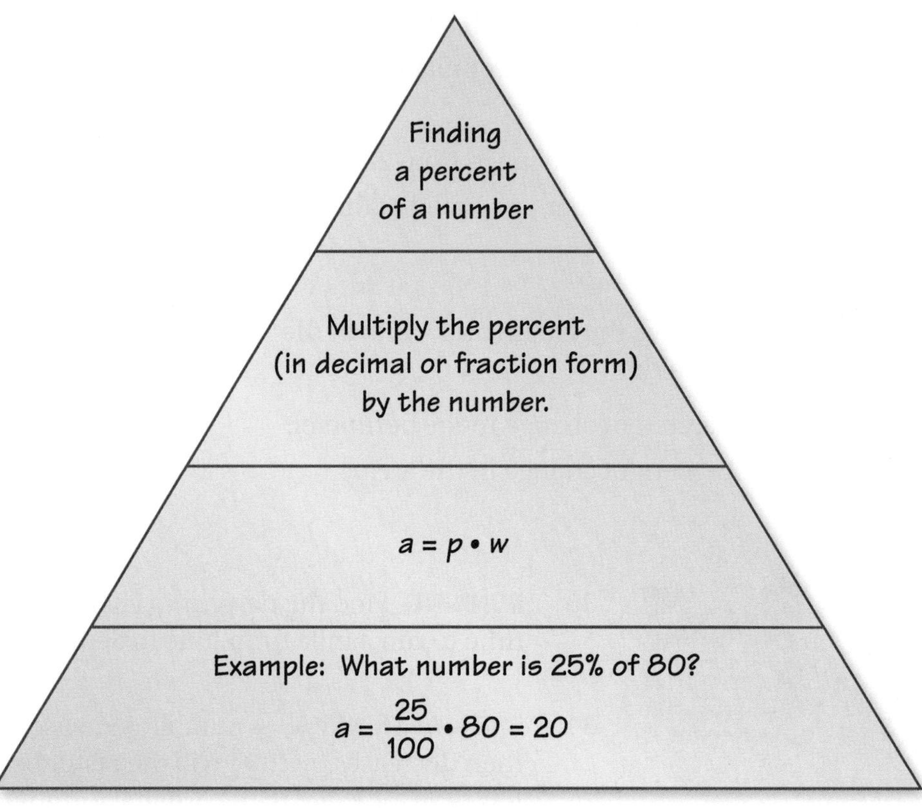

Finding a percent of a number
Multiply the percent (in decimal or fraction form) by the number.
$a = p \cdot w$
Example: What number is 25% of 80?
$a = \frac{25}{100} \cdot 80 = 20$

On Your Own

Make a summary triangle to help you study these topics.

1. finding the percent given a number and a part of the number
2. finding the number given a part of the number and a percent
3. percent of increase
4. percent of decrease

After you complete this chapter, make summary triangles for the following topics.

5. discount
6. markup
7. simple interest

"I'm posting my new summary triangle on my daily blog. Do you think it will get me more hits?"

4.1–4.2 Quiz

Write and solve an equation to answer the question. *(Section 4.1)*

1. What number is 28% of 75?
2. 42 is 21% of what number?
3. 36 is what percent of 45?
4. What number is 68% of 12?
5. 66 is what percent of 55?

Identify the percent of change as an *increase* or *decrease*. Then find the percent of change. Round to the nearest tenth of a percent, if necessary. *(Section 4.2)*

6. 8 inches to 24 inches
7. 300 miles to 210 miles
8. $42.00 to $16.00
9. 32 points to 46 points
10. 185 pounds to 153 pounds
11. 35 people to 70 people

12. **TEXT MESSAGES** You have 44 text messages in your inbox. How many messages can your cell phone hold? *(Section 4.1)*

13. **COMPLETIONS** A quarterback completed 68% of his passes in a game. He threw 25 passes. How many passes did the quarterback complete? *(Section 4.1)*

14. **QUIZ** You answered 14 questions correctly on a 15-question quiz. What percent did you receive on the quiz? Round to the nearest hundredth. *(Section 4.1)*

15. **FRUIT JUICE** The graph shows the amount of fruit juice available per person in the United States during a six-year period. *(Section 4.2)*

    a. What is the percent of change from 2002 to 2005?

    b. What is the percent of change from 2002 to 2003?

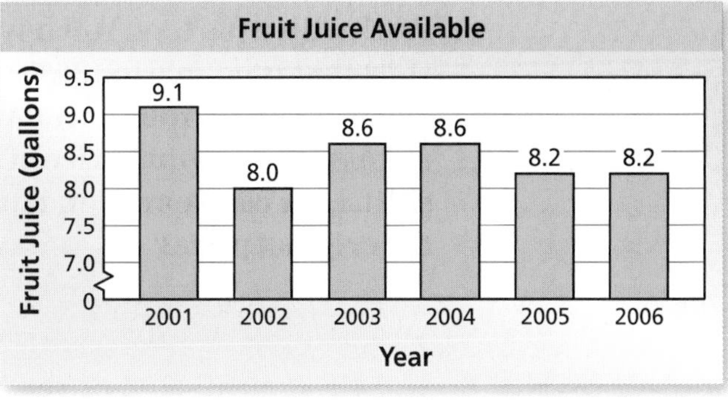

16. **CAR** A car loses 15% of its original value each year. After one year, a car has a value of $13,600. What is the original value of the car? *(Section 4.2)*

4.3 Discounts and Markups

STANDARDS OF LEARNING
8.3

Essential Question How can you find discounts and markups efficiently?

1 ACTIVITY: Comparing Discounts

Work with a partner. The same pair of sneakers is on sale at three stores. Which one is the best buy?

a. Regular Price: $45 **b.** Regular Price: $49 **c.** Regular Price: $39

a.

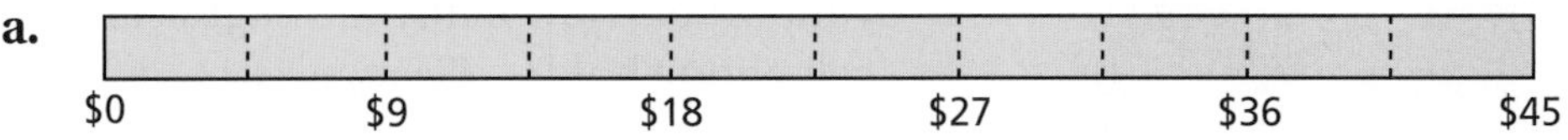

b.

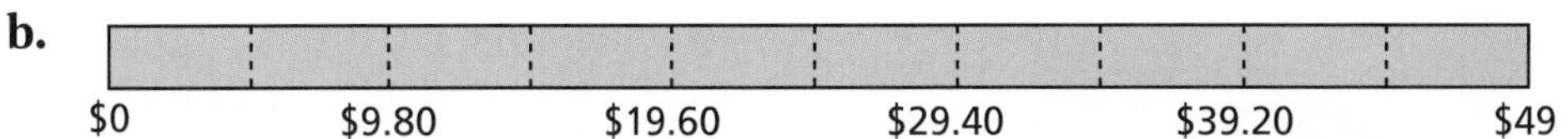

c.

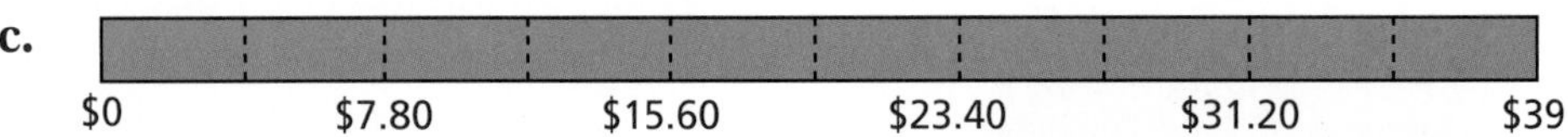

2 ACTIVITY: Finding the Original Price

Work with a partner. You buy a shirt that is on sale for 30% off. You pay $22.40. Your friend wants to know the original price of the shirt. How can your friend find the original price?

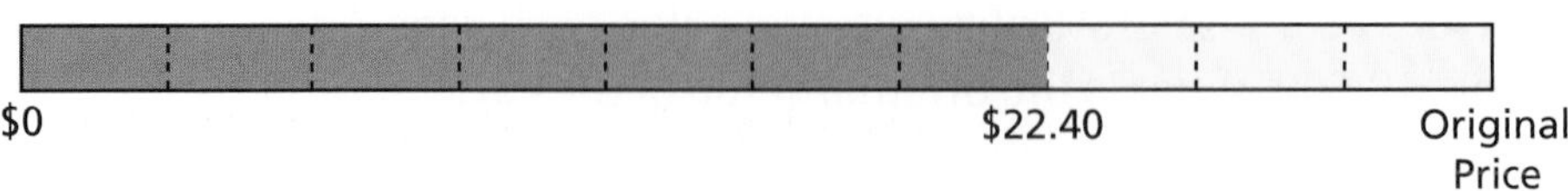

3 ACTIVITY: Calculating Markup

You own a small jewelry store. You increase the price of the jewelry by 125%.

Work with a partner. Use a model to estimate the selling price of the jewelry. Then use a calculator to find the selling price.

a. Your cost is $250.

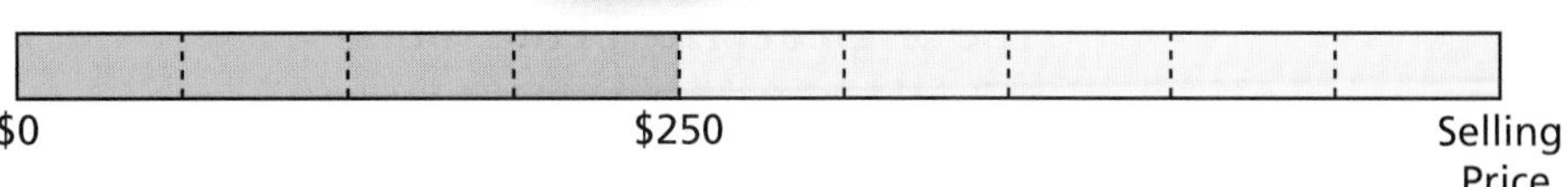

b. Your cost is $50.

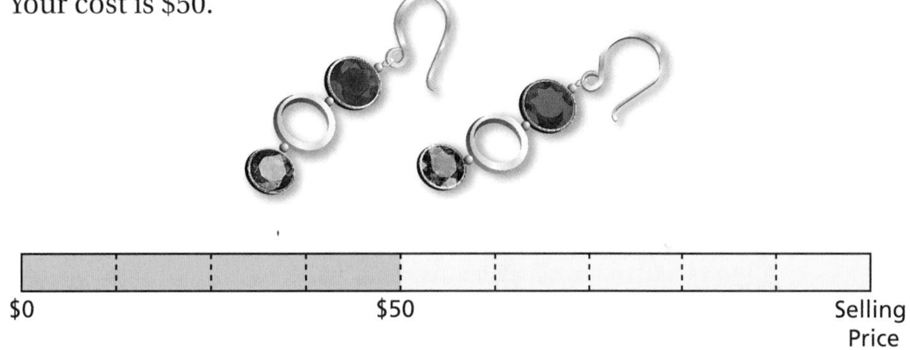

c. Your cost is $20.

What Is Your Answer?

4. IN YOUR OWN WORDS How can you find discounts and markups efficiently? Give examples of each.

Practice Use what you learned about discounts and markups to complete Exercises 4, 9, 14, and 18–20 on pages 180 and 181.

4.3 Lesson

Key Vocabulary
discount, *p. 178*
markup, *p. 178*

Key Ideas

Discounts

A **discount** is a decrease in the original price of an item.

Markups

To make a profit, stores charge more than what they pay. The increase from what the store pays to the selling price is called a **markup**.

EXAMPLE 1 Finding a Sale Price

The original price of the shorts is \$35. What is the sale price?

Method 1: First, find the discount. The discount is 25% of \$35.

$a = p \cdot w$ — Write percent equation.

$= 0.25 \cdot 35$ — Subsitute 0.25 for p and 35 for w.

$= 8.75$ — Multiply.

Next, find the sale price.

sale price	=	original price	−	discount
	=	35	−	8.75
	= 26.25			

∴ The sale price is \$26.25.

Method 2: First, find the percent of the original price.

$100\% - 25\% = 75\%$

Next, find the sale price.

sale price $= 75\%$ of \$35

$= 0.75 \cdot 35$

$= 26.25$

∴ The sale price is \$26.25. **Check**

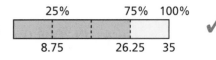

25% | 75% | 100%
8.75 | 26.25 | 35 ✓

Study Tip

A 25% discount is the same as paying 75% of the original price.

On Your Own

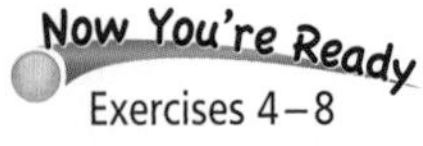

Exercises 4–8

1. The original price of a skateboard is \$50. The sale price includes a 20% discount. What is the sale price?

Multi-Language Glossary at BigIdeasMath.com.

EXAMPLE 2 Finding an Original Price

What is the original price of the shoes?

The sale price is
100% − 40% = 60%
of the original price.

Answer the question: 33 is 60% of what number?

$a = p \cdot w$	Write percent equation.
$33 = 0.6 \cdot w$	Substitute 33 for *a* and 0.6 for *p*.
$55 = w$	Divide each side by 0.6.

∴ The original price of the shoes is $55.

Check: 60% — 33; 100% — 55 ✓

EXAMPLE 3 Finding a Selling Price

A store pays $70 for a bicycle. The percent of markup is 20%. What is the selling price?

First, find the markup. The markup is 20% of $70.

$a = p \cdot w$	Write percent equation.
$= 0.20 \cdot 70$	Substitute 0.20 for *p* and 70 for *w*.
$= 14$	Multiply.

Next, find the selling price.

selling price = cost to store + markup

= 70 + 14

= 84

∴ The selling price is $84.

On Your Own

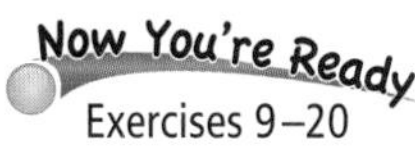

Exercises 9–20

2. The discount on a DVD is 50%. It is on sale for $10. What is the original price of the DVD?
3. A store pays $75 for an aquarium. The markup is 20%. What is the selling price?
4. Solve Example 3 using a different method.

4.3 Exercises

Vocabulary and Concept Check

1. **WRITING** Describe how to find the sale price of an item that has been discounted 25%.
2. **WRITING** Describe how to find the selling price of an item that has been marked up 110%.
3. **REASONING** Which would you rather pay? Explain your reasoning.

   a. 6% tax on a discounted price or 6% tax on the original price

   b. 30% markup on a $30 shirt or $30 markup on a $30 shirt

Practice and Problem Solving

Copy and complete the table.

		Original Price	Percent of Discount	Sale Price
1	4.	$80	20%	
	5.	$42	15%	
	6.	$120	80%	
	7.	$112	32%	
	8.	$69.80	60%	
2	9.		25%	$40
	10.		5%	$57
	11.		80%	$90
	12.		64%	$72
	13.		15%	$146.54
	14.	$60		$45
	15.	$82		$65.60
	16.	$95		$61.75

17. **YOU BE THE TEACHER** The cost to a store for an MP3 player is $60. The selling price is $105. A classmate says that the markup is 175% because $\frac{\$105}{\$60} = 1.75$. Is your classmate correct? If not, explain how to find the correct percent of markup.

Find the cost to store, percent of markup, or selling price.

3 **18.** Cost to store: \$70
Markup: 10%
Selling price: ▢

19. Cost to store: ▢
Markup: 75%
Selling price: \$63

20. Cost to store: \$75
Markup: ▢
Selling price: \$180

21. **SCOOTER** The scooter is on sale for 90% off the original price. Which of the methods can you use to find the sale price? Which method do you prefer? Explain.

- Multiply \$45.85 by 0.9.
- Multiply \$45.85 by 0.1.
- Multiply \$45.85 by 0.9, then add to \$45.85.
- Multiply \$45.85 by 0.9, then subtract from \$45.85.

22. **GAMING** You are shopping for a video game system.

a. At which store should you buy the system?

b. Store A has a weekend sale. How can this change your decision in part (a)?

Store	Cost to Store	Markup
A	\$162	40%
B	\$155	30%
C	\$160	25%

23. **STEREO** A \$129.50 stereo is discounted 40%. The next month, the sale price is discounted 60%. Is the stereo now "free"? If not, what is the sale price?

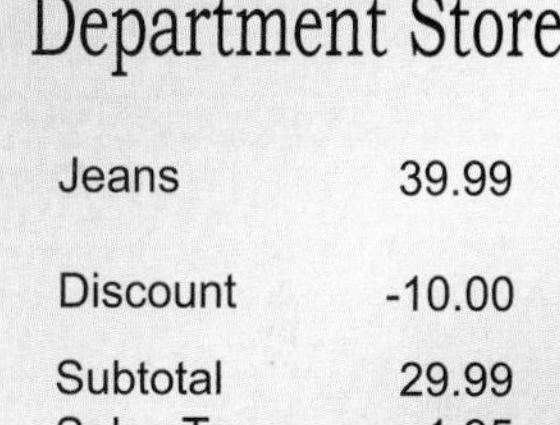

Department Store

Jeans	39.99
Discount	-10.00
Subtotal	29.99
Sales Tax	1.95
Total	31.94

Thank You

24. **CLOTHING** You buy a pair of jeans at a department store.

a. What is the percent of discount to the nearest percent?

b. What is the percent of sales tax to the nearest tenth of a percent?

c. The price of the jeans includes a 60% markup. After the discount, what is the percent of markup to the nearest percent?

25. Critical Thinking You buy a bicycle helmet for \$22.26, which includes 6% sales tax. The helmet is discounted 30% off the selling price. What is the original price?

Fair Game Review What you learned in previous grades & lessons

Evaluate. *(Skills Review Handbook)*

26. 2000(0.085)

27. 1500(0.04)(3)

28. 3200(0.045)(8)

29. **MULTIPLE CHOICE** Which measurement is greater than 1 meter? *(Skills Review Handbook)*

(A) 38 inches (B) 1 yard (C) 3.4 feet (D) 98 centimeters

4.4 Simple Interest

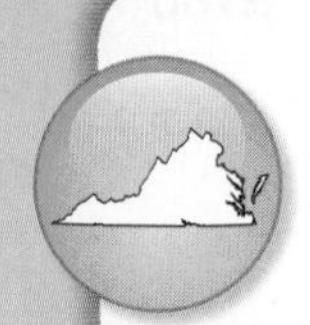

STANDARDS OF LEARNING

8.3

Essential Question How can you find the amount of simple interest earned on a savings account? How can you find the amount of interest owed on a loan?

Simple interest is money earned on a savings account or an investment. It can also be money you pay for borrowing money.

Write the annual interest rate in decimal form.

Simple Interest	=	Principal	×	Annual Interest Rate	×	Time
($)		($)		(% per yr)		(Years)

$I = Prt$

1 ACTIVITY: Finding Simple Interest

Work with a partner. You put $100 in a savings account. The account earns 6% simple interest per year. (a) Find the interest earned and the balance at the end of 6 months. (b) Copy and complete the table. Then make a bar graph that shows how the balance grows in 6 months.

a. $I = Prt$ — Write simple interest formula.

$= 100(0.06)\left(\frac{6}{12}\right)$ — Substitute values.

$= 3$ — Multiply.

At the end of 6 months, you earn $3 in interest. So, your balance is $100 + $3 = $103.

b.

Time	Interest	Balance
0 month	$0	$100
1 month		
2 months		
3 months		
4 months		
5 months		
6 months	$3	$103

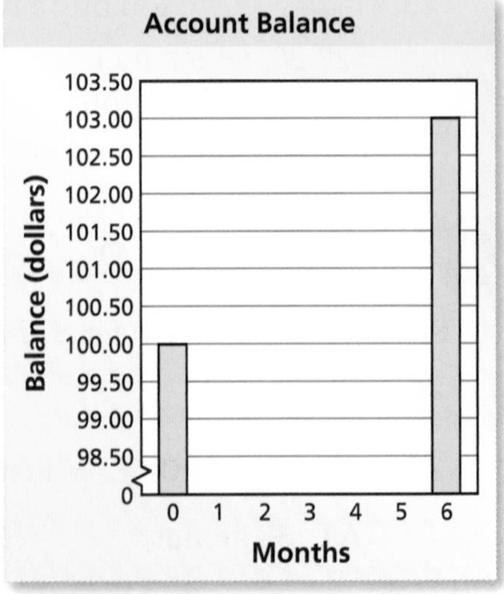

2 ACTIVITY: Financial Literacy

Work with a partner. Use the following information to write a report about credit cards. In the report, describe how a credit card works. Include examples that show the amount of interest paid each month on a credit card.

U.S. Credit Card Data

- A typical family in the United States owes about $5000 in credit card debt.
- A typical credit card interest rate is 18% to 20% per year. This is called the annual percentage rate.

3 ACTIVITY: The National Debt

Work with a partner. In 2010, the United States owed about $12 trillion in debt. The interest rate on the national debt is about 3% per year.

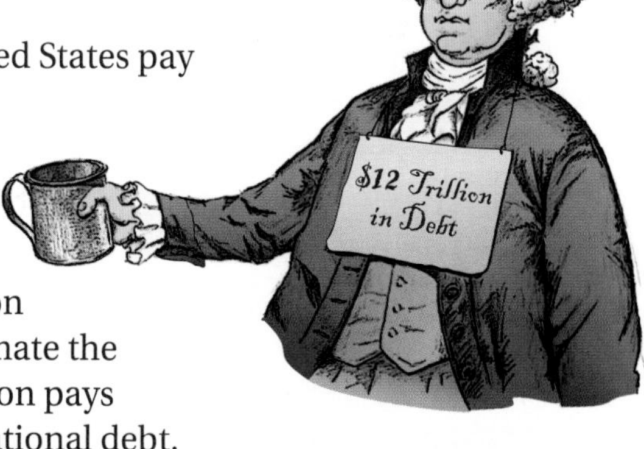

a. Write $12 trillion in decimal form. How many zeros does this number have?

b. How much interest does the United States pay each year on its national debt?

c. How much interest does the United States pay each day on its national debt?

d. The United States has a population of about 310 million people. Estimate the amount of interest that each person pays per year toward interest on the national debt.

What Is Your Answer?

4. **IN YOUR OWN WORDS** How can you find the amount of simple interest earned on a savings account? How can you find the amount of interest owed on a loan? Give examples with your answer.

Practice Use what you learned about simple interest to complete Exercises 4–7 on page 186.

4.4 Lesson

Check It Out
Lesson Tutorials
BigIdeasMath.com

Key Vocabulary
interest, *p. 184*
principal, *p. 184*
simple interest, *p. 184*

Interest is money paid or earned for the use of money. The **principal** is the amount of money borrowed or deposited.

Key Idea

Simple Interest

Words **Simple interest** is money paid or earned only on the principal.

Algebra

$$I = Prt$$

- I: Simple interest
- P: Principal
- r: Annual interest rate (in decimal form)
- t: Time (in years)

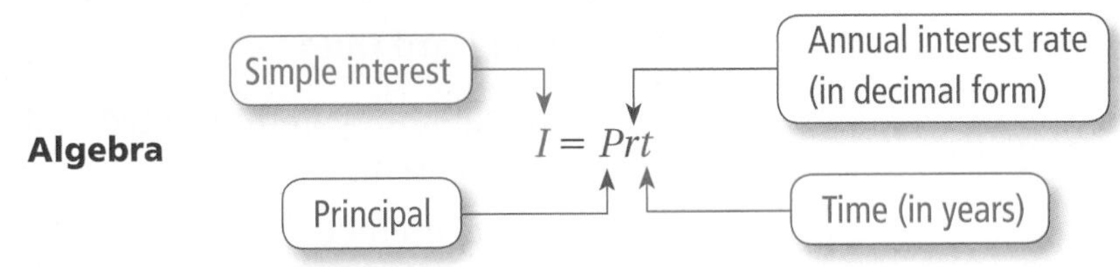

EXAMPLE 1 Finding Interest Earned

You put \$500 in a savings account. The account earns 3% simple interest per year. (a) What is the interest earned after 3 years? (b) What is the balance after 3 years?

a. $I = Prt$ — Write simple interest formula.

$= 500(0.03)(3)$ — Substitute 500 for *P*, 0.03 for *r*, and 3 for *t*.

$= 45$ — Multiply.

The interest earned is \$45 after 3 years.

b. To find the balance, add the interest to the principal.

So, the balance is \$500 + \$45 = \$545 after 3 years.

EXAMPLE 2 Finding an Annual Interest Rate

You put \$1000 in an account. The account earns \$100 simple interest in 4 years. What is the annual interest rate?

$I = Prt$ — Write simple interest formula.

$100 = 1000(r)(4)$ — Substitute 100 for *I*, 1000 for *P*, and 4 for *t*.

$100 = 4000r$ — Simplify.

$0.025 = r$ — Divide each side by 4000.

The annual interest rate of the account is 0.025, or 2.5%.

Multi-Language Glossary at BigIdeasMath.com.

On Your Own

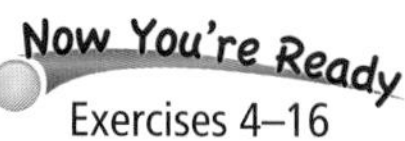
Now You're Ready
Exercises 4–16

1. In Example 1, what is the balance of the account after 9 months?
2. You put \$350 in an account. The account earns \$17.50 simple interest in 2.5 years. What is the annual interest rate?

EXAMPLE 3 Finding an Amount of Time

A bank offers three savings accounts. The simple interest rate is determined by the principal. How long does it take an account with a principal of \$800 to earn \$100 interest?

1.5% Less than \$500

2.0% \$500-\$5000

3.0% More than \$5000

The pictogram shows that the interest rate for a principal of \$800 is 2%.

$I = Prt$	Write simple interest formula.
$100 = 800(0.02)(t)$	Substitute 100 for I, 800 for P, and 0.02 for r.
$100 = 16t$	Simplify.
$6.25 = t$	Divide each side by 16.

∴ The account earns \$100 in interest in 6.25 years.

EXAMPLE 4 Finding Amount Paid on a Loan

You borrow \$600 to buy a violin. The simple interest rate is 15%. You pay off the loan after 5 years. How much do you pay for the loan?

$I = Prt$	Write simple interest formula.
$= 600(0.15)(5)$	Substitute 600 for P, 0.15 for r, and 5 for t.
$= 450$	Multiply.

To find the amount you pay, add the interest to the loan amount.

∴ So, you pay \$600 + \$450 = \$1050 for the loan.

On Your Own

Now You're Ready
Exercises 17–27

3. In Example 3, how long does it take an account with a principal of \$10,000 to earn \$750 interest?
4. **WHAT IF?** In Example 4, you pay off the loan after 2 years. How much money do you save?

4.4 Exercises

Vocabulary and Concept Check

1. **VOCABULARY** Define each variable in $I = Prt$.
2. **WRITING** In each situation, tell whether you would want a *higher* or *lower* interest rate. Explain your reasoning.

   a. You borrow money

   b. You open a savings account
3. **REASONING** An account earns 6% simple interest. You want to find the interest earned on \$200 after 8 months. What conversions do you need to make before you can use the formula $I = Prt$?

Practice and Problem Solving

An account earns simple interest. (a) Find the interest earned. (b) Find the balance of the account.

1 4. \$600 at 5% for 2 years

5. \$1500 at 4% for 5 years

6. \$350 at 3% for 10 years

7. \$1800 at 6.5% for 30 months

8. \$700 at 8% for 6 years

9. \$1675 at 4.6% for 4 years

10. \$925 at 2% for 2.4 years

11. \$5200 at 7.36% for 54 months

12. **ERROR ANALYSIS** Describe and correct the error in finding the simple interest earned on \$500 at 6% for 18 months.

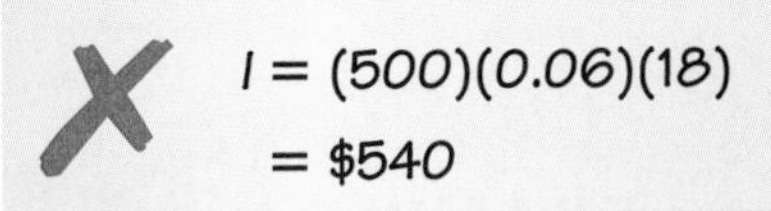

Find the annual simple interest rate.

2 13. $I = \$24, P = \$400, t = 2$ years

14. $I = \$562.50, P = \$1500, t = 5$ years

15. $I = \$54, P = \$900, t = 18$ months

16. $I = \$160.67, P = \$2000, t = 8$ months

Find the amount of time.

3 17. $I = \$30, P = \$500, r = 3\%$

18. $I = \$720, P = \$1000, r = 9\%$

19. $I = \$54, P = \$800, r = 4.5\%$

20. $I = \$450, P = \$2400, r = 7.5\%$

21. **BANKING** A savings account earns 5% annual simple interest. The principal is \$1200. What is the balance after 4 years?

22. **SAVINGS** You put \$400 in an account. The account earns \$18 simple interest in 9 months. What is the annual interest rate?

23. **CD** You put \$3000 in a CD (certificate of deposit) at the promotional rate. How long will it take to earn \$336 in interest?

Find the amount paid for the loan.

④ **24.** \$1500 at 9% for 2 years

25. \$2000 at 12% for 3 years

26. \$2400 at 10.5% for 5 years

27. \$4800 at 9.9% for 4 years

Copy and complete the table.

	Principal	Interest Rate	Time	Simple Interest
28.	\$12,000	4.25%	5 years	
29.		6.5%	18 months	\$828.75
30.	\$15,500	8.75%		\$5425.00
31.	\$18,000		54 months	\$4252.50

32. **ZOO** A family charges a trip to the zoo on a credit card. The simple interest rate is 12%. The charges are paid after 3 months. What is the total amount paid for the trip?

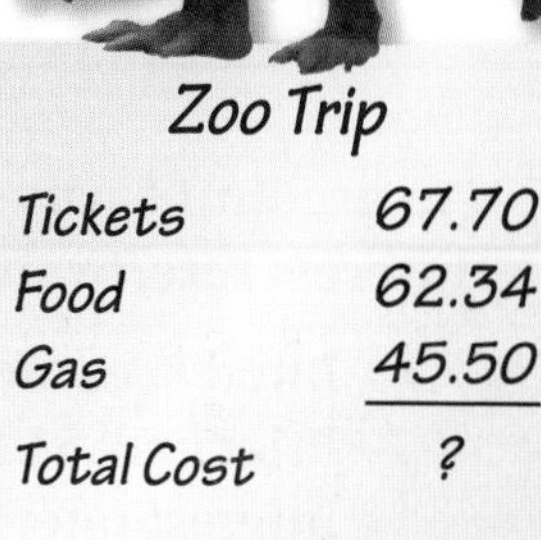

33. **MONEY MARKET** You deposit \$5000 in an account earning 7.5% simple interest. How long will it take for the balance of the account to be \$6500?

34. **LOANS** A music company offers a loan to buy a drum set for \$1500. What is the monthly payment?

35. **REASONING** How many years will it take for \$2000 to double at a simple interest rate of 8%? Explain how you found your answer.

36. **LOANS** You have two loans, for 2 years each. The total interest for the two loans is \$138. On the first loan, you pay 7.5% simple interest on a principal of \$800. On the second loan, you pay 3% simple interest. What is the principal for the second loan?

37. Critical Thinking You put \$500 in an account that earns 4% annual interest. The interest earned each year is added to the principal to create a new principal. Find the total amount in your account after each year for 3 years.

Fair Game Review What you learned in previous grades & lessons

Write the next three terms of the arithmetic sequence. *(Skills Review Handbook)*

38. $-5, 3, 11, 19, \ldots$

39. $100, 85, 70, 55, \ldots$

40. **MULTIPLE CHOICE** What is the solution of $4x + 5 = -11$? *(Section 1.2)*

Ⓐ -4 Ⓑ -1.5 Ⓒ 1.5 Ⓓ 4

4.3–4.4 Quiz

Find the price, discount, markup, or cost to store. *(Section 4.3)*

1. Original price: $30
Discount: 10%
Sale price: ?

2. Original price: $55
Discount: ?
Sale price: $46.75

3. Original price: ?
Discount: 75%
Sale price: $74.75

4. Cost to store: $152
Markup: 50%
Selling price: ?

5. Cost to store: $20
Markup: ?
Selling price: $32

6. Cost to store: ?
Markup: 80%
Selling price: $21.60

An account earns simple interest. Find the interest earned, principal, interest rate, or time. *(Section 4.4)*

7. Interest earned: ?
Principal: $1200
Interest rate: 2%
Time: 5 years

8. Interest earned: $25
Principal: $500
Interest rate: 5%
Time: ?

9. Interest earned: $76
Principal: $800
Interest rate: ?
Time: 2 years

10. Interest earned: $119.88
Principal: ?
Interest rate: 3.6%
Time: 3 years

11. DIGITAL CAMERA A digital camera costs $229. The camera is on sale for 30% off and you have a coupon for an additional 15% off the original price. What is the final price? *(Section 4.3)*

12. WATER SKIS The original price of the water skis was $200. What is the percent of discount? *(Section 4.3)*

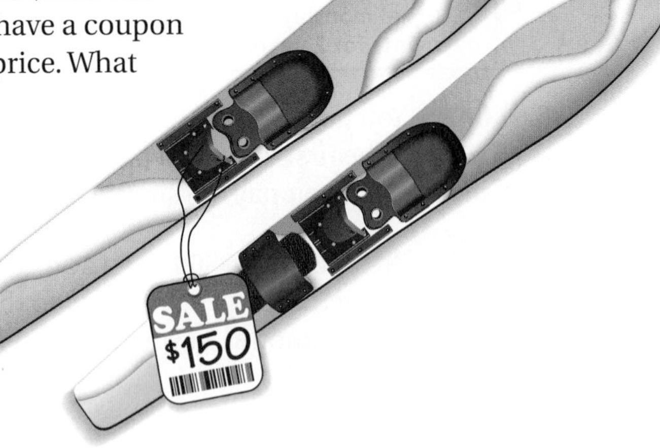

2 Ways to Own:
1. $75 cash back with 3.5% simple interest
2. No interest for 2 years

13. SAXOPHONE A saxophone costs $1200. A store offers two loan options. Which option saves more money if you pay the loan in 2 years? *(Section 4.4)*

14. LOAN You borrow $200. The simple interest rate is 12%. You pay off the loan after 2 years. How much do you pay for the loan? *(Section 4.4)*

4 Chapter Review

Check It Out
Vocabulary Help
BigIdeasMath.com

Review Key Vocabulary

percent, *p. 164*
percent of change, *p. 170*
percent of increase, *p. 170*
percent of decrease, *p. 170*
discount, *p. 178*
markup, *p. 178*
interest, *p. 184*
principal, *p. 184*
simple interest, *p. 184*

Review Examples and Exercises

4.1 The Percent Equation *(pp. 162–167)*

What number is 72% of 25?

$a = p \cdot w$ — Write percent equation.

$= 0.72 \cdot 25$ — Substitute 0.72 for p and 25 for w.

$= 18$ — Multiply.

So, 72% of 25 is 18.

28 is what percent of 70?

$a = p \cdot w$ — Write percent equation.

$28 = p \cdot 70$ — Substitute 28 for a and 70 for w.

$0.4 = p$ — Divide each side by 70.

Because 0.4 = 40%, 28 is 40% of 70.

22.1 is 26% of what number?

$a = p \cdot w$ — Write percent equation.

$22.1 = 0.26 \cdot w$ — Substitute 22.1 for a and 0.26 for p.

$85 = w$ — Divide each side by 0.26.

So, 22.1 is 26% of 85.

Exercises

Write and solve an equation to answer the question.

1. What number is 24% of 25?
2. 9 is what percent of 20?
3. 85% of what number is 10.2?
4. 83% of 20 is what number?
5. **PARKING** 15% of the school parking spaces are handicap spaces. The school has 18 handicap spaces. How many parking spaces are there?

4.2 Percents of Increase and Decrease (pp. 168–173)

The table shows the number of skim boarders at a beach on Saturday and Sunday. What was the percent of change in boarders from Saturday to Sunday?

The number of skim boarders on Sunday is less than the number of skim boarders on Saturday. So, the percent of change is a percent of decrease.

Day	Number of Skim Boarders
Saturday	12
Sunday	9

$$\text{percent of decrease} = \frac{\text{original amount} - \text{new amount}}{\text{original amount}}$$

$= \frac{12 - 9}{12}$ Substitute.

$= \frac{3}{12}$ Subtract.

$= 0.25 = 25\%$ Write as a percent.

∴ The number of skim boarders decreased by 25% from Saturday to Sunday.

Exercises

Identify the percent of change as an *increase* or *decrease*. Then find the percent of change. Round to the nearest tenth of a percent, if necessary.

6. 6 yards to 36 yards

7. 6 hits to 3 hits

8. 120 meals to 52 meals

9. 35 words to 115 words

4.3 Discounts and Markups (pp. 176–181)

What is the original price of the tennis racquet?

The sale price is 100% − 30% = 70% of the original price.

Answer the question: 21 is 70% of what number?

$a = p \cdot w$ Write percent equation.

$21 = 0.7 \cdot w$ Substitute 21 for a and 0.7 for p.

$30 = w$ Divide each side by 0.7.

∴ The original price of the tennis racquet is $30.

Exercises

Find the price.

10. Original price: $50
Discount: 15%
Sale price: ?

11. Original price: ?
Discount: 20%
Sale price: $75

4.4 Simple Interest (pp. 182–187)

You put $200 in a savings account. The account earns 2% simple interest per year.

a. What is the interest after 4 years?

b. What is the balance after 4 years?

a. $I = Prt$ — Write simple interest formula.

$= 200(0.02)(4)$ — Substitute 200 for *P*, 0.02 for *r*, and 4 for *t*.

$= 16$ — Multiply.

∴ The interest earned is $16 after 4 years.

b. The balance is the principal plus the interest.

∴ So, the balance is $200 + $16 = $216 after 4 years.

You put $500 in an account. The account earns $55 simple interest in 5 years. What is the annual interest rate?

$I = Prt$ — Write simple interest formula.

$55 = 500(r)(5)$ — Substitute 55 for *I*, 500 for *P*, and 5 for *t*.

$55 = 2500r$ — Simplify.

$0.022 = r$ — Divide each side by 2500.

∴ The annual interest rate of the account is 0.022, or 2.2%.

Exercises

An account earns simple interest.

a. Find the interest earned.

b. Find the balance of the account.

12. $300 at 4% for 3 years

13. $2000 at 3.5% for 4 years

Find the annual simple interest rate.

14. $I = \$17, P = \$500, t = 2$ years

15. $I = \$426, P = \$1200, t = 5$ years

Find the amount of time.

16. $I = \$60, P = \$400, r = 5\%$

17. $I = \$237.90, P = \$1525, r = 2.6\%$

18. SAVINGS You put $100 in an account. The account earns $2 simple interest in 6 months. What is the annual interest rate?

4 Chapter Test

Write and solve an equation to answer the question.

1. 16% of 150 is what number?
2. 10 is 40% of what number?
3. 27 is what percent of 75?
4. What number is 35% of 56?

Identify the percent of change as an *increase* or *decrease*. Then find the percent of change. Round to the nearest tenth of a percent, if necessary.

5. 4 strikeouts to 10 strikeouts
6. $24.00 to $18.00

Find the price, discount, or markup.

7. Original price: $15
   Discount: 5%
   Sale price: ?
8. Original price: $189
   Discount: ?
   Sale price: $75.60
9. Cost to store: $15
   Markup: ?
   Selling price: $24.75
10. Cost to store: $5.50
    Markup: 75%
    Selling price: ?

An account earns simple interest. Find the interest earned, principal, interest rate, or time.

11. Interest earned: ?
    Principal: $450
    Interest rate: 6%
    Time: 8 years
12. Interest earned: $27
    Principal: ?
    Interest rate: 1.5%
    Time: 2 years
13. Interest earned: $116.25
    Principal: $1550
    Interest rate: ?
    Time: 9 months
14. Interest earned: $45.60
    Principal: $2400
    Interest rate: 3.8%
    Time: ?

15. **MOVIE PREVIEWS** There are eight previews before a movie. Seventy-five percent of the previews are for comedies. How many previews are for comedies?

16. **BOOK** What was the original price of the book?

17. **TEXT MESSAGES** The cost of a text message increases from $0.10 per message to $0.25 per message. What is the percent increase in the cost of sending a text message?

18. **INVESTMENT** You put $800 in an account that earns 4% simple interest. Find the total amount in your account after each year for 3 years.

4 Standardized Test Practice

Test-Taking Strategy
Read Question Before Answering

About 0.4 of cats are polydactyl. Of 80 cats, how many have 5 toes per paw?
Ⓐ 32 Ⓑ 30% Ⓒ 48 Ⓓ 58

Not fair. I'm a cartoon character and I have only 4 toes per paw.

"Keep on your toes and read the questions before choosing your answer."

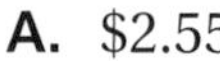

1. A movie theater offers 30% off the price of a movie ticket to students from your school. The regular price of a movie ticket is \$8.50. What is the discounted price that you would pay for a ticket?

A. \$2.55 **C.** \$5.95

B. \$5.50 **D.** \$8.20

2. You are comparing the prices of four boxes of cereal. Two of the boxes contain free extra cereal.

- Box F costs \$3.59 and contains 16 ounces.
- Box G costs \$3.79 and contains 16 ounces, plus an additional 10% for free.
- Box H costs \$4.00 and contains 500 grams.
- Box I costs \$4.69 and contains 500 grams, plus an additional 20% for free.

Which box has the least unit cost? (1 ounce = 28.35 grams)

F. Box F **H.** Box H

G. Box G **I.** Box I

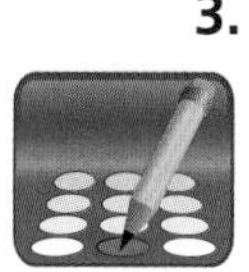

3. James is getting ready for wrestling season. As part of his preparation, he plans to lose 5% of his body weight. James currently weighs 160 pounds. How much will he weigh, in pounds, after he loses 5% of his weight?

4. Which proportion represents the problem below?

"17% of a number is 43. What is the number?"

A. $\frac{17}{43} = \frac{n}{100}$ **C.** $\frac{n}{43} = \frac{17}{100}$

B. $\frac{n}{17} = \frac{43}{100}$ **D.** $\frac{43}{n} = \frac{17}{100}$

The graph below shows how many calories c are burned during m minutes of playing basketball. Use the graph for Exercises 5 and 6.

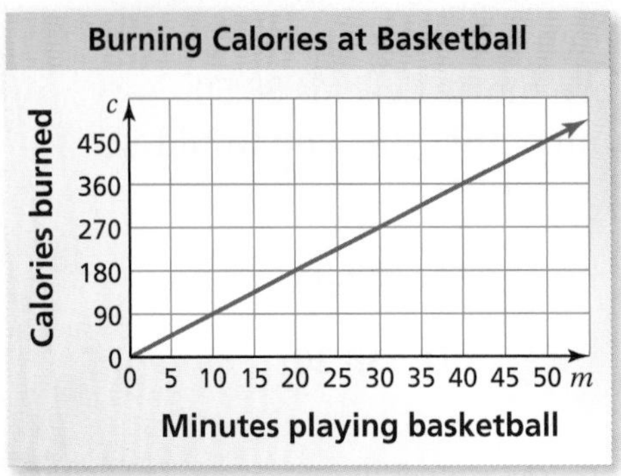

5. How many calories are burned in 25 minutes?

F. 180 cal

G. 185 cal

H. 225 cal

I. 270 cal

6. Which equation fits the data given in the graph?

A. $c = 9m$

B. $c = 90m$

C. $c = m + 80$

D. $m = 9c$

7. The line shown in the graph below has a slope of -3. What is the equation of the line?

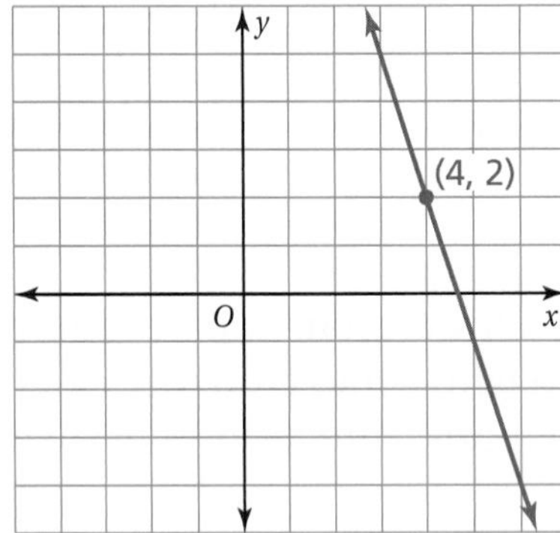

F. $y = 3x - 10$

G. $y = -3x + 10$

H. $y = -3x + 14$

I. $y = -3x - 14$

8. A lighting store is holding a clearance sale. The store is offering discounts on all the lamps it sells. As the sale progresses, the store will increase the percent of discount it is offering.

You want to buy a lamp that has an original price of \$40. You will buy the lamp when its price is marked down to \$10. What percent discount will you have received?

9. A student scored 600 the first time she took the mathematics portion of her college entrance exam. The next time she took the exam, she scored 660. Her second score represents what percent increase over her first score?

A. 9.1% **C.** 39.6%

B. 10% **D.** 60%

10. Solve the formula below for I.

$$A = P + PI$$

F. $I = A - 2P$ **H.** $I = A - \frac{P}{P}$

G. $I = \frac{A}{P} - P$ **I.** $I = \frac{A - P}{P}$

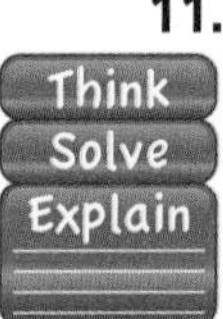

11. You are planning to deposit \$4000 in an account that earns 5% simple interest per year. You will not make any other deposits or withdrawals.

Part A How long would it take for your account to contain \$4500? Show your work and explain your reasoning.

Part B You would like the account to contain \$5100 after 4 years. Would your initial \$4000 deposit be large enough? Show your work and explain your reasoning.

12. Brad was solving the equation in the box shown.

$$-3(2 - 5w) = -45$$
$$-6 + 15w = -45$$
$$9w = -45$$
$$\frac{9w}{9} = \frac{-45}{9}$$
$$w = -5$$

What should Brad do to correct the error that he made?

A. Distribute -3 to get $6 - 15w$.

B. Distribute -3 to get $-6 - 15w$.

C. Add 6 to both sides to get $15w = -51$.

D. Add 6 to both sides to get $15w = -39$.

13. What is the slope of the line given by $3x - 6y = 33$?

F. -3 **H.** $\frac{1}{2}$

G. $-\frac{1}{2}$ **I.** 3

5 Angles and Polygons

"Start with any triangle."

"Tear off the angles. You can always rearrange the angles so that they form a straight line."

"What does that prove?"

"Let's use shadows and similar triangles to indirectly measure the height of the giant hyena standing right behind you."

What You Learned Before

"I just remember that C comes before S and 90 comes before 180. That makes it easy."

Finding Unknown Measures in Similar Polygons

Example 1 **The two triangles are similar. Find the value of *x*.**

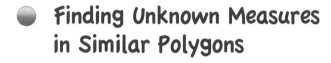

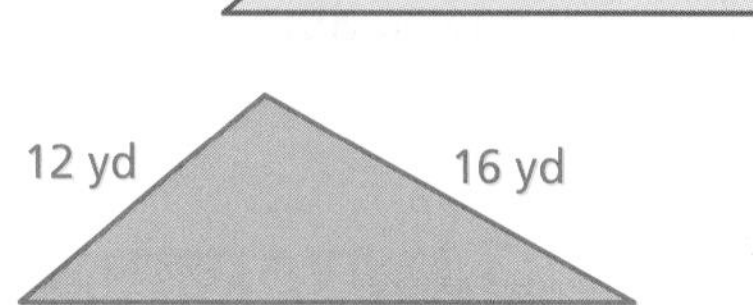

$\frac{16}{18} = \frac{12}{x}$	Write a proportion.
$16x = 216$	Use Cross Products Property.
$x = 13.5$	Divide each side by 16.

So, x is 13.5 yards.

Example 2 **The two quadrilaterals are similar. The ratio of their perimeters is 4 : 5. Find the value of *x*.**

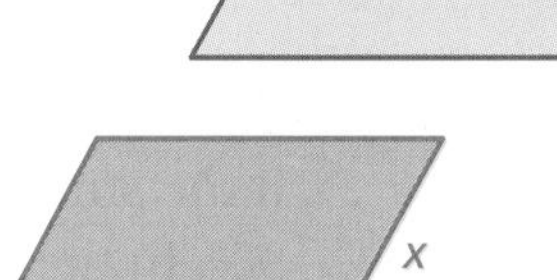

$\frac{4}{5} = \frac{x}{25}$	Write a proportion.
$100 = 5x$	Use Cross Products Property.
$20 = x$	Divide each side by 5.

So, x is 20 centimeters.

Try It Yourself

The polygons are similar. Find the value of *x*.

1.

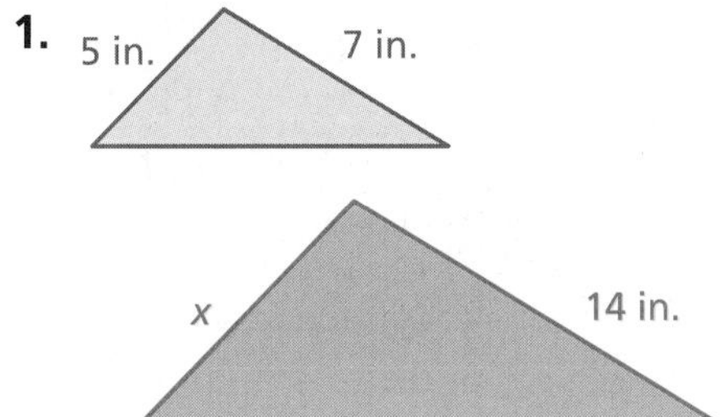

2. The ratio of the perimeters is $2:1$.

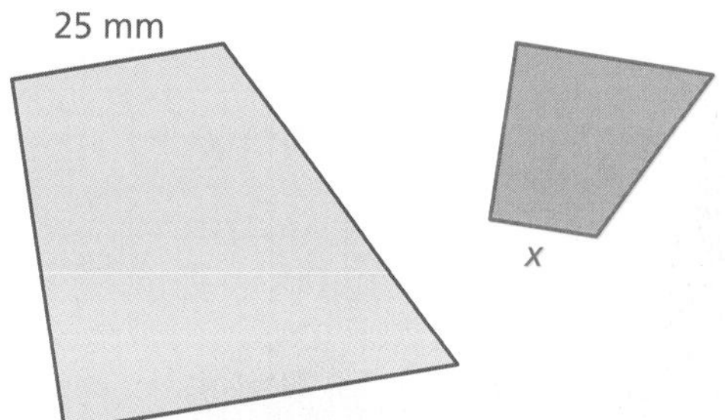

5.1 Classifying Angles

STANDARDS OF LEARNING
8.6

Essential Question How can you classify two angles as complementary or supplementary?

Classification of Angles

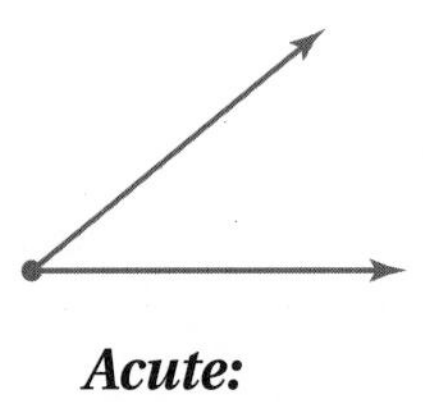

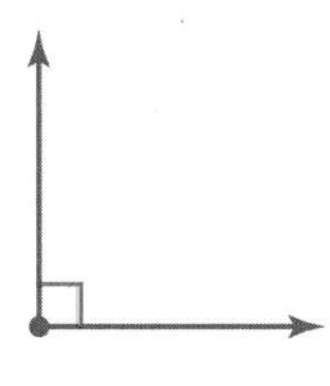

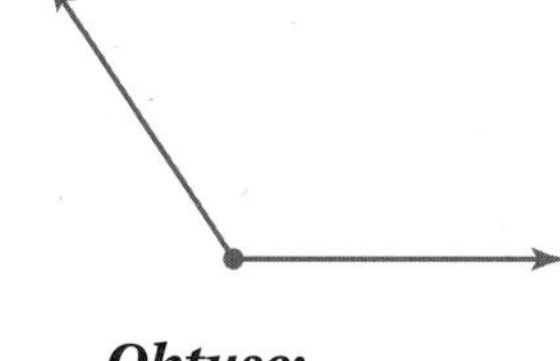

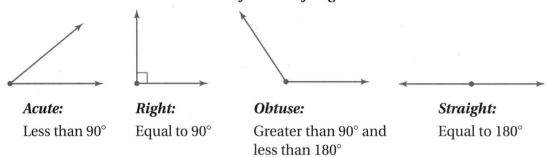

Acute: Less than 90°

Right: Equal to 90°

Obtuse: Greater than 90° and less than 180°

Straight: Equal to 180°

1 ACTIVITY: Complementary and Supplementary Angles

Work with a partner.

- **Copy and complete each table.**
- **Graph each function. Is the function linear?**
- **Write an equation for *y* as a function of *x*.**
- **Describe the domain of each function.**

a. Two angles are **complementary** if the sum of their measures is 90°. In the table, *x* and *y* are complementary.

x	15°	30°	45°	60°	75°
y					

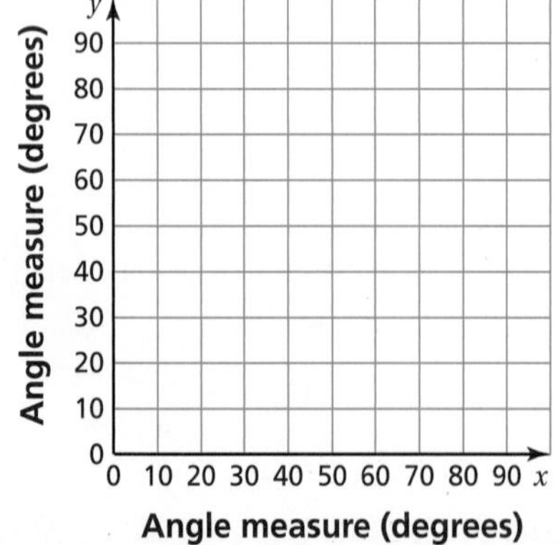

b. Two angles are **supplementary** if the sum of their measures is 180°. In the table, *x* and *y* are supplementary.

x	30°	60°	90°	120°	150°
y					

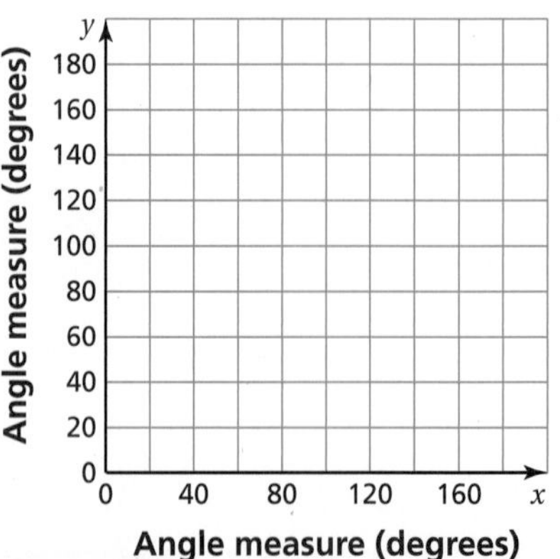

2 ACTIVITY: Exploring Rules About Angles

Work with a partner. Copy and complete each sentence with *always*, *sometimes*, or *never*.

a. If x and y are complementary angles, then both x and y are ________ acute.

b. If x and y are supplementary angles, then x is ________ acute.

c. If x is a right angle, then x is ________ acute.

3 ACTIVITY: Naming Angles

Some angles, such as $\angle A$, can be named by a single letter. When this does not clearly identify an angle, you should use three letters, as follows.

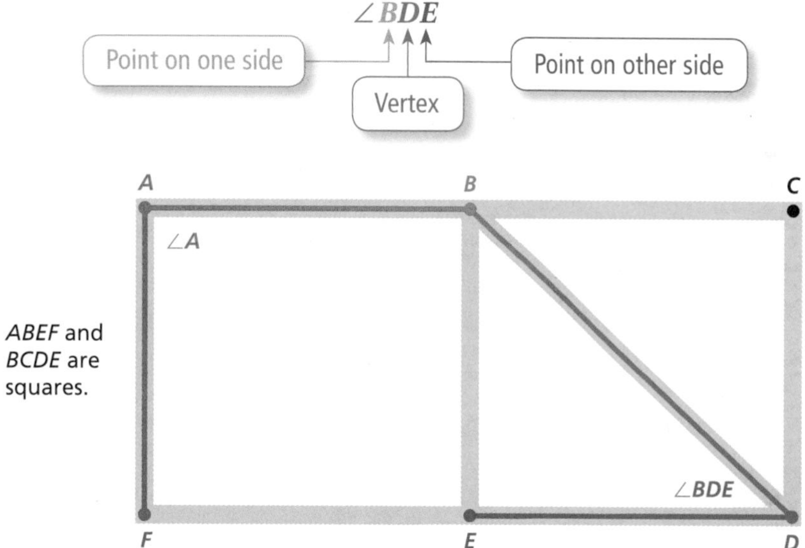

Work with a partner.

a. Name all pairs of complementary angles in the diagram above.

b. Name all pairs of supplementary angles in the diagram above.

What Is Your Answer?

4. **IN YOUR OWN WORDS** How can you classify two angles as complementary or supplementary? Give examples of each type.

5. Find examples of real-life objects that use complementary and supplementary angles. Make a drawing of each object and approximate the degree measure of each angle.

Practice Use what you learned about classifying angles to complete Exercises 3–5 on page 202.

Key Vocabulary
complementary angles, *p. 200*
supplementary angles, *p. 200*
adjacent angles, *p. 201*
vertical angles, *p. 201*

Key Ideas

Complementary Angles

Words Two angles are **complementary angles** if the sum of their measures is 90°.

Examples

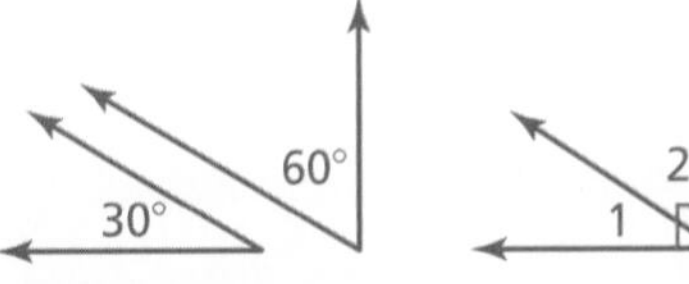

$\angle 1$ and $\angle 2$ are complementary angles.

Supplementary Angles

Words Two angles are **supplementary angles** if the sum of their measures is 180°.

Examples

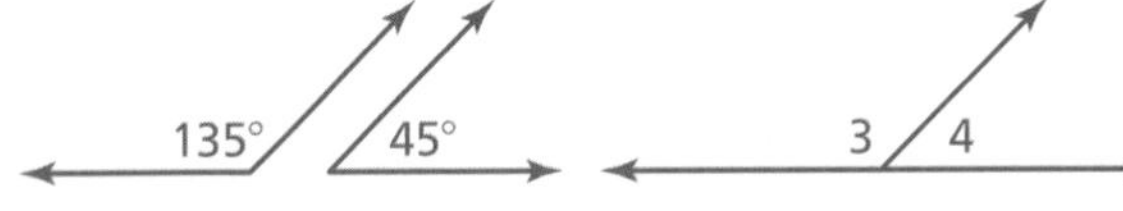

$\angle 3$ and $\angle 4$ are supplementary angles.

EXAMPLE 1 Classifying Pairs of Angles

Tell whether the angles are *complementary*, *supplementary*, or *neither*.

a. $70° + 110° = 180°$

So, the angles are supplementary.

b.

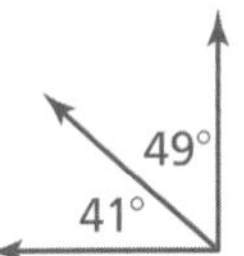

$41° + 49° = 90°$

So, the angles are complementary.

c. $128° + 62° = 190°$

So, the angles are *neither* complementary nor supplementary.

On Your Own

Now You're Ready
Exercises 6–11

Tell whether the angles are *complementary*, *supplementary*, or *neither*.

1.

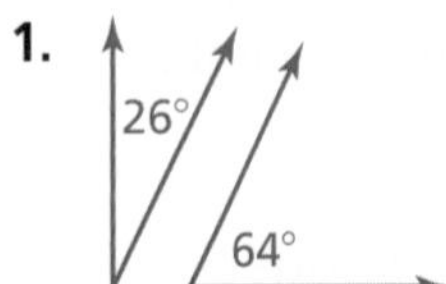

2.

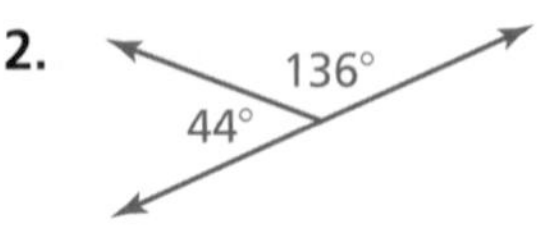

3.

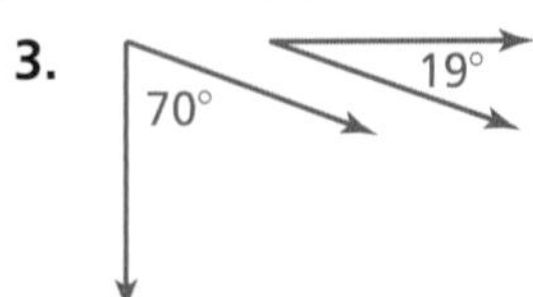

Multi-Language Glossary at BigIdeasMath.com.

Key Ideas

Adjacent Angles

Words Two angles are **adjacent angles** if they share a common side and have the same vertex.

Examples

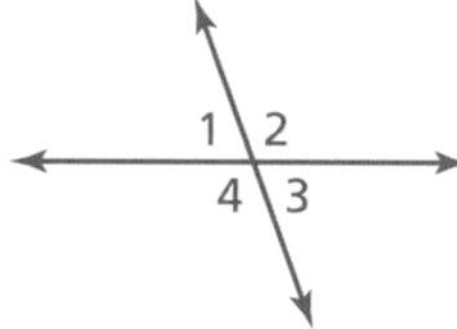

$\angle 1$ and $\angle 2$ are adjacent.

$\angle 2$ and $\angle 4$ are not adjacent.

Vertical Angles

Remember

Two angles are congruent if they have the same measure.

Words Two angles are **vertical angles** if they are opposite angles formed by the intersection of two lines. Vertical angles are congruent.

Examples

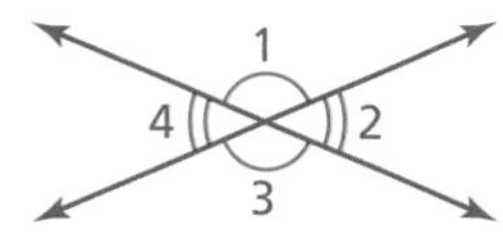

$\angle 1$ and $\angle 3$ are vertical angles.

$\angle 2$ and $\angle 4$ are vertical angles.

EXAMPLE 2 Finding Angle Measures

Tell whether the angles are *adjacent* or *vertical*. Then find the value of x.

a.

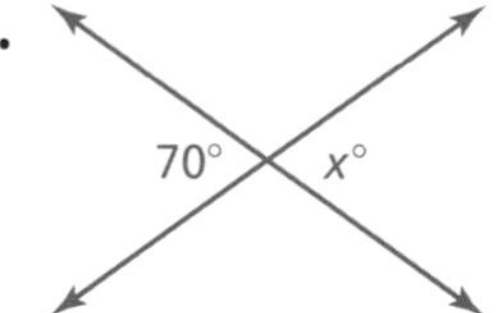

The angles are vertical angles. Because vertical angles are congruent, the angles have the same measure.

∴ So, x is 70.

b.

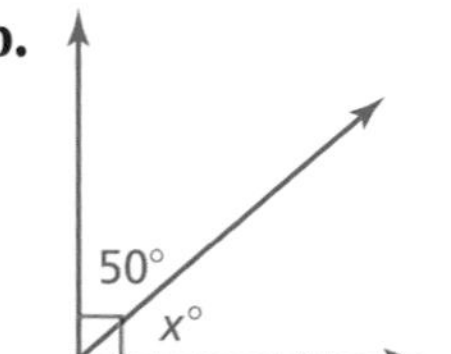

The angles are adjacent angles. Because the angles are complementary, the sum of their measures is 90°.

$$x + 50 = 90$$

$$x = 40$$

∴ So, x is 40.

On Your Own

Now You're Ready
Exercises 12–14

Tell whether the angles are *adjacent* or *vertical*. Then find the value of x.

4. **5.**

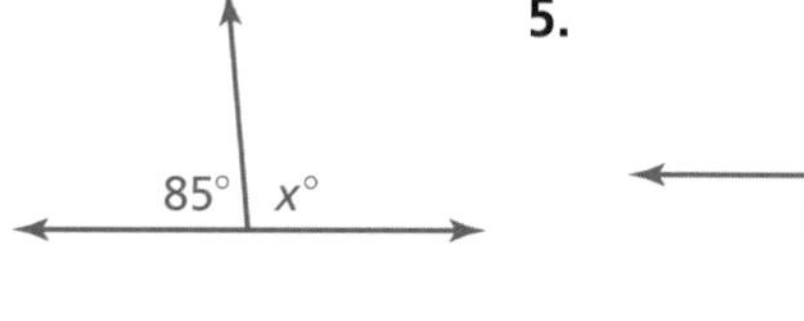

6.

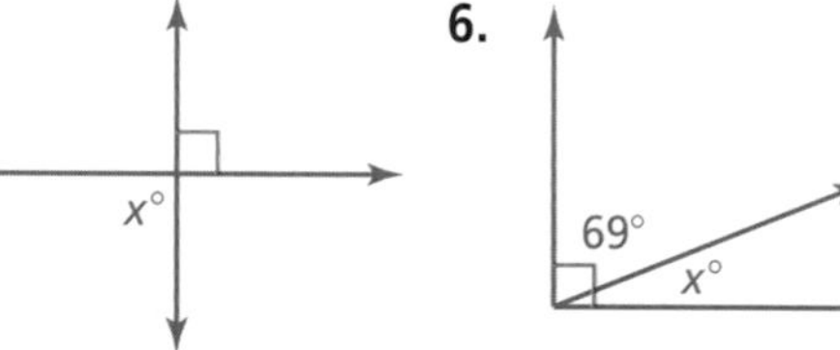

5.1 Exercises

Vocabulary and Concept Check

1. **VOCABULARY** Explain how complementary angles and supplementary angles are different.
2. **WRITING** When two lines intersect, how many pairs of vertical angles are formed? How many pairs of adjacent angles are formed? Explain.

Practice and Problem Solving

Tell whether the statement is *always, sometimes,* or *never* true. Explain.

3. If x and y are supplementary angles, then x is obtuse.
4. If x and y are right angles, then x and y are supplementary angles.
5. If x and y are complementary angles, then y is a right angle.

Tell whether the angles are *complementary, supplementary,* or *neither*.

1 6.
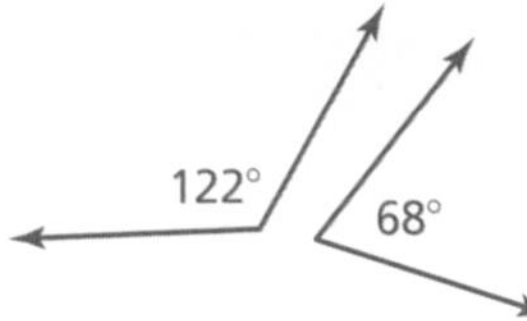

7.
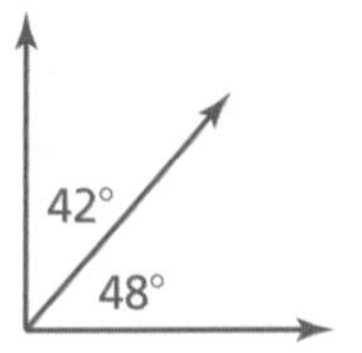

8.
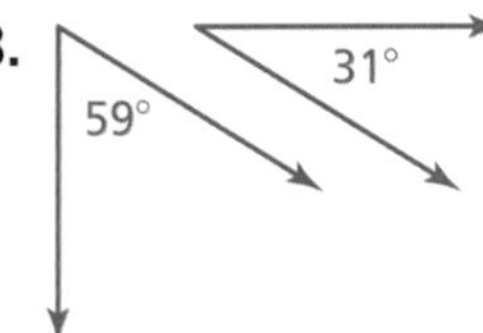

9.
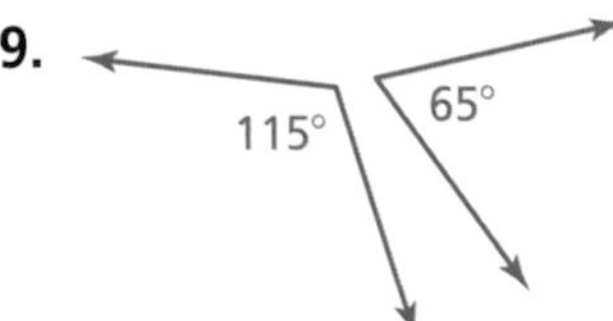

10.
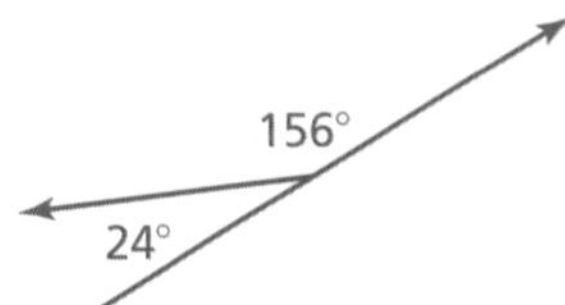

11.
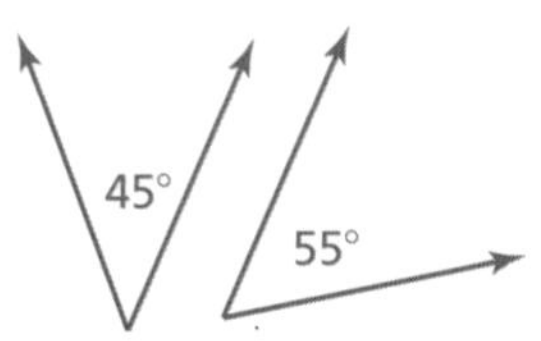

Tell whether the angles are *adjacent* or *vertical*. Then find the value of x.

2 12.
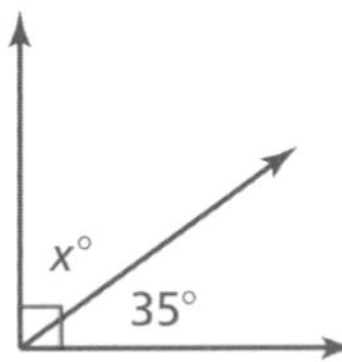

13.
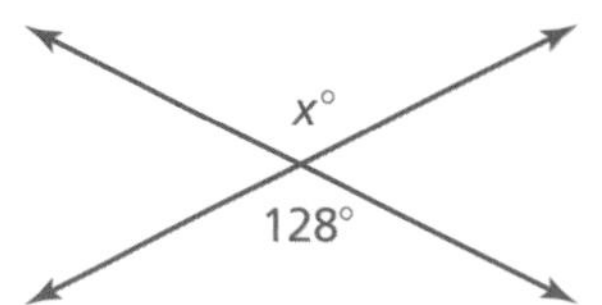

14.
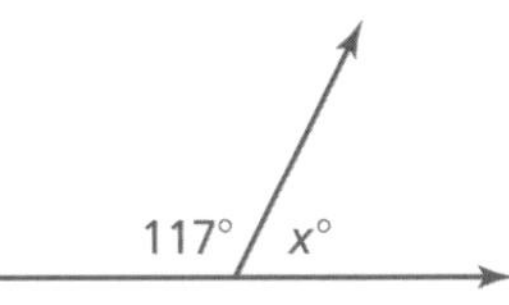

15. **ERROR ANALYSIS** Describe and correct the error in finding the value of x.

The value of x is 55 because vertical angles are complementary.

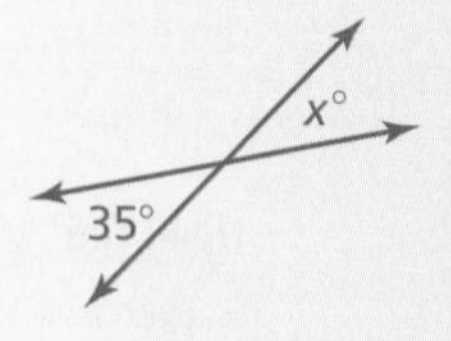

16. **TRIBUTARY** A tributary joins a river at an angle. Find the value of x.

x° 127°

Tell whether the angles are *adjacent* or *vertical*. Then find the measure of each angle.

17.

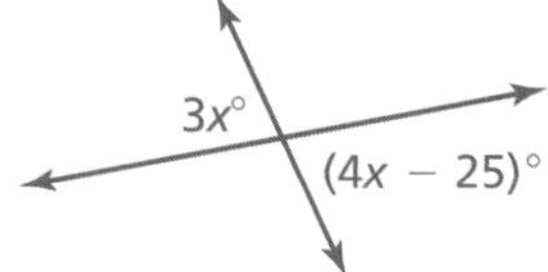

18.

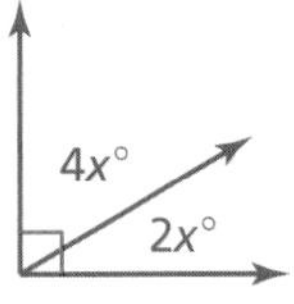

19.

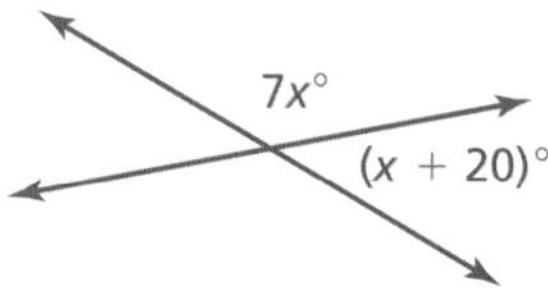

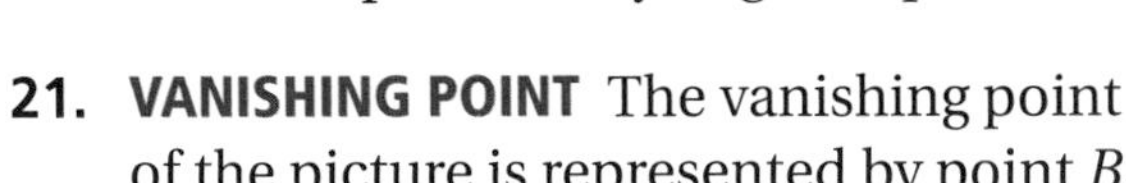

20. OPEN-ENDED Give an example of an angle that can be a supplementary angle but cannot be a complementary angle. Explain.

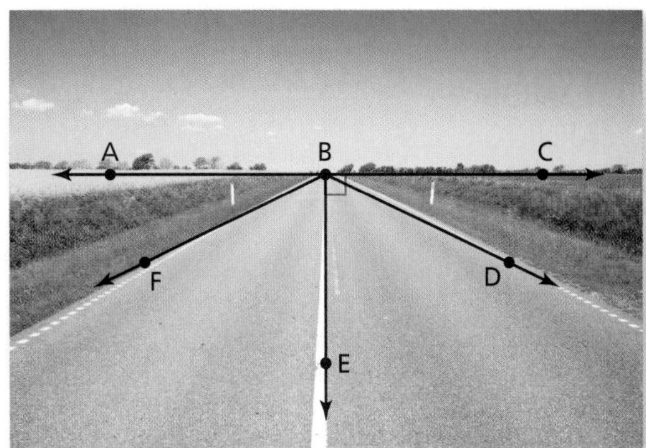

21. VANISHING POINT The vanishing point of the picture is represented by point *B*.

a. Name two pairs of complementary angles.

b. Name three pairs of supplementary angles.

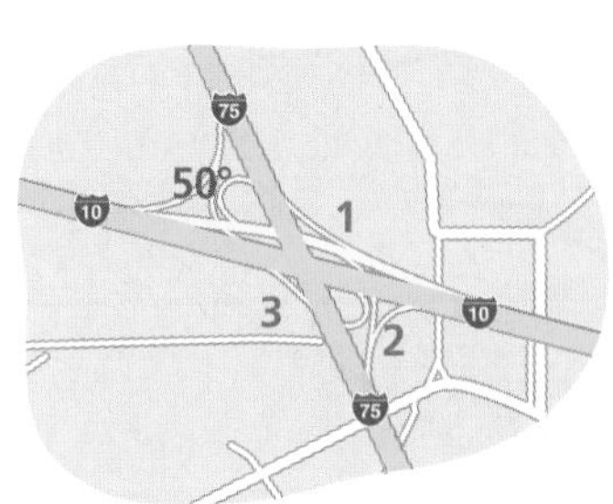

22. INTERSECTION What are the measures of the other three angles formed by the intersection?

23. REASONING Can adjacent angles be supplementary? complementary? neither? Explain.

24. RATIO The measures of two complementary angles have a ratio of 3 : 2. What is the measure of the larger angle?

25. REASONING Two angles are vertical angles. What are their measures if they are also complementary angles? supplementary angles?

26. Critical Thinking Find the values of x and y.

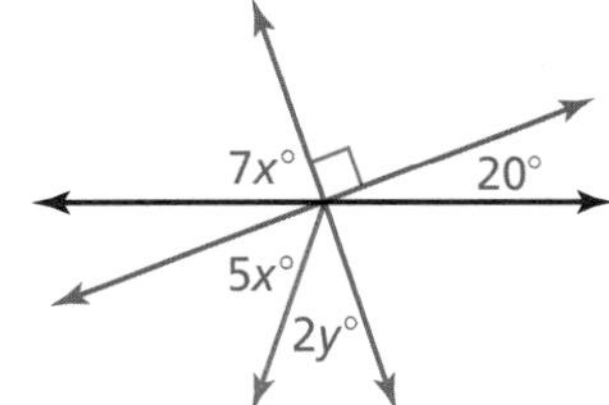

Fair Game Review What you learned in previous grades & lessons

Solve the equation. Check your solution. *(Section 1.1 and Section 1.2)*

27. $x + 60 + 45 = 180$

28. $x + 58.5 + 92.2 = 180$

29. $x + x + 110 = 180$

30. MULTIPLE CHOICE The graph of which equation has a slope of $-\frac{1}{2}$ and passes through the point (6, 4)? *(Section 2.6)*

Ⓐ $y = x + 3$ Ⓑ $y = -\frac{1}{2}x + 7$ Ⓒ $y = -\frac{1}{2}x + 1$ Ⓓ $y = \frac{1}{2}x - 3$

5.2 Angles and Sides of Triangles

STANDARDS OF LEARNING
8.6
8.15

Essential Question How can you classify triangles by their angles?

1 ACTIVITY: Exploring the Angles of a Triangle

Work with a partner.

a. Draw a triangle that has an obtuse angle. Label the angles *A*, *B*, and *C*.

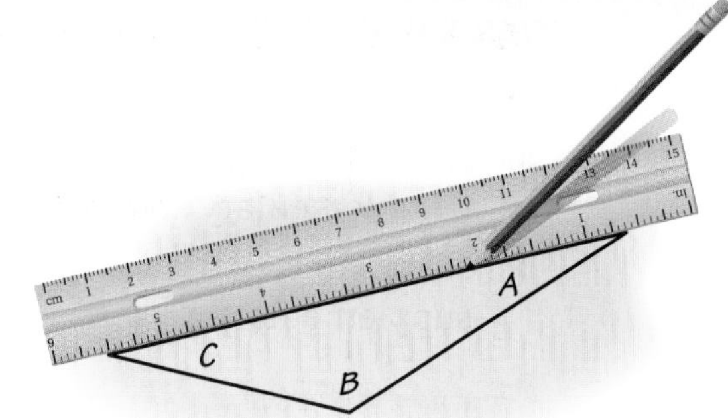

b. Carefully cut out the triangle. Tear off the three corners of the triangle.

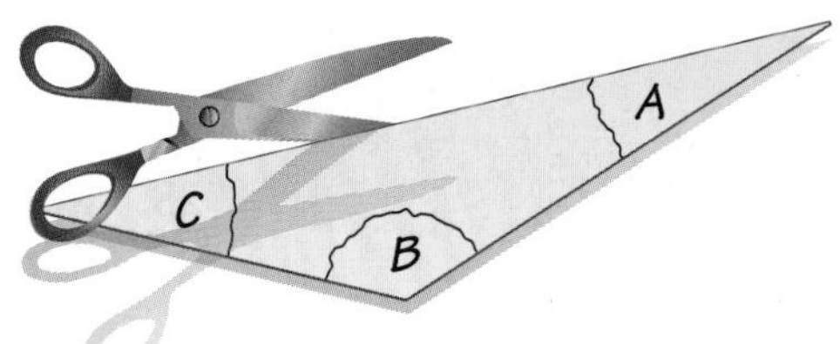

c. Draw a straight line on a piece of paper. Arrange angles *A* and *B* as shown.

d. Place the third angle as shown. What does this tell you about the sum of the measures of the angles?

e. Draw three other triangles that have different shapes. Repeat parts (b)–(d) for each one. Do you get the same result as in part (d)? Explain.

f. Write a rule about the sum of the measures of the angles of a triangle. Compare your rule with the rule you wrote in Activity 2 in Section 1.1. Did you get the same result? Explain.

2 ACTIVITY: Thinking About Vocabulary

Work with a partner. Talk about the meaning of each name. Use reasoning to define each name. Then match each name with a triangle.

Note: Each triangle has at least one name, but some have more than one name.

a. Right triangle

b. Acute triangle

c. Obtuse triangle

d. Equiangular triangle

e. Scalene triangle

f. Equilateral triangle

g. Isosceles triangle

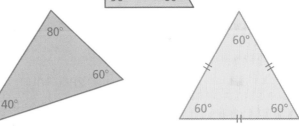

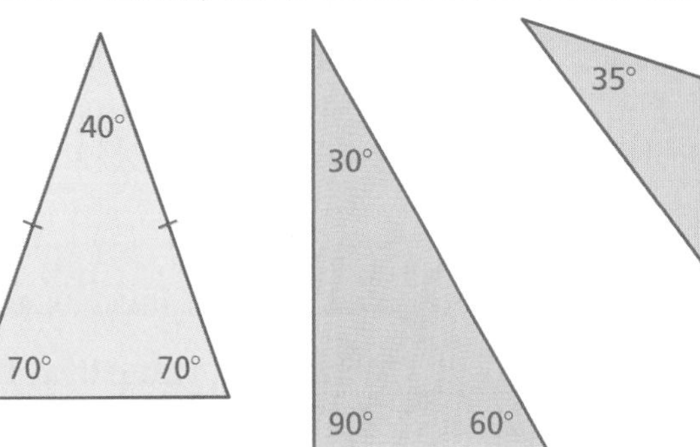

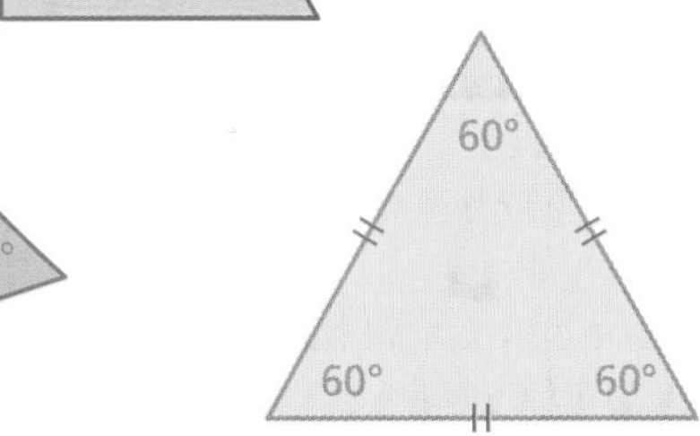

3 ACTIVITY: Triangles in Art

Work with a partner.

a. Trace four triangles in the painting. Classify each triangle using the names in Activity 2.

b. Design your own abstract art painting. How many different types of triangles did you use in your painting?

Abstract II by Linda Bahner
www.spiritartist.com

What Is Your Answer?

4. **IN YOUR OWN WORDS** How can you classify triangles by their angles?

5. Find examples of real-life triangles in architecture. Name each type of triangle that you find.

Practice Use what you learned about angles of triangles to complete Exercises 3–5 on page 208.

5.2 Lesson

Key Vocabulary

isosceles triangle, *p. 206*
congruent sides, *p. 206*
equilateral triangle, *p. 206*
equiangular triangle, *p. 206*

Key Idea

Angle Measures of a Triangle

Words The sum of the angle measures of a triangle is 180°.

Algebra $x + y + z = 180$

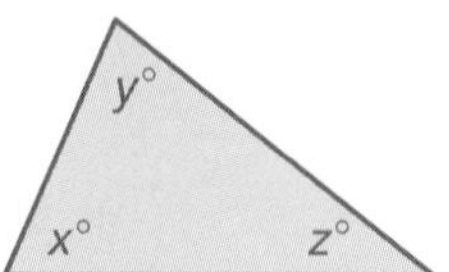

EXAMPLE 1 Finding Angle Measures

Remember

An *acute triangle* has all acute angles.
A *right triangle* has one right angle.
An *obtuse triangle* has one obtuse angle.

Find each value of x. Then classify each triangle.

a.

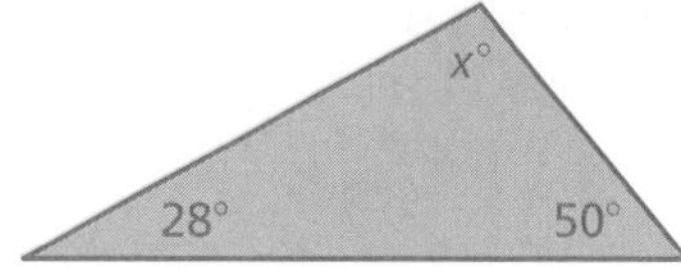

$$x + 28 + 50 = 180$$
$$x + 78 = 180$$
$$x = 102$$

The value of x is 102. The triangle has an obtuse angle. So, it is an obtuse triangle.

b.

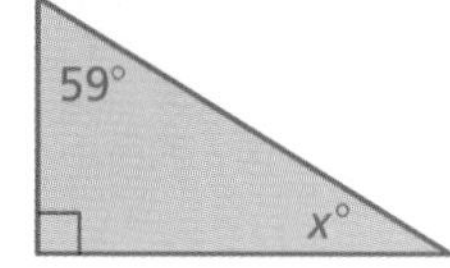

$$x + 59 + 90 = 180$$
$$x + 149 = 180$$
$$x = 31$$

The value of x is 31. The triangle has a right angle. So, it is a right triangle.

On Your Own

Now You're Ready
Exercises 6–8

Find the value of x. Then classify the triangle.

1.

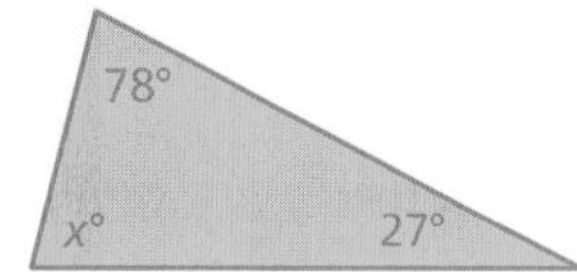

2.

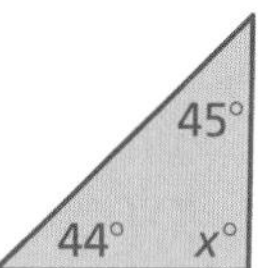

Key Ideas

Remember

A *scalene triangle* has no congruent sides.

Isosceles Triangle

An **isosceles triangle** has at least two sides that are **congruent** (have the same length).

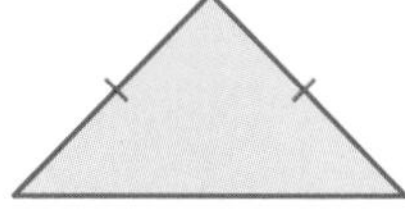

Equilateral Triangle

An **equilateral triangle** has three congruent sides.

An equilateral triangle is also **equiangular** (three congruent angles).

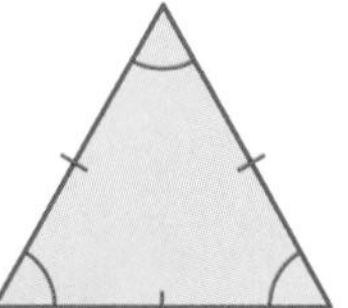

Multi-Language Glossary at BigIdeasMath.com.

EXAMPLE 2 Finding Angle Measures

Find the value of x. Then classify each triangle.

a. Flag of Jamaica

$$x + x + 128 = 180$$
$$2x + 128 = 180$$
$$2x = 52$$
$$x = 26$$

The value of x is 26. Two of the sides are congruent. So, it is an isosceles triangle.

b. Flag of Cuba

$$x + x + 60 = 180$$
$$2x + 60 = 180$$
$$2x = 120$$
$$x = 60$$

The value of x is 60. All three angles are congruent. So, it is an equilateral and equiangular triangle.

EXAMPLE  3 Standardized Test Practice

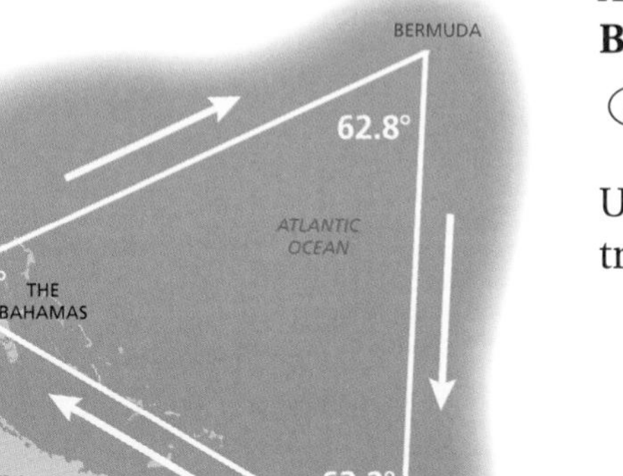

An airplane leaves from Miami and travels around the Bermuda Triangle. What is the value of x?

Ⓐ 26.8 Ⓑ 27.2 Ⓒ 54 Ⓓ 64

Use what you know about the angle measures of a triangle to write an equation.

$x + 62.8 + 63.2 = 180$	Write equation.
$x + 126 = 180$	Add.
$x = 54$	Subtract 126 from each side.

The value of x is 54. The correct answer is Ⓒ.

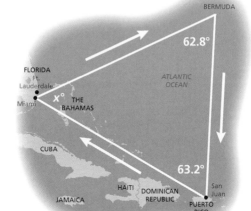

On Your Own

Find the value of x. Then classify the triangle in as many ways as possible.

3.

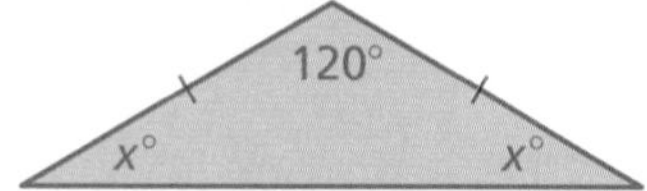

4.

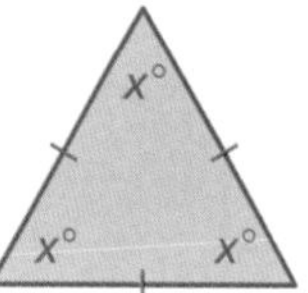

5. In Example 3, the airplane leaves from Fort Lauderdale. The angle measure at Bermuda is 63.9° and the angle measure at San Juan is 61.8°. Find the value of x.

5.2 Exercises

Vocabulary and Concept Check

1. **VOCABULARY** Compare equilateral and isosceles triangles.
2. **REASONING** Describe how to find the missing angle of the triangle.

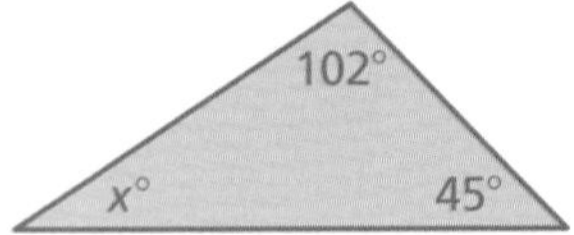

Practice and Problem Solving

Classify the triangle in as many ways as possible.

3. 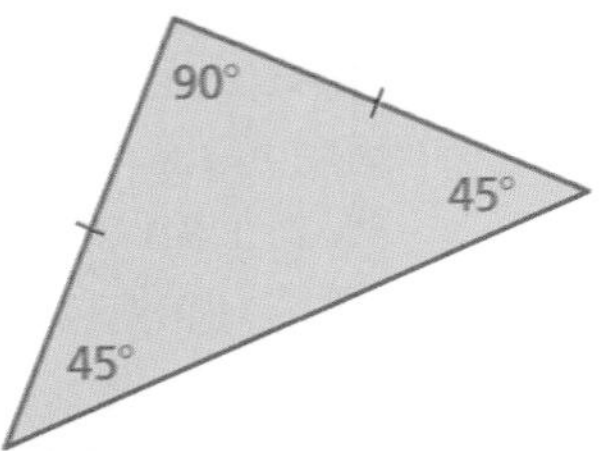

4. 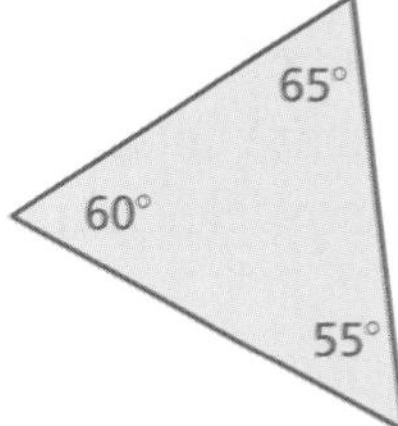

5. 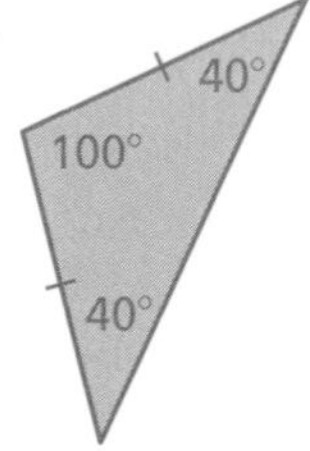

Find the value of *x*. Then classify the triangle in as many ways as possible.

1 6. 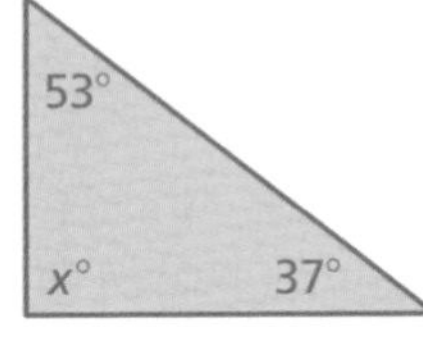

7. 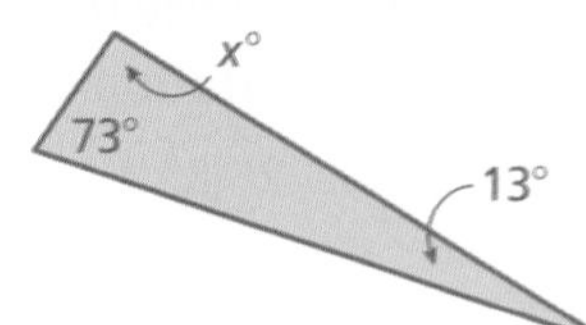

8. 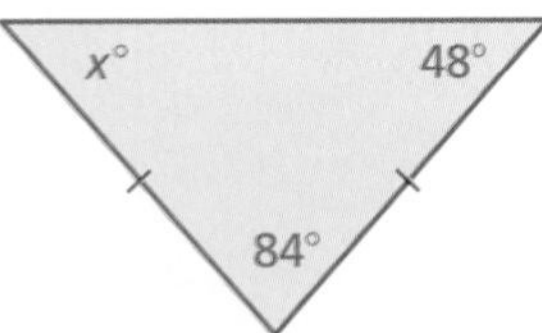

2 9. 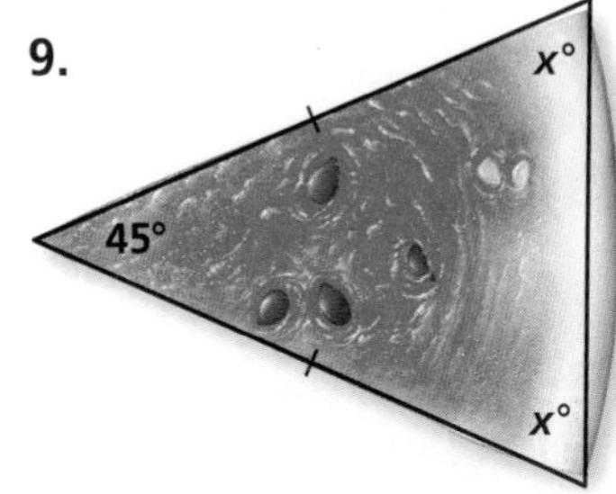

10. 

11. 

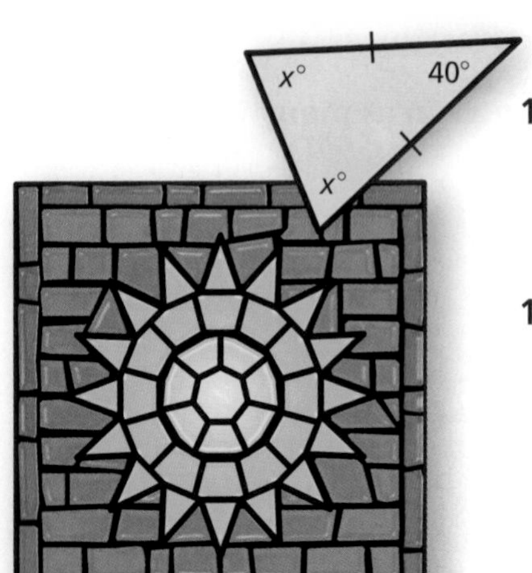

12. **ERROR ANALYSIS** Describe and correct the error in classifying the triangle.

98°
41°
41°

The triangle is an acute triangle, because it has acute angles.

13. **MOSAIC TILE** A mosaic is a pattern or picture made of small pieces of colored material.

    a. Find the value of x.

    b. Classify the triangle used in the mosaic in two ways.

Tell whether a triangle can have the given angle measures. If not, change the first angle measure so that the angle measures form a triangle.

14. $76.2°, 81.7°, 22.1°$

15. $115.1°, 47.5°, 93°$

16. $5\frac{2}{3}°, 64\frac{1}{3}°, 87°$

17. $31\frac{3}{4}°, 53\frac{1}{2}°, 94\frac{3}{4}°$

18. CRITICAL THINKING Consider the three isosceles triangles.

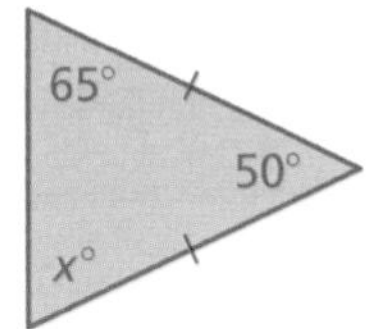

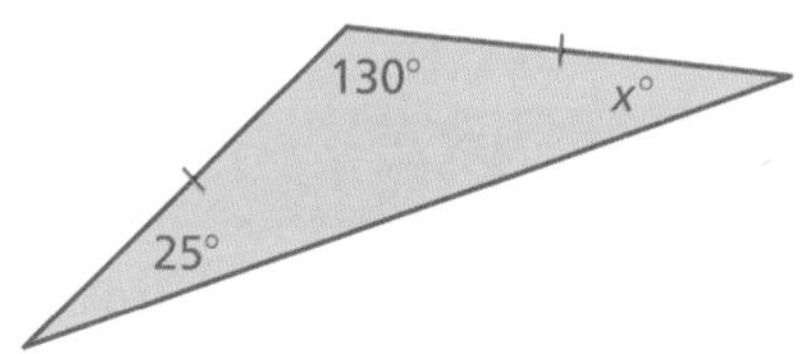

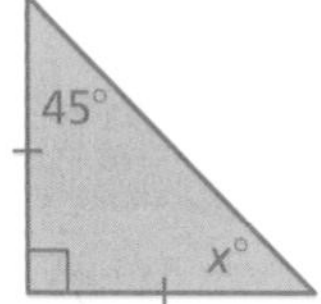

a. Find the value of x for each triangle.

b. What do you notice about the angle measures of each triangle?

c. Write a rule about the angle measures of an isosceles triangle.

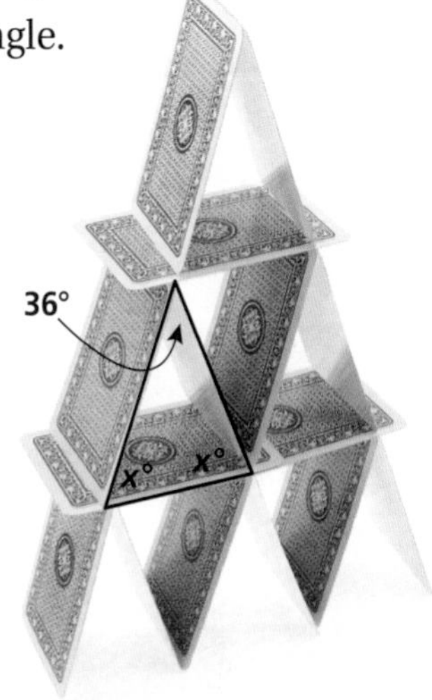

19. REASONING Explain why all triangles have at least two acute angles.

20. CARDS One method of stacking cards is shown.

a. Find the value of x.

b. Critical Thinking Describe how to stack the cards with different angles. Is the value of x limited? If so, what are the limitations? Explain your reasoning.

Fair Game Review What you learned in previous grades & lessons

Write and solve an equation to find x. *(Skills Review Handbook)*

21. $P = 28$ cm

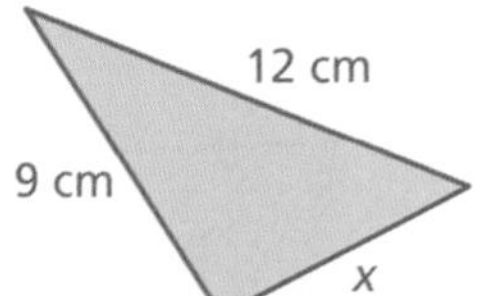

22. $P = 22$ in.

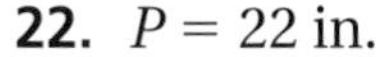

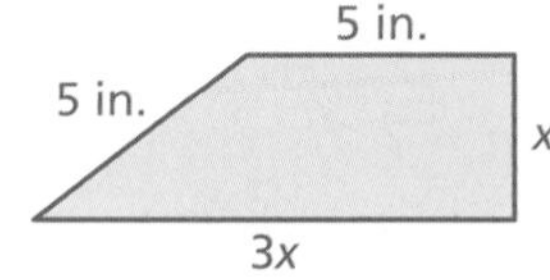

23. $P = 30$ m

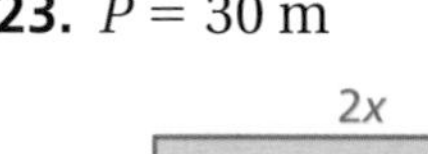

24. MULTIPLE CHOICE You have \$10 for text messages. Each message costs \$0.25. Which equation represents the amount of money you have after x messages? *(Section 2.1)*

Ⓐ $y = -0.25x + 10$

Ⓑ $y = 0.25x - 10$

Ⓒ $y = -0.25x - 10$

Ⓓ $y = 0.25x + 10$

5.3 Angles of Polygons

STANDARDS OF LEARNING
8.6

Essential Question How can you find a formula for the sum of the angle measures of any polygon?

1 ACTIVITY: The Sum of the Angle Measures of a Polygon

Work with a partner. Find the sum of the angle measures of each polygon with n sides.

a. **Sample:** Quadrilateral: $n = 4$

Draw a line that divides the quadrilateral into two triangles.

Because the sum of the angle measures of each triangle is 180°, the sum of the angle measures of the quadrilateral is 360°.

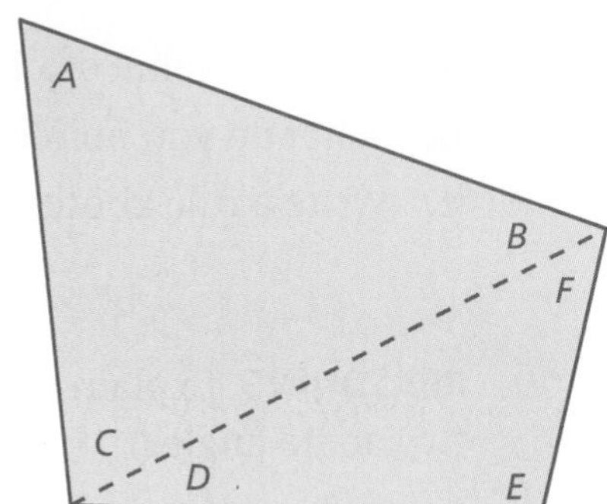

$$(A + B + C) + (D + E + F) = 180^\circ + 180^\circ$$
$$= 360^\circ$$

b. Pentagon: $n = 5$

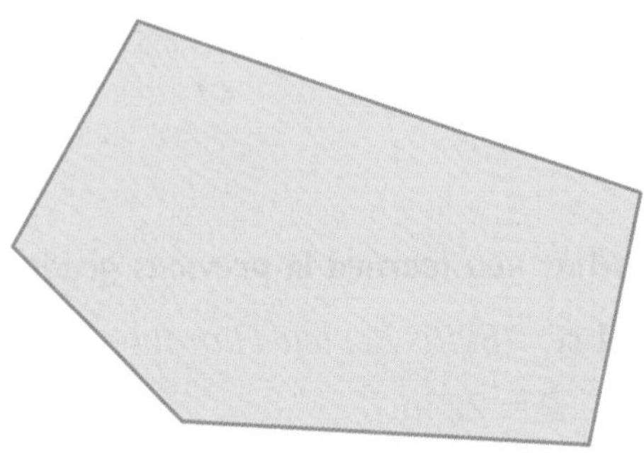

c. Hexagon: $n = 6$

d. Heptagon: $n = 7$

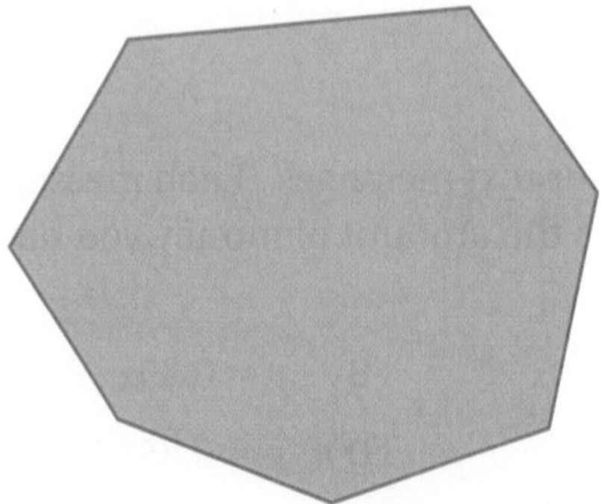

e. Octagon: $n = 8$

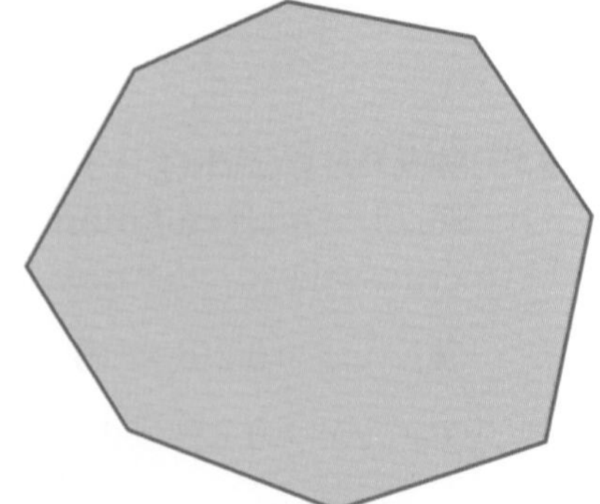

2 ACTIVITY: The Sum of the Angle Measures of a Polygon

Work with a partner.

a. Use the table to organize your results from Activity 1.

Sides, *n*	3	4	5	6	7	8
Angle Sum, *S*						

b. Plot the points in the table in a coordinate plane.

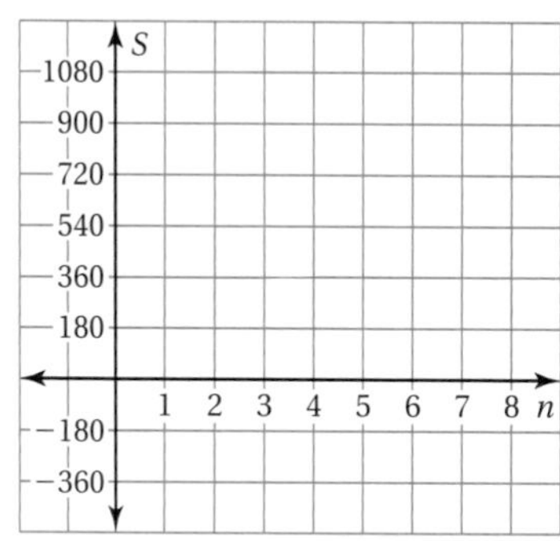

c. Write a linear equation that relates S to n.

d. What is the domain of the function? Explain your reasoning.

e. Use the function to find the sum of the angle measures of a polygon with 10 sides.

3 ACTIVITY: The Sum of the Angle Measures of a Polygon

Work with a partner.

A polygon is convex if the line segment connecting any two vertices lies entirely inside the polygon. A polygon that is not convex is called concave.

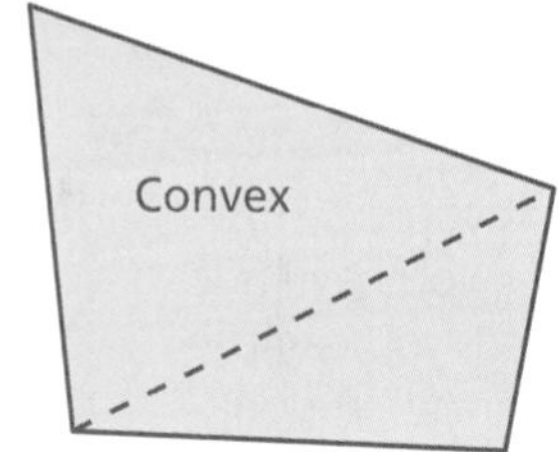

Measure each angle of the concave polygon. Then find the sum of the angle measures.

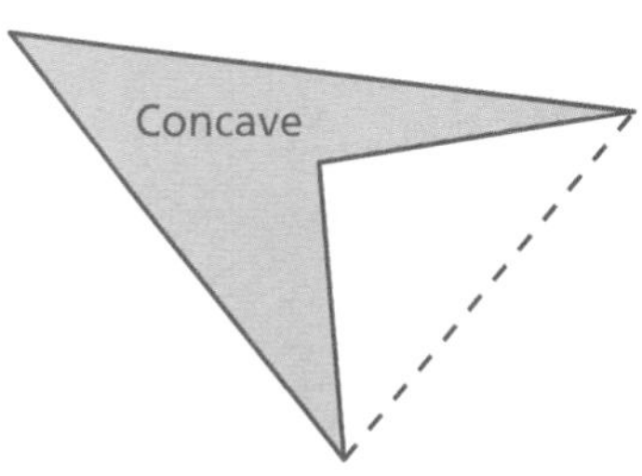

Does the equation you found in Activity 2 apply to concave polygons? Explain.

What Is Your Answer?

4. **IN YOUR OWN WORDS** How can you find a formula for the sum of the angle measures of any polygon?

Practice Use what you learned about angles of polygons to complete Exercises 4–6 on page 215.

Key Vocabulary
polygon, *p. 212*
regular polygon, *p. 213*
convex polygon, *p. 214*
concave polygon, *p. 214*

A **polygon** is a closed plane figure made up of three or more line segments that intersect only at their endpoints.

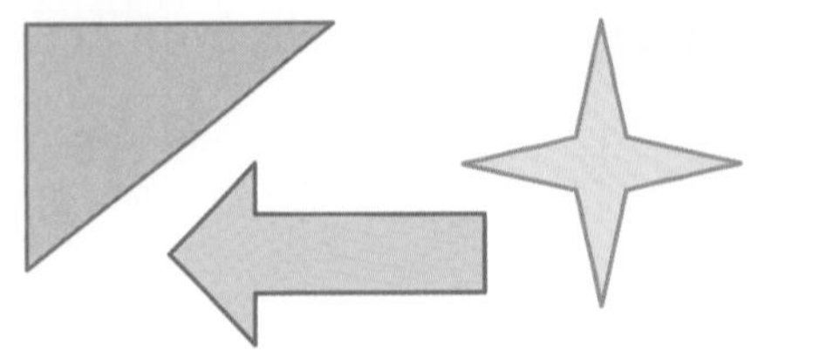

Polygons **Not polygons**

Key Idea

Angle Measures of a Polygon

The sum S of the angle measures of a polygon with n sides is

$$S = (n - 2) \cdot 180°.$$

Reading

For polygons whose names you have not learned, you can use the phrase "n-gon," where n is the number of sides. For example, a 15-gon is a polygon with 15 sides.

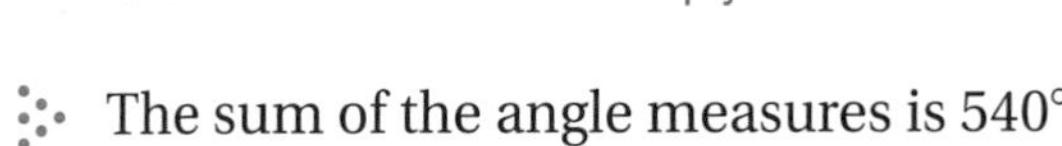

EXAMPLE 1 Finding the Sum of the Angle Measures of a Polygon

Find the sum of the angle measures of the school crossing sign.

The sign is in the shape of a pentagon. It has 5 sides.

$S = (n - 2) \cdot 180°$	Write the formula.
$= (5 - 2) \cdot 180°$	Substitute 5 for n.
$= 3 \cdot 180°$	Subtract.
$= 540°$	Multiply.

The sum of the angle measures is 540°.

On Your Own

Now You're Ready
Exercises 7–9

Find the sum of the angle measures of the green polygon.

1. 

2. 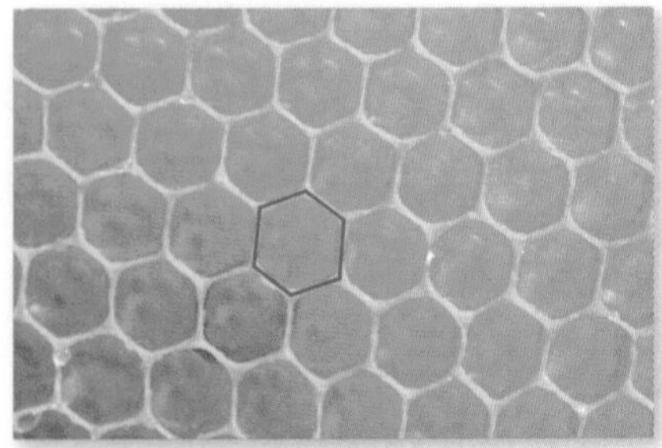

Multi-Language Glossary at BigIdeasMath.com.

EXAMPLE 2 Finding an Angle Measure of a Polygon

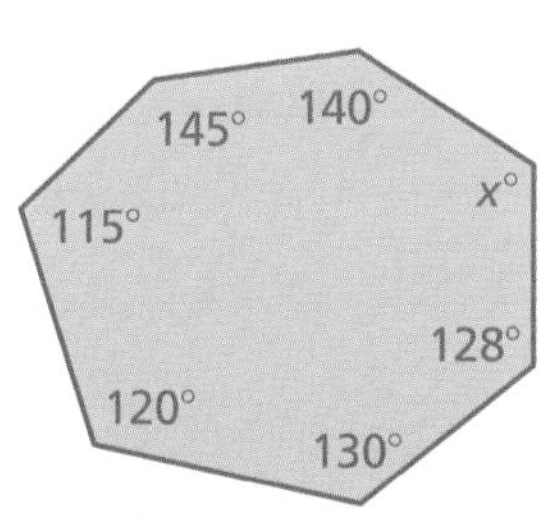

Find the value of x.

Step 1: The polygon has 7 sides. Find the sum of the angle measures.

$S = (n - 2) \cdot 180°$ Write the formula.

$= (7 - 2) \cdot 180°$ Substitute 7 for n.

$= 900°$ Simplify. The sum of the angle measures is 900°.

Step 2: Write and solve an equation.

$$140 + 145 + 115 + 120 + 130 + 128 + x = 900$$

$$778 + x = 900$$

$$x = 122$$

∴ The value of x is 122.

On Your Own

Now You're Ready
Exercises 12–14

Find the value of x.

3. 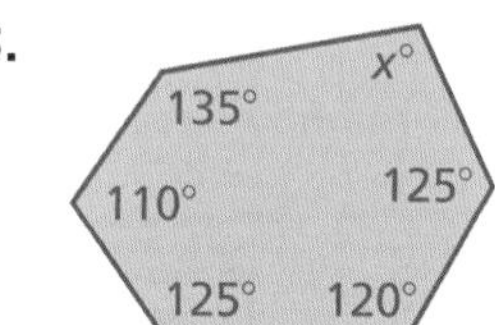

4. 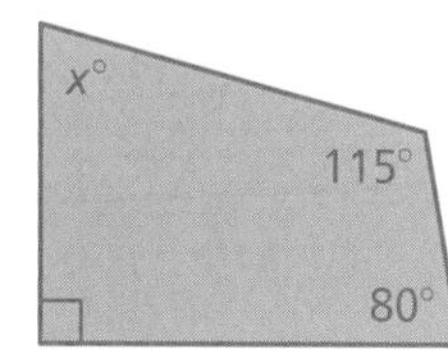

5. 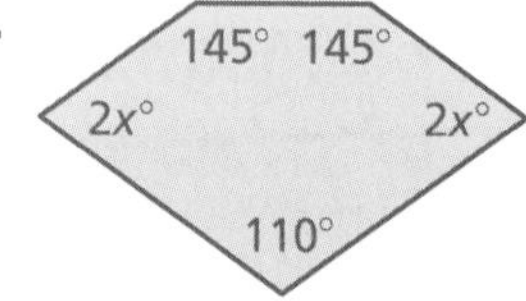

In a **regular polygon**, all of the sides are congruent and all of the angles are congruent.

EXAMPLE 3 Real-Life Application

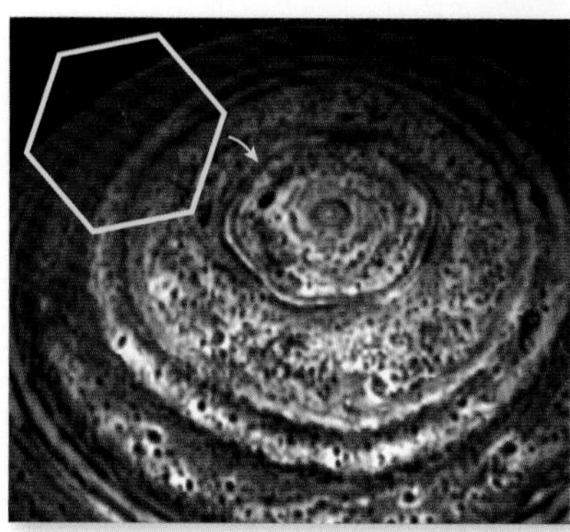

The hexagon is about 15,000 miles across. Approximately four Earths could fit inside it.

A cloud system discovered on Saturn is in the approximate shape of a regular hexagon. Find the measure of each angle of the hexagon.

Step 1: A hexagon has 6 sides. Find the sum of the angle measures.

$S = (n - 2) \cdot 180°$ Write the formula.

$= (6 - 2) \cdot 180°$ Substitute 6 for n.

$= 720°$ Simplify. The sum of the angle measures is 720°.

Step 2: Divide the sum by the number of angles, 6.

$$720° \div 6 = 120°$$

∴ The measure of each angle is 120°.

On Your Own

Find the measure of each angle of the regular polygon.

6. octagon **7.** decagon **8.** 18-gon

Key Idea

Convex and Concave Polygons

A polygon is **convex** if every line segment connecting any two vertices lies entirely inside the polygon.

A polygon is **concave** if at least one line segment connecting any two vertices lies outside the polygon.

EXAMPLE 4 Identifying Convex and Concave Polygons

Tell whether the polygon is *convex* or *concave*. Explain.

a.

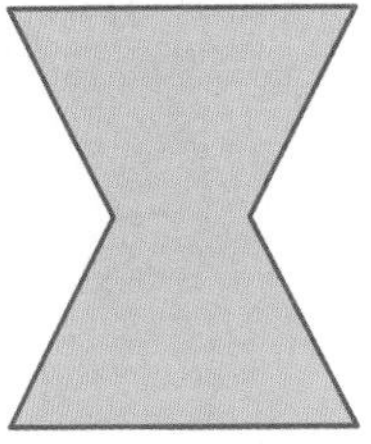

A line segment connecting two vertices lies outside the polygon. So, the polygon is concave.

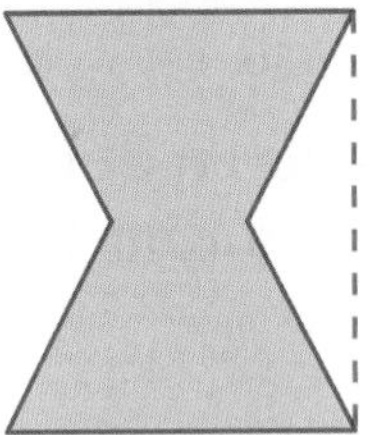

b.

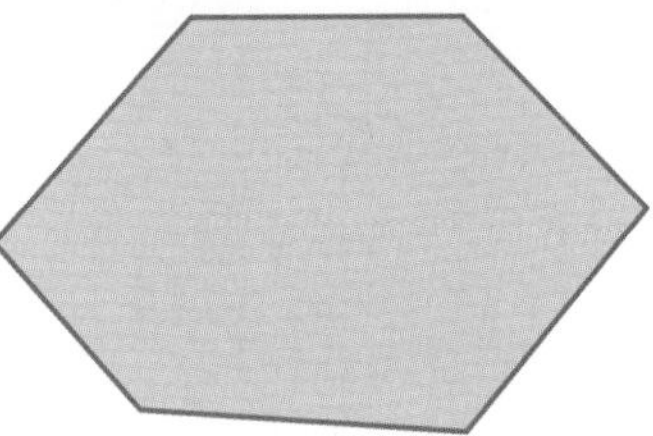

No line segment connecting two vertices lies outside the polygon. So, the polygon is convex.

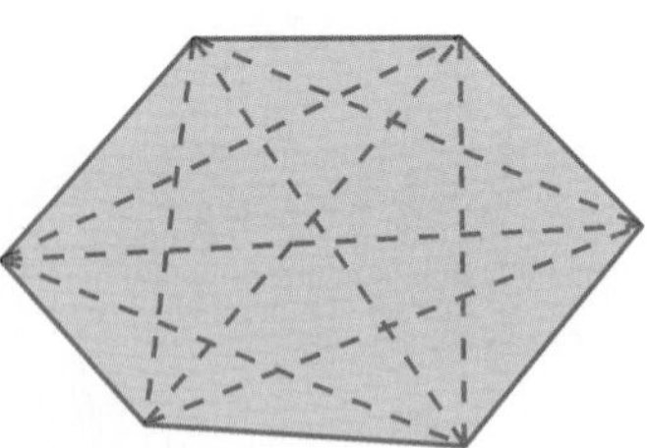

The Meaning of a Word

Concave

To remember the term con**cave**, think of a polygon that is "**cave**d in."

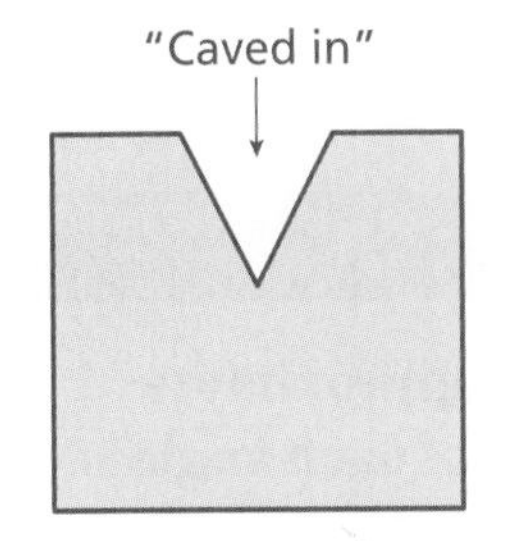

On Your Own

Now You're Ready
Exercises 22–24

Tell whether the polygon is *convex* or *concave*. Explain.

9.

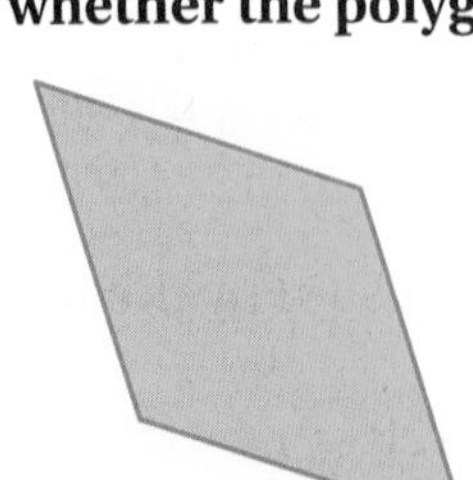

10.

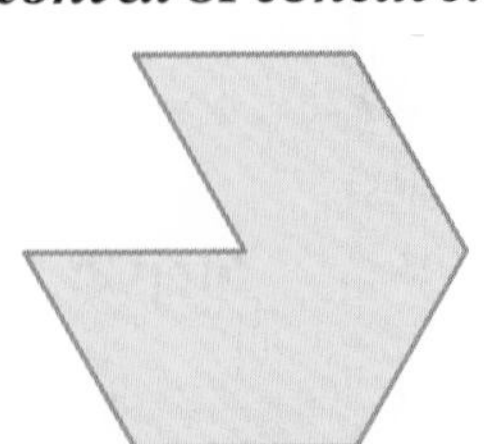

11.

Vocabulary and Concept Check

1. **VOCABULARY** Draw a regular polygon that has three sides.

2. **WHICH ONE DOESN'T BELONG?** Which figure does *not* belong with the other three? Explain your reasoning.

   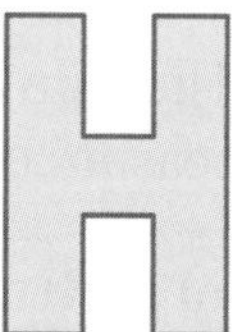

3. **DIFFERENT WORDS, SAME QUESTION** Which is different? Find "both" answers.

What is the measure of an angle of a regular pentagon?	What is the sum of the angle measures of a convex pentagon?
What is the sum of the angle measures of a regular pentagon?	What is the sum of the angle measures of a concave pentagon?

Practice and Problem Solving

Use triangles to find the sum of the angle measures of the polygon.

4. 

5. 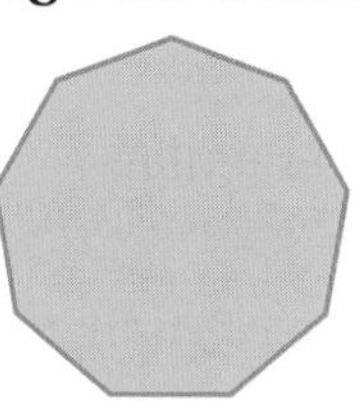

6. 

Find the sum of the angle measures of the polygon.

1 7. 

8. 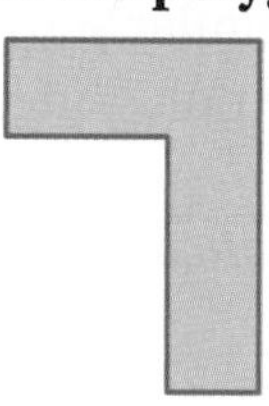

9. 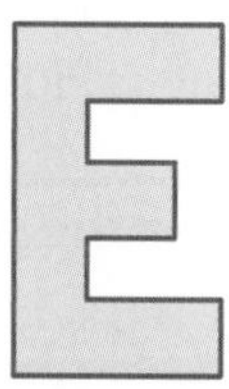

10. **ERROR ANALYSIS** Describe and correct the error in finding the sum of the angle measures of a 13-gon.

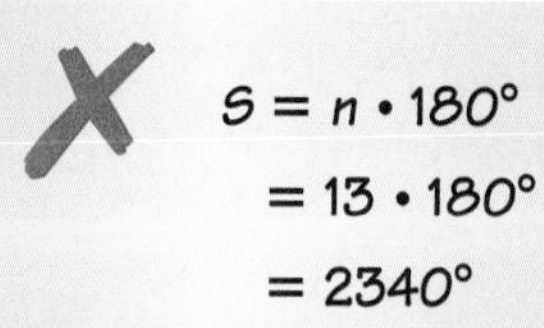

11. **NUMBER SENSE** Can a pentagon have angles that measure 120°, 105°, 65°, 150°, and 95°? Explain.

Find the value of x.

2 12. 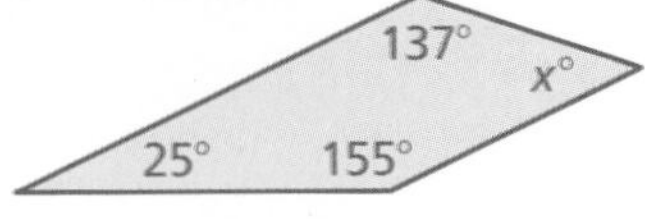

13. 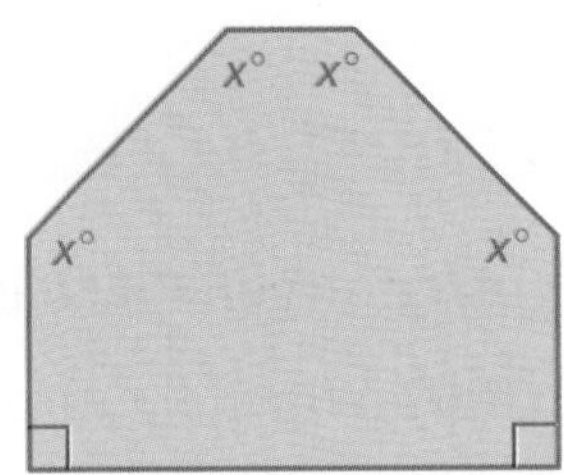

14. 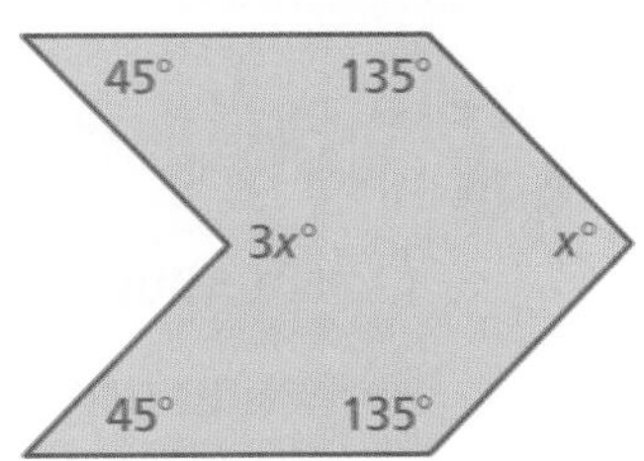

15. **REASONING** The sum of the angle measures in a regular polygon is 1260°. What is the measure of one of the angles of the polygon?

Find the measure of each angle of the regular polygon.

3 16. 

17. 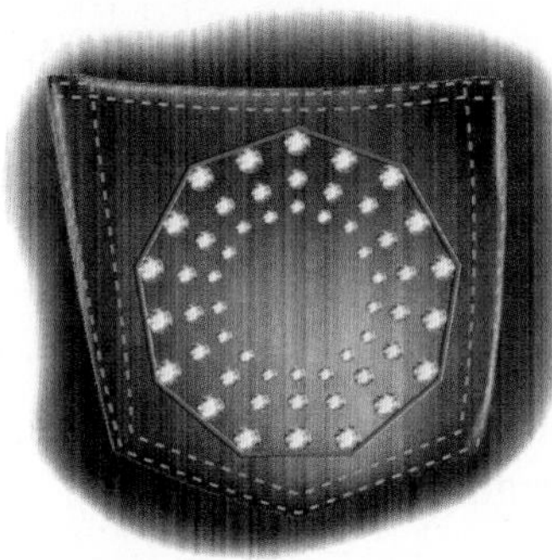

18. 

19. **ERROR ANALYSIS** Describe and correct the error in finding the measure of each angle of a regular 20-gon.

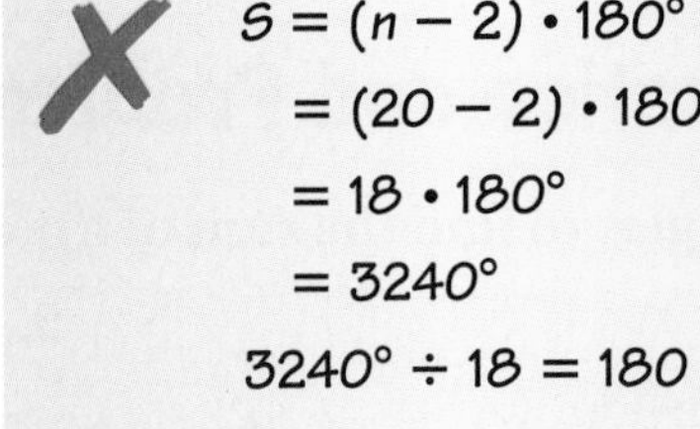

$S = (n - 2) \cdot 180°$
$= (20 - 2) \cdot 180°$
$= 18 \cdot 180°$
$= 3240°$

$3240° \div 18 = 180$

The measure of each angle is 180°.

20. **FIRE HYDRANT** A fire hydrant bolt is in the shape of a regular pentagon.
    a. What is the measure of each angle?
    b. Why are fire hydrants made this way?

21. **PUZZLE** The angles of a regular polygon each measure 165°. How many sides does the polygon have?

Tell whether the polygon is *convex* or *concave*. Explain.

4 22. 

23. 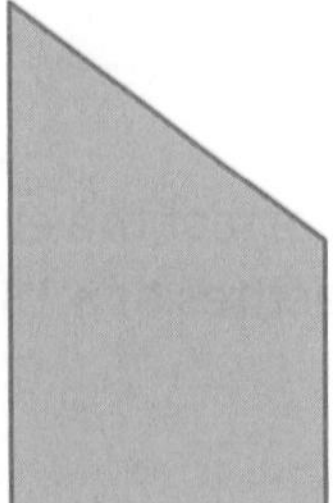

24. 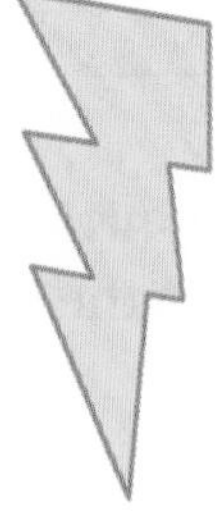

25. **CRITICAL THINKING** Can a concave polygon be regular? Explain.

26. **OPEN-ENDED** Draw a polygon that has congruent sides but is not regular.

27. **STAINED GLASS** The center of the stained glass window is in the shape of a regular polygon. What is the measure of each angle of the polygon?

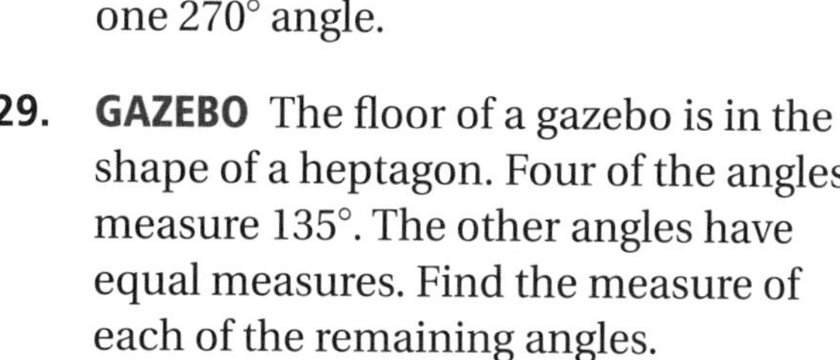

28. **PENTAGON** Draw a pentagon that has two right angles, two 45° angles, and one 270° angle.

29. **GAZEBO** The floor of a gazebo is in the shape of a heptagon. Four of the angles measure 135°. The other angles have equal measures. Find the measure of each of the remaining angles.

30. **MONEY** The border of a Susan B. Anthony dollar is in the shape of a regular polygon.

    a. How many sides does the polygon have?

    b. What is the measure of each angle of the border? Round your answer to the nearest degree.

31. **REASONING** Copy and complete the table. Does the table represent a linear function? Explain.

Sides of a Regular Polygon, n	3	4	5	6	7	8	9	10
Measure of One Angle, a								

32. **Geometry** When tiles can be used to cover a floor with no empty spaces, the collection of tiles is called a *tessellation*.

    a. Create a tessellation using equilateral triangles.

    b. Find two more regular polygons that form tessellations.

    c. Create a tessellation that uses two different regular polygons.

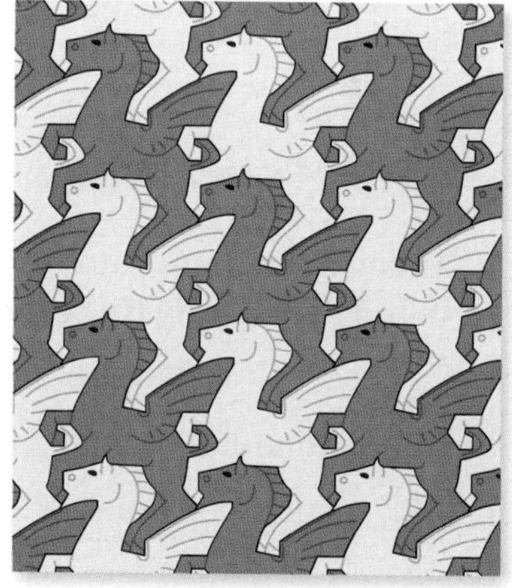

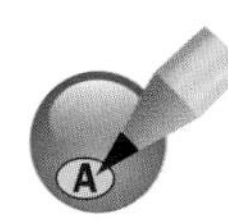

Fair Game Review What you learned in previous grades & lessons

Solve the proportion. *(Skills Review Handbook)*

33. $\frac{x}{12} = \frac{3}{4}$

34. $\frac{14}{21} = \frac{x}{3}$

35. $\frac{x}{9} = \frac{2}{6}$

36. $\frac{4}{10} = \frac{x}{15}$

37. **MULTIPLE CHOICE** The ratio of tulips to daisies is 3 : 5. Which of the following could be the total number of tulips and daisies? *(Skills Review Handbook)*

    Ⓐ 6 Ⓑ 10 Ⓒ 15 Ⓓ 16

5 Study Help

You can use an **example and non-example chart** to list examples and non-examples of a vocabulary word or item. Here is an example and non-example chart for complementary angles.

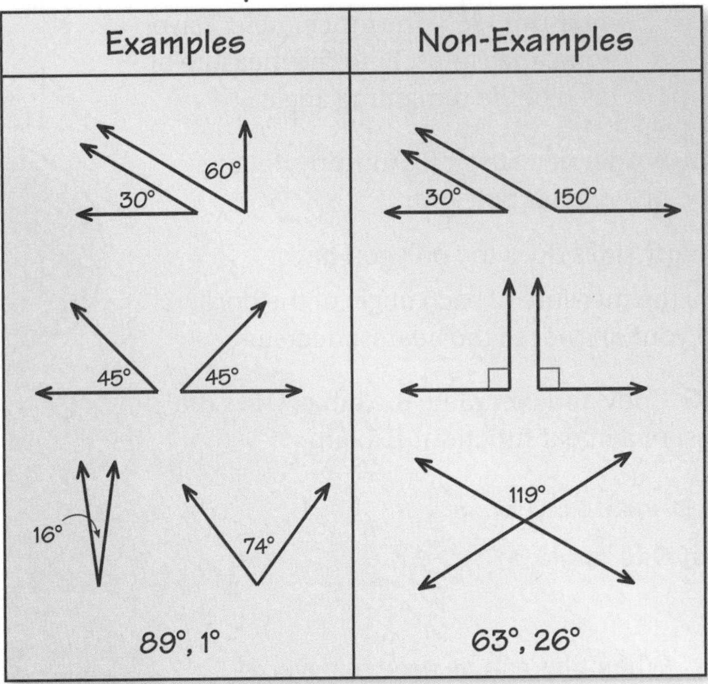

On Your Own

Make an example and non-example chart to help you study these topics.

1. isosceles triangles
2. equilateral triangles
3. regular polygons
4. convex polygons
5. concave polygons

After you complete this chapter, make example and non-example charts for the following topics.

6. similar triangles
7. transformations
8. composite figures

"What do you think of my example & non-example chart for popular cat toys?"

5.1–5.3 Quiz

Check It Out
Progress Check
BigIdeasMath.com

Tell whether the angles are *complementary*, *supplementary*, or *neither*. *(Section 5.1)*

1. 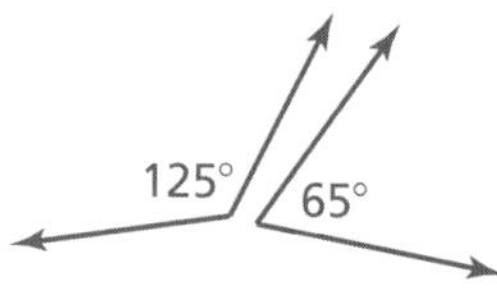

2. 

3. 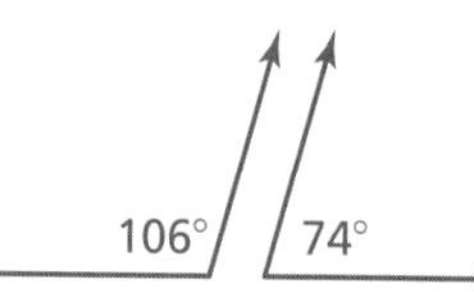

Tell whether the angles are *adjacent* or *vertical*. Then find the value of x. *(Section 5.1)*

4. 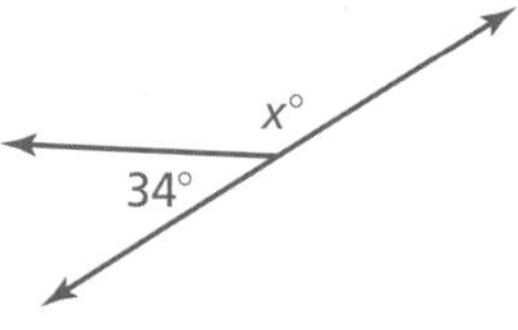

5. 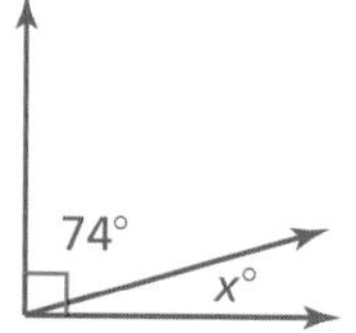

6. 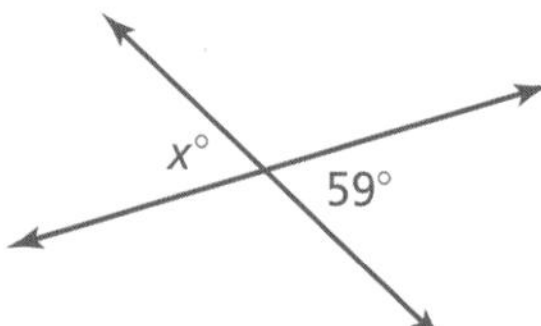

Find the value of x. Then classify the triangle in as many ways as possible. *(Section 5.2)*

7. 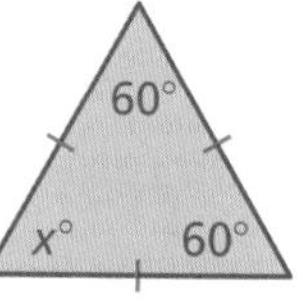

8. 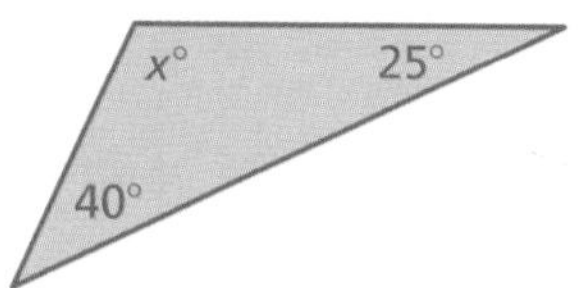

9. 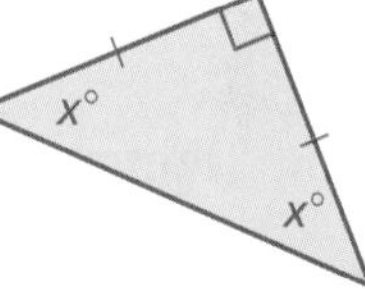

10. Find the sum of the angle measures of the polygon. *(Section 5.3)*

11. Tell whether the polygon is concave or convex. *(Section 5.3)*

Find the value of x. *(Section 5.3)*

12. 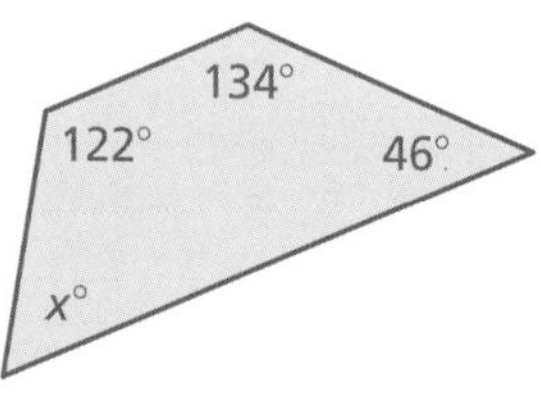

13. 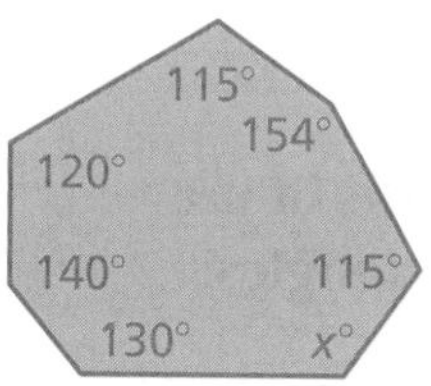

14. 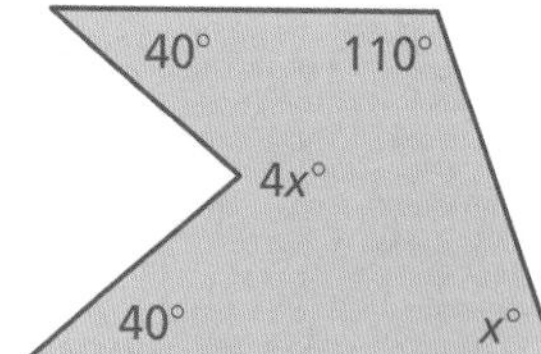

15. **RAILROAD CROSSING** What are the measures of the other three angles formed by the intersection of the road and the railroad tracks? *(Section 5.1)*

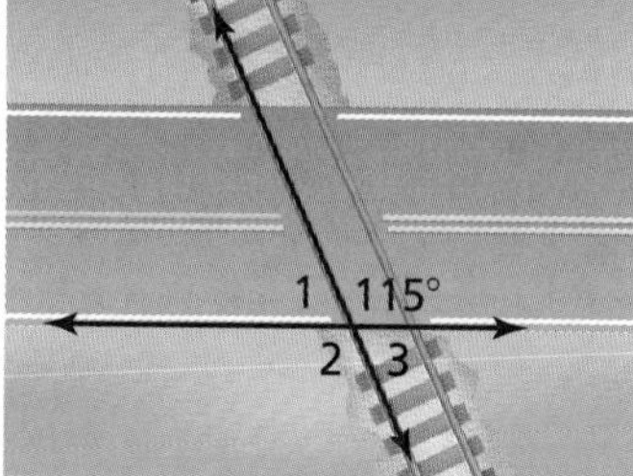

16. **REASONING** The sum of the angle measures of a polygon is 4140°. How many sides does the polygon have? *(Section 5.3)*

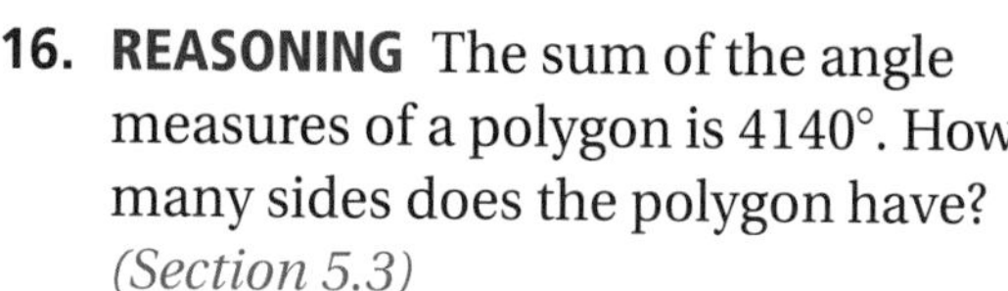

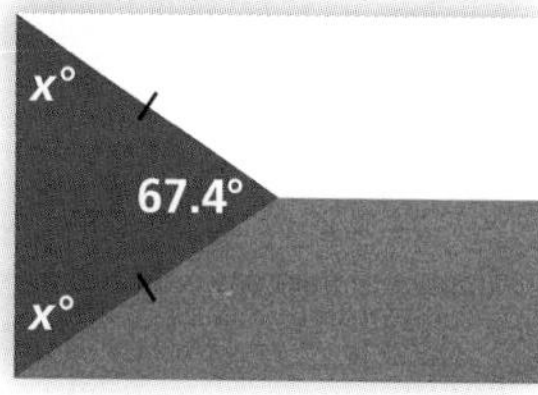

17. **FLAG** Classify the triangle on the flag of the Czech Republic in as many ways as possible. *(Section 5.2)*

5.4 Using Similar Triangles

STANDARDS OF LEARNING
8.3

Essential Question Which properties of triangles make them special among all other types of polygons?

You already know that two triangles are **similar** if and only if the ratios of their corresponding side lengths are equal.

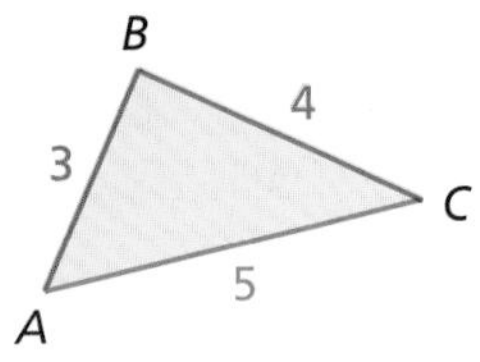

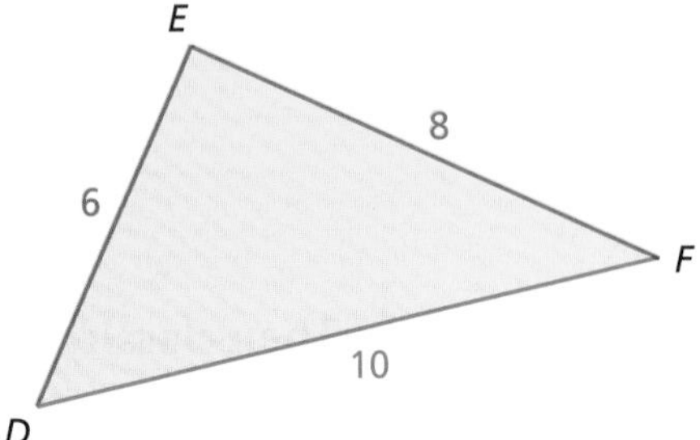

For example, $\triangle ABC$ is similar to $\triangle DEF$ because the ratios of their corresponding side lengths are equal.

$$\frac{6}{3} = \frac{10}{5} = \frac{8}{4}$$

1 ACTIVITY: Angles of Similar Triangles

Work with a partner.

- **Discuss how to make a triangle that is larger than $\triangle XYZ$ and has the *same* angle measures as $\triangle XYZ$.**

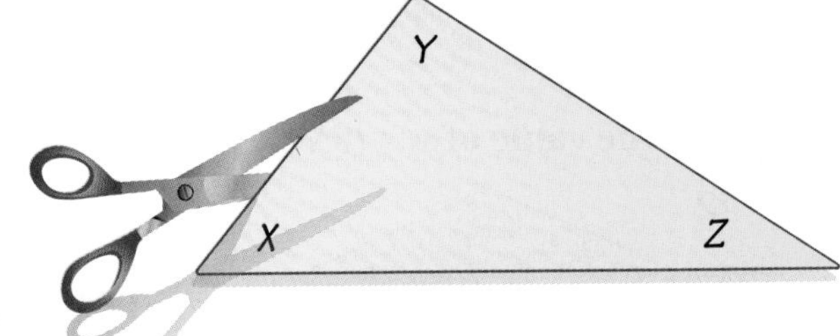

- **Measure the lengths of the sides of the two triangles.**
- **Find the ratios of the corresponding side lengths. Are they all the same? What can you conclude?**

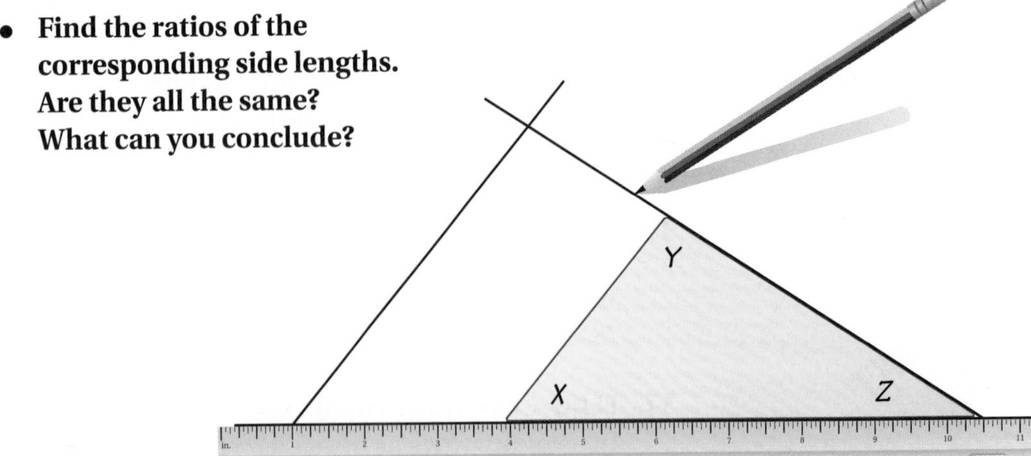

2 ACTIVITY: Amazing Triangles

Work with a partner. Use what you know about polygons to decide whether each statement is true. In each case, explain your reasoning.

a. 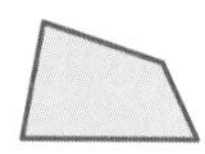 If two triangles are similar, then the ratios of their corresponding side lengths are equal.

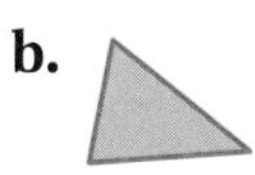 If two quadrilaterals are similar, then the ratios of their corresponding side lengths are equal.

b. 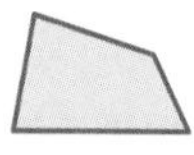 If the ratios of the corresponding sides of two triangles are equal, then the triangles are similar.

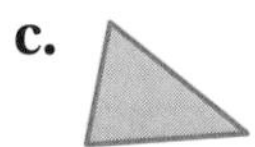 If the ratios of the corresponding sides of two quadrilaterals are equal, then the quadrilaterals are similar.

c. 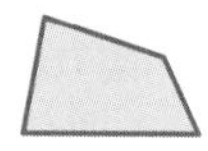 If two triangles are similar, then their corresponding angles are congruent.

 If two quadrilaterals are similar, then their corresponding angles are congruent.

d. 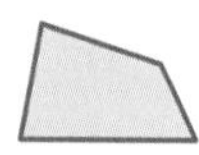 If the corresponding angles in two triangles are congruent, then the triangles are similar.

 If the corresponding angles in two quadrilaterals are congruent, then the quadrilaterals are similar.

e. 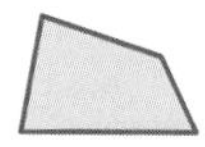 If the corresponding sides of two triangles are congruent, then the two triangles have identical shapes.

If the corresponding sides of two quadrilaterals are congruent, then the two quadrilaterals have identical shapes.

What Is Your Answer?

3. **IN YOUR OWN WORDS** Which properties of triangles make them special among all other types of polygons? Describe two careers in which the special properties of triangles are used.

Use what you learned about similar triangles to complete Exercises 3 and 4 on page 224.

5.4 Lesson

Key Vocabulary
similar triangles, *p. 222*
indirect measurement, *p. 223*

Triangles that have the same shape but not necessarily the same size are **similar triangles**.

Key Idea

Angles of Similar Triangles

Words Two triangles have the same angle measures if and only if they are similar.

Example

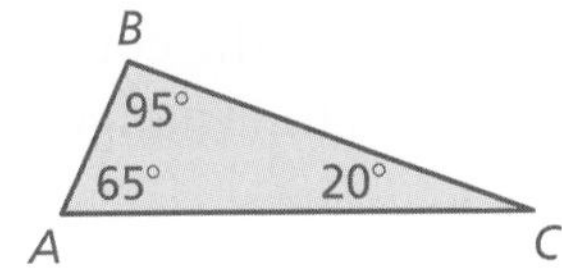

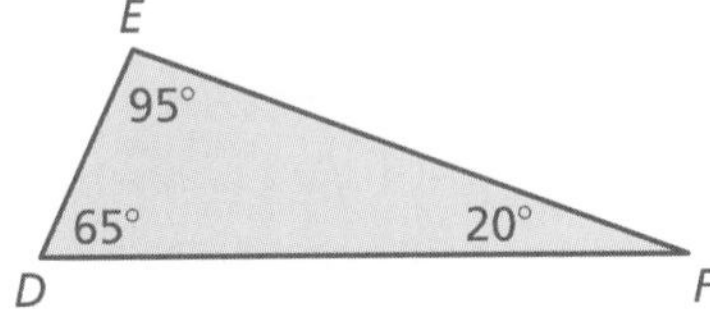

Triangle ABC is similar to triangle DEF: $\triangle ABC \sim \triangle DEF$.

Study Tip

If two angles in one triangle are congruent to two angles in another triangle, then the third angles are also congruent.

EXAMPLE 1 Identifying Similar Triangles

Tell whether the triangles are similar. Explain.

a.

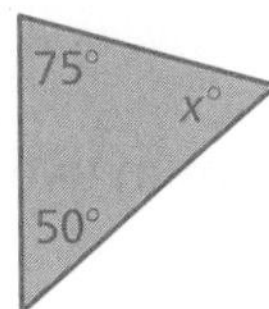

y°
55°
50°

$75 + 50 + x = 180$

$125 + x = 180$

$x = 55$

$y + 50 + 55 = 180$

$y + 105 = 180$

$y = 75$

The triangles have the same angle measures, 75°, 50°, and 55°. So, they are similar.

b.

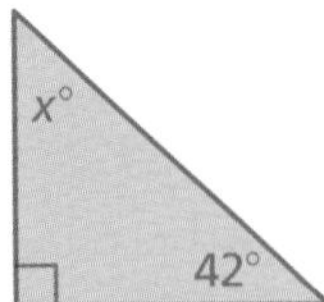

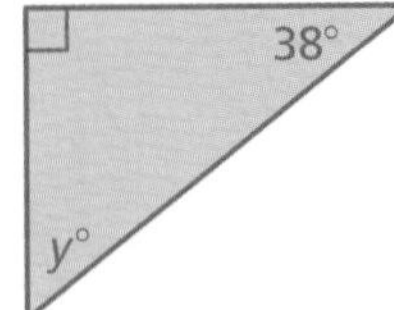

$x + 90 + 42 = 180$

$x + 132 = 180$

$x = 48$

$90 + 38 + y = 180$

$128 + y = 180$

$y = 52$

The triangles do not have the same angle measures. So, they are not similar.

Multi-Language Glossary at BigIdeasMath.com.

On Your Own

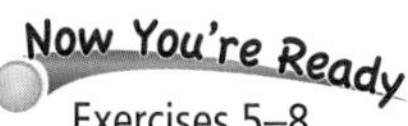

Tell whether the triangles are similar. Explain.

1.

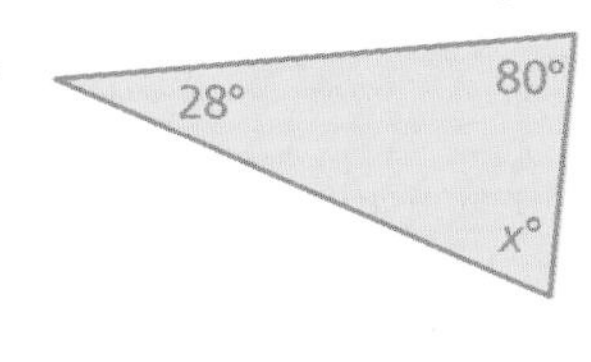

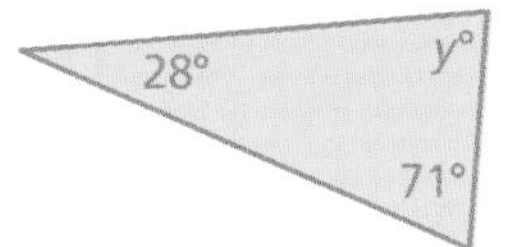

2.

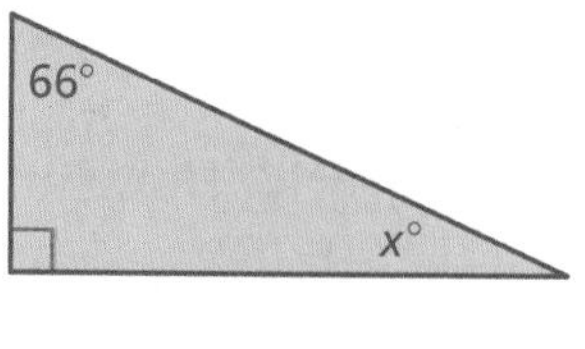

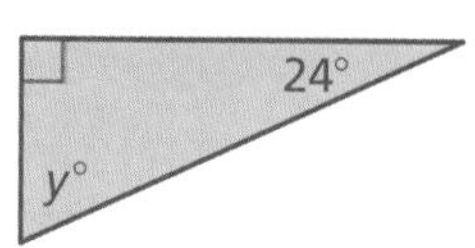

Indirect measurement uses similar figures to find a missing measure when it is difficult to find directly.

EXAMPLE 2 Using Indirect Measurement

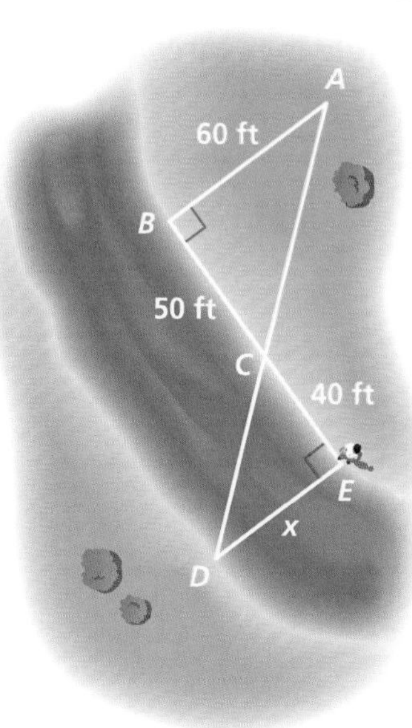

You plan to cross a river and want to know how far it is to the other side. You take measurements on your side of the river and make the drawing shown. (a) Explain why $\triangle ABC$ and $\triangle DEC$ are similar. (b) What is the distance x across the river?

a. $\angle B$ and $\angle E$ are right angles, so they are congruent. $\angle ACB$ and $\angle DCE$ are vertical angles, so they are congruent.

Because two angles in $\triangle ABC$ are congruent to two angles in $\triangle DEC$, the third angles are also congruent. The triangles have the same angle measures, so they are similar.

b. The ratios of the corresponding side lengths in similar triangles are equal. Write and solve a proportion to find x.

$$\frac{x}{60} = \frac{40}{50}$$ Write a proportion.

$$60 \cdot \frac{x}{60} = 60 \cdot \frac{40}{50}$$ Multiply each side by 60.

$$x = 48$$ Simplify.

∴ The distance across the river is 48 feet.

On Your Own

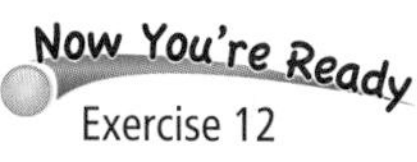

3. WHAT IF? The distance from vertex A to vertex B is 55 feet. What is the distance across the river?

5.4 Exercises

Vocabulary and Concept Check

1. **REASONING** How can you use similar triangles to find a missing measurement?

2. **WHICH ONE DOESN'T BELONG?** Which triangle does *not* belong with the other three? Explain your reasoning.

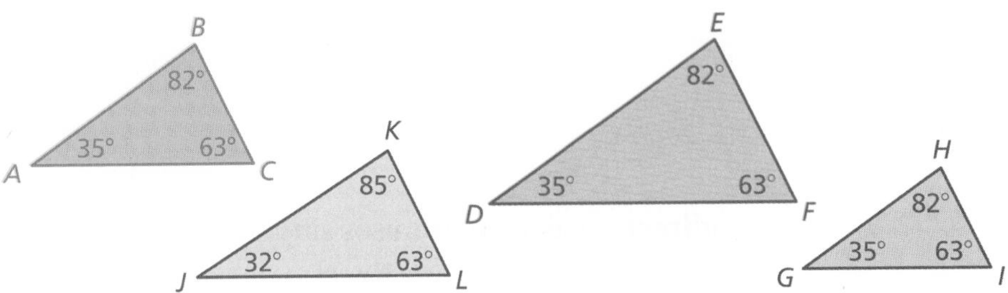

Practice and Problem Solving

Make a triangle that is larger than the one given and has the same angle measures. Find the ratios of the corresponding side lengths.

3.

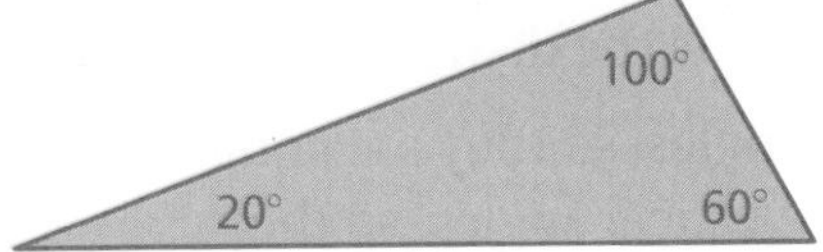

4.

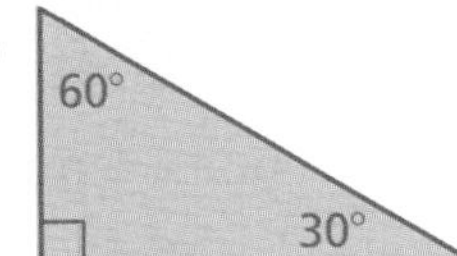

Tell whether the triangles are similar. Explain.

1 5.

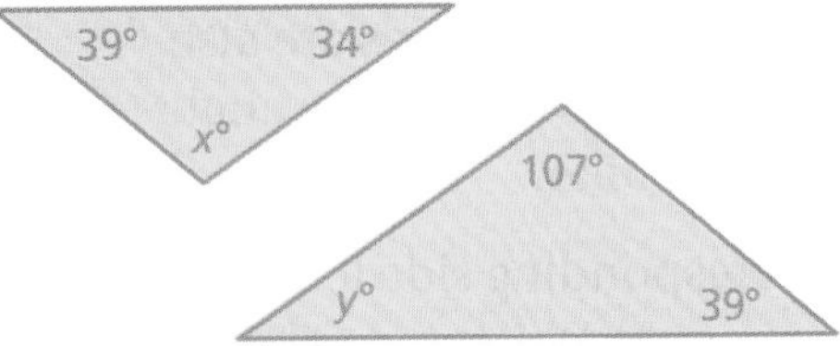

6.

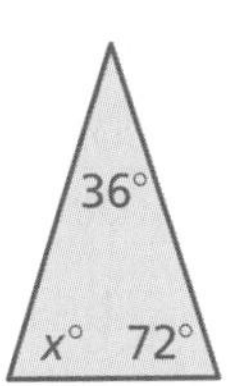

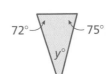

7.

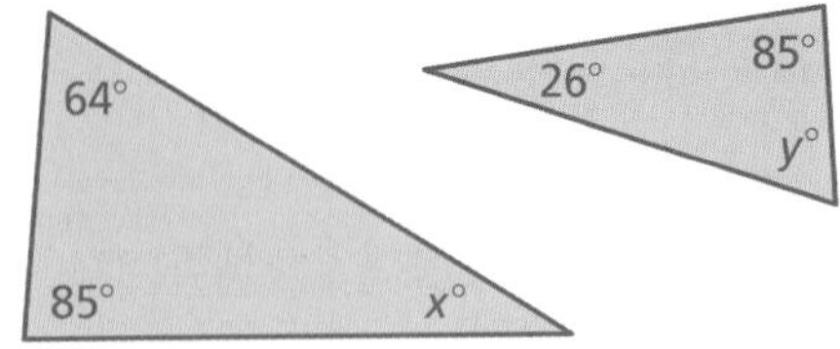

8.

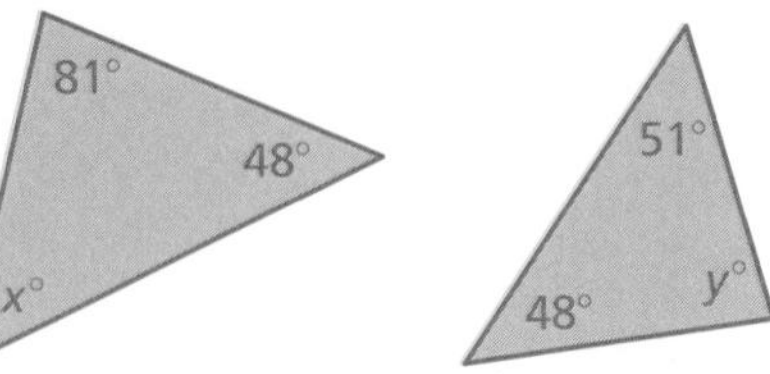

9. **ERROR ANALYSIS** Describe and correct the error in using indirect measurement.

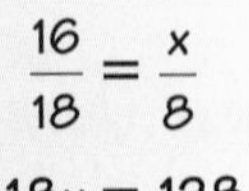

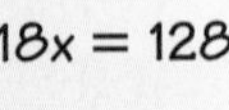

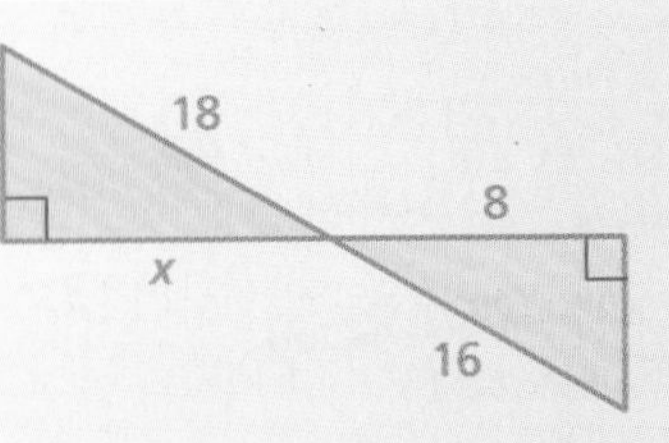

The triangles are similar. Find the value of x.

10.

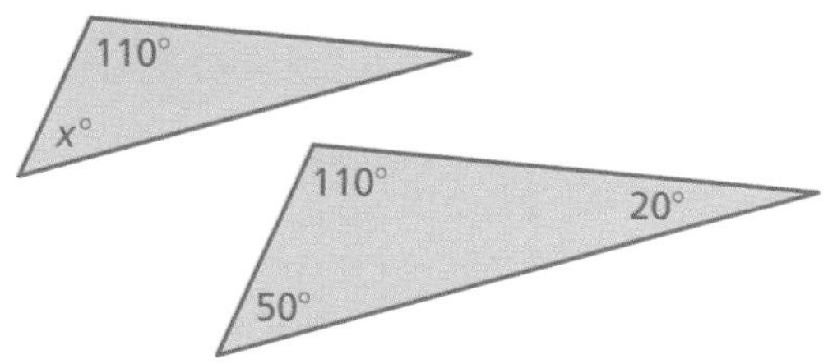

11.

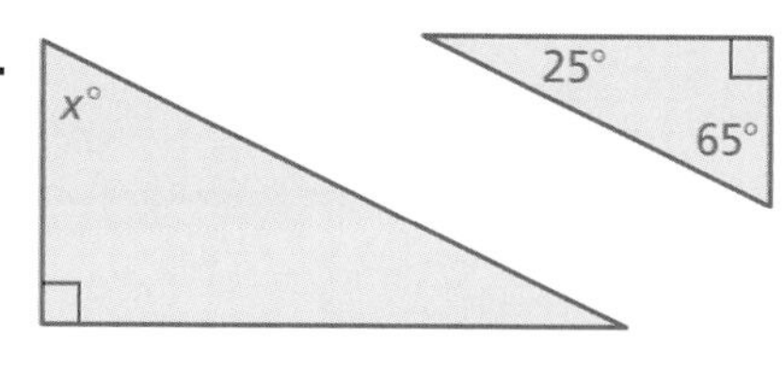

2 **12. TREASURE** The map shows the number of steps you must take to get to the treasure. However, the map is old and the last dimension is unreadable. How many steps do you take from the pyramids to the treasure?

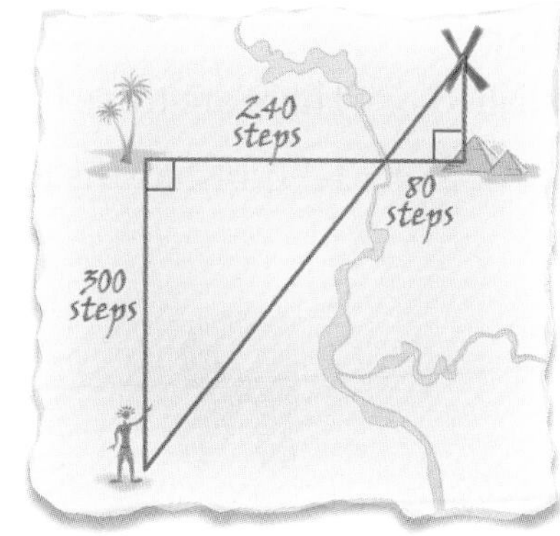

13. CRITICAL THINKING The side lengths of a triangle are increased by 50% to make a similar triangle. Does the area increase by 50% as well? Explain.

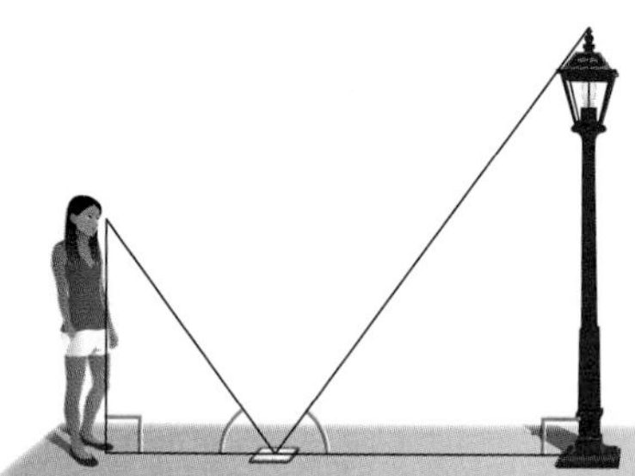

14. PROJECT Using a mirror, a tape measure, and indirect measurement, you can find the height of a lamppost. Place the mirror flat on the ground 6 feet from the lamppost. Move away from the mirror and the lamppost until you can see the top of the lamppost in the mirror. Measure the distance between yourself and the mirror. Then use similar triangles to find the height of the lamppost.

15. Geometry The drawing shows the scoring zone of a standard shuffleboard court. $\triangle DAE \sim \triangle BAG \sim \triangle CAF$. The lengths of segments AG, GF, and FE are equal.

a. Find x.

b. Find CF.

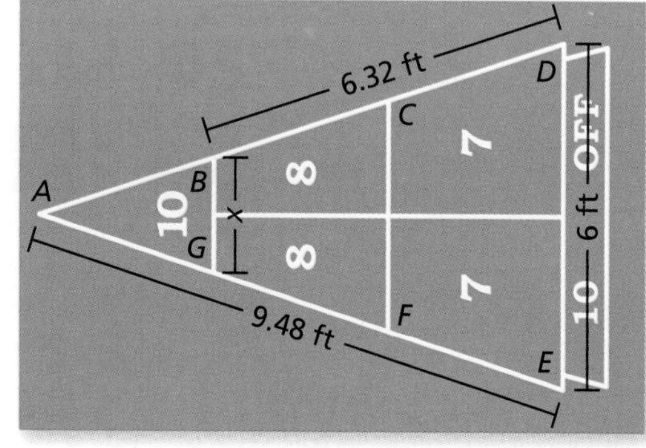

Fair Game Review What you learned in previous grades & lessons

Does the equation represent a *linear* or *nonlinear* function? Explain. *(Section 3.4)*

16. $y = \dfrac{5}{x}$

17. $y = -5.4x + \pi$

18. $y = 2x - 8$

19. $y = 6x^2 + x - 1$

20. MULTIPLE CHOICE Which two lines are parallel? *(Section 2.2)*

(A) blue and red

(B) red and green

(C) green and blue

(D) all three are parallel

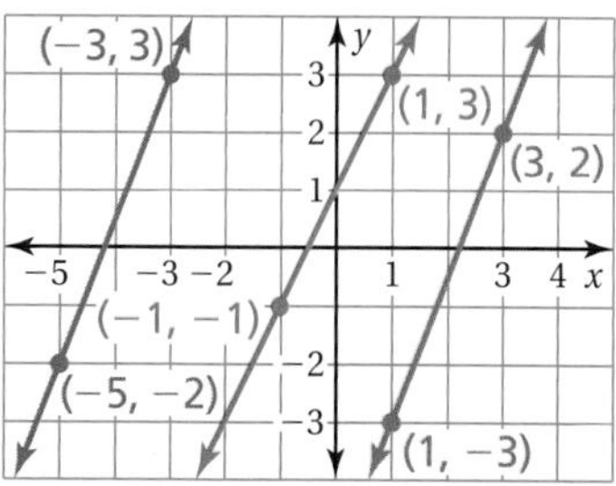

5.5 Polygons and Transformations

STANDARDS OF LEARNING
8.8

Essential Question How can transformations be used in calligraphy?

There are three basic ways to move objects on a flat surface.

1. Translate the object.
2. Reflect the object.
3. Rotate the object.

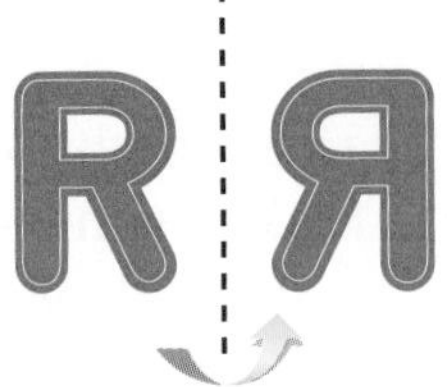

1 ACTIVITY: Making Ambigrams for Names

Work with a partner. An *ambigram* is a word that is the same when it is rotated 180°.

a. Some names can be made into ambigrams. Identify each person's name.

b. Make an ambigram of your own name or the name of someone you know. Use a name that is different from the 6 names shown above.

2 ACTIVITY: Making Palindrome Names

Work with a partner. A *palindrome* is a word that is the same forwards and backwards. Some palindrome names are also *reflective* because they can be reflected horizontally or vertically to produce the same name.

a. Decide whether each palindrome name is reflective. Explain.

HANNAH EVE

OTTO ANNA BOB

b. Find other names that are palindromes. Are they reflective horizontally? vertically?

3 ACTIVITY: Making Anagram Name Pairs

Work with a partner. Two names are *anagrams* if the letters in one name can be translated to make the other name.

a. Find common names that are anagrams of the following names.

MYRA HAMLET ARNOLD

EDNA AILEEN

MAY GALEN BRYAN

b. Find other pairs of anagram names. Can you make another name from the letters in your name?

What Is Your Answer?

4. **IN YOUR OWN WORDS** How can transformations be used in calligraphy?
5. Use the Internet or some other resource to find ways that mathematics (including geometry) is used in calligraphy.

Practice Use what you learned about ambigrams to complete Exercises 3 and 4 on page 231.

5.5 Lesson

Key Vocabulary
translation, *p. 228*
reflection, *p. 228*
rotation, *p. 228*
dilation, *p. 230*

Translations

A **translation**, or *slide*, is a transformation in which a figure moves but does not turn. Every point of the figure moves the same distance and in the same direction.

Reflections

A **reflection**, or *flip*, is a transformation in which a figure is reflected in a line called the *line of reflection*. A reflection creates a mirror image of the original figure.

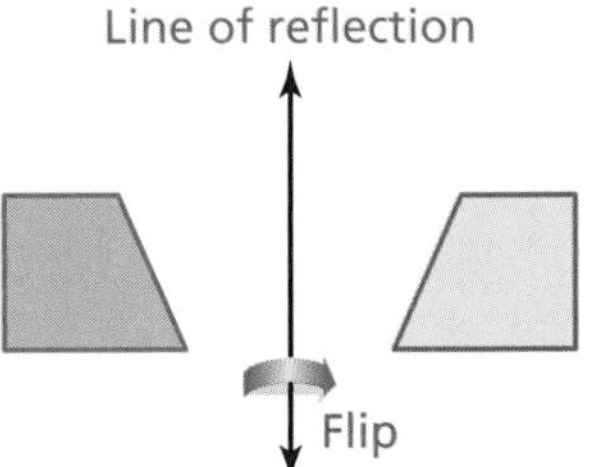

Rotations

A **rotation**, or *turn*, is a transformation in which a figure is rotated about a point called the *center of rotation*. The number of degrees a figure rotates is the *angle of rotation*.

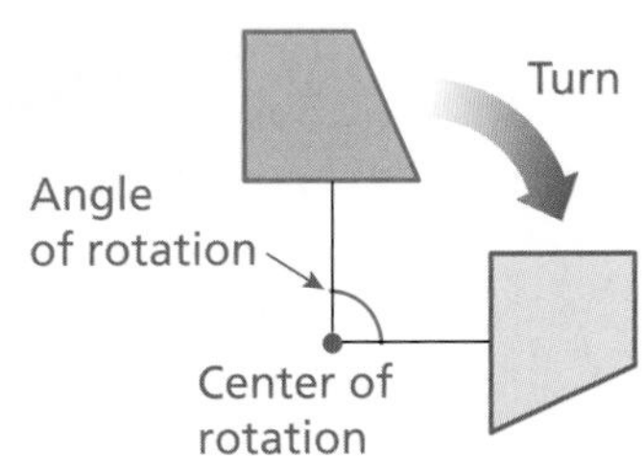

For these transformations, the original figure and its image are congruent.

Remember

A *transformation* changes a figure into another figure. The new figure is called the *image*.

EXAMPLE 1 Translating a Figure

The vertices of a parallelogram are $A(-4, -3)$, $B(-2, -2)$, $C(3, -4)$, and $D(1, -5)$. Translate the parallelogram 2 units left and 4 units up. What are the coordinates of the image?

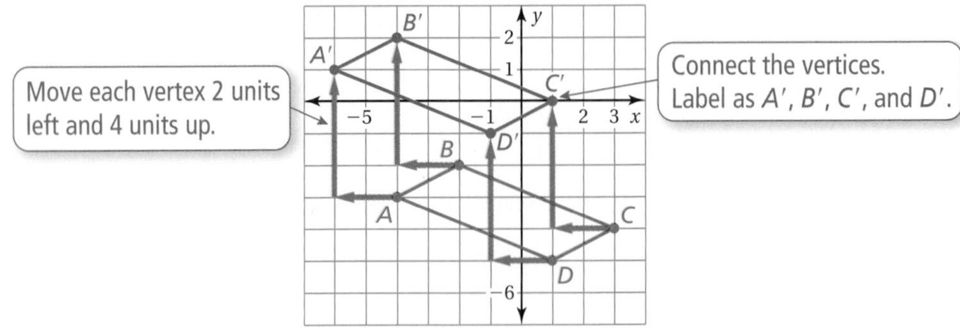

∴ The coordinates of the image are $A'(-6, 1)$, $B'(-4, 2)$, $C'(1, 0)$, and $D'(-1, -1)$.

EXAMPLE 2 Reflecting a Figure

The vertices of a pentagon are $V(-4, -5)$, $W(-4, -1)$, $X(-2, -1)$, $Y(-1, -3)$, and $Z(-2, -5)$. Reflect the pentagon in the y-axis. What are the coordinates of the image?

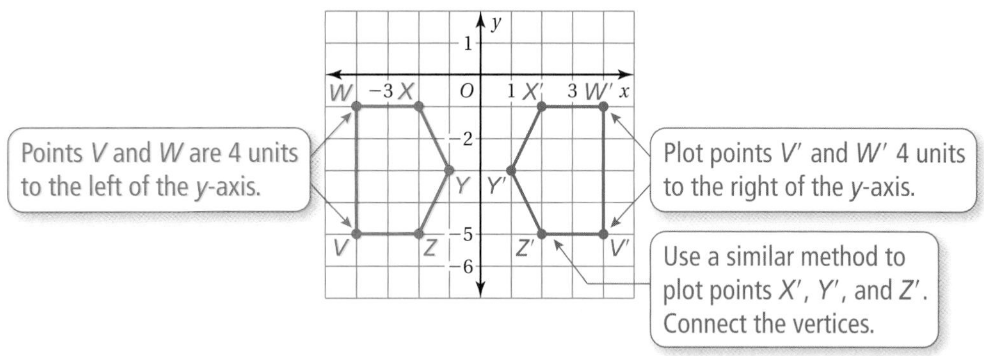

Points V and W are 4 units to the left of the y-axis.
Plot points V′ and W′ 4 units to the right of the y-axis.
Use a similar method to plot points X′, Y′, and Z′. Connect the vertices.

The coordinates of the image are $V'(4, -5)$, $W'(4, -1)$, $X'(2, -1)$, $Y'(1, -3)$, and $Z'(2, -5)$.

EXAMPLE 3 Rotating a Figure

The vertices of a trapezoid are $P(2, -2)$, $Q(4, -2)$, $R(5, -5)$, and $S(4, -5)$. Rotate the trapezoid 90° clockwise about the origin. What are the coordinates of the image?

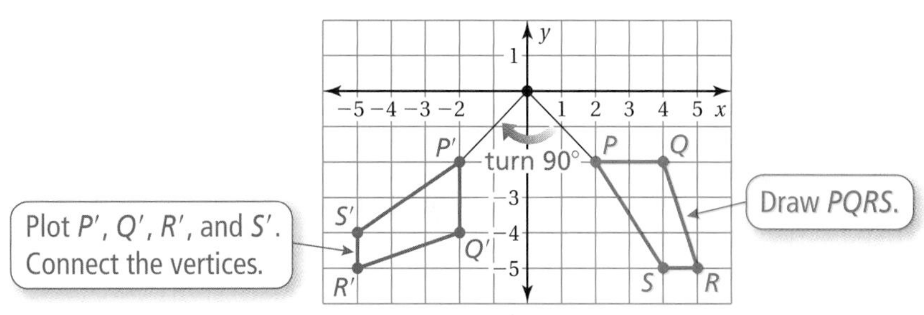

The coordinates of the image are $P'(-2, -2)$, $Q'(-2, -4)$, $R'(-5, -5)$, and $S'(-5, -4)$.

On Your Own

Now You're Ready
Exercises 5–10

Find the coordinates of the image after the transformation.

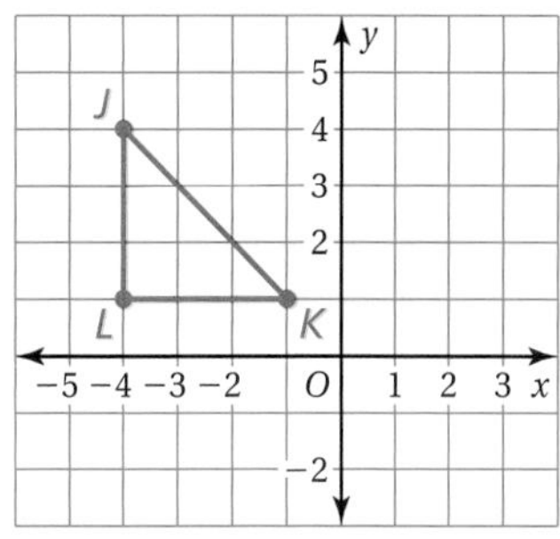

1. a translation of 3 units right and 5 units down
2. a reflection in the x-axis
3. a rotation of 180° about the origin

Key Idea

Dilations

A **dilation** is a transformation in which a figure is made larger or smaller with respect to a fixed point called the *center of dilation.*

The original figure and its image are similar.

The ratio of the side lengths of the image to the corresponding side lengths of the original figure is the *scale factor* of the dilation. To dilate a figure in the coordinate plane with respect to the origin, multiply the coordinates of each vertex by the scale factor k.

- When $k > 1$, the dilation is called an *enlargement.*
- When $k > 0$ and $k < 1$, the dilation is called a *reduction.*

EXAMPLE 4 Dilating a Figure

Draw the image of kite *FGHJ* after a dilation with a scale factor of 2. Identify the type of dilation.

Multiply each x- and y-coordinate by the scale factor 2.

Vertices of $FGHJ$	$(x \cdot 2, y \cdot 2)$	Vertices of $F'G'H'J'$
$F(1, 3)$	$(1 \cdot 2, 3 \cdot 2)$	$F'(2, 6)$
$G(2, 4)$	$(2 \cdot 2, 4 \cdot 2)$	$G'(4, 8)$
$H(3, 3)$	$(3 \cdot 2, 3 \cdot 2)$	$H'(6, 6)$
$J(2, 1)$	$(2 \cdot 2, 1 \cdot 2)$	$J'(4, 2)$

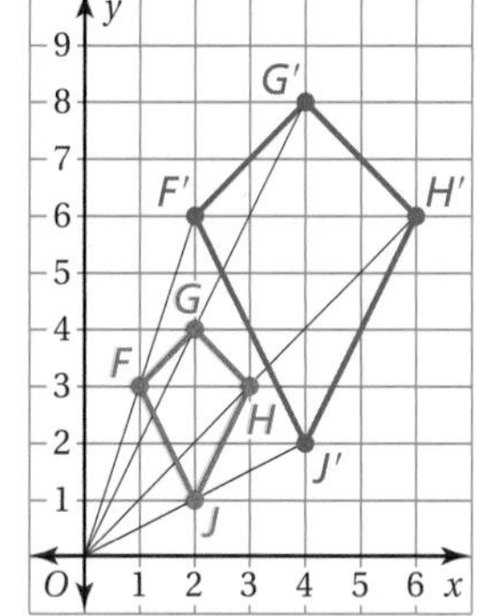

The dilation is an *enlargement* because the scale factor is greater than 1.

Study Tip

You can check your answer by drawing a line from the origin through each vertex of the original figure. The vertices of the image should lie on these lines.

On Your Own

Now You're Ready
Exercises 11–13

4. Draw the image of rhombus $JKLM$ after a dilation with a scale factor of $\frac{1}{2}$. Identify the type of dilation.

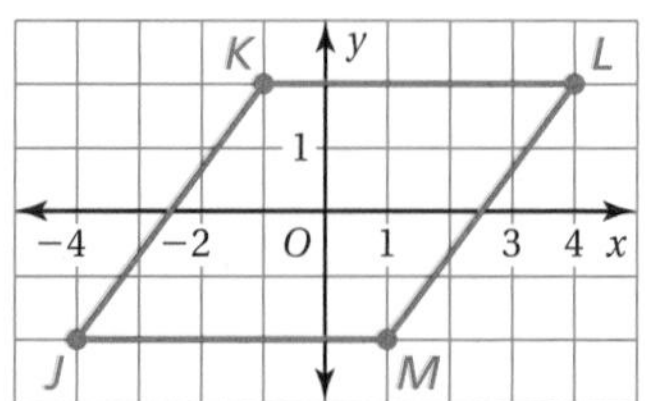

5.5 Exercises

Vocabulary and Concept Check

1. **VOCABULARY** Identify the transformation shown.

a. 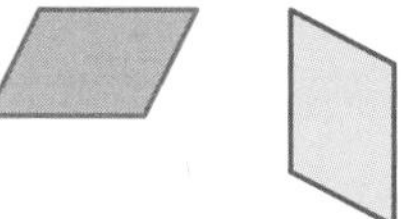

b. 

c. 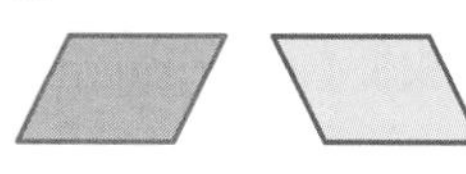

d. 

2. **WHICH ONE DOESN'T BELONG?** Which transformation does *not* belong with the other three? Explain your reasoning.

translation	reflection	rotation	dilation

Practice and Problem Solving

Identify the name. Is the name an ambigram? Explain.

3. 4.

Find the coordinates of the image after the transformation.

1 5. a translation of 2 units left and 1 unit up

6. a translation of 5 units right and 3 units down

2 7. a reflection in the y-axis

8. a reflection in the x-axis

3 9. a rotation of 90° clockwise about the origin

10. a rotation of 90° counterclockwise about the origin

4 11. a dilation with a scale factor of 3

12. a dilation with a scale factor of $\frac{1}{4}$

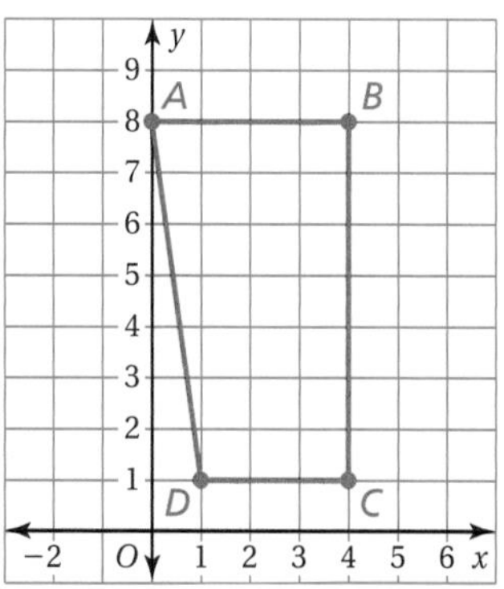

13. Identify each type of dilation in Exercises 11 and 12.

14. **ERROR ANALYSIS** Describe and correct the error in reflecting the blue triangle in the y-axis.

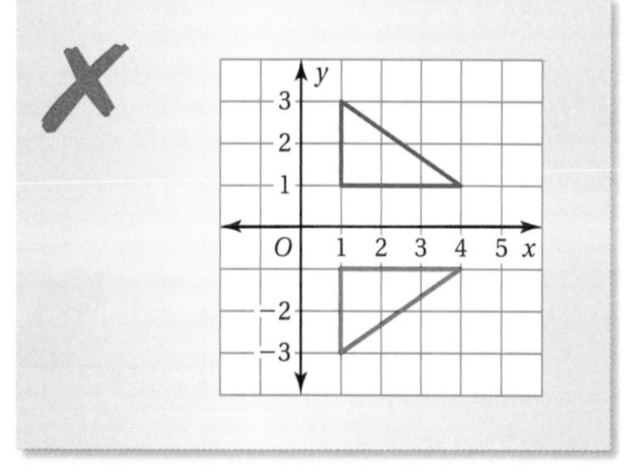

15. **OPEN-ENDED** Draw a polygon in a coordinate plane. Translate the polygon 4 units left and 5 units down.

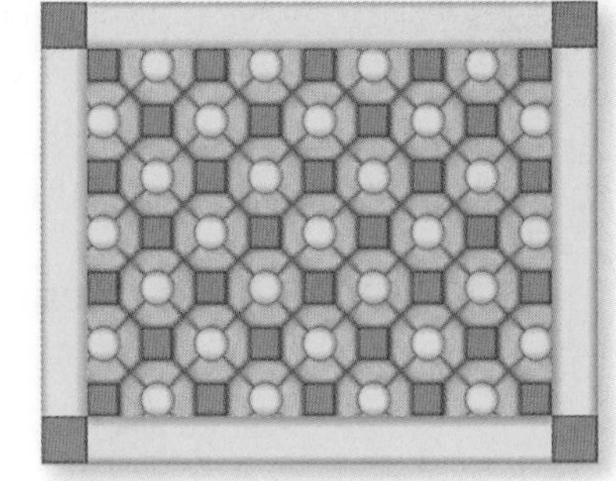

16. **AREA RUG** Describe how translations are used in the design of the area rug.

17. **ERROR ANALYSIS** Describe and correct the error in describing the transformation.

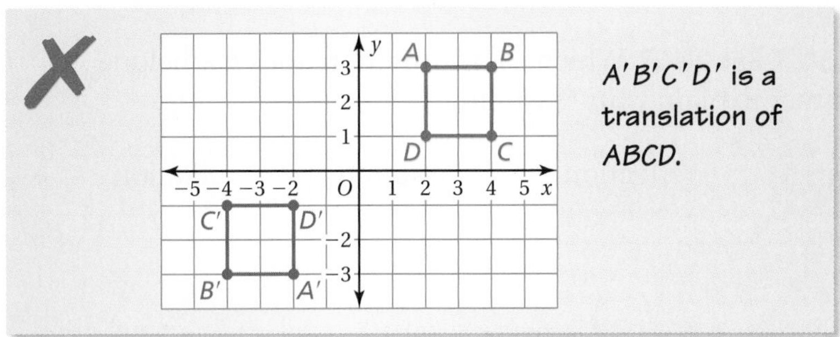

Tell whether a polygon and its image are congruent after the transformation. Explain.

18. translation
19. reflection
20. rotation
21. dilation

REASONING A polygon lies entirely in Quadrant I. In which quadrant will the image lie after the given transformation?

22. a reflection in the x-axis
23. a reflection in the y-axis
24. a rotation of 180° about the origin
25. a dilation with a scale factor of 2

26. **CRITICAL THINKING** The blue square is the image of the red square after a transformation. How can the vertices of each figure be labeled so that the transformation is a translation? a reflection? a rotation? Explain.

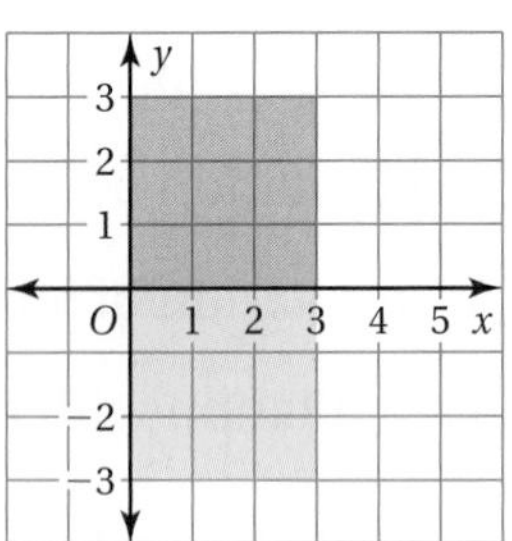

27. **CARTOON** A cartoonist enlarges Newton as shown. What is the scale factor?

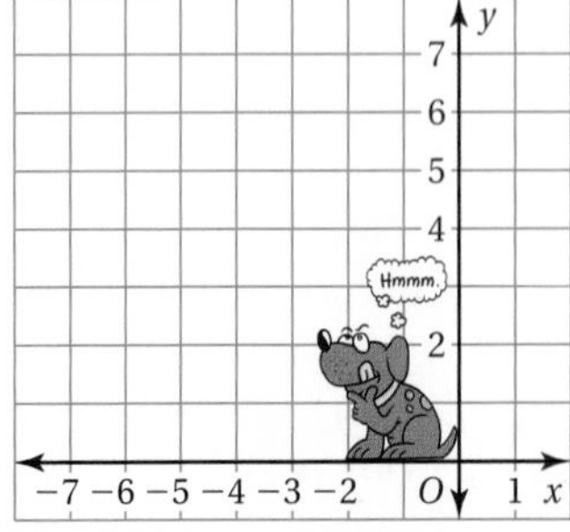

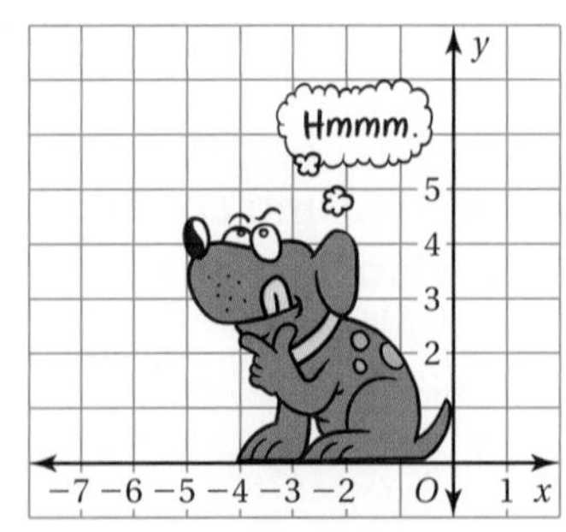

28. **REASONING** The vertices of a polygon are $A(-8, 4)$, $B(6, 4)$, $C(10, -12)$, and $D(-8, -12)$. The coordinates of the image are $A'(-4, 2)$, $B'(3, 2)$, $C'(5, -6)$, and $D'(-4, -6)$. Identify the type of transformation.

29. **KALEIDOSCOPE** A pattern has a line of symmetry if the pattern can be mapped onto itself by a reflection in the line. Find the number of lines of symmetry in each kaleidoscope pattern.

a.

b.

30. **OPEN-ENDED** Describe the transformation(s) you can use to rearrange the letters to spell DANCE.

31. **REASONING** What rotation is the same as 90° clockwise? 90° counterclockwise?

32. 

A vertex of a figure is (x, y). Find the coordinates of the vertex after the given transformation.

a. a translation of 3 units left and 2 units up
b. a reflection in the y-axis
c. a rotation of 180° about the origin
d. a dilation with a scale factor of 5

Fair Game Review What you learned in previous grades & lessons

Find the domain and range of the function represented by the graph. *(Section 3.1)*

33. 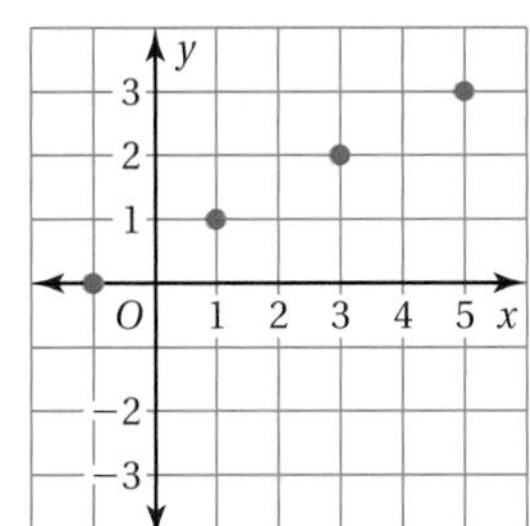

34. 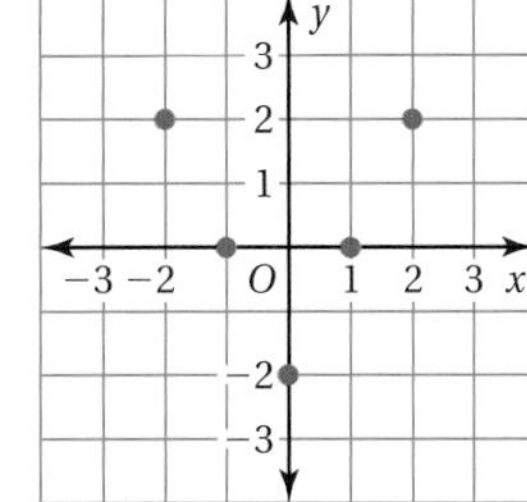

35. 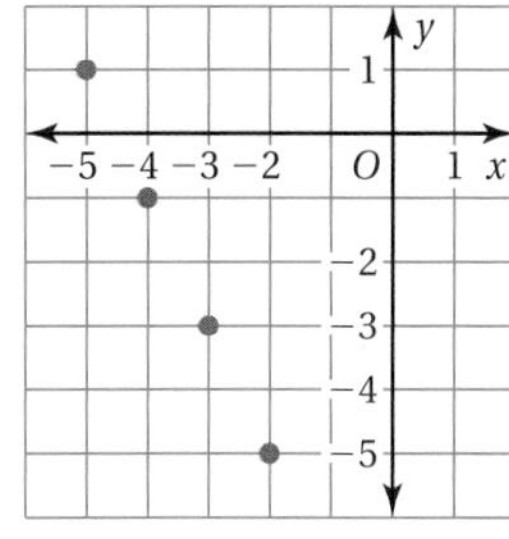

36. **MULTIPLE CHOICE** A store pays \$25 for a video game. The percent of markup is 80%. What is the selling price? *(Section 4.3)*

Ⓐ \$20 Ⓑ \$30 Ⓒ \$45 Ⓓ \$70

5.6 Perimeters of Composite Figures

STANDARDS OF LEARNING
8.11

Essential Question How can you find the perimeter of a composite figure?

1 ACTIVITY: Finding a Pattern

Work with a partner. Describe the pattern of the perimeters. Use your pattern to find the perimeter of the tenth figure in the sequence. (Each small square has a perimeter of 4.)

a.

b.

c.

2 ACTIVITY: Finding a Distance

Work with a partner.

a. Estimate the distance to the gold.

b. Estimate the distance to the silver.

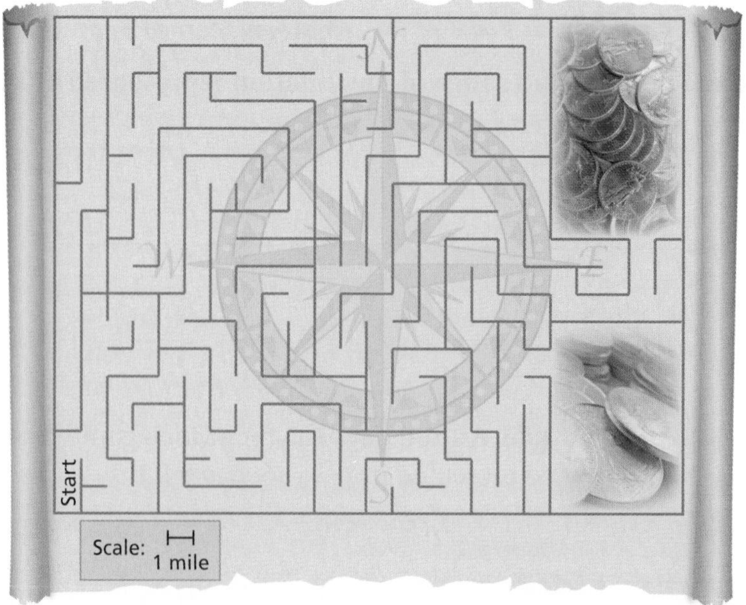

3 ACTIVITY: Submitting a Bid

Work with a partner. You want to bid on a tiling contract. You will be supplying and installing the brown tile that borders the swimming pool.

- **Your cost for the tile is $4 per linear foot.**
- **It takes about 15 minutes to prepare, install, and clean each foot of tile.**

a. How many brown tiles are needed for the border?

b. Write a bid for how much you will charge to supply and install the tile. Include what you want to charge as an hourly wage. Estimate what you think your profit will be.

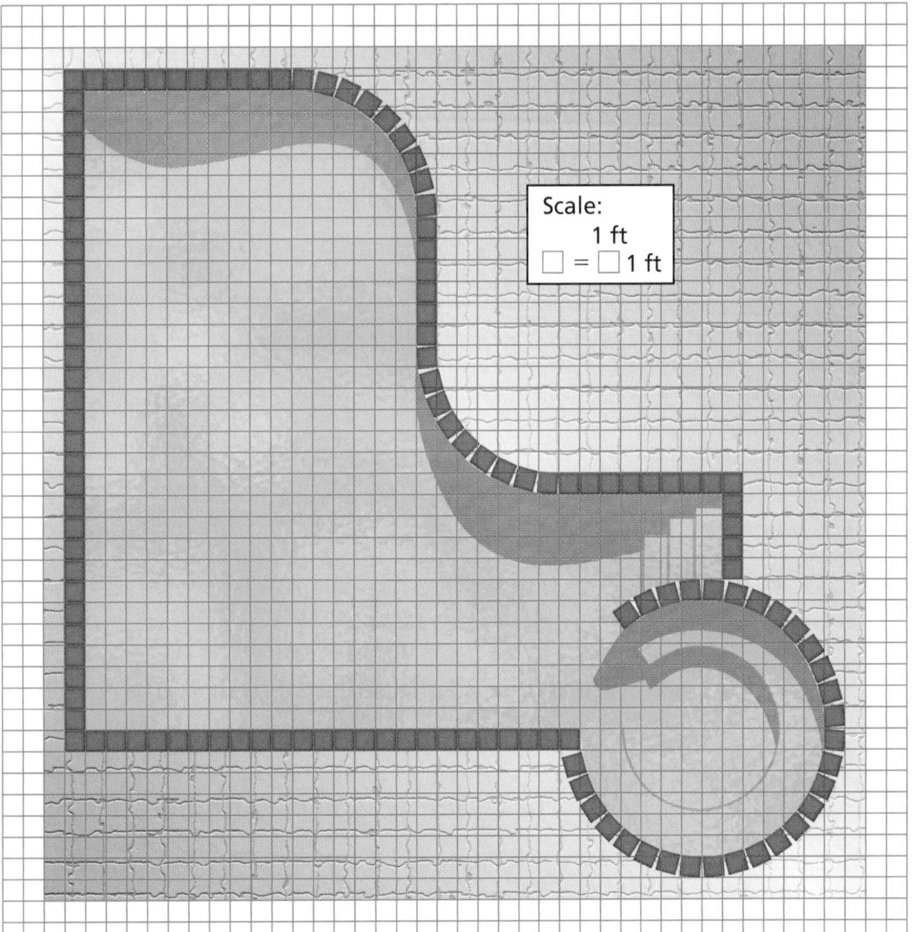

What Is Your Answer?

4. **IN YOUR OWN WORDS** How can you find the perimeter of a composite figure? Use a semicircle, a triangle, and a parallelogram to draw a composite figure. Label the dimensions. Find the perimeter of the figure.

Practice Use what you learned about perimeters of composite figures to complete Exercises 3–5 on page 238.

5.6 Lesson

Check It Out
Lesson Tutorials
BigIdeasMath.com

Key Vocabulary
composite figure, *p. 236*

A **composite figure** is made up of triangles, squares, rectangles, semicircles, and other two-dimensional figures. Here are two examples.

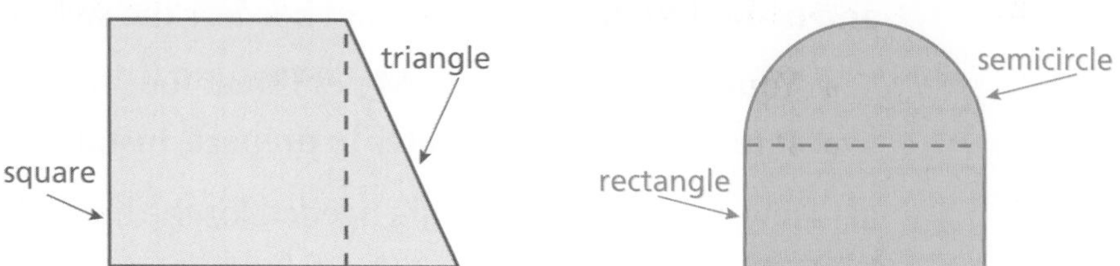
triangle
square
semicircle
rectangle

To find the perimeter of a composite figure, find the distance around the figure.

EXAMPLE 1 Finding a Perimeter Using Grid Paper

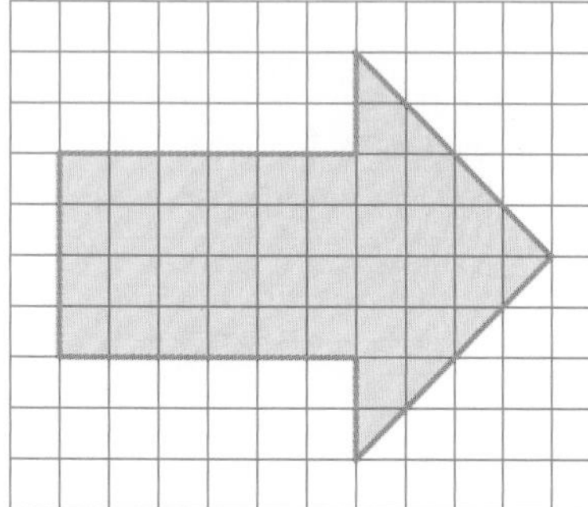

Each square on the grid paper is 1 square inch. Estimate the perimeter of the arrow.

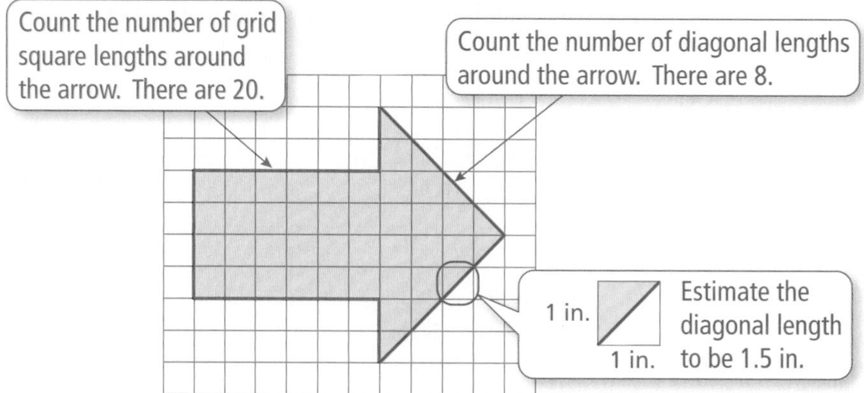
Count the number of grid square lengths around the arrow. There are 20.
Count the number of diagonal lengths around the arrow. There are 8.
1 in.
1 in.
Estimate the diagonal length to be 1.5 in.

Length of 20 grid square lengths: $20 \times 1 = 20$ inches

Length of 8 diagonal lengths: $8 \times 1.5 = 12$ inches

The perimeter is about $20 + 12 = 32$ inches.

On Your Own

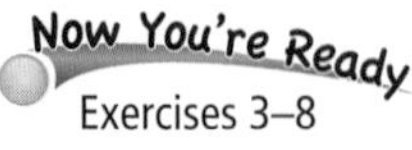
Now You're Ready
Exercises 3–8

1. Each square on the grid paper is 1 square foot. Estimate the perimeter of the red figure.
2. Measure the diagonal of a square whose area is exactly one square foot. Is the diagonal length closer to 1.5 feet or 1.4 feet? Explain.

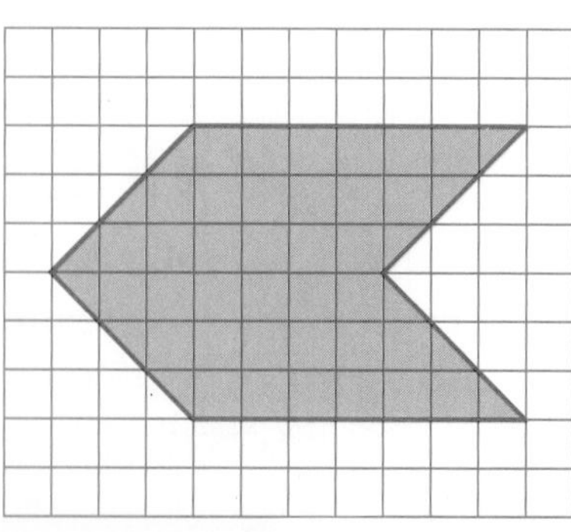

EXAMPLE 2 Finding a Perimeter

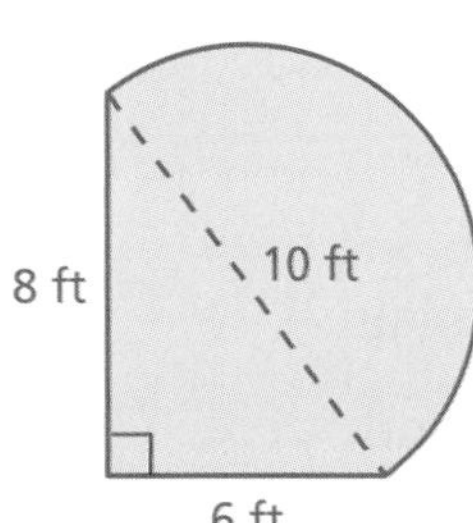

The figure is made up of a semicircle and a triangle. Find the perimeter.

The distance around the triangular part of the figure is $6 + 8 = 14$ feet.

The distance around the semicircle is one-half the circumference of a circle with a diameter of 10 feet.

$\frac{C}{2} = \frac{\pi d}{2}$ Divide the circumference by 2.

$\approx \frac{3.14 \cdot 10}{2}$ Substitute 3.14 for π and 10 for d.

$= 15.7$ Simplify.

The perimeter is about $14 + 15.7 = 29.7$ feet.

EXAMPLE 3 Finding a Perimeter

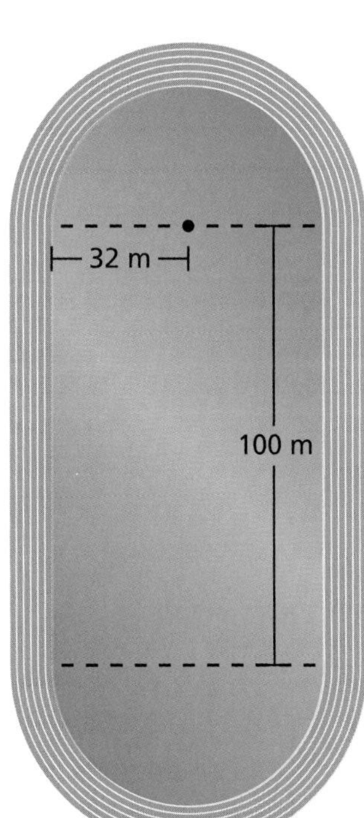

The running track is made up of a rectangle and two semicircles. Find the perimeter.

The semicircular ends of the track form a circle with a radius of 32 meters. Find its circumference.

$C = 2\pi r$ Write formula for circumference.

$\approx 2 \cdot 3.14 \cdot 32$ Substitute 3.14 for π and 32 for r.

$= 200.96$ Multiply.

The perimeter is about $100 + 100 + 200.96 = 400.96$ meters.

On Your Own

3. The figure is made up of a square and two semicircles. Find the perimeter.

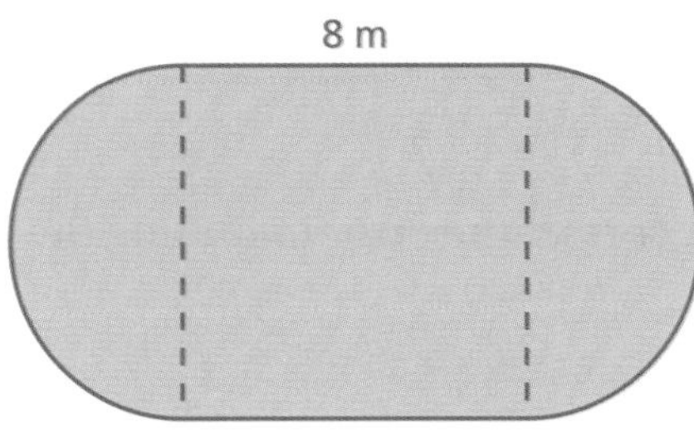

4. Running at 4 ft/sec, how long would it take a person to run around the baseball field?

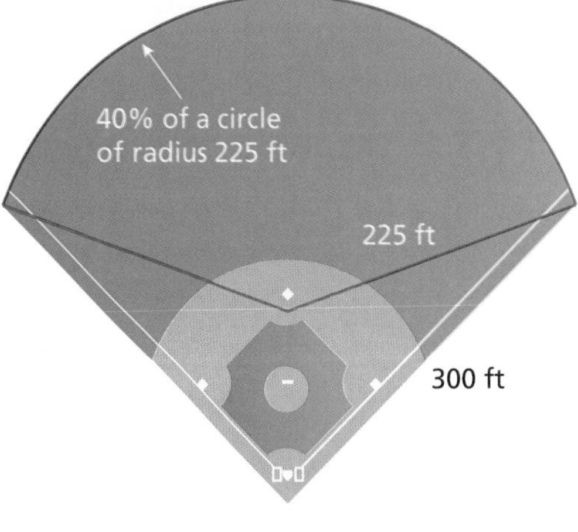

5.6 Exercises

Vocabulary and Concept Check

1. **NUMBER SENSE** Is the perimeter of a composite figure *greater than*, *less than*, or *equal to* the sum of the perimeters of each figure separately? Explain.
2. **OPEN-ENDED** Draw a composite figure formed by a parallelogram and a trapezoid.

Practice and Problem Solving

Each square on the grid paper is 1 square inch. Estimate the perimeter of the figure.

1 **3.**

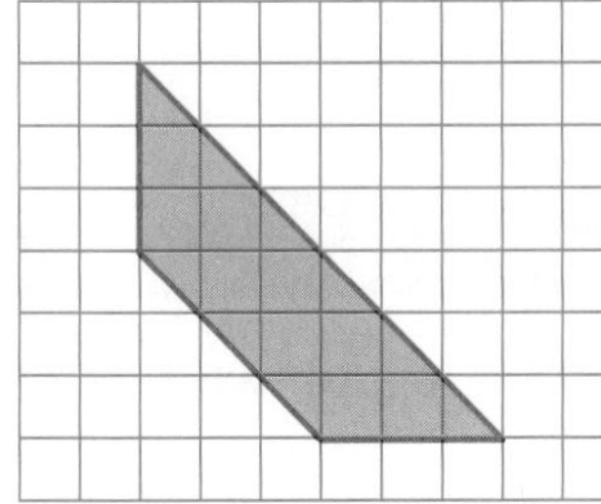

4.

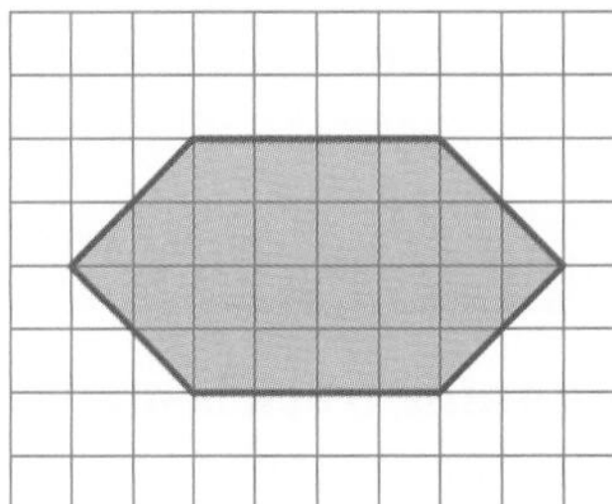

5.

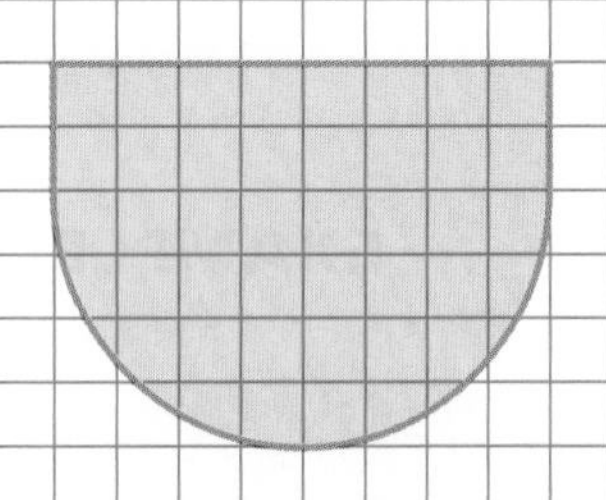

6.

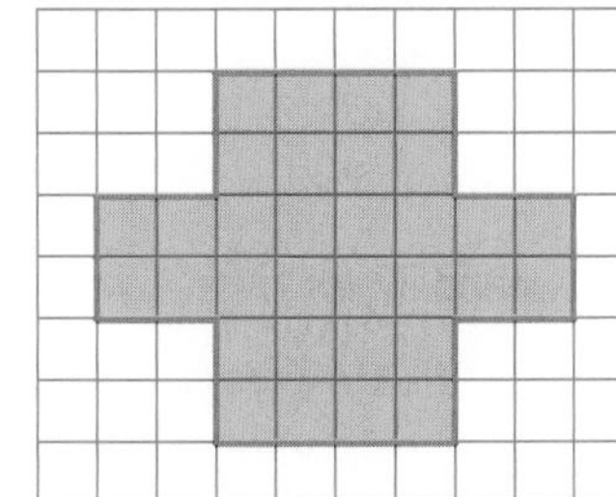

7.

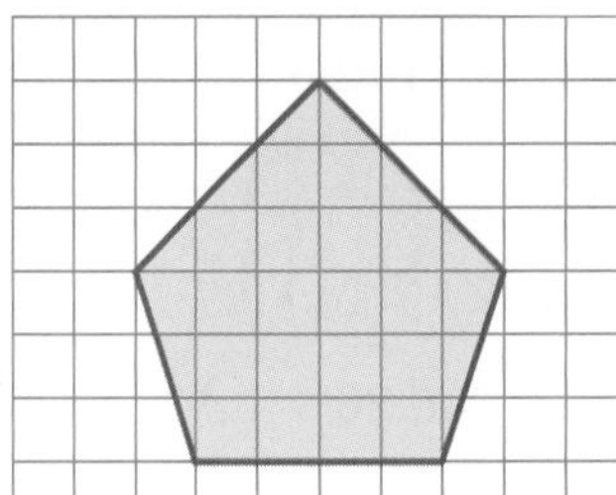

8.

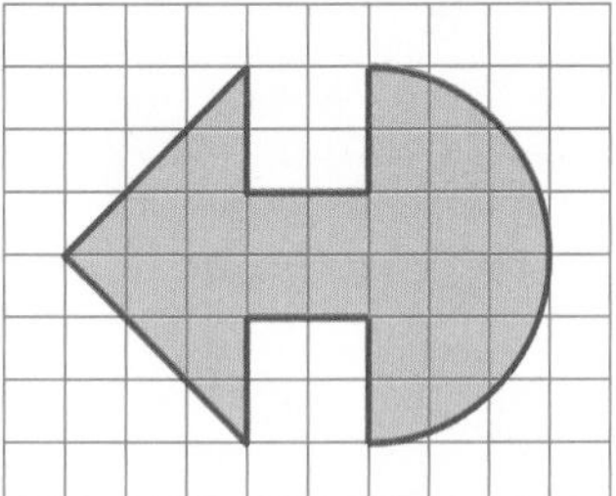

Find the perimeter of the figure.

2 **9.**

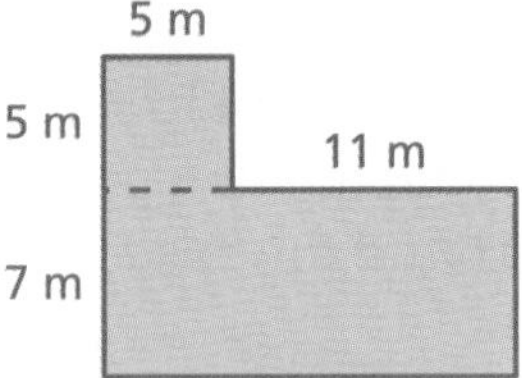

10.

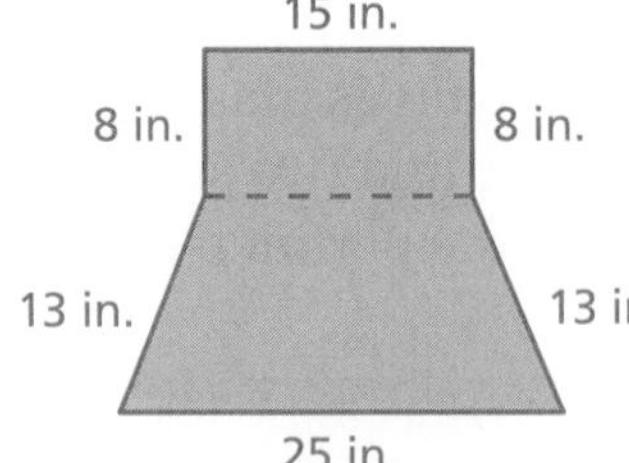

11.

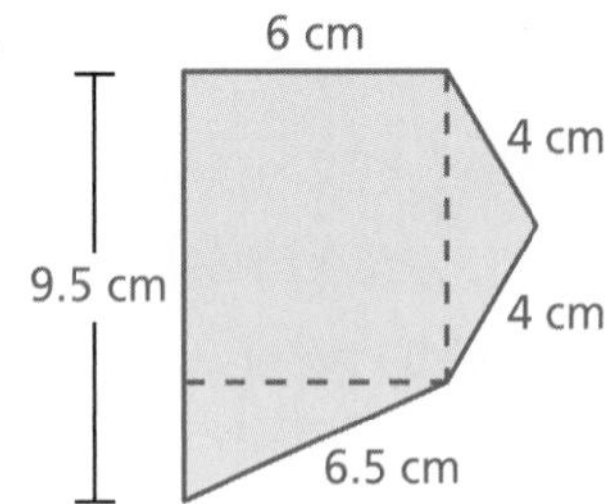

12. **ERROR ANALYSIS** Describe and correct the error in finding the perimeter of the figure.

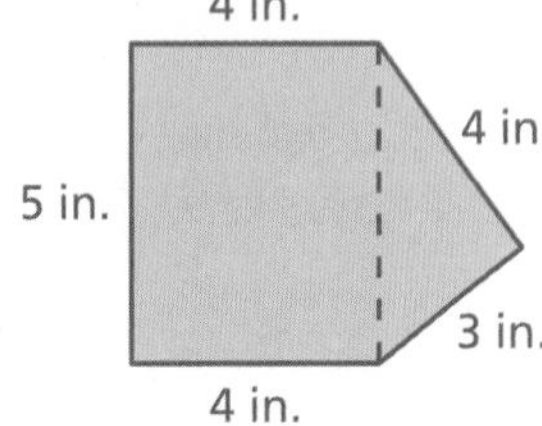

✗ Perimeter $= 4 + 3 + 4 + 5 + 4 + 5$
$= 25$ in.

Find the perimeter of the figure.

13.

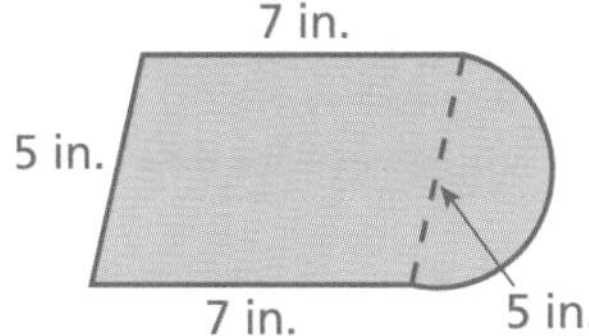

14.

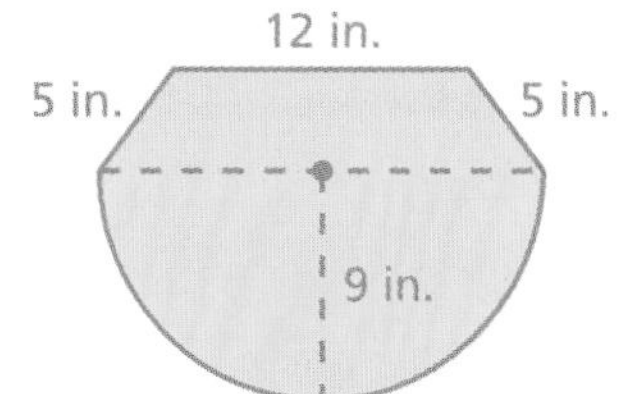

15.

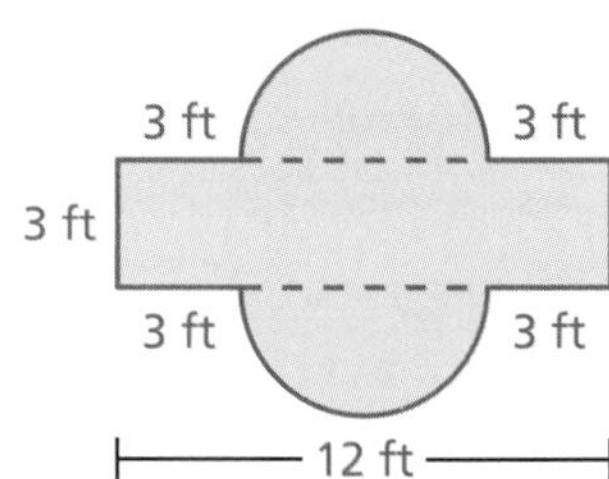

240 ft 285 ft

450 ft 450 ft

450 ft

16. PASTURE A section of land is to be fenced in for a horse pasture.

a. Find the perimeter of the pasture.

b. Fencing costs $27 per yard. How much will it cost to fence in the pasture?

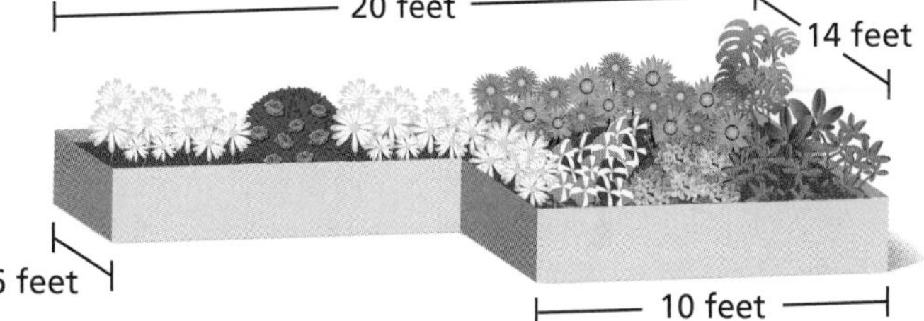

17. GARDEN A garden is built on a rooftop.

a. Find the perimeter of the garden.

b. You want to increase the perimeter by 15 feet. Draw a diagram of how you would do this. Is there more than one way? Explain.

18. In Example 3 on page 237, the track has six lanes. Explain why the starting points for the six runners are staggered. Draw a diagram as part of your explanation.

19. Critical Thinking Is it possible to add a figure to a composite figure without increasing its perimeter? Explain and draw a diagram to support your answer.

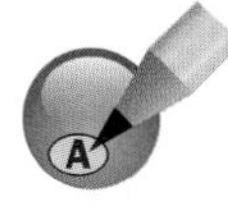

Fair Game Review What you learned in previous grades & lessons

Evaluate the expression. *(Skills Review Handbook)*

20. $2.15(3)^2$ **21.** $4.37(8)^2$ **22.** $3.14(7)^2$ **23.** $8.2(5)^2$

24. MULTIPLE CHOICE Which expression represents "6 less than 5 times a number x?" *(Skills Review Handbook)*

Ⓐ $(6 - 5)x$ Ⓑ $6 - 5x$ Ⓒ $\frac{6}{5x}$ Ⓓ $5x - 6$

5.7 Areas of Composite Figures

STANDARDS OF LEARNING
8.11

Essential Question How can you find the area of a composite figure?

1 ACTIVITY: Estimating Area

Work with a partner.

a. Choose a state. On grid paper, draw a larger outline of the state.

b. Use your drawing to estimate the area (in square miles) of the state.

c. Which state areas are easy to find? Which are difficult? Why?

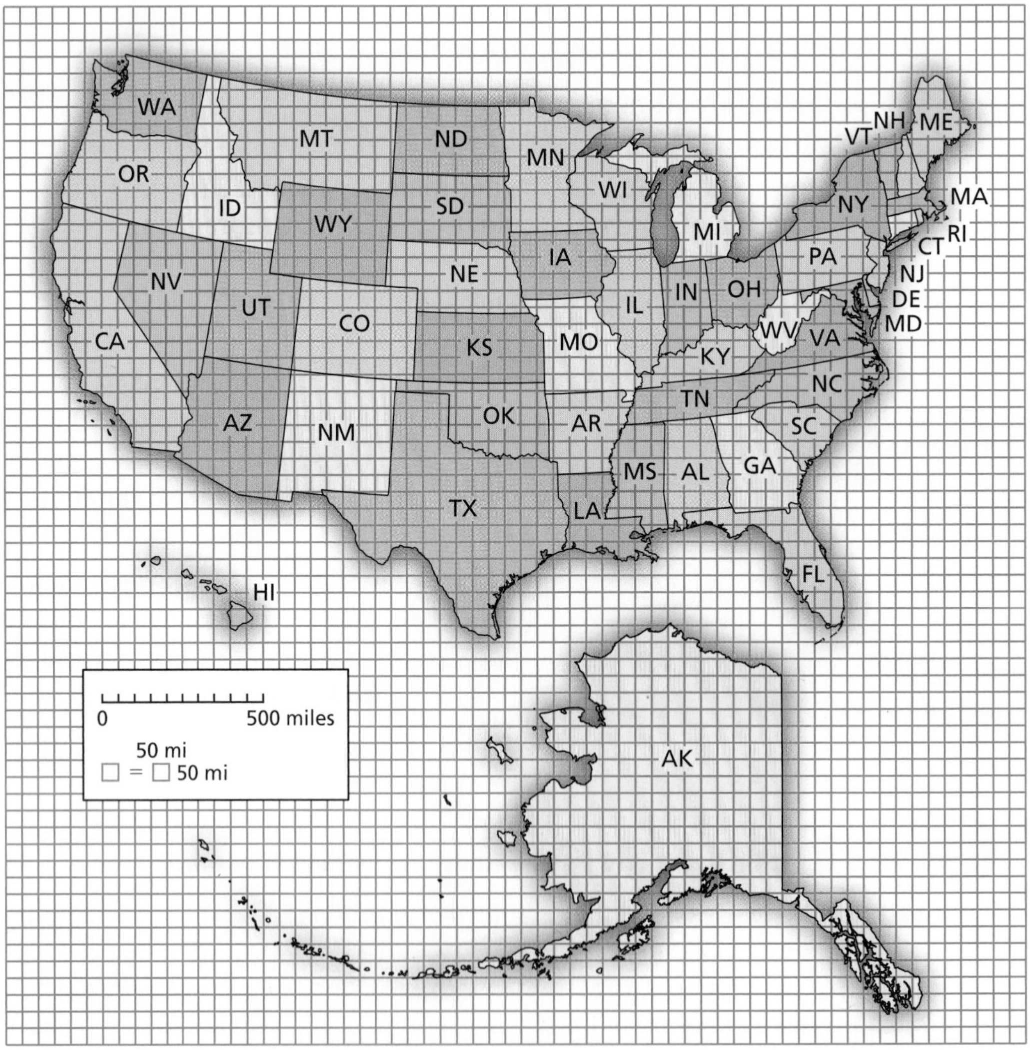

0 500 miles

50 mi
□ = □ 50 mi

2 ACTIVITY: Estimating Areas

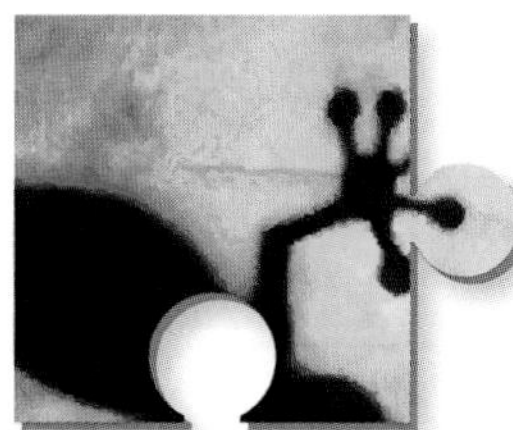

Work with a partner. The completed puzzle has an area of 150 square centimeters.

a. Estimate the area of each puzzle piece.

b. Check your work by adding the six areas. Why is this a check?

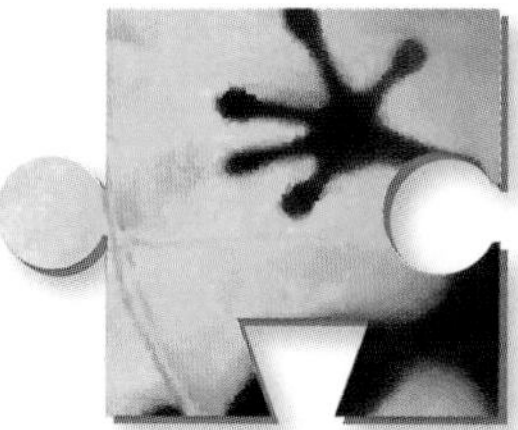

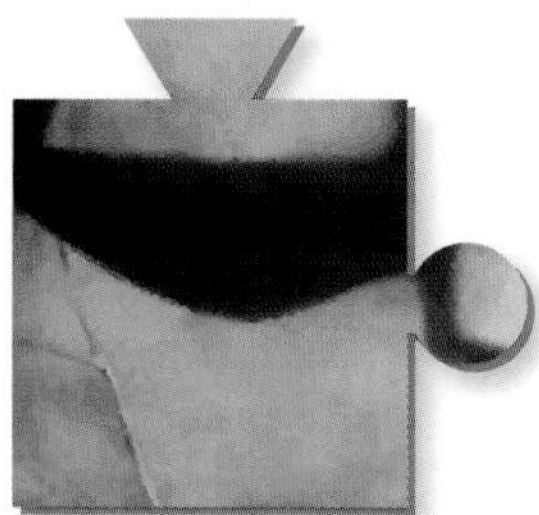

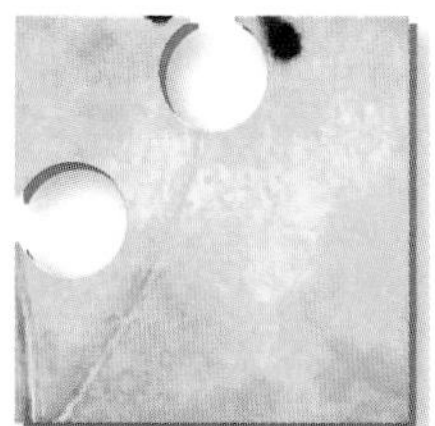

3 ACTIVITY: Filling a Square with Circles

Work with a partner. Which pattern fills more of the square with circles? Explain.

a.

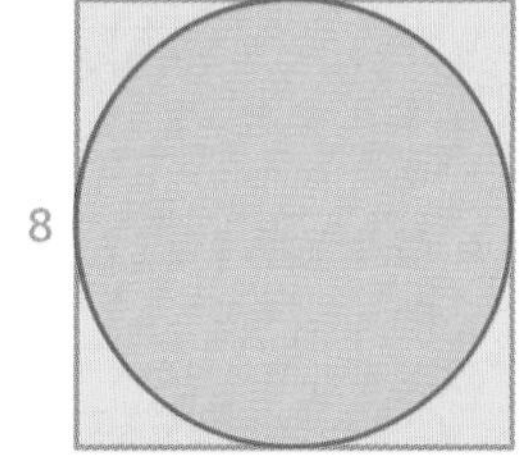

b.

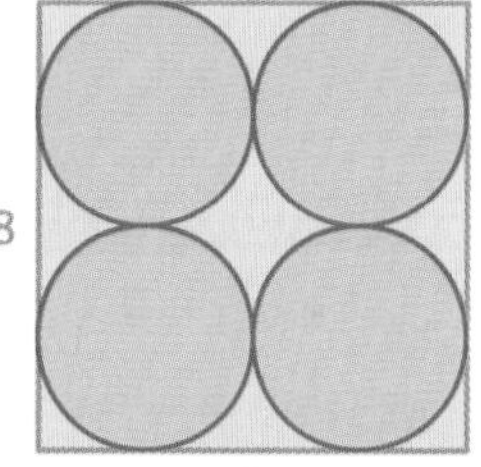

c.

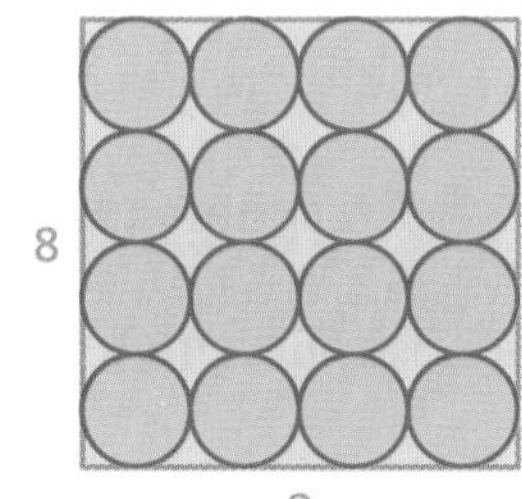

d.

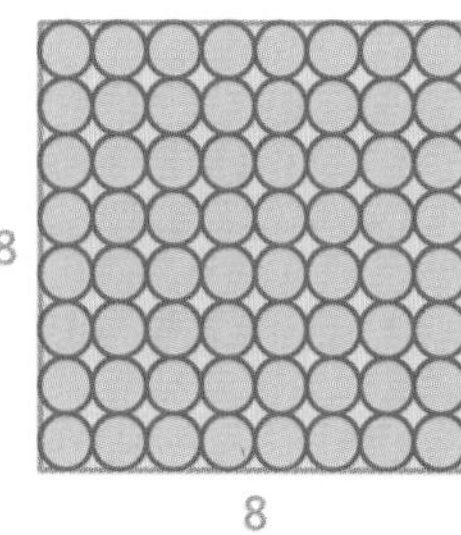

What Is Your Answer?

4. **IN YOUR OWN WORDS** How can you find the area of a composite figure?

5. Summarize the area formulas for all the basic figures you have studied. Draw a single composite figure that has each type of basic figure. Label the dimensions and find the total area.

Use what you learned about areas of composite figures to complete Exercises 3–5 on page 244.

To find the area of a composite figure, split it up into figures with areas you know how to find. Then add the areas of those figures.

EXAMPLE 1 Finding an Area Using Grid Paper

Each square on the grid paper is 1 square meter. Find the area of the yellow figure.

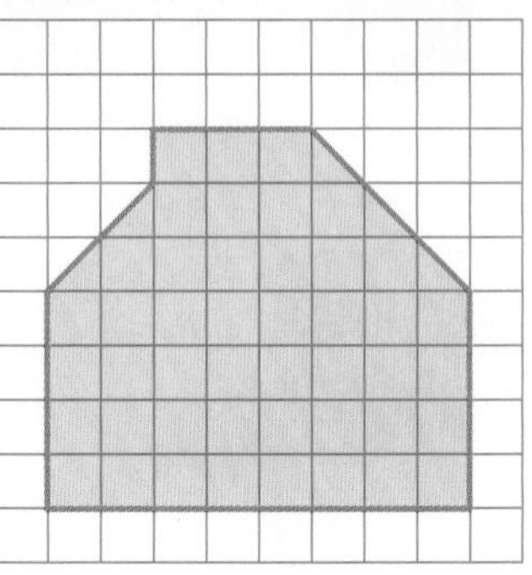

Count the number of squares that lie entirely in the figure. There are 45.

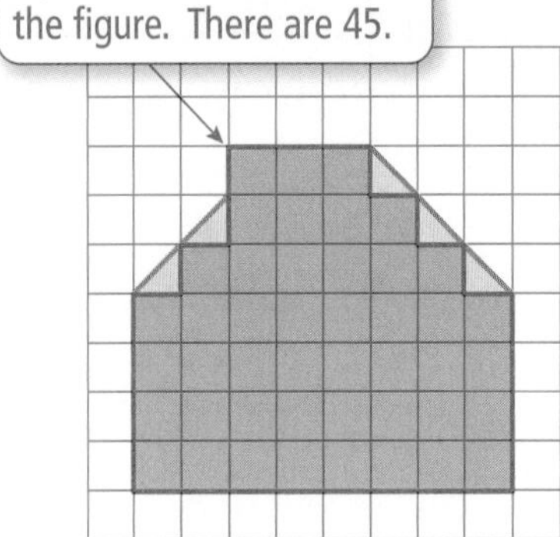

Count the number of half-squares in the figure. There are 5.

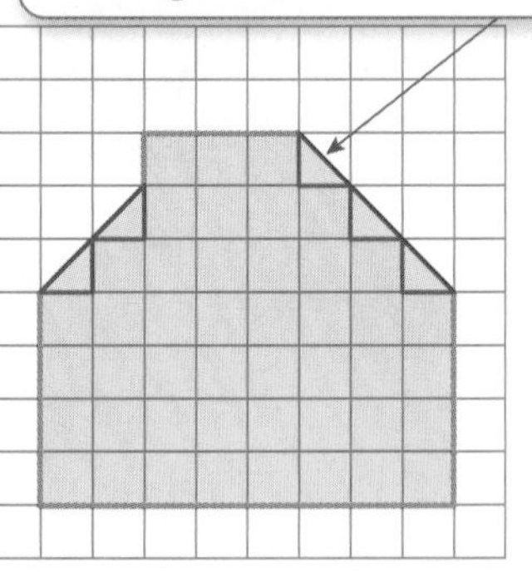

The area of a half-square is $1 \div 2 = 0.5$ square meter.

Area of 45 squares: $45 \times 1 = 45$ square meters

Area of 5 half-squares: $5 \times 0.5 = 2.5$ square meters

So, the area is $45 + 2.5 = 47.5$ square meters.

On Your Own

Now You're Ready
Exercises 3–8

Find the area of the shaded figure.

1.

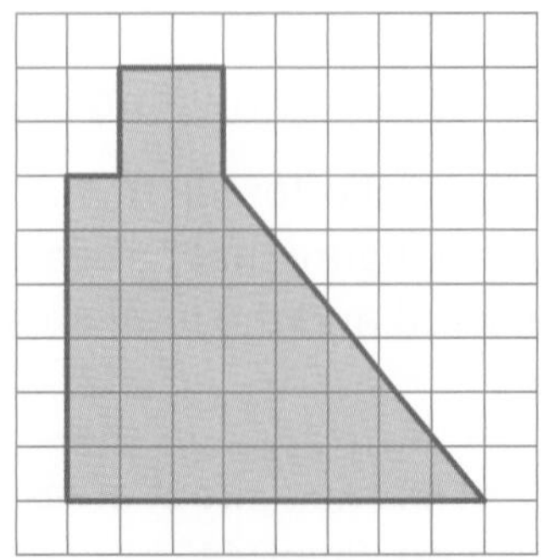

2.

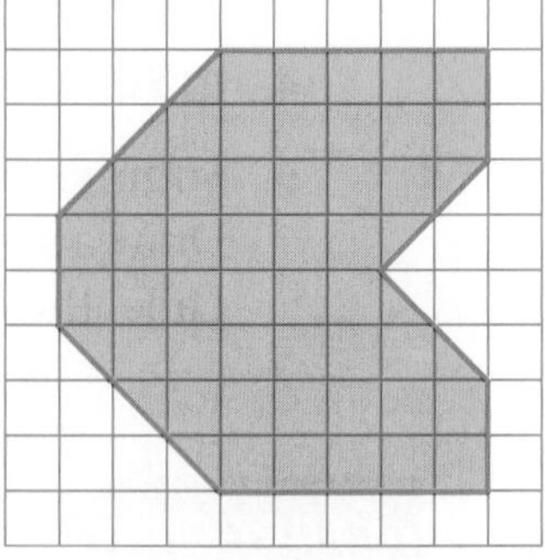

EXAMPLE 2 Finding an Area

Find the area of the portion of the basketball court shown.

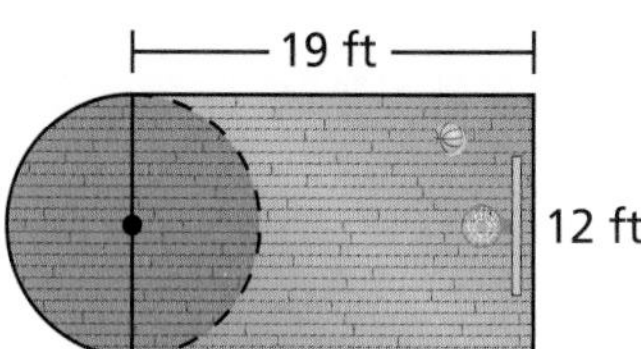

The figure is made up of a rectangle and a semicircle. Find the area of each figure.

Area of rectangle

$$A = \ell w$$
$$= (19)(12)$$
$$= 228$$

Area of semicircle

$$A = \frac{\pi r^2}{2}$$
$$\approx \frac{3.14 \cdot (6)^2}{2}$$
$$= 56.52$$

The semicircle has a radius of $\frac{12}{2} = 6$ feet.

So, the area is about $228 + 56.52 = 284.52$ square feet.

EXAMPLE 3 Finding an Area

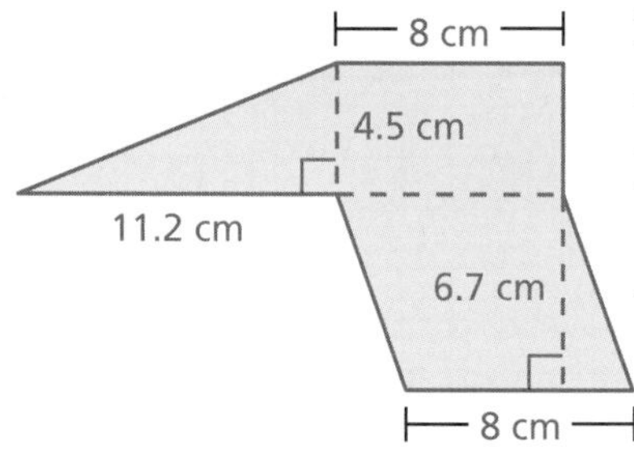

Find the area of the figure.

The figure is made up of a triangle, a rectangle, and a parallelogram. Find the area of each figure.

Area of triangle

$$A = \frac{1}{2}bh$$
$$= \frac{1}{2}(11.2)(4.5)$$
$$= 25.2$$

Area of rectangle

$$A = \ell w$$
$$= (8)(4.5)$$
$$= 36$$

Area of parallelogram

$$A = bh$$
$$= (8)(6.7)$$
$$= 53.6$$

So, the area is $25.2 + 36 + 53.6 = 114.8$ square centimeters.

On Your Own

Now You're Ready
Exercises 9 and 10

Find the area of the figure.

3.

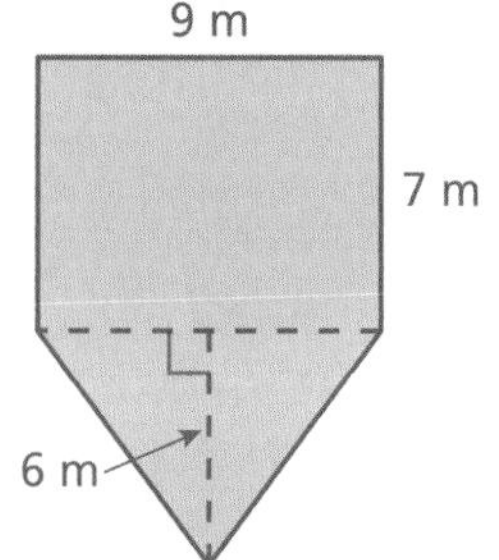

4.

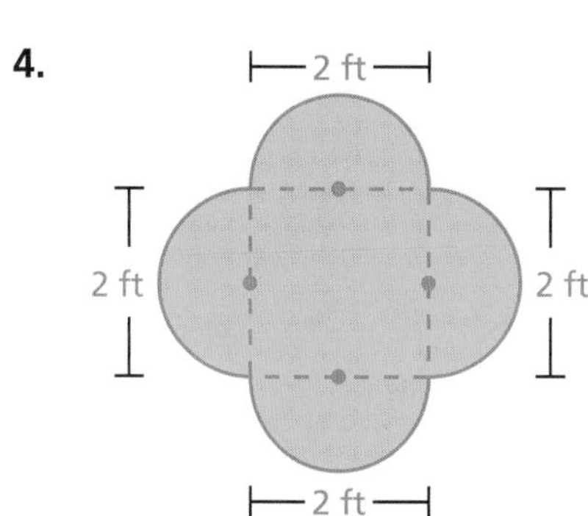

5.7 Exercises

Vocabulary and Concept Check

1. **REASONING** Describe two different ways to find the area of the figure. Name the types of figures you used and the dimensions of each.

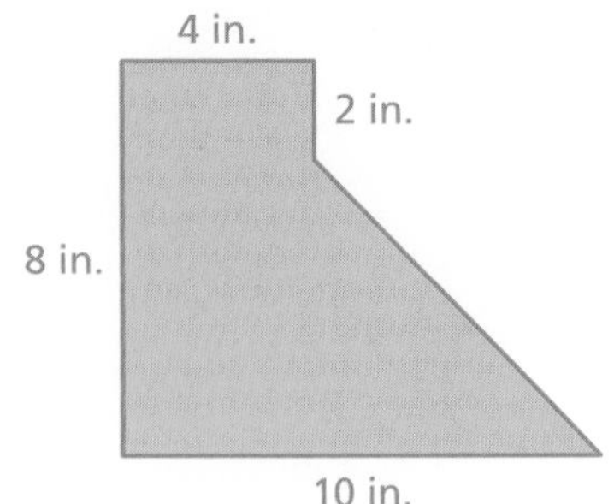

2. **REASONING** Draw a trapezoid. Suppose you can't remember the formula for the area of a trapezoid. Explain how you can think of the trapezoid as a composite figure to find its area.

Practice and Problem Solving

Each square on the grid paper is 1 square inch. Find the area of the figure.

1 3. 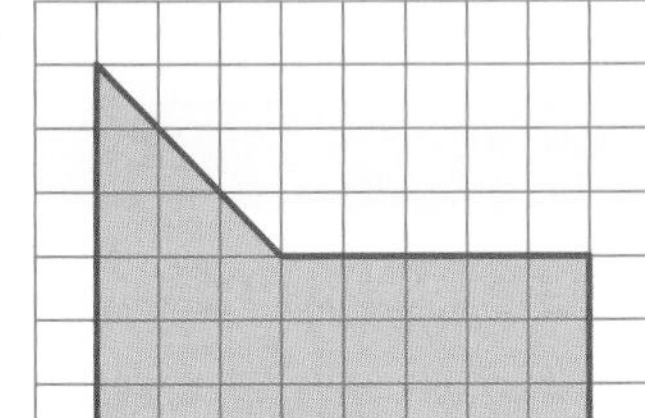

4. 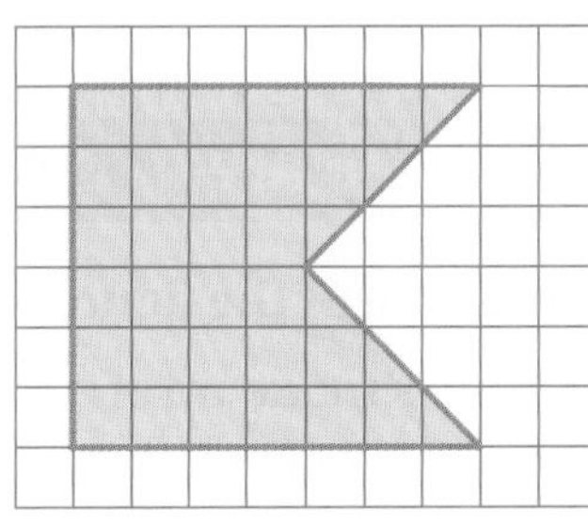

5. 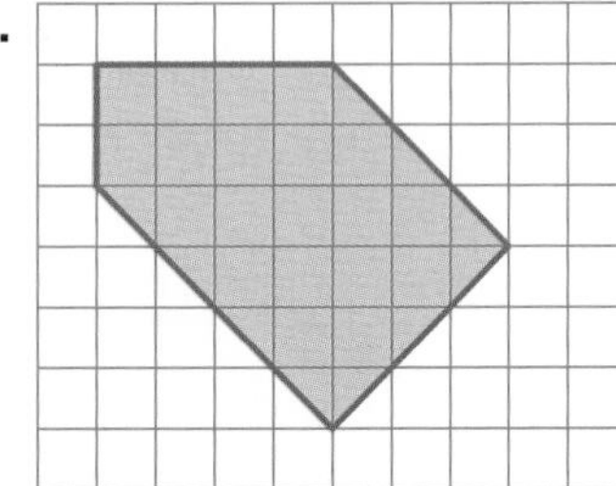

6. 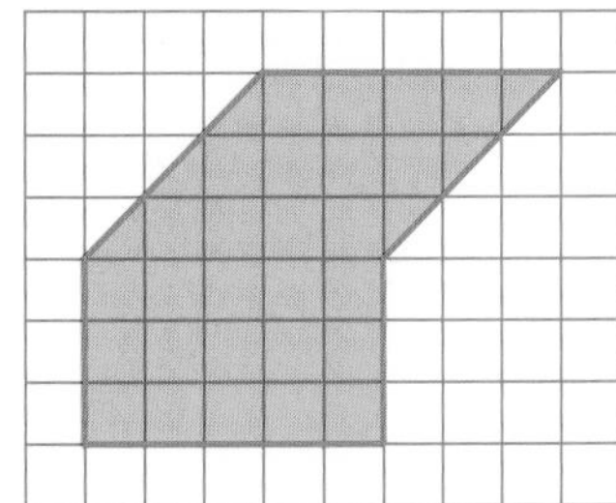

7. 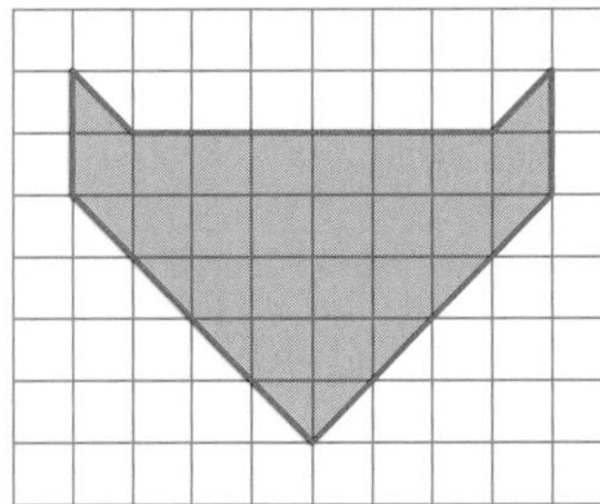

8. 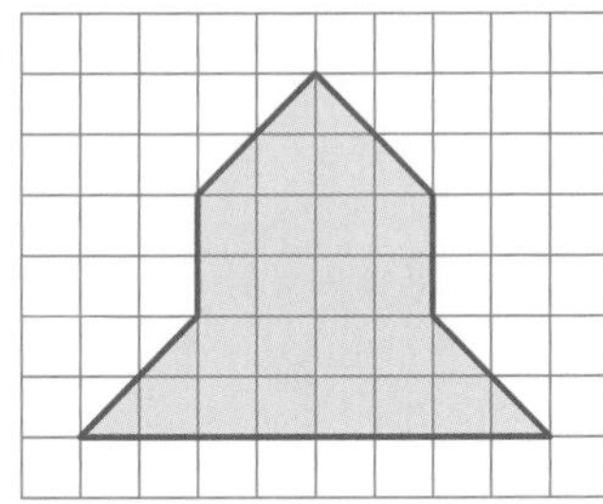

Find the area of the figure.

2 3 9.

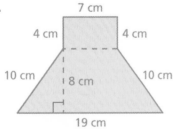

10. 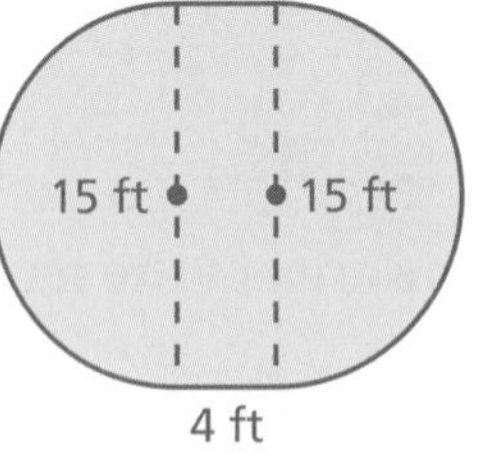

11. **OPEN-ENDED** Trace your hand and your foot on grid paper. Then estimate the area of each. Which one has the greater area?

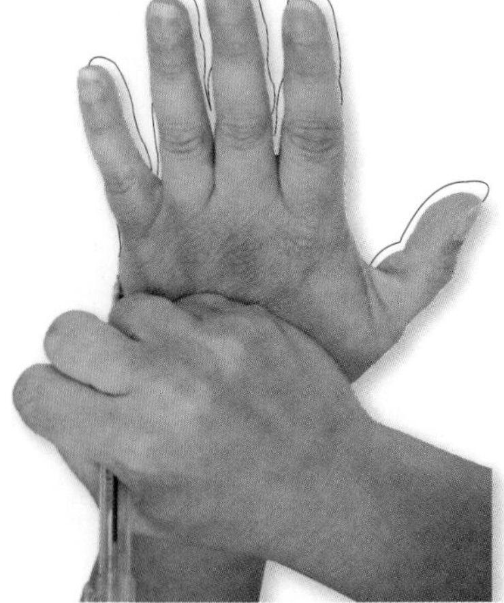

Find the area of the figure.

12. 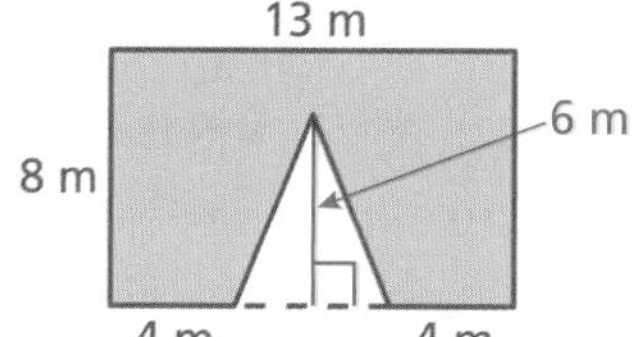

13. 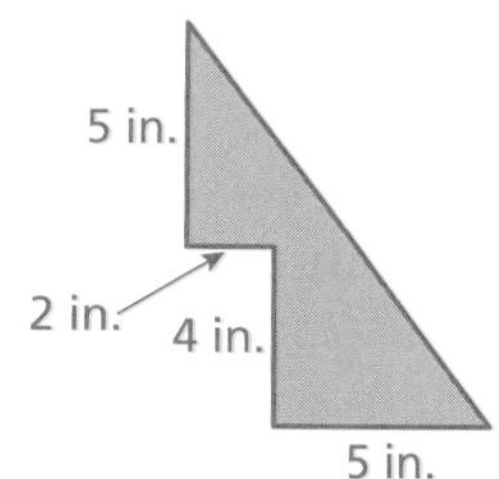

14. 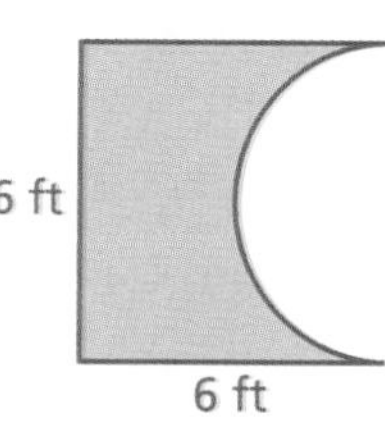

15. **AREA** The figure is made up of a square and a rectangle. Find the area of the shaded region.

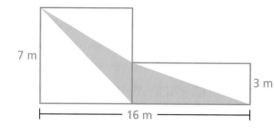

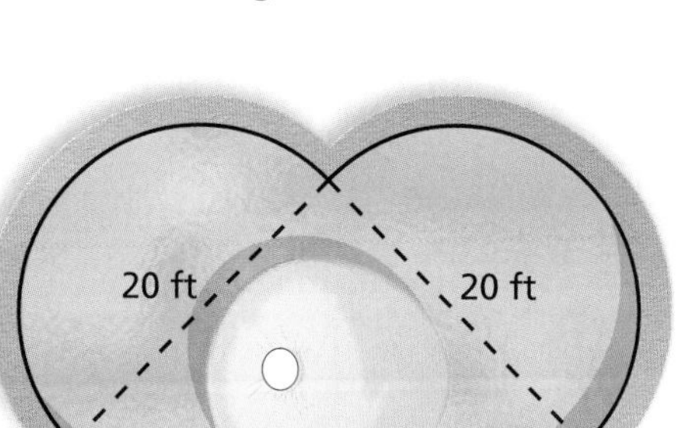

16. **FOUNTAIN** The fountain is made up of two semicircles and a quarter circle. Find the perimeter and area of the fountain.

17.  You are deciding on two different designs for envelopes.

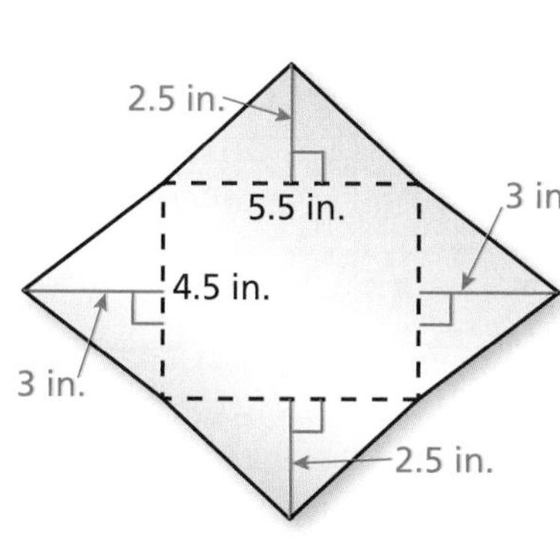

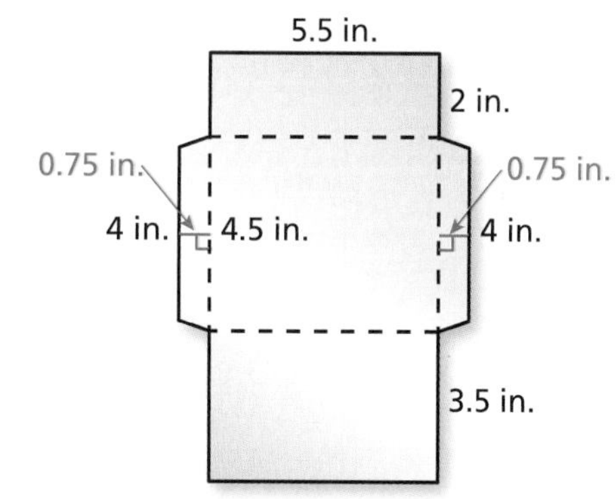

a. Which design has the greater area?

b. You make 500 envelopes using the design with the greater area. Using the same amount of paper, how many more envelopes can you make with the other design?

Fair Game Review What you learned in previous grades & lessons

Write the phrase as an expression. *(Skills Review Handbook)*

18. 12 less than a number x

19. a number y divided by 6

20. a number b increased by 3

21. the product of 7 and a number w

22. **MULTIPLE CHOICE** What number is 0.02% of 50? *(Section 4.1)*

Ⓐ 0.01 Ⓑ 0.1 Ⓒ 1 Ⓓ 100

5.4–5.7 Quiz

The triangles are similar. Find the value of *x*. *(Section 5.4)*

1.

2.

The vertices of a triangle are $L(1, -1)$, $M(3, -1)$, and $N(3, -4)$. Find the coordinates of the image after the transformation. *(Section 5.5)*

3. a translation of 2 units right and 7 units up

4. a reflection in the *y*-axis

5. a rotation of 180° about the origin

6. a dilation with a scale factor of 2

Find the perimeter and area of the figure. *(Section 5.6 and Section 5.7)*

7.

8.

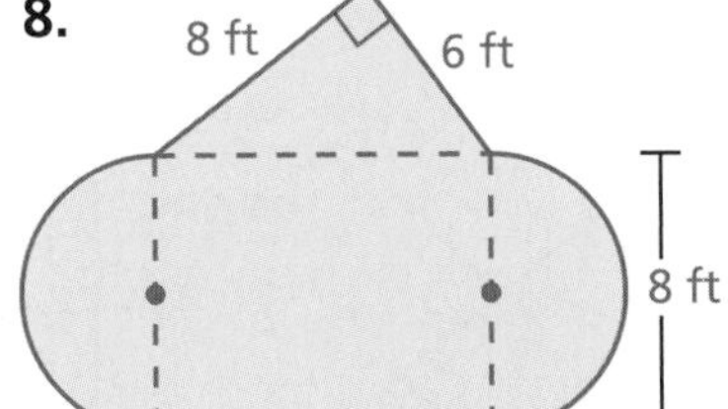

9.

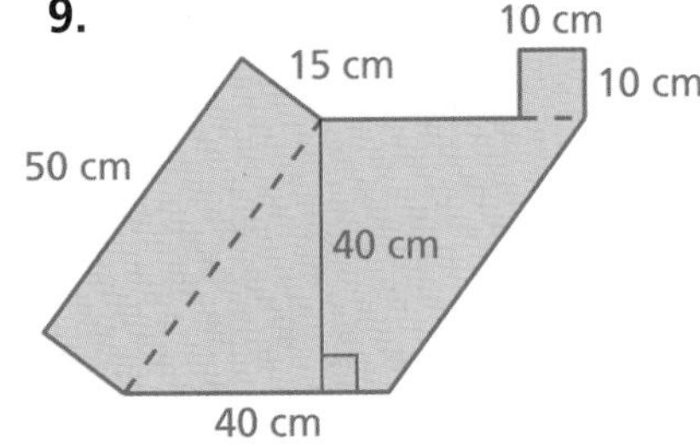

10. GARDEN Part of a yard is being fenced in to make a vegetable garden. How many feet of fencing are needed to surround the garden? *(Section 5.6)*

11. PERIMETER The side lengths of a right triangle are doubled to make a similar triangle. Does the perimeter double as well? Explain. *(Section 5.4)*

12. CARD The heart-shaped card is made by placing a square and two semicircles together. What is the area of the card? *(Section 5.7)*

5 Chapter Review

Check It Out
Vocabulary Help
BigIdeasMath.com

Review Key Vocabulary

complementary angles, *p. 200*
supplementary angles, *p. 200*
adjacent angles, *p. 201*
vertical angles, *p. 201*
isosceles triangle, *p. 206*
congruent sides, *p. 206*
equilateral triangle, *p. 206*
equiangular triangle, *p. 206*
polygon, *p. 212*
regular polygon, *p. 213*
convex polygon, *p. 214*
concave polygon, *p. 214*
similar triangles, *p. 222*
indirect measurement, *p. 223*
translation, *p. 228*
reflection, *p. 228*
rotation, *p. 228*
dilation, *p. 230*
composite figure, *p. 236*

Review Examples and Exercises

5.1 Classifying Angles *(pp. 198–203)*

Tell whether the angles are *adjacent* or *vertical*. Then find the value of *x*.

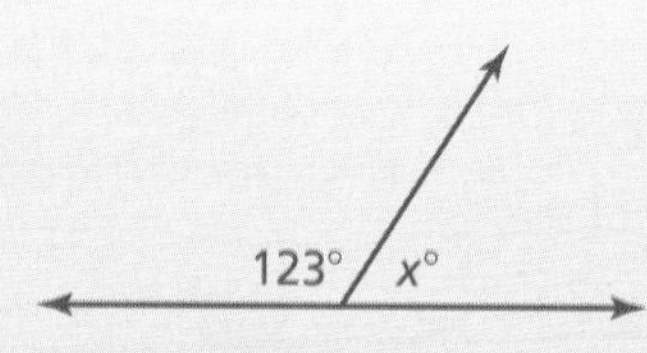

The angles are adjacent angles. Because the angles are supplementary, the sum of their measures is 180°.

$$x + 123 = 180$$

$$x = 57$$

So, x is 57.

Exercises

Tell whether the angles are *adjacent* or *vertical*. Then find the value of *x*.

1. 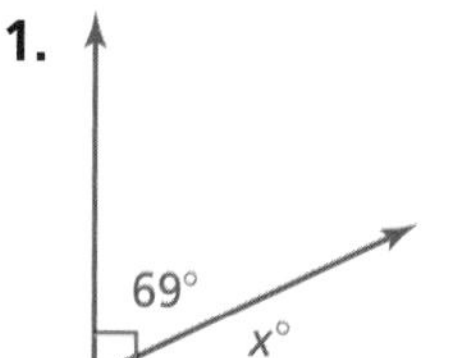

2. 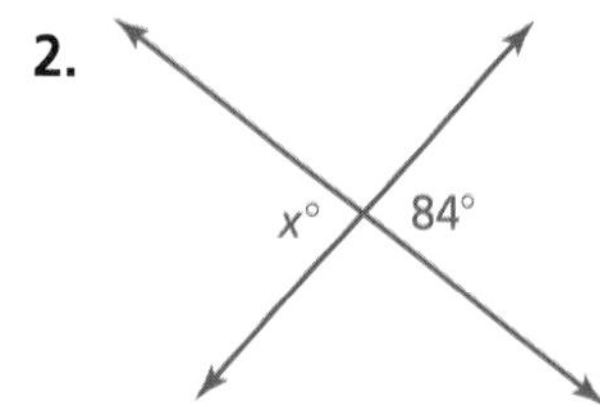

5.2 Angles and Sides of Triangles *(pp. 204–209)*

Find the value of *x*. Then classify the triangle.

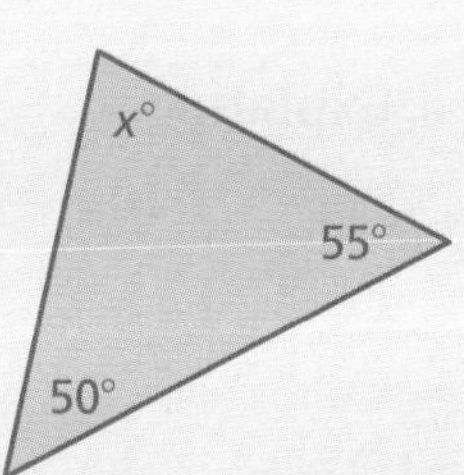

$$x + 50 + 55 = 180$$

$$x + 105 = 180$$

$$x = 75$$

The value of x is 75. The triangle has three acute angle measures, 50°, 55°, and 75°. So, it is an acute triangle.

Exercises

Find the value of x. Then classify the triangle in as many ways as possible.

3. 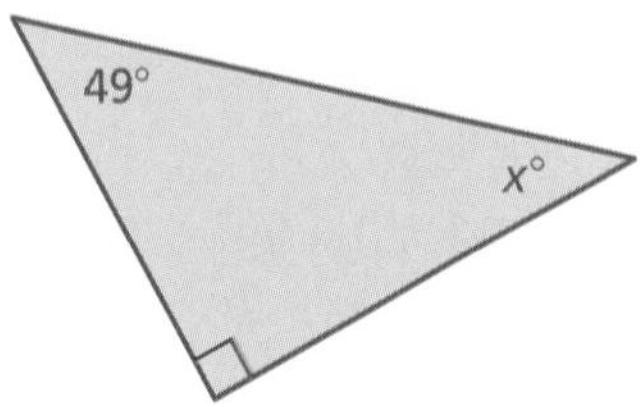

4. 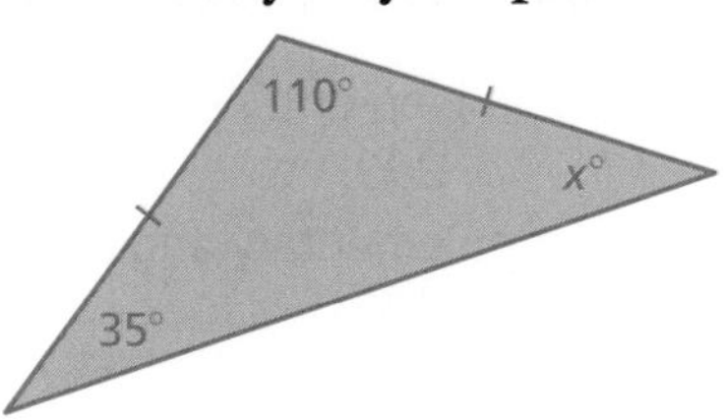

5.3 Angles of Polygons *(pp. 210–217)*

Find the value of x.

Step 1: The polygon has 6 sides. Find the sum of the angle measures.

$S = (n - 2) \cdot 180°$	Write the formula.
$= (6 - 2) \cdot 180°$	Substitute 6 for n.
$= 720$	Simplify. The sum of the angle measures is 720°.

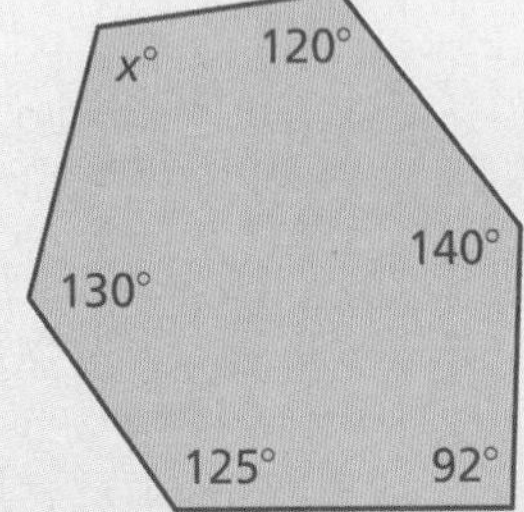

Step 2: Write and solve an equation.

$$130 + 125 + 92 + 140 + 120 + x = 720$$

$$607 + x = 720$$

$$x = 113$$

The value of x is 113.

Exercises

Find the value of x.

5. 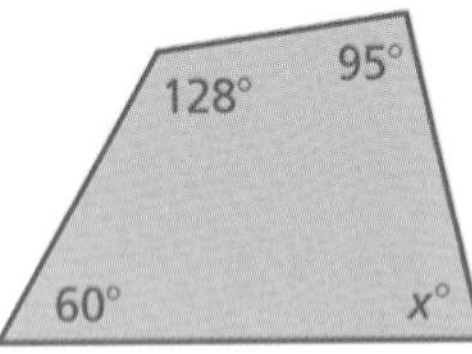

6. 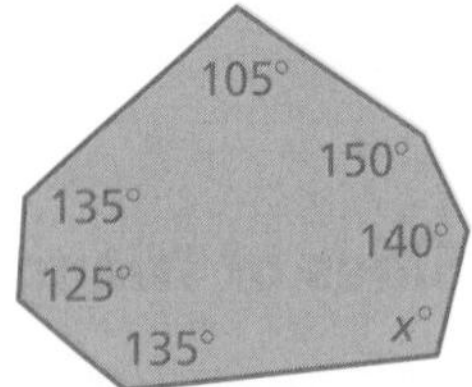

7. 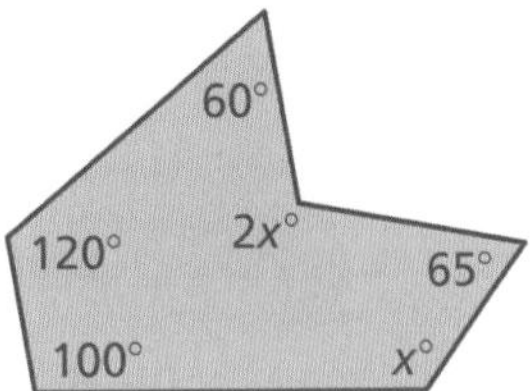

Tell whether the polygon is *convex* or *concave*. Explain.

8. 

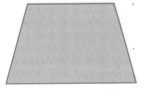

9. 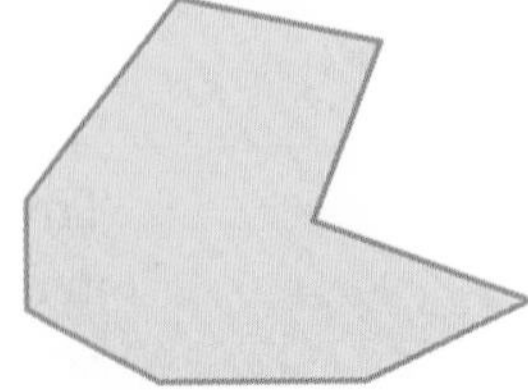

10. 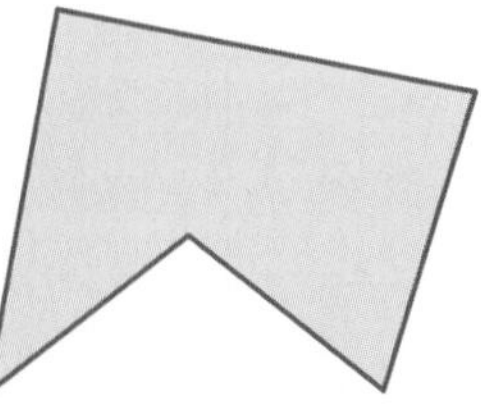

5.4 Using Similar Triangles (pp. 220–225)

Tell whether the triangles are similar. Explain.

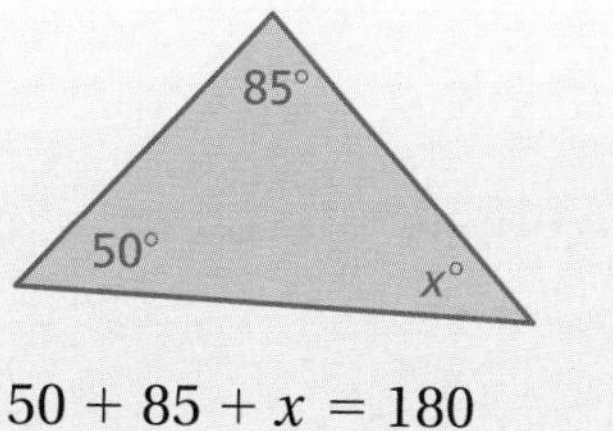

$50 + 85 + x = 180$ $\qquad$ $y + 85 + 35° = 180$

$135 + x = 180$ $\qquad$ $y + 120 = 180$

$x = 45$ $\qquad$ $y = 60$

∴ The triangles do not have the same angle measures. So, they are not similar.

Exercises

11. Tell whether the triangles are similar. Explain.

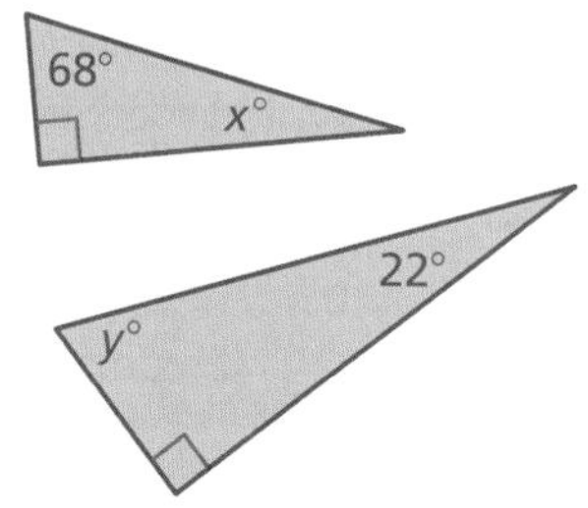

12. The triangles are similar. Find the value of x.

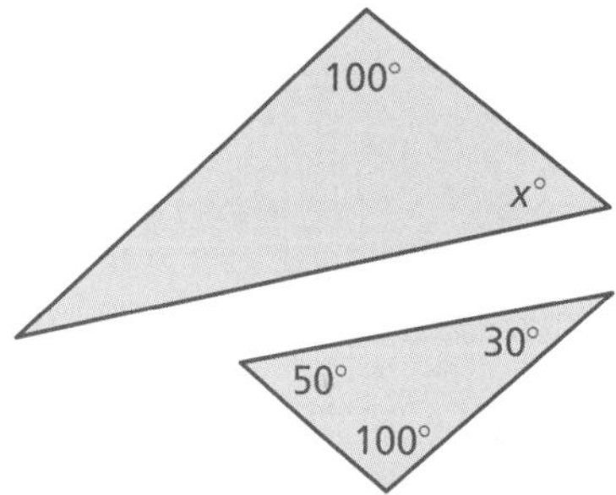

5.5 Polygons and Transformations (pp. 226–233)

The vertices of a trapezoid are $A(0, -1)$, $B(4, 1)$, $C(3, -2)$, and $D(1, -3)$. Translate the trapezoid 5 units right and 5 units up. What are the coordinates of the image?

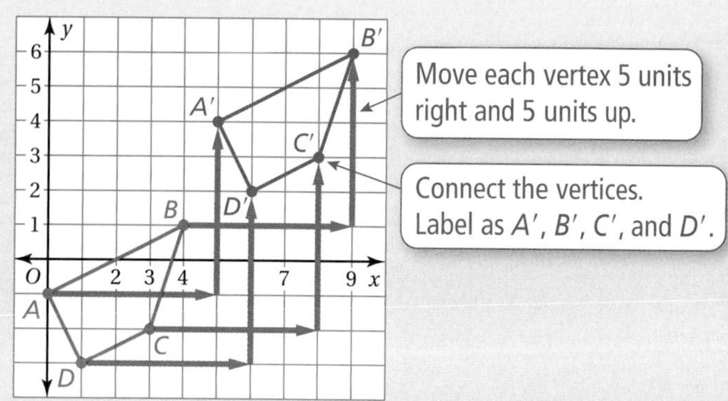

Move each vertex 5 units right and 5 units up.
Connect the vertices. Label as A′, B′, C′, and D′.

∴ The coordinates of the image are $A'(5, 4)$, $B'(9, 6)$, $C'(8, 3)$, and $D'(6, 2)$.

Exercises

Find the coordinates of the image after the transformation.

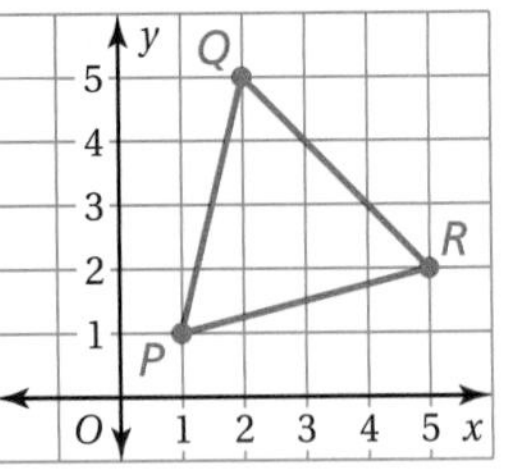

13. a translation of 3 units left and 4 units down

14. a reflection in the y-axis

15. a rotation of 180° about the origin

16. a dilation with a scale factor of 3

5.6 Perimeters of Composite Figures (pp. 234–239)

The figure is made up of a semicircle and a square. Find the perimeter. Use 3.14 for π.

The distance around the square part is $6 + 6 + 6 = 18$ meters. The distance around the curved part is one-half the circumference of a circle with $d = 6$ meters.

$\frac{C}{2} = \frac{\pi d}{2}$ Divide the circumference by 2.

$\approx \frac{3.14 \cdot 6}{2}$ Substitute 3.14 for π and 6 for d.

$= 9.42$ Simplify.

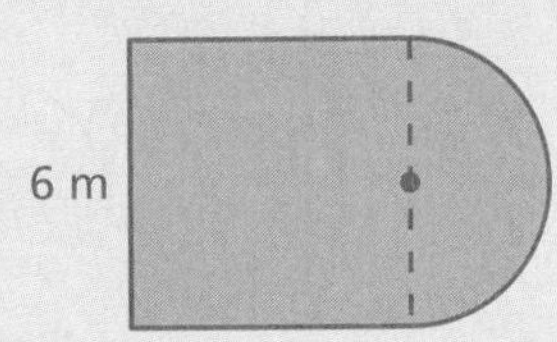

The perimeter of the figure is about $18 + 9.42 = 27.42$ meters.

Exercises

Find the perimeter of the figure.

17.

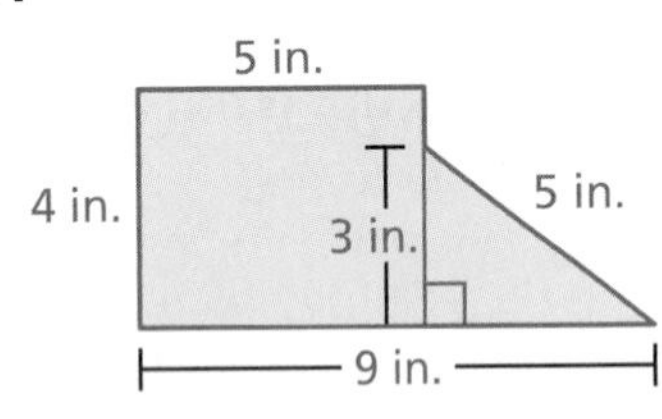

18.

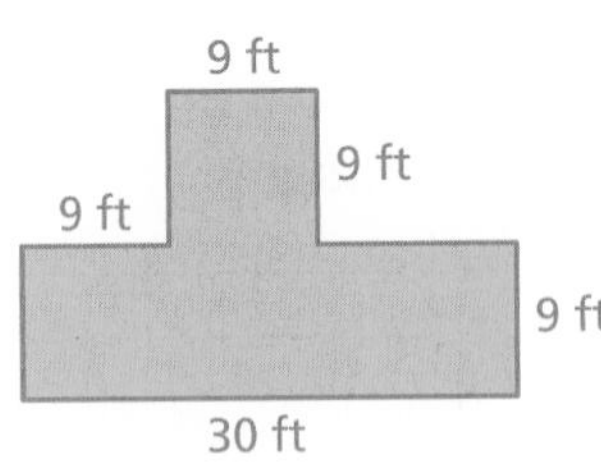

19.

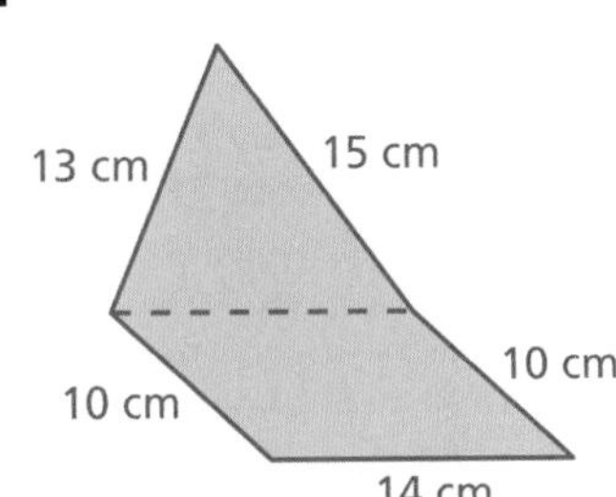

20.

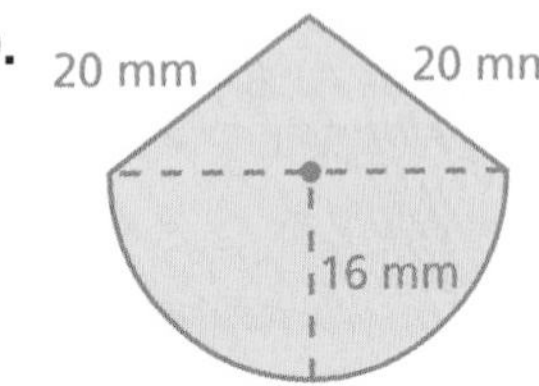

21.

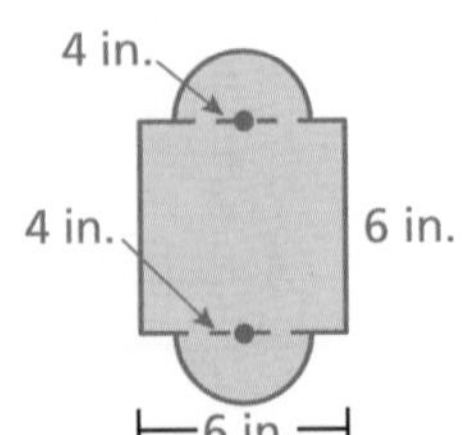

22.

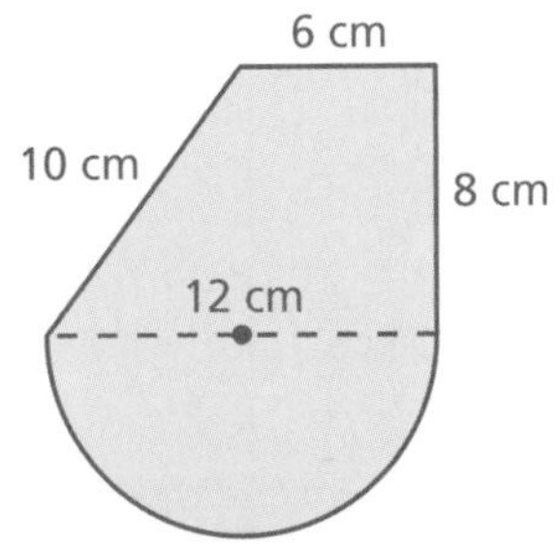

5.7 Areas of Composite Figures (pp. 240–245)

Find the area of the figure.

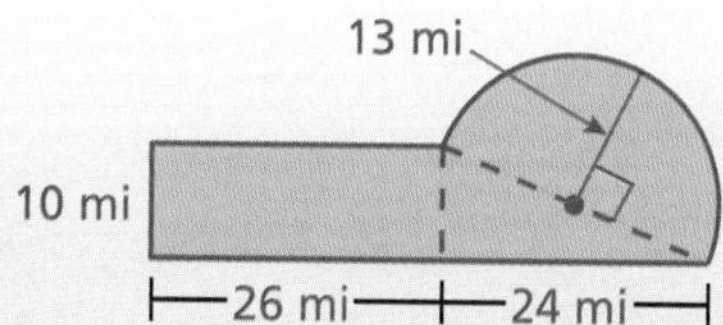

The figure is made up of a rectangle, a triangle, and a semicircle. Find the area of each figure.

Area of rectangle	***Area of triangle***	***Area of semicircle***
$A = \ell w$	$A = \frac{1}{2}bh$	$A = \frac{\pi r^2}{2}$
$= (26)(10)$	$= \frac{1}{2}(10)(24)$	$\approx \frac{3.14 \cdot (13)^2}{2}$
$= 260$	$= 120$	$= 265.33$

So, the area of the figure is about $260 + 120 + 265.33 = 645.33$ square miles.

Exercises

Find the area of the figure.

23.

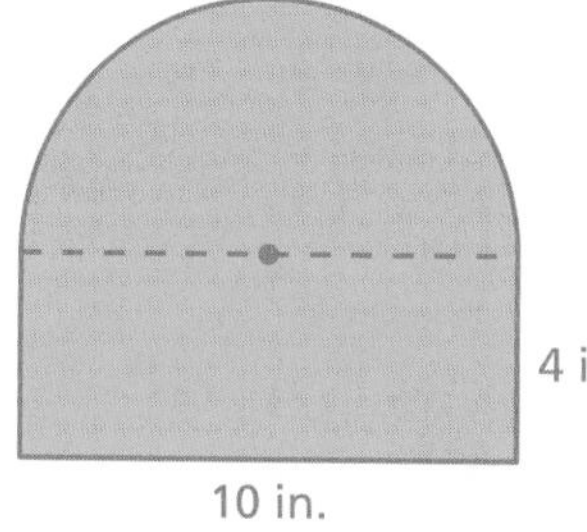

24.

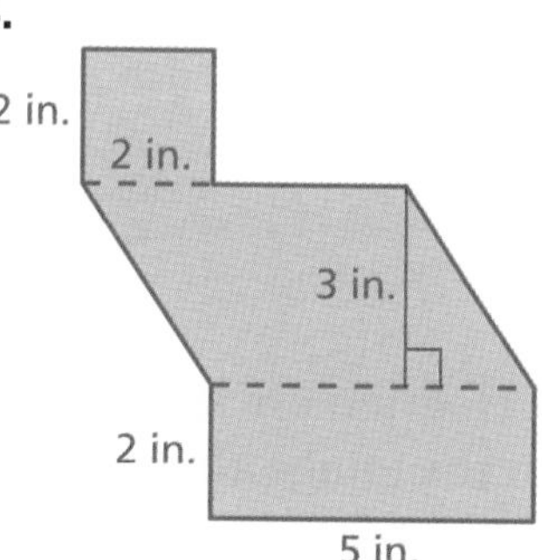

25.

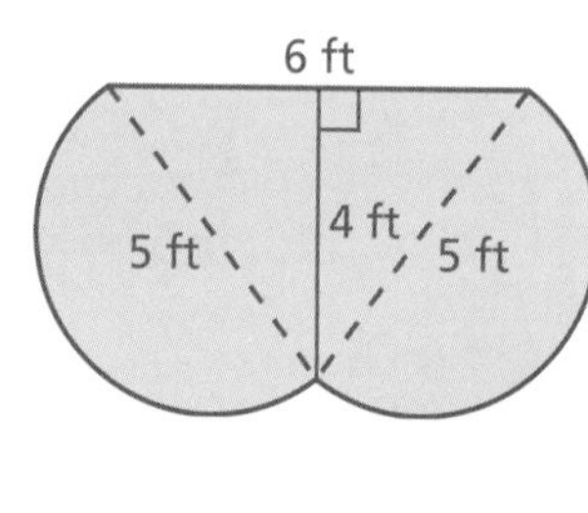

26. FLOORING Oak flooring costs \$4 per square foot. Estimate how much it costs to buy oak flooring for the room shown?

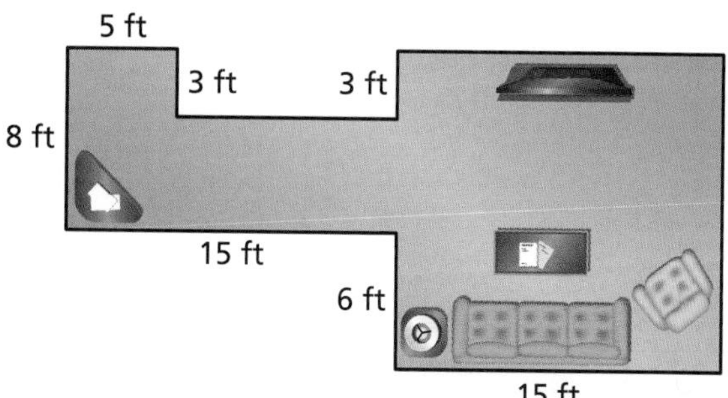

5 Chapter Test

Tell whether the angles are *adjacent* or *vertical*. Then find the value of *x*.

1. 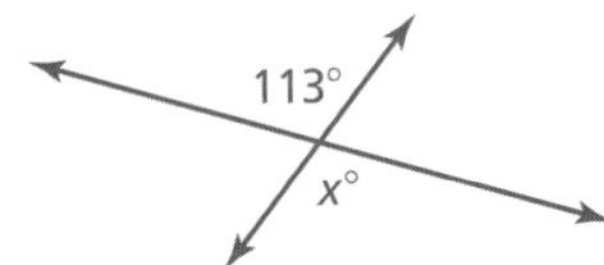

2. 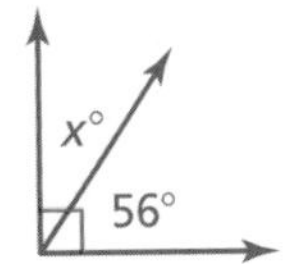

3. 

Find the value of *x*. Then classify the triangle in as many ways as possible.

4. 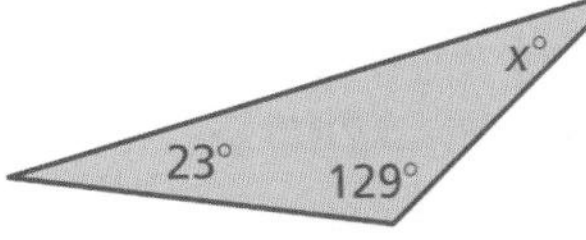

5. 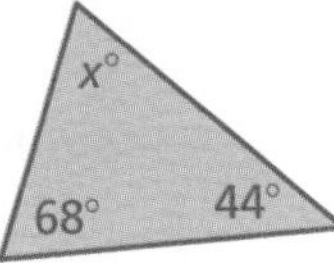

6. 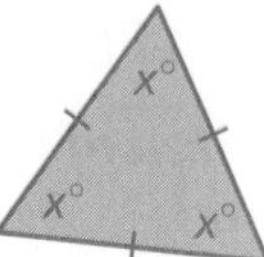

7. Tell whether the polygon is *convex* or *concave*. Explain.

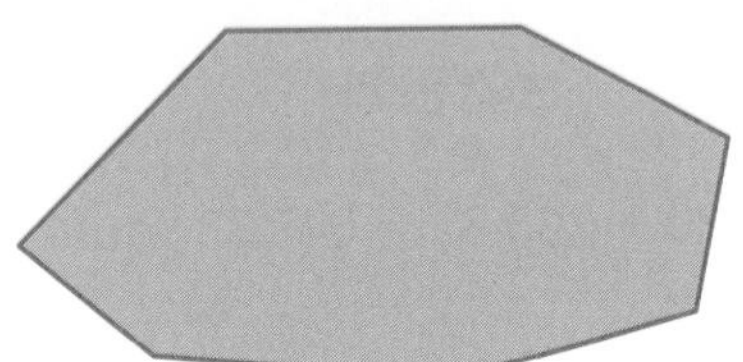

8. Find the value of x.

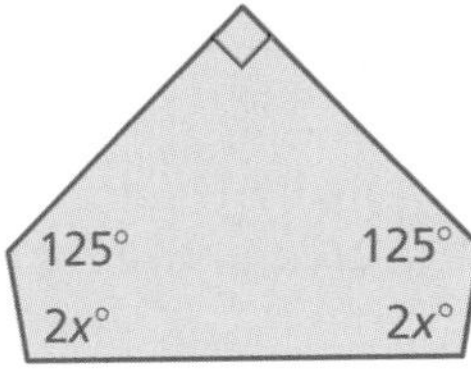

Find the perimeter and area of the figure.

9. 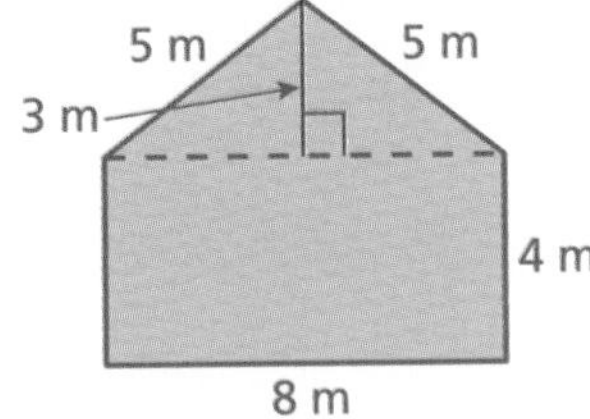

10. 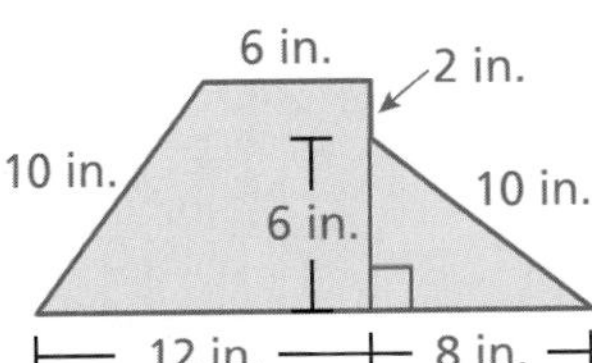

11. 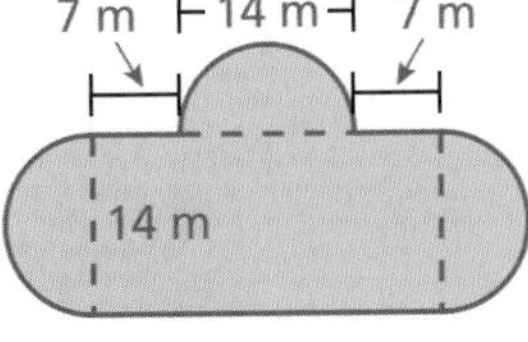

The vertices of a parallelogram are $W(4, 4)$, $X(8, 4)$, $Y(10, 1)$, and $Z(6, 1)$. Find the coordinates of the image after the transformation.

12. a translation of 4 units left and 5 units down

13. a reflection in the x-axis

14. a rotation of 90° counterclockwise about the origin

15. a dilation with a scale factor of $\frac{1}{2}$

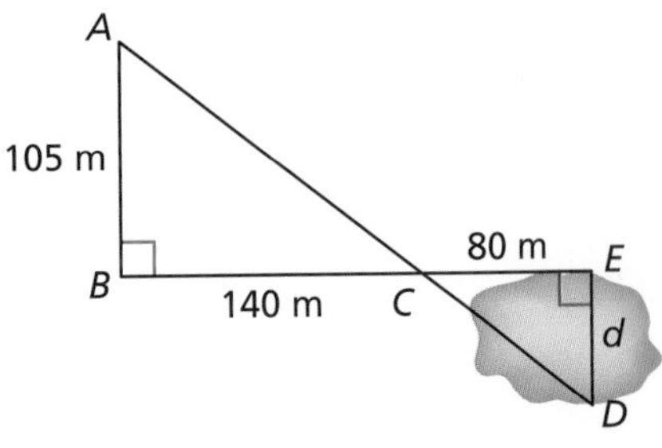

16. **POND** Use the given measurements to find the distance d across the pond.

5 Standardized Test Practice

1. The border of a Canadian one-dollar coin is shaped like an 11-sided regular polygon. The shape was chosen to help visually-impaired people identify the coin. How many degrees are in each angle along the border? Round your answer to the nearest degree.

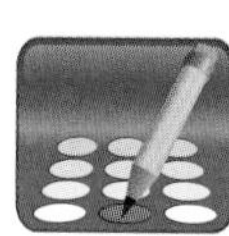

2. A public utility charges its residential customers for natural gas based on the number of therms used each month. The formula below shows how the monthly cost C in dollars is related to the number t of therms used.

$$C = 11 + 1.6t$$

Solve this formula for t.

A. $t = \dfrac{C}{12.6}$

B. $t = \dfrac{C - 11}{1.6}$

C. $t = \dfrac{C}{1.6} - 11$

D. $t = C - 12.6$

3. Which equation matches the line shown in the graph?

F. $y = x - 5$

G. $y = x + 5$

H. $y = -x - 5$

I. $y = -x + 5$

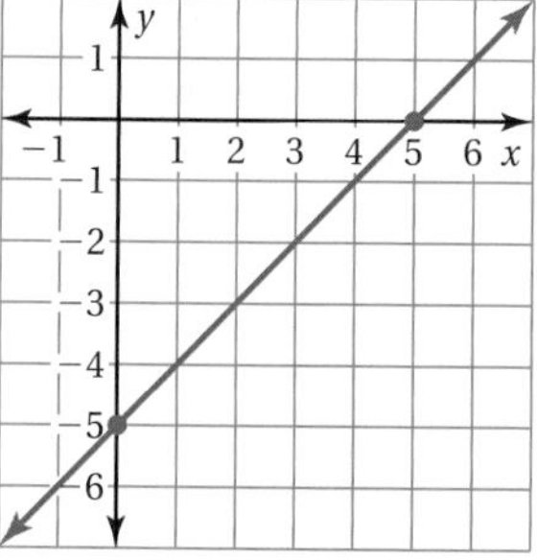

4. $\angle 1$ and $\angle 2$ form a straight angle. $\angle 1$ has a measure of 28°. Find the measure of $\angle 2$, in degrees.

2 1

5. Which equation represents a linear function?

A. $y = x^2$

B. $y = \dfrac{2}{x}$

C. $xy = 1$

D. $x + y = 1$

6. At which point does the graph of the equation $4x + 5y = 12$ cross the x-axis?

F. (0, 2.4) H. (2.4, 0)

G. (0, 3) I. (3, 0)

7. What is the domain of the function graphed in the coordinate plane?

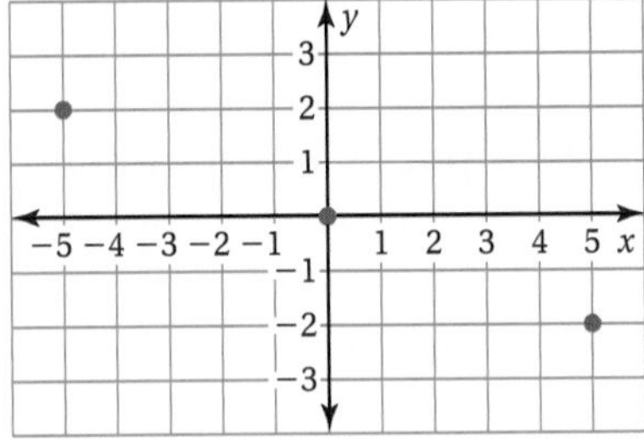

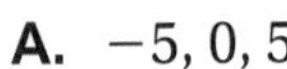

A. −5, 0, 5 C. −5, −2, 0, 2, 5

B. −2, 0, 2 D. −5, 2

8. The sum S of the angle measures of a polygon with n sides can be found using a formula.

Part A Write the formula.

Part B A quadrilateral has angles measuring 100, 90, and 90 degrees. Find the measure of its fourth angle. Show your work and explain your reasoning.

Part C The sum of the measures of the angles of the pentagon shown is 540 degrees. Divide the pentagon into triangles to show why this must be true. Show your work and explain your reasoning.

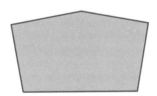

9. The line shown in the graph has a slope of $\frac{2}{5}$.

What is the equation of the line?

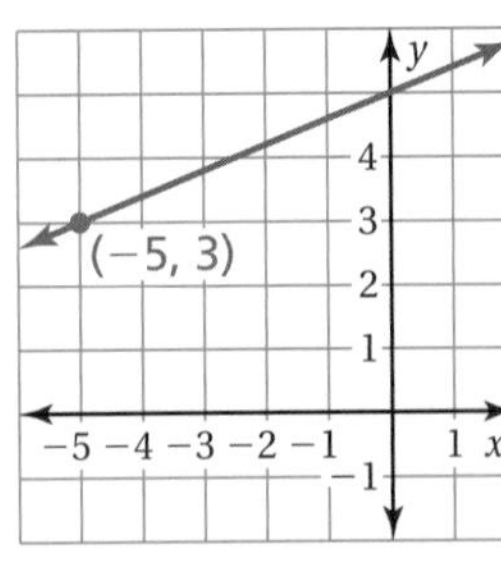

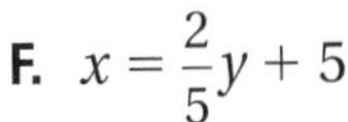

F. $x = \frac{2}{5}y + 5$ H. $x = \frac{2}{5}y + 1$

G. $y = \frac{2}{5}x + 5$ I. $y = \frac{2}{5}x + 1$

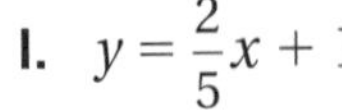

10. On a hot summer day, the temperature was 95°F, the relative humidity was 75%, and the Heat Index was 122°F. For every degree that the temperature rises, the Heat Index increases by 4 degrees. The temperature rises to 98°F. What is the Heat Index?

A. 99°F

B. 107°F

C. 126°F

D. 134°F

11. Which value of x makes the equation below true?

$$5x - 3 = 11$$

F. 1.6

G. 2.8

H. 40

I. 70

12. In the diagram below, $\triangle ABC \sim \triangle DEF$. What is the value of x?

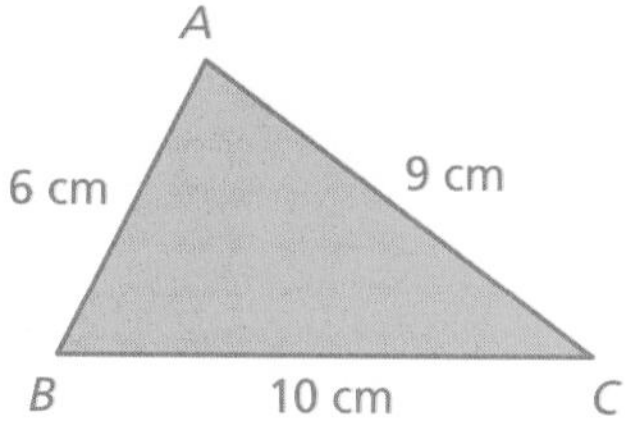

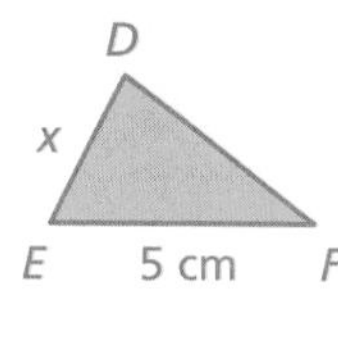

A. 1 cm

B. 3 cm

C. 4.5 cm

D. 6 cm

13. Two lines have the same y-intercept. The slope of one line is 1 and the slope of the other line is -1. What can you conclude?

F. The lines are parallel.

G. The lines meet at exactly one point.

H. The lines meet at more than one point.

I. The situation described is impossible.

6 Surface Areas of Solids

6.1 Drawing 3-Dimensional Figures

6.2 Surface Areas of Prisms

6.3 Surface Areas of Cylinders

6.4 Surface Areas of Pyramids

6.5 Surface Areas of Cones

6.6 Surface Areas of Composite Solids

"I want to paint my dog house. To make sure I buy the correct amount of paint, I want to calculate the lateral surface area."

"Then, because I want to paint the inside and the outside, I will multiply by 2. Does this seem right to you?"

"Dear Sir: Why do you sell dog food in tall cans and sell cat food in short cans?"

"Neither of these shapes is the optimal use of surface area when compared to volume."

Polly Prism, Prissy Pyramid, Cici Cylinder, and Connie Cone

"Name these shapes."

What You Learned Before

Finding Areas of Composite Figures

Example 1 **Find the area.**

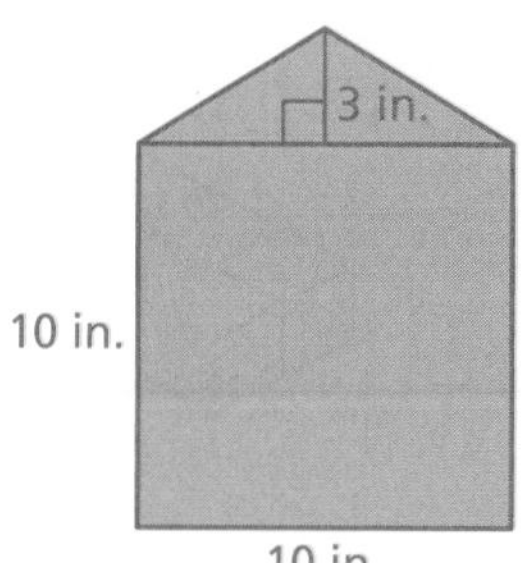

Area = Area of square + Area of triangle

$$A = s^2 + \frac{1}{2}bh$$

$$= 10^2 + \left(\frac{1}{2} \cdot 10 \cdot 3\right)$$

$$= 100 + 15$$

$$= 115 \text{ in.}^2$$

Try It Yourself

Find the area.

1.

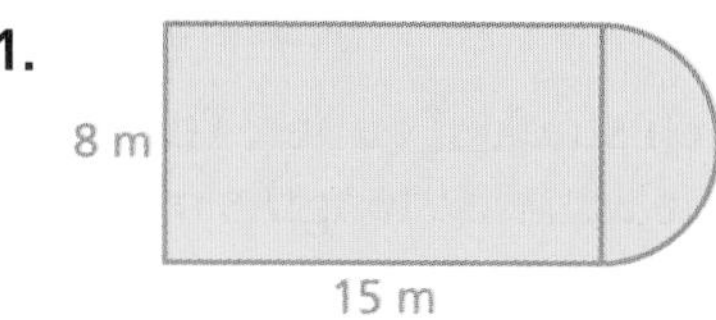

2.

14 cm

5 cm

9 cm

4 cm

Finding Areas of Circles

Example 2 **Find the area.**

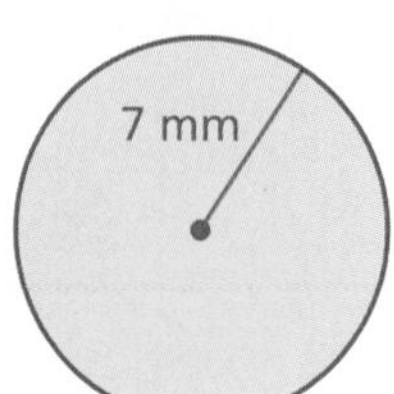

$$A = \pi r^2$$

$$= \pi \cdot (7)^2$$

$$= 49\pi$$

$$\approx 153.9 \text{ mm}^2$$

Example 3 **Find the area.**

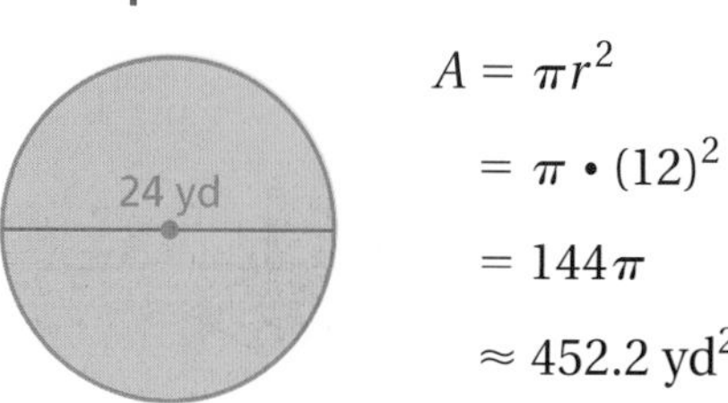

$$A = \pi r^2$$

$$= \pi \cdot (12)^2$$

$$= 144\pi$$

$$\approx 452.2 \text{ yd}^2$$

Try It Yourself

Find the area.

3.

5 ft

4.

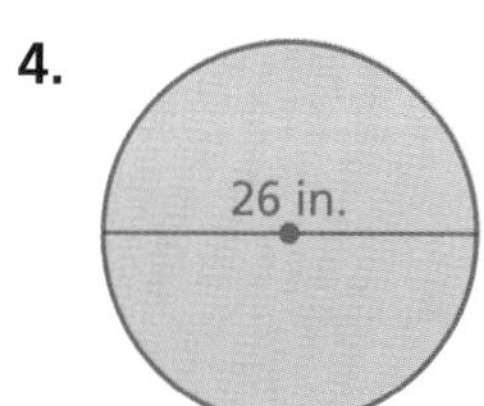

5.

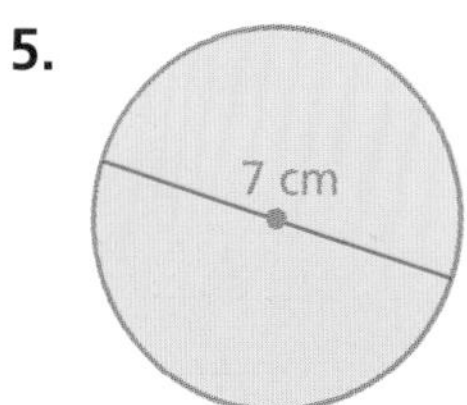

6.1 Drawing 3-Dimensional Figures

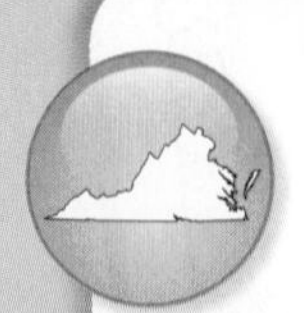

STANDARDS OF LEARNING
8.9

Essential Question How can you draw three-dimensional figures?

Dot paper can help you draw three-dimensional figures, or solids. Shading parallel sides the same color helps create a three-dimensional illusion.

Square Dot Paper

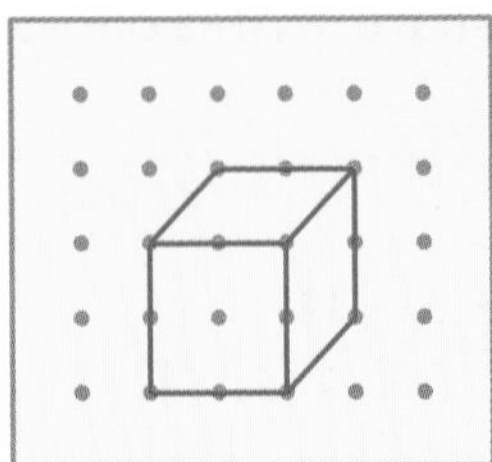

Face-On View

Isometric Dot Paper

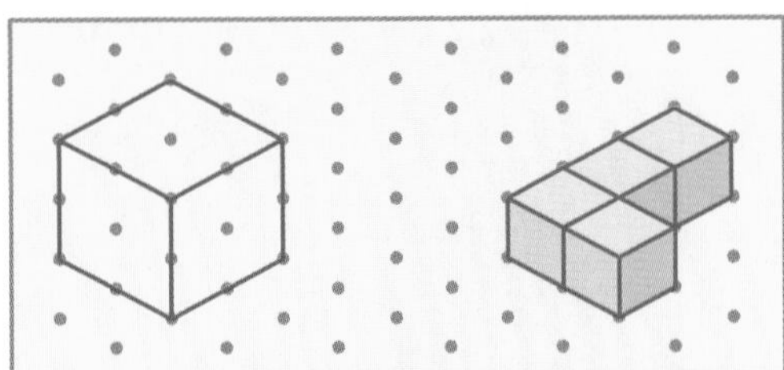

Corner View

1 ACTIVITY: Finding Surface Areas and Volumes

Work with a partner.

Draw the front, side, and top views of each stack of cubes. Then find the surface area and volume. Each small cube has side lengths of 1 unit.

a. Sample:

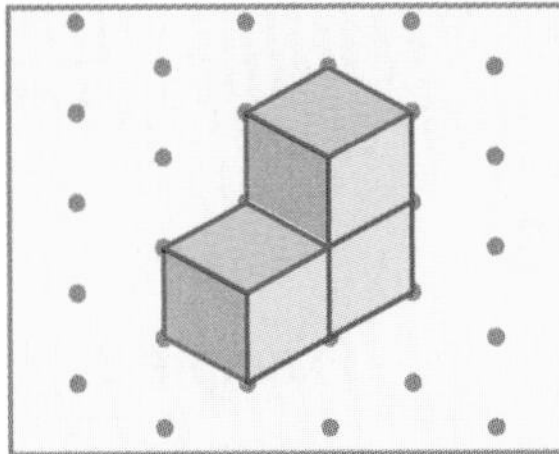

Volume: 3 cubic units

Surface Area: 14 square units

b.

c.

d.

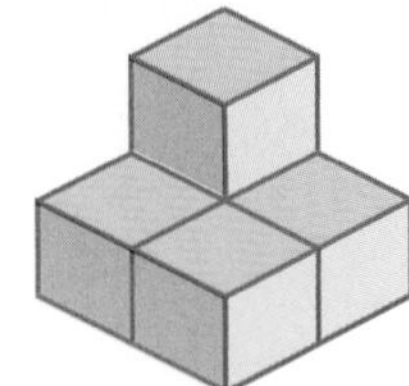

e.

f.

g.

2 ACTIVITY: Drawing Solids

Work with a partner.

a. Draw all the different solids you can make by joining four cubes. (Two have been drawn.) Cubes must be joined on faces, not on edges only. Translations, reflections, and rotations do not count as different solids.

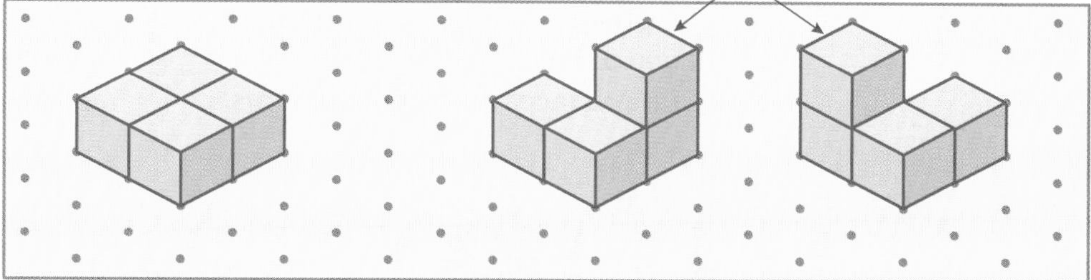

b. Do all the solids have the same surface area? Do all the solids have the same volume? Explain your reasoning.

What Is Your Answer?

3. **IN YOUR OWN WORDS** How can you draw three-dimensional figures? Draw and shade two prisms that have the same volume but different surface areas.

4. Maurits Escher (1898–1972) was a popular artist who drew optical illusions.

   a. What is the illusion in Escher's drawing?

   b. Why is the cartoon funny? What is the illusion in the cartoon?

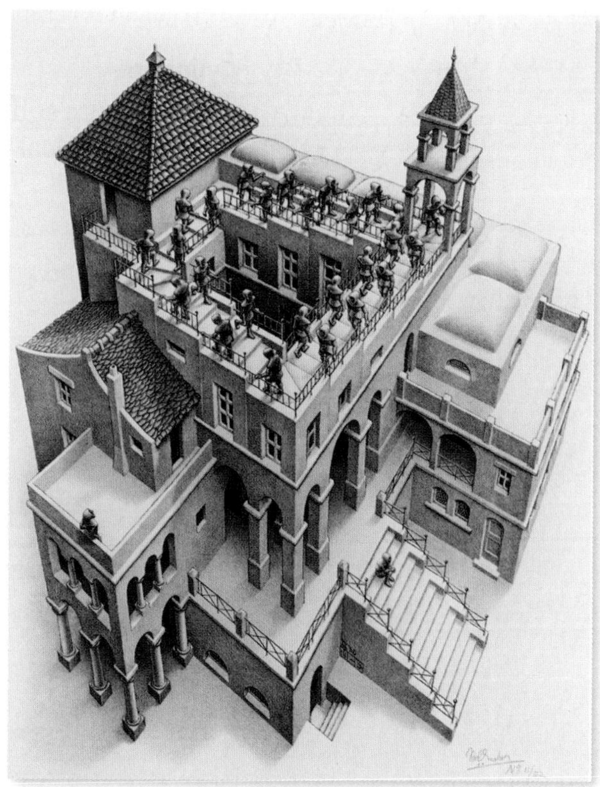

Practice Use what you learned about three-dimensional figures to complete Exercises 7–9 on page 262.

6.1 Lesson

Key Vocabulary
solid, *p. 260*
polyhedron, *p. 260*
lateral face, *p. 260*

A **solid** is a three-dimensional figure that encloses a space. A **polyhedron** is a solid whose faces are all polygons.

Prisms

A prism is a polyhedron that has two parallel, identical bases. The **lateral faces** are parallelograms.

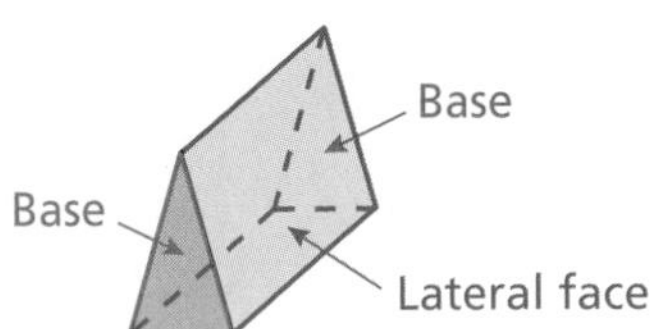

Triangular Prism

Pyramids

A pyramid is a polyhedron that has one base. The lateral faces are triangles.

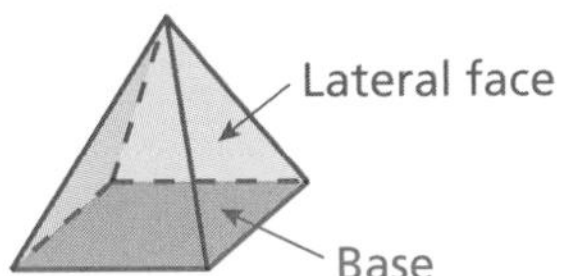

Rectangular Pyramid

The shape of the base tells the name of the prism or the pyramid.

Cylinders

A cylinder is a solid that has two parallel, identical circular bases.

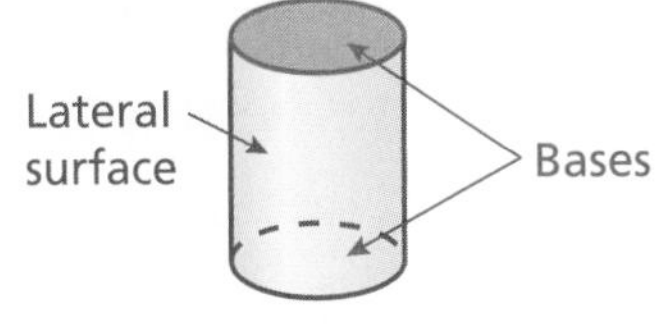

Cones

A cone is a solid that has one circular base and one vertex.

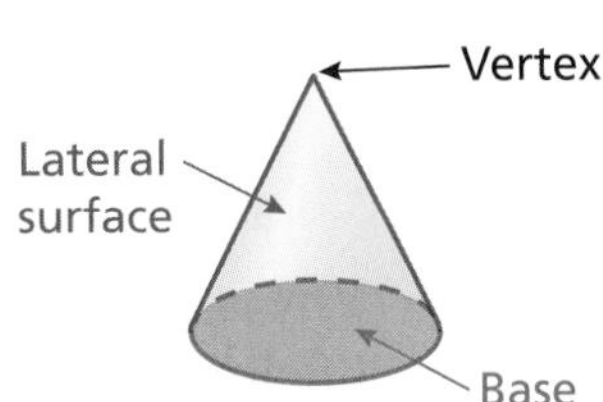

EXAMPLE 1 Drawing a Prism

Draw a rectangular prism.

Step 1

Draw identical rectangular bases.

Step 2

Connect corresponding vertices.

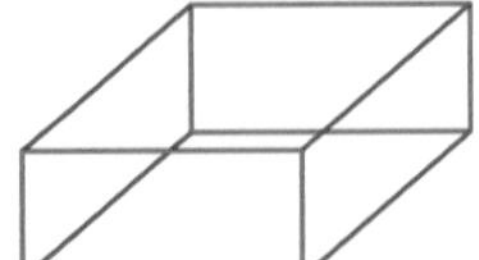

Step 3

Change any *hidden* lines to dashed lines.

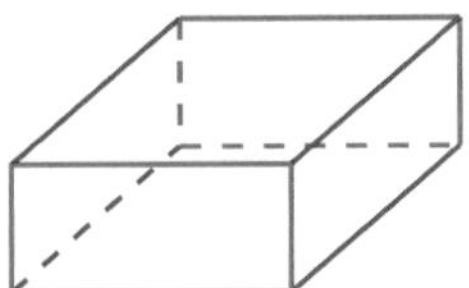

EXAMPLE 2 Drawing a Pyramid

Draw a triangular pyramid.

Step 1

Draw a triangular base and a point.

Step 2

Connect the vertices of the triangle to the point.

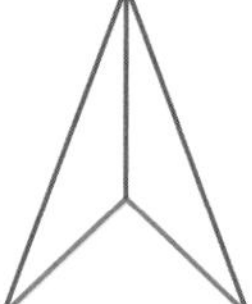

Step 3

Change any *hidden* lines to dashed lines.

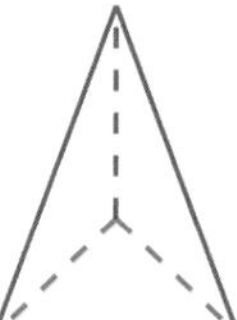

On Your Own

Now You're Ready
Exercises 10–15

Draw the solid.

1. Square prism
2. Pentagonal pyramid

EXAMPLE 3 Drawing Views of a Solid

Draw the front, side, and top views of the paper cup.

The front view is a triangle.

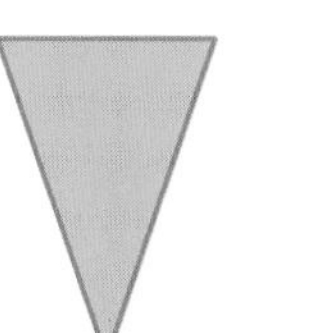

The side view is a triangle.

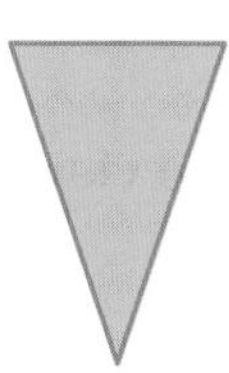

The top view is a circle.

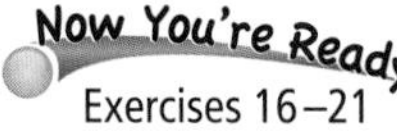

Now You're Ready
Exercises 16–21

Draw the front, side, and top views of the solid.

3.

4.

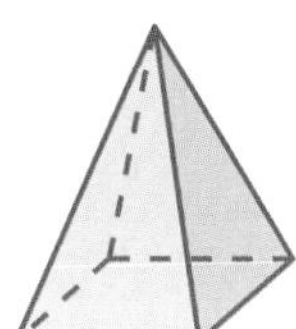

5.

6.1 Exercises

Vocabulary and Concept Check

1. **VOCABULARY** Compare and contrast prisms and cylinders.
2. **VOCABULARY** Compare and contrast pyramids and cones.
3. **WRITING** Give examples of prisms, pyramids, cylinders, and cones in real life.

Identify the shape of the base. Then name the solid.

4. 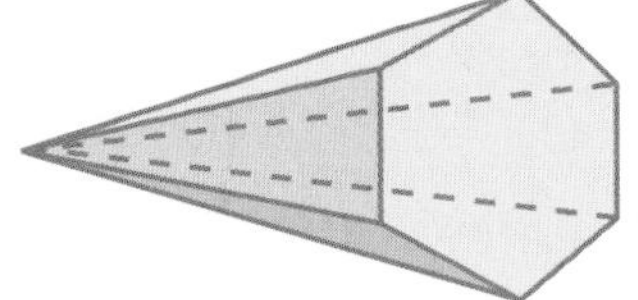

5. 

6. 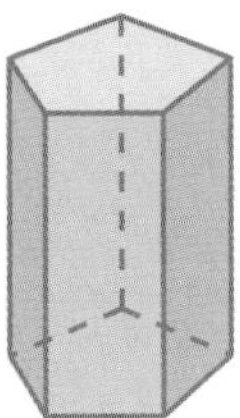

Practice and Problem Solving

Draw the front, side, and top views of the stack of cubes. Then find the surface area and volume.

7. 

8. 

9. 

Draw the solid.

(1) (2) 10. Triangular prism
11. Pentagonal prism
12. Rectangular pyramid
13. Hexagonal pyramid
14. Cone
15. Cylinder

Draw the front, side, and top views of the solid.

(3) 16. 

17. 

18. 

19. 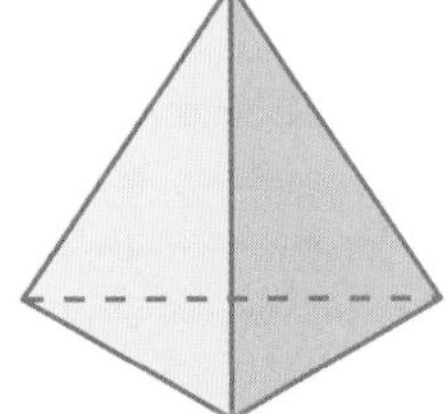

20. 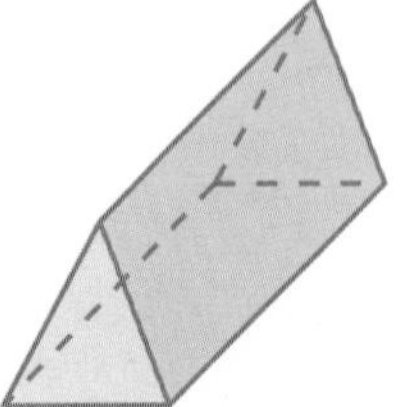

21. 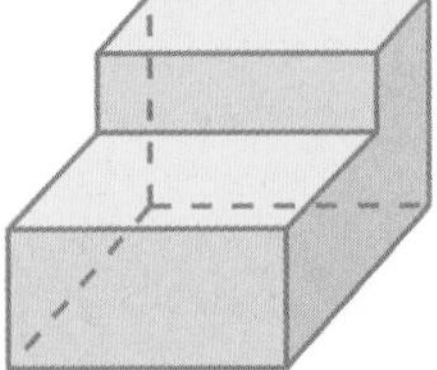

22. **PYRAMID ARENA** The Pyramid of Caius Cestius in Rome is in the shape of a square pyramid. Draw a sketch of the pyramid.

23. **RESEARCH** Use the Internet to find a picture of the Washington Monument. Describe its shape.

Draw a solid with the following front, side, and top views.

24. 25.

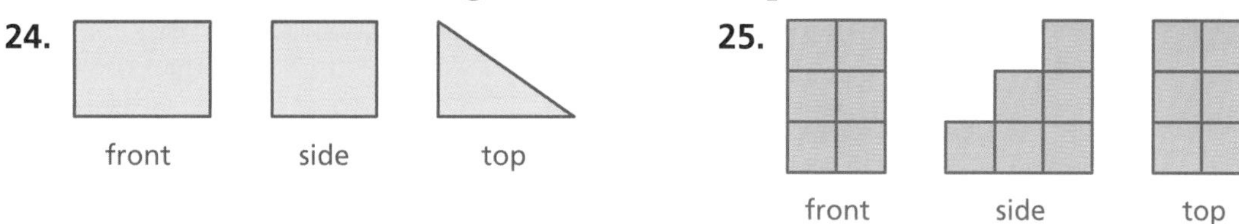

26. **PROJECT** Design and draw a house. Name the different solids that can be used to make a model of the house.

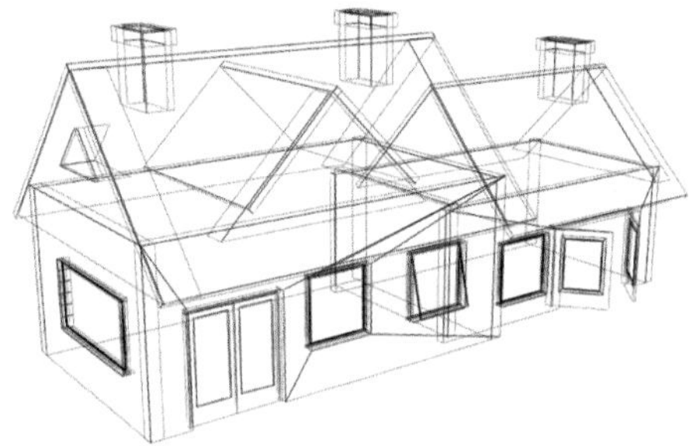

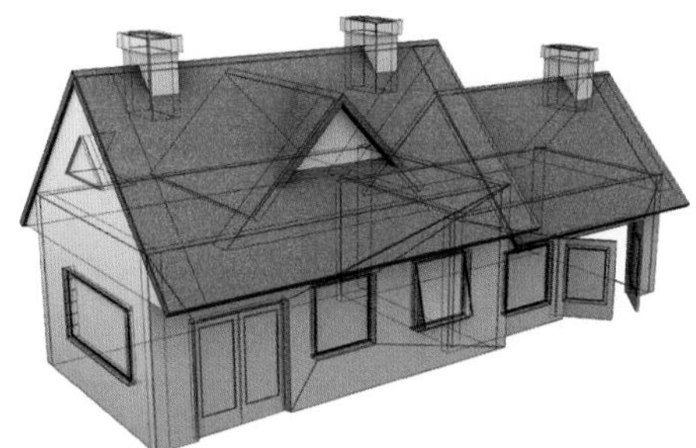

27. **REASONING** Two of the three views of a solid are shown.
    a. What is the greatest number of unit cubes in the solid?
    b. What is the least number of unit cubes in the solid?
    c. Draw the front views of both solids in parts (a) and (b).

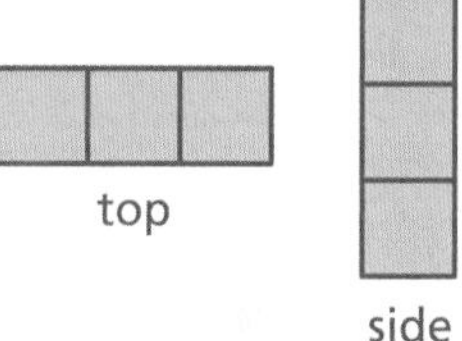

28. **Reasoning** Draw two different solids with five faces.
    a. Write the number of vertices and edges for each solid.
    b. Explain how knowing the numbers of edges and vertices helps you draw a three-dimensional figure.

Fair Game Review What you learned in previous grades & lessons

Find the area. *(Skills Review Handbook)*

29.

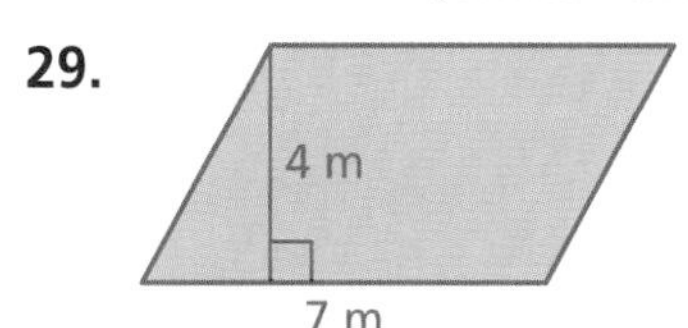

30.

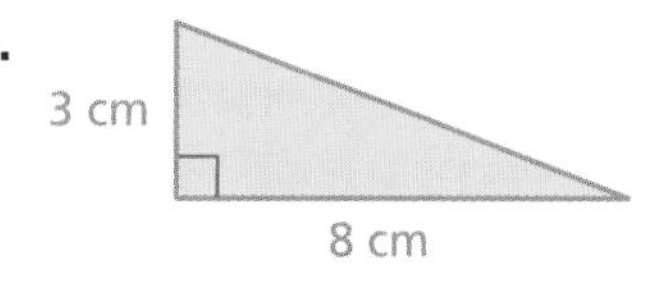

31.

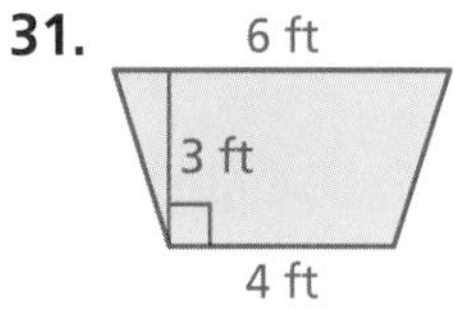

32. **MULTIPLE CHOICE** You borrow $200 and agree to repay $240 at the end of 2 years. What is the simple interest rate per year? *(Section 4.4)*

Ⓐ 5% Ⓑ 10% Ⓒ 15% Ⓓ 20%

6.2 Surface Areas of Prisms

STANDARDS OF LEARNING
8.7

Essential Question How can you use a formula to find the surface area of a prism?

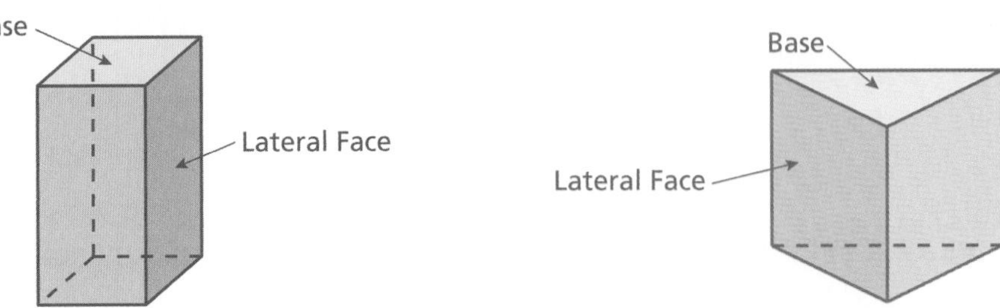

The **surface area** of a prism is the sum of the areas of all its faces. A two-dimensional representation of a solid is called a **net**.

1 ACTIVITY: Surface Area of a Triangular Prism

Work with a partner.

a. Use the net for the triangular prism to find its surface area.

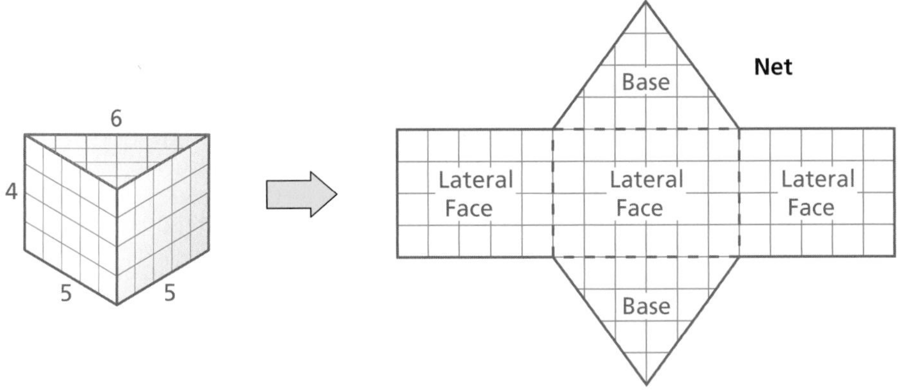

b. Copy the net for a triangular prism. Label each side. Then use your drawing to write a formula for the surface area of a triangular prism.

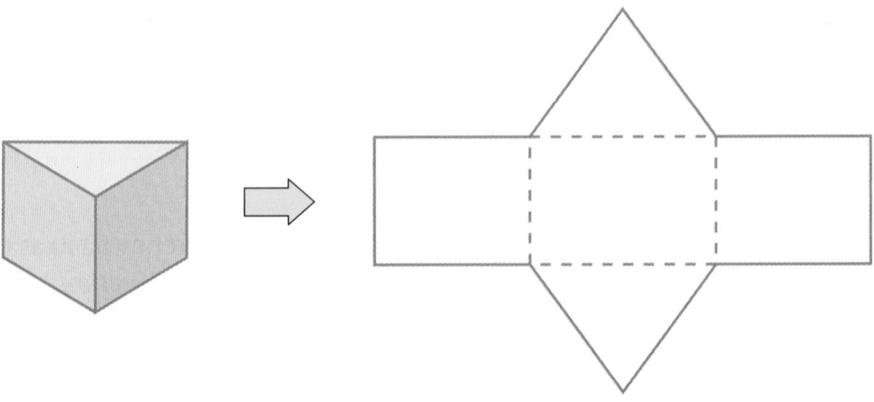

2 ACTIVITY: Finding Surface Area

Work with a partner.

a. Find the surface area of the solid shown by the net. Copy the net, cut it out, and fold it to form a solid. Identify the solid.

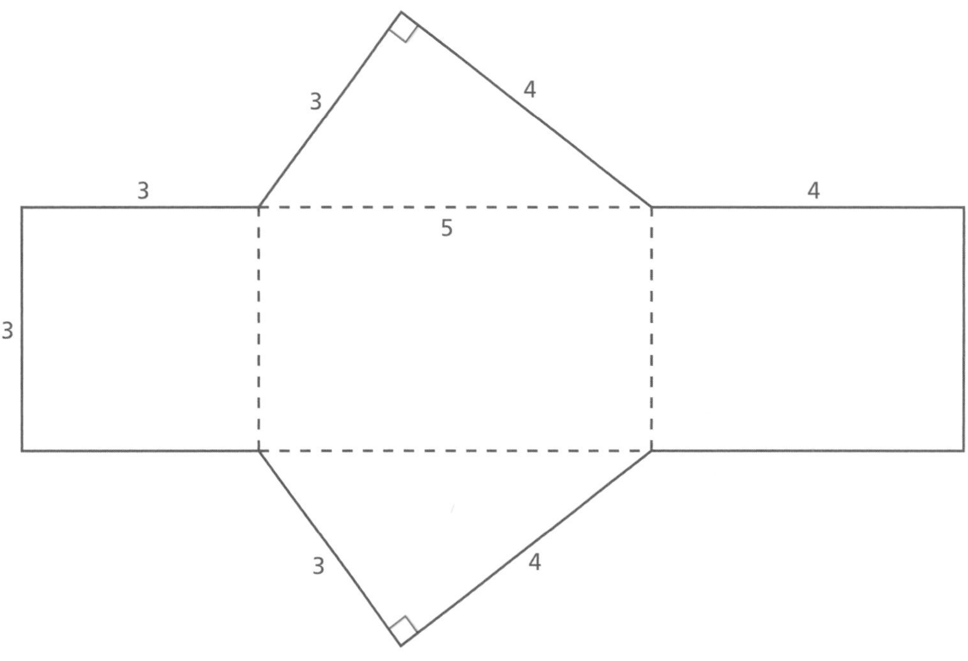

b. Which of the surfaces of the solid are bases? Why?

c. Double the height of the solid. Does this double the surface area? Explain your reasoning.

What Is Your Answer?

3. **IN YOUR OWN WORDS** How can you use a formula to find the surface area of a prism?

4. Find examples of prisms in your classroom. Measure each item and determine its surface area. For each item, give an example of how finding the surface area is important in knowing how much money is needed to manufacture or build the item.

Practice Use what you learned about the surface area of a prism to complete Exercises 6–8 on page 268.

6.2 Lesson

Key Vocabulary
surface area, *p. 264*
net, *p. 264*

Surface Area of a Rectangular Prism

Words The surface area S of a rectangular prism is the sum of the areas of the bases and the lateral faces.

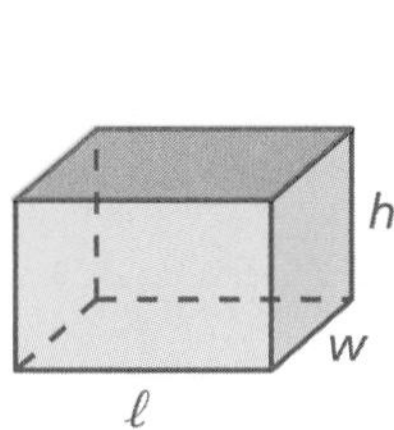

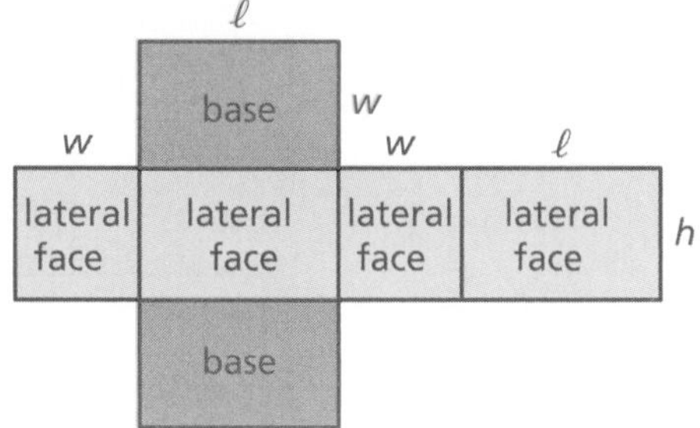

Algebra $S = 2\ell w + 2\ell h + 2wh$

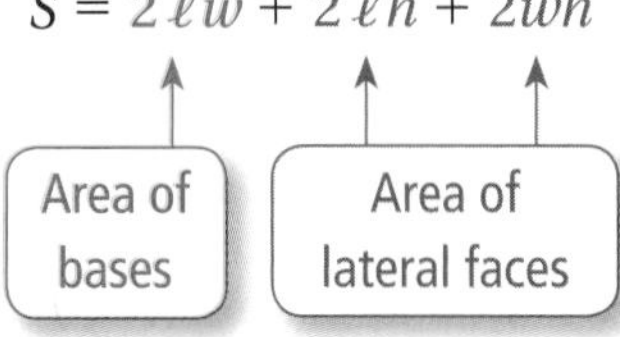

EXAMPLE 1 Finding the Surface Area of a Rectangular Prism

Find the surface area of the prism.

$$S = 2\ell w + 2\ell h + 2wh$$
$$= 2(5)(3) + 2(5)(6) + 2(3)(6)$$
$$= 30 + 60 + 36$$
$$= 126$$

6 in.
5 in.
3 in.

The surface area is 126 square inches.

On Your Own

Find the surface area of the prism.

1. 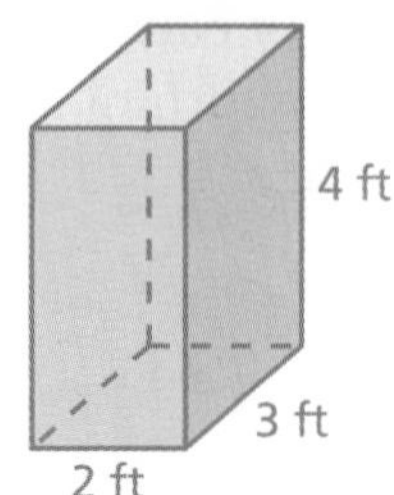

2. 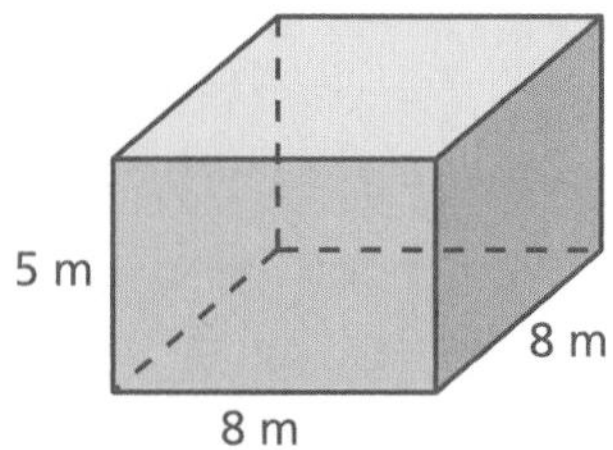

Surface Area of a Prism

The surface area S of any prism is the sum of the areas of the bases and the lateral faces.

$$S = \text{areas of bases} + \text{areas of lateral faces}$$

EXAMPLE 2 Finding the Surface Area of a Triangular Prism

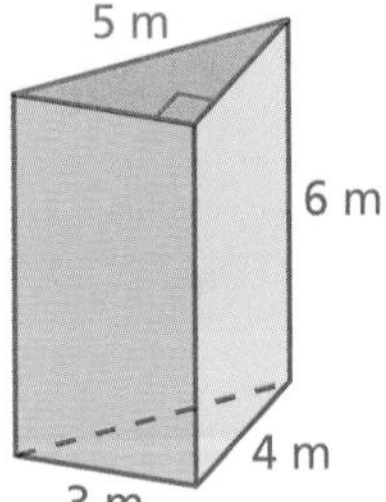

Find the surface area of the prism.

Draw a net.

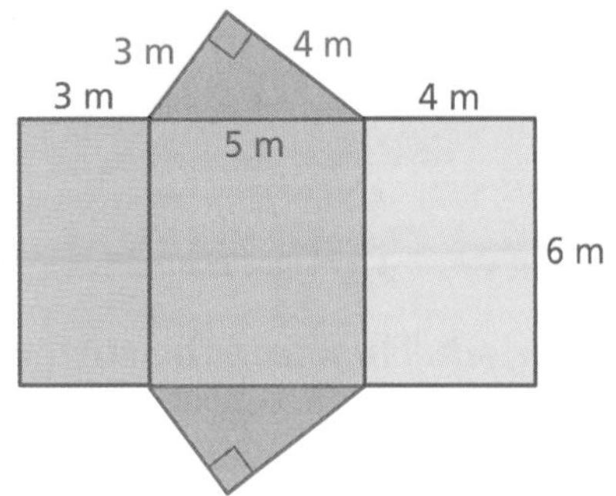

Remember

The area A of a triangle with base b and height h is $A = \frac{1}{2}bh$.

Area of a base	*Areas of lateral faces*
Red base: $\frac{1}{2} \cdot 3 \cdot 4 = 6$	Green lateral face: $6 \cdot 3 = 18$
	Purple lateral face: $6 \cdot 5 = 30$
	Blue lateral face: $6 \cdot 4 = 24$

Add the areas of the bases and the lateral faces.

$$S = \text{areas of bases} + \text{areas of lateral faces}$$

$$= 6 + 6 + 18 + 30 + 24$$

There are two identical bases. Count the area twice.

$$= 84$$

The surface area is 84 square meters.

On Your Own

Find the surface area of the prism.

3.

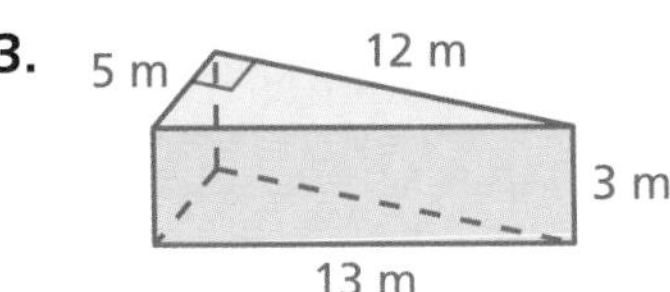

4.

4 cm

5 cm

4 cm

3 cm

6.2 Exercises

Vocabulary and Concept Check

1. **OPEN-ENDED** Describe a real-world situation in which you would want to find the surface area of a prism.

Find the indicated area for the rectangular prism.

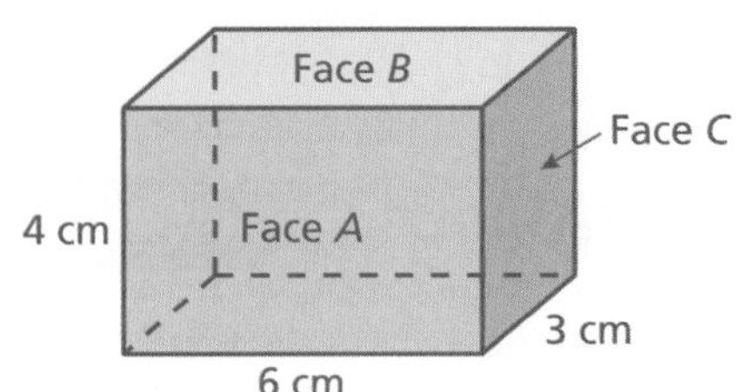

2. Area of Face *A*
3. Area of Face *B*
4. Area of Face *C*
5. Surface area of the prism

Practice and Problem Solving

Draw a net for the prism. Then find the surface area.

6.

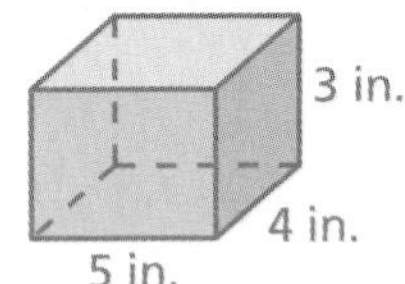

7.

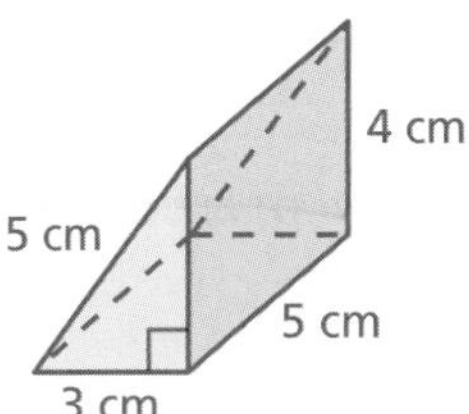

8.

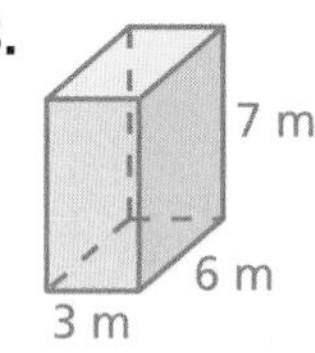

Find the surface area of the prism.

1 9.

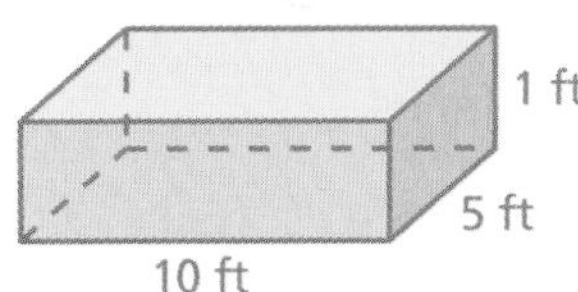

10.

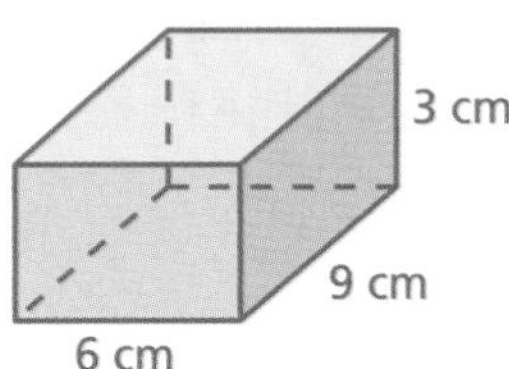

11.

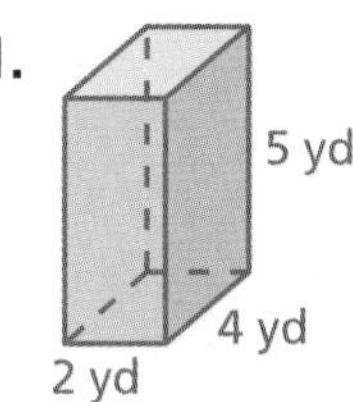

2 12.

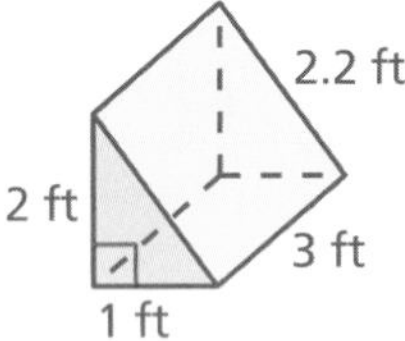

13.

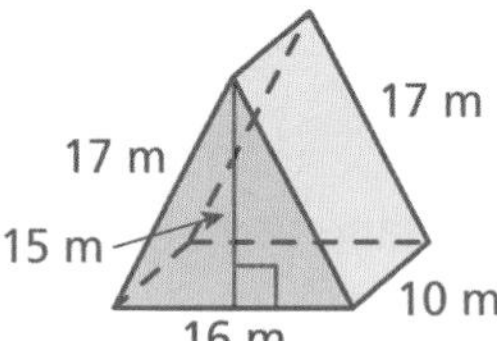

14.

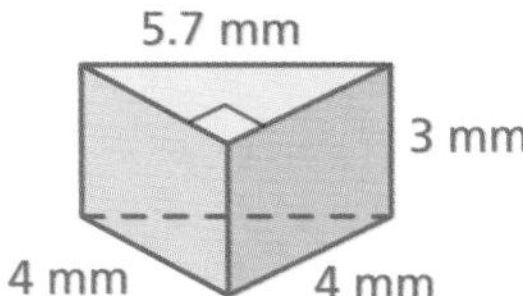

15. **GIFT BOX** What is the least amount of wrapping paper needed to wrap a gift box that measures 8 inches by 8 inches by 10 inches? Explain.

16. **TENT** What is the least amount of fabric needed to make the tent?

Find the surface area of the prism.

17.

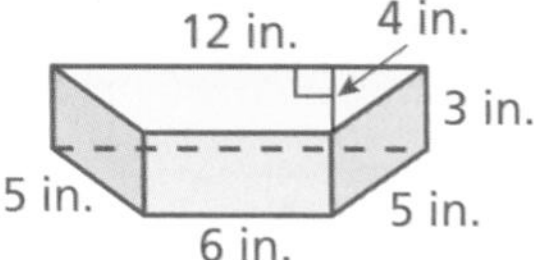

18.

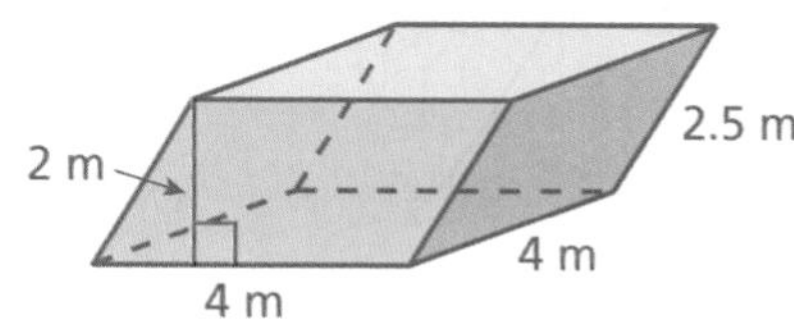

2.5 ft   6 ft   4 ft

19. AQUARIUM An aquarium is in the shape of a rectangular prism.

a. How many square feet of glass were used to build the aquarium? (The top of the aquarium is open.)

b. All three dimensions of a second aquarium are twice the size of the first aquarium. How much glass is needed to build this aquarium?

c. How does doubling all of the dimensions affect the amount of glass needed to build the aquarium?

20. STORAGE BOX The material used to make a storage box costs $1.25 per square foot. The boxes have the same volume. How much does a company save by choosing to make 50 of Box 2 instead of 50 of Box 1?

	Length	Width	Height
Box 1	20 in.	6 in.	4 in.
Box 2	15 in.	4 in.	8 in.

21. LABEL A label that wraps around a box of golf balls covers 75% of its lateral surface area. What is the value of x?

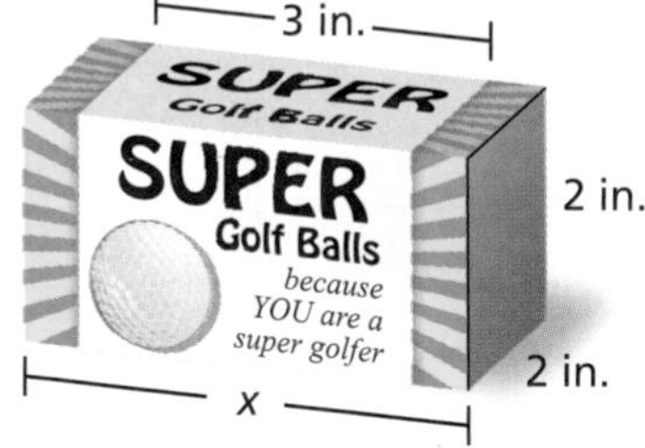

22. Critical Thinking Write a formula for the surface area of a rectangular prism using the height h, the perimeter P of a base, and the area B of a base.

Fair Game Review What you learned in previous grades & lessons

Find the perimeter. *(Skills Review Handbook)*

23.

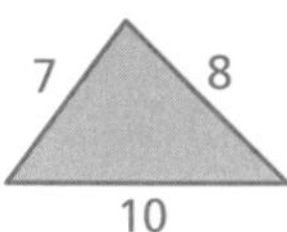

24.

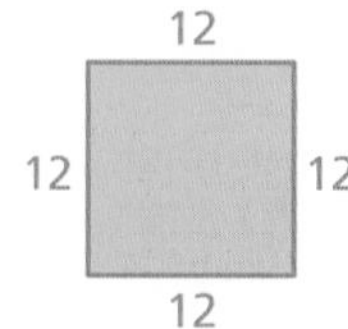

25.

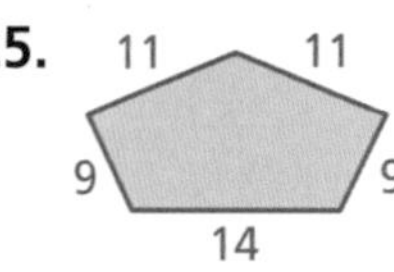

26. MULTIPLE CHOICE The class size increased 25% to 40 students. What was the original class size? *(Section 4.2)*

Ⓐ 10   Ⓑ 30   Ⓒ 32   Ⓓ 50

6.3 Surface Areas of Cylinders

STANDARDS OF LEARNING
8.7

Essential Question How can you derive a formula for the surface area of a cylinder?

You already know that the surface area of a cylinder is the sum of the areas of the bases and the lateral surface.

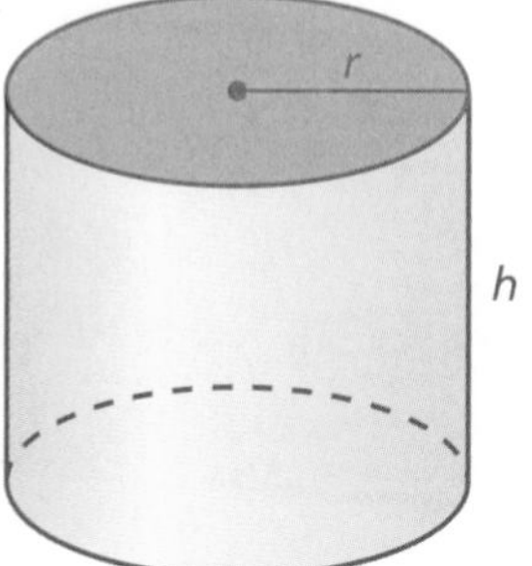

$$S = 2\pi r^2 + 2\pi rh$$

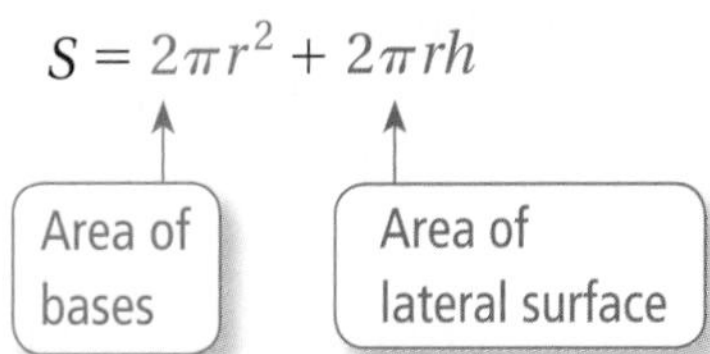

1 ACTIVITY: Writing an Activity

Work with a partner. Imagine that you are a math teacher and are introducing a lesson.

a. Design and write an activity in which your students can derive a formula for the surface area of a cylinder. Consider using any of the following objects. You can also use other objects, such as sheets of paper and tape.

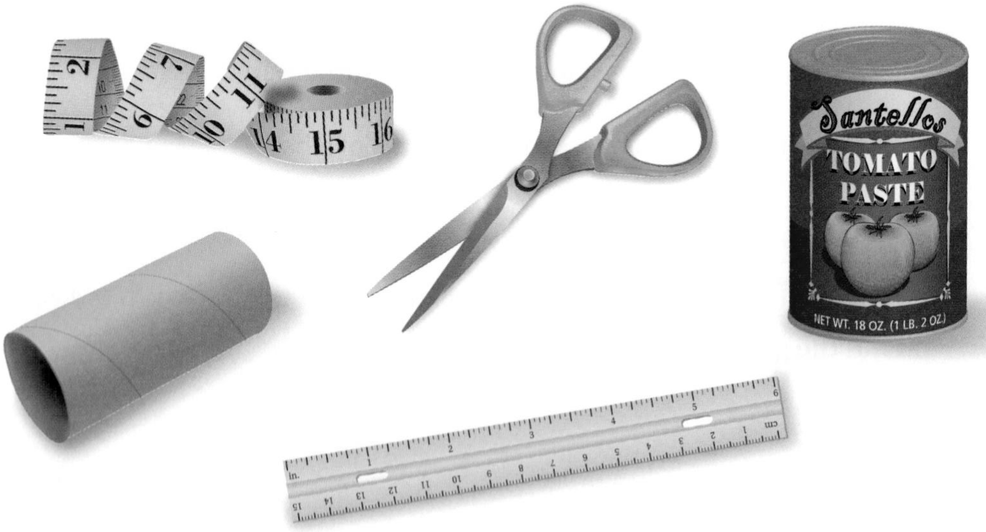

b. Perform the activity with your partner and write conclusions about your results.

2 ACTIVITY: Writing a Math Lesson

Work with a partner. Use your results from Activity 1 to write a lesson on finding the surface area of a cylinder.

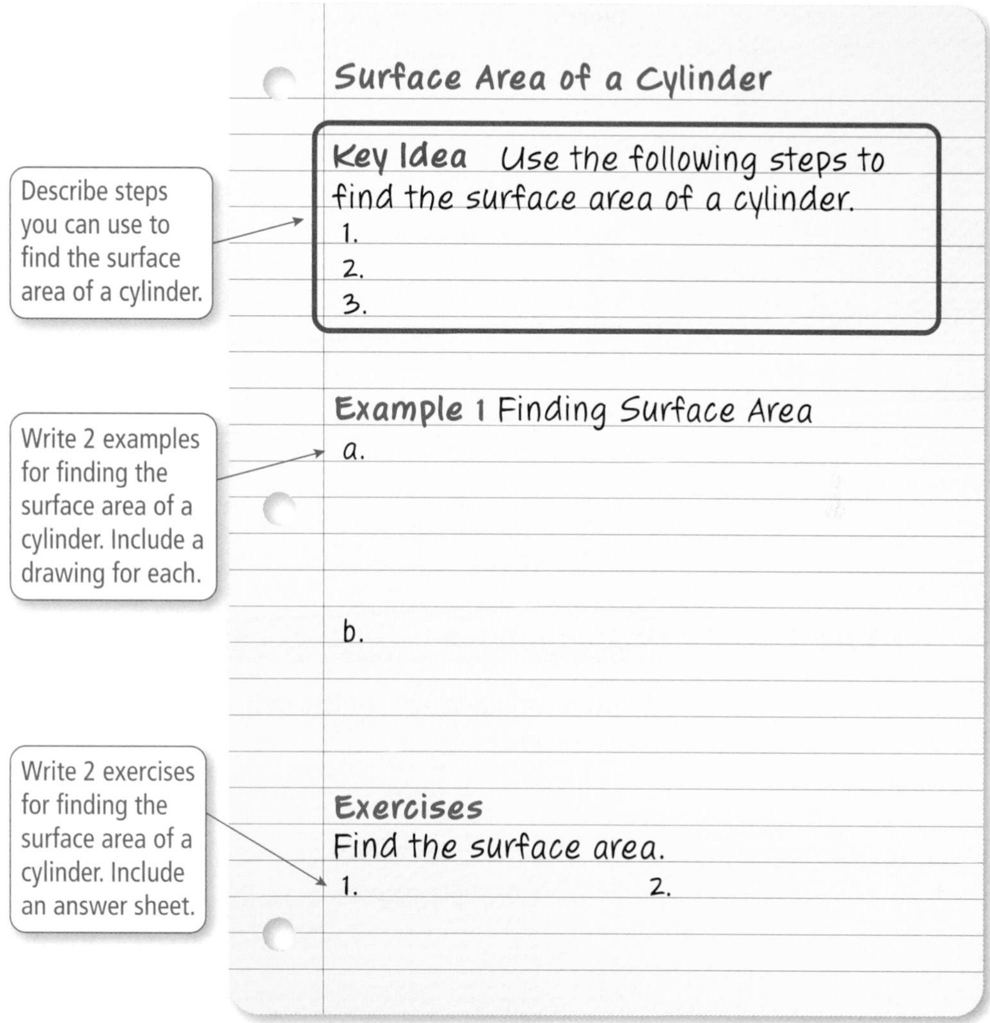

Surface Area of a Cylinder
Key Idea Use the following steps to find the surface area of a cylinder.
1.
2.
3.
Describe steps you can use to find the surface area of a cylinder.
Example 1 Finding Surface Area
a.
b.
Write 2 examples for finding the surface area of a cylinder. Include a drawing for each.
Exercises
Find the surface area.
1.
2.
Write 2 exercises for finding the surface area of a cylinder. Include an answer sheet.

What Is Your Answer?

3. **IN YOUR OWN WORDS** How can you derive a formula for the surface area of a cylinder?

4. Find examples of cylinders in your classroom. Measure each item and determine its surface area. For each item, give an example of how finding the surface area is important in knowing how much money is needed to manufacture or build the item.

Practice Use what you learned about the surface area of a cylinder to complete Exercises 4–6 on page 274.

6.3 Lesson

Surface Area of a Cylinder

Words The surface area S of a cylinder is the sum of the areas of the bases and the lateral surface.

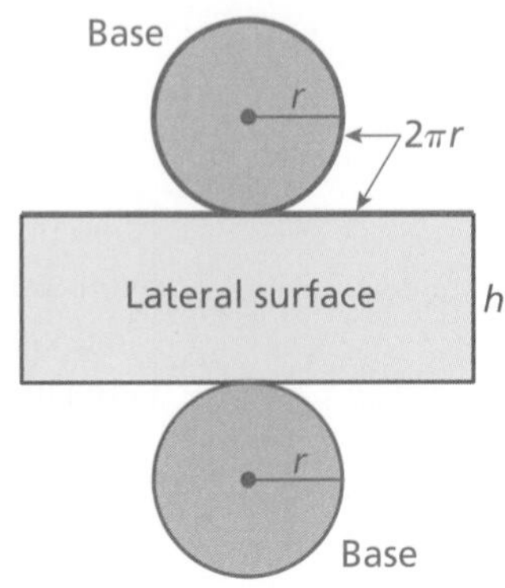

Algebra $S = 2\pi r^2 + 2\pi rh$

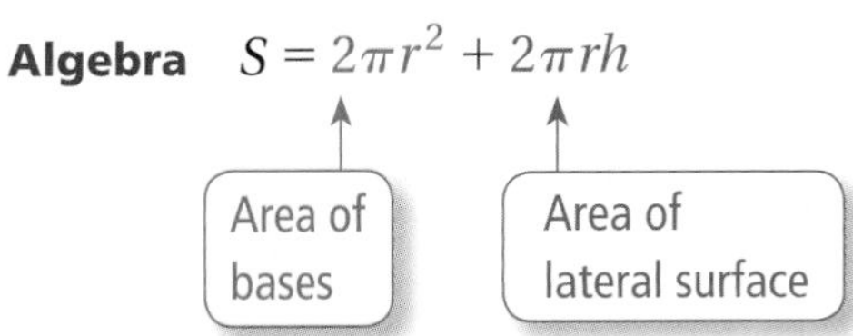

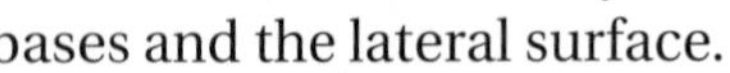

EXAMPLE 1 Finding the Surface Area of a Cylinder

Find the surface area of the cylinder. Round your answer to the nearest tenth.

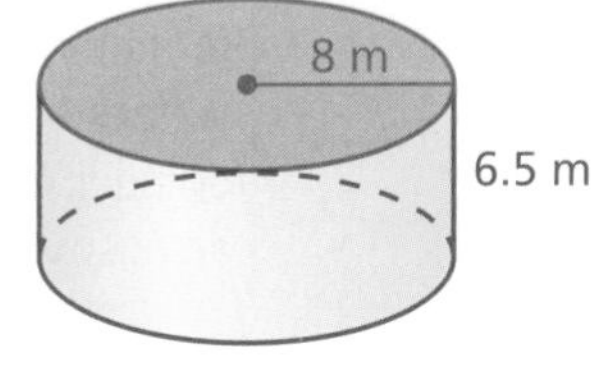

$$\begin{aligned} S &= 2\pi r^2 + 2\pi rh \\ &= 2\pi(8)^2 + 2\pi(8)(6.5) \\ &= 128\pi + 104\pi \\ &= 232\pi \\ &\approx 728.5 \end{aligned}$$

The surface area is about 728.5 square meters.

On Your Own

Now You're Ready
Exercises 4–9

Find the surface area of the cylinder. Round your answer to the nearest tenth.

1.

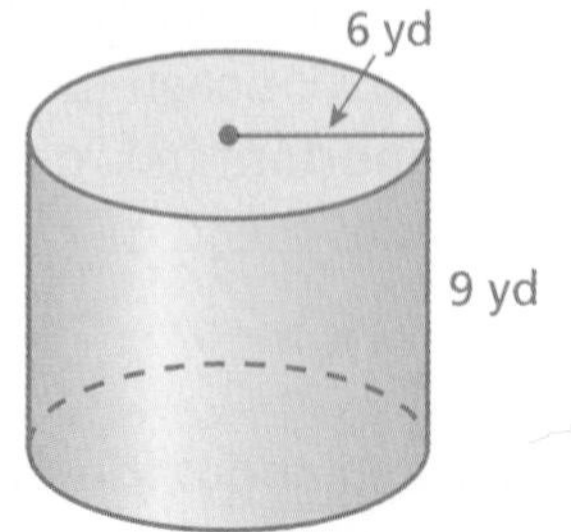

2.

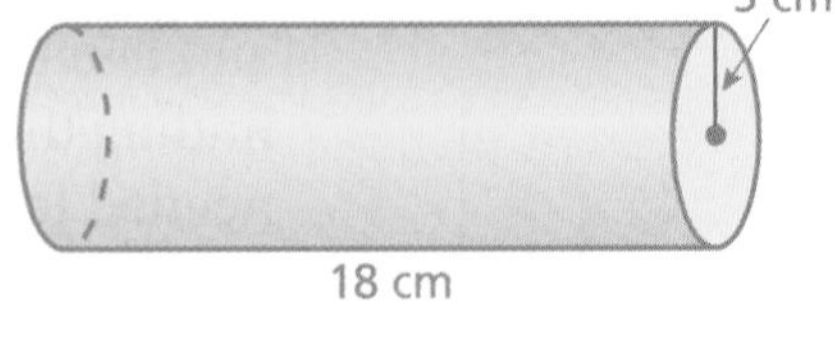

EXAMPLE 2 Changing Dimensions of a Cylinder

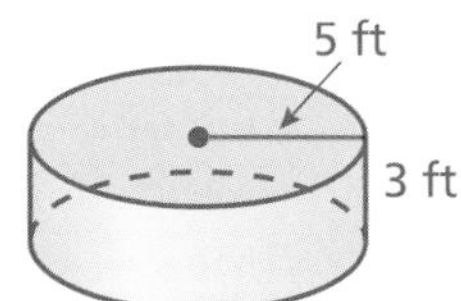

The dimensions of the red cylinder are twice the dimensions of the blue cylinder. How many times greater is the surface area of the red cylinder than the surface area of the blue cylinder?

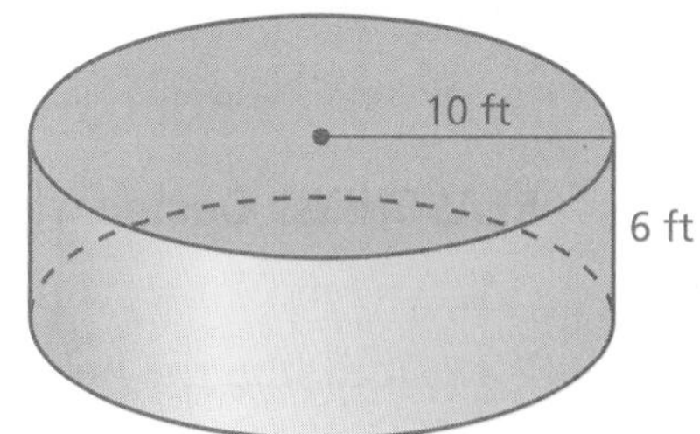

Find the surface area of each cylinder.

Blue Cylinder

$S = 2\pi r^2 + 2\pi rh$

$= 2\pi(5)^2 + 2\pi(5)(3)$

$= 50\pi + 30\pi = 80\pi \text{ ft}^2$

Red Cylinder

$S = 2\pi r^2 + 2\pi rh$

$= 2\pi(10)^2 + 2\pi(10)(6)$

$= 200\pi + 120\pi = 320\pi \text{ ft}^2$

The ratio of the surface areas is $\frac{320\pi \cancel{\text{ft}^2}}{80\pi \cancel{\text{ft}^2}} = 4$. So, the surface area of the red cylinder is 4 times greater than the surface area of the blue cylinder.

EXAMPLE 3 Real-Life Application

Find the ratio of the amount of paper used for the label of the large can to the amount of paper used for the label of the small can. What can you conclude?

Find the *lateral* surface area of each can.

Small Can

$S = 2\pi rh$

$= 2\pi(2)(3)$

$= 12\pi \text{ in.}^2$

Large Can

$S = 2\pi rh$

$= 2\pi(2)(6)$

$= 24\pi \text{ in.}^2$

The ratio of the amounts of paper is $\frac{24\pi \cancel{\text{in.}^2}}{12\pi \cancel{\text{in.}^2}} = 2$. So, the amount of paper used for the label of the large can is twice the amount of paper used for the label of the small can.

On Your Own

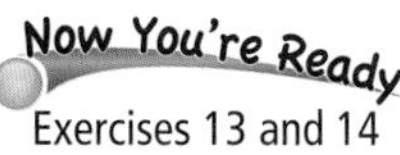

3. **WHAT IF?** The dimensions of a green cylinder are three times the dimensions of the blue cylinder in Example 2. How many times greater is the surface area of the green cylinder than the surface area of the blue cylinder?

4. **WHAT IF?** A jumbo can of beans has a height of 6 inches and a radius of 3 inches. Find the ratio of the amount of paper used for the label of the jumbo can to the amount of paper used for the label of the large can in Example 3. What can you conclude?

6.3 Exercises

Vocabulary and Concept Check

REASONING **Decide whether the statement is *true* or *false*. If false, explain your reasoning.**

1. The net for a cylinder consists of two circles and a rectangle.
2. Doubling the height of a cylinder doubles its surface area.
3. The area of the bases of a cylinder is always greater than its lateral surface area.

Practice and Problem Solving

Find the surface area of the cylinder. Round your answer to the nearest tenth.

1 **4.**

5.

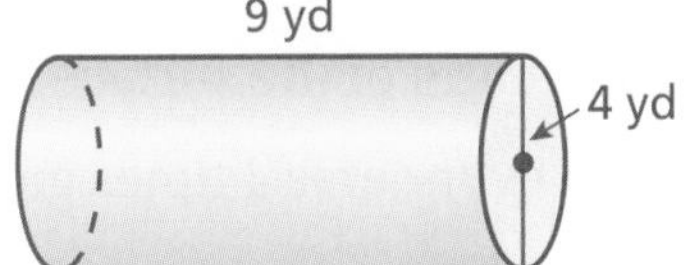

6.

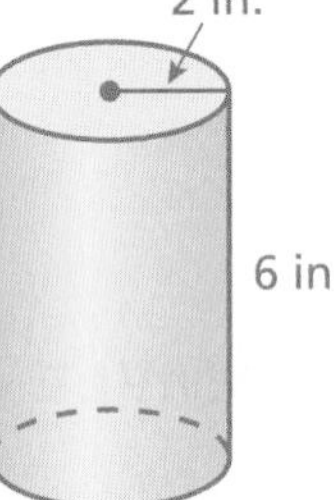

7.

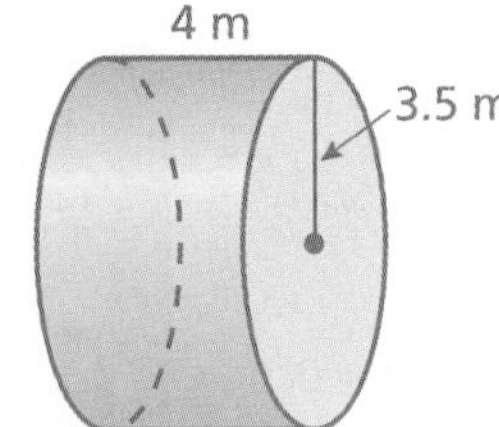

8.

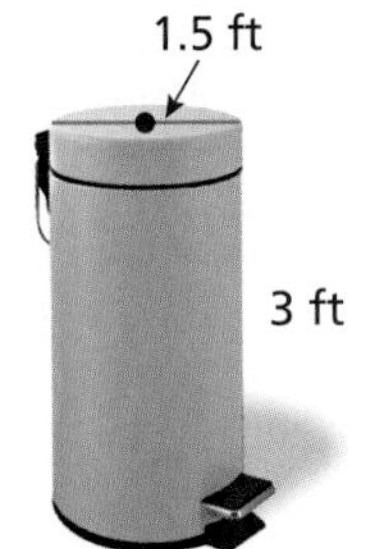

9.

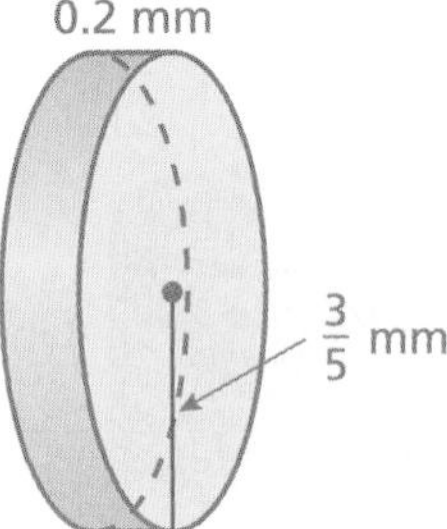

10. **ERROR ANALYSIS** Describe and correct the error in finding the surface area of the cylinder.

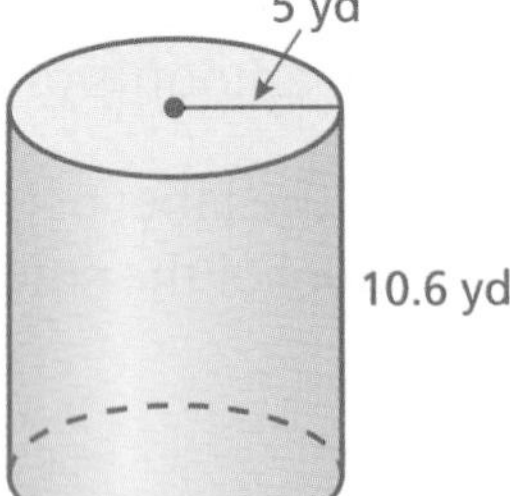

$$\begin{aligned} S &= \pi r^2 + 2\pi rh \\ &= \pi(5)^2 + 2\pi(5)(10.6) \\ &= 25\pi + 106\pi \\ &= 131\pi \approx 411.3 \text{ yd}^2 \end{aligned}$$

11. **FRUITCAKE** A cylindrical fruitcake container has a radius of 10 centimeters and a height of 5.3 centimeters. What is the surface area of the container?

12. **POPCORN** Which popcorn canister has the greater surface area? Explain.

Compare the dimensions of the cylinders. How many times greater is the surface area of the red cylinder than the surface area of the blue cylinder?

2 **13.**

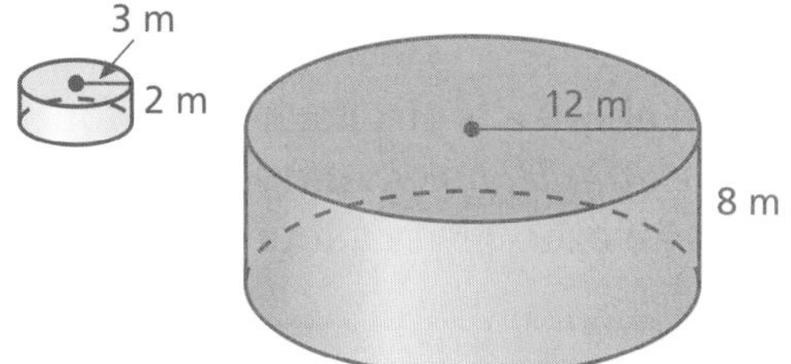

14.

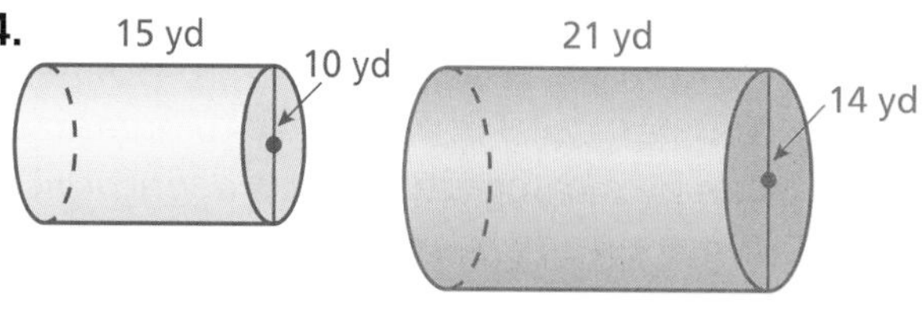

15. HAMSTER A hamster cage has a cylindrical tube for a hamster to crawl through and hide.

a. Find the lateral surface area of the tube.

b. You replace the tube. The new tube is three times longer. How does tripling the length affect the lateral surface area?

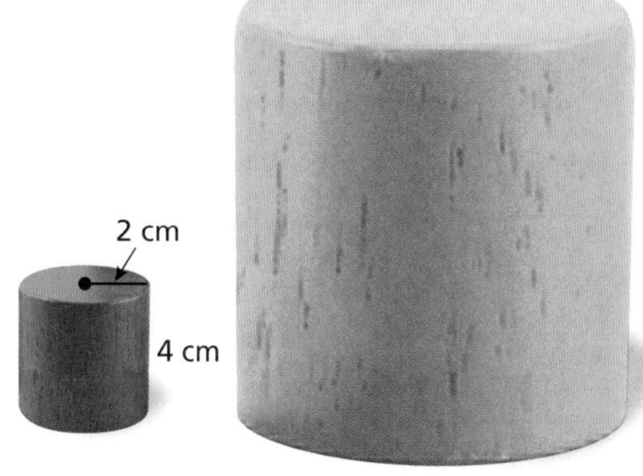

16. TOY BLOCKS You are painting toy blocks. You need 1 ounce of paint to paint 50 blue blocks.

a. The dimensions of the red block are one-half the dimensions of the blue block. How much paint do you need to paint 50 red blocks?

b. The dimensions of the orange block are triple the dimensions of the blue block. How much paint do you need to paint 50 orange blocks?

17. Critical Thinking A cylinder has radius r and height h.

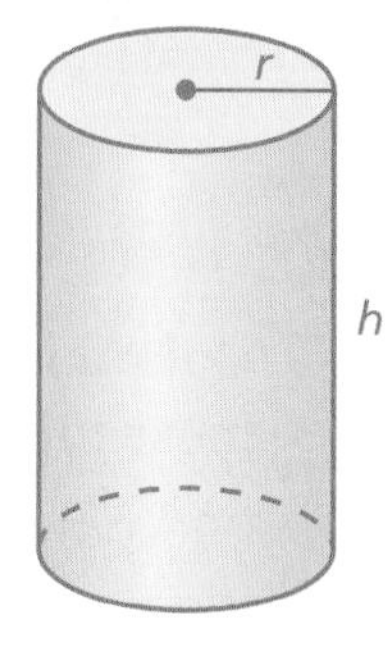

a. How many times greater is the surface area of a cylinder when both dimensions are multiplied by a factor of 2? 3? 5? 10?

b. Describe the pattern in part (a). How many times greater is the surface area of a cylinder when both dimensions are multiplied by a factor of 20?

Fair Game Review What you learned in previous grades & lessons

Use the table to write a linear function that relates y to x. *(Section 3.3)*

18.

x	-2	-1	0	1
y	5	4	3	2

19.

x	-1	0	1	2
y	-3	-1	1	3

20. MULTIPLE CHOICE What is the solution of $2x - 4 = 18$? *(Section 1.2)*

(A) 7 (B) 11 (C) 14 (D) 22

6 Study Help

You can use a **four square** to organize information about a topic. Each of the four squares can be a category, such as *definition, vocabulary, example, non-example, words, algebra, table, numbers, visual, graph,* or *equation*. Here is an example of a four square for a solid.

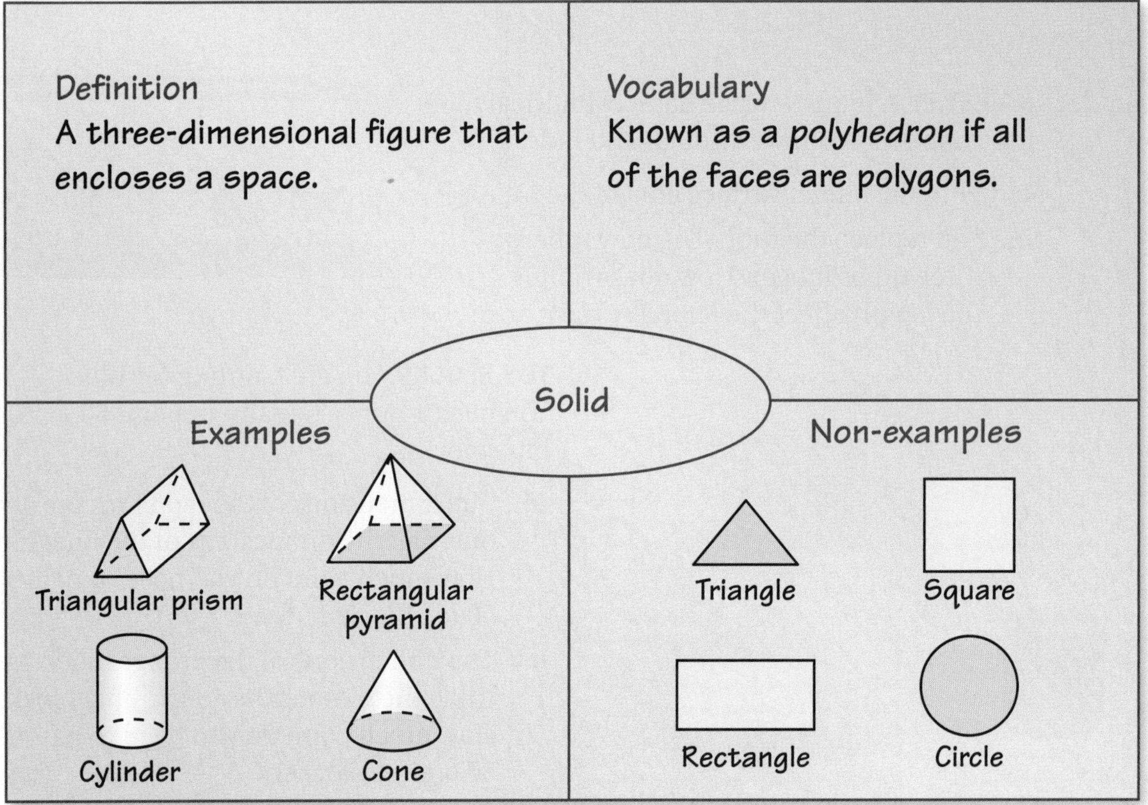

On Your Own

Make a four square to help you study these topics.

1. polyhedron
2. prism
3. pyramid
4. cylinder
5. cone
6. drawing a solid
7. surface area

    a. of a prism b. of a cylinder

After you complete this chapter, make four squares for the following topics.

8. surface area

    a. of a pyramid b. of a cone c. of a composite solid

"I'm taking a survey for my four square. How many fleas do you have?"

6.1–6.3 Quiz

Draw the front, side, and top views of the solid. *(Section 6.1)*

1. 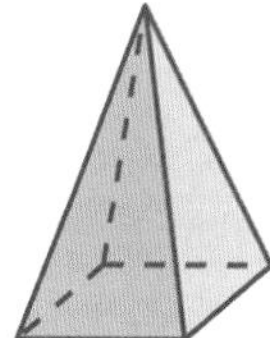

2. 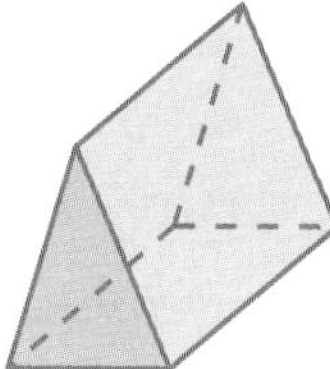

3. 

Find the surface area of the prism. *(Section 6.2)*

4. 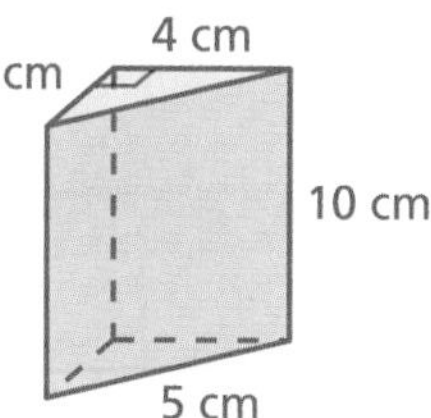

5. 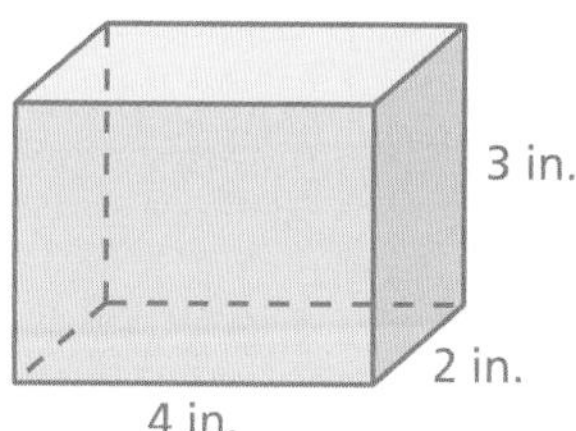

Find the surface area of the cylinder. Round your answer to the nearest tenth. *(Section 6.3)*

6. 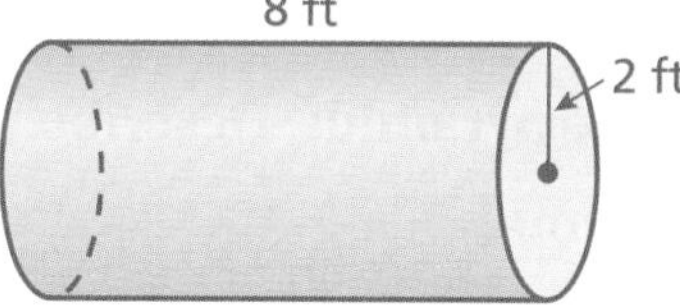

7. 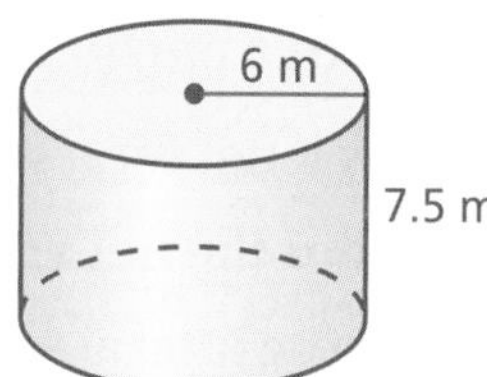

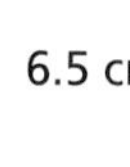

8. GIFT BOX Find the surface area of the gift box. *(Section 6.2)*

9. PILLOW A cylindrical pillow has a height of 14 inches and a radius of 2 inches. Triple the dimensions of the pillow. How many times greater is the surface area of the new pillow? *(Section 6.3)*

10. CAT FOOD Does doubling both dimensions of the can of cat food double the amount of metal needed to make the can? Explain. *(Section 6.3)*

6.4 Surface Areas of Pyramids

STANDARDS OF LEARNING
8.7

Essential Question How can you find the surface area of a pyramid?

Even though many well-known **pyramids** have square bases, the base of a pyramid can be any polygon.

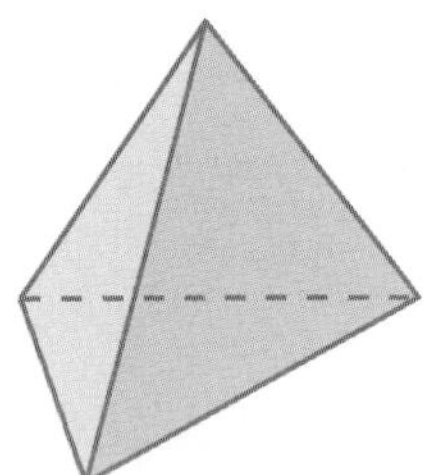
Triangular Base

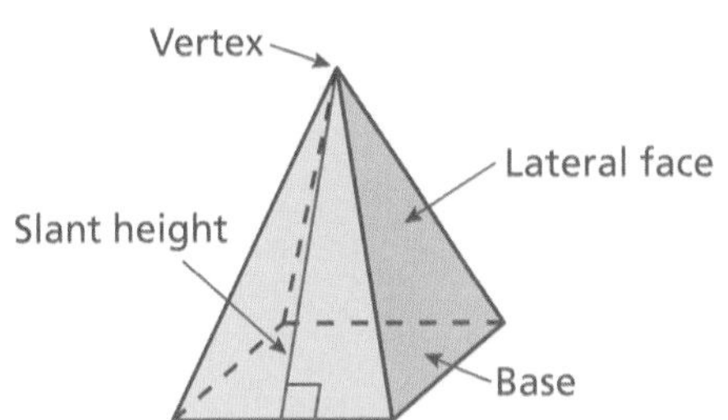

Square Base

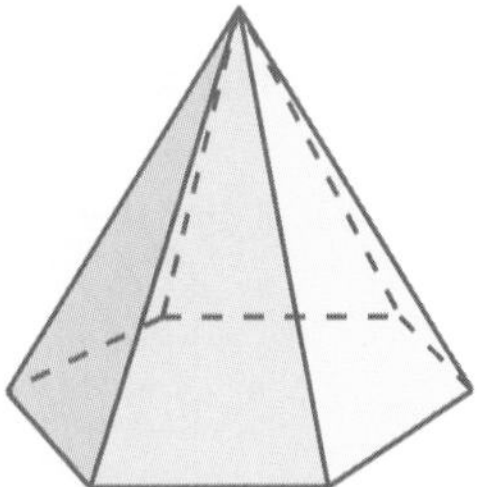
Hexagonal Base

1 ACTIVITY: Making a Scale Model

Work with a partner. Each pyramid has a square base.

- **Draw a net for a scale model of one of the pyramids. Describe your scale.**
- **Cut out the net and fold it to form a pyramid.**
- **Find the lateral surface area of the real-life pyramid.**

a. Cheops Pyramid in Egypt

Side = 230 m, Slant height ≈ 186 m

b. Muttart Conservatory in Edmonton

Side = 26 m, Slant height ≈ 27 m

c. Louvre Pyramid in Paris

Side = 35 m, Slant height ≈ 28 m

d. Pyramid of Caius Cestius in Rome

Side = 22 m, Slant height ≈ 29 m

2 ACTIVITY: Estimation

Work with a partner. There are many different types of gemstone cuts. Here is one called a brilliant cut.

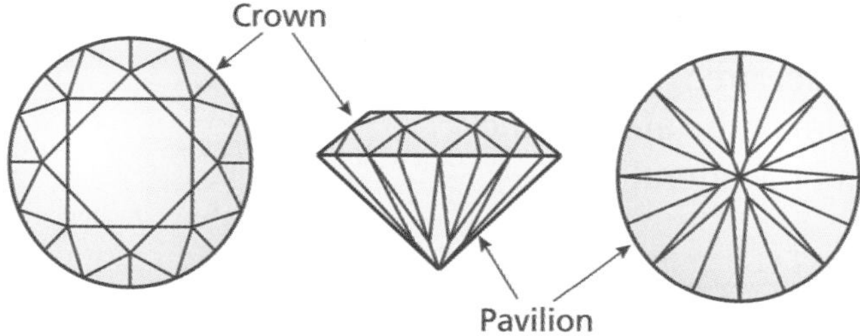

The size and shape of the pavilion can be approximated by an octagonal pyramid.

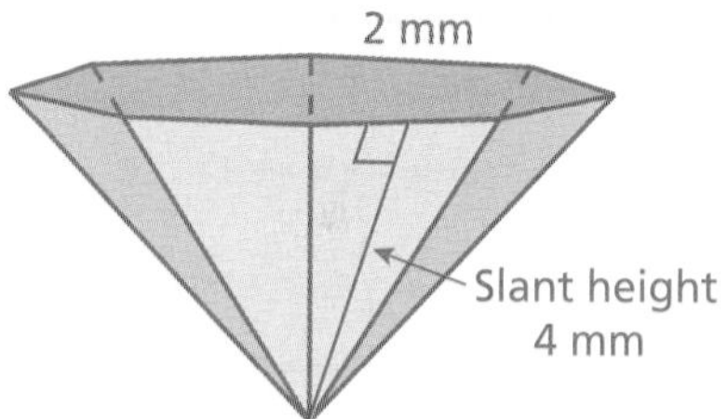

a. What does octagonal mean?

b. Draw a net for the pyramid.

c. Find the lateral surface area of the pyramid.

3 ACTIVITY: Building a Skylight

Work with a partner. The skylight has 12 triangular pieces of glass. Each piece has a base of 1 foot and a slant height of 3 feet.

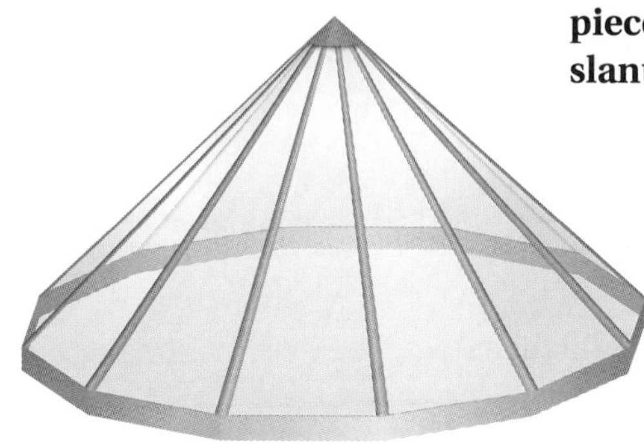

a. How much glass will you need to make the skylight?

b. Can you cut the 12 glass triangles from a sheet of glass that is 4 feet by 8 feet? If so, draw a diagram showing how this can be done.

What Is Your Answer?

4. **IN YOUR OWN WORDS** How can you find the surface area of a pyramid? Draw a diagram with your explanation.

Practice Use what you learned about the surface area of a pyramid to complete Exercises 4–6 on page 282.

6.4 Lesson

Key Vocabulary
regular pyramid, *p. 280*
slant height, *p. 280*

A **regular pyramid** is a pyramid whose base is a regular polygon. The lateral faces are triangles. The height of each triangle is the **slant height** of the pyramid.

Surface Area of a Pyramid

The surface area S of a pyramid is the sum of the areas of the base and the lateral faces.

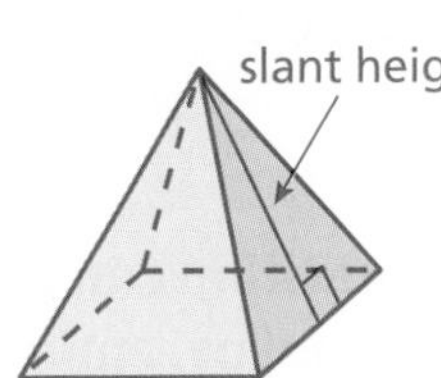

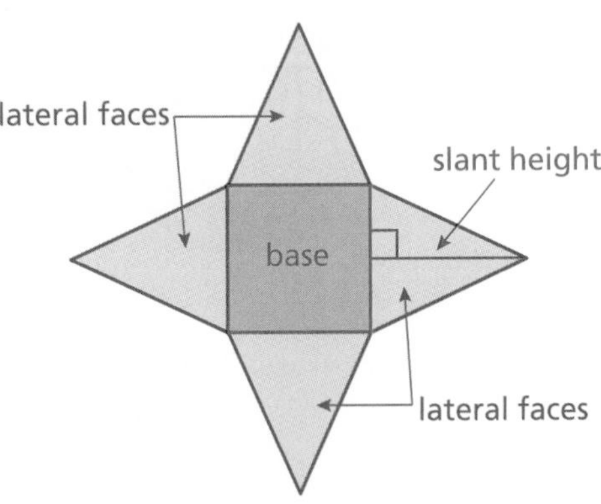

S = area of base + areas of lateral faces

Remember

In a regular polygon, all of the sides have the same length and all of the angles have the same measure.

EXAMPLE 1 Finding the Surface Area of a Square Pyramid

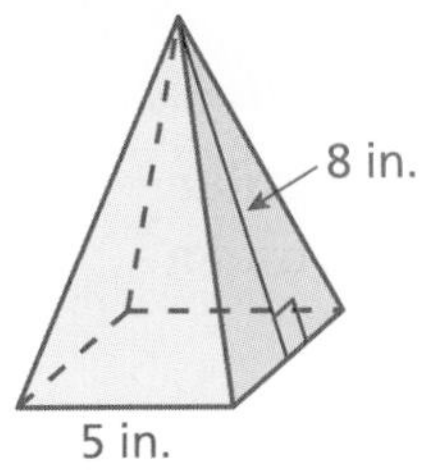

Find the surface area of the regular pyramid.

Draw a net.

Area of base	*Area of a lateral face*
$5 \cdot 5 = 25$	$\frac{1}{2} \cdot 5 \cdot 8 = 20$

5 in.
8 in.
5 in.

Find the sum of the areas of the base and the lateral faces.

S = area of base + areas of lateral faces

$= 25 + 20 + 20 + 20 + 20$

$= 105$

There are 4 identical lateral faces. Count the area 4 times.

∴ The surface area is 105 square inches.

1. What is the surface area of a square pyramid with a base side length of 9 centimeters and a slant height of 7 centimeters?

Multi-Language Glossary at BigIdeasMath.com.

EXAMPLE 2 Finding the Surface Area of a Triangular Pyramid

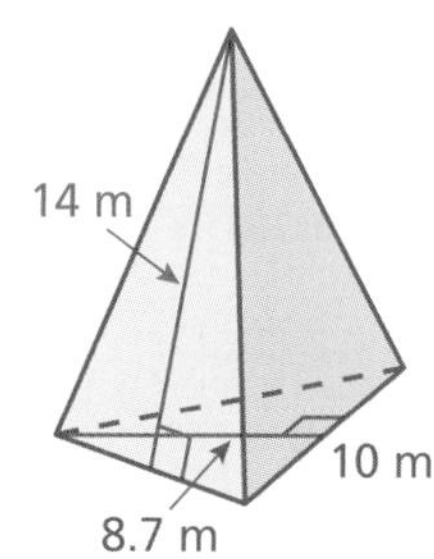

Find the surface area of the regular pyramid.

Draw a net.

Area of base	***Area of a lateral face***
$\frac{1}{2} \cdot 10 \cdot 8.7 = 43.5$	$\frac{1}{2} \cdot 10 \cdot 14 = 70$

Find the sum of the areas of the base and the lateral faces.

$$S = \text{area of base} + \text{areas of lateral faces}$$

$$= 43.5 + \underbrace{70 + 70 + 70}$$

$$= 253.5$$

There are 3 identical lateral faces. Count the area 3 times.

∴ The surface area is 253.5 square meters.

EXAMPLE 3 Real-Life Application

A roof is shaped like a square pyramid. One bundle of shingles covers 25 square feet. How many bundles should you buy to cover the roof?

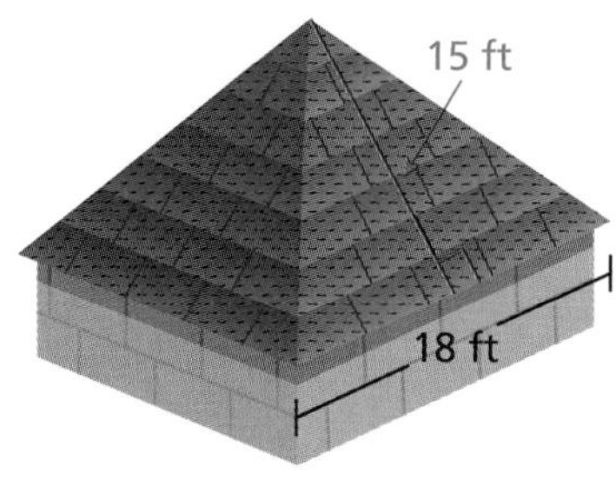

The base of the roof does not need shingles. So, find the sum of the areas of the lateral faces of the pyramid.

Area of a lateral face

$\frac{1}{2} \cdot 18 \cdot 15 = 135$

There are four identical lateral faces. So, the sum of the areas of the lateral faces is

$$135 + 135 + 135 + 135 = 540.$$

Because one bundle of shingles covers 25 square feet, it will take $540 \div 25 = 21.6$ bundles to cover the roof.

∴ So, you should buy 22 bundles of shingles.

On Your Own

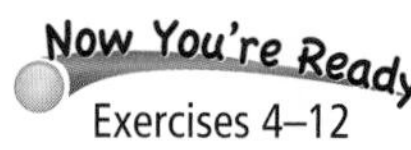

2. What is the surface area of the pyramid at the right?

3. **WHAT IF?** In Example 3, one bundle of shingles covers 32 square feet. How many bundles should you buy to cover the roof?

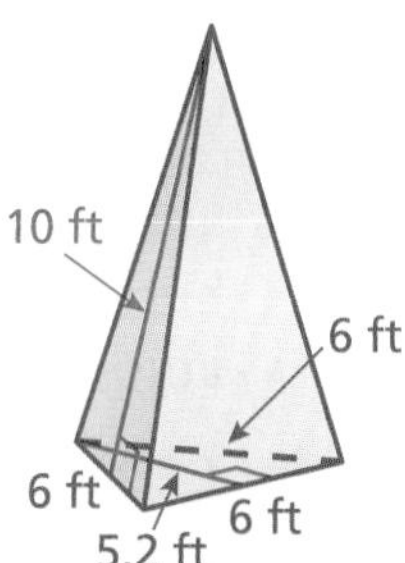

6.4 Exercises

Vocabulary and Concept Check

1. **VOCABULARY** Which of the polygons could be the base for a regular pyramid?

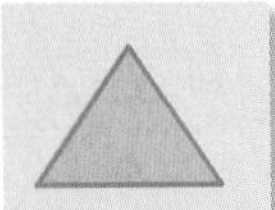 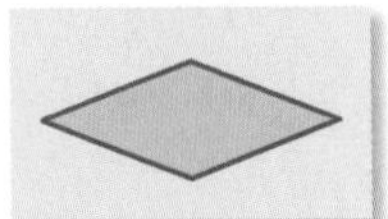 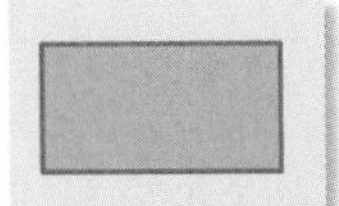 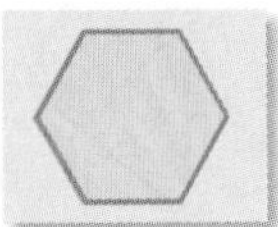

2. **VOCABULARY** Can a pyramid have rectangles as lateral faces? Explain.

3. **CRITICAL THINKING** Why is it helpful to know the slant height of a pyramid to find its surface area?

Practice and Problem Solving

Use the net to find the surface area of the regular pyramid.

4. 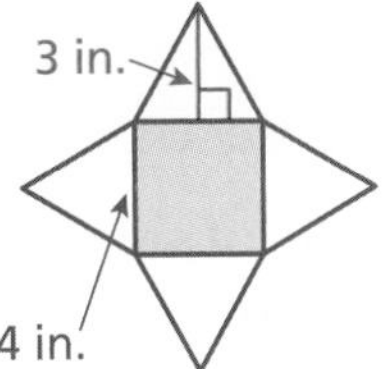

5. 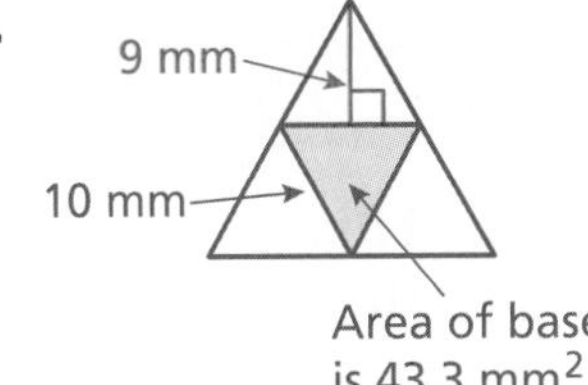

6. 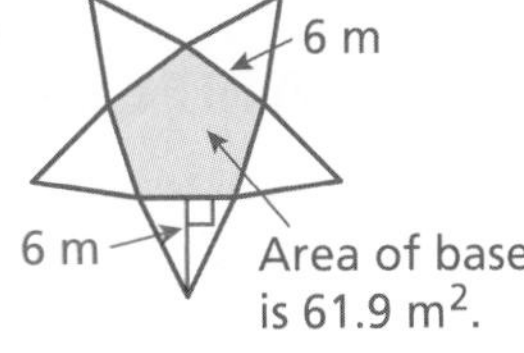

In Exercises 7–11, find the surface area of the regular pyramid.

7. 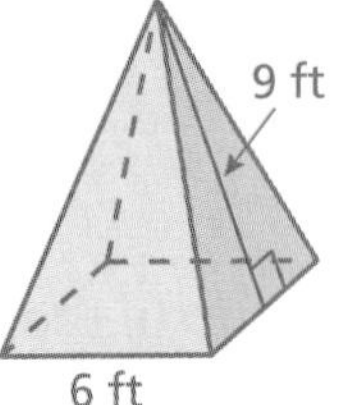

8. 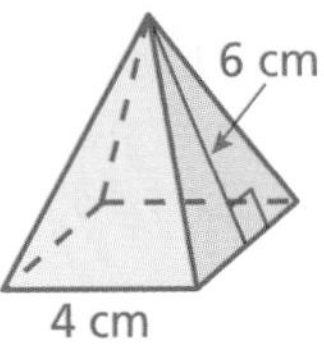

9. 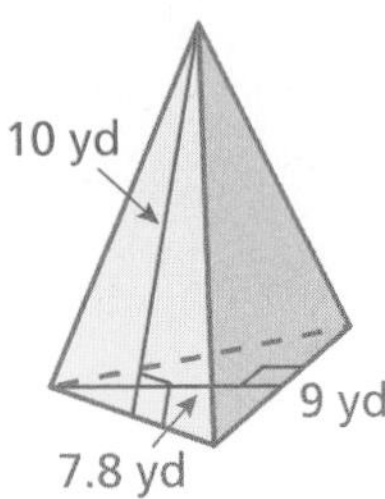

10. 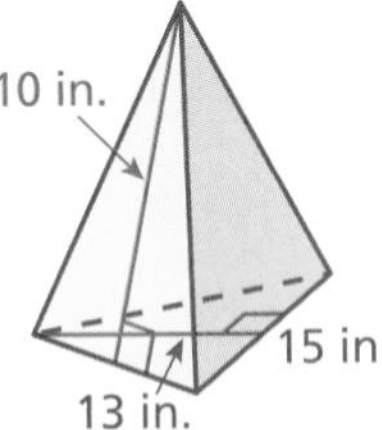

11. 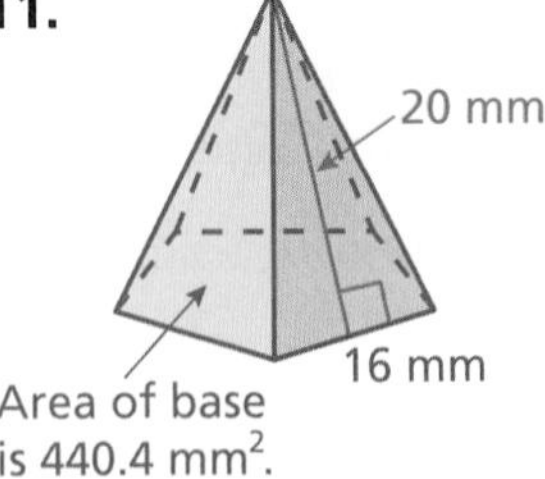

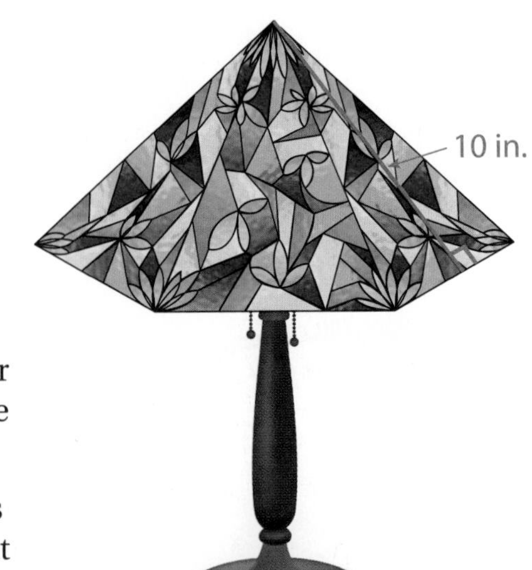

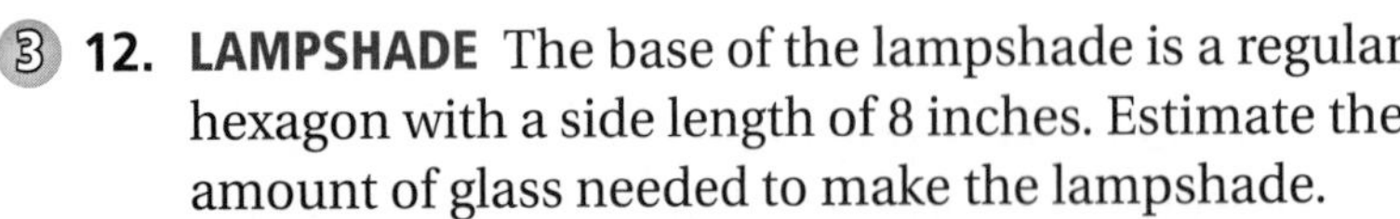

3 12. **LAMPSHADE** The base of the lampshade is a regular hexagon with a side length of 8 inches. Estimate the amount of glass needed to make the lampshade.

13. **GEOMETRY** The surface area of a square pyramid is 85 square meters. The base length is 5 meters. What is the slant height?

14. **BMX** You are building a bike ramp that is shaped like a square pyramid. You use two 4-foot by 8-foot sheets of plywood. How much plywood do you have left over?

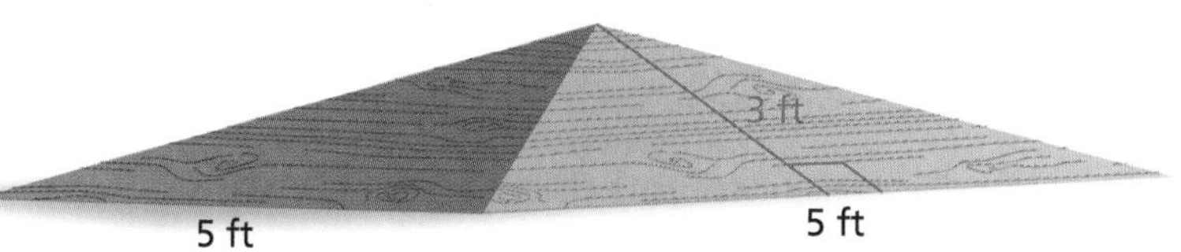

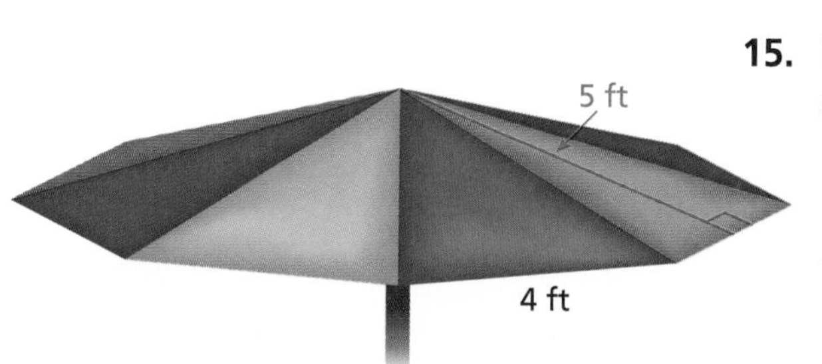

15. **UMBRELLA** You are making an umbrella that is shaped like a regular octagonal pyramid.

    a. Estimate the amount of fabric that is needed to make the umbrella.

    b. The fabric comes in rolls that are 72 inches wide. You don't want to cut the fabric "on the bias." Find out what this means. Then, draw a diagram of how you can cut the fabric most efficiently.

    c. How much fabric is wasted?

16. **REASONING** The *height* of a pyramid is the perpendicular distance between the base and the top of the pyramid. Which is greater, the height of a pyramid or the slant height? Explain your reasoning.

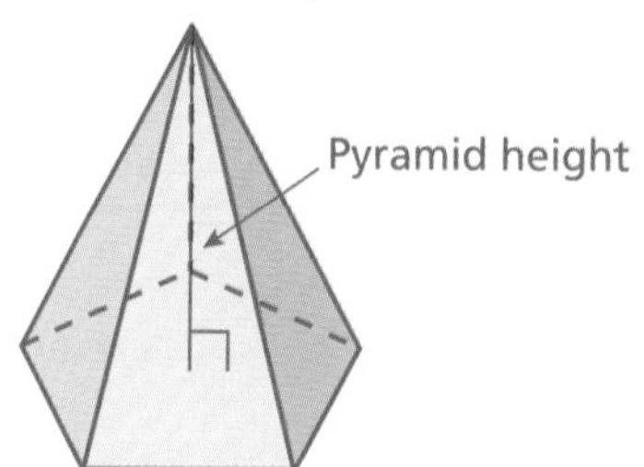

17. **TETRAHEDRON** A tetrahedron is a triangular pyramid whose four faces are identical equilateral triangles. The total lateral surface area is 93 square centimeters. Find the surface area of the tetrahedron.

18. **Reasoning** Is the total area of the lateral faces of a pyramid *greater than*, *less than*, or *equal to* the area of the base? Explain.

Fair Game Review What you learned in previous grades & lessons

Find the area and circumference of the circle. Use 3.14 for π. *(Skills Review Handbook)*

19. 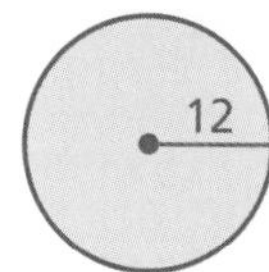

20. 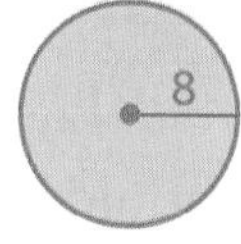

21. 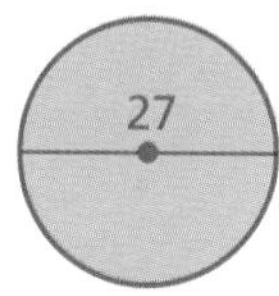

22. **MULTIPLE CHOICE** A youth baseball diamond is similar to a professional baseball diamond. The ratio of the perimeters is 2 : 3. The distance between bases on a youth diamond is 60 feet. What is the distance between bases on a professional diamond? *(Skills Review Handbook)*

    Ⓐ 40 ft   Ⓑ 90 ft   Ⓒ 120 ft   Ⓓ 180 ft

6.5 Surface Areas of Cones

STANDARDS OF LEARNING
8.7

Essential Question How can you find the surface area of a cone?

A cone is a solid with one circular base and one vertex.

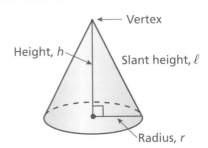

Vertex
Height, h
Slant height, ℓ
Radius, r

1 ACTIVITY: Finding the Surface Area of a Cone

Work with a partner.

- **Draw a circle with a radius of 3 inches.**
- **Mark the circumference of the circle into six equal parts.**
- **The circumference of the circle is $2(\pi)(3) = 6\pi$. So each of the six parts on the circle has a length of π. Label each part.**
- **Cut out one part as shown. Then, make a cone.**

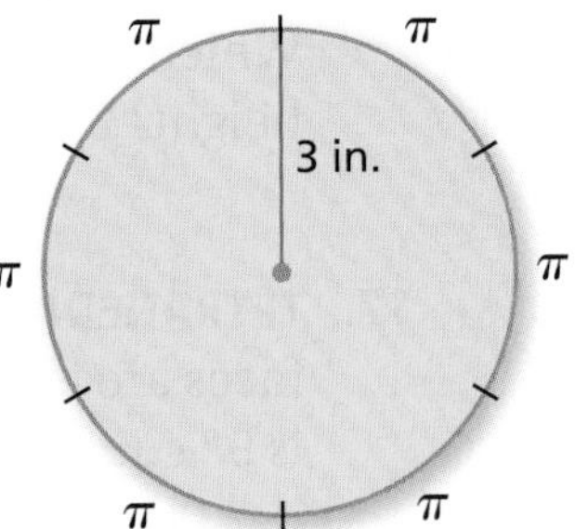

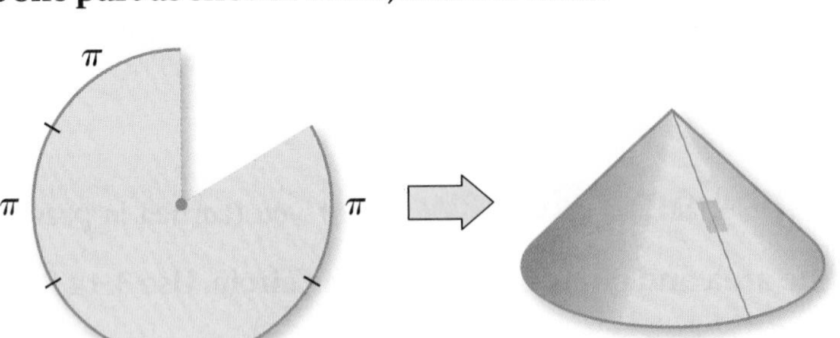

a. The base of the cone should be a circle. Explain why the circumference of the base is 5π.

b. Find the radius of the base.

c. What is the area of the original circle?

d. What is the area of the circle with one part missing?

e. Describe the surface area of the cone. Use your description to find the surface area, including the base.

2 ACTIVITY: Experimenting with Surface Area

Work with a partner.

- **Cut out another part from the circle in Activity 1 and make a cone.**
- **Find the radius of the base and the surface area of the cone.**
- **Record your results in the table.**
- **Repeat this three times.**
- **Describe the pattern.**

Shape					
Radius of Base					
Slant Height					
Surface Area					

3 ACTIVITY: Writing a Story

Write a story that uses real-life cones. Include a diagram and label the dimensions. In your story, explain why you would want to know the surface area of the cone. Then, estimate the surface area.

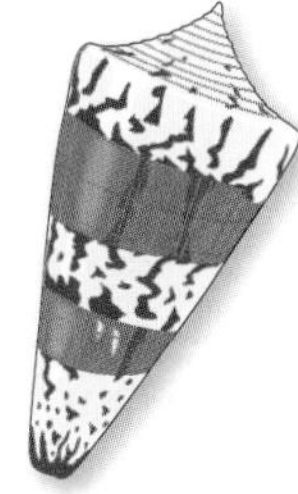

What Is Your Answer?

4. **IN YOUR OWN WORDS** How can you find the surface area of a cone? Draw a diagram with your explanation.

Use what you learned about the surface area of a cone to complete Exercises 4–6 on page 288.

6.5 Lesson

Key Vocabulary
slant height, *p. 286*

The distance from the vertex of a cone to any point on the edge of its base is called the **slant height** of the cone.

Surface Area of a Cone

Words The surface area S of a cone is the sum of the areas of the base and the lateral surface.

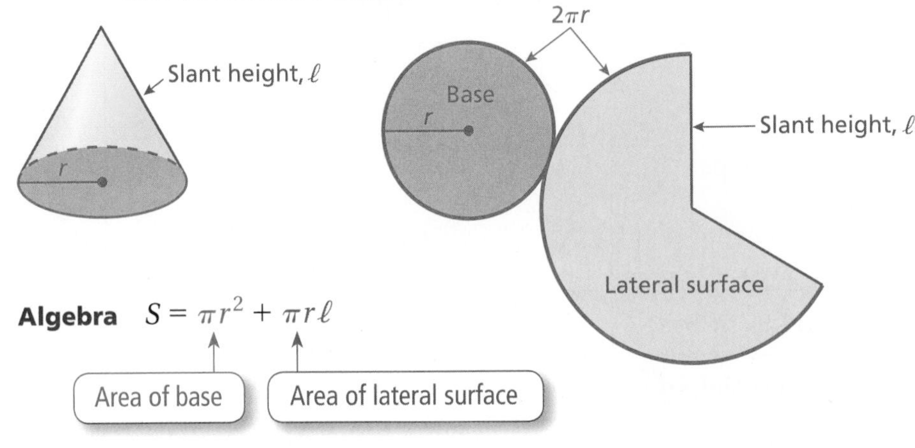

Algebra $S = \pi r^2 + \pi r \ell$

Area of base ↑ (πr^2); Area of lateral surface ↑ ($\pi r \ell$)

EXAMPLE 1 Finding the Surface Area of a Cone

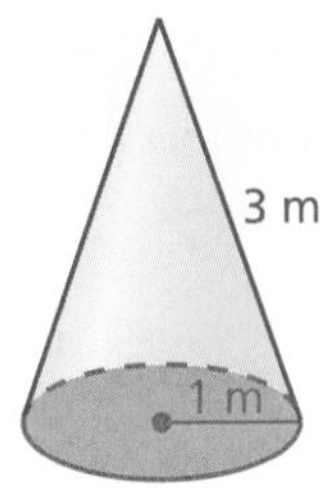

Find the surface area of the cone. Round your answer to the nearest tenth.

Draw a net.

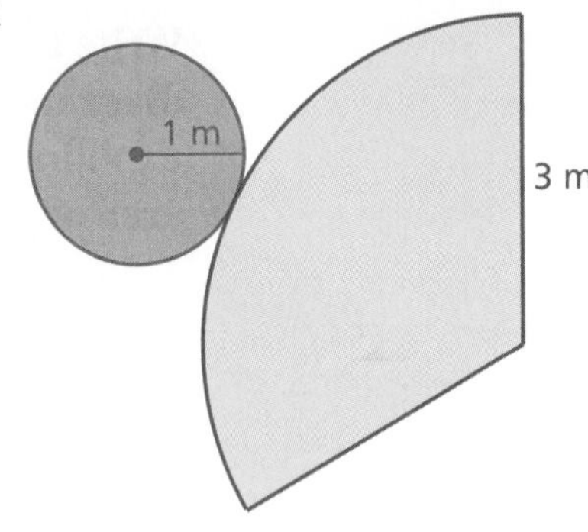

$$S = \pi r^2 + \pi r \ell$$
$$= \pi(1)^2 + \pi(1)(3)$$
$$= \pi + 3\pi$$
$$= 4\pi \approx 12.6$$

The surface area is about 12.6 square meters.

On Your Own

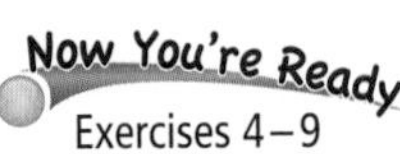

Find the surface area of the cone. Round your answer to the nearest tenth.

1. 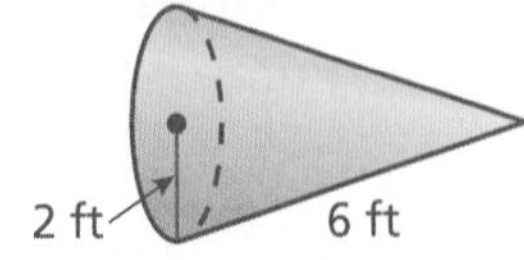

2. 8 cm, 4 cm

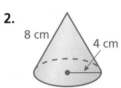

Multi-Language Glossary at BigIdeasMath.com.

EXAMPLE 2 Finding the Slant Height of a Cone

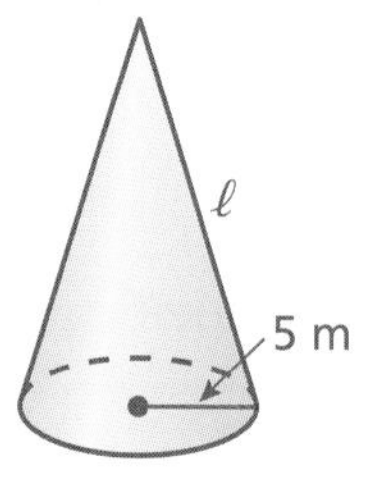

The surface area of the cone is 100π square meters. What is the slant height ℓ of the cone?

$S = \pi r^2 + \pi r \ell$	Write formula.
$100\pi = \pi(5)^2 + \pi(5)(\ell)$	Substitute.
$100\pi = 25\pi + 5\pi\ell$	Simplify.
$75\pi = 5\pi\ell$	Subtract 25π from each side.
$15 = \ell$	Divide each side by 5π.

∴ The slant height is 15 meters.

EXAMPLE 3 Real-Life Application

You design a party hat. You attach a piece of elastic along a diameter. (a) How long is the elastic? (b) How much paper do you need to make the hat?

a. To find the length of the elastic, find the diameter of the base.

$C = \pi d$	Write formula.
$22 \approx (3.14)d$	Substitute.
$7.0 \approx d$	Solve for d.

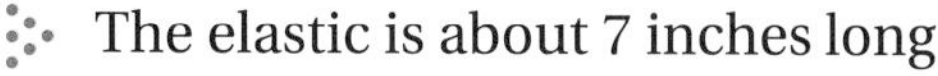

∴ The elastic is about 7 inches long.

5 in.

$C = 22$ in.

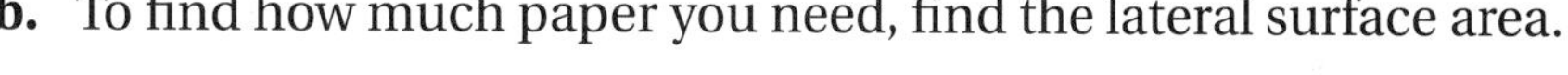

b. To find how much paper you need, find the lateral surface area.

Remember

The diameter d of a circle is two times the radius r.

$d = 2r$

$S = \pi r \ell$	← Do not include the area of the base in the formula.
$= \pi(3.5)(5)$	Substitute.
$= 17.5\pi \approx 55$	Multiply.

∴ You need about 55 square inches of paper to make the hat.

On Your Own

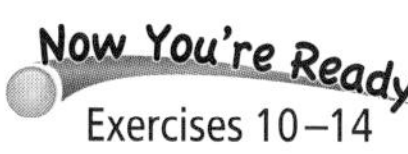

Now You're Ready
Exercises 10–14

3. **WHAT IF?** In Example 2, the surface area is 50π square meters. What is the slant height of the cone?

4. **WHAT IF?** In Example 3, the slant height of the party hat is doubled. Does the amount of paper used double? Explain.

6.5 Exercises

Vocabulary and Concept Check

1. **VOCABULARY** Is the base of a cone a polygon? Explain.
2. **CRITICAL THINKING** In the formula for the surface area of a cone, what does $\pi r \ell$ represent? What does πr^2 represent?
3. **REASONING** Write an inequality comparing the slant height ℓ and the radius r of a cone.

Practice and Problem Solving

Find the surface area of the cone. Round your answer to the nearest tenth.

① 4.
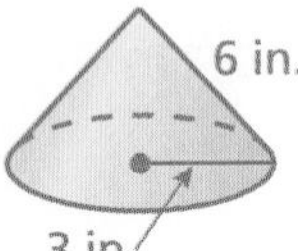

5.
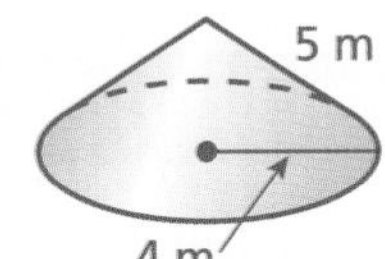

6.
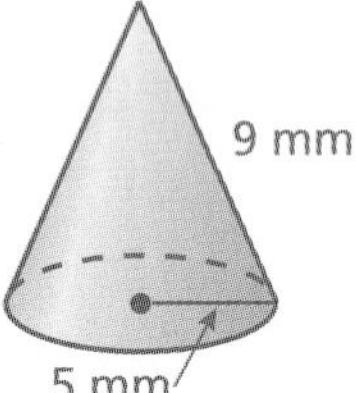

7.
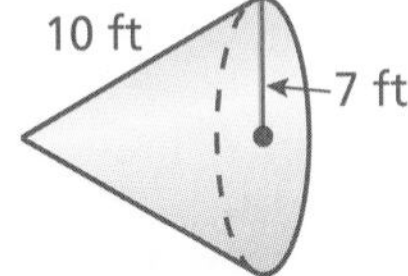

8.
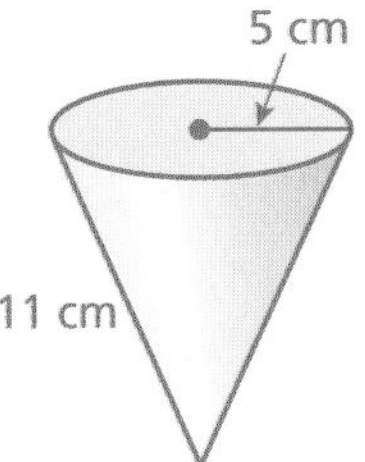

9.
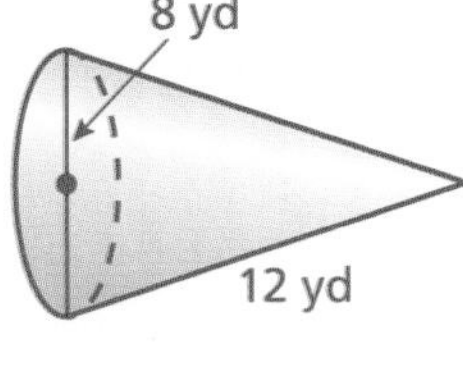

Find the slant height ℓ of the cone.

② 10. $S = 33\pi$ in.^{2}

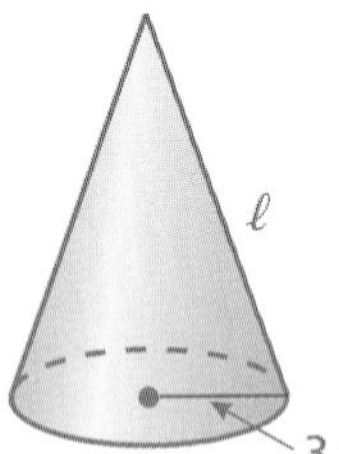

11. $S = 126\pi$ cm^2

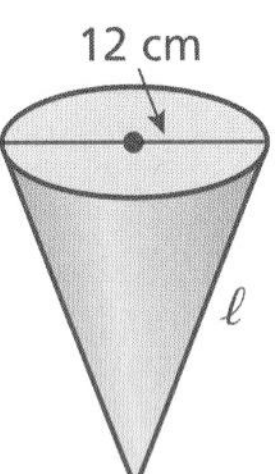

12. $S = 60\pi$ ft^2

③ 13. **NÓN LÁ** How much material is needed to make the Nón Lá Vietnamese leaf hat?

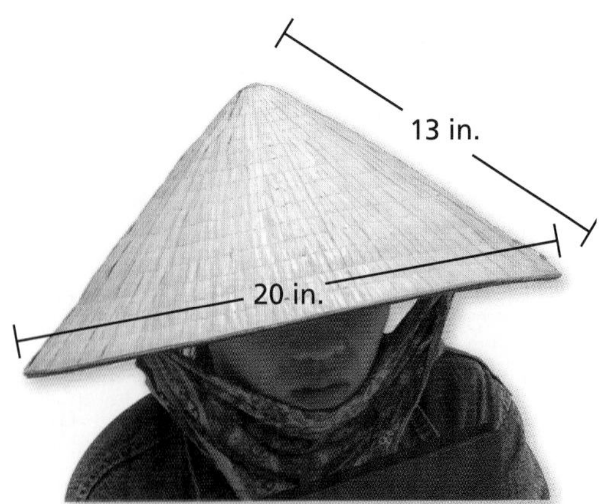

14. **PAPER CUP** A paper cup shaped like a cone has a diameter of 6 centimeters and a slant height of 7.5 centimeters. How much paper is needed to make the cup?

Find the surface area of the cone with diameter d and slant height ℓ.

15. $d = 2$ ft
$\ell = 18$ in.

16. $d = 12$ cm
$\ell = 85$ mm

17. $d = 4$ yd
$\ell = 10$ ft

18. ROOF A roof is shaped like a cone with a diameter of 12 feet. One bundle of shingles covers 32 square feet. How many bundles should you buy to cover the roof?

19. MEGAPHONE Two stickers are placed on opposite sides of the megaphone. Estimate the percent of the surface area of the megaphone covered by the stickers. Round your answer to the nearest percent.

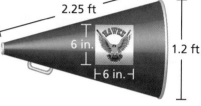

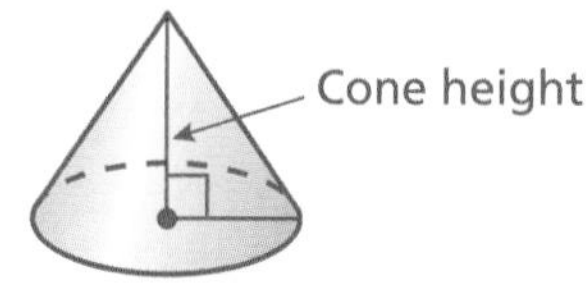

20. REASONING The *height* of a cone is the perpendicular distance from the base to the vertex. Which is greater, the height of a cone or the slant height? Explain your reasoning.

21. GEOMETRY The surface area of a cone is also given as $S = \frac{1}{2}C\ell + B$, where C is the circumference and ℓ is the slant height. What does $\frac{1}{2}C\ell$ represent?

22. Critical Thinking A cone has a diameter of x millimeters and a slant height of y millimeters. A square pyramid has a base side length of x millimeters and a slant height of y millimeters. Which has the greater surface area? Explain.

Fair Game Review What you learned in previous grades & lessons

Find the area of the figure. *(Section 5.7)*

23.

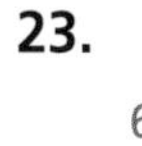

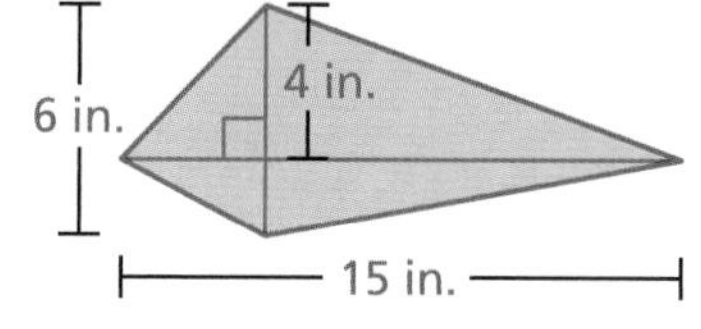

24.

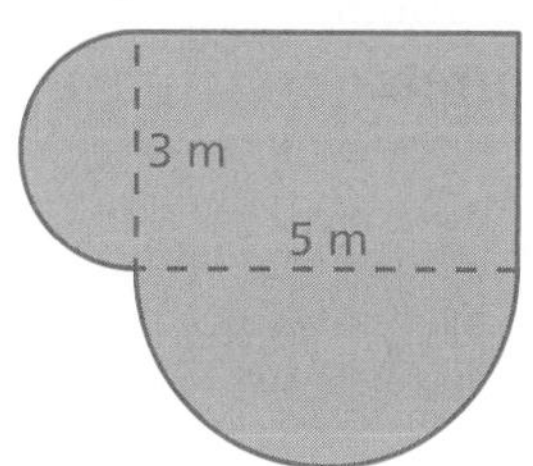

25.

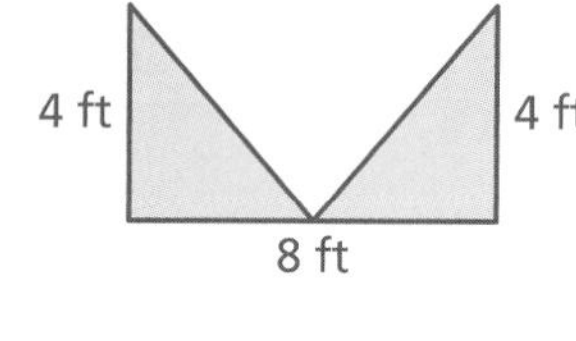

26. MULTIPLE CHOICE Which best describes a translation? *(Section 5.5)*

Ⓐ a flip
Ⓑ a slide
Ⓒ a turn
Ⓓ an enlargement

6.6 Surface Areas of Composite Solids

STANDARDS OF LEARNING
8.7

Essential Question How can you find the surface area of a composite solid?

1 ACTIVITY: Finding a Surface Area

Work with a partner. You are manufacturing scale models of old houses.

a. Name the four basic solids of this composite figure.

b. Determine a strategy for finding the surface area of this model. Would you use a scale drawing? Would you use a net? Explain.

Many castles have cylindrical towers with conical roofs. These are called turrets.

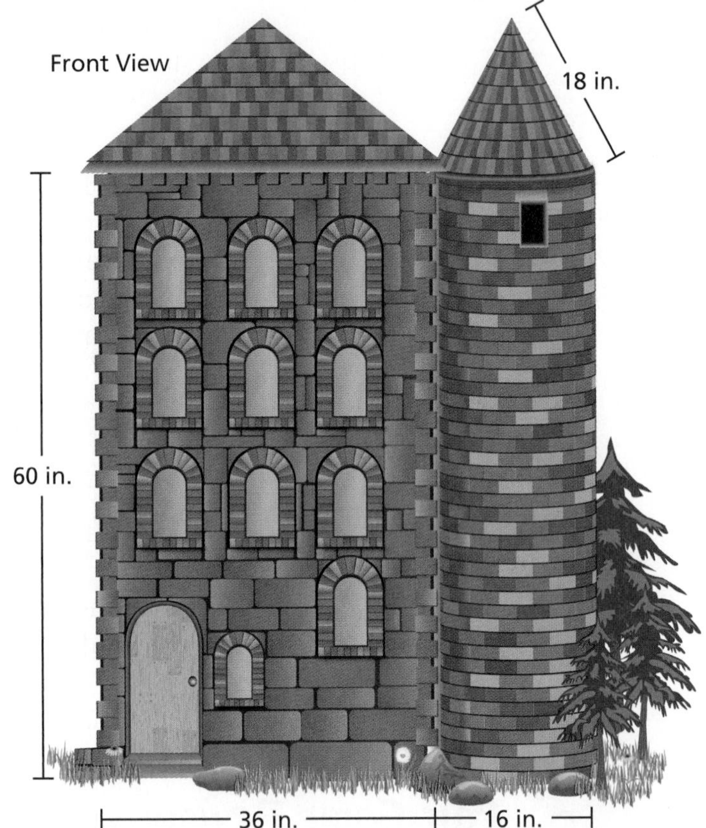

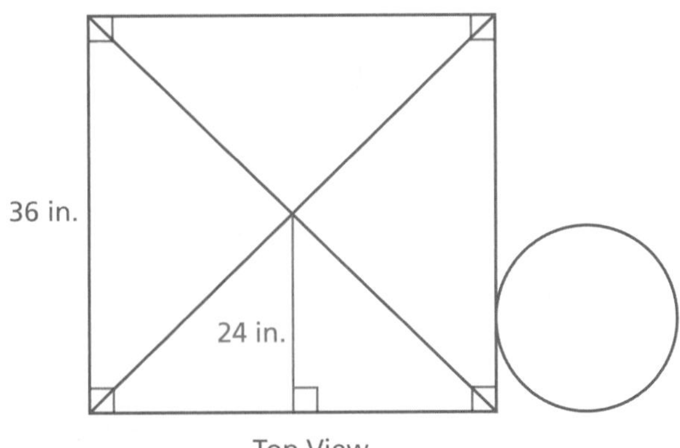

2 ACTIVITY: Finding and Using a Pattern

Work with a partner.

- Find the surface area of each figure.
- Use a table to organize your results.
- Describe the pattern in the table.
- Use the pattern to find the surface area of the figure that has a base of 10 blocks.

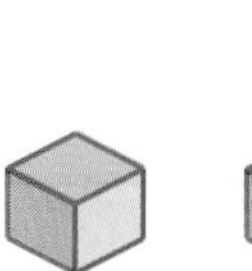    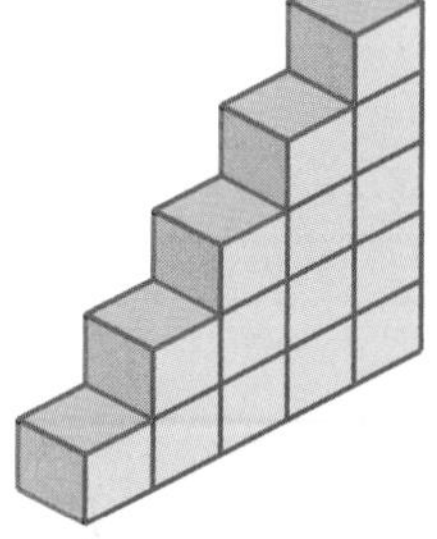

3 ACTIVITY: Finding and Using a Pattern

Work with a partner. You own a roofing company. Each building has the same base area. Which roof would be cheapest? Which would be the most expensive? Explain your reasoning.

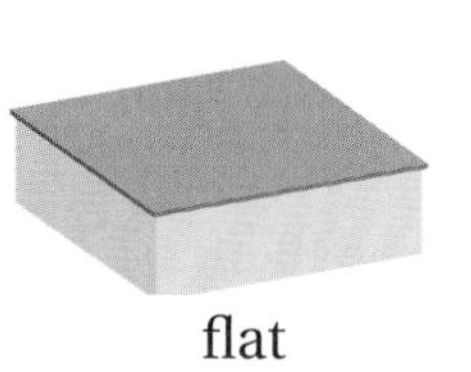
flat

lean-to

gable

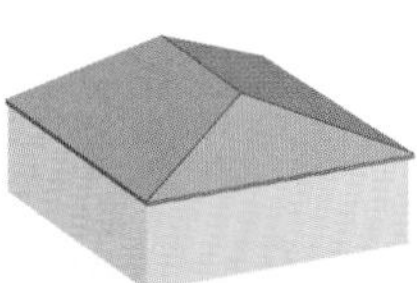
hip

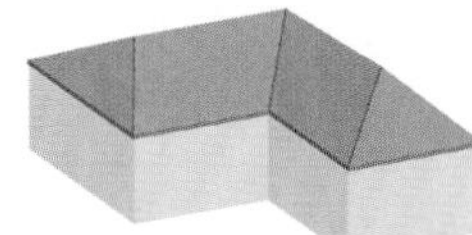
cross-hipped

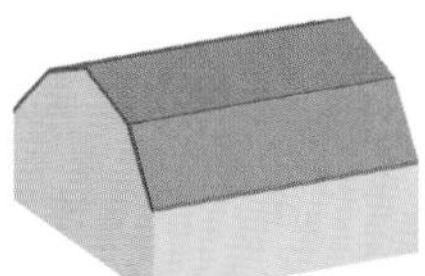
gambrel

mansard

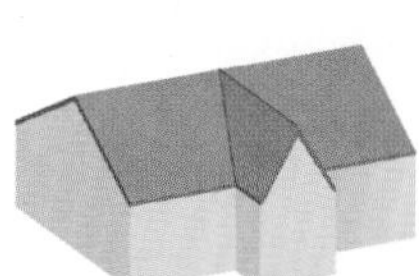
cross-gabled

What Is Your Answer?

4. **IN YOUR OWN WORDS** How can you find the surface area of a composite solid?

5. Design a building that has a turret and also has a mansard roof. Find the surface area of the roof.

Practice Use what you learned about the surface area of a composite solid to complete Exercises 6–8 on page 294.

6.6 Lesson

Key Vocabulary
composite solid, *p. 292*

A **composite solid** is a figure that is made up of more than one solid.

EXAMPLE 1 Identifying Solids

Identify the solids that make up Fort Matanzas.

EXAMPLE 2 Standardized Test Practice

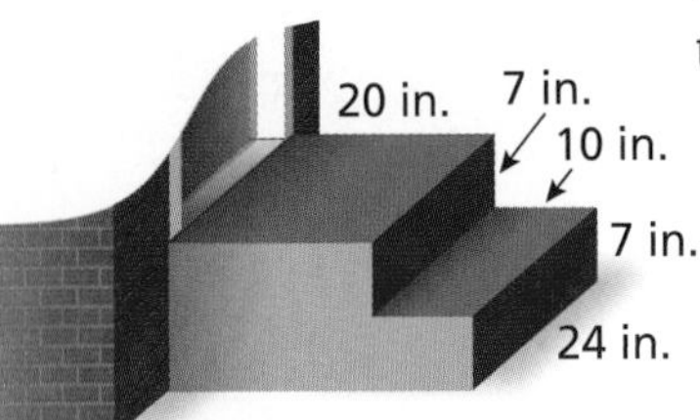

You painted the steps to an apartment green. What is the surface area that you painted?

Ⓐ 210 in.^{2} Ⓑ 408 in.^{2} Ⓒ 648 in.^{2} Ⓓ 1056 in.^{2}

Find the area of each green face.

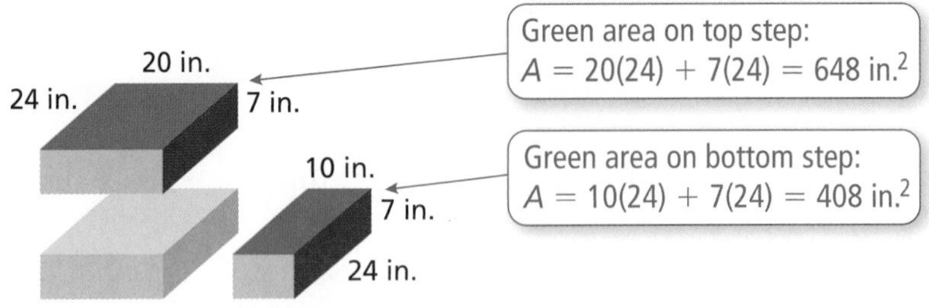

Green area on top step: $A = 20(24) + 7(24) = 648 \text{ in.}^2$

Green area on bottom step: $A = 10(24) + 7(24) = 408 \text{ in.}^2$

You painted $648 + 408 = 1056$ square inches.

∴ The correct answer is Ⓓ.

On Your Own

1. **WHAT IF?** In Example 2, you also painted the sides of the steps green. What is the surface area that you painted?

Multi-Language Glossary at BigIdeasMath.com.

EXAMPLE 3 Finding the Surface Area of a Composite Solid

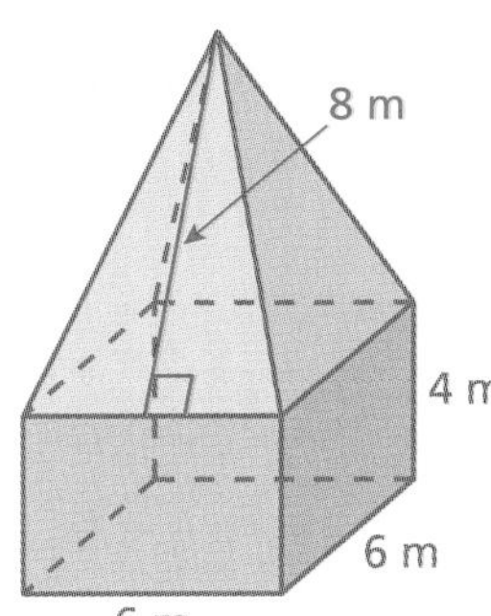

Find the surface area of the composite solid.

The solid is made up of a square prism and a square pyramid. Use the surface area formulas for a prism and a pyramid, but do not include the areas of the sides that overlap.

4 m
6 m
6 m

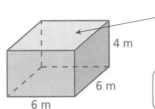

Do not include the top base of the prism in the surface area.

8 m
6 m
6 m

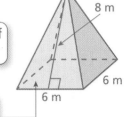

Do not include the base of the pyramid in the surface area.

Square prism

$S = \ell w + 2\ell h + 2wh$	Write formula.
$= 6(6) + 2(6)(4) + 2(6)(4)$	Substitute.
$= 36 + 48 + 48$	Multiply.
$= 132$	Add.

Square pyramid

$S =$ areas of lateral faces	Write formula.
$= 4\left(\frac{1}{2} \cdot 6 \cdot 8\right)$	Substitute.
$= 96$	Multiply.

Find the sum of the surface areas: $132 + 96 = 228$.

The surface area is 228 square meters.

On Your Own

Identify the solids that make up the composite solid. Then find the surface area. Round your answer to the nearest tenth.

2.

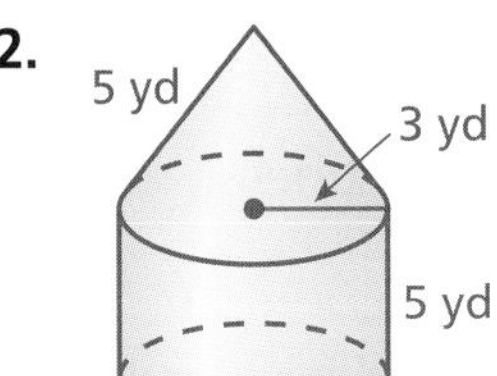

3.

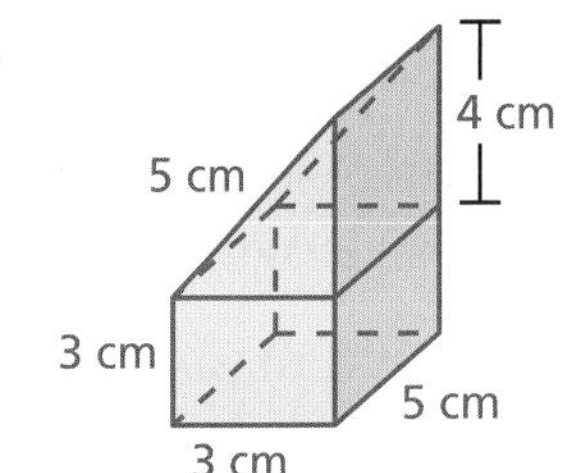

6.6 Exercises

Vocabulary and Concept Check

1. **OPEN-ENDED** Draw a composite solid formed by a triangular prism and a cone.
2. **REASONING** Explain how to find the surface area of the composite solid.

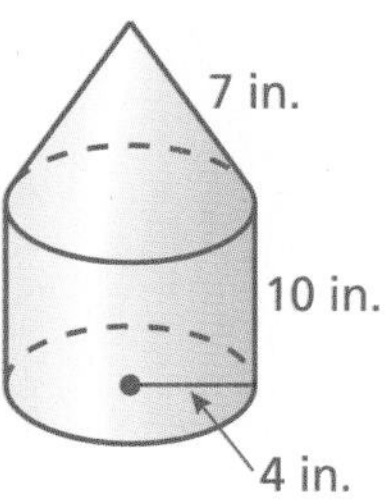

Practice and Problem Solving

Identify the solids that form the composite solid.

3. 

4. 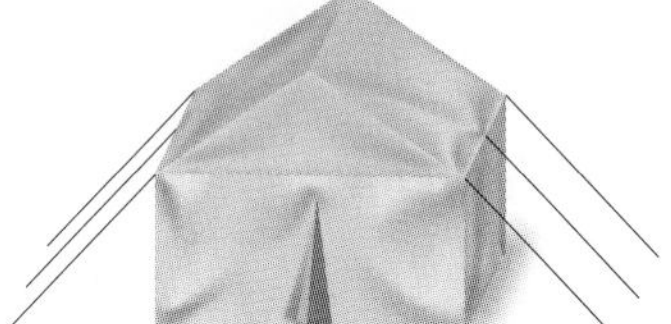

5. 

Identify the solids that form the composite solid. Then find the surface area. Round your answer to the nearest tenth.

6. 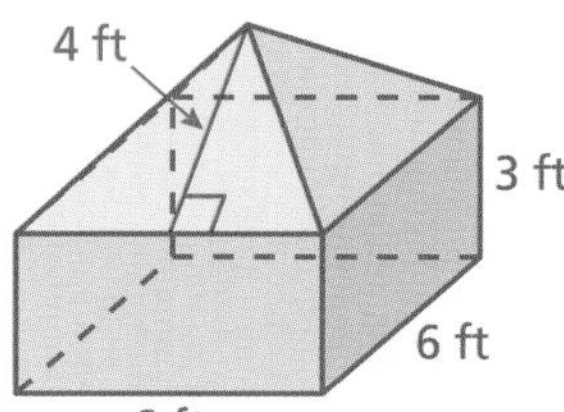

7. 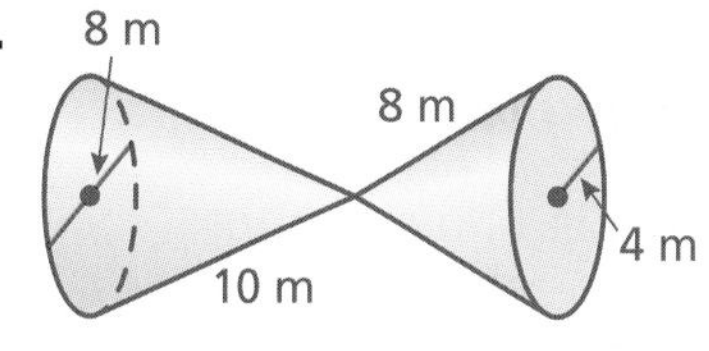

8. 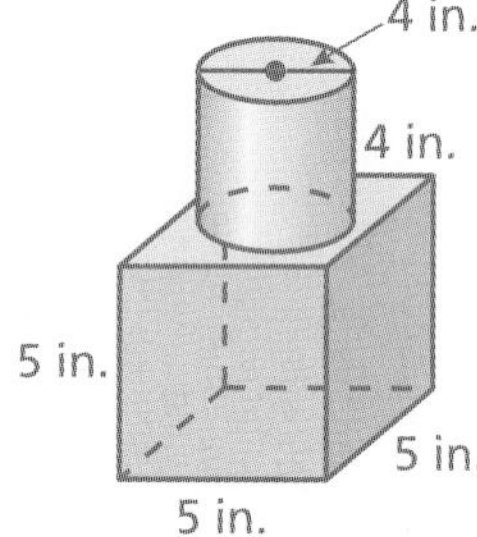

9. 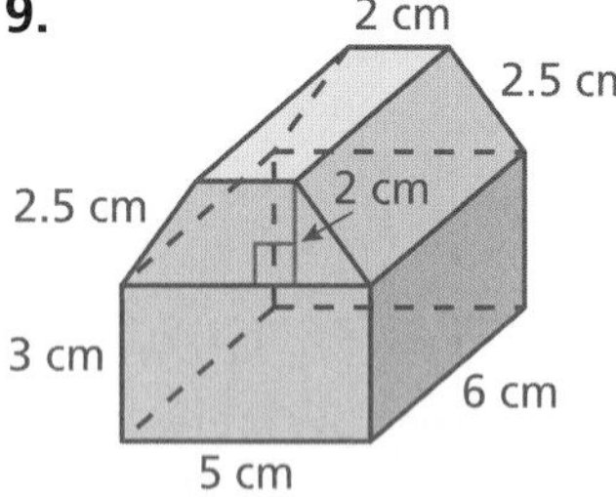

10. 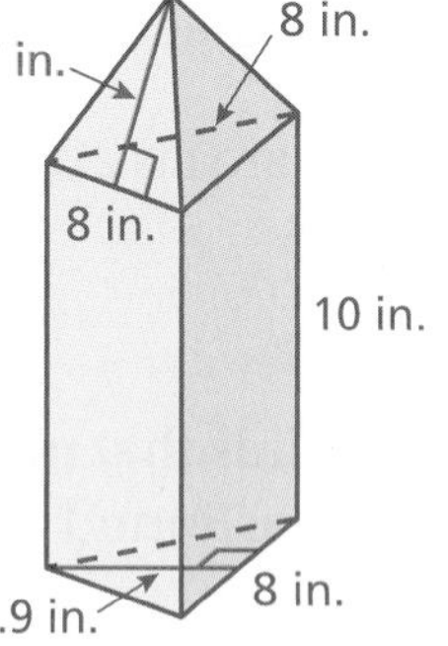

11. 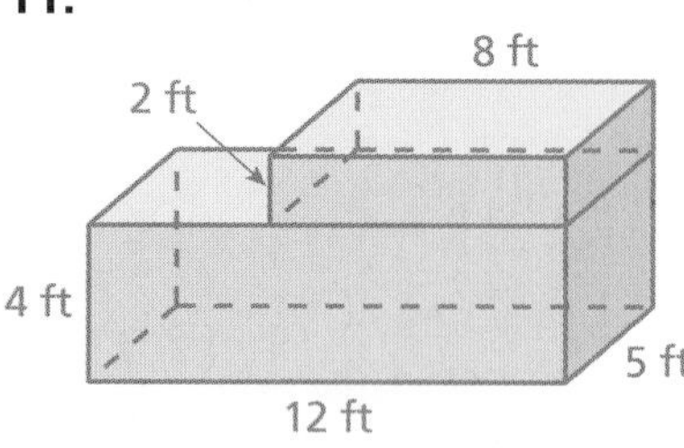

12. **OPEN-ENDED** The solid is made using eight cubes with side lengths of 1 centimeter.

    a. Draw a new solid using eight cubes that has a surface area less than that of the original solid.

    b. Draw a new solid using eight cubes that has a surface area greater than that of the original solid.

13. **BATTERIES** What is the percent increase in the surface area of the AAA battery to the AA battery? Round your answer to the nearest tenth of a percent.

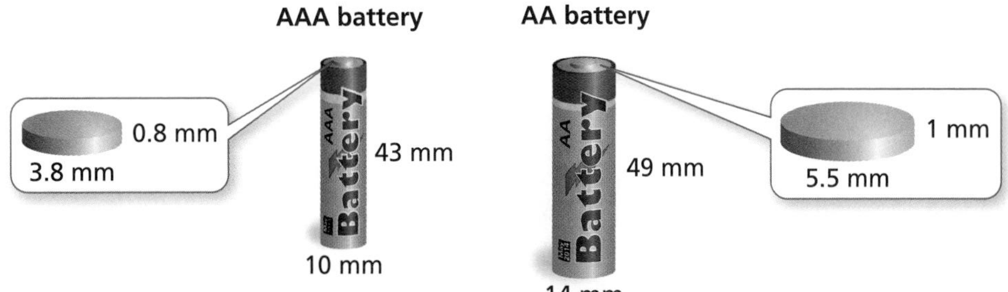

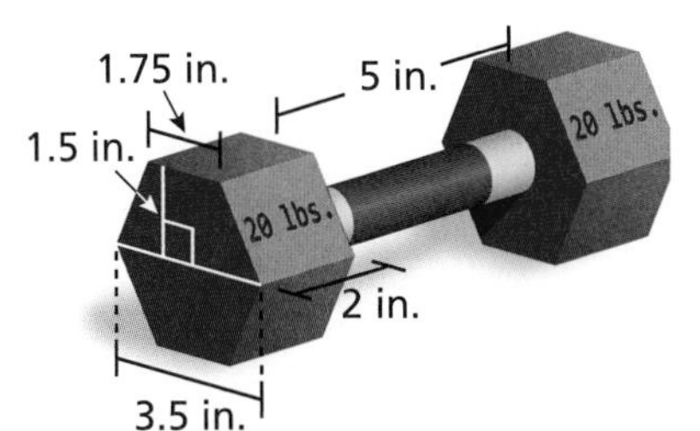

14. **BARBELL** The diameter of the handle of a barbell is 1 inch. The hexagonal weights are identical. What is the surface area of the barbell?

REASONING **Find the surface area of the solid. Round your answer to the nearest tenth.**

15. 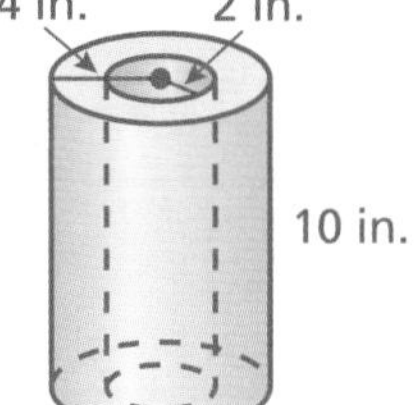

16. 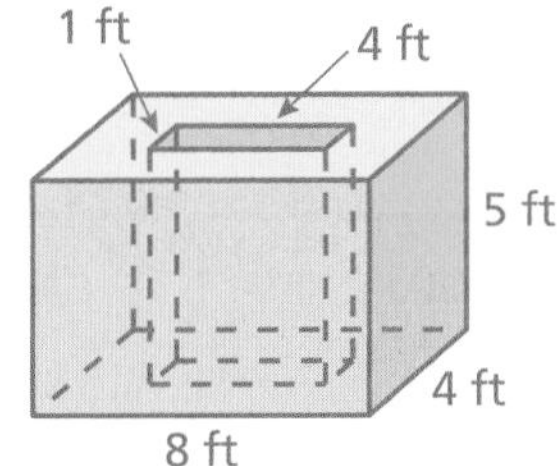

17. 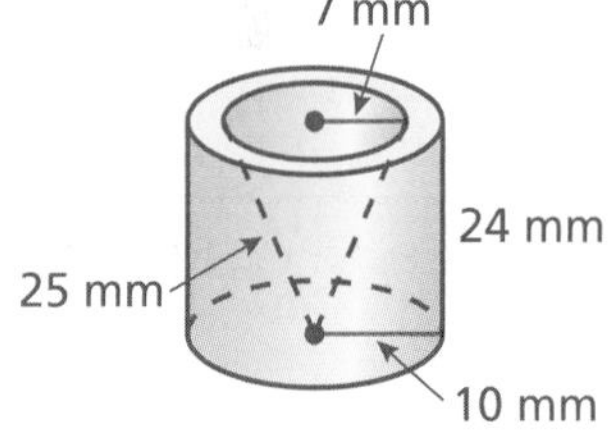

18. **Critical Thinking** The cube is made with 27 identical cubes. All cubes that cannot be seen are orange. Is the surface area of the solid formed without the purple cubes *greater than, less than,* or *equal to* the surface area of the solid formed without the green cubes? Explain your reasoning.

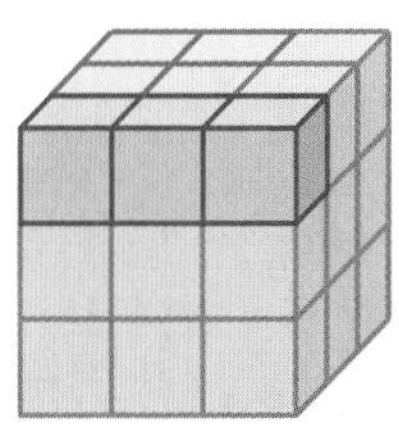

Fair Game Review What you learned in previous grades & lessons

Find the area. *(Skills Review Handbook)*

19. 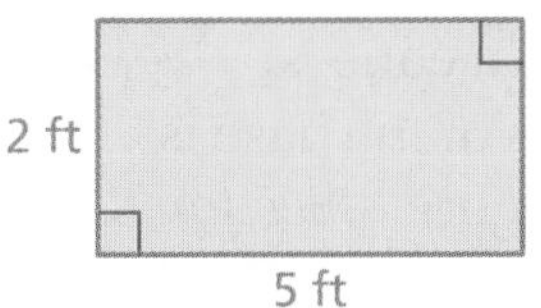

20. 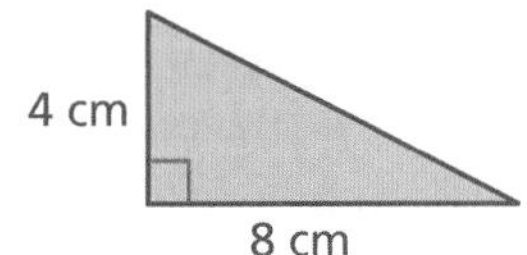

21. 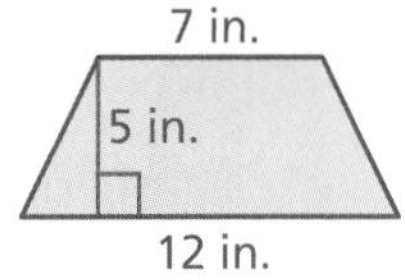

22. **MULTIPLE CHOICE** A cliff swallow nest is 86 meters above a canyon floor. The elevation of the nest is −56 meters. What is the elevation of the canyon floor? *(Section 1.1)*

Ⓐ −142 Ⓑ −30 Ⓒ 30 Ⓓ 142

6.4–6.6 Quiz

Identify the solids that form the composite solid. *(Section 6.6)*

1. 

2. 

3. 

Find the surface area of the regular pyramid. *(Section 6.4)*

4. 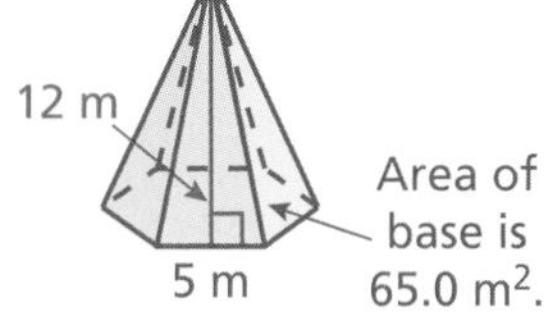

5. 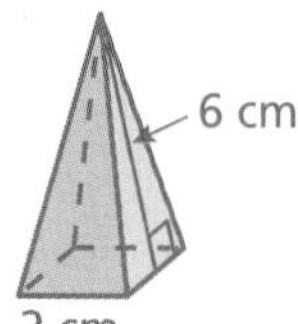

Find the surface area of the cone. Round your answer to the nearest tenth. *(Section 6.5)*

6. 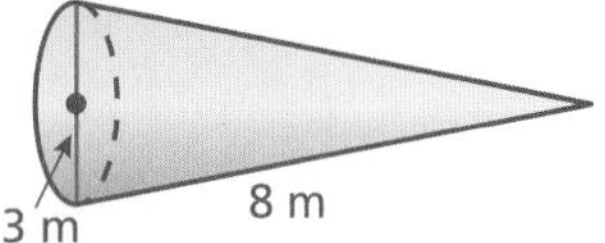

7. 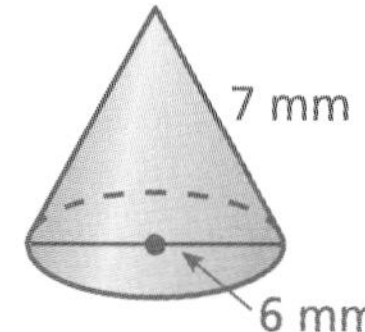

Find the surface area of the composite solid. Round your answer to the nearest tenth. *(Section 6.6)*

8. 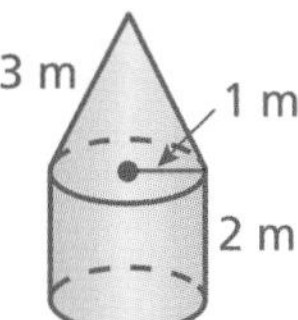

9. 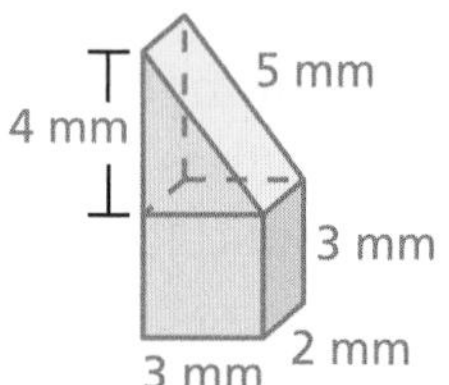

99 cm

12 cm

12 cm

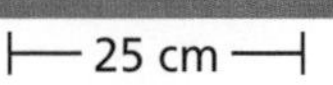

10. TRAFFIC CONE A square reflective sticker is placed on a traffic cone to make it more visible at night. Estimate the percent of the surface area of the traffic cone covered by the sticker to the nearest percent. *(Section 6.5)*

11. GEOMETRY The surface area of a cone is 150π square inches. The radius of the base is 10 inches. What is the slant height? *(Section 6.5)*

12. TOOLBOX Find the surface area of the toolbox. *(Section 6.6)*

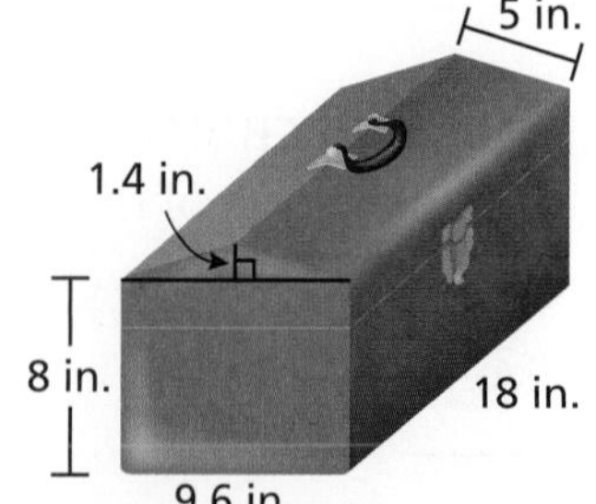

6 Chapter Review

Check It Out
Vocabulary Help
BigIdeasMath.com

Review Key Vocabulary

solid, *p. 260*
polyhedron, *p. 260*
lateral face, *p. 260*
surface area, *p. 264*
net, *p. 264*
regular pyramid, *p. 280*
slant height, *pp. 280, 286*
composite solid, *p. 292*

Review Examples and Exercises

6.1 Drawing 3-Dimensional Figures *(pp. 258–263)*

Draw a triangular prism.

Draw identical triangular bases.

Connect corresponding vertices.

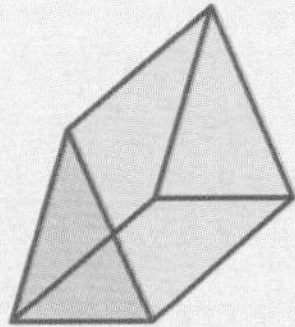

Change any *hidden* lines to dashed lines.

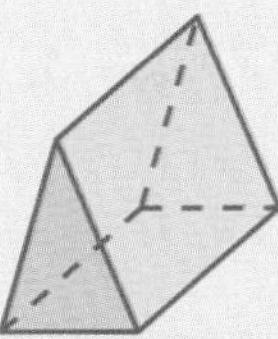

Exercises

Draw the solid.

1. Square pyramid
2. Hexagonal prism
3. Cylinder

6.2 Surface Areas of Prisms *(pp. 264–269)*

Find the surface area of the prism.

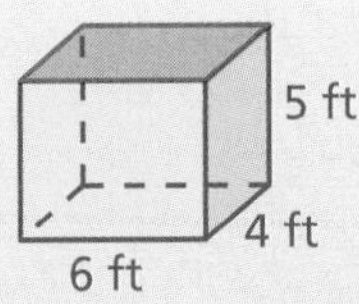

Draw a net.

$S = 2\ell w + 2\ell h + 2wh$

$= 2(6)(4) + 2(6)(5) + 2(4)(5)$

$= 48 + 60 + 40$

$= 148$

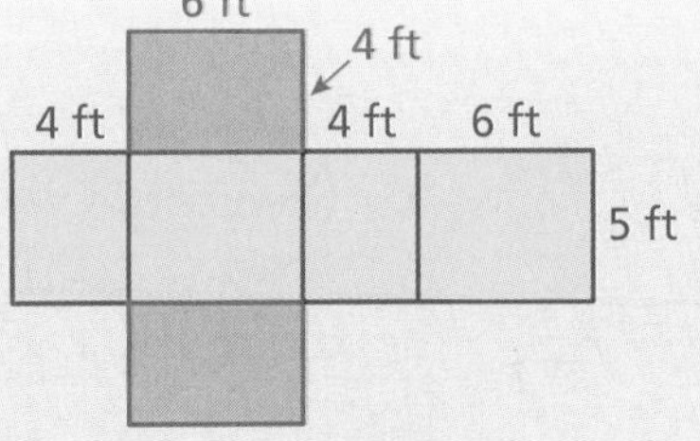

∴ The surface area is 148 square feet.

Exercises

Find the surface area of the prism.

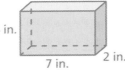

4. 4 in. 7 in. 2 in.

5. 17 cm 15 cm 8 cm 7 cm

6. 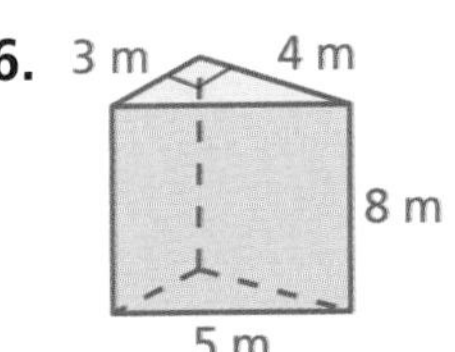

6.3 Surface Areas of Cylinders (pp. 270–275)

Find the surface area of the cylinder. Round your answer to the nearest tenth.

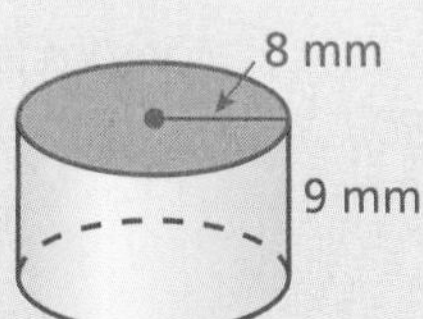

Draw a net.

$$S = 2\pi r^2 + 2\pi rh$$
$$= 2\pi(8)^2 + 2\pi(8)(9)$$
$$= 128\pi + 144\pi$$
$$= 272\pi \approx 854.1$$

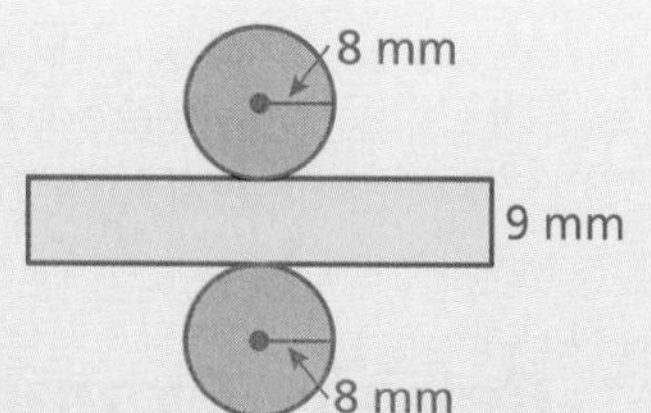

The surface area is about 854.1 square millimeters.

Exercises

Find the surface area of the cylinder. Round your answer to the nearest tenth.

7. 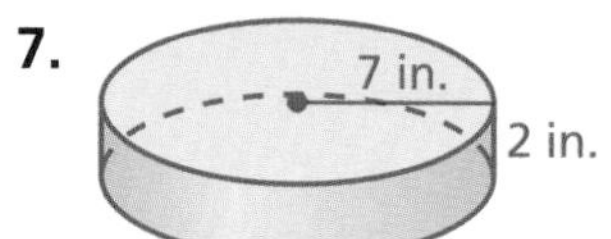

8. 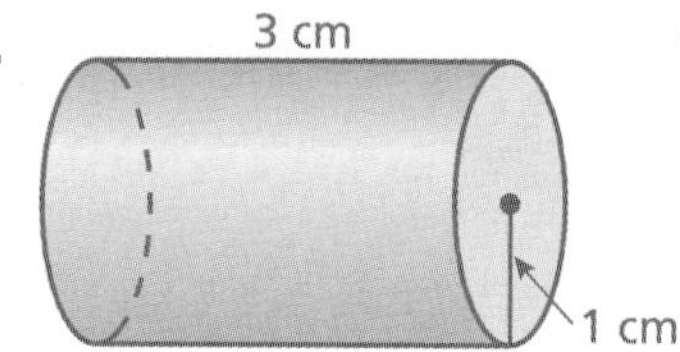

9. 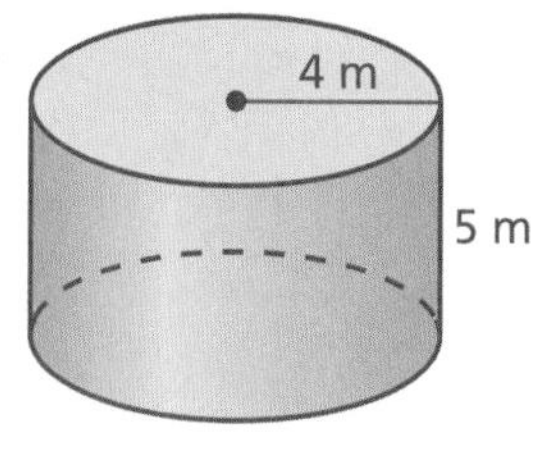

6.4 Surface Areas of Pyramids (pp. 278–283)

Find the surface area of the regular pyramid.

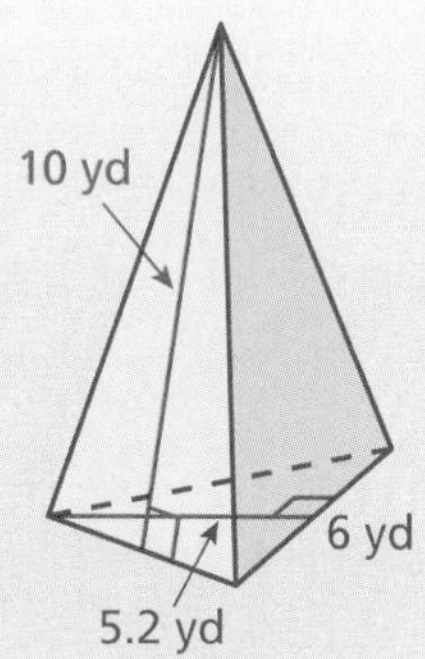

Draw a net.

Area of base

$\frac{1}{2} \cdot 6 \cdot 5.2 = 15.6$

Area of a lateral face

$\frac{1}{2} \cdot 6 \cdot 10 = 30$

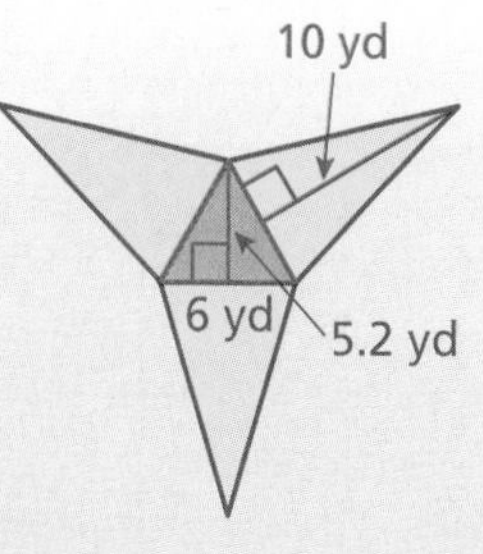

Find the sum of the areas of the base and all 3 lateral faces.

$$S = 15.6 + 30 + 30 + 30 = 105.6$$

The surface area is 105.6 square yards.

Exercises

Find the surface area of the regular pyramid.

10. 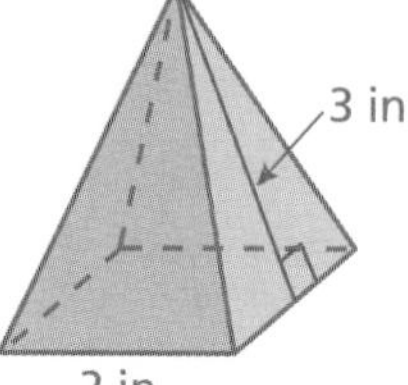

11. 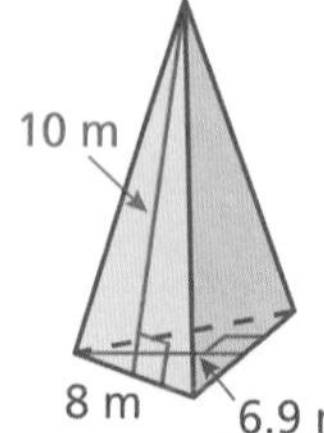

12. 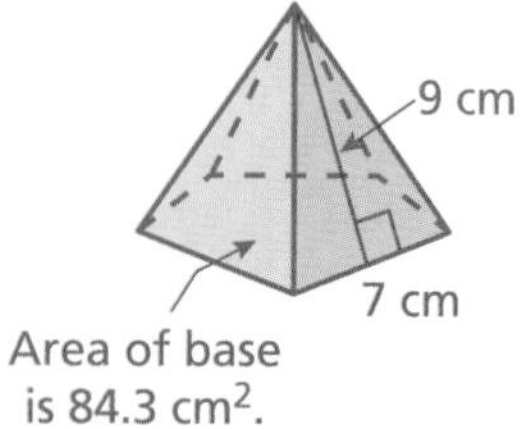

6.5 Surface Areas of Cones (pp. 284–289)

Find the surface area of the cone. Round your answer to the nearest tenth.

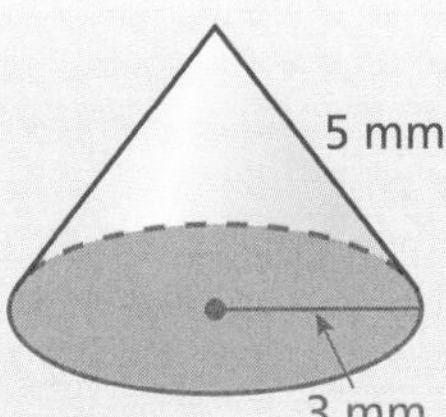

Draw a net.

$$S = \pi r^2 + \pi r \ell$$
$$= \pi(3)^2 + \pi(3)(5)$$
$$= 9\pi + 15\pi$$
$$= 24\pi \approx 75.4$$

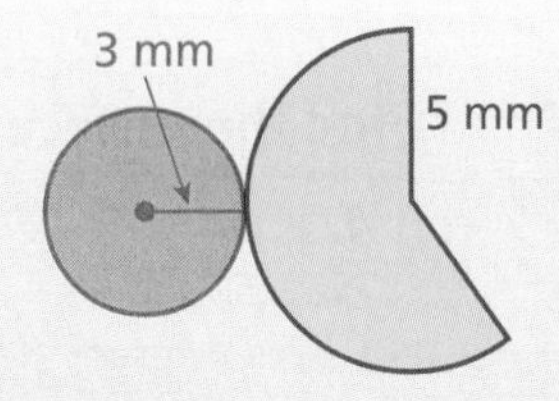

∴ The surface area is about 75.4 square millimeters.

Exercises

Find the surface area of the cone. Round your answer to the nearest tenth.

13. 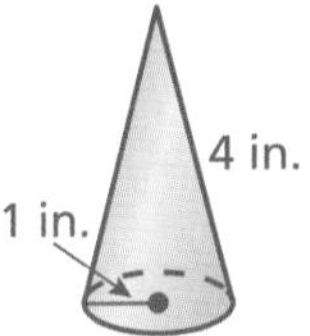

14. 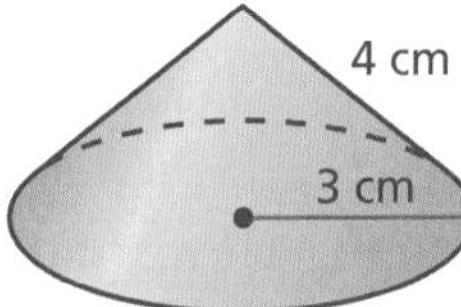

15. 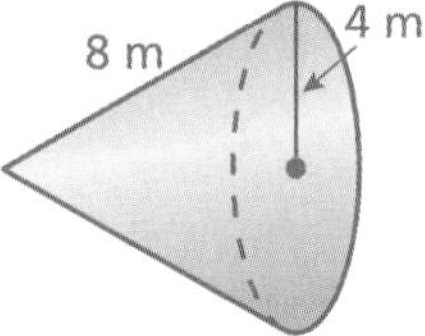

6.6 Surface Areas of Composite Solids (pp. 290–295)

Find the surface area of the composite solid. Round your answer to the nearest tenth.

The solid is made of a cone and a cylinder. Use the surface area formulas. Do not include the areas of the bases that overlap.

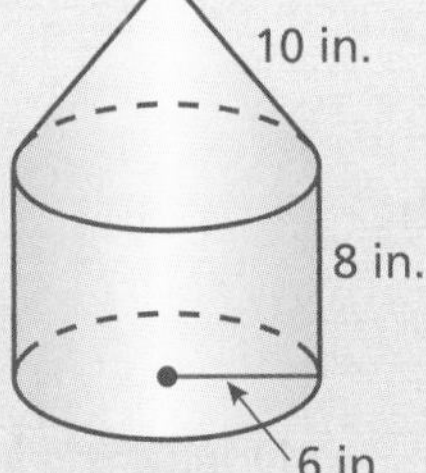

Cone

$$S = \pi r \ell$$
$$= \pi(6)(10)$$
$$= 60\pi \approx 188.4$$

Cylinder

$$S = \pi r^2 + 2\pi r h$$
$$= \pi(6)^2 + 2\pi(6)(8)$$
$$= 36\pi + 96\pi$$
$$= 132\pi \approx 414.5$$

∴ The surface area is about 188.4 + 414.5 = 602.9 square inches.

Exercises

Find the surface area of the composite solid. Round your answer to the nearest tenth.

16. 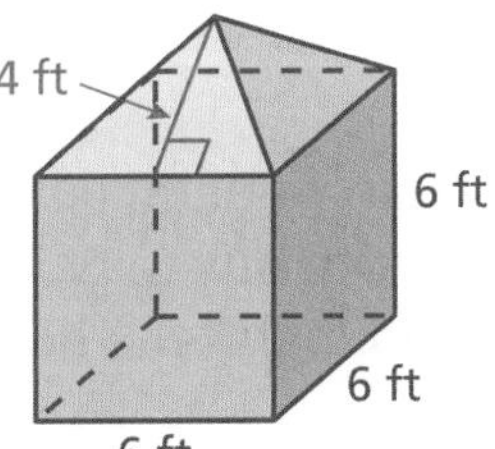

17. 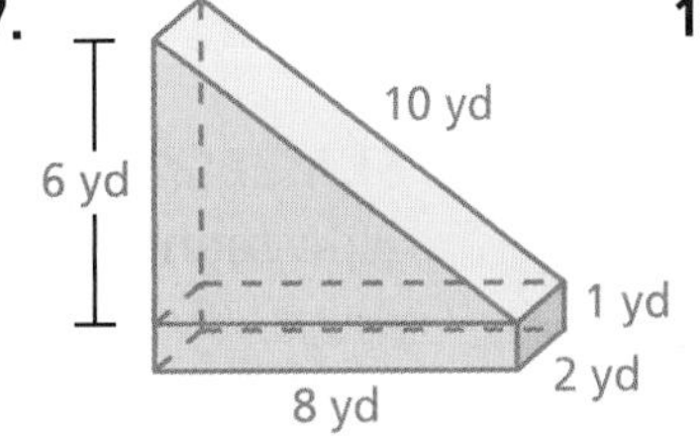

18. 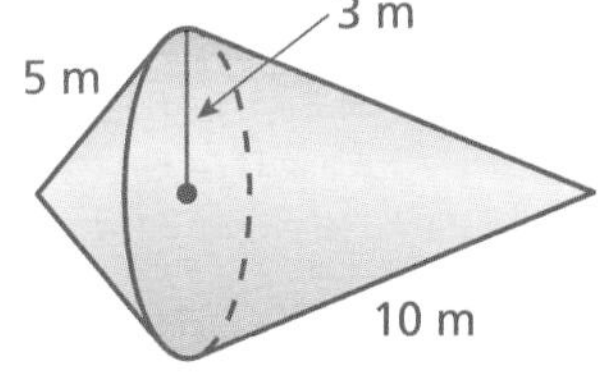

6 Chapter Test

Check It Out
Test Practice
BigIdeasMath.com

Draw the solid.

1. Square prism
2. Pentagonal pyramid
3. Cone

Find the surface area of the prism or regular pyramid.

4. 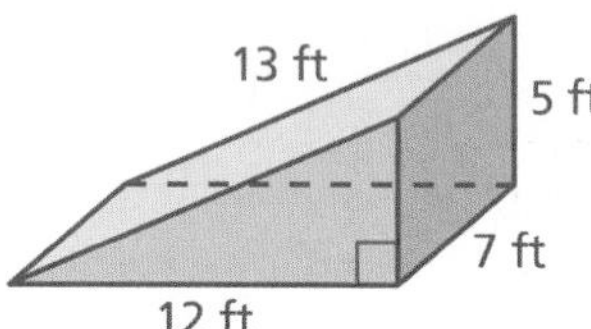

5. 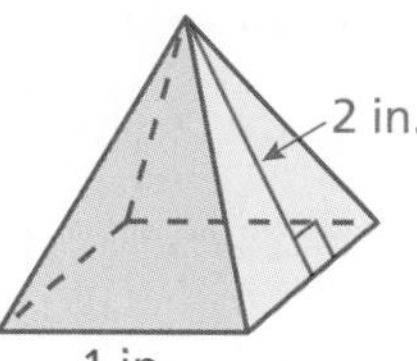

6. 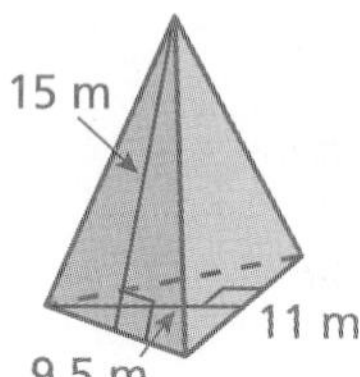

Find the surface area of the cylinder or cone. Round your answer to the nearest tenth.

7. 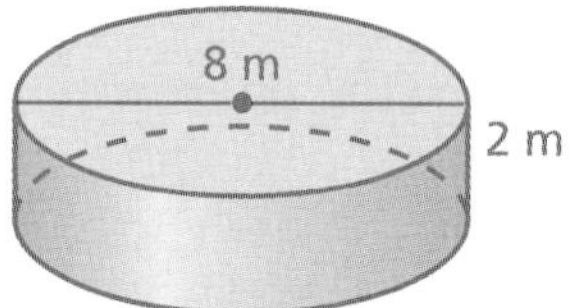

8. 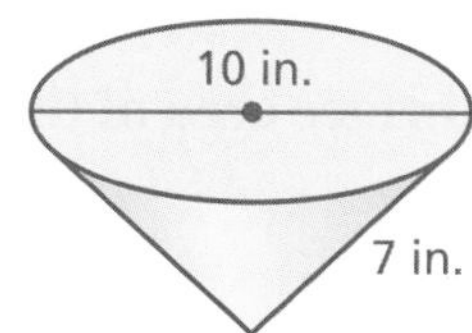

9. Draw the front, side, and top views of the solid in Exercise 8.

Identify the solids that form the composite solid. Then find the surface area. Round your answer to the nearest tenth.

10. 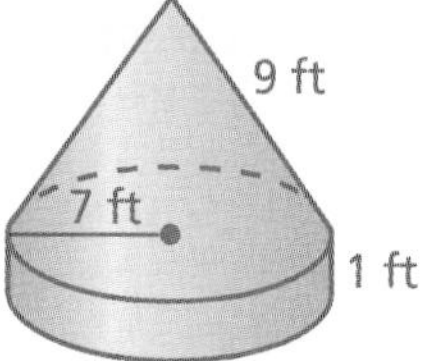

11. 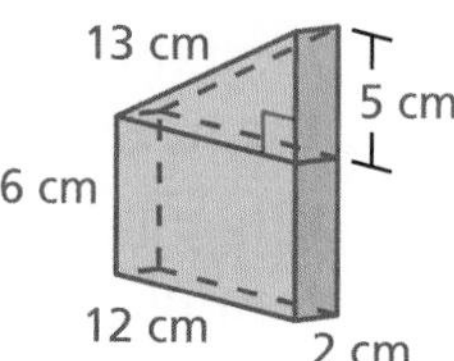

12. **CORN MEAL** A cylindrical corn meal container has a height of 5 inches and a diameter of 4 inches. How much paper is used for the label of the corn meal container?

13. **COSTUME** The cone-shaped hat will be part of a costume for a school play. What is the least amount of material needed to make this hat?

14. **GEOMETRY** A cylinder has a surface area of 80 square inches. You double both dimensions. What is the surface area of the new cylinder?

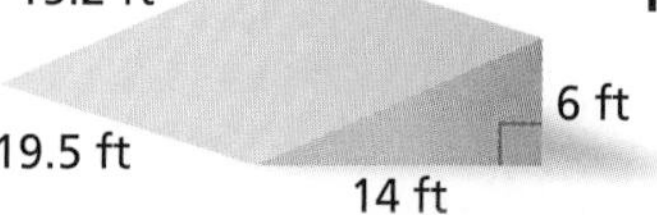

15. **SKATEBOARD RAMP** A quart of paint covers 80 square feet. How many quarts should you buy to paint the ramp with two coats? (Assume you will not paint the bottom of the ramp.)

6 Standardized Test Practice

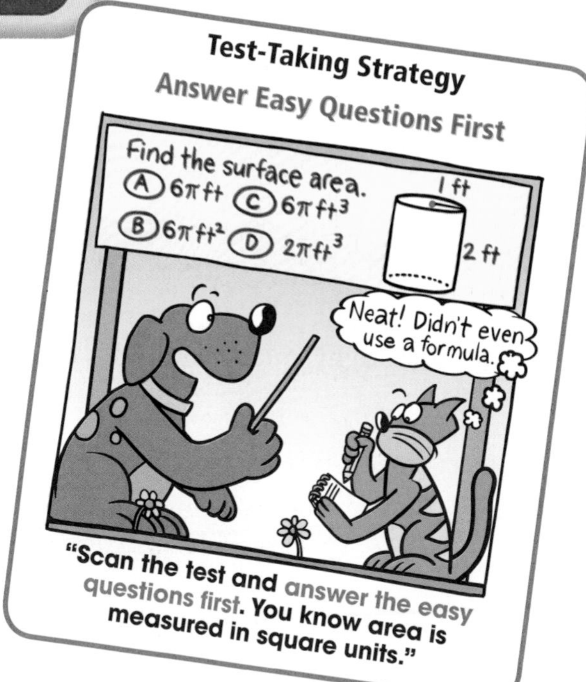

1. In the figure below, $\triangle PQR \sim \triangle STU$.

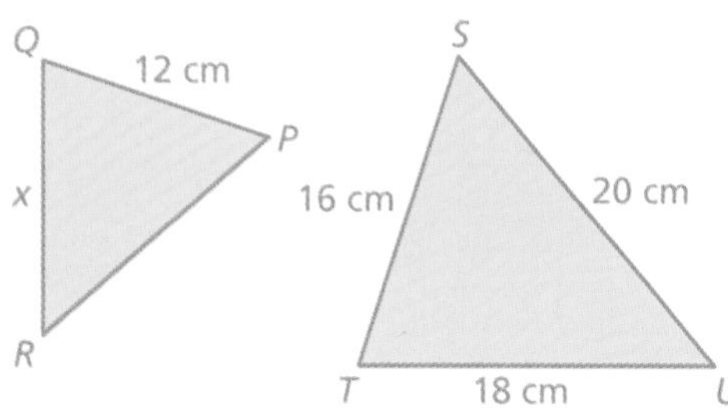

What is the value of x?

A. 9.6 cm **C.** 13.5 cm

B. $10\frac{2}{3}$ cm **D.** 15 cm

2. The rectangle below is divided into six regions.

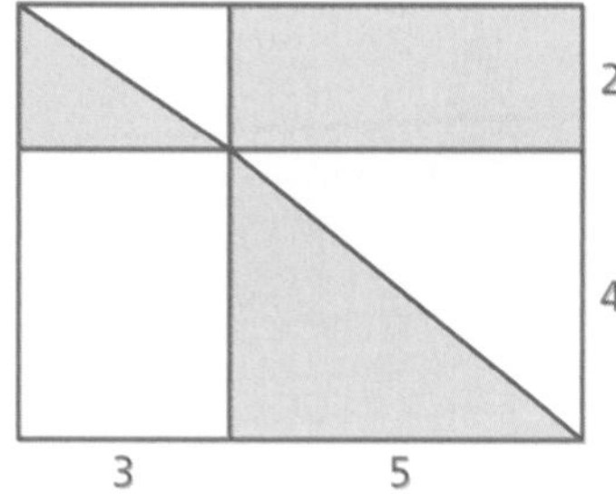

What is the area of the part of the figure that is shaded?

F. 23 units^2 **H.** 25 units^2

G. 24 units^2 **I.** 28 units^2

3. A right rectangular prism and its dimensions are shown below.

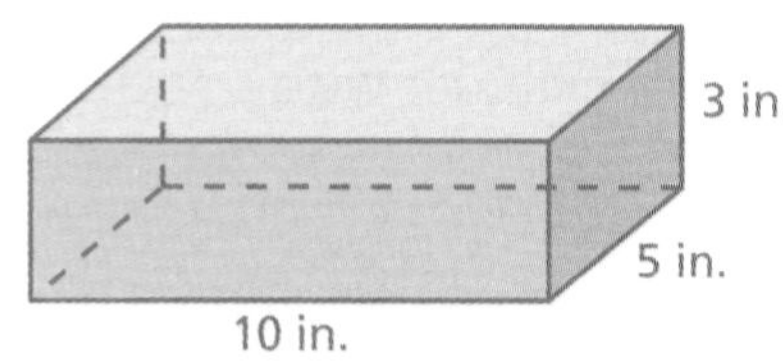

What is the total surface area, in square inches, of the right rectangular prism?

4. You ride 6 miles on your bicycle in 15 minutes and 18 miles in 45 minutes. Which equation represents the distance y (in miles) you ride in x minutes?

A. $y = \frac{2}{5}x + 6$

C. $y = \frac{5}{2}x + 6$

B. $y = \frac{2}{5}x$

D. $y = \frac{5}{2}x$

5. A right square pyramid is shown below.

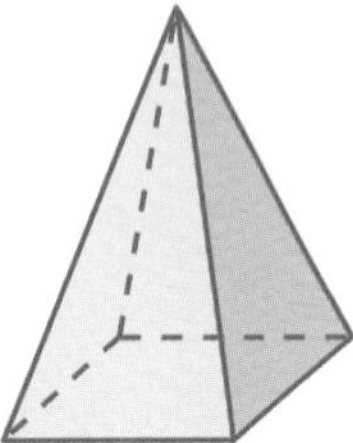

The square base and one of the triangular faces of the right square pyramid are shown below with their dimensions.

Square Base

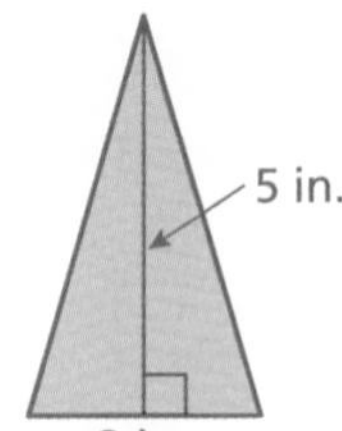

A Triangular Face

What is the total surface area of the right square pyramid?

F. 16.5 in.^2

H. 39 in.^2

G. 31.5 in.^2

I. 69 in.^2

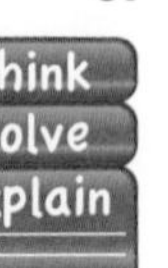

6. A right circular cylinder with a radius of 3 centimeters and a height of 7 centimeters will be carved out of wood.

Part A Draw and label a right circular cylinder with a radius of 3 centimeters and a height of 7 centimeters.

The two bases of the right circular cylinder will be painted blue. The rest of the cylinder will be painted red.

Part B What is the surface area, in square centimeters, that will be painted blue? Show your work and explain your reasoning. (Use 3.14 for π.)

Part C What is the surface area, in square centimeters, that will be painted red? Show your work and explain your reasoning. (Use 3.14 for π.)

7. Anna was solving the inequality in the box below.

$$\begin{aligned} 18 &> -5x + 3 \\ -3 & \quad\;\; -3 \\ 15 &> -5x \\ \frac{15}{-5} &> \frac{-5x}{-5} \\ -3 &> x \end{aligned}$$

What should Anna do to correct the error that she made?

A. Add 3 to both sides.

B. Multiply both sides by -5.

C. Reverse the inequality symbol when dividing by -5.

D. Divide both sides by 5.

8. Which equation has the greatest solution?

F. $-3x + 9 = -15$

G. $12 = 2x + 28$

H. $\frac{x}{2} - 13 = -7$

I. $6 = \frac{x}{3} + 10$

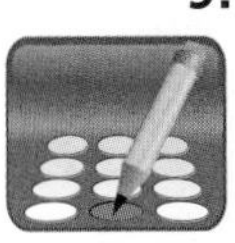

9. A cube has a total surface area of 600 square inches. What is the length, in inches, of each edge of the cube?

10. A line contains the two points plotted in the coordinate plane below.

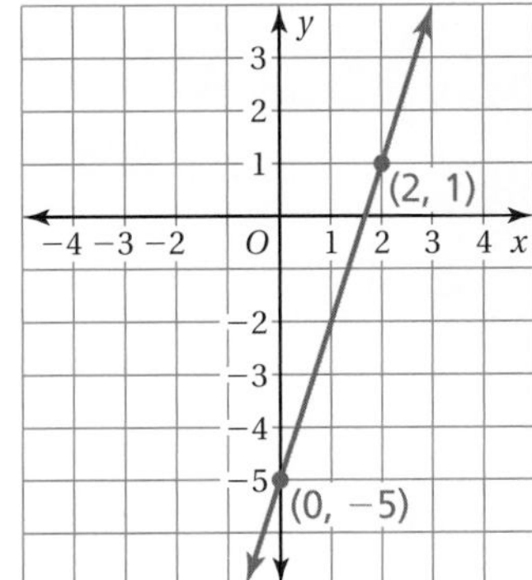

What is the slope of the line?

A. $\frac{1}{3}$

B. 3

C. $-\frac{1}{3}$

D. -3

7 Volumes of Solids

"I petitioned my owner for a dog house with greater volume."

Add a bunk bed and we can have a sleep over.

"And this is what he built for me."

This setup is too good to be true.

"Do you know why the volume of a cone is one-third the volume of the cylinder with the same height and base?"

What You Learned Before

Number one on America's list of 10 worst ideas.

"I just figured out how to find your volume. We'll immerse you in a barrel of water and measure the water that overflows."

Identifying Similar Figures

Example 1 **Which rectangle is similar to Rectangle A?**

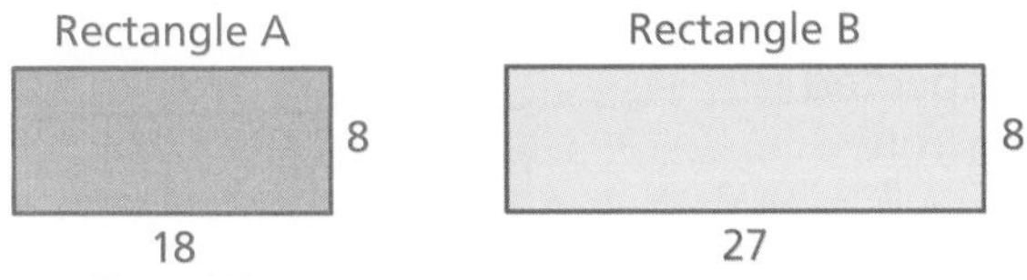

Rectangle C

12

27

Rectangle A and Rectangle B

$\frac{\text{Length of A}}{\text{Length of B}} = \frac{18}{27} = \frac{2}{3}$ $\quad \frac{\text{Width of A}}{\text{Width of B}} = \frac{8}{8} = 1$ Not proportional

Rectangle A and Rectangle C

$\frac{\text{Length of A}}{\text{Length of C}} = \frac{18}{27} = \frac{2}{3}$ $\quad \frac{\text{Width of A}}{\text{Width of C}} = \frac{8}{12} = \frac{2}{3}$ Proportional

So, Rectangle C is similar to Rectangle A.

Finding Measures in Similar Figures

Example 2 **The two triangles are similar. Find the value of x.**

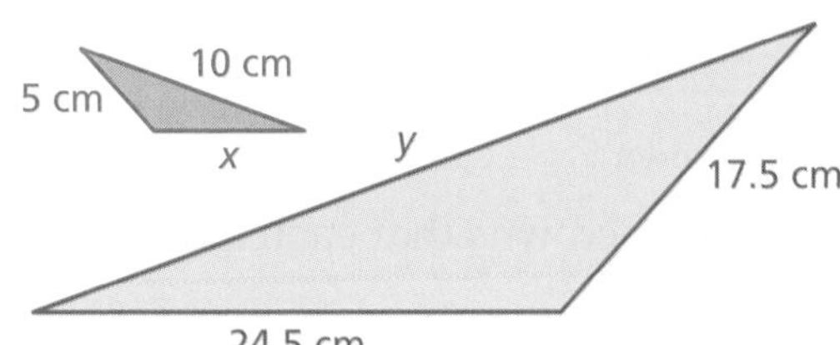

$\frac{5}{17.5} = \frac{x}{24.5}$ Write a proportion.

$122.5 = 17.5x$ Use Cross Products Property.

$7 = x$ Divide each side by 17.5.

So, x is 7 centimeters.

Try It Yourself

1. Construct two more rectangles that are similar to Rectangle A in Example 1.
2. Find the value of y in Example 2.

7.1 Volumes of Prisms

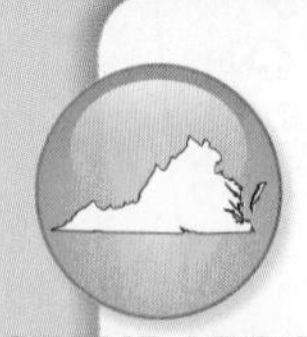

STANDARDS OF LEARNING
8.7

Essential Question How can you find the volume of any prism?

1 ACTIVITY: A Famous Discovery

A famous story tells how Archimedes used volume to solve a royal mystery.

Archimedes (c. 287 B.C.–c. 212 B.C.)

A king had a special gold crown made for himself. Afterward, he suspected that the jeweler had not used 100% gold to make the crown, but had mixed less valuable silver into the molten gold.

The king asked Archimedes if he could prove that the crown was not pure gold without destroying the crown.

When he was taking a bath, it occurred to Archimedes that the amount of water that overflowed out of the tub must have the same volume as his body. With this realization, he jumped out of the tub and ran home shouting "Eureka, I have found it!"

King's Crown

After Archimedes got home, he made two crowns that each had exactly the same weight as the king's new crown.

100% Gold Crown

100% Silver Crown

Work with a partner. Explain how Archimedes used the three crowns to solve the mystery.

2 ACTIVITY: Finding a General Formula for Volume

Work with a partner. You already know how to find the volume of a rectangular prism. Extend this concept to explain how to find the volume of any prism.

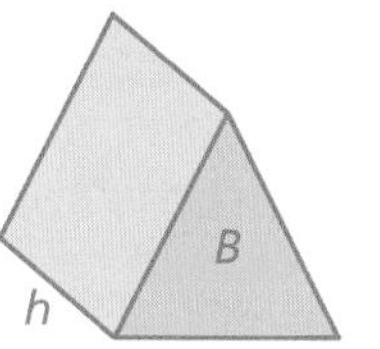

Triangular Prism

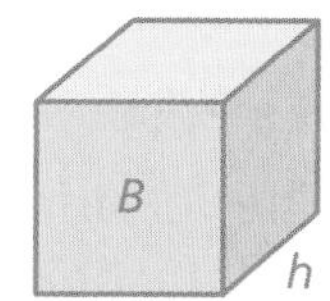

Rectangular Prism

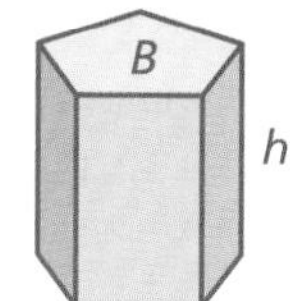

Pentagonal Prism

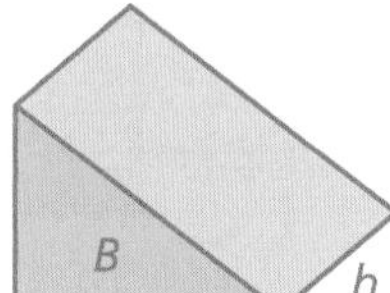

Triangular Prism

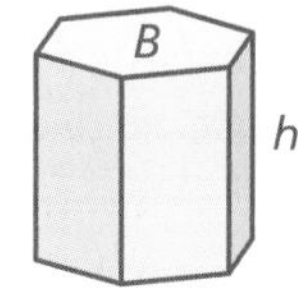

Hexagonal Prism

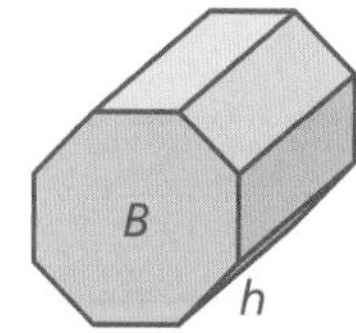

Octagonal Prism

3 ACTIVITY: Using a Formula

Work with a partner. A ream of paper has 500 sheets.

a. Does a single sheet of paper have a volume? Why or why not?

b. If so, explain how you can find the volume of a single sheet of paper.

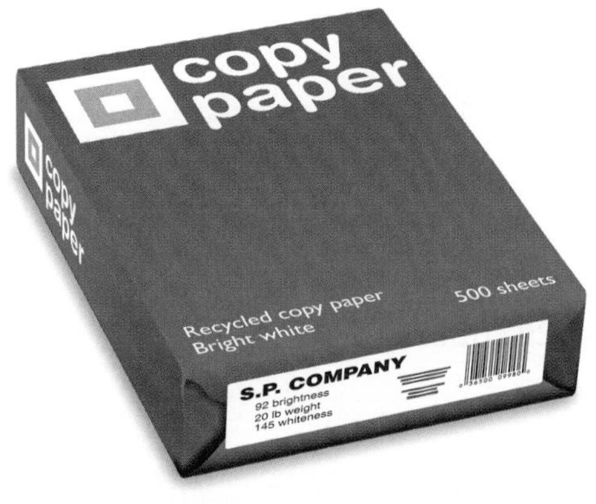

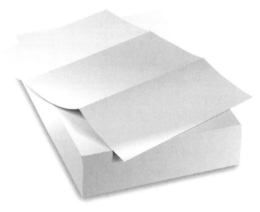

What Is Your Answer?

4. **IN YOUR OWN WORDS** How can you find the volume of any prism? Give examples with your explanation.

5. Draw a prism that has a trapezoid as its base. Use your formula to find the volume of the prism.

Practice Use what you learned about the volumes of prisms to complete Exercises 4–6 on page 310.

7.1 Lesson

Key Vocabulary
volume, *p. 308*

The **volume** of a three-dimensional figure is a measure of the amount of space that it occupies. Volume is measured in cubic units.

Volume of a Prism

Words The volume V of a prism is the product of the area of the base and the height of the prism.

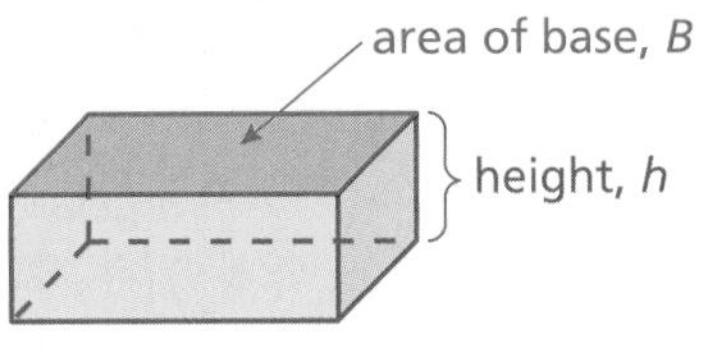

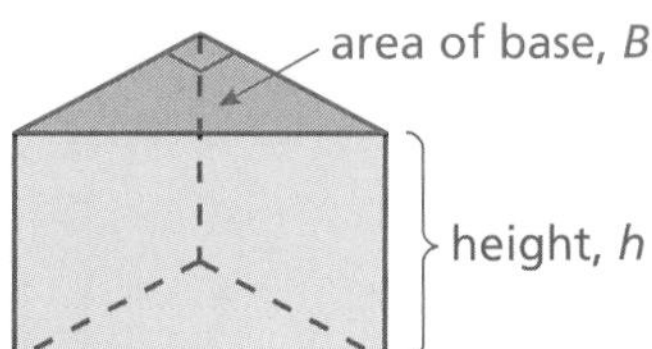

Algebra $V = Bh$

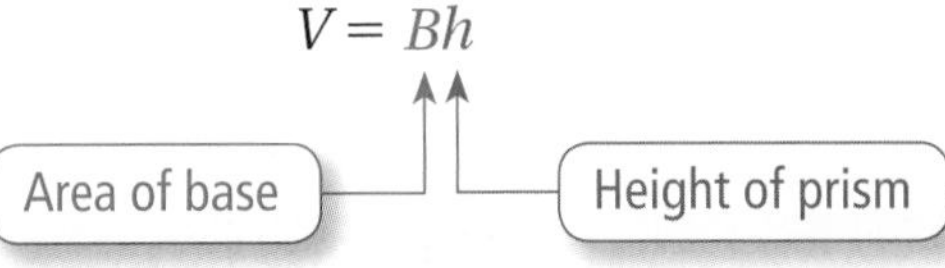

EXAMPLE 1 Finding the Volume of a Prism

Study Tip

The area of the base of a rectangular prism is the product of the length ℓ and the width w.

You can use $V = \ell wh$ to find the volume of a rectangular prism.

Find the volume of the prism.

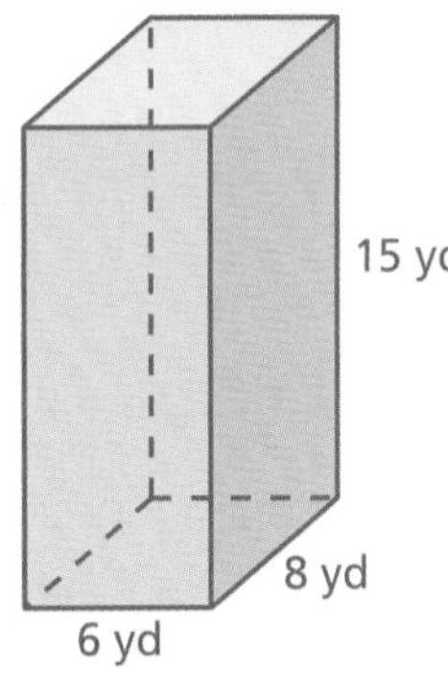

$V = Bh$	Write formula for volume.
$= 8(6) \cdot 15$	Substitute.
$= 48 \cdot 15$	Simplify.
$= 720$	Multiply.

The volume is 720 cubic yards.

EXAMPLE 2 Finding the Volume of a Prism

Find the volume of the prism.

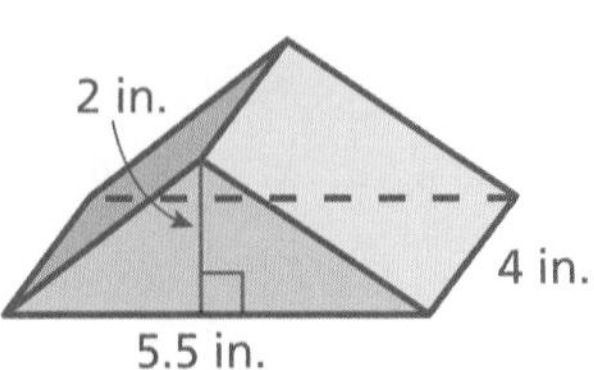

$V = Bh$	Write formula for volume.
$= \frac{1}{2}(5.5)(2) \cdot 4$	Substitute.
$= 5.5 \cdot 4$	Simplify.
$= 22$	Multiply.

The volume is 22 cubic inches.

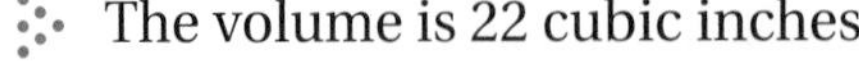

On Your Own

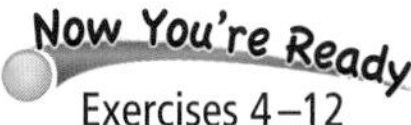

Find the volume of the prism.

1.

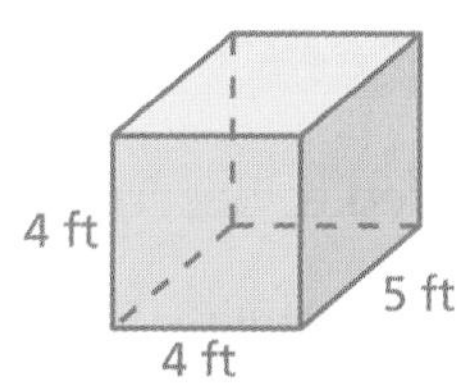

2.

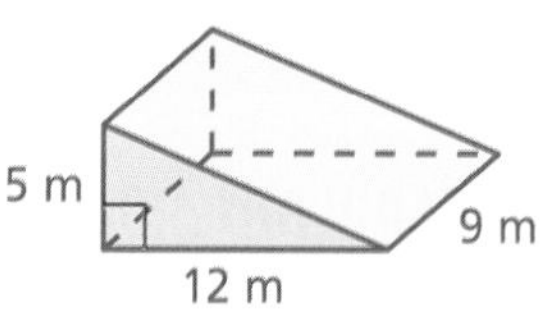

EXAMPLE 3 Real-Life Application

A movie theater designs two bags to hold 96 cubic inches of popcorn. (a) Find the height of each bag. (b) Which bag should the theater choose to reduce the amount of paper needed? Explain.

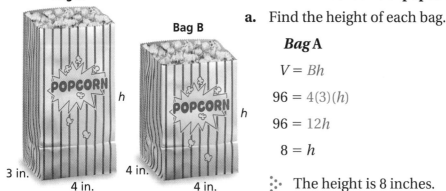

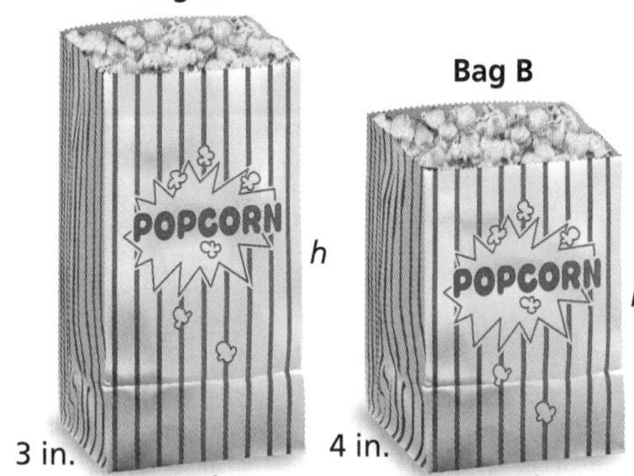

a. Find the height of each bag.

***Bag* A**	***Bag* B**
$V = Bh$	$V = Bh$
$96 = 4(3)(h)$	$96 = 4(4)(h)$
$96 = 12h$	$96 = 16h$
$8 = h$	$6 = h$
The height is 8 inches.	The height is 6 inches.

b. To determine the amount of paper needed, find the surface area of each bag. Do not include the top base.

***Bag* A**	***Bag* B**
$S = \ell w + 2\ell h + 2wh$	$S = \ell w + 2\ell h + 2wh$
$= 4(3) + 2(4)(8) + 2(3)(8)$	$= 4(4) + 2(4)(6) + 2(4)(6)$
$= 12 + 64 + 48$	$= 16 + 48 + 48$
$= 124 \text{ in.}^2$	$= 112 \text{ in.}^2$

The surface area of Bag B is less than the surface area of Bag A. So, the theater should choose Bag B.

On Your Own

3. You design Bag C that has a volume of 96 cubic inches. Should the theater in Example 3 choose your bag? Explain.

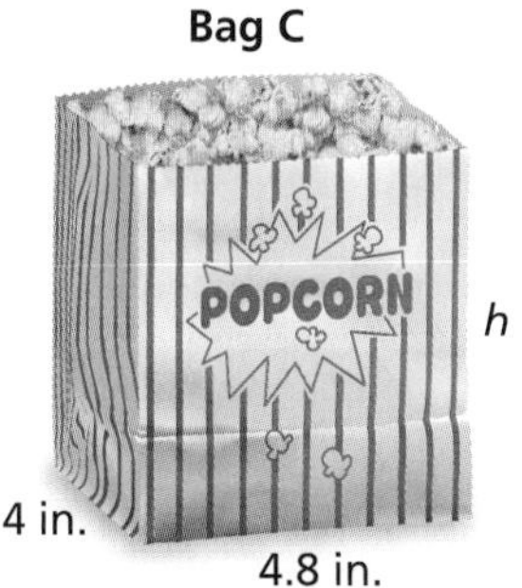

7.1 Exercises

Vocabulary and Concept Check

1. **VOCABULARY** What types of units are used to describe volume?
2. **CRITICAL THINKING** How are volume and surface area different?
3. **CRITICAL THINKING** You are ordering packaging for a product. Should you be more concerned with volume or surface area? Explain.

Practice and Problem Solving

Find the volume of the prism.

4. 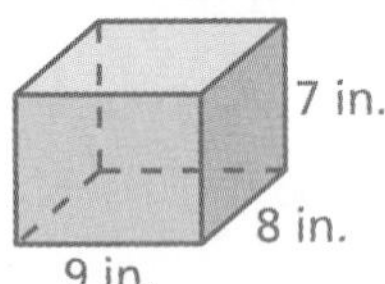

5. 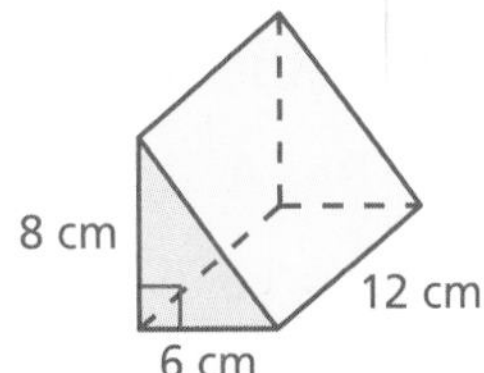

6. 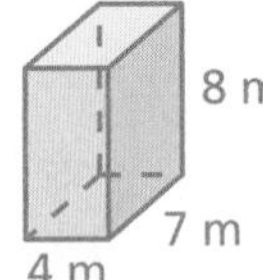

7. 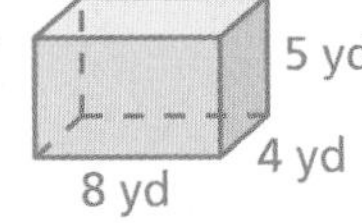

8. 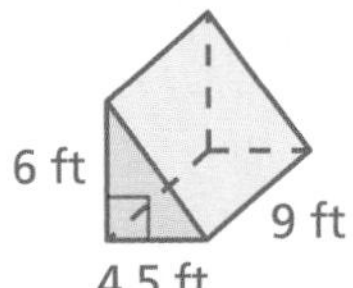

9. 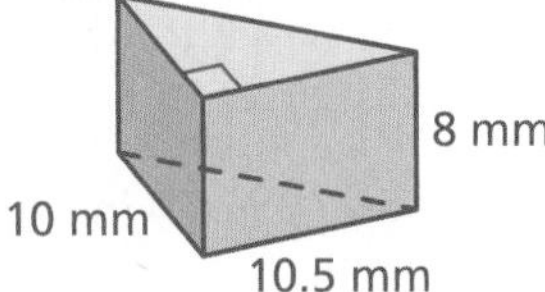

10. 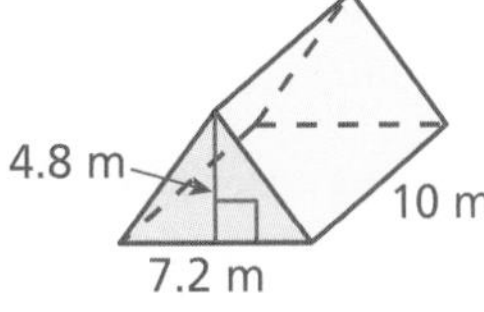

11. 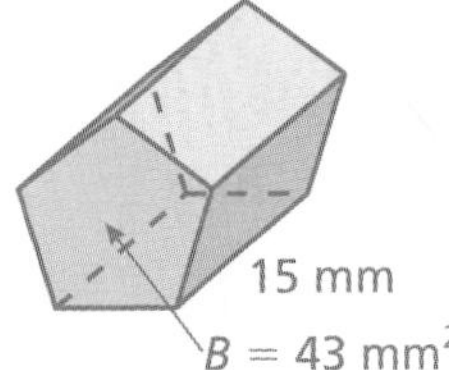

12. 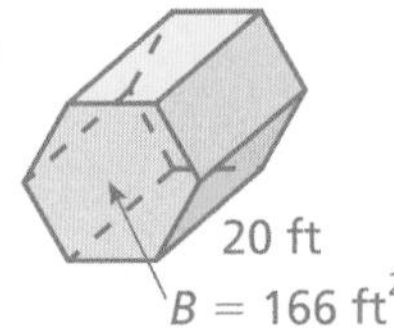

13. **ERROR ANALYSIS** Describe and correct the error in finding the volume of the triangular prism.

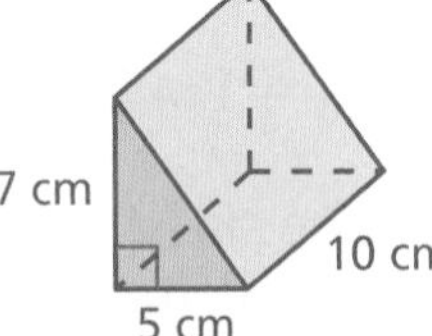

✗
$$\begin{aligned} V &= Bh \\ &= 10(5)(7) \\ &= 50 \cdot 7 \\ &= 350 \text{ cm}^3 \end{aligned}$$

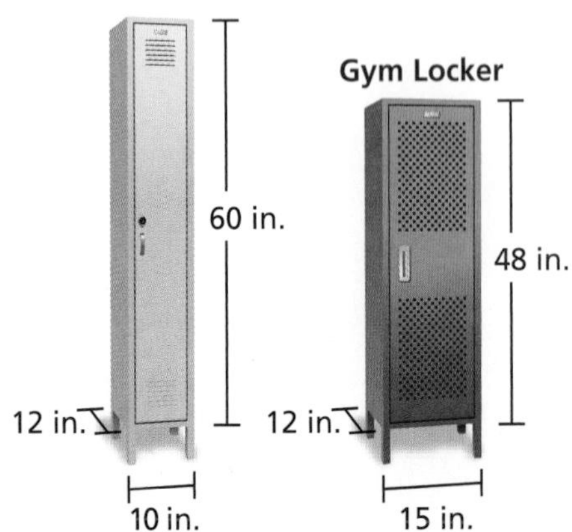

14. **LOCKER** Each locker is shaped like a rectangular prism. Which has more storage space? Explain.

15. **CEREAL BOX** A cereal box is 9 inches by 2.5 inches by 10 inches. What is the volume of the box?

Find the volume of the prism.

16. 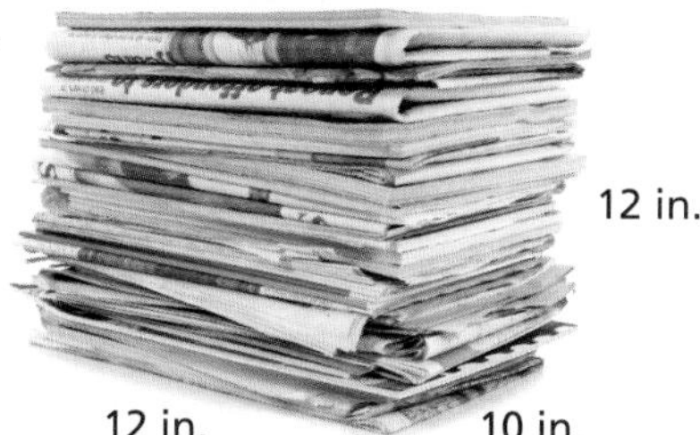

17. 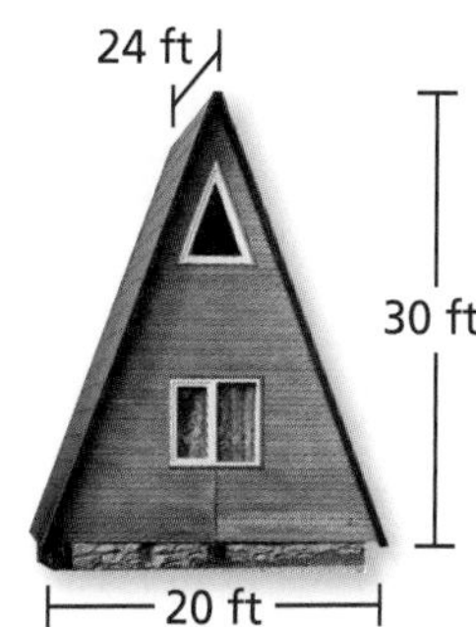

18. **REASONING** Two prisms have the same volume. Do they *always*, *sometimes*, or *never* have the same surface area? Explain.

19. **CUBIC UNITS** How many cubic inches are in a cubic foot? Use a sketch to explain your reasoning.

20. **CAPACITY** As a gift, you fill the calendar with packets of chocolate candy. Each packet has a volume of 2 cubic inches. Find the maximum number of packets you can fit inside the calendar.

21. **HEIGHT** Two liters of water are poured into an empty vase shaped like an octagonal prism. The base area is 100 square centimeters. What is the height of the water? ($1 \text{ L} = 1000 \text{ cm}^3$)

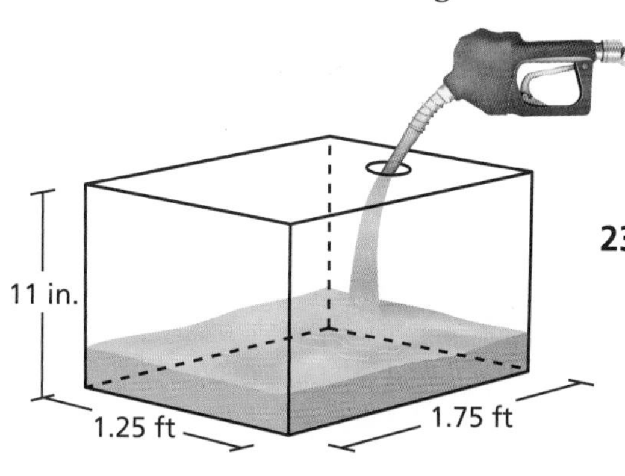

22. **GAS TANK** The gas tank is 20% full. Use the current price of gas in your community to find the cost to fill the tank. ($1 \text{ gal} = 231 \text{ in.}^3$)

23. **OPEN-ENDED** You visit an aquarium. One of the tanks at the aquarium holds 450 gallons of water. Draw a diagram to show one possible set of dimensions of the tank. ($1 \text{ gal} = 231 \text{ in.}^3$)

24. **Critical Thinking** How many times greater is the volume of a triangular prism when one of its dimensions is doubled? when all three dimensions are doubled?

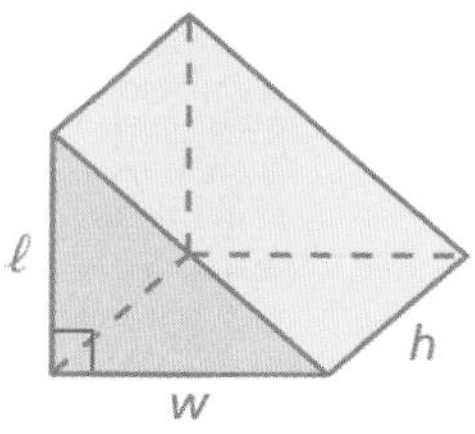

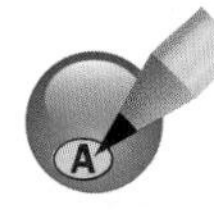

Fair Game Review What you learned in previous grades & lessons

Identify the transformation. *(Skills Review Handbook)*

25.  

26.  

27.  

28. **MULTIPLE CHOICE** What is the approximate surface area of a cylinder with a radius of 3 inches and a height of 10 inches? *(Section 6.3)*

Ⓐ 30 in.^2 Ⓑ 87 in.^2 Ⓒ 217 in.^2 Ⓓ 245 in.^2

7.2 Volumes of Cylinders

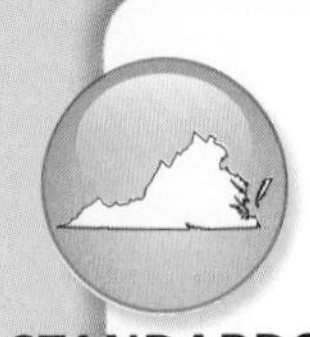

STANDARDS OF LEARNING
8.7

Essential Question How can you find a pattern for changes in volume that occur in nature?

1 ACTIVITY: A Research Project by Descartes

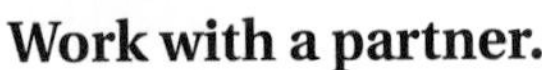

The French mathematician René Descartes was fascinated by the shell of a chambered nautilus.

In one of his experiments, Descartes measured the volumes of several of the chambers to try to find a pattern for the changes in volume.

Work with a partner.

a. Explain how Descartes might have measured the volumes of the different chambers.

b. What is meant by "using mathematics to model a real-life situation"?

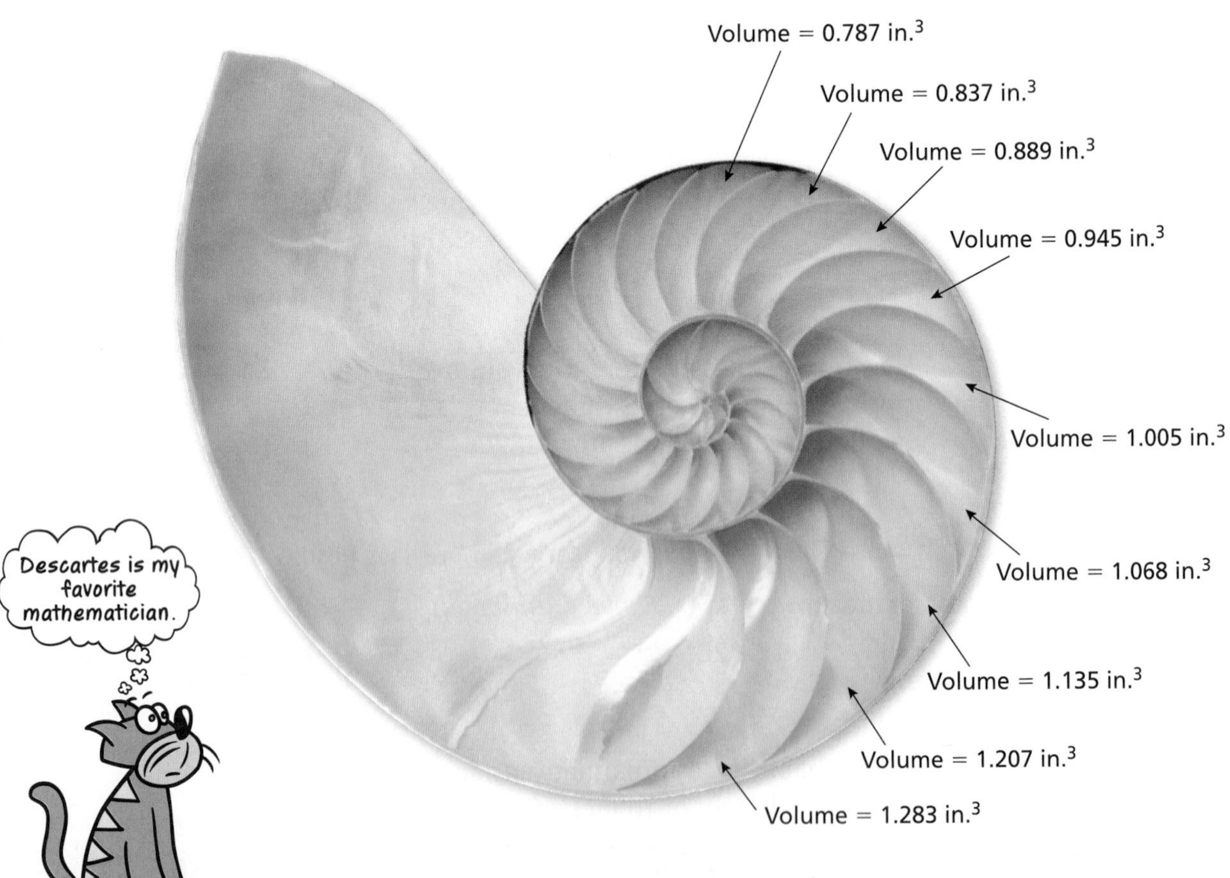

2 ACTIVITY: Finding a Pattern

Work with a partner.

a. Organize the data in Activity 1 in a table.

Chamber	1	2	3	4	5	6	7	8	9
Volume (in.^{3})	0.787								

b. Describe the pattern in the table. Is the pattern linear or nonlinear? Explain your reasoning.

c. Draw a graph of the data. Does the graph agree with your conclusion in part (b)? Explain.

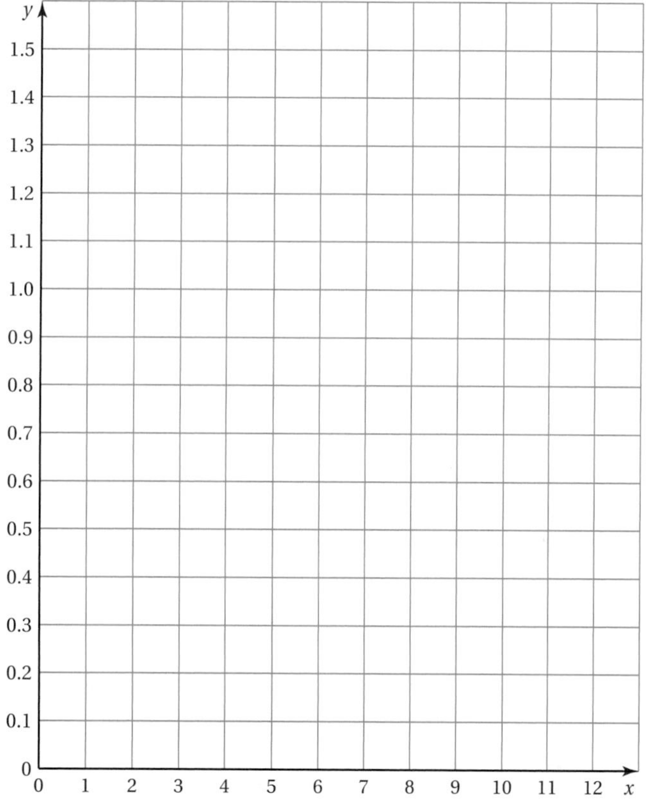

What Is Your Answer?

3. How can you find a pattern for changes in volume that occur in nature? Find other examples in nature where there are patterns of change in volume.

Use what you learned about volumes of cylinders to complete Exercises 3–5 on page 316.

7.2 Lesson

Volume of a Cylinder

Words The volume V of a cylinder is the product of the area of the base and the height of the cylinder.

Algebra $V = Bh$

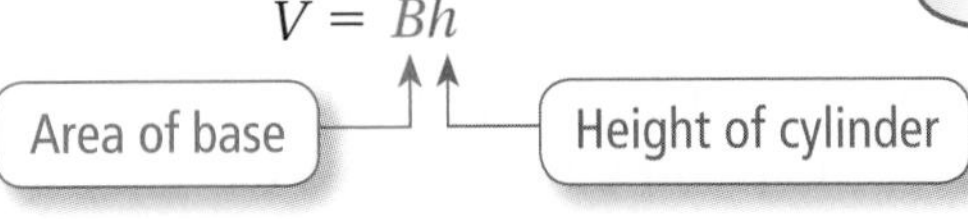

area of base, B

height, h

EXAMPLE 1 Finding the Volume of a Cylinder

Find the volume of the cylinder. Round your answer to the nearest tenth.

$V = Bh$	Write formula for volume.
$= \pi(8)^2(4)$	Substitute.
$= 256\pi \approx 803.8$	Simplify.

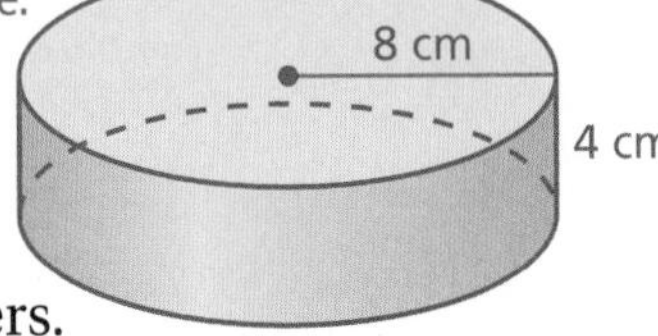

∴ The volume is about 803.8 cubic centimeters.

Study Tip

Because $B = \pi r^2$, you can use $V = \pi r^2 h$ to find the volume of a cylinder.

EXAMPLE 2 Finding the Height of a Cylinder

Find the height of the cylinder. Round your answer to the nearest whole number.

The diameter is 5 inches. So, the radius is 2.5 inches.

$V = Bh$	Write formula for volume.
$157 = \pi(2.5)^2(h)$	Substitute.
$157 = 6.25\pi h$	Simplify.
$8 \approx h$	Divide each side by 6.25π.

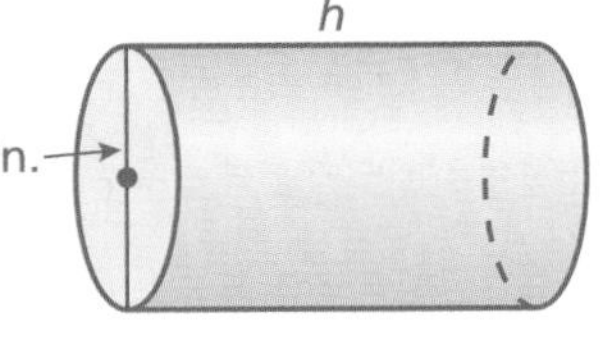

Volume = 157 in.^{3}

∴ The height is about 8 inches.

On Your Own

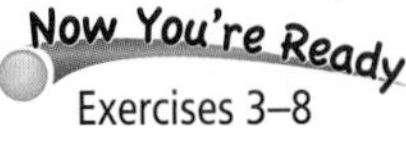

Exercises 3–8

Find the volume V or height h of the cylinder. Round your answer to the nearest tenth.

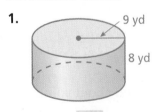

1. 9 yd, 8 yd

$V \approx$

2. 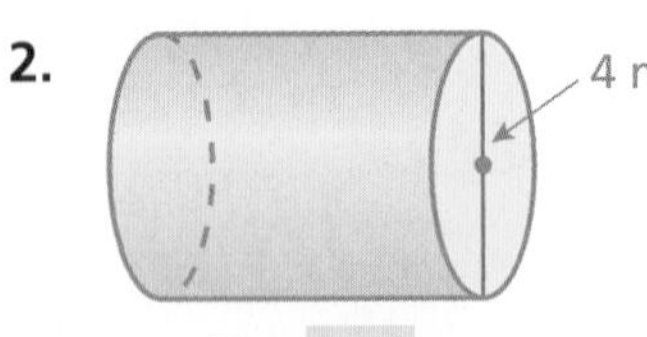

$h \approx$

Volume = 62.8 m^3

EXAMPLE 3 Changing One Dimension of a Cylinder

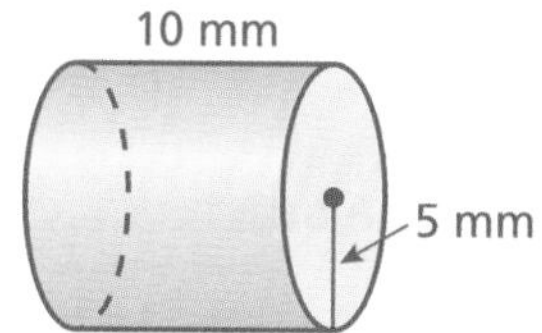

Does doubling the height of the cylinder (a) double its volume? (b) double its surface area? Explain.

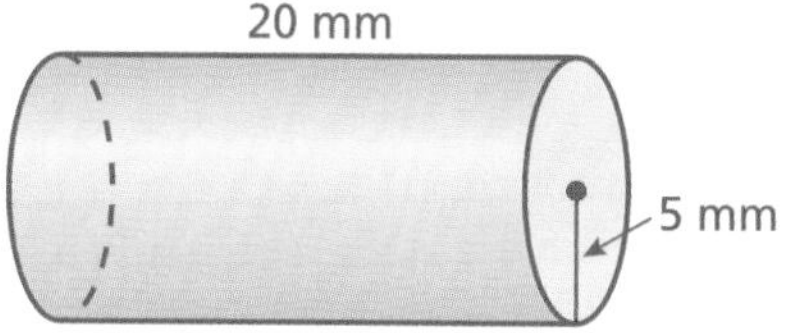

	Cylinder A	*Cylinder B*
a.	$V = Bh = \pi(5)^2(10)$	$V = Bh = \pi(5)^2(20)$
	$= 250\pi \text{ mm}^3$	$= 500\pi \text{ mm}^3$

The ratio of the volumes is $\frac{500\pi \text{ mm}^2}{250\pi \text{ mm}^2} = 2$. So, doubling the height of the cylinder doubles the volume.

	Cylinder A	*Cylinder B*
b.	$S = 2\pi r^2 + 2\pi rh$	$S = 2\pi r^2 + 2\pi rh$
	$= 2\pi(5)^2 + 2\pi(5)(10)$	$= 2\pi(5)^2 + 2\pi(5)(20)$
	$= 50\pi + 100\pi = 150\pi \text{ mm}^2$	$= 50\pi + 200\pi = 250\pi \text{ mm}^2$

The ratio of the surface areas is $\frac{250\pi \text{ mm}^2}{150\pi \text{ mm}^2} \approx 1.7$. So, doubling the height of the cylinder does *not* double the surface area.

EXAMPLE 4 Real-Life Application

The cylindrical bottom layer of a Quinceañera cake has a radius of 8 inches and a height of 4 inches. The dimensions of each of the other layers are one-half of the dimensions of the layer beneath. How many times greater is the volume of the middle layer than the volume of the top layer?

Middle Layer	*Top Layer*
$r = 8\left(\frac{1}{2}\right) = 4,\ h = 4\left(\frac{1}{2}\right) = 2$	$r = 4\left(\frac{1}{2}\right) = 2,\ h = 2\left(\frac{1}{2}\right) = 1$
$V = Bh$	$V = Bh$
$= \pi(4)^2(2)$	$= \pi(2)^2(1)$
$= 32\pi \text{ in.}^3$	$= 4\pi \text{ in.}^3$

The ratio of the volumes is $\frac{32\pi \text{ in.}^3}{4\pi \text{ in.}^3} = 8$. So, the volume of the middle layer is 8 times greater than the volume of the top layer.

On Your Own

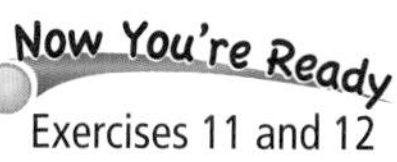

3. In Example 3, does tripling the height (a) triple the volume? (b) triple the surface area? Explain.
4. In Example 4, how many times greater is the volume of the bottom layer than the volume of the middle layer?

7.2 Exercises

Vocabulary and Concept Check

1. **VOCABULARY** How are the formulas for surface area and volume of a cylinder the same? different?

2. **WHICH ONE DOESN'T BELONG?** Which formula does *not* belong with the other three? Explain your reasoning.

$V = \pi r^2 h$	$V = Bh$	$V = \ell wh$	$V = \pi\left(\frac{d}{2}\right)^2 h$

Practice and Problem Solving

Find the volume of the cylinder. Round your answer to the nearest tenth.

3. 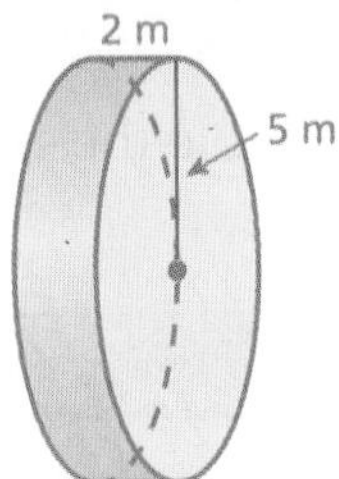

4. 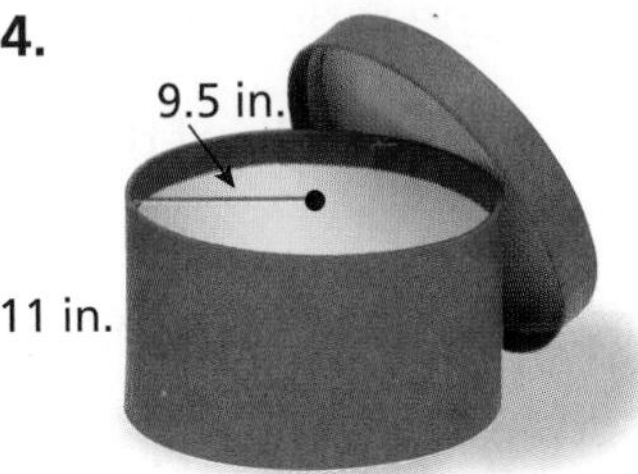

5. 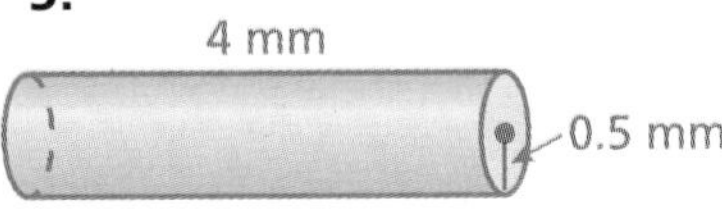

Find the volume V or height h of the cylinder. Round your answer to the nearest tenth.

6. 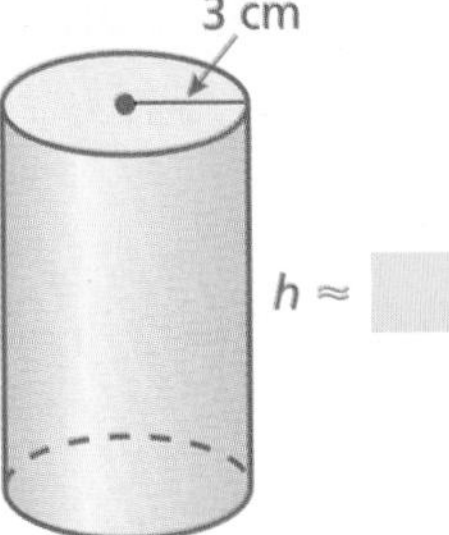

7. 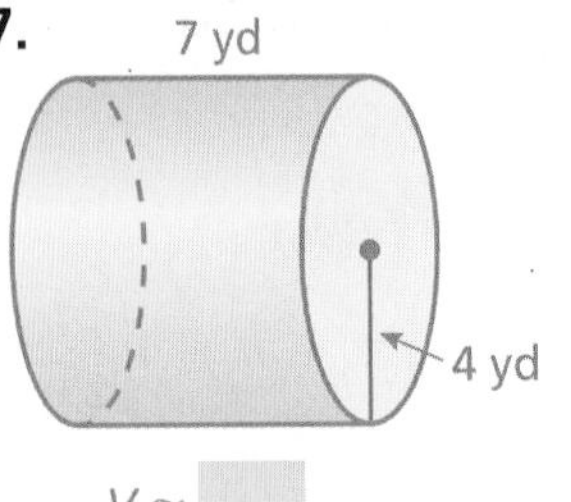

8. 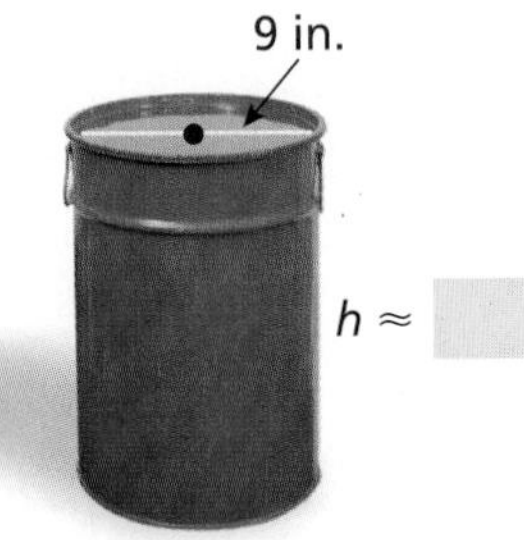

9. **ERROR ANALYSIS** Describe and correct the error in finding the volume of the cylinder.

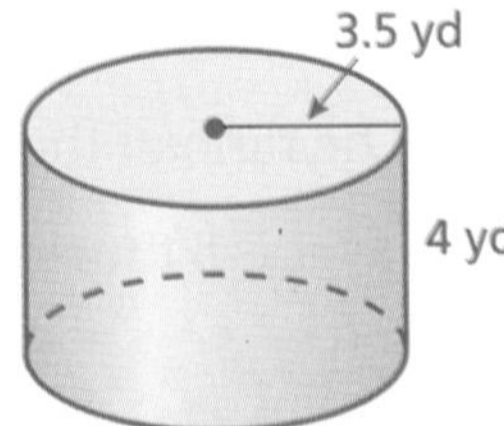

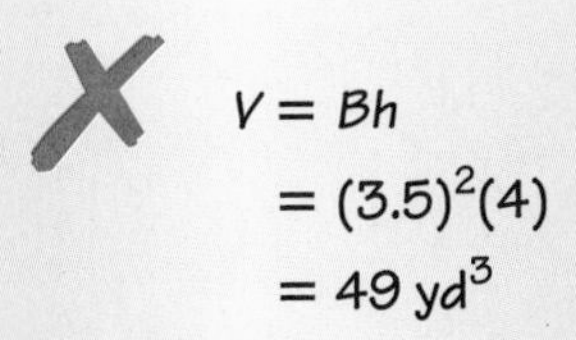

$$V = Bh$$
$$= (3.5)^2(4)$$
$$= 49 \text{ yd}^3$$

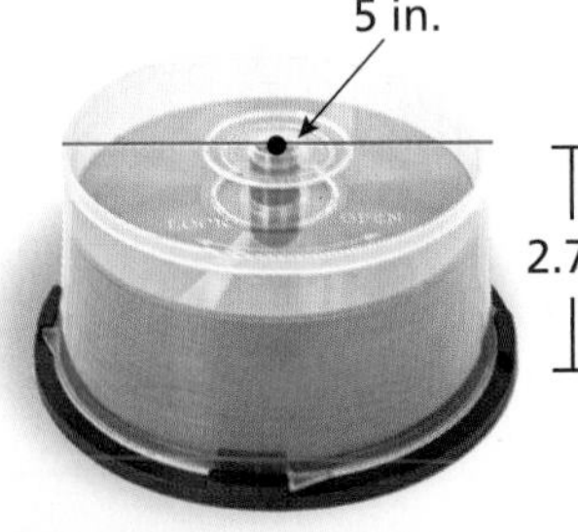

10. **BLANK CDS** You purchase a case of blank CDs.

 a. Find the volume of the case.

 b. Each CD has a volume of about 1.2 cubic inches. How many CDs can fit into the case?

In Exercises 11 and 12, use the cylinder shown.

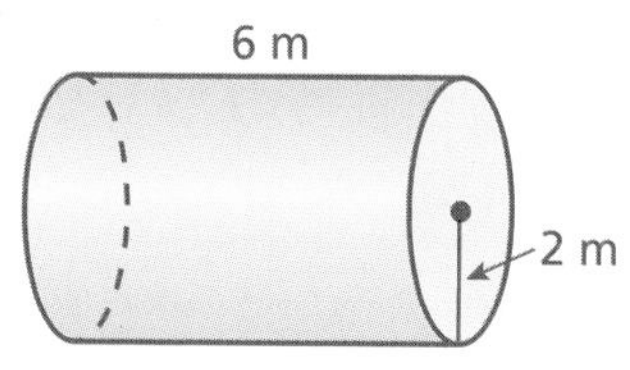

3 **11.** Double the radius of the cylinder. How many times greater is the volume of the new cylinder than the volume of the original cylinder?

12. Triple the height of the cylinder. How many times greater is the volume of the new cylinder than the volume of the original cylinder?

13. REASONING Are your results in Exercises 11 and 12 true for any cylinder? Are these results true for surface area? Explain.

14. PEANUT BUTTER You are comparing two jars of peanut butter at the grocery store. Which is the better buy? Explain your reasoning.

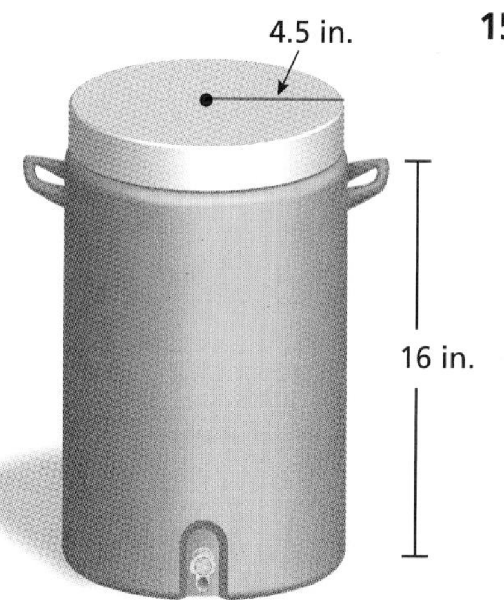

15. SPORTS COOLER You are making a sports drink for a soccer game. (1 in.$^3 \approx 0.6$ fluid ounce)

a. Each scoop of drink mix needs to be combined with 8 cups of water. Approximately how many scoops of mix do you need to fill the cooler with the sports drink?

b. Halfway through the game, $\frac{1}{4}$ of the sports drink is gone. Approximately how many scoops of mix are needed to refill the cooler with the sports drink?

c. At the next game, you use a smaller cooler with dimensions that are one-half the dimensions of the cooler shown. How many times do you need to fill the smaller cooler to have the same amount of sports drink as in part (a)?

16. Critical Thinking How does the given change affect the volume and surface area of a cylinder?

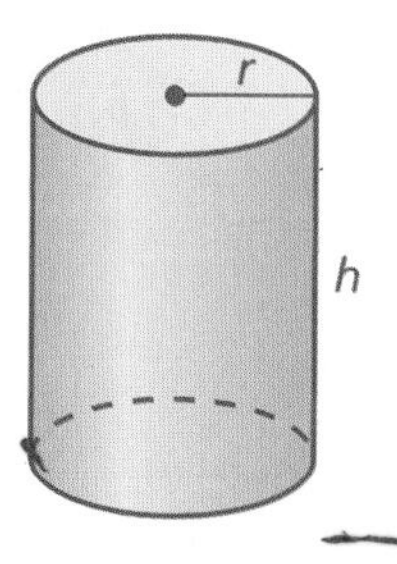

a. Height doubles
b. Height triples
c. Both dimensions double
d. Both dimensions triple

Fair Game Review What you learned in previous grades & lessons

Solve the inequality. Graph the solution. *(Section 1.7)*

17. $2x + 8 \geq 14$

18. $\frac{w}{-4} + 7 < 11$

19. $17.5 \leq -1.5 - 3y$

20. MULTIPLE CHOICE What is the surface area of the regular pyramid? *(Section 6.4)*

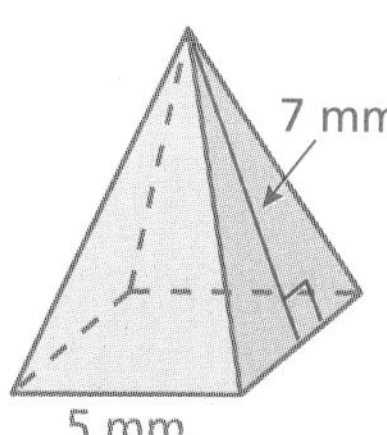

Ⓐ 42.5 mm^2
Ⓑ 60 mm^2
Ⓒ 77.5 mm^2
Ⓓ 95 mm^2

7.3 Volumes of Pyramids

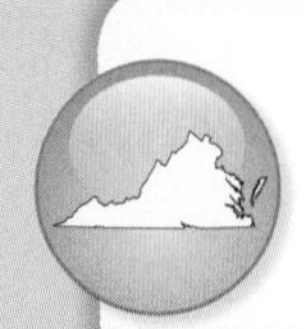

STANDARDS OF LEARNING

8.7

Essential Question How can you find the volume of a pyramid?

1 ACTIVITY: Finding a Formula Experimentally

Work with a partner.

- **Draw the two nets on cardboard and cut them out.**

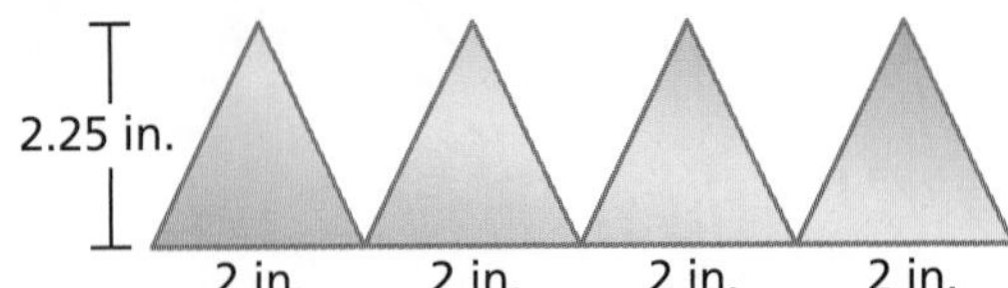

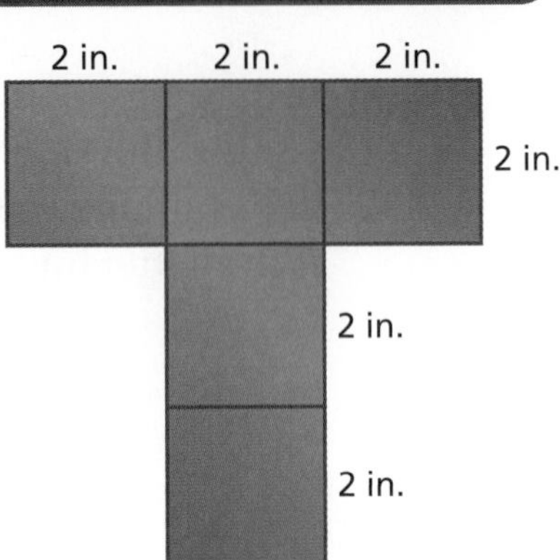

- **Fold and tape the nets to form an open square box and an open pyramid.**
- **Both figures should have the same size square base and the same height.**
- **Fill the pyramid with pebbles. Then pour the pebbles into the box. Repeat this until the box is full. How many pyramids does it take to fill the box?**
- **Use your result to find a formula for the volume of a pyramid.**

2 ACTIVITY: Comparing Volumes

Work with a partner. You are an archeologist studying two ancient pyramids. What factors would affect how long it took to build each pyramid? Given similar conditions, which pyramid took longer to build? Explain your reasoning.

Cholula Pyramid in Mexico
Height: about 217 ft
Base: about 1476 ft by 1476 ft

Cheops Pyramid in Egypt
Height: about 480 ft
Base: about 755 ft by 755 ft

3 ACTIVITY: Finding and Using a Pattern

Work with a partner.

- **Find the volumes of the pyramids.**
- **Organize your results in a table.**
- **Describe the pattern.**
- **Use your pattern to find the volume of a pyramid with a side length and height of 20.**

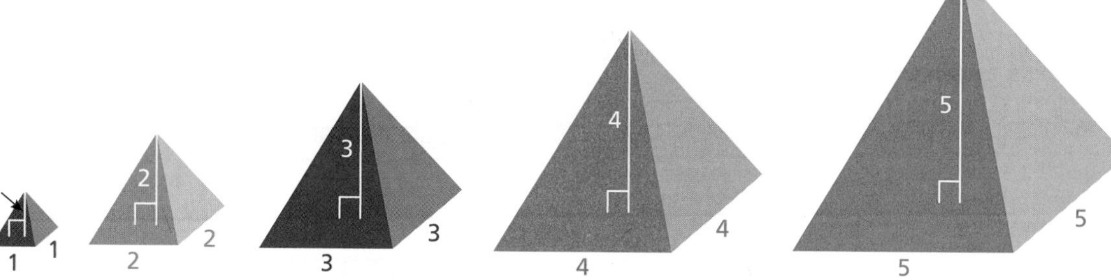

4 ACTIVITY: Breaking a Prism into Pyramids

Work with a partner. The rectangular prism can be cut to form three pyramids. Show that the sum of the volumes of the three pyramids is equal to the volume of the prism.

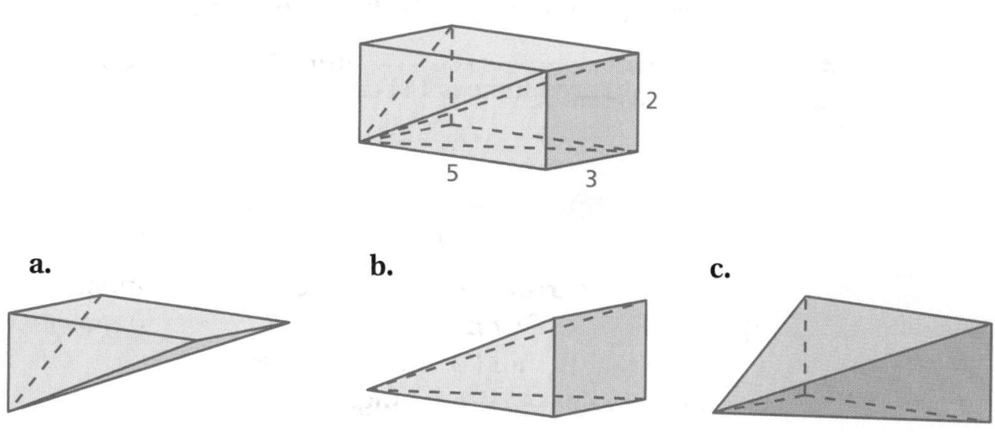

What Is Your Answer?

5. **IN YOUR OWN WORDS** How can you find the volume of a pyramid?
6. Write a general formula for the volume of a pyramid.

Use what you learned about the volumes of pyramids to complete Exercises 4–6 on page 322.

7.3 Lesson

Study Tip

The *height* of a pyramid is the perpendicular distance from the base to the vertex.

Volume of a Pyramid

Words The volume V of a pyramid is one-third the product of the area of the base and the height of the pyramid.

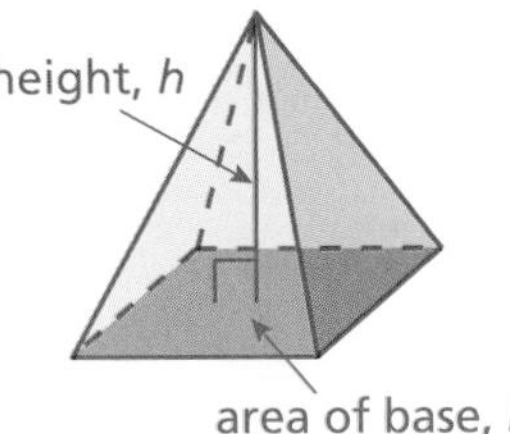

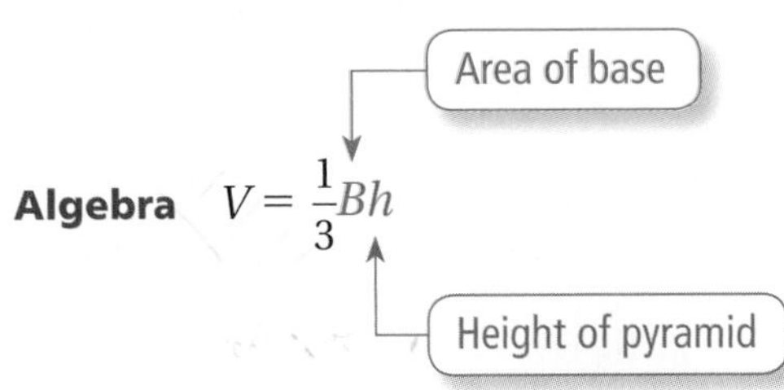

Algebra $V = \frac{1}{3}Bh$

EXAMPLE 1 Finding the Volume of a Pyramid

Find the volume of the pyramid.

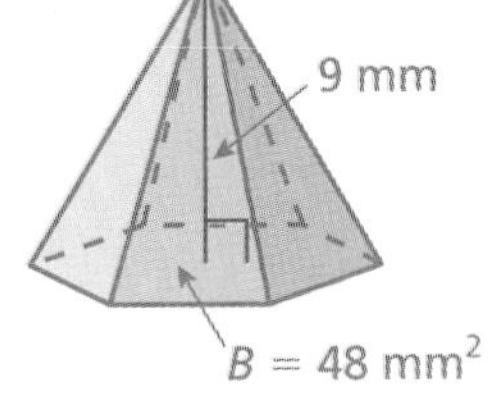

$V = \frac{1}{3}Bh$ Write formula for volume.

$= \frac{1}{3}(48)(9)$ Substitute.

$= 144$ Multiply.

The volume is 144 cubic millimeters.

EXAMPLE 2 Finding the Volume of a Pyramid

Study Tip

The area of the base of a rectangular pyramid is the product of the length ℓ and the width w.

You can use $V = \frac{1}{3}\ell wh$ to find the volume of a rectangular pyramid.

Find the volume of the pyramid.

a.

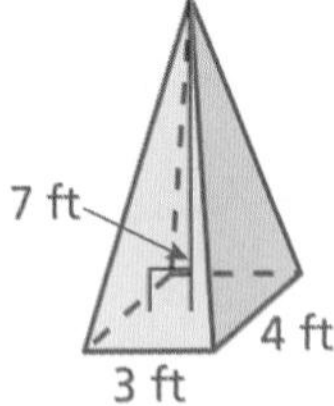

$V = \frac{1}{3}Bh$

$= \frac{1}{3}(4)(3)(7)$

$= 28$

The volume is 28 cubic feet.

b.

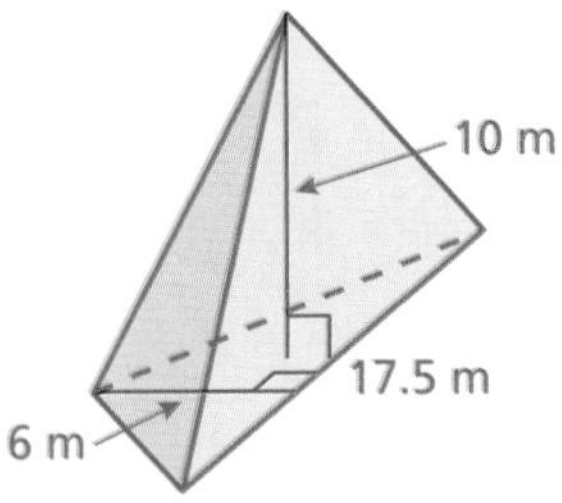

$V = \frac{1}{3}Bh$

$= \frac{1}{3}\left(\frac{1}{2}\right)(17.5)(6)(10)$

$= 175$

The volume is 175 cubic meters.

On Your Own

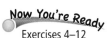

Now You're Ready
Exercises 4–12

Find the volume of the pyramid.

1. 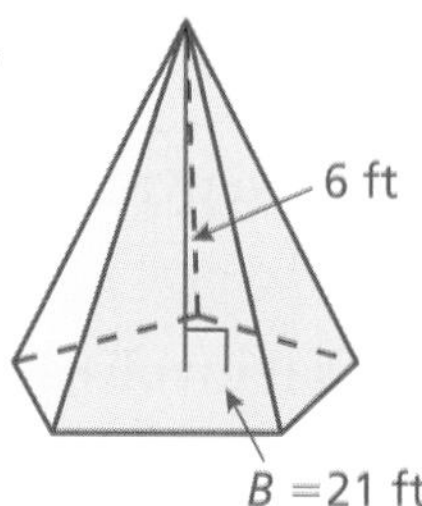

2. 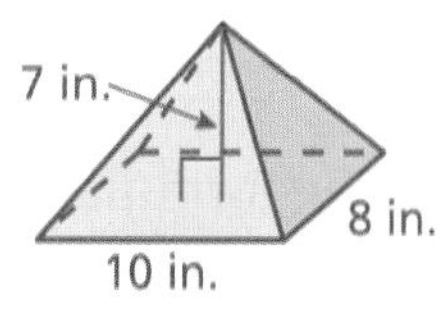

3. 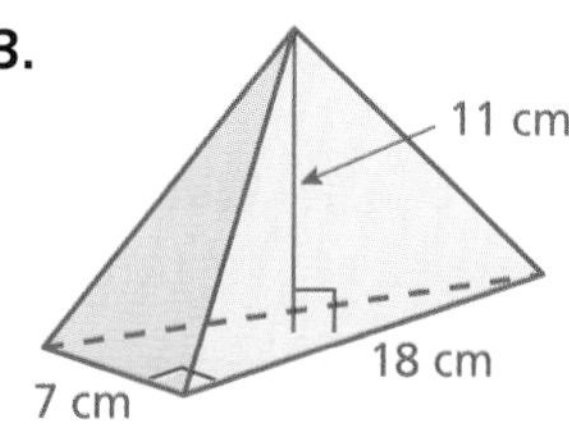

EXAMPLE 3 Real-Life Application

a. The volume of sunscreen in Bottle B is how many times the volume in Bottle A?

b. Which is the better buy?

Bottle A
$9.96

Bottle B
$14.40

a. Use the formula for the volume of a pyramid to estimate the amount of sunscreen in each bottle.

***Bottle* A**	***Bottle* B**
$V = \frac{1}{3}Bh$	$V = \frac{1}{3}Bh$
$= \frac{1}{3}(2)(1)(6)$	$= \frac{1}{3}(3)(1.5)(4)$
$= 4 \text{ in.}^3$	$= 6 \text{ in.}^3$

So, the volume of sunscreen in Bottle B is $\frac{6}{4}$, or 1.5 times the volume in Bottle A.

b. Find the unit cost for each bottle.

***Bottle* A**	***Bottle* B**
$\frac{\text{cost}}{\text{volume}} = \frac{\$9.96}{4 \text{ in.}^3}$	$\frac{\text{cost}}{\text{volume}} = \frac{\$14.40}{6 \text{ in.}^3}$
$= \frac{\$2.49}{1 \text{ in.}^3}$	$= \frac{\$2.40}{1 \text{ in.}^3}$

The unit cost of Bottle B is less than the unit cost of Bottle A. So, Bottle B is the better buy.

On Your Own

4. Bottle C is on sale for $13.20. Is Bottle C a better buy than Bottle B in Example 3? Explain.

Bottle C

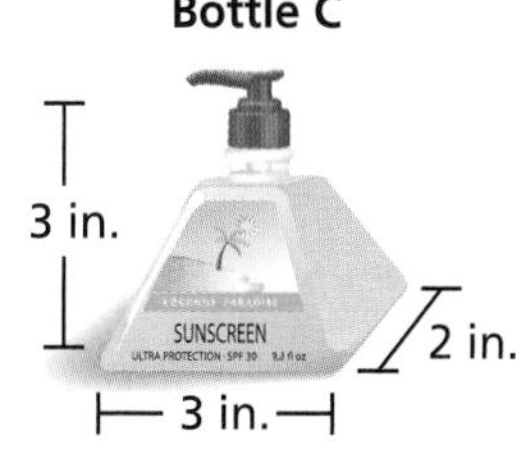

7.3 Exercises

Vocabulary and Concept Check

1. **WRITING** How is the formula for the volume of a pyramid different from the formula for the volume of a prism?
2. **OPEN-ENDED** Describe a real-life situation that involves finding the volume of a pyramid.
3. **REASONING** A triangular pyramid and a triangular prism have the same base and height. The volume of the prism is how many times the volume of the pyramid?

Practice and Problem Solving

Find the volume of the pyramid.

1 2 **4.**

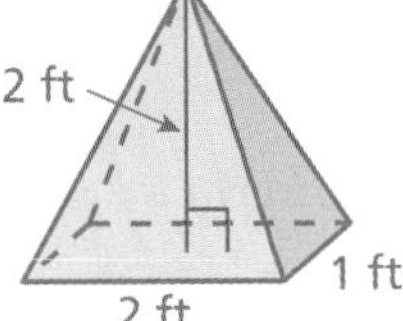

5.

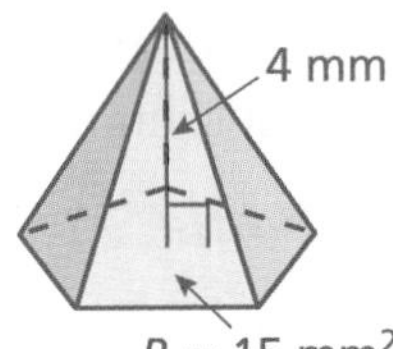

6.

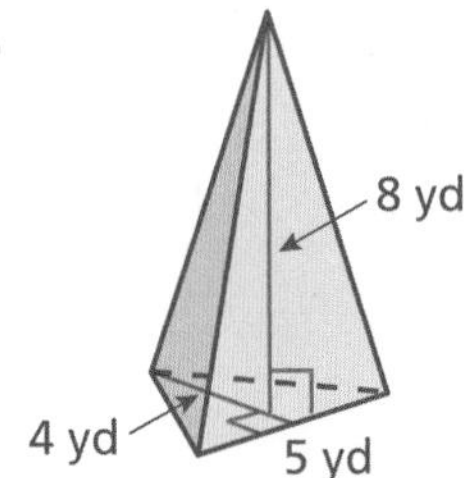

7.

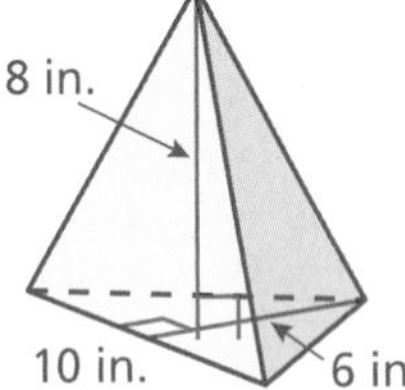

8.

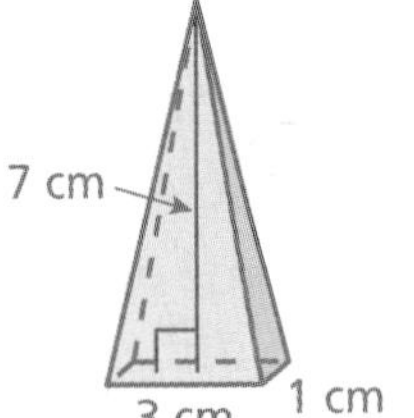

9.

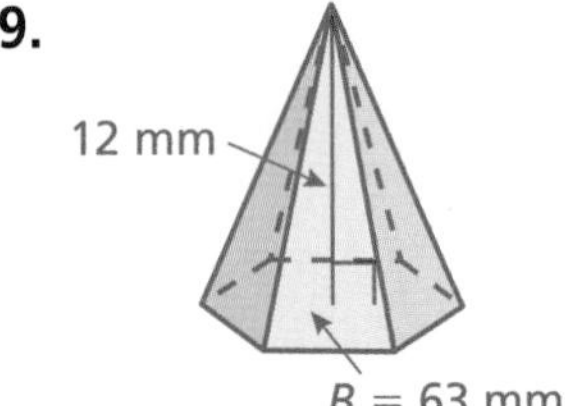

10.

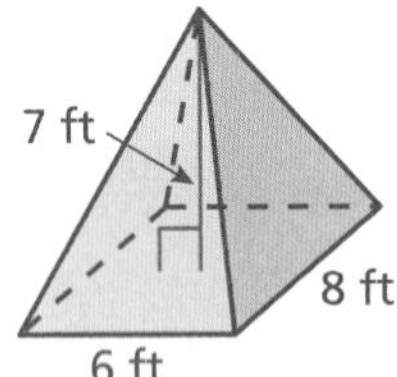

11.

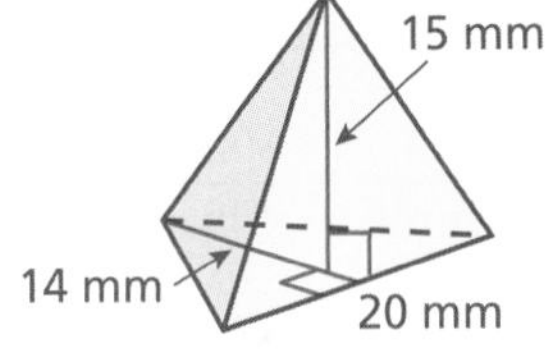

12. **PARACHUTE** In 1483, Leonardo da Vinci designed a parachute. It is believed that this was the first parachute ever designed. In a notebook, he wrote "If a man is provided with a length of gummed linen cloth with a length of 12 yards on each side and 12 yards high, he can jump from any great height whatsoever without injury." Find the volume of air inside Leonardo's parachute.

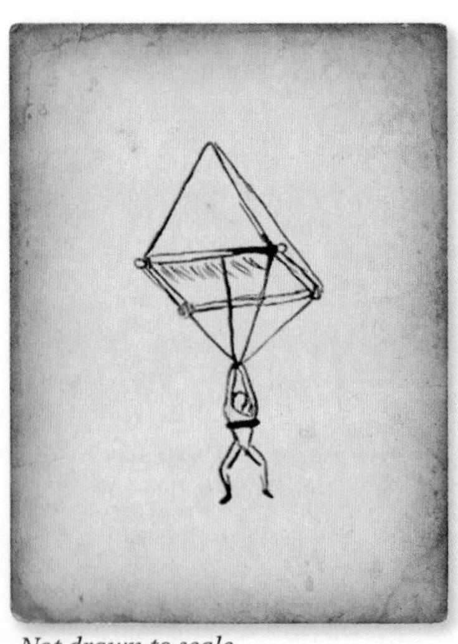

Not drawn to scale

Copy and complete the table to find the area of the base B or the height h of the pyramid.

	Volume, V	Area of Base, B	Height, h
13.	60 in.^{3}		6 in.
14.	144 cm^3	48 cm^2	
15.	135 ft^3	54 ft^2	

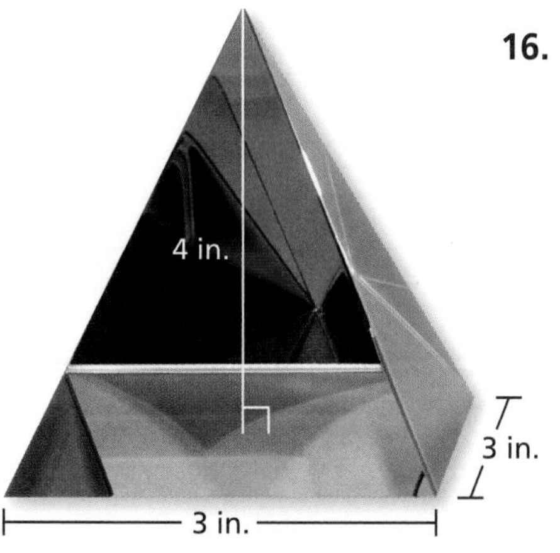

Paperweight

16. TEEPEE Use the photo of the teepee.

a. What is the shape of the base? How can you tell?

b. The teepee's height is about 10 feet. Estimate the volume of the teepee.

17. PAPERWEIGHT How much glass is needed to manufacture 1000 paperweights? Explain your reasoning.

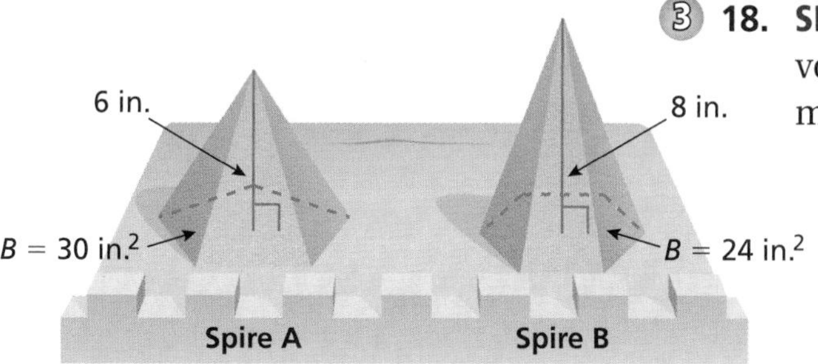

3 **18. SPIRE** Which sandcastle spire has a greater volume? How much more sand is required to make the spire with the greater volume?

19. OPEN-ENDED A pyramid has a volume of 40 cubic feet and a height of 6 feet. Find one possible set of dimensions of the rectangular base.

20. Reasoning Do the two solids have the same volume? Explain.

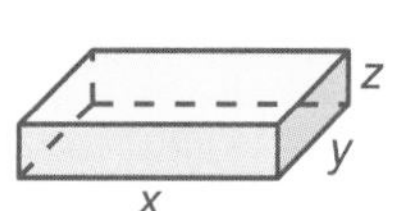

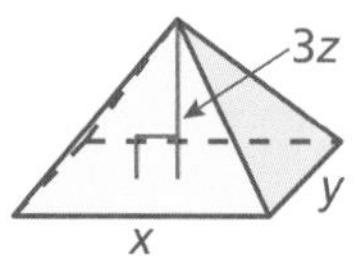

Fair Game Review What you learned in previous grades & lessons

Simplify the expression. *(Skills Review Handbook)*

21. $\frac{1}{3} \times 12 \times 7$ **22.** $\frac{1}{3} \times 8 \times 27$ **23.** $\frac{1}{3} \times 6^2 \times 5$ **24.** $\frac{1}{3} \times 2^2 \times 15$

25. MULTIPLE CHOICE You spend 25% of your money on a shirt. Then you spend $\frac{1}{6}$ of the remainder on lunch. Lunch costs \$8. What percent of your money is spent on lunch? *(Section 4.1)*

Ⓐ 4.2% Ⓑ 12.5% Ⓒ 16.7% Ⓓ 32%

7.4 Volumes of Cones

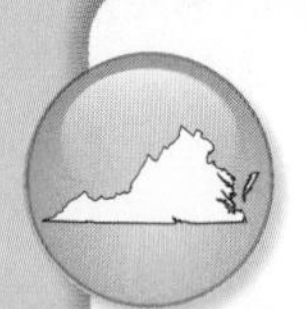

STANDARDS OF LEARNING

8.7

Essential Question How can you remember the formulas for surface area and volume?

You discovered that the volume of a pyramid is one-third the volume of a prism that has the same base and same height. You can use a similar activity to discover that the volume of a cone is one-third the volume of a cylinder that has the same base and height.

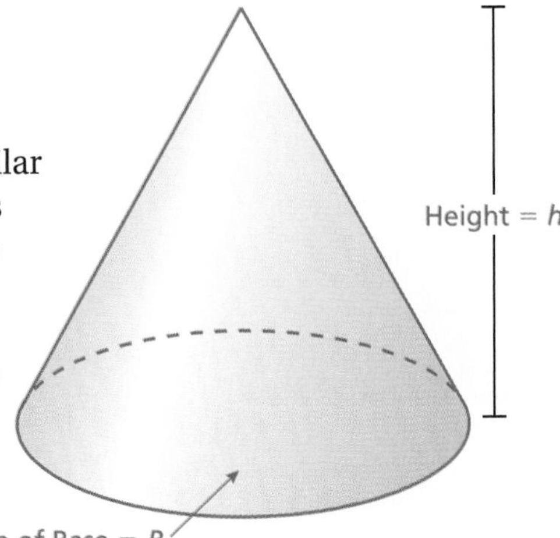

Volume of a Cone = $\frac{1}{3}$(Area of Base) × (Height)

1 ACTIVITY: Summarizing Volume Formulas

Work with a partner. You can remember the volume formulas for all of the solids shown with just two concepts.

Volumes of Prisms and Cylinders

Volume = (Area of Base) × (Height)

Volumes of Pyramids and Cones

Volume = $\frac{1}{3}$ (Volume of Prism or Cylinder with same base and height)

Make a list of all the formulas you need to remember to find the area of a base. Talk about strategies for remembering these formulas.

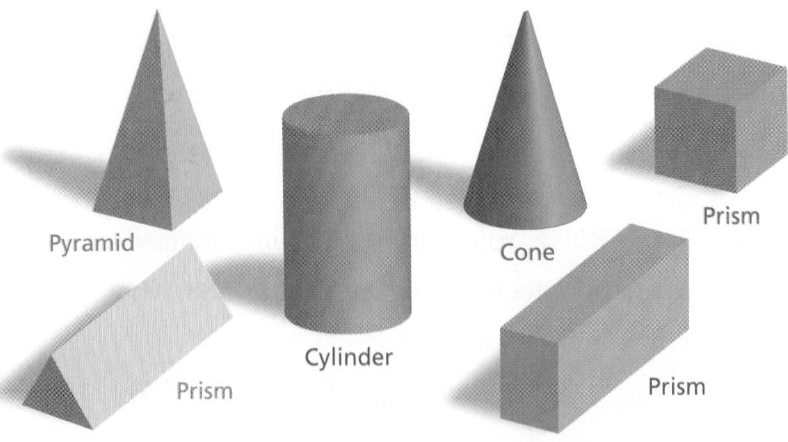

2 ACTIVITY: Volumes of Oblique Solids

Work with a partner. Think of a stack of paper. If you adjust the stack so that the sides are oblique (slanted), do you change the volume of the stack? If the volume of the stack does not change, then the formulas for volumes of right solids also apply to oblique solids.

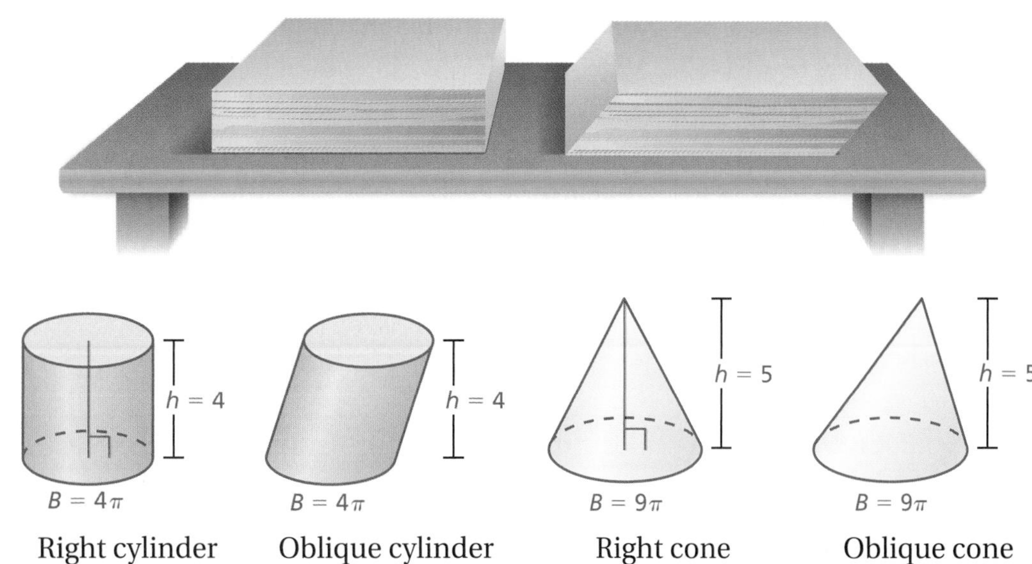

3 ACTIVITY: Summarizing Surface Area Formulas

Work with a partner. Make a list of the formulas for surface area that you studied in Chapter 6. Organize these formulas in a way similar to what you did in Activity 1.

Surface Area of a Right Prism =

Surface Area of a Right Pyramid =

Surface Area of a Right Cylinder =

Surface Area of a Right Cone =

What Is Your Answer?

4. **IN YOUR OWN WORDS** How can you remember the formulas for surface area and volume? Write all of the surface area and volume formulas on a summary sheet. Make the list short so that you do not have to memorize many formulas.

Practice Use what you learned about the volumes of cones to complete Exercises 4–6 on page 328.

7.4 Lesson

Study Tip

The *height* of a cone is the perpendicular distance from the base to the vertex.

Volume of a Cone

Words The volume V of a cone is one-third the product of the area of the base and the height of the cone.

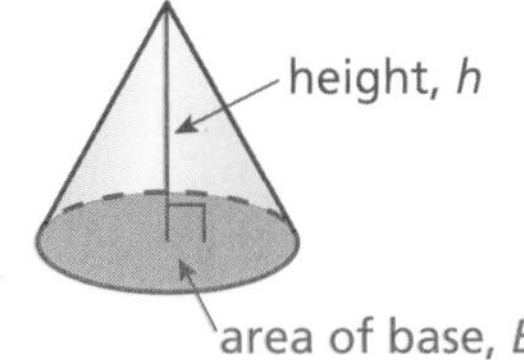

Algebra $V = \frac{1}{3}Bh$

Area of base (B)
Height of cone (h)

EXAMPLE 1 Finding the Volume of a Cone

Study Tip

Because $B = \pi r^2$, you can use $V = \frac{1}{3}\pi r^2 h$ to find the volume of a cone.

Find the volume of the cone. Round your answer to the nearest tenth.

The diameter is 4 meters. So, the radius is 2 meters.

$V = \frac{1}{3}Bh$ Write formula.

$= \frac{1}{3}\pi(2)^2(6)$ Substitute.

$= 8\pi \approx 25.1$ Simplify.

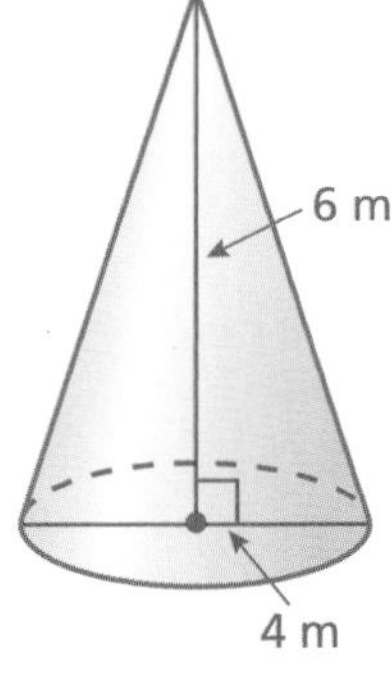

The volume is about 25.1 cubic meters.

EXAMPLE 2 Finding the Height of a Cone

Find the height of the cone. Round your answer to the nearest tenth.

$V = \frac{1}{3}Bh$ Write formula.

$956 = \frac{1}{3}\pi(9)^2(h)$ Substitute.

$956 = 27\pi h$ Simplify.

$11.3 \approx h$ Divide each side by 27π.

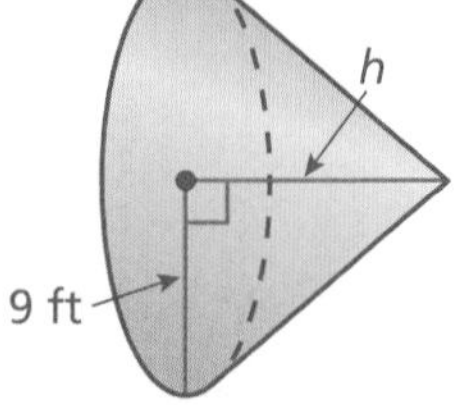

The height is about 11.3 feet.

On Your Own

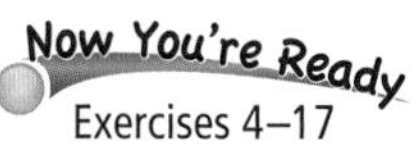

Find the volume V or height h of the cone. Round your answer to the nearest tenth.

1. 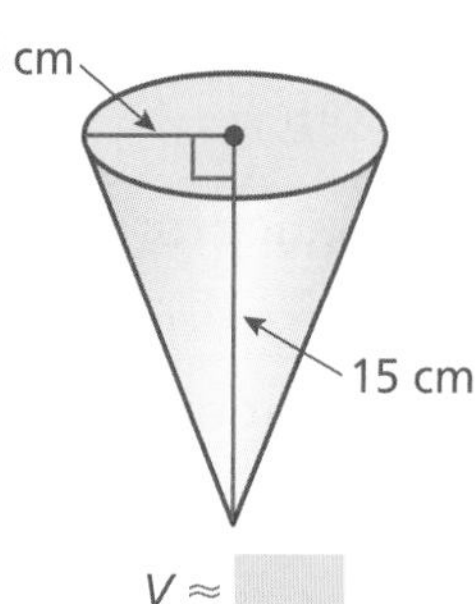

2. 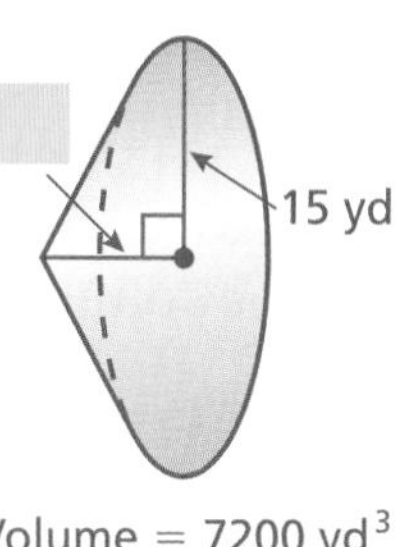

EXAMPLE 3 Real-Life Application

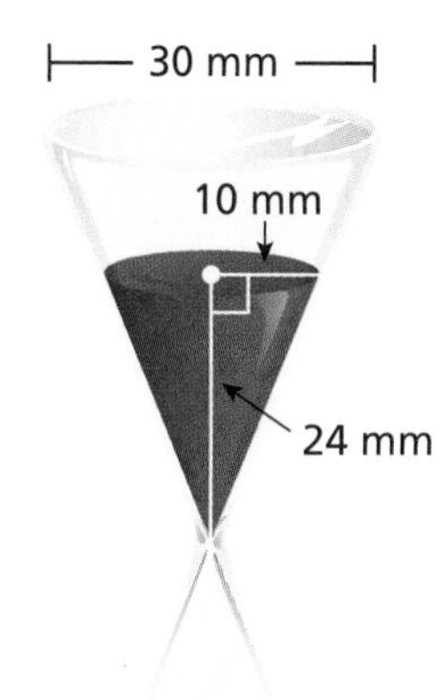

You must answer a trivia question before the sand in the timer falls to the bottom. The sand falls at a rate of 50 cubic millimeters per second. How much time do you have to answer the question?

Use the formula for the volume of a cone to find the volume of the sand in the timer.

$$V = \frac{1}{3}Bh \qquad \text{Write formula.}$$

$$= \frac{1}{3}\pi(10)^2(24) \qquad \text{Substitute.}$$

$$= 800\pi \approx 2512 \qquad \text{Simplify.}$$

The volume of the sand is about 2512 cubic millimeters. To find the amount of time you have to answer the question, multiply the volume by the rate at which the sand falls.

$$2512\ \cancel{\text{mm}^3} \times \frac{1\text{ sec}}{50\ \cancel{\text{mm}^3}} = 50.24\text{ sec}$$

∴ You have about 50 seconds to answer the question.

On Your Own

3. **WHAT IF?** In Example 3, the sand falls at a rate of 60 cubic millimeters per second. How much time do you have to answer the question?

4. **WHAT IF?** In Example 3, the height of the sand in the timer is 12 millimeters and the radius is 5 millimeters. How much time do you have to answer the question?

7.4 Exercises

Vocabulary and Concept Check

1. **VOCABULARY** Describe the height of a cone.
2. **WRITING** Compare and contrast the formulas for the volume of a pyramid and the volume of a cone.
3. **REASONING** You know the volume of a cylinder. How can you find the volume of a cone with the same base and height?

Practice and Problem Solving

Find the volume of the cone. Round your answer to the nearest tenth.

1 4.

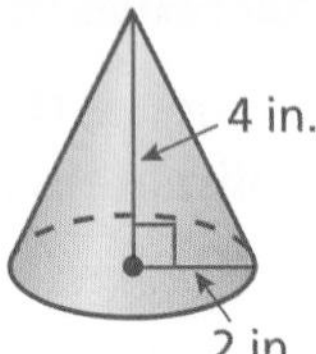

5.

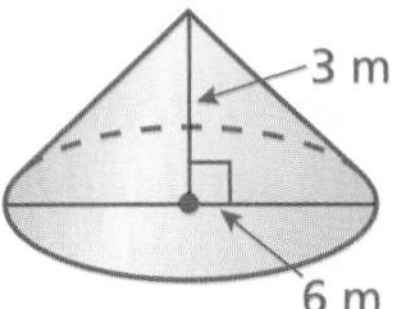

6.

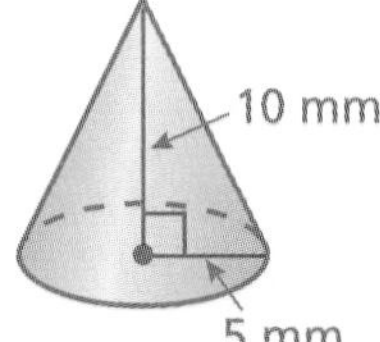

7.

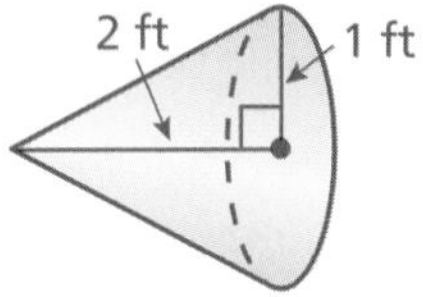

8.

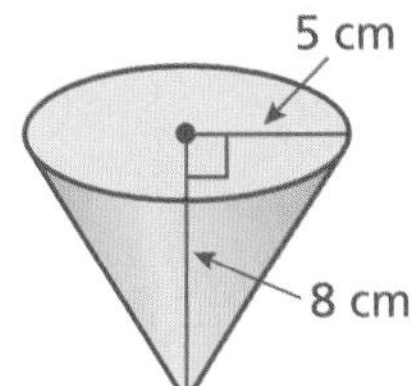

9.

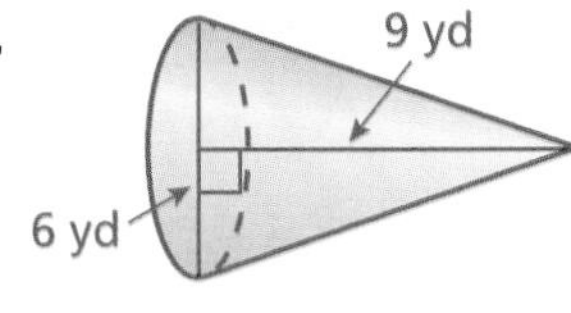

10.

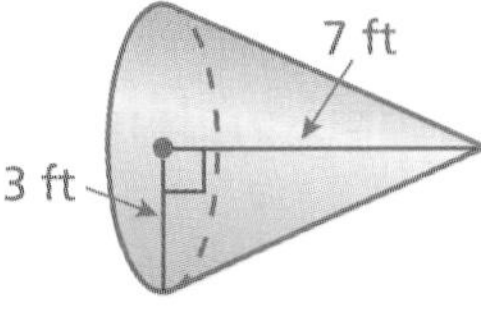

11.

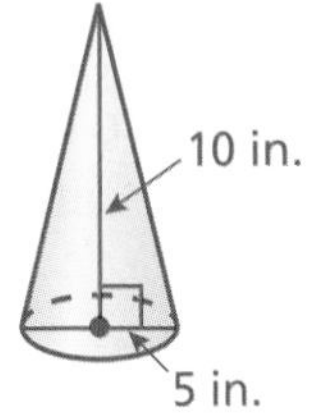

12.

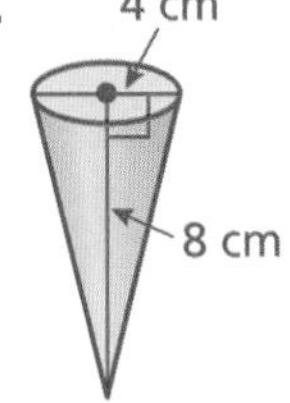

13. **ERROR ANALYSIS** Describe and correct the error in finding the volume of the cone.

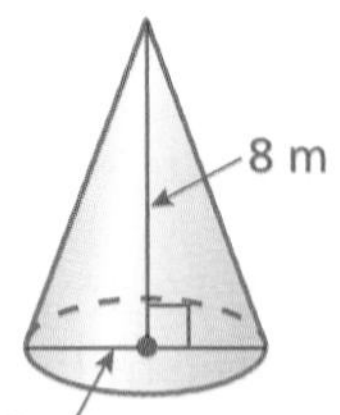

$$V = \frac{1}{3}Bh$$
$$= \frac{1}{3}(\pi)(6)^2(8)$$
$$= 96\pi \text{ m}^3$$

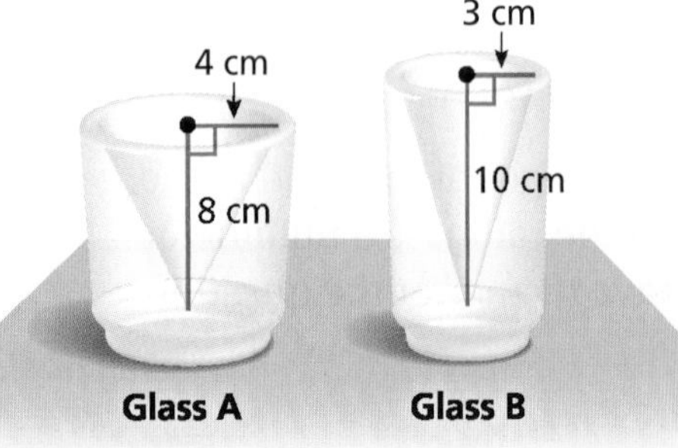

14. **GLASS** The inside of each glass is shaped like a cone. Which glass can hold more liquid? How much more?

Find the height of the cone. Round your answer to the nearest tenth.

2 **15.** Volume $= \frac{1}{18}\pi$ ft^3

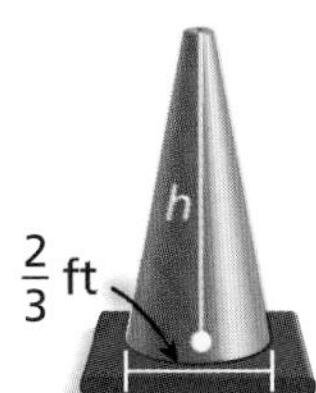

16. Volume $= 225$ cm^3

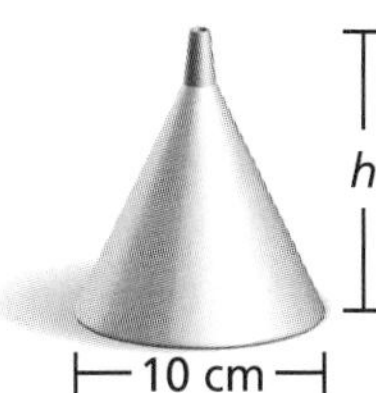

17. Volume $= 3.6$ in.^{3}

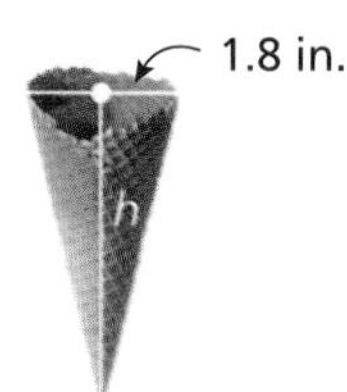

18. REASONING The volume of a cone is 20π cubic meters. What is the volume of a cylinder having the same base and same height?

19. VASE Water leaks from a crack in a vase at a rate of 0.5 cubic inch per minute. How long does it take for 20% of the water to leak from a full vase?

4.8 in.

10 in.

20. LEMONADE STAND You have 10 gallons of lemonade to sell. (1 gal $\approx$ 3785 cm^3)

a. Each customer uses one paper cup. How many paper cups will you need?

b. The cups are sold in packages of 50. How many packages should you buy?

c. How many cups will be left over if you sell 80% of the lemonade?

21. REASONING The cylinder and the cone have the same volume. What is the height of the cone?

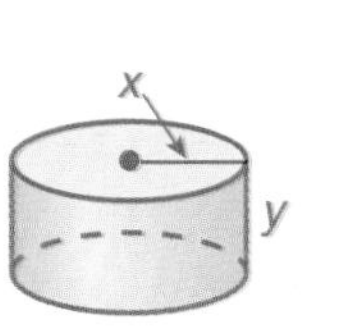

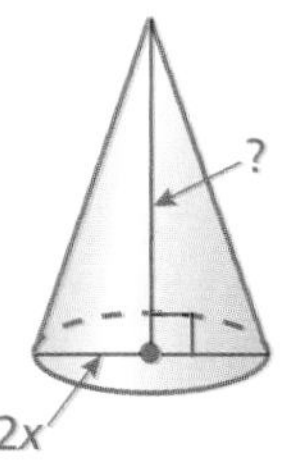

22. Critical Thinking Cone A has the same height but twice the radius of Cone B. What is the ratio of the volume of Cone A to the volume of Cone B?

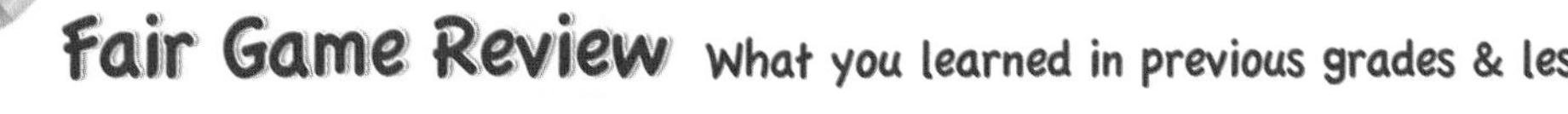

Fair Game Review What you learned in previous grades & lessons

Find the volume of the solid. *(Section 7.1, Section 7.2, and Section 7.3)*

23.

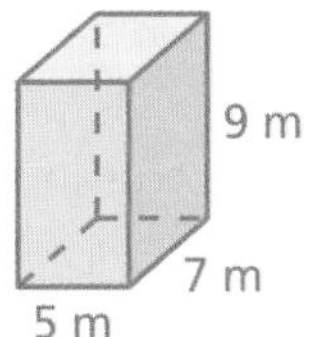

24.

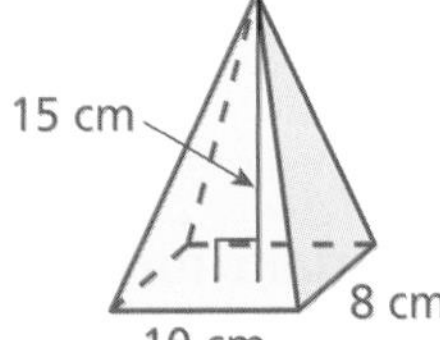

25.

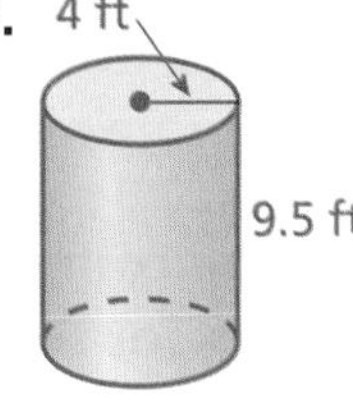

26. MULTIPLE CHOICE A triangle has angle measures of 55.4°, 23.4°, and x°. What is the value of x? *(Section 5.2)*

Ⓐ 11.2 Ⓑ 12.2 Ⓒ 101.2 Ⓓ 281.2

7 Study Help

Check It Out
Graphic Organizer
BigIdeasMath.com

You can use a **formula triangle** to arrange variables and operations of a formula. Here is an example of a formula triangle for volume of a prism.

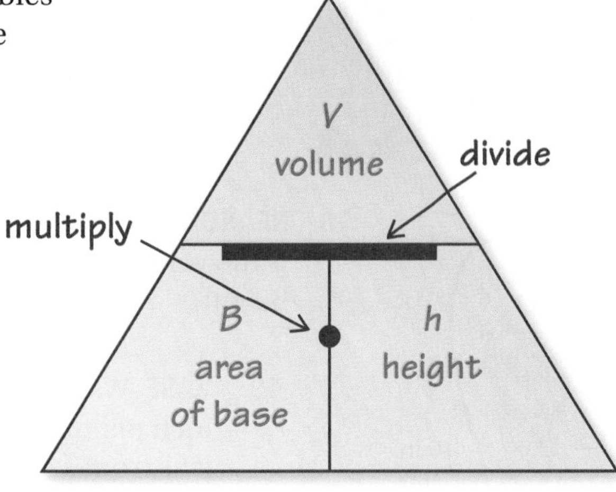

To find an unknown variable, use the other variables and the operation between them. For example, to find the area *B* of the base, cover up the *B*. Then you can see that you divide the volume *V* by the height *h*.

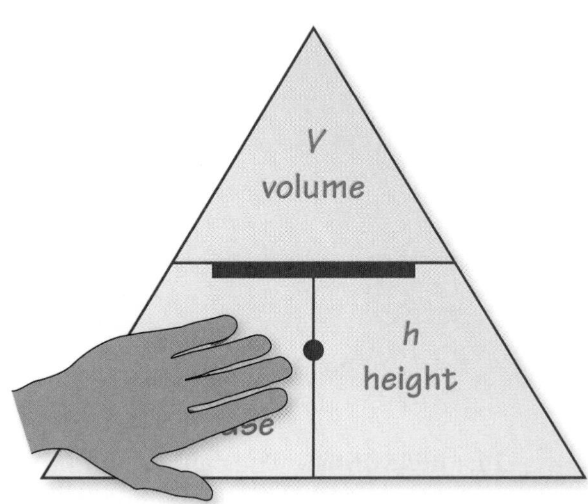

On Your Own

Make a formula triangle to help you study these topics. *Hint:* Your formula triangles may have a different form than what is shown in the example.

1. volume of a cylinder
2. volume of a pyramid
3. volume of a cone

After you complete this chapter, make formula triangles for the following topics.

4. volume of a composite solid
5. surface areas of similar solids
6. volumes of similar solids

"See how a formula triangle works? Cover any variable and you get its formula."

7.1–7.4 Quiz

Check It Out
Progress Check
BigIdeasMath.com

Find the volume of the prism. *(Section 7.1)*

1.

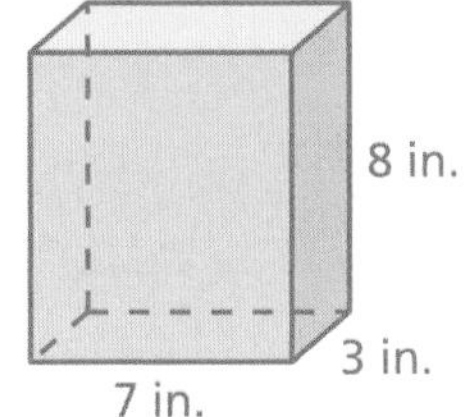

2.

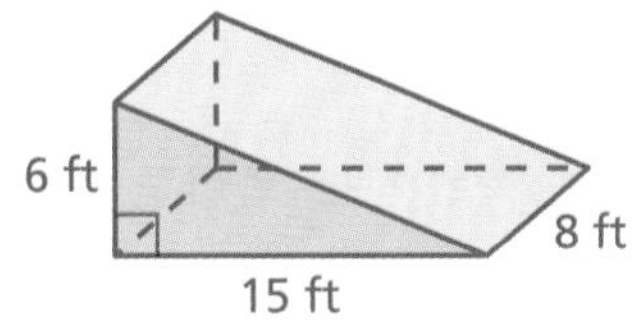

3.

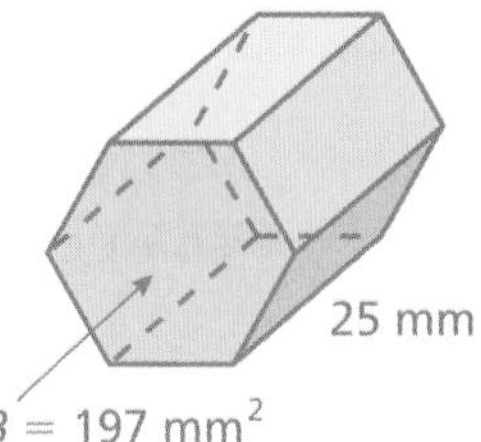

Find the volume of the solid. Round your answer to the nearest tenth, if necessary. *(Section 7.2, Section 7.3, and Section 7.4)*

4.

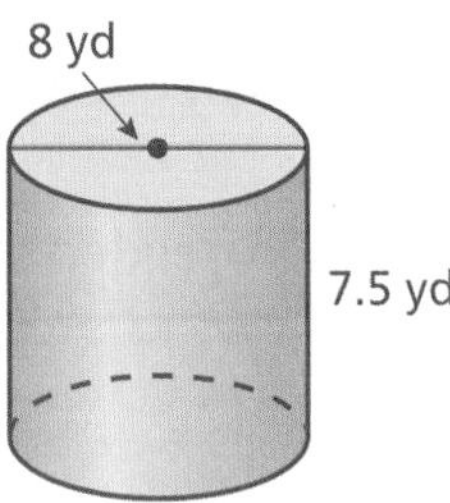

5.

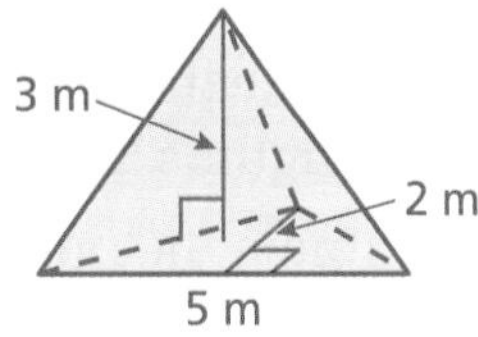

6.

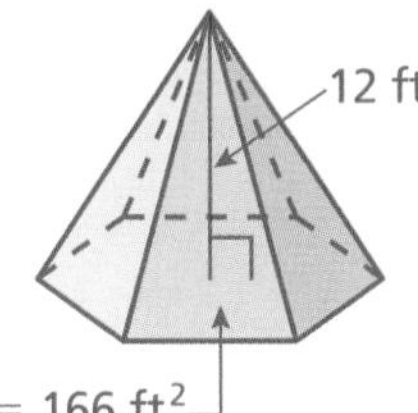

7.

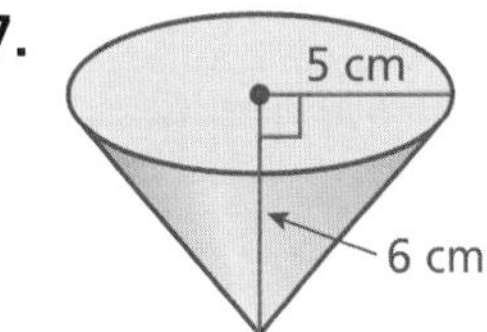

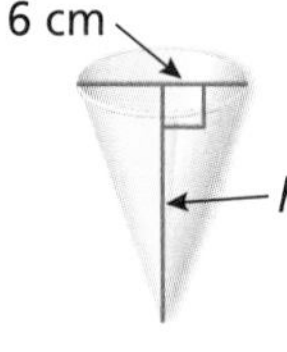

8. PAPER CONE The paper cone can hold 84.78 cubic centimeters of water. What is the height of the cone? *(Section 7.4)*

20 ft

40 ft

40 ft

9. ROOF A pyramid hip roof is a good choice for a house in a hurricane area. What is the volume of the roof to the nearest tenth? *(Section 7.3)*

10. CUBIC UNITS How many cubic feet are there in a cubic yard? Use a sketch to explain your reasoning. *(Section 7.1)*

11. GEOMETRY Triple both dimensions of the cylinder. How many times greater is the volume of the new cylinder than the volume of the original cylinder? *(Section 7.2)*

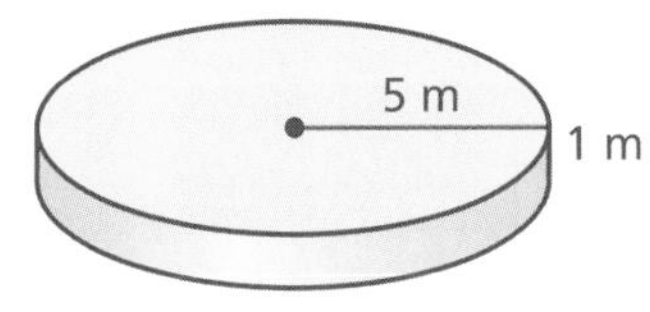

1.5 in.

16 in.

12. SAND ART There are 42.39 cubic inches of blue sand and 28.26 cubic inches of red sand in the cylindrical container. How many cubic inches of white sand are in the container? *(Section 7.2)*

7.5 Volumes of Composite Solids

STANDARDS OF LEARNING
8.7

Essential Question How can you estimate the volume of a composite solid?

1 ACTIVITY: Estimating Volume

Work with a partner. You work for a toy company and need to estimate the volume of a Minifigure that will be molded out of plastic.

a. Estimate the number of cubic inches of plastic that is needed to mold the Minifigure's head. Show your work.

b. Estimate the number of cubic inches of plastic that is needed to mold one of the Minifigure's legs. Show your work.

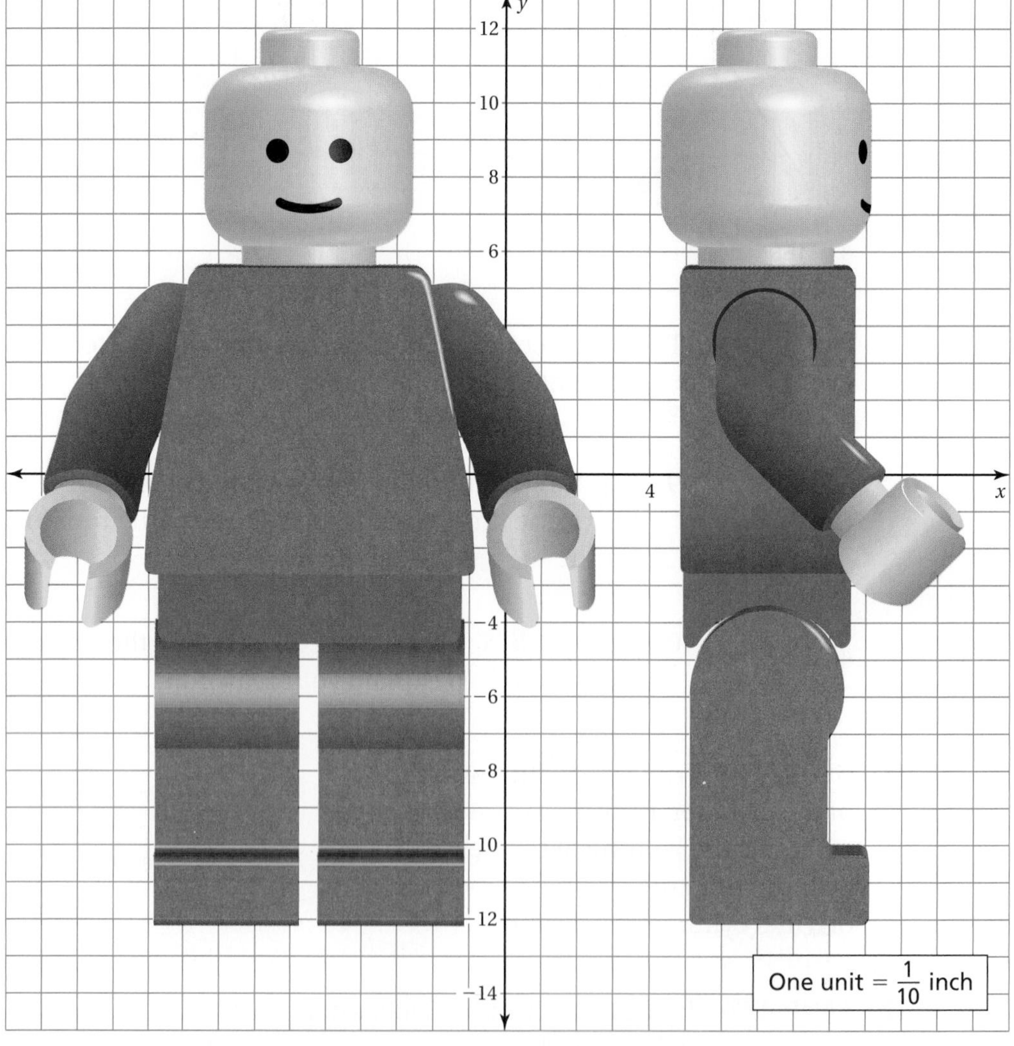

2 ACTIVITY: Finding the Volumes of Composite Solids

Work with a partner.

a. Make a plan for estimating the amount of plastic it takes to make a standard eight-stud LEGO® Brick.

© 2010 The LEGO Group, used with permission

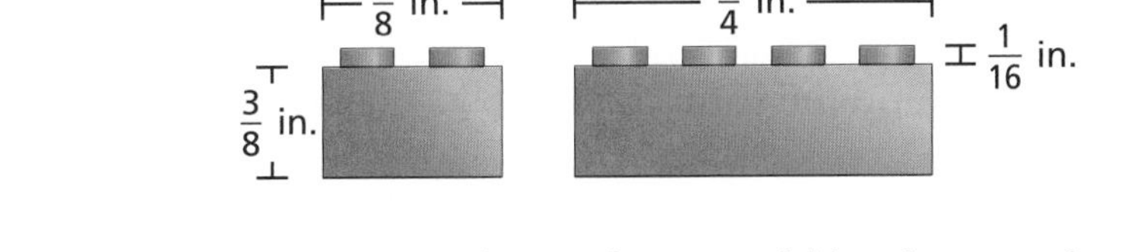

b. How much water, in cubic inches, would it take to make ten LEGO® Brick ice cubes?

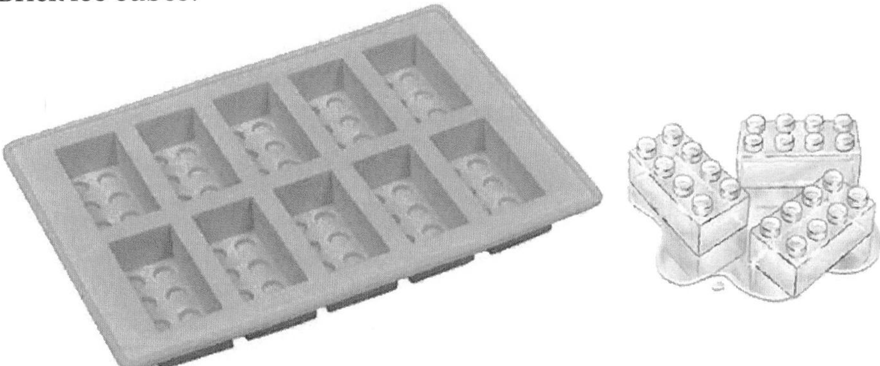

What Is Your Answer?

3. IN YOUR OWN WORDS How can you estimate the volume of a composite solid? Try thinking of some alternative strategies.

Practice Use what you learned about the volumes of composite solids to complete Exercises 4–6 on page 336.

7.5 Lesson

EXAMPLE 1 Finding the Volume of a Composite Solid

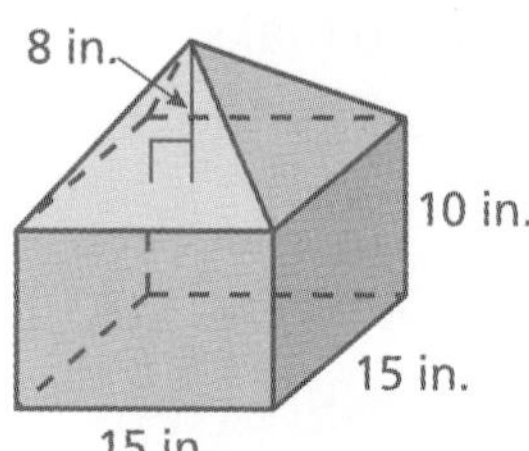

Find the volume of the composite solid.

The solid is made up of a square prism and a square pyramid. Find each volume.

Square prism

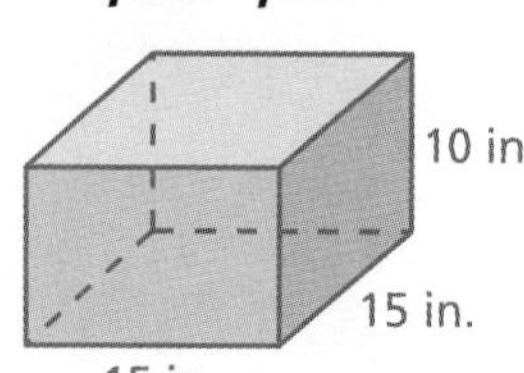

$V = Bh$

$= 15(15)(10)$

$= 2250$

Square pyramid

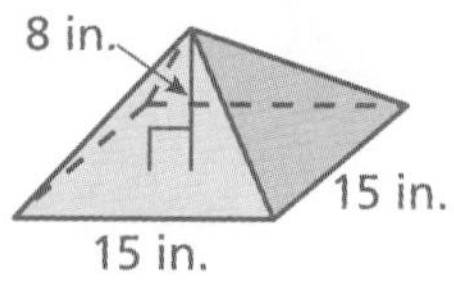

$V = \frac{1}{3}Bh$

$= \frac{1}{3}(15)(15)(8)$

$= 600$

Find the sum: $2250 + 600 = 2850 \text{ in.}^3$.

The volume of the composite solid is 2850 cubic inches.

EXAMPLE 2 Finding the Volume of a Composite Solid

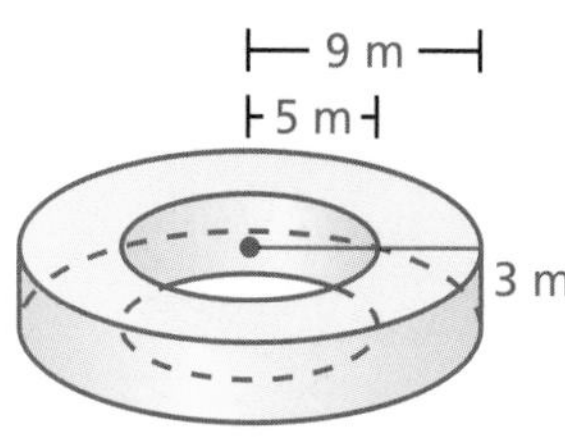

Find the volume of the composite solid. Round your answer to the nearest tenth.

The solid is a cylinder with a cylinder-shaped hole. Find each volume.

Entire Cylinder

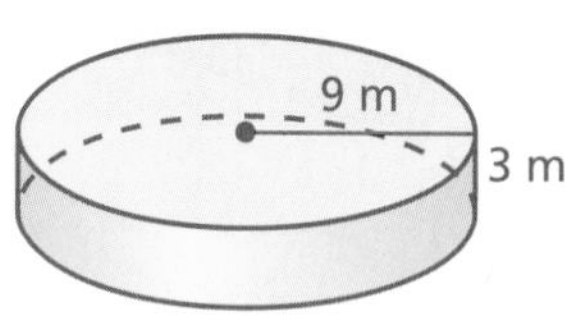

$V = Bh$

$= \pi(9)^2(3)$

$= 243\pi$

Cylinder-Shaped Hole

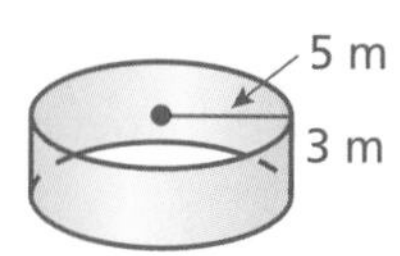

$V = Bh$

$= \pi(5)^2(3)$

$= 75\pi$

Find the difference: $243\pi - 75\pi = 168\pi \approx 527.5 \text{ m}^3$.

The volume of the composite solid is about 527.5 cubic meters.

On Your Own

Now You're Ready
Exercises 4–11

Find the volume of the composite solid. Round your answer to the nearest tenth.

1.

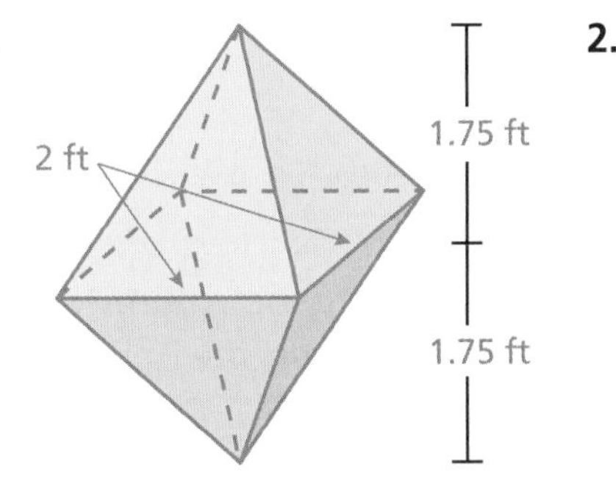

2.

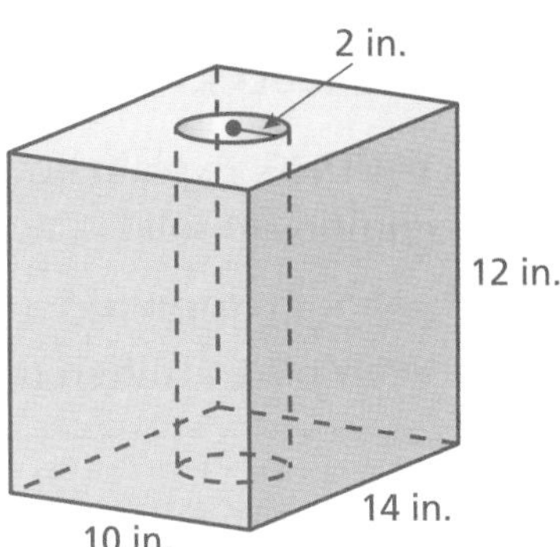

EXAMPLE 3 **Real-Life Application**

What is the volume of the silver ring in an Argentine peso? Round your answer to the nearest tenth.

The coin is a cylinder. The silver ring is the portion remaining when the inner cylinder is removed. Find the volume of each cylinder.

Entire cylinder

$V = Bh$

$= \pi(11.5)^2(2.2)$

$= 290.95\pi$

Inner cylinder

$V = Bh$

$= \pi(8.5)^2(2.2)$

$= 158.95\pi$

Subtract the volume of the inner cylinder from the volume of the entire cylinder: $290.95\pi - 158.95\pi = 132\pi \approx 414.5 \text{ mm}^3$.

∴ The volume of the silver ring is about 414.5 cubic millimeters.

On Your Own

3. **WHAT IF?** In Example 3, how would the volume of the silver ring change if the coin were only half as thick?

4. Find the volume of the composite solid. Round your answer to the nearest tenth.

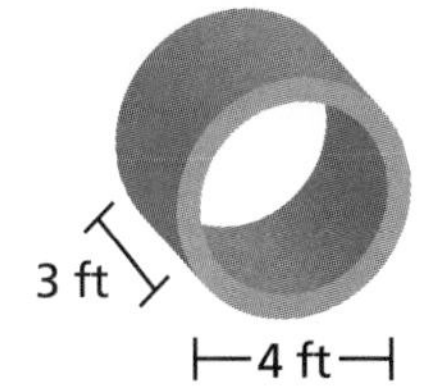

7.5 Exercises

Vocabulary and Concept Check

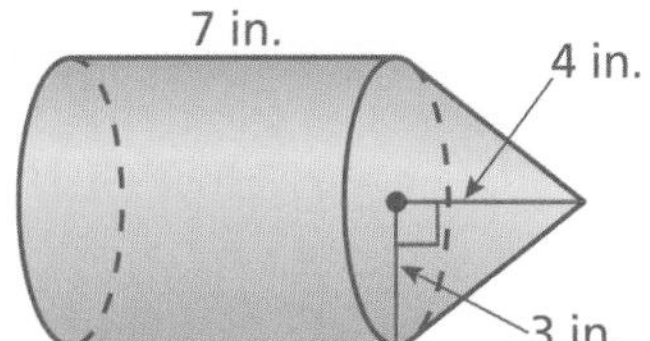

1. **VOCABULARY** What is a composite solid?
2. **WRITING** Explain how to find the volume of the composite solid.
3. **CRITICAL THINKING** Explain how finding the volume in Example 2 is different from finding the volume in Example 1.

Practice and Problem Solving

Find the volume of the composite solid. Round your answer to the nearest tenth.

4.

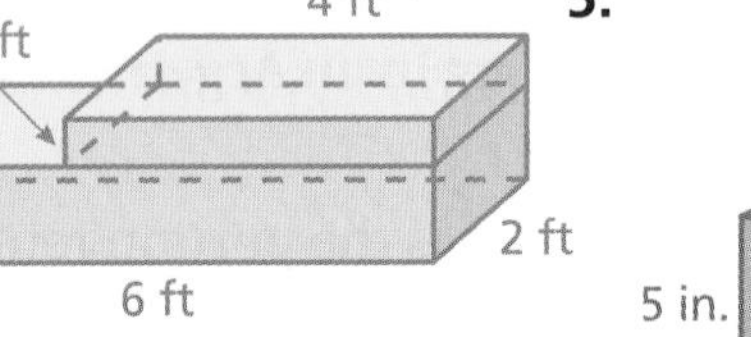

5.

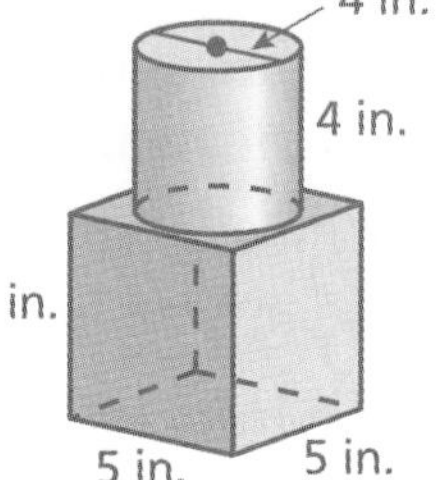

6.

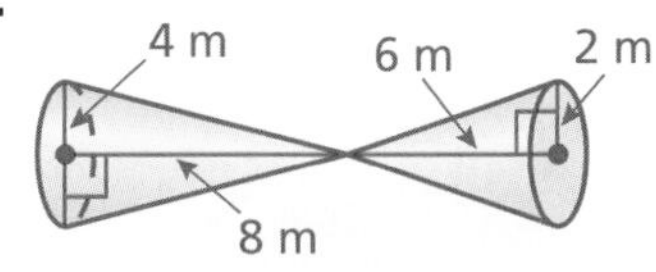

7.

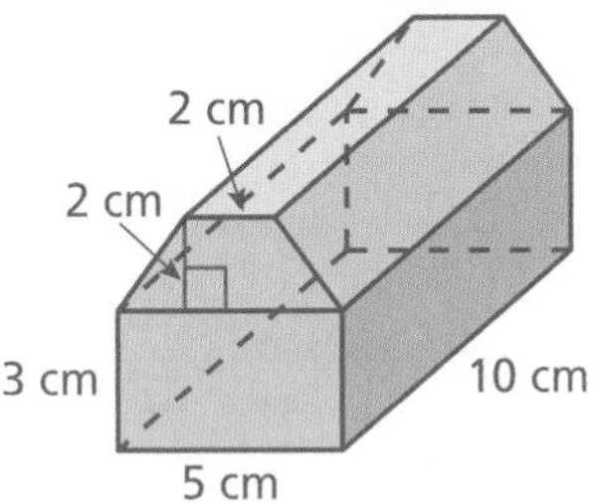

8.

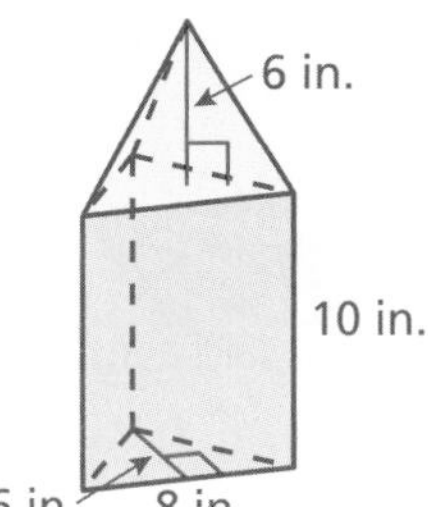

9.

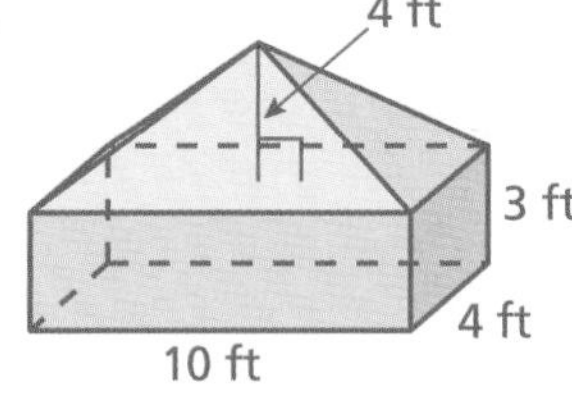

10.

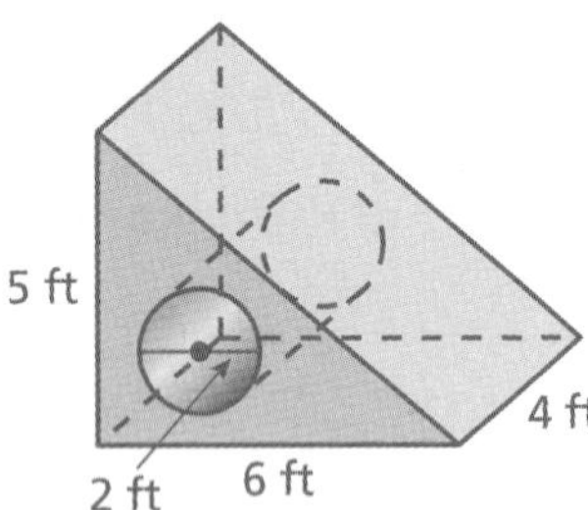

11.

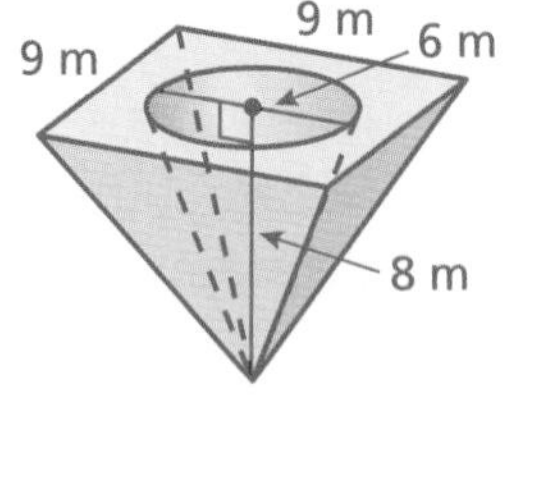

12. **BIRD FEEDER** The cedar waxwing measures about 6 inches from head to tail. The green hexagonal part of the bird feeder has a base area of 18 square inches. Estimate how much bird seed the bird feeder will hold. Explain how you found your estimate.

13. **CAKE** The raspberry layer cake has a diameter of 10 inches and a height of 5 inches.

 a. About what percent of the cake is remaining?

 b. Estimate the volume of the remaining cake.

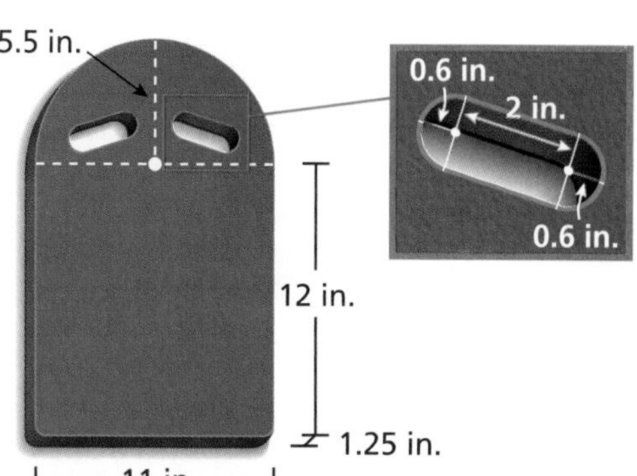

14. **KICKBOARD** A foam kickboard used for swimming has two identical hand grips.

 a. Find the volume of the kickboard.

 b. One cubic inch of foam weighs about 0.007 pound. How much does the kickboard weigh?

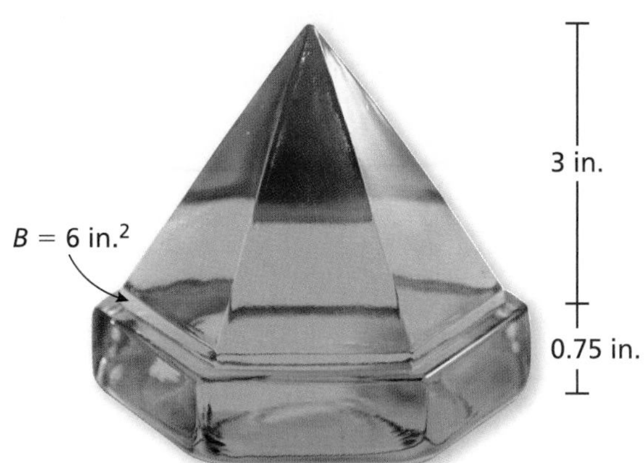

15. **PAPERWEIGHT** Estimate the amount of glass in the paperweight. Explain how you found your estimate.

16. **Puzzle** The volume of each group of solids is given. Find the volume of each of the four types of blocks.

$V = 8\pi + 8$

$V = 8\pi + 28$

$V = 8\pi + 20$

Fair Game Review What you learned in previous grades & lessons

The two figures are similar. Find the ratio (red to blue) of the areas. *(Skills Review Handbook)*

17.

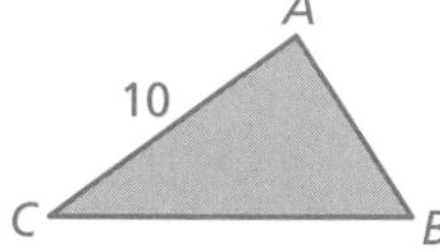

18.

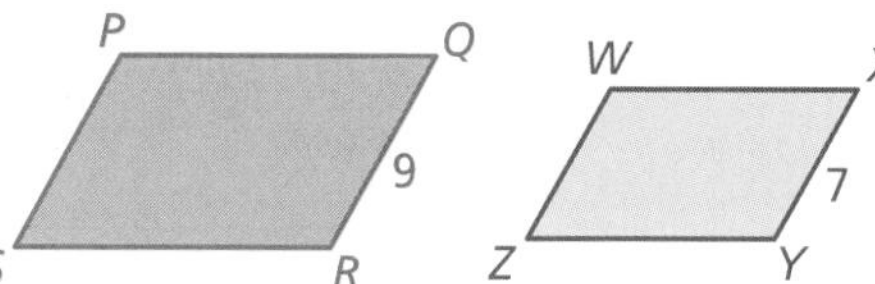

19. **MULTIPLE CHOICE** A fire hydrant releases 1200 gallons of water in 4 minutes. What is the rate of release in gallons per second? *(Skills Review Handbook)*

 Ⓐ 3 gal/sec Ⓑ 5 gal/sec Ⓒ 30 gal/sec Ⓓ 300 gal/sec

7.6 Surface Areas and Volumes of Similar Solids

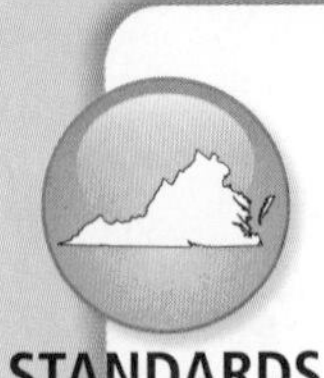

STANDARDS OF LEARNING
8.7

Essential Question When the dimensions of a solid increase by a factor of k, how does the surface area change? How does the volume change?

1 ACTIVITY: Comparing Volumes and Surface Areas

Work with a partner. Copy and complete the table. Describe the pattern. Are the solids similar? Explain your reasoning.

a.

Radius	1	1	1	1	1
Height	1	2	3	4	5
Surface Area					
Volume					

b.

Radius	1	2	3	4	5
Height	1	2	3	4	5
Surface Area					
Volume					

2 ACTIVITY: Comparing Volumes and Surface Areas

Work with a partner. Copy and complete the table. Describe the pattern. Are the solids similar? Explain.

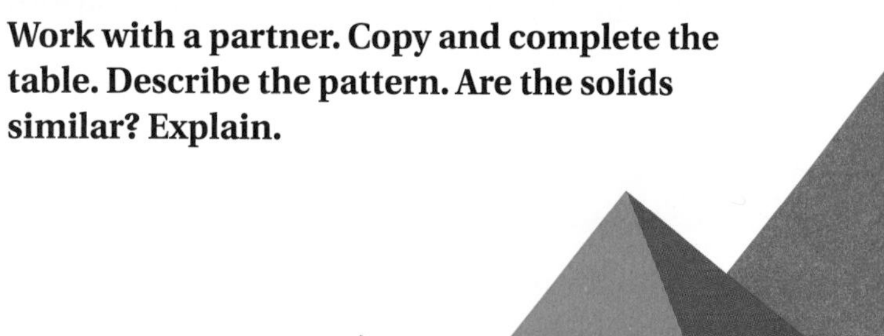

Base Side	6	12	18	24	30
Height	4	8	12	16	20
Slant Height	5	10	15	20	25
Surface Area					
Volume					

What Is Your Answer?

3. **IN YOUR OWN WORDS** When the dimensions of a solid increase by a factor of k, how does the surface area change?
4. **IN YOUR OWN WORDS** When the dimensions of a solid increase by a factor of k, how does the volume change?
5. All the dimensions of a cone increase by a factor of 5.

   a. How many times greater is the surface area? Explain.

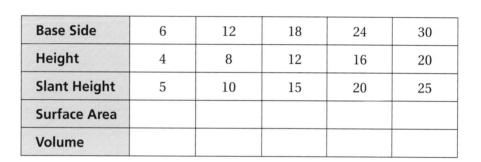

   5   10   25   125

   b. How many times greater is the volume? Explain.

   5   10   25   125

Practice Use what you learned about the surface areas and volumes of similar solids to complete Exercises 4–6 on page 343.

7.6 Lesson

Check It Out
Lesson Tutorials
BigIdeasMath.com

Key Vocabulary
similar solids, *p. 340*

Solids of the same type that have proportional corresponding linear measures are **similar solids**.

EXAMPLE 1 Identifying Similar Solids

Cylinder B

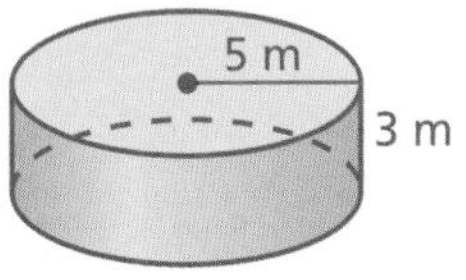

Cylinder C

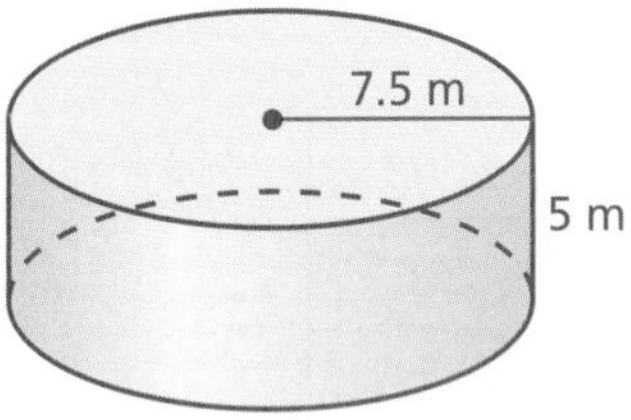

Cylinder A

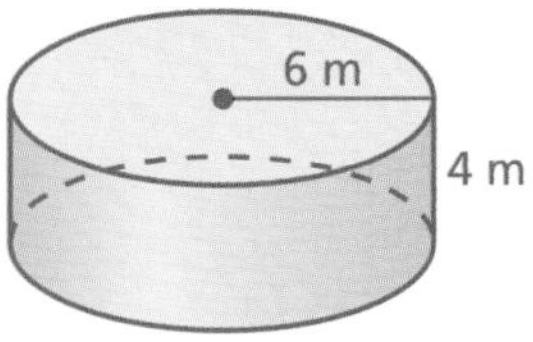

Which cylinder is similar to Cylinder A?

Check to see if corresponding linear measures are proportional.

***Cylinder* A *and Cylinder* B**

$$\frac{\text{Height of A}}{\text{Height of B}} = \frac{4}{3} \qquad \frac{\text{Radius of A}}{\text{Radius of B}} = \frac{6}{5}$$

Not proportional

***Cylinder* A *and Cylinder* C**

$$\frac{\text{Height of A}}{\text{Height of C}} = \frac{4}{5} \qquad \frac{\text{Radius of A}}{\text{Radius of C}} = \frac{6}{7.5} = \frac{4}{5}$$

Proportional

So, Cylinder C is similar to Cylinder A.

EXAMPLE 2 Finding Missing Measures in Similar Solids

Cone X

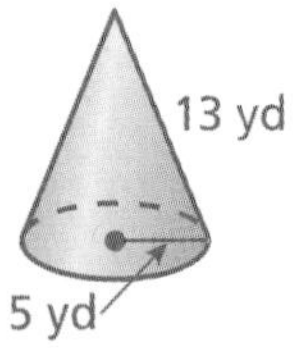

Cone Y

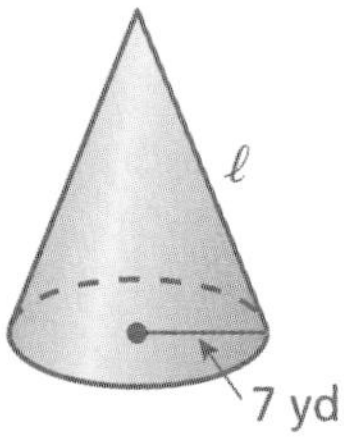

The cones are similar. Find the missing slant height ℓ.

$$\frac{\text{Radius of X}}{\text{Radius of Y}} = \frac{\text{Slant height of X}}{\text{Slant height of Y}}$$

$$\frac{5}{7} = \frac{13}{\ell}$$ Substitute.

$$5\ell = 91$$ Use Cross Products Property.

$$\ell = 18.2$$ Divide each side by 5.

The slant height is 18.2 yards.

On Your Own

Now You're Ready
Exercises 4–9

1. Cylinder D has a radius of 7.5 meters and a height of 4.5 meters. Which cylinder in Example 1 is similar to Cylinder D?
2. The prisms are similar. Find the missing width and length.

Prism A

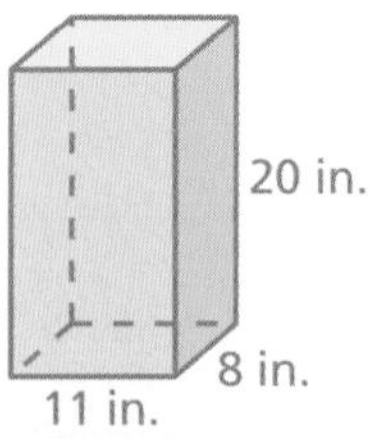

Prism B

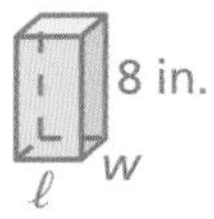

Multi-Language Glossary at BigIdeasMath.com.

Key Ideas

Linear Measures

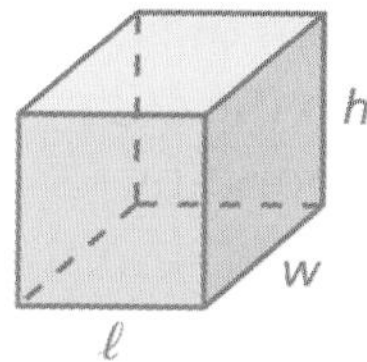

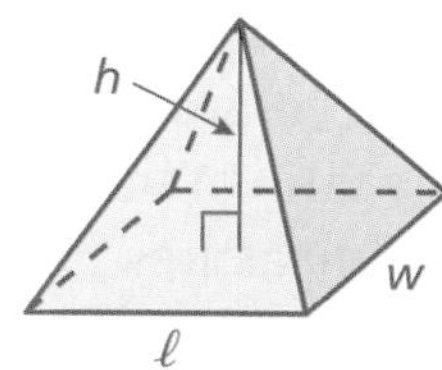

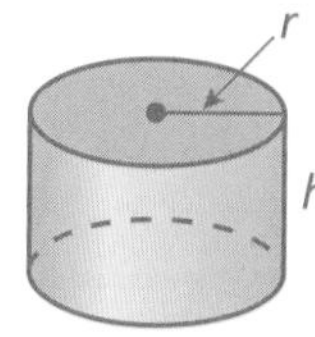

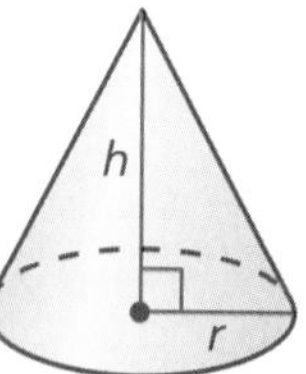

Surface Areas of Similar Solids

If two solids are similar, then the ratio of their surface areas is equal to the square of the ratio of their corresponding linear measures.

$$\frac{\text{Surface Area of A}}{\text{Surface Area of B}} = \left(\frac{a}{b}\right)^2$$

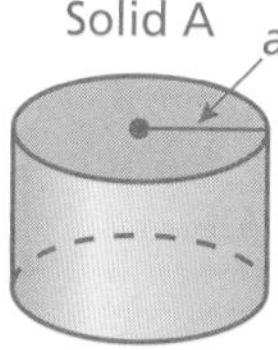

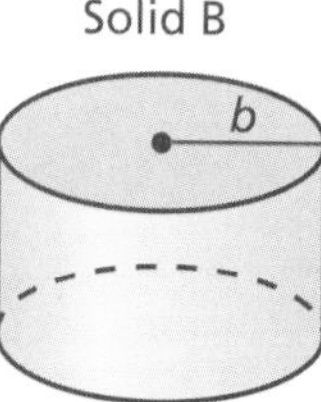

EXAMPLE 3 Finding Surface Area

Pyramid A

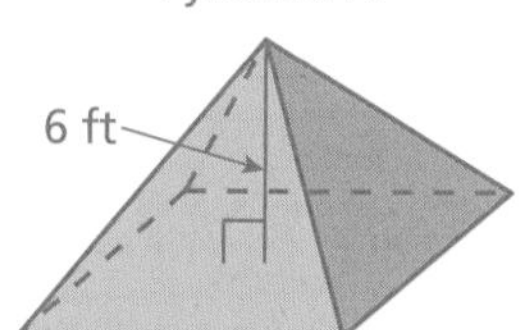

Pyramid B

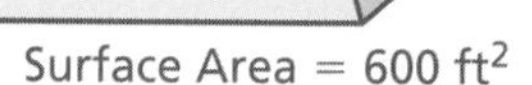

Surface Area = 600 ft²

The pyramids are similar. What is the surface area of Pyramid A?

$$\frac{\text{Surface Area of A}}{\text{Surface Area of B}} = \left(\frac{\text{Height of A}}{\text{Height of B}}\right)^2$$

$$\frac{S}{600} = \left(\frac{6}{10}\right)^2 \qquad \text{Substitute.}$$

$$\frac{S}{600} = \frac{36}{100} \qquad \text{Evaluate power.}$$

$$\frac{S}{600} \cdot 600 = \frac{36}{100} \cdot 600 \qquad \text{Multiply each side by 600.}$$

$$S = 216 \qquad \text{Simplify.}$$

∴ The surface area of Pyramid A is 216 square feet.

On Your Own

The solids are similar. Find the surface area of the red solid. Round your answer to the nearest tenth.

3.

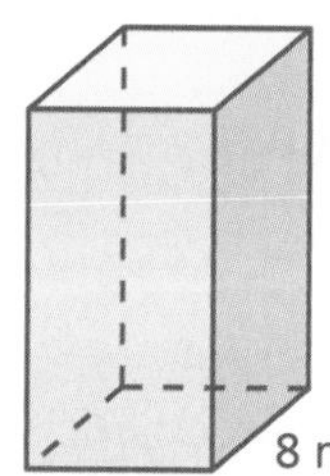

Surface Area = 608 m²

4.

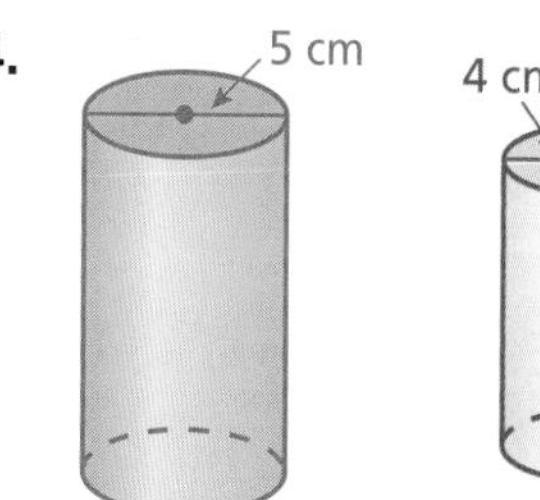

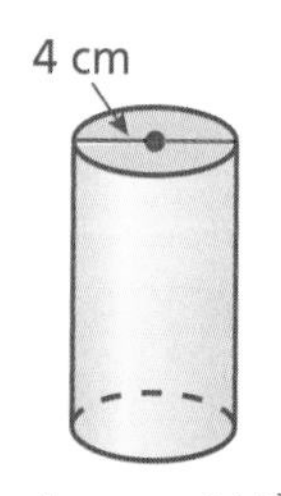

Surface Area = 110 cm²

Key Idea

Volumes of Similar Solids

If two solids are similar, then the ratio of their volumes is equal to the cube of the ratio of their corresponding linear measures.

$$\frac{\text{Volume of A}}{\text{Volume of B}} = \left(\frac{a}{b}\right)^3$$

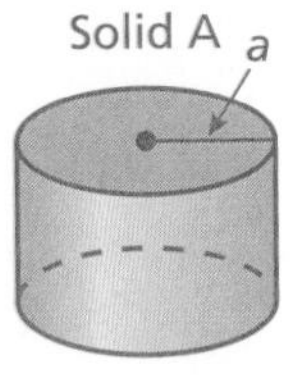

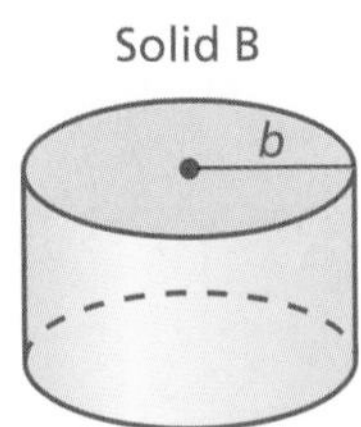

EXAMPLE 4 Standardized Test Practice

Original Tank

Volume = 2000 ft^3

The dimensions of the touch tank at an aquarium are doubled. What is the volume of the new touch tank?

Ⓐ 150 ft^3 Ⓑ 4000 ft^3

Ⓒ 8000 ft^3 Ⓓ 16,000 ft^3

The dimensions are doubled, so the ratio of the dimensions in the original tank to the dimensions in the new tank is 1 : 2.

$$\frac{\text{Original volume}}{\text{New volume}} = \left(\frac{\text{Original dimension}}{\text{New dimension}}\right)^3$$

$$\frac{2000}{V} = \left(\frac{1}{2}\right)^3 \quad \text{Substitute.}$$

$$\frac{2000}{V} = \frac{1}{8} \quad \text{Evaluate power.}$$

$$16{,}000 = V \quad \text{Use Cross Products Property.}$$

∴ The volume of the new tank is 16,000 cubic feet. The correct answer is Ⓓ.

Study Tip

When the dimensions of a solid are multiplied by k, the surface area is multiplied by k^2 and the volume is multiplied by k^3.

On Your Own

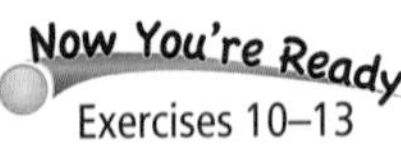

The solids are similar. Find the volume of the red solid. Round your answer to the nearest tenth.

5.

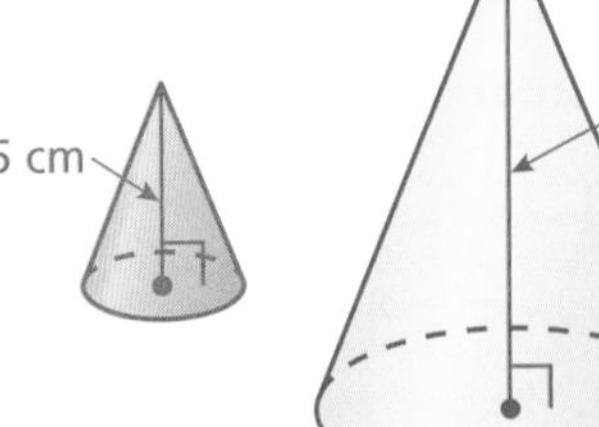

6.

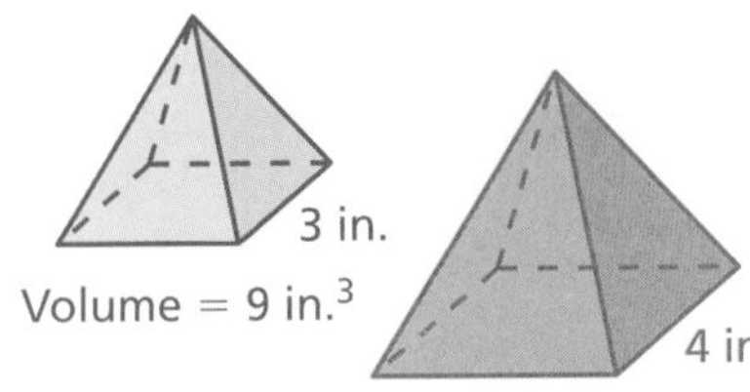

7.6 Exercises

Vocabulary and Concept Check

1. **VOCABULARY** What are similar solids?
2. **OPEN-ENDED** Draw two similar solids and label their corresponding linear measures.
3. **REASONING** The ratio of the corresponding linear measures of Cube A to Cube B is $\frac{2}{3}$.
   a. Find the ratio of the area of one face of Cube A to the area of one face of Cube B.
   b. Find the ratio of the volume of Cube A to the volume of Cube B.

Practice and Problem Solving

Determine whether the solids are similar.

1 **4.**

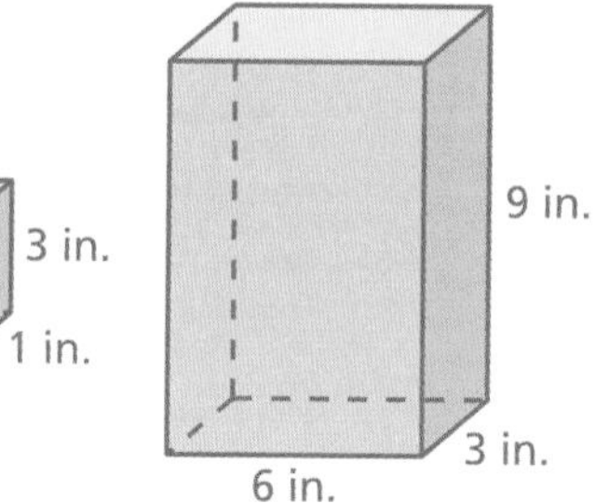

5.

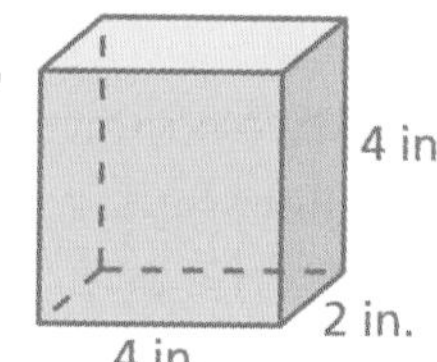

6.

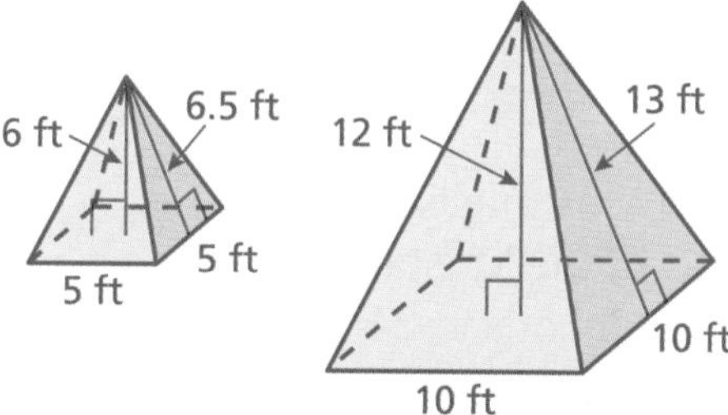

7.

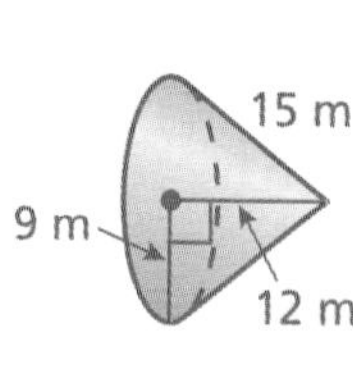

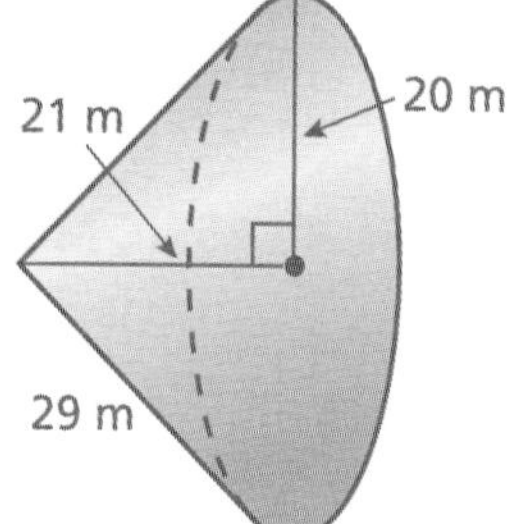

The solids are similar. Find the missing dimension(s).

2 **8.**

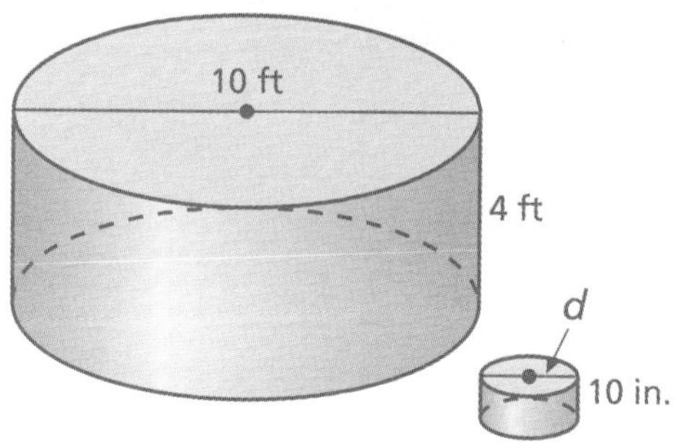

9.

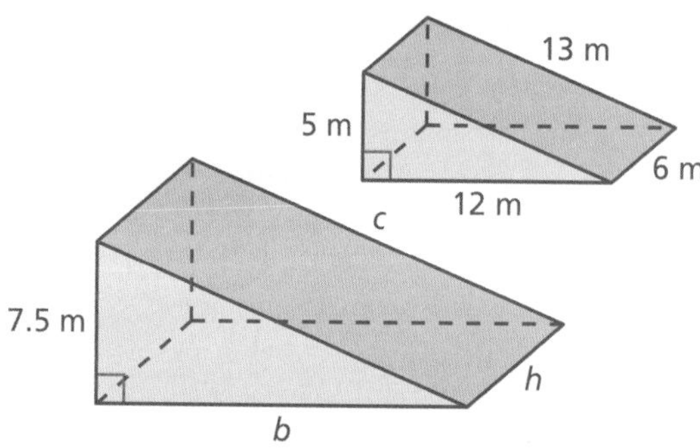

The solids are similar. Find the surface area S or volume V of the red solid. Round your answer to the nearest tenth.

③ ④ **10.**

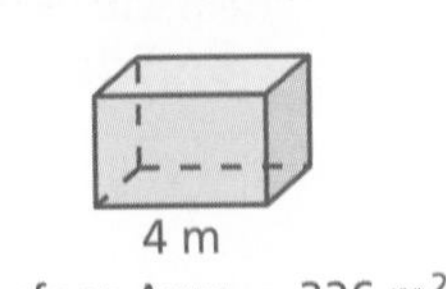

Surface Area = 336 m^2

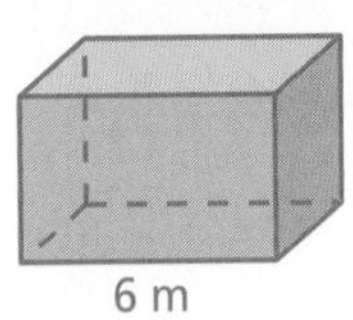

11.

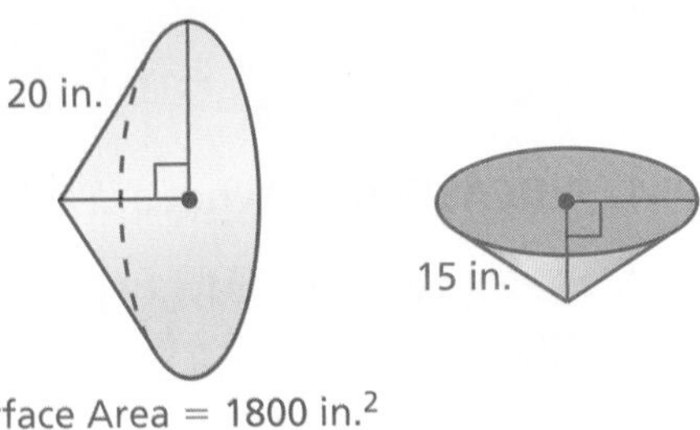

Surface Area = 1800 in.^{2}

12.

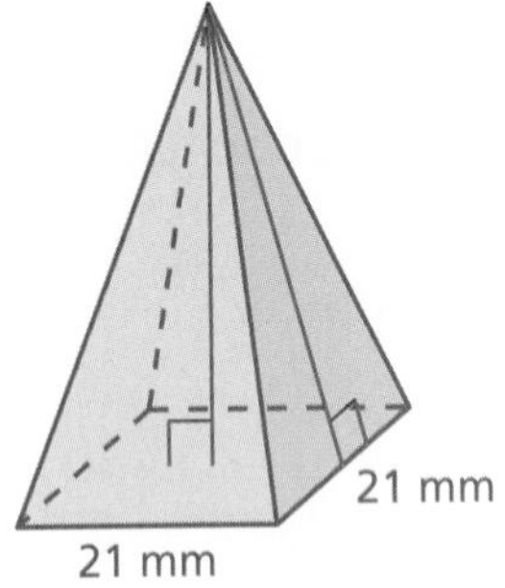

Volume = 5292 mm^3

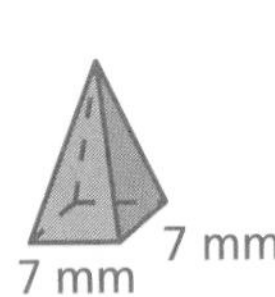

13.

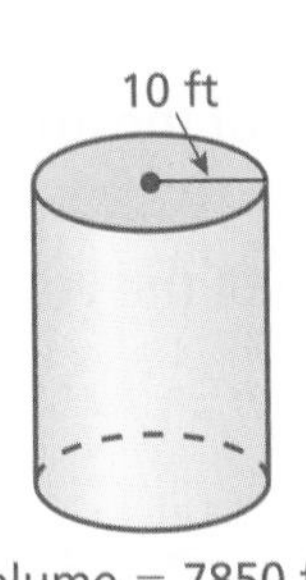

Volume = 7850 ft^3

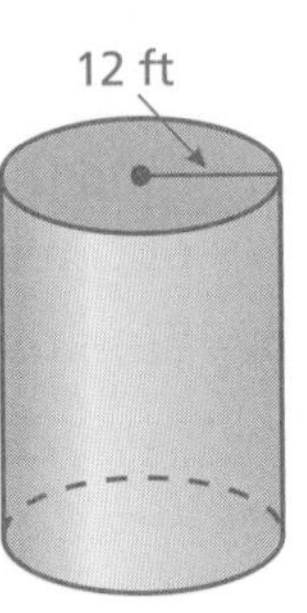

14. **ERROR ANALYSIS** The ratio of the corresponding linear measures of two similar solids is 3 : 5. The volume of the smaller solid is 108 cubic inches. Describe and correct the error in finding the volume of the larger solid.

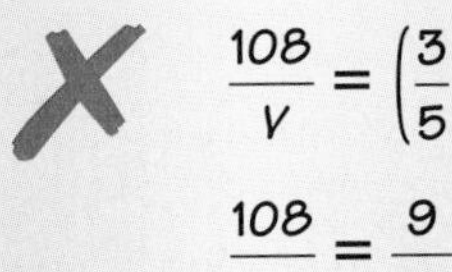

$\frac{108}{V} = \left(\frac{3}{5}\right)^2$
$\frac{108}{V} = \frac{9}{25}$
$300 = V$
The volume of the larger solid is 300 cubic inches.

15. **MIXED FRUIT** The ratio of the corresponding linear measures of two similar cans of fruit is 4 to 7. The smaller can has a surface area of 220 square centimeters. Find the surface area of the larger can.

16. **CLASSIC MUSTANG** The volume of a 1968 Ford Mustang GT engine is 390 cubic inches. Which scale model of the Mustang has the greater engine volume, a 1 : 18 scale model or a 1 : 24 scale model? How much greater?

17. **Critical Thinking** You and a friend make paper cones to collect beach glass. You cut out the largest possible three-fourths circle from each piece of paper.

a. Are the cones similar? Explain your reasoning.

b. Your friend says that because your sheet of paper is twice as large, your cone will hold exactly twice the volume of beach glass. Is this true? Explain your reasoning.

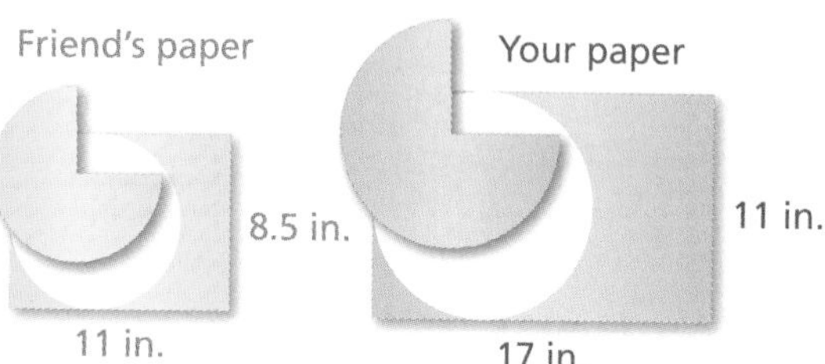

18. **MARBLE STATUE** You have a small marble statue of Wolfgang Mozart that is 10 inches tall and weighs 16 pounds. The original statue in Vienna is 7 feet tall.

a. Estimate the weight of the original statue. Explain your reasoning.

b. If the original statue were 20 feet tall, how much would it weigh?

Wolfgang Mozart

19. **RUSSIAN DOLLS** The largest doll is 7 inches tall. Each of the other dolls is 1 inch shorter than the next larger doll. Make a table that compares the surface areas and volumes of the seven dolls.

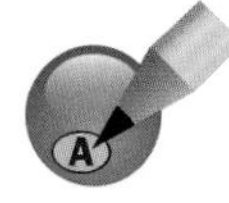

Fair Game Review What you learned in previous grades & lessons

Add. *(Skills Review Handbook)*

20. $69 + (-31) + 7 + (-6)$

21. $-2 + (-5) + (-12) + 20$

22. $10 + (-6) + (-5) + 1$

23. **MULTIPLE CHOICE** What is the mean of the numbers below? *(Skills Review Handbook)*

14, 6, 21, 8, 14, 19, 30

Ⓐ 6 Ⓑ 15 Ⓒ 16 Ⓓ 56

7.5–7.6 Quiz

1. Determine whether the solids are similar. *(Section 7.6)*

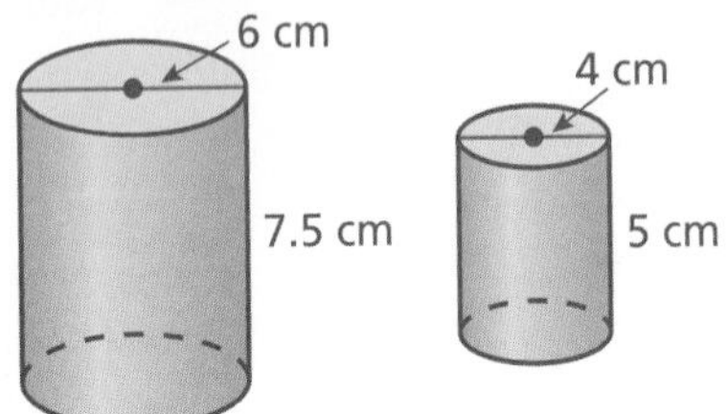

2. The prisms are similar. Find the missing width and height. *(Section 7.6)*

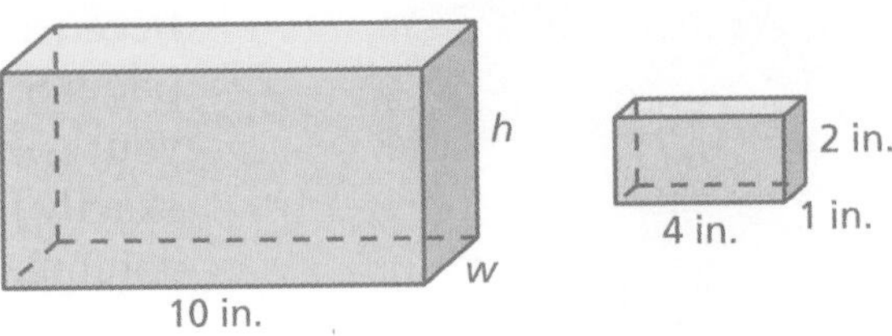

Find the volume of the composite solid. Round your answer to the nearest tenth. *(Section 7.5)*

3. 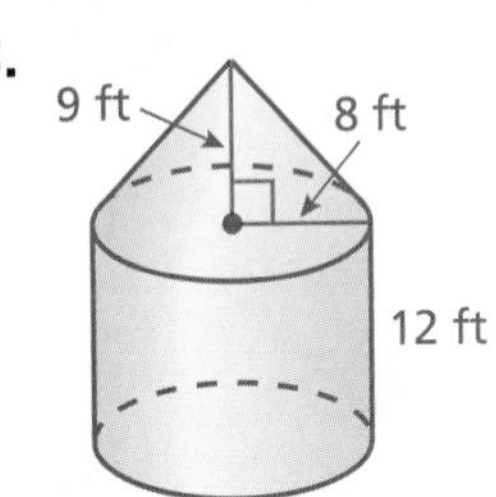

4. 2 mm 2 mm 4 mm 4.5 mm 4.5 mm

5. The solids are similar. Find the surface area of the red solid. *(Section 7.6)*

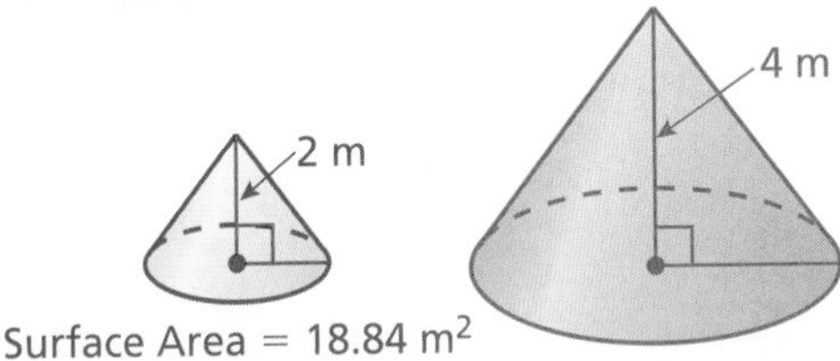

6. **ARCADE** You win a token after playing an arcade game. What is the volume of the gold ring? Round your answer to the nearest tenth. *(Section 7.5)*

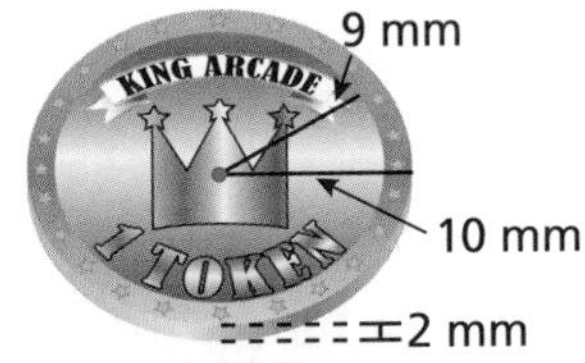

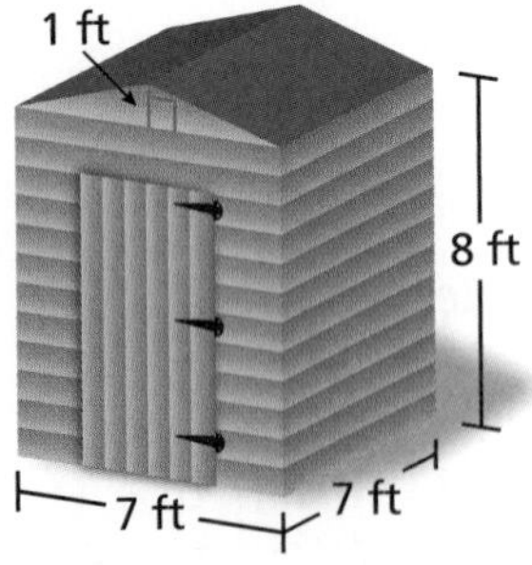

7. **SHED** What is the volume of the storage shed? *(Section 7.5)*

8. **JEWELRY BOXES** The ratio of the corresponding linear measures of two similar jewelry boxes is 2 to 3. The larger box has a volume of 162 cubic inches. Find the volume of the smaller jewelry box. *(Section 7.6)*

9. **GELATIN** You make a dessert with lemon gelatin and lime gelatin. What percent of the dessert is lime-flavored? Explain. *(Section 7.5)*

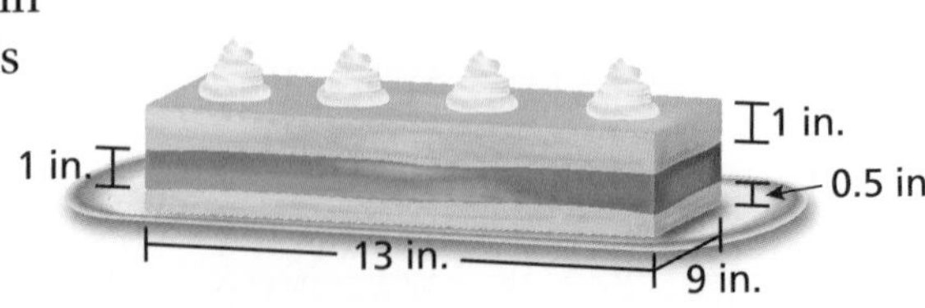

7 Chapter Review

Review Key Vocabulary

volume, *p. 308*

similar solids, *p. 340*

Review Examples and Exercises

7.1 Volumes of Prisms *(pp. 306–311)*

Find the volume of the prism.

$V = Bh$ Write formula for volume.

$= \frac{1}{2}(7)(3) \cdot 5$ Substitute.

$= 52.5$ Multiply.

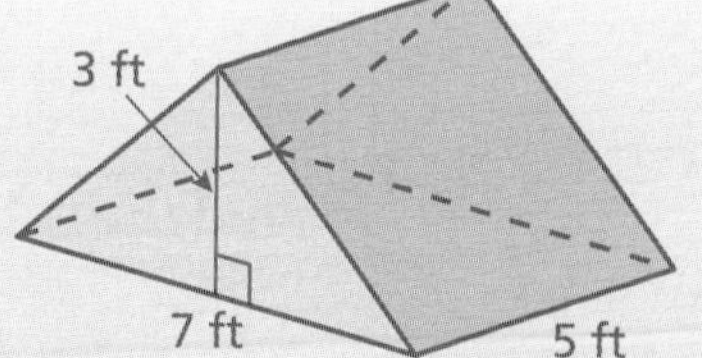

The volume is 52.5 cubic feet.

Exercises

Find the volume of the prism.

1. 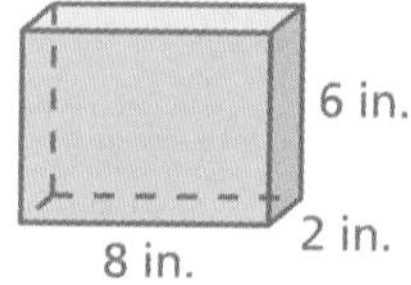

2. 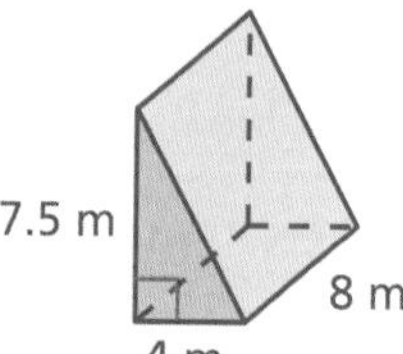

3. 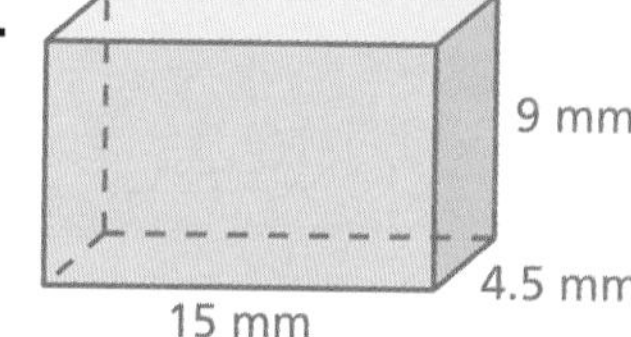

7.2 Volumes of Cylinders *(pp. 312–317)*

Find the height of the cylinder. Round your answer to the nearest whole number.

$V = Bh$ Write formula for volume.

$565 = \pi(6)^2(h)$ Substitute.

$565 = 36\pi h$ Simplify.

$5 \approx h$ Divide each side by 36π.

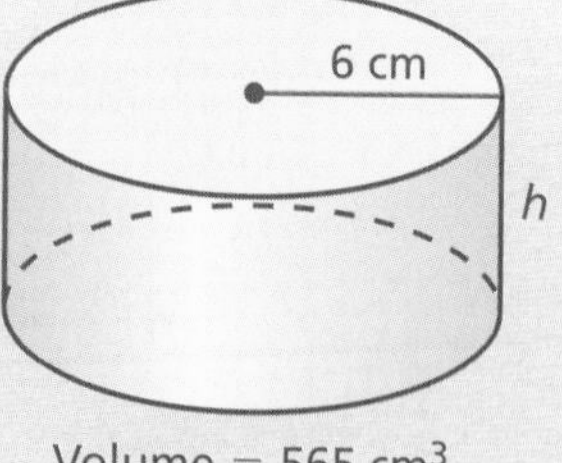

The height is about 5 centimeters.

Exercises

Find the volume V or height h of the cylinder. Round your answer to the nearest tenth.

4. 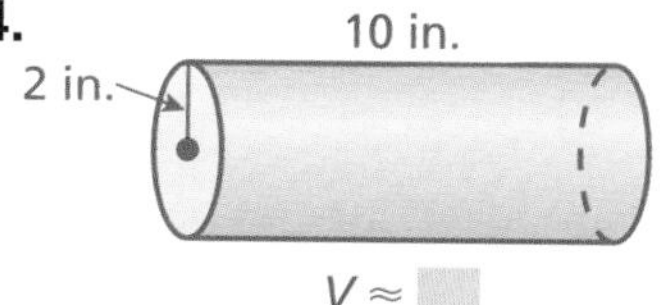

5. 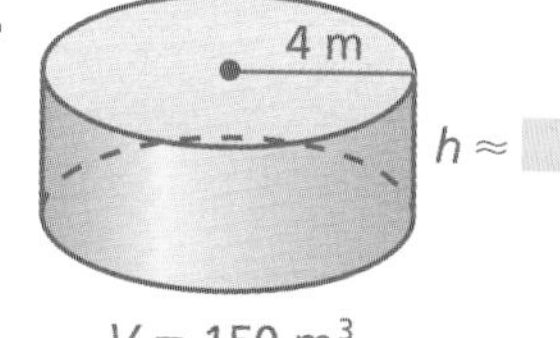

6. 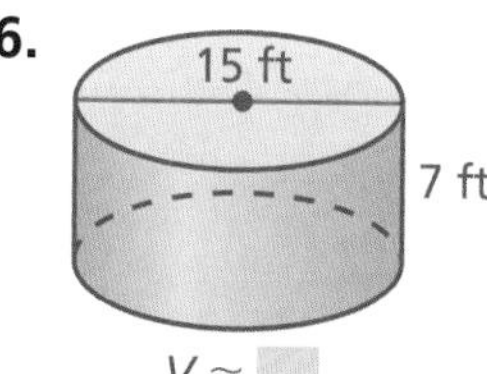

7.3 Volumes of Pyramids (pp. 318–323)

Find the volume of the pyramid.

$V = \frac{1}{3}Bh$ Write formula for volume.

$= \frac{1}{3}(6)(5)(10)$ Substitute.

$= 100$ Multiply.

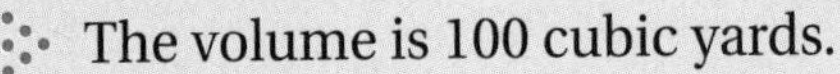
The volume is 100 cubic yards.

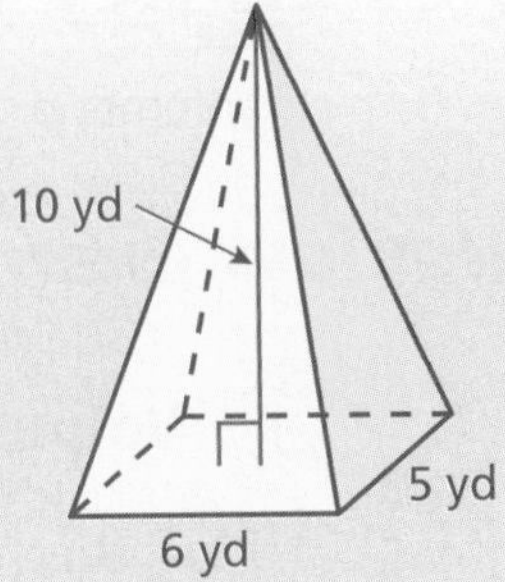

Exercises

Find the volume of the pyramid.

7.

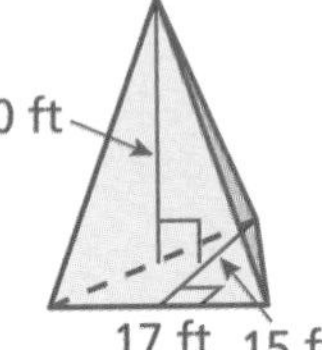

8.

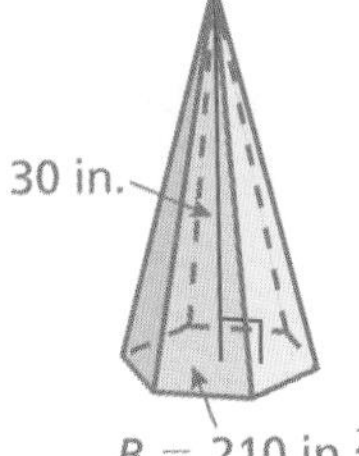

9.

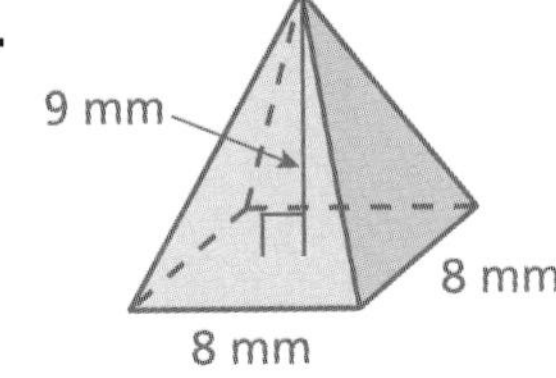

7.4 Volumes of Cones (pp. 324–329)

Find the height of the cone. Round your answer to the nearest tenth.

$V = \frac{1}{3}Bh$ Write formula for volume.

$900 = \frac{1}{3}\pi(6)^2(h)$ Substitute.

$900 = 12\pi h$ Simplify.

$23.9 \approx h$ Divide each side by 12π.

The height is about 23.9 millimeters.

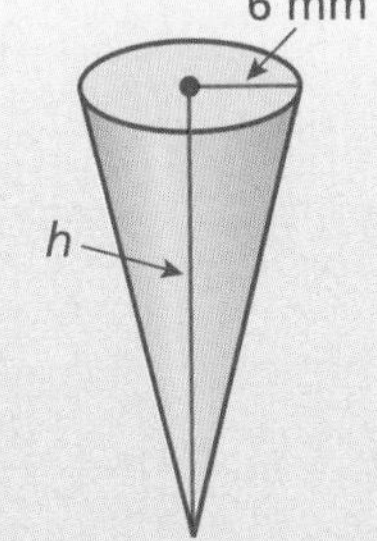

Exercises

Find the volume *V* or height *h* of the cone. Round your answer to the nearest tenth.

10.

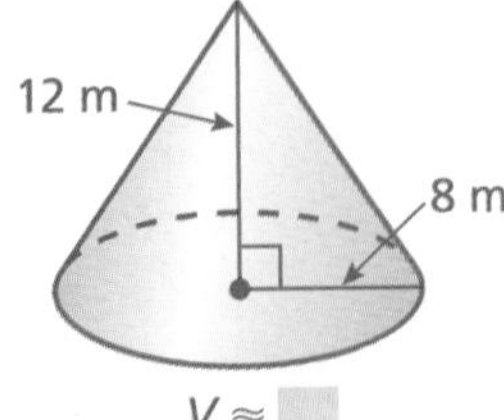

11.

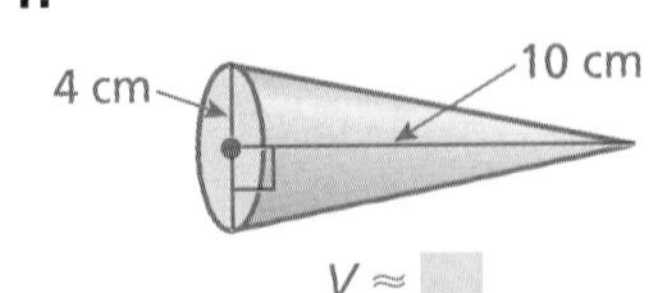

12.

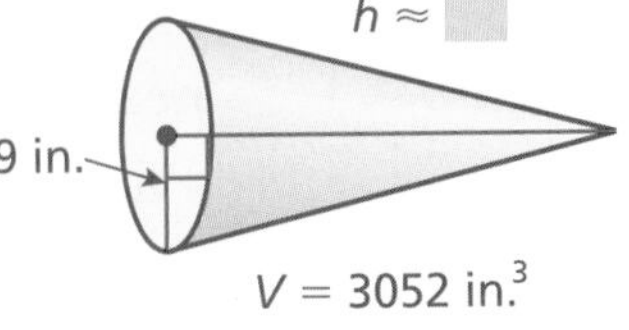

7.5 Volumes of Composite Solids (pp. 332–337)

Find the volume of the composite solid. Round your answer to the nearest tenth.

Square Prism

$V = Bh$

$= (12)(12)(9)$

$= 1296$

Cylinder

$V = Bh$

$= \pi(5)^2(9)$

$= 225\pi \approx 706.5$

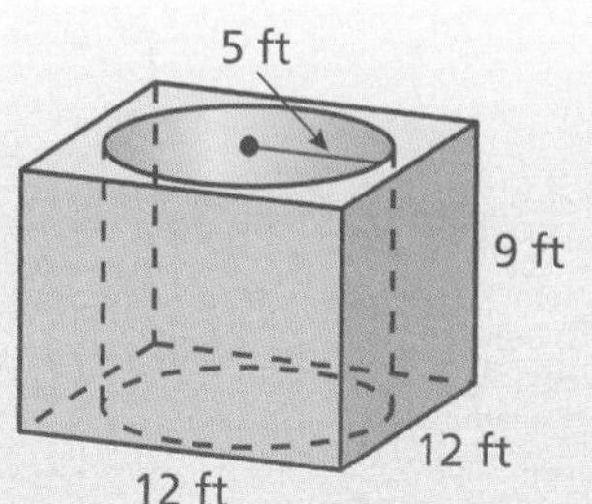

Find the difference: $1296 - 706.5 = 589.5$.

∴ The volume of the composite solid is about 589.5 cubic feet.

Exercises

Find the volume of the composite solid. Round your answer to the nearest tenth.

13.

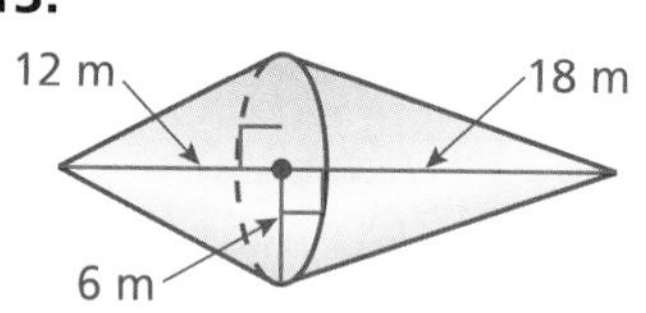

14.

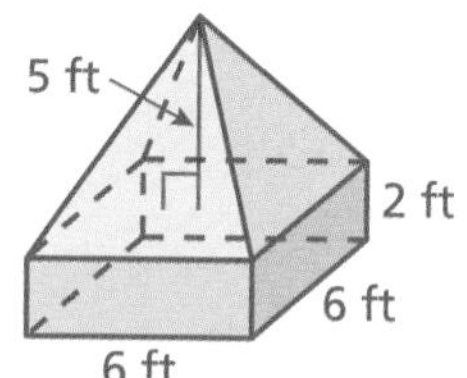

15.

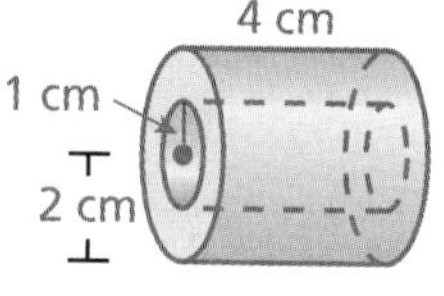

7.6 Surface Areas and Volumes of Similar Solids (pp. 338–345)

The cones are similar. What is the volume of the red cone? Round your answer to the nearest tenth.

$$\frac{\text{Volume of A}}{\text{Volume of B}} = \left(\frac{\text{Height of A}}{\text{Height of B}}\right)^3$$

$\frac{V}{157} = \left(\frac{4}{6}\right)^3$ Substitute.

$\frac{V}{157} = \frac{64}{216}$ Evaluate power.

$V \approx 46.5$ Multiply each side by 157.

Cone A

4 in.

Cone B

6 in.

Volume = 157 in.^{3}

∴ The volume is about 46.5 cubic inches.

Exercises

The solids are similar. Find the surface area *S* or volume *V* of the red solid.

16.

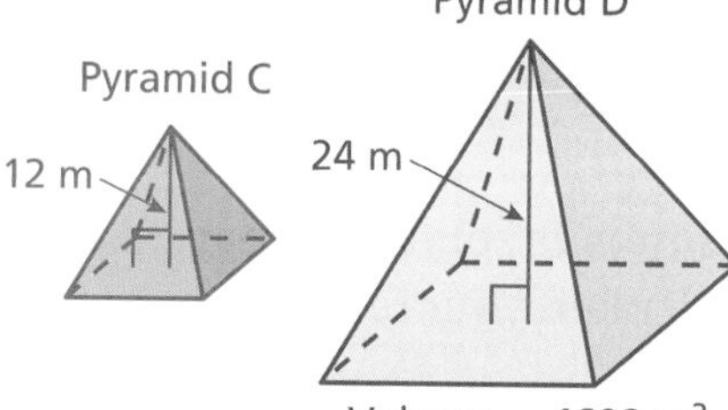

17.

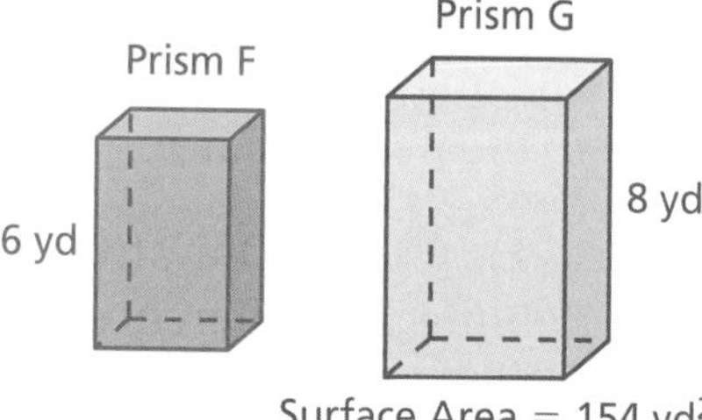

7 Chapter Test

Find the volume of the solid. Round your answer to the nearest tenth.

1.

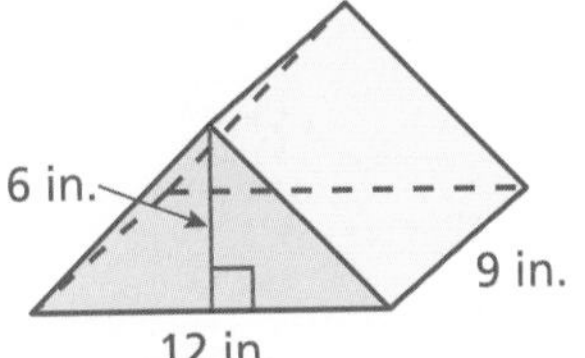

2.

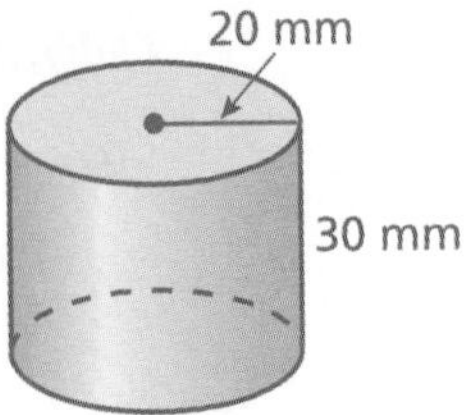

3.

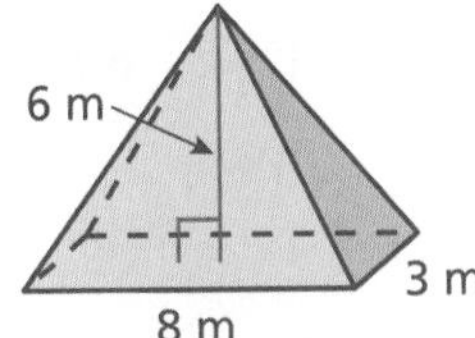

4.

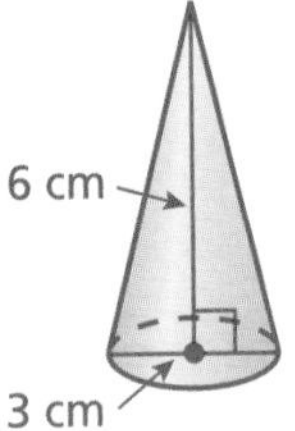

5.

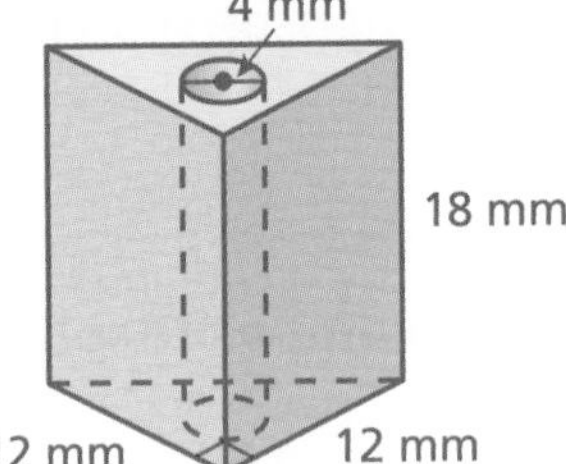

6.

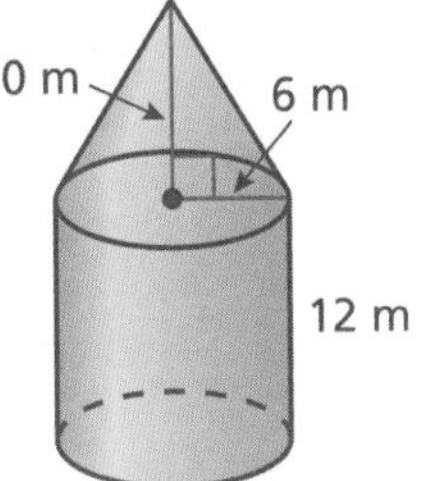

7. The pyramids are similar.

a. Find the missing dimension.

b. Find the surface area of the red pyramid.

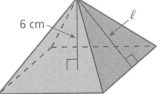

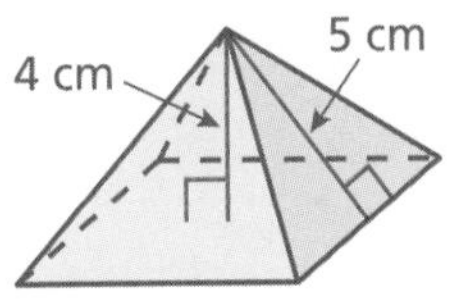

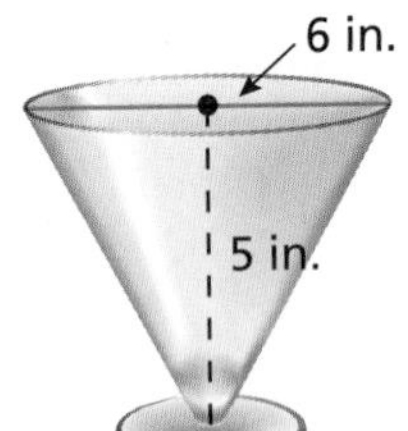

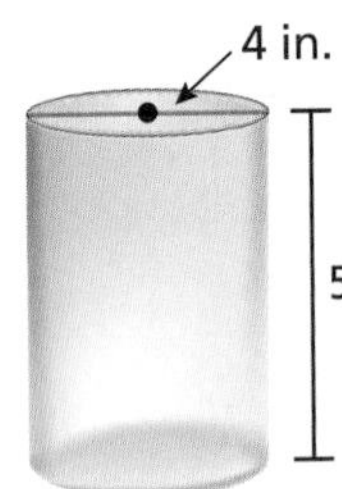

8. SMOOTHIES You are making smoothies. You will use either the cone-shaped glass or the cylindrical glass. Which glass holds more? About how much more?

9. CAPACITY A baseball team uses a heated tub to treat injuries. What is the capacity of the tub in liters? $(1\text{ L} = 1000\text{ cm}^3)$

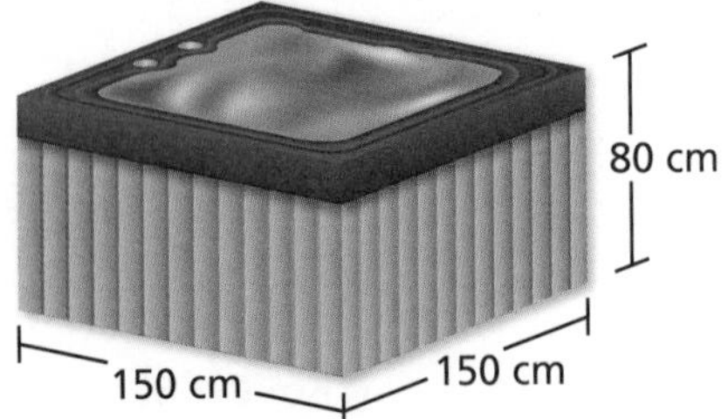

10. WAFFLE CONES The ratio of the corresponding linear measures of two similar waffle cones is 3 to 4. The smaller cone has a volume of about 18 cubic inches. Find the volume of the larger cone. Round your answer to the nearest tenth.

11. OPEN-ENDED Draw two different composite solids that have the same volume, but different surface areas. Explain your reasoning.

7 Standardized Test Practice

1. What is the value of x?

$$5(x - 4) = 3x$$

A. -10

B. 2

C. $2\frac{1}{2}$

D. 10

2. A right circular cone and its dimensions are shown below.

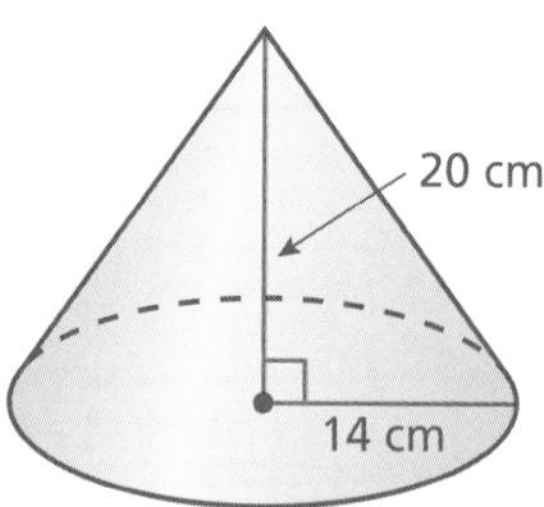

What is the volume of the right circular cone? $\left(\text{Use } \frac{22}{7} \text{ for } \pi.\right)$

F. $1{,}026\frac{2}{3}$ cm^3

G. $3{,}080$ cm^3

H. $4{,}106\frac{2}{3}$ cm^3

I. $12{,}320$ cm^3

3. A right triangular prism and its dimensions are shown below.

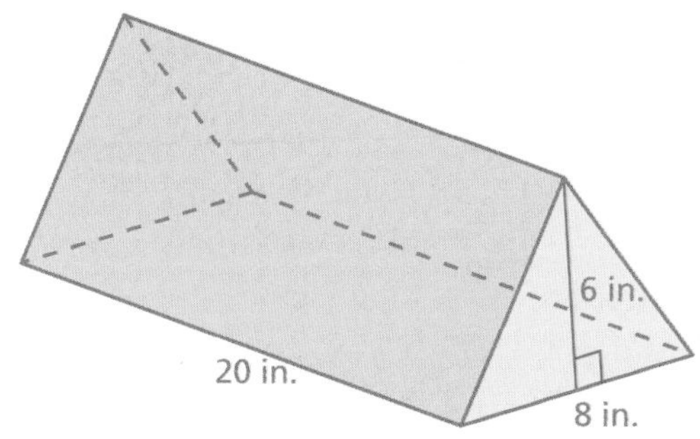

What is the volume of the right triangular prism?

4. A tropical storm has maximum sustained surface winds of at least 39 miles per hour but less than 74 miles per hour. Which graph correctly represents the possible wind speeds of a tropical storm?

A.
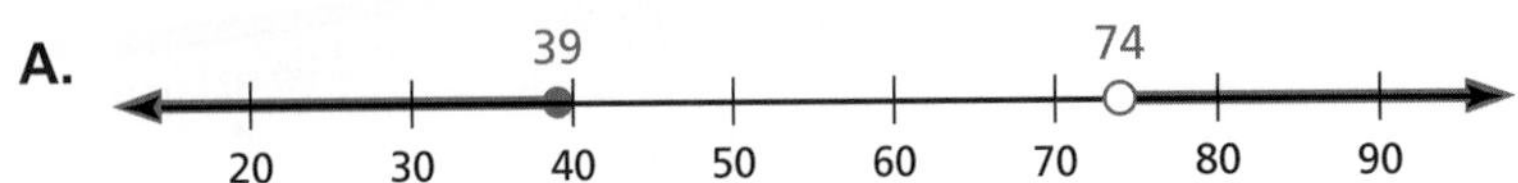

B.
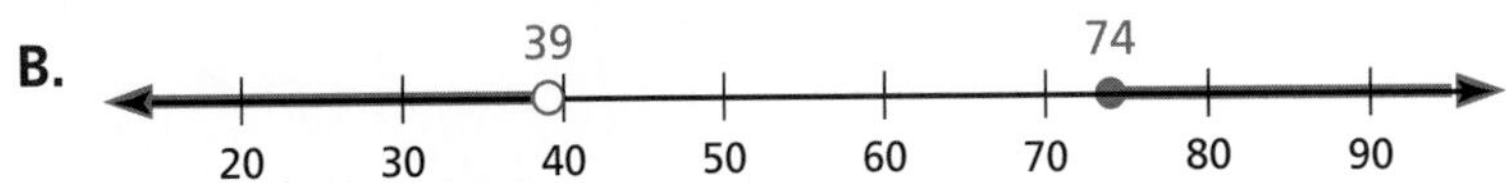

C.
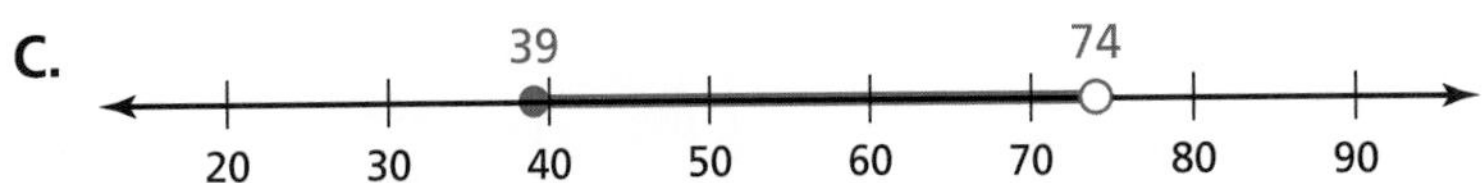

D.
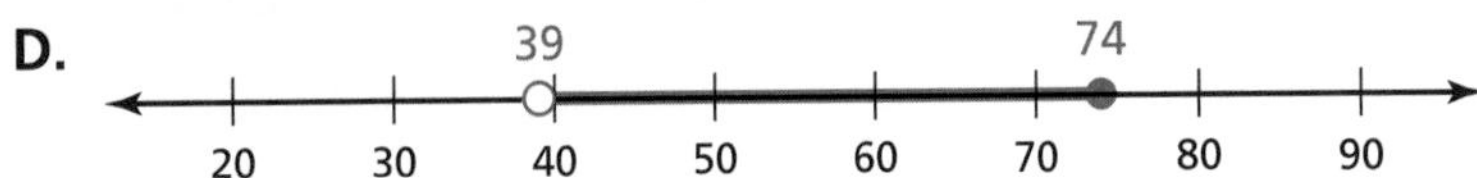

5. Use the coordinate plane to answer the question below.

Which point does *not* lie on the same line as the other three?

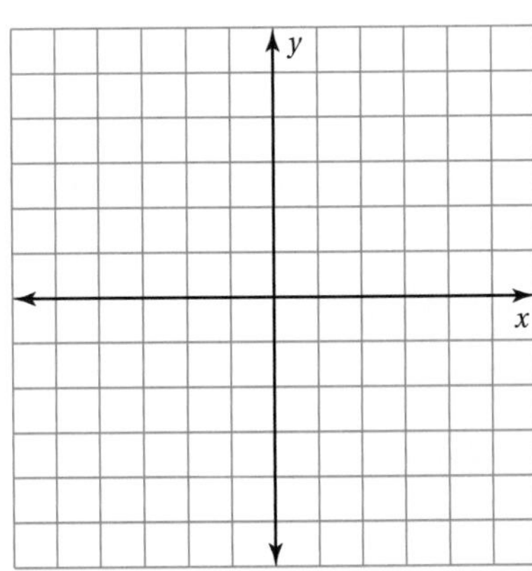

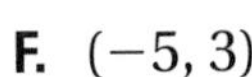

F. $(-5, 3)$ H. $(-1, -1)$

G. $(-3, 2)$ I. $(1, -4)$

6. Olga was solving an equation in the box shown.

What should Olga do to correct the error that she made?

$$-\frac{2}{5}(10x - 15) = -30$$
$$10x - 15 = -30\left(-\frac{2}{5}\right)$$
$$10x - 15 = 12$$
$$10x - 15 + 15 = 12 + 15$$
$$10x = 27$$
$$\frac{10x}{10} = \frac{27}{10}$$
$$x = \frac{27}{10}$$

A. Multiply both sides by $-\frac{5}{2}$ instead of $-\frac{2}{5}$.

B. Multiply both sides by $\frac{2}{5}$ instead of $-\frac{2}{5}$.

C. Distribute $-\frac{2}{5}$ to get $-4x - 6$.

D. Add 15 to -30.

7. It has been raining at a rate of 0.08 inch per hour. At this rate, how much rain will fall in $2\frac{1}{2}$ hours?

F. 0.032 in.

G. 0.2 in.

H. 0.3125 in.

I. 0.33 in.

8. A right circular cylinder has a volume of 1296 cubic inches. If the radius of the cylinder is divided by 12, what would be the volume, in cubic inches, of the smaller cylinder?

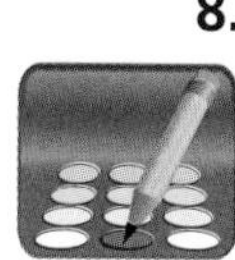

9. If 9 friends share equally a large box of baseball cards, each friend gets 240 cards. If 6 friends share equally the same box of cards, how many cards does each friend get?

A. 80

B. 160

C. 360

D. 400

10. All students in a class were surveyed to find out their preferences for writing instruments. The survey found that 12 students prefer to write with a pencil and 20 students prefer to write with a pen. What percent of students in the class prefer to write with a pencil?

F. 12%

G. 37.5%

H. 60%

I. 62.5%

11. The figure below is a diagram for making a tin lantern.

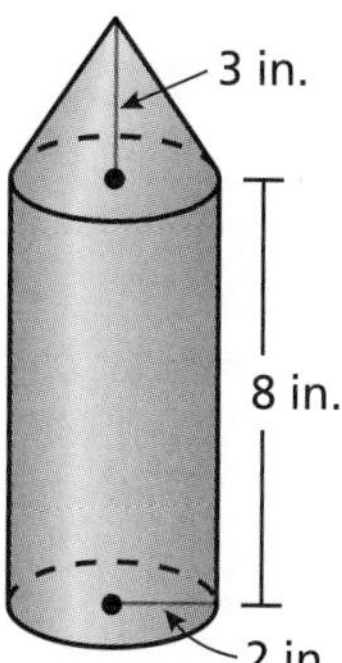

The figure consists of a right circular cylinder without its top base and a right circular cone without its base. What is the volume, in cubic inches, of the entire lantern? Show your work and explain your reasoning. (Use 3.14 for π.)

8 Square Roots and the Pythagorean Theorem

"I'm pretty sure that Pythagoras was a Greek."

"I said 'Greek', not 'Geek'."

"Leonardo da Vinci claimed that the human face is made up of golden ratios."

"Let's see if the same is true of a cat's face."

What You Learned Before

Can't I just use a calculator?

"Here's how I remember the square root of 2. February is the 2nd month. It has 28 days. Split 28 into 14 and 14. Move the decimal to get 1.414."

Comparing Decimals

Complete the number sentence with <, >, or =.

Example 1 **1.1 ☐ 1.01**

Because $\frac{110}{100}$ is greater than $\frac{101}{100}$, 1.1 is greater than 1.01.

So, $1.1 > 1.01$.

Example 2 **−0.3 ☐ −0.003**

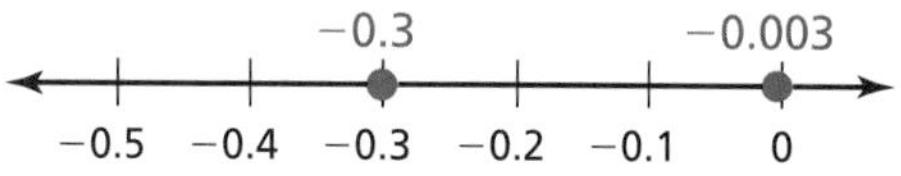

Because −0.3 is to the left of −0.003, $-0.3 < -0.003$.

Example 3 **Find three decimals that make the number sentence $-5.12 >$ ☐ true.**

Any decimal less than −5.12 will make the sentence true.

Sample answer: −10.1, −9.05, −8.25

Try It Yourself

Complete the number sentence with <, >, or =.

1. 2.10 ☐ 2.1 **2.** −4.5 ☐ −4.25 **3.** π ☐ 3.2

Find three decimals that make the number sentence true.

4. $-0.01 \leq$ ☐ **5.** $1.75 >$ ☐ **6.** $0.75 \geq$ ☐

Using Order of Operations

Example 4 **Evaluate $8^2 \div (32 \div 2) + 2(3 - 5)$.**

$8^2 \div (32 \div 2) + 2(3 - 5)$	$= 8^2 \div 16 + 2(-2)$	Perform operations in parentheses.
	$= 64 \div 16 + 2(-2)$	Evaluate the power.
	$= 4 + (-4)$	Multiply and divide from left to right.
	$= 0$	Add.

Try It Yourself

Evaluate the expression.

7. $15\left(\frac{12}{3}\right) - 7^2 - 2 \cdot 7$ **8.** $3^2 \cdot 4 \div 18 + 30 \cdot 6 - 1$ **9.** $-1 + \left(\frac{4}{2}(6 - 1)\right)^2$

8.1 Finding Square Roots

STANDARDS OF LEARNING
8.5

Essential Question How can you find the dimensions of a square or circle when you are given its area?

1 ACTIVITY: Finding Square Roots

Work with a partner. Use a square root symbol to write the side length of the square. Then find the square root. Check your answer by multiplying.

a. Sample: $s = \sqrt{144} = 12$ ft

Area = 144 ft^2

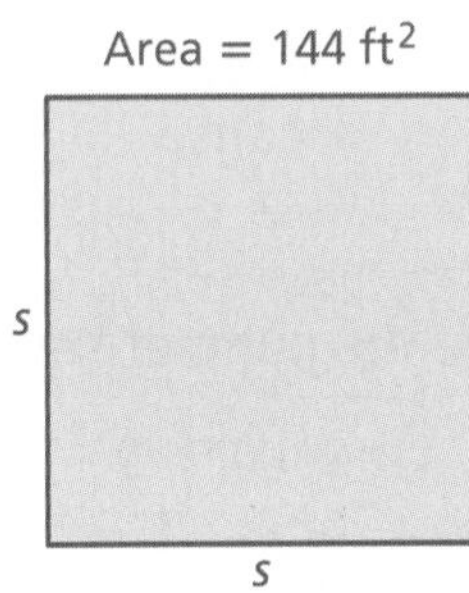

Check

$$\begin{array}{r} 12 \\ \times\ 12 \\ \hline 24 \\ 120 \\ \hline 144 \end{array}$$ ✓

The side length of the square is 12 feet.

b. Area = 225 mi^2

c. Area = 2.89 in.^{2}

d. Area = $\frac{4}{9}$ ft^2

2 ACTIVITY: Using Square Roots

Work with a partner. Find the radius of each circle.

a.

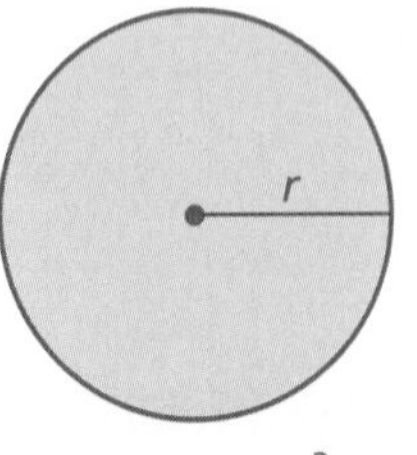

$A = 36\pi$ in.^{2}

b.

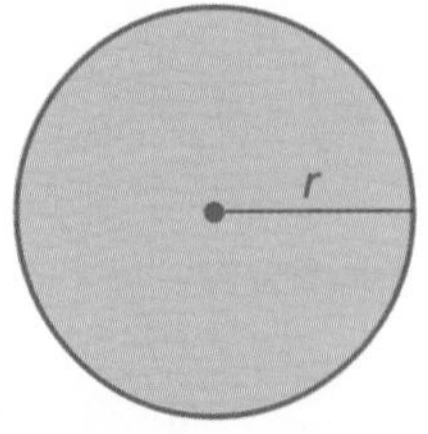

$A = 81\pi$ yd^2

c.

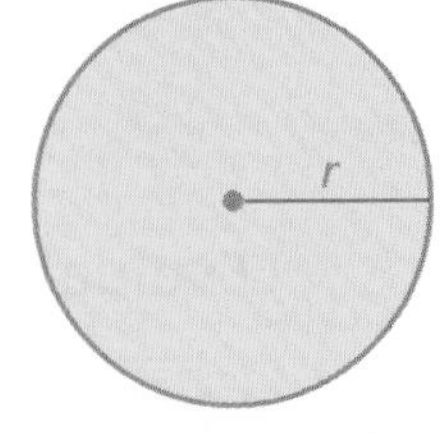

$A = 0.25\pi$ ft^2

3 ACTIVITY: The Period of a Pendulum

Work with a partner.

The period of a pendulum is the time (in seconds) it takes the pendulum to swing back *and* forth.

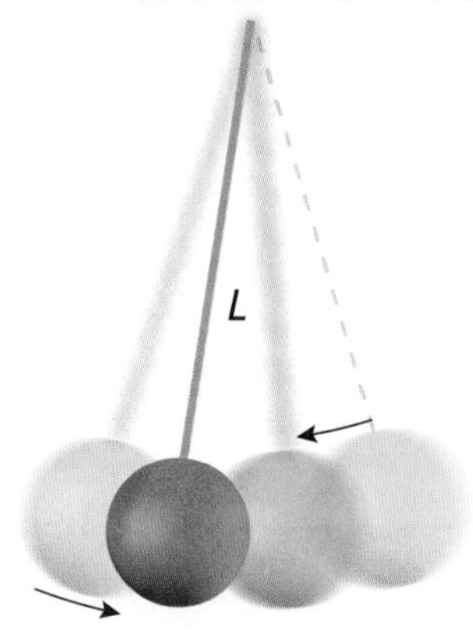

The period T is represented by $T = 1.1\sqrt{L}$, where L is the length of the pendulum (in feet).

Copy and complete the table. Then graph the function. Is the function linear?

L	1.00	1.96	3.24	4.00	4.84	6.25	7.29	7.84	9.00
T									

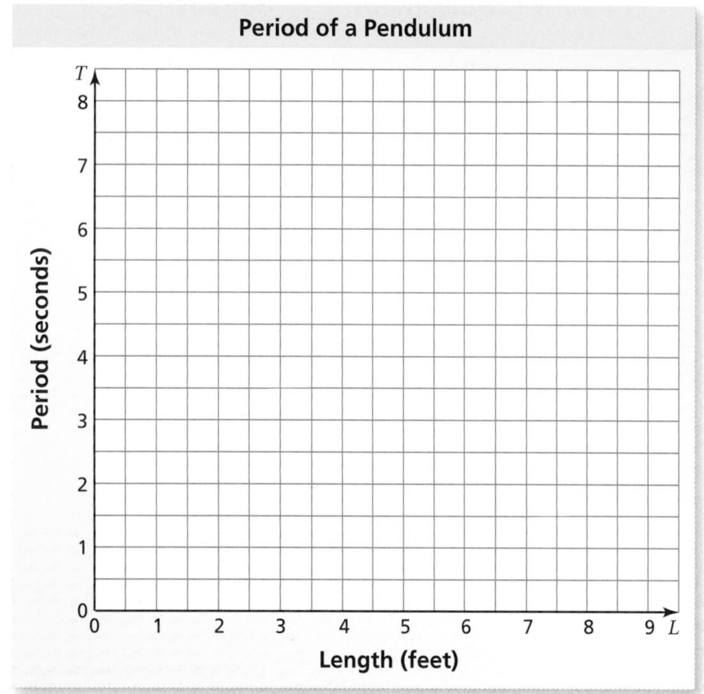

What Is Your Answer?

4. **IN YOUR OWN WORDS** How can you find the dimensions of a square or circle when you are given its area? Give an example of each. How can you check your answers?

Practice Use what you learned about finding square roots to complete Exercises 4–6 on page 360.

8.1 Lesson

Key Vocabulary
square root, *p. 358*
perfect square, *p. 358*
radical sign, *p. 358*
radicand, *p. 358*

A **square root** of a number is a number that when multiplied by itself, equals the given number. Every positive number has a positive *and* a negative square root. A **perfect square** is a number with integers as its square roots.

EXAMPLE 1 Finding Square Roots of a Perfect Square

Study Tip

Zero has one square root, which is 0.

Find the two square roots of 49.

$7 \cdot 7 = 49$ and $(-7) \cdot (-7) = 49$

So, the square roots of 49 are 7 and −7.

The symbol $\sqrt{}$ is called a **radical sign**. It is used to represent a square root. The number under the radical sign is called the **radicand**.

Positive Square Root $\sqrt{}$	Negative Square Root $-\sqrt{}$	Both Square Roots $\pm\sqrt{}$
$\sqrt{16} = 4$	$-\sqrt{16} = -4$	$\pm\sqrt{16} = \pm 4$

EXAMPLE 2 Finding Square Roots

Find the square root(s).

a. $\sqrt{25}$

$\sqrt{25}$ represents the *positive* square root.

Because $5^2 = 25$, $\sqrt{25} = \sqrt{5^2} = 5$.

b. $-\sqrt{\frac{9}{16}}$

$-\sqrt{\frac{9}{16}}$ represents the *negative* square root.

Because $\left(\frac{3}{4}\right)^2 = \frac{9}{16}$, $-\sqrt{\frac{9}{16}} = -\sqrt{\left(\frac{3}{4}\right)^2} = -\frac{3}{4}$.

c. $\pm\sqrt{2.25}$

$\pm\sqrt{2.25}$ represents both the *positive and negative* square roots.

Because $1.5^2 = 2.25$, $\pm\sqrt{2.25} = \pm\sqrt{1.5^2} = 1.5$ and -1.5.

On Your Own

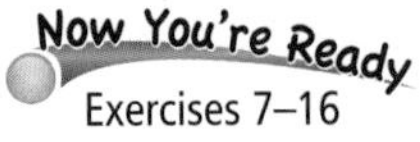

Exercises 7–16

Find the two square roots of the number.

1. 36 **2.** 100 **3.** 121

Find the square root(s).

4. $-\sqrt{1}$ **5.** $\pm\sqrt{\frac{4}{25}}$ **6.** $\sqrt{12.25}$

Multi-Language Glossary at BigIdeasMath.com.

EXAMPLE 3 Evaluating Expressions Involving Square Roots

Evaluate the expression.

a. $5\sqrt{36} + 7$

$$\begin{aligned} 5\sqrt{36} + 7 &= 5(6) + 7 && \text{Evaluate the square root.} \\ &= 30 + 7 && \text{Multiply.} \\ &= 37 && \text{Add.} \end{aligned}$$

b. $\frac{1}{4} + \sqrt{\frac{18}{2}}$

$$\begin{aligned} \frac{1}{4} + \sqrt{\frac{18}{2}} &= \frac{1}{4} + \sqrt{9} && \text{Simplify.} \\ &= \frac{1}{4} + 3 && \text{Evaluate the square root.} \\ &= 3\frac{1}{4} && \text{Add.} \end{aligned}$$

Squaring a positive number and finding a square root are inverse operations. Use this relationship to solve equations involving squares.

EXAMPLE 4 Real-Life Application

The area of a crop circle is 45,216 square feet. What is the radius of the crop circle? Use 3.14 for π.

$$\begin{aligned} A &= \pi r^2 && \text{Write the formula for the area of a circle.} \\ 45{,}216 &\approx 3.14r^2 && \text{Substitute 45,216 for } A \text{ and 3.14 for } \pi. \\ 14{,}400 &= r^2 && \text{Divide each side by 3.14.} \\ \sqrt{14{,}400} &= \sqrt{r^2} && \text{Take positive square root of each side.} \\ 120 &= r && \text{Simplify.} \end{aligned}$$

∴ The radius of the crop circle is about 120 feet.

On Your Own

Now You're Ready
Exercises 18–23

Evaluate the expression.

7. $12 - 3\sqrt{25}$

8. $\sqrt{\frac{28}{7}} + 2.4$

9. $5(\sqrt{49} - 10)$

10. The area of a circle is 2826 square feet. Write and solve an equation to find the radius of the circle. Use 3.14 for π.

8.1 Exercises

Vocabulary and Concept Check

1. **VOCABULARY** Is 26 a perfect square? Explain.
2. **REASONING** Can the square of an integer be a negative number? Explain.
3. **NUMBER SENSE** Does $\sqrt{256}$ represent the positive square root of 256, the negative square root of 256, or both? Explain.

Practice and Problem Solving

Find the dimensions of the square or circle. Check your answer.

4. Area = 441 cm^2

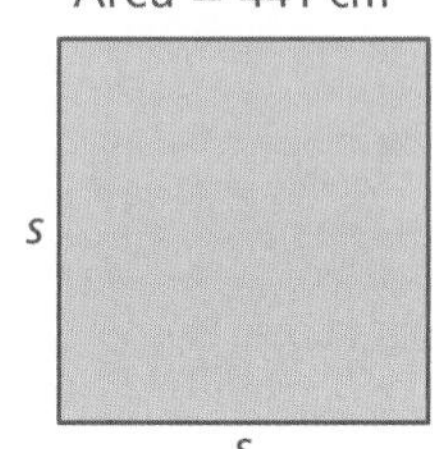

5. Area = 1.69 km^2

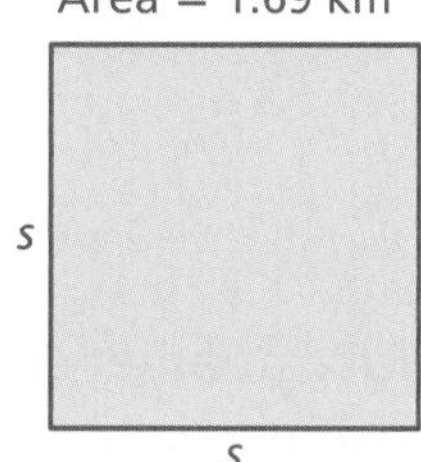

6.

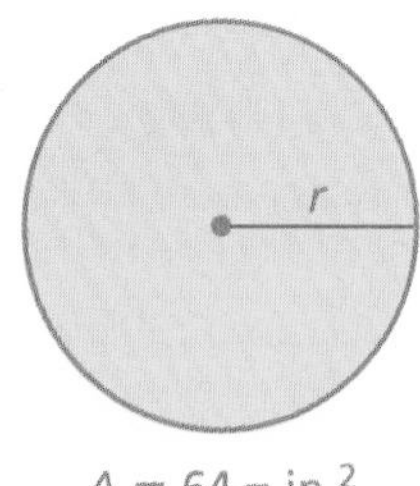

$A = 64\pi$ in.^{2}

Find the two square roots of the number.

1 7. 9 8. 64 9. 4 10. 144

Find the square root(s).

2 11. $\sqrt{625}$ 12. $-\sqrt{\frac{9}{100}}$ 13. $\pm\sqrt{\frac{1}{961}}$

14. $\sqrt{7.29}$ 15. $\pm\sqrt{4.84}$ 16. $-\sqrt{361}$

17. **ERROR ANALYSIS** Describe and correct the error in finding the square roots.

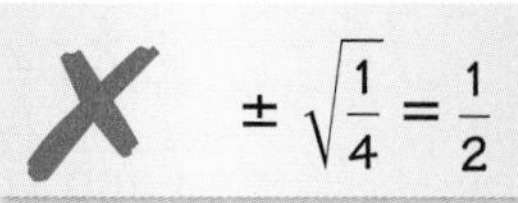

$\pm\sqrt{\frac{1}{4}} = \frac{1}{2}$

Evaluate the expression.

3 18. $3\sqrt{16} - 5$ 19. $10 - 4\sqrt{\frac{1}{16}}$ 20. $\sqrt{6.76} + 5.4$

21. $8\sqrt{8.41} + 1.8$ 22. $2\left(\sqrt{\frac{80}{5}} - 5\right)$ 23. $4\left(\sqrt{\frac{147}{3}} + 3\right)$

24. **NOTEPAD** The area of the base of a square notepad is 9 square inches. What is the length of one side of the base of the notepad?

25. **CRITICAL THINKING** There are two square roots of 25. Why is there only one answer for the radius of the button?

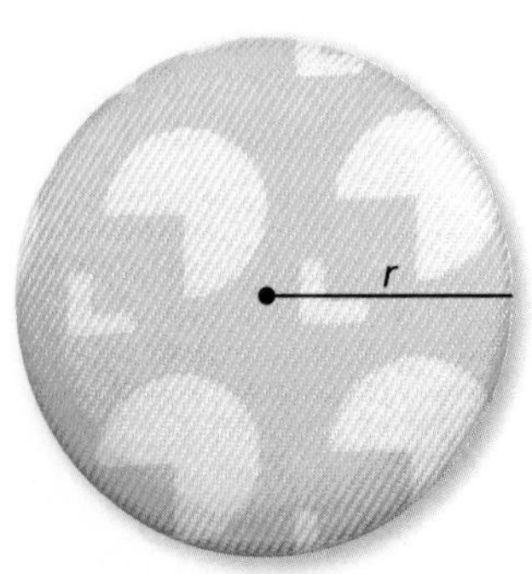

$A = 25\pi$ mm^2

Copy and complete the statement with <, >, or =.

26. $\sqrt{81}$ ▢ 8 **27.** 0.5 ▢ $\sqrt{0.25}$ **28.** $\frac{3}{2}$ ▢ $\sqrt{\frac{25}{4}}$

29. SAILBOAT The area of a sail is $40\frac{1}{2}$ square feet. The base and the height of the sail are equal. What is the height of the sail (in feet)?

30. REASONING Is the product of two perfect squares always a perfect square? Explain your reasoning.

31. ENERGY The kinetic energy K (in joules) of a falling apple is represented by $K = \frac{v^2}{2}$, where v is the speed of the apple (in meters per second). How fast is the apple traveling when the kinetic energy is 32 joules?

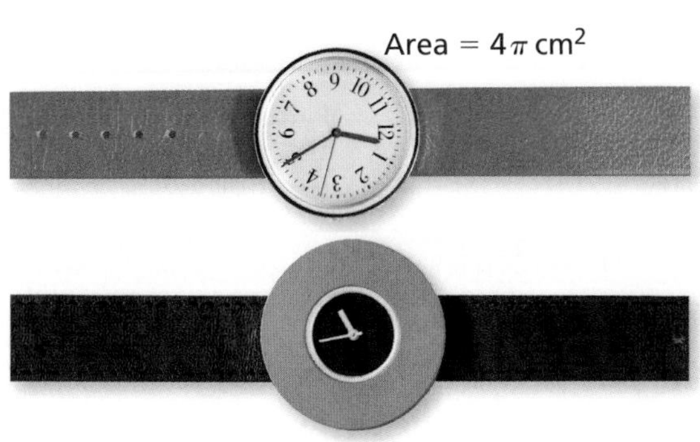

32. WATCHES The areas of the two watch faces have a ratio of 16 : 25.

a. What is the ratio of the radius of the smaller watch face to the radius of the larger watch face?

b. What is the radius of the larger watch face?

33. WINDOW The cost C (in dollars) of making a square window with a side length of n inches is represented by $C = \frac{n^2}{5} + 175$. A window costs \$355. What is the length (in feet) of the window?

34. Geometry The area of the triangle is represented by the formula $A = \sqrt{s(s-21)(s-17)(s-10)}$, where s is equal to half the perimeter. What is the height of the triangle?

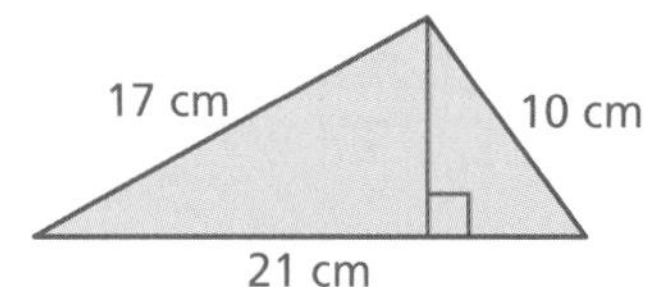

Fair Game Review What you learned in previous grades & lessons

Evaluate the expression. *(Skills Review Handbook)*

35. $3^2 + 4^2$ **36.** $8^2 + 15^2$ **37.** $13^2 - 5^2$ **38.** $25^2 - 24^2$

39. MULTIPLE CHOICE Which of the following describes the triangle? *(Section 5.2)*

Ⓐ Acute Ⓑ Right

Ⓒ Obtuse Ⓓ Equiangular

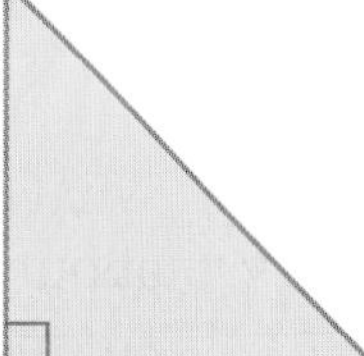

8.2 The Pythagorean Theorem

STANDARDS OF LEARNING
8.10

Essential Question How are the lengths of the sides of a right triangle related?

Pythagoras
(c. 570 B.C.–c. 490 B.C.)

Pythagoras was a Greek mathematician and philosopher who discovered one of the most famous rules in mathematics. In mathematics, a rule is called a **theorem**. So, the rule that Pythagoras discovered is called the Pythagorean Theorem.

1 ACTIVITY: Discovering the Pythagorean Theorem

Work with a partner.

a. On grid paper, draw any right triangle. Label the lengths of the two shorter sides (the **legs**) a and b.

b. Label the length of the longest side (the **hypotenuse**) c.

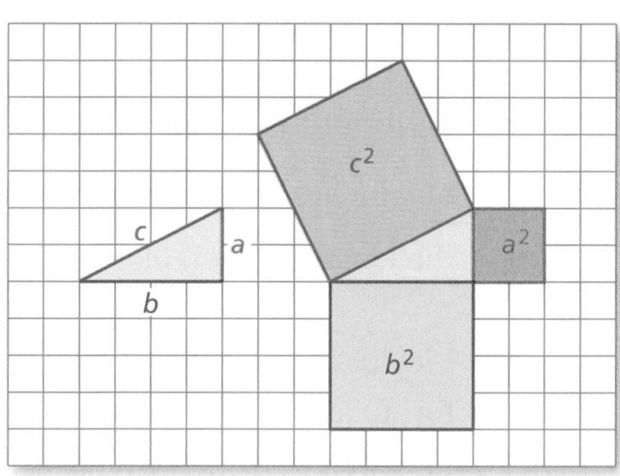

c. Draw squares along each of the three sides. Label the areas of the three squares a^2, b^2, and c^2.

d. Cut out the three squares. Make eight copies of the right triangle and cut them out. Arrange the figures to form two identical larger squares.

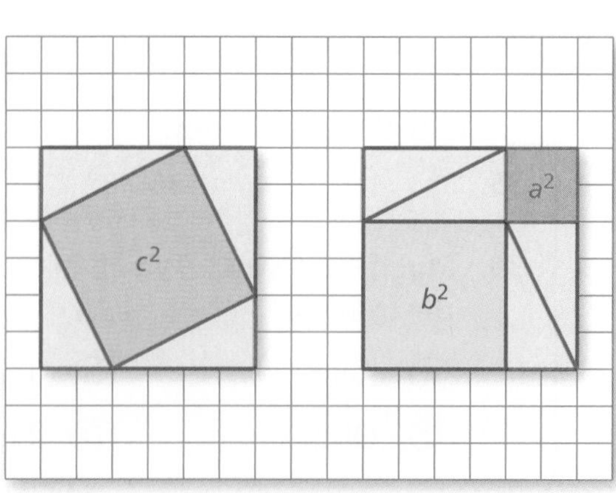

e. What does this tell you about the relationship among a^2, b^2, and c^2?

2 ACTIVITY: Finding the Length of the Hypotenuse

Work with a partner. Use the result of Activity 1 to find the length of the hypotenuse of each right triangle.

a.

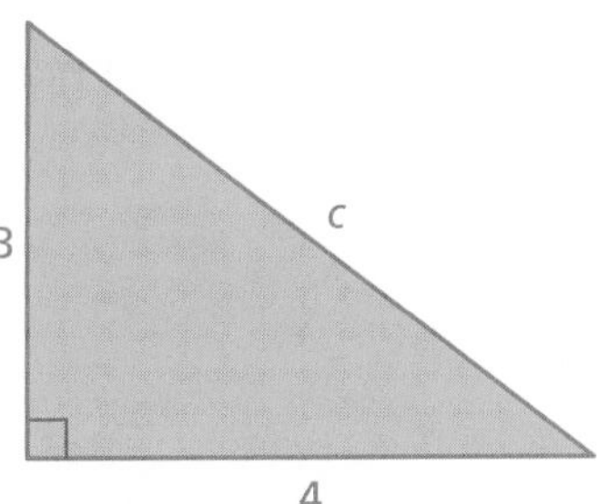

b.

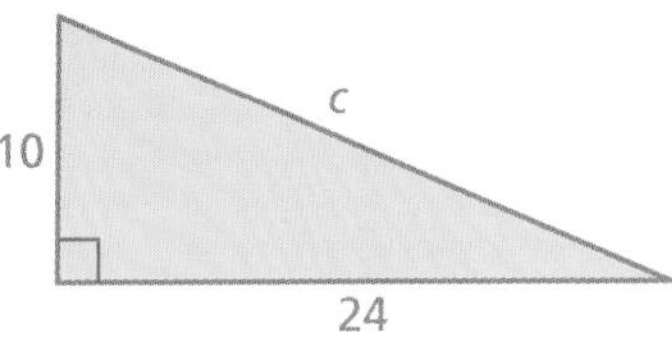

c.

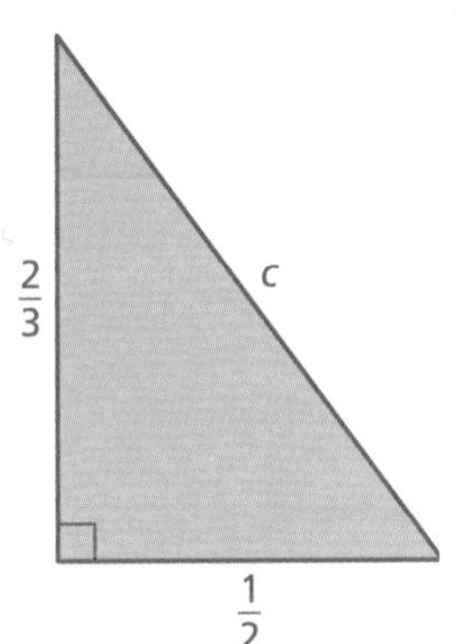

d.

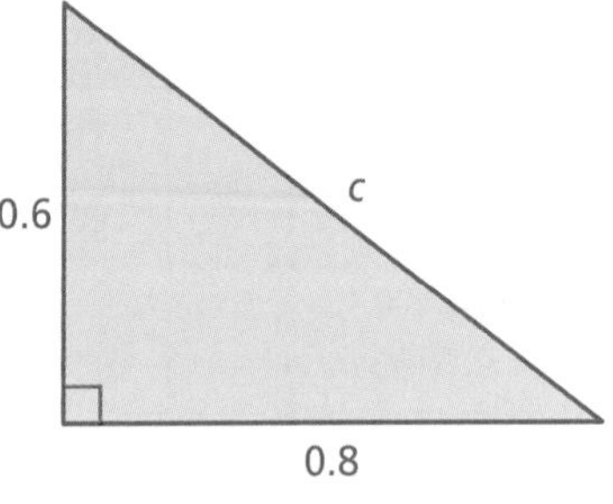

3 ACTIVITY: Finding the Length of a Leg

Work with a partner. Use the result of Activity 1 to find the length of the leg of each right triangle.

a.

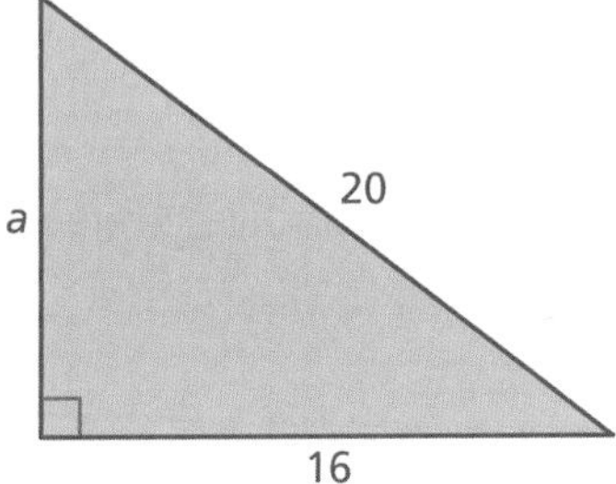

b.

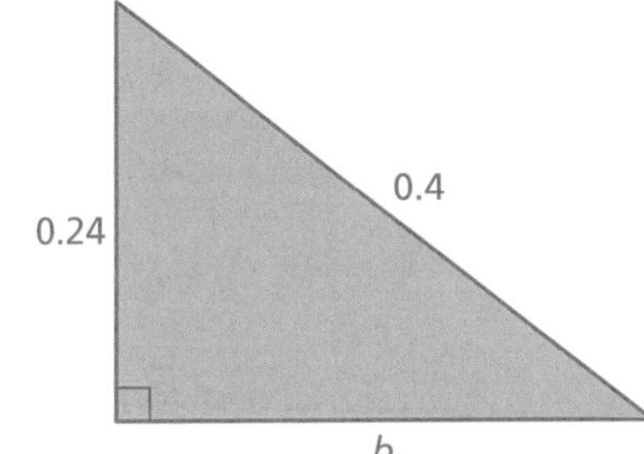

What Is Your Answer?

4. **IN YOUR OWN WORDS** How are the lengths of the sides of a right triangle related? Give an example using whole numbers.

Practice Use what you learned about the Pythagorean Theorem to complete Exercises 3–5 on page 366.

8.2 Lesson

Key Vocabulary
theorem, *p. 362*
legs, *p. 364*
hypotenuse, *p. 364*
Pythagorean Theorem, *p. 364*

Sides of a Right Triangle

The sides of a right triangle have special names.

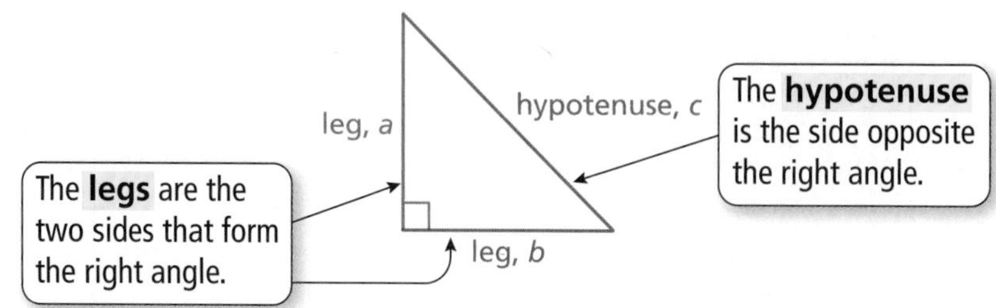

The Pythagorean Theorem

Words In any right triangle, the sum of the squares of the lengths of the legs is equal to the square of the length of the hypotenuse.

Algebra $a^2 + b^2 = c^2$

Study Tip

In a right triangle, the legs are the shorter sides and the hypotenuse is always the longest side.

EXAMPLE 1 Finding the Length of a Hypotenuse

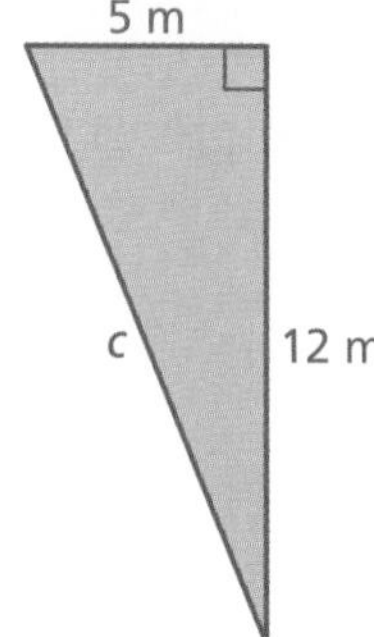

Find the length of the hypotenuse of the triangle.

$a^2 + b^2 = c^2$	Write the Pythagorean Theorem.
$5^2 + 12^2 = c^2$	Substitute 5 for *a* and 12 for *b*.
$25 + 144 = c^2$	Evaluate powers.
$169 = c^2$	Add.
$\sqrt{169} = \sqrt{c^2}$	Take positive square root of each side.
$13 = c$	Simplify.

The length of the hypotenuse is 13 meters.

On Your Own

Find the length of the hypotenuse of the triangle.

1. 2.

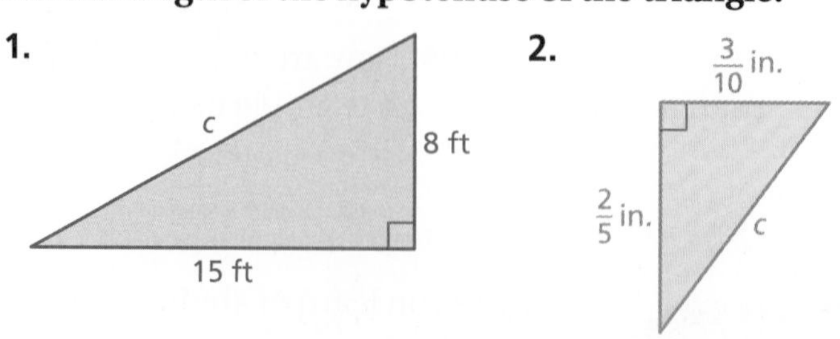

EXAMPLE 2 Finding the Length of a Leg

Find the missing length of the triangle.

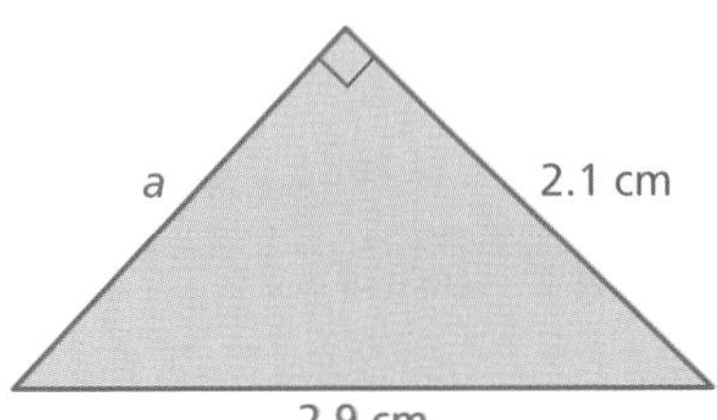

$a^2 + b^2 = c^2$	Write the Pythagorean Theorem.
$a^2 + 2.1^2 = 2.9^2$	Substitute 2.1 for *b* and 2.9 for *c*.
$a^2 + 4.41 = 8.41$	Evaluate powers.
$a^2 = 4$	Subtract 4.41 from each side.
$a = 2$	Take positive square root of each side.

∴ The length of the leg is 2 centimeters.

EXAMPLE 3 Standardized Test Practice

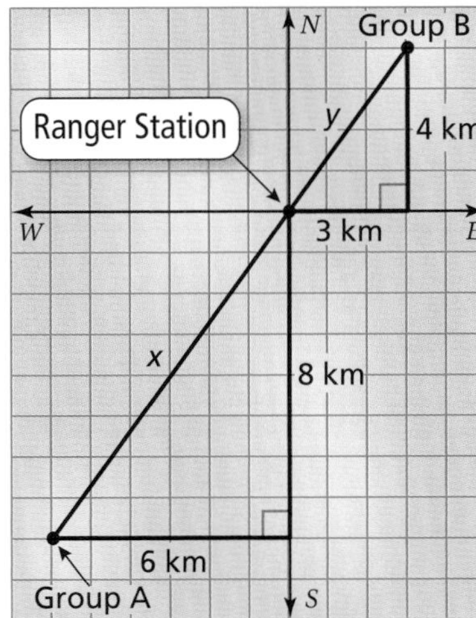

Hiking Group A leaves a ranger station and hikes 8 kilometers south then 6 kilometers west. Group B leaves the station and hikes 3 kilometers east then 4 kilometers north. Using the figure, how far apart are the two groups of hikers?

Ⓐ 5 km Ⓑ 10 km Ⓒ 15 km Ⓓ 21 km

The distance between the groups is the sum of the hypotenuses, *x* and *y*. Use the Pythagorean Theorem to find *x* and *y*.

$a^2 + b^2 = c^2$	Write the Pythagorean Theorem.	$a^2 + b^2 = c^2$
$6^2 + 8^2 = x^2$	Substitute.	$3^2 + 4^2 = y^2$
$36 + 64 = x^2$	Evaluate powers.	$9 + 16 = y^2$
$100 = x^2$	Add.	$25 = y^2$
$10 = x$	Take positive square root of each side.	$5 = y$

∴ The distance between the groups of hikers is $10 + 5 = 15$ kilometers. So, the correct answer is Ⓒ.

On Your Own

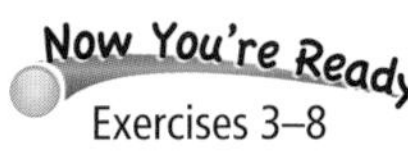

Find the missing length of the triangle.

3.

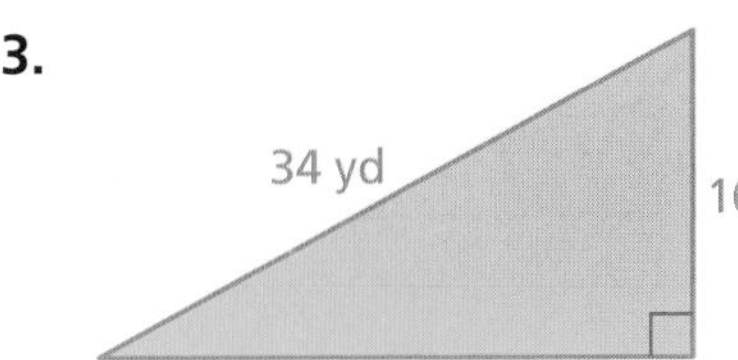

4.

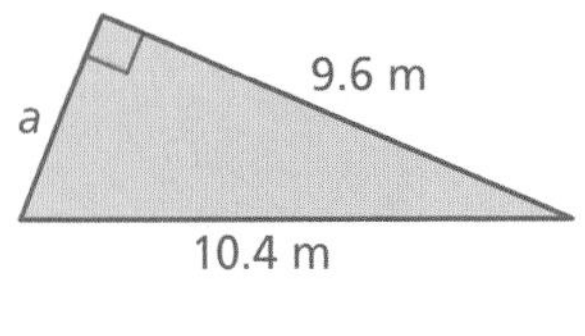

5. **WHAT IF?** In Example 3, Group A hikes 12 kilometers south and 9 kilometers west. How far apart are the hikers?

8.2 Exercises

Vocabulary and Concept Check

1. **VOCABULARY** In a right triangle, how can you tell which sides are the legs and which side is the hypotenuse?

2. **DIFFERENT WORDS, SAME QUESTION** Which is different? Find "both" answers.

Which side is the hypotenuse?

Which side is the longest?

Which side is a leg?

Which side is opposite the right angle?

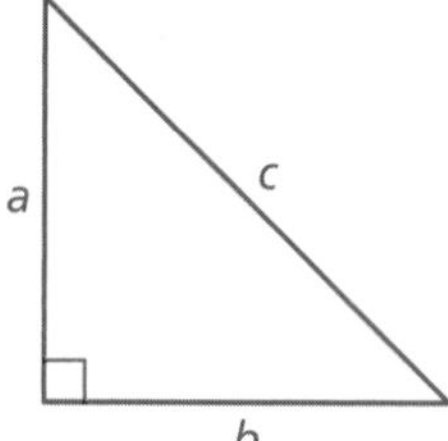

Practice and Problem Solving

Find the missing length of the triangle.

3. 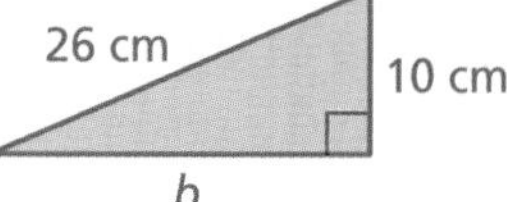

4. 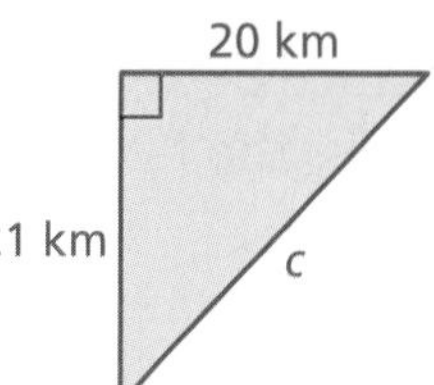

5. 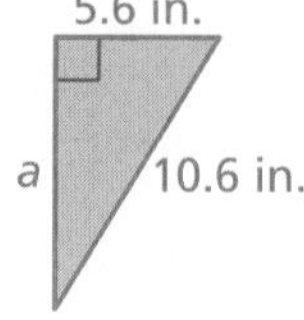

6. 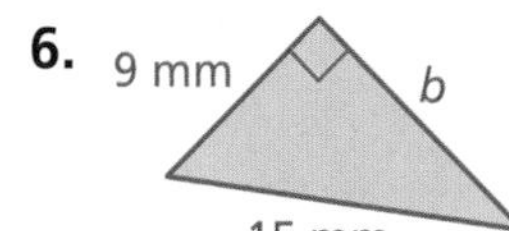

7. 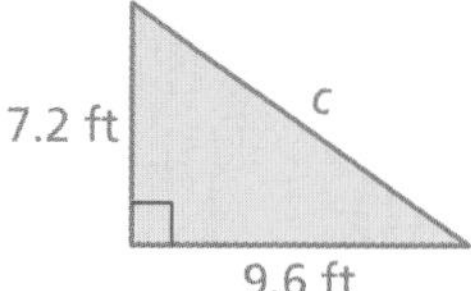

8. 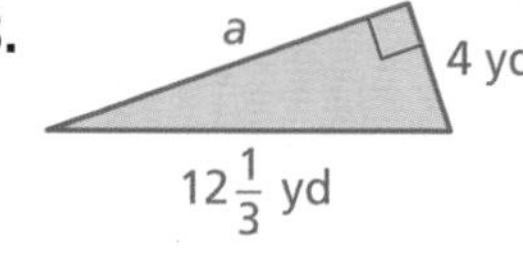

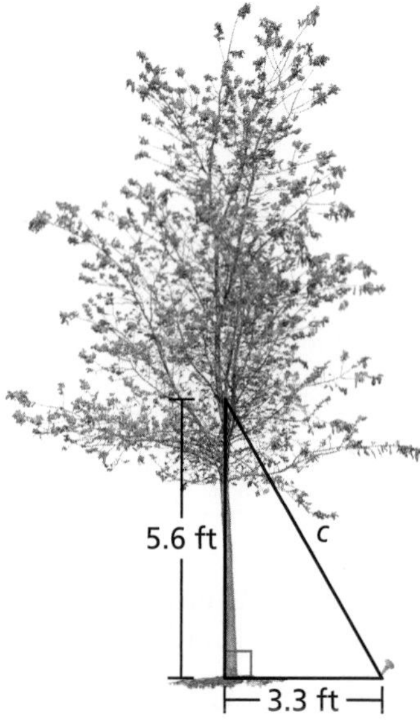

9. **ERROR ANALYSIS** Describe and correct the error in finding the missing length of the triangle.

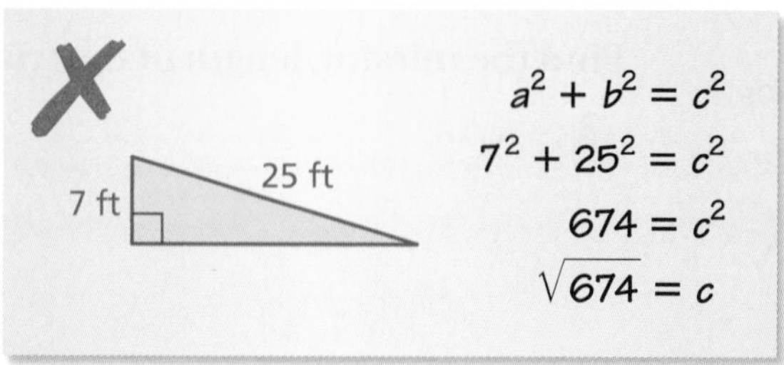

10. **TREE SUPPORT** How long is the wire that supports the tree?

Find the value of *x*.

11.

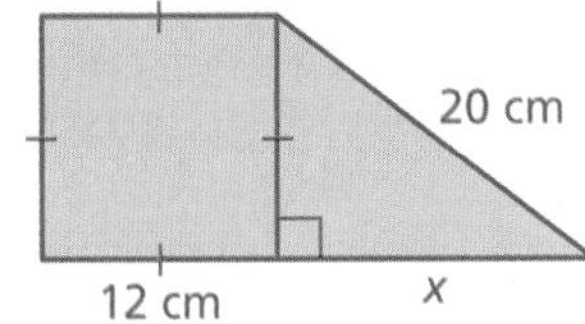

12.

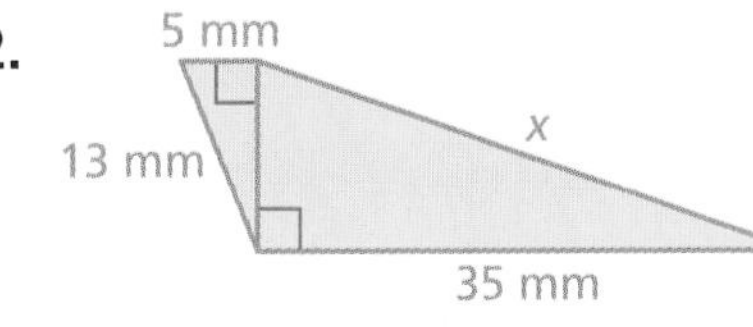

13.

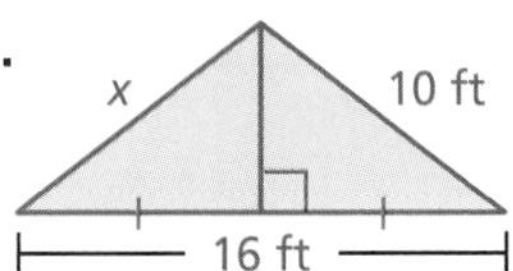

14. FLAT SCREEN Televisions are advertised by the lengths of their diagonals. A store has a sale on televisions 40 inches and larger. Is the television on sale? Explain.

15. BUTTERFLY Approximate the wingspan of the butterfly.

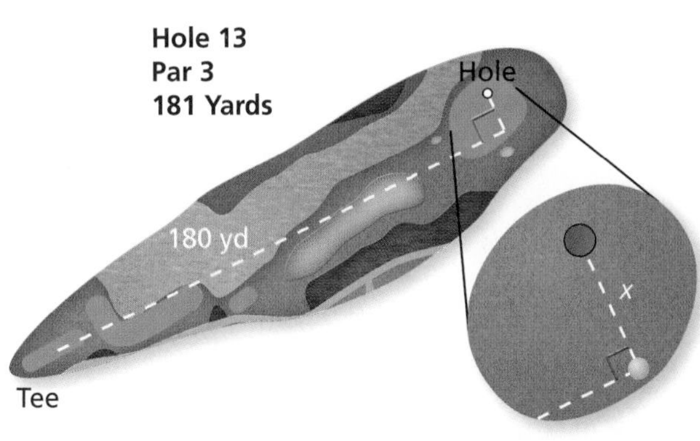

16. GOLF The figure shows the location of a golf ball after a tee shot. How many feet from the hole is the ball?

17. SNOWBALLS You and a friend stand back-to-back. You run 20 feet forward then 15 feet to your right. At the same time, your friend runs 16 feet forward then 12 feet to her right. She stops and hits you with a snowball.

a. Draw the situation in a coordinate plane.

b. How far does your friend throw the snowball?

18. Algebra The legs of a right triangle have lengths of 28 meters and 21 meters. The hypotenuse has a length of $5x$ meters. What is the value of x?

Fair Game Review What you learned in previous grades & lessons

Find the square root(s). *(Section 8.1)*

19. $\pm\sqrt{36}$ **20.** $-\sqrt{121}$ **21.** $\sqrt{169}$ **22.** $-\sqrt{225}$

23. MULTIPLE CHOICE Which type of triangle can have an obtuse angle? *(Section 5.2)*

Ⓐ equiangular Ⓑ right Ⓒ isosceles Ⓓ equilateral

8 Study Help

You can use a **summary triangle** to explain a topic. Here is an example of a summary triangle for finding the length of the hypotenuse of a triangle.

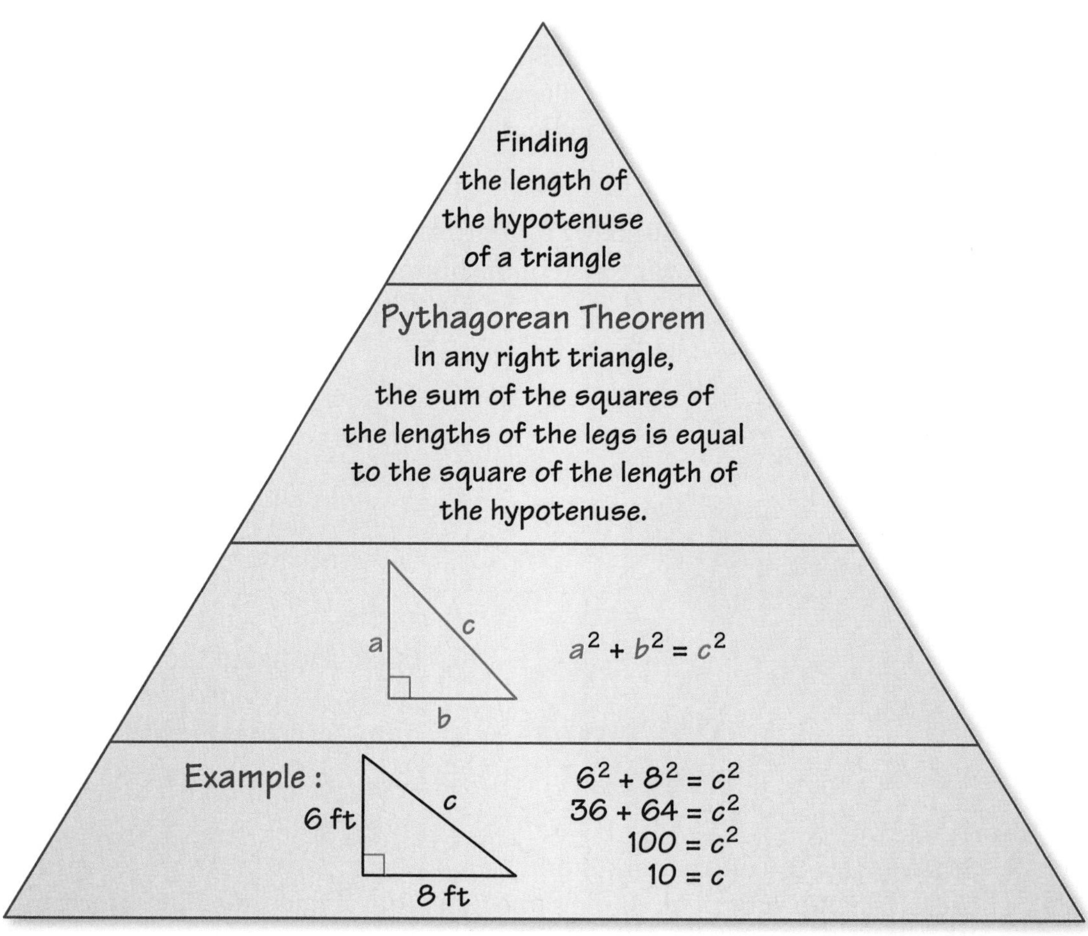

Finding the length of the hypotenuse of a triangle
Pythagorean Theorem
In any right triangle, the sum of the squares of the lengths of the legs is equal to the square of the length of the hypotenuse.
a
b
c
$a^2 + b^2 = c^2$
Example :
6 ft
8 ft
c
$6^2 + 8^2 = c^2$
$36 + 64 = c^2$
$100 = c^2$
$10 = c$

On Your Own

Make a summary triangle to help you study these topics.

1. finding square roots
2. evaluating expressions involving square roots
3. finding the length of a leg of a right triangle

After you complete this chapter, make summary triangles for the following topics.

4. approximating square roots
5. simplifying square roots

"What do you call a cheese summary triangle that isn't yours?"

8.1–8.2 Quiz

Find the two square roots of the number. *(Section 8.1)*

1. 196

2. 49

3. 400

Find the square root(s). *(Section 8.1)*

4. $-\sqrt{4}$

5. $\sqrt{\dfrac{16}{25}}$

6. $\pm\sqrt{6.25}$

Evaluate the expression. *(Section 8.1)*

7. $3\sqrt{49} + 5$

8. $10 - 4\sqrt{16}$

9. $\dfrac{1}{4} + \sqrt{\dfrac{100}{4}}$

Find the missing length of the triangle. *(Section 8.2)*

10.

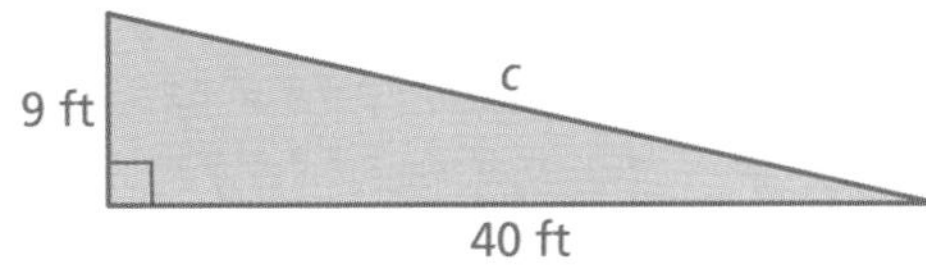

11.

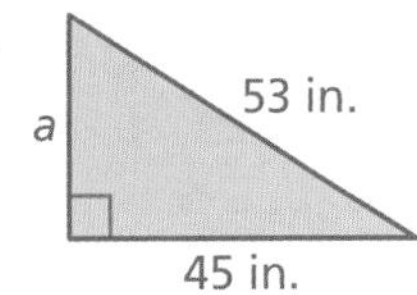

12.

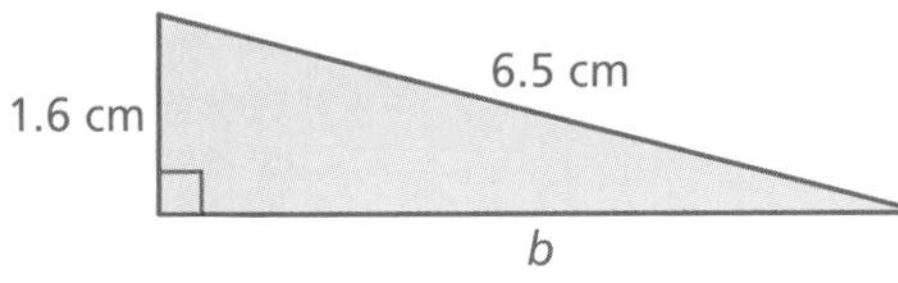

13.

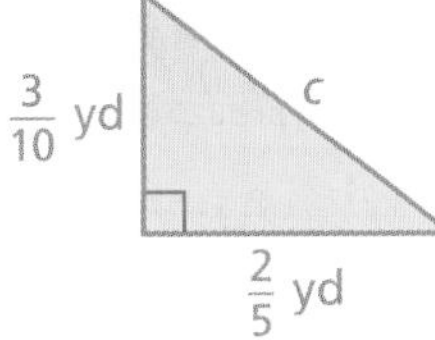

14. POOL The area of a circular pool cover is 314 square feet. Write and solve an equation to find the diameter of the pool cover. Use 3.14 for π. *(Section 8.1)*

15. LAND A square parcel of land has an area of 1 million square feet. What is the length of one side of the parcel? *(Section 8.1)*

16. FABRIC You are cutting a rectangular piece of fabric in half along the diagonal. The fabric measures 28 inches wide and $1\frac{1}{4}$ yards long. What is the length (in inches) of the diagonal? *(Section 8.2)*

8.3 Approximating Square Roots

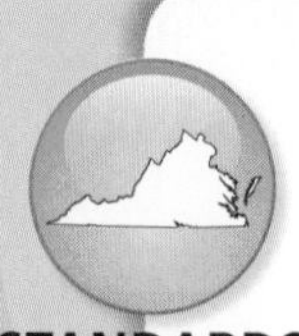

STANDARDS OF LEARNING
8.2
8.5

Essential Question How can you find decimal approximations of square roots that are irrational?

You already know that a rational number is a number that can be written as the ratio of two integers. Numbers that cannot be written as the ratio of two integers are called **irrational**.

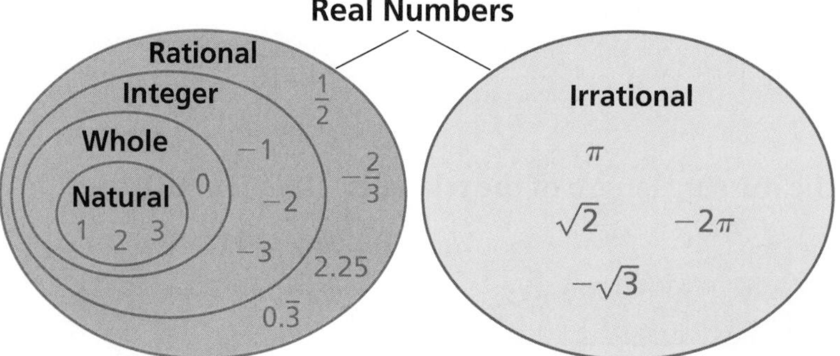

1 ACTIVITY: Approximating Square Roots

Work with a partner.

Archimedes was a Greek mathematician, physicist, engineer, inventor, and astronomer.

Archimedes
(c. 287 B.C.–c. 212 B.C.)

a. Archimedes tried to find a rational number whose square is 3. Here are two that he tried.

$$\frac{265}{153} \text{ and } \frac{1351}{780}$$

Are either of these numbers equal to $\sqrt{3}$? How can you tell?

b. Use a calculator with a square root key to approximate $\sqrt{3}$.

Write the number on a piece of paper. Then enter it into the calculator and square it. Then subtract 3. Do you get 0? Explain.

c. Calculators did not exist in the time of Archimedes. How do you think he might have approximated $\sqrt{3}$?

2 ACTIVITY: Approximating Square Roots Geometrically

Work with a partner.

a. Use grid paper and the given scale to draw a horizontal line segment 1 unit in length. Label this segment *AC*.

b. Draw a vertical line segment 2 units in length. Label this segment *DC*.

c. Set the point of a compass on *A*. Set the compass to 2 units. Swing the compass to intersect segment *DC*. Label this intersection as *B*.

d. Use the Pythagorean Theorem to show that the length of segment *BC* is $\sqrt{3}$ units.

e. Use the grid paper to approximate $\sqrt{3}$.

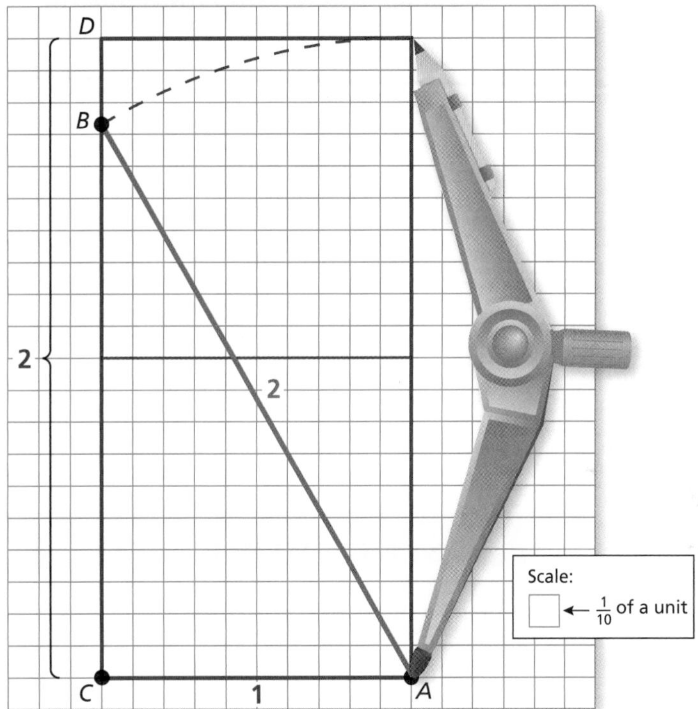

What Is Your Answer?

3. Repeat Activity 2 for a triangle in which segment *CA* is 2 units and segment *BA* is 3 units. Use the Pythagorean Theorem to show that segment *BC* is $\sqrt{5}$ units. Use the grid paper to approximate $\sqrt{5}$.

4. **IN YOUR OWN WORDS** How can you find decimal approximations of square roots that are irrational?

Practice Use what you learned about approximating square roots to complete Exercises 5–8 on page 375.

8.3 Lesson

Key Vocabulary
irrational number, *p. 372*
real numbers, *p. 372*

A rational number is a number that can be written as the ratio of two integers. An **irrational number** cannot be written as the ratio of two integers.

- The square root of any whole number that is not a perfect square is irrational.
- The decimal form of an irrational number neither terminates nor repeats.

Key Idea

Real Numbers

Rational numbers and irrational numbers together form the set of **real numbers**.

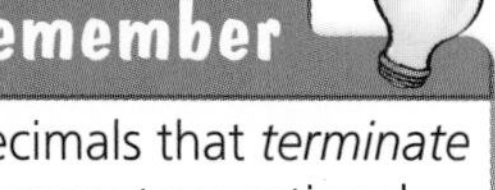

Decimals that *terminate* or *repeat* are rational.

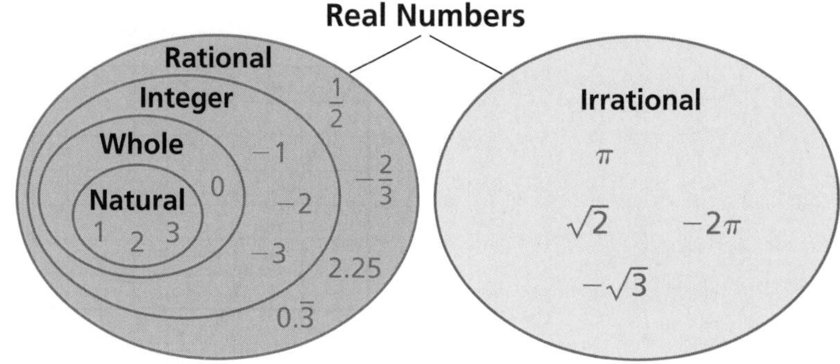

EXAMPLE 1 Classifying Real Numbers

Classify each real number.

Study Tip

When classifying a real number, list all the subsets in which the number belongs.

	Number	Subset(s)	Reasoning
a.	$\sqrt{12}$	Irrational	12 is not a perfect square.
b.	$-0.36\overline{4}$	Rational	$-0.36\overline{4}$ is a repeating decimal.
c.	$-\sqrt{9}$	Integer, Rational	$-\sqrt{9}$ is equal to -3.
d.	$\frac{72}{4}$	Natural, Whole, Integer, Rational	$\frac{72}{4}$ is equal to 18.
e.	π	Irrational	The decimal form of π neither terminates nor repeats.

On Your Own

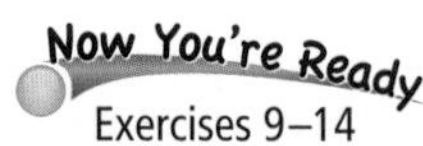

Exercises 9–14

Classify the real number.

1. 0.121221222. . . **2.** $-\sqrt{196}$ **3.** $\sqrt{2}$

EXAMPLE 2 Approximating Square Roots

Estimate $\sqrt{52}$ to the nearest integer.

Use a number line and the square roots of the perfect squares nearest to the radicand. The nearest perfect square less than 52 is 49. The nearest perfect square greater than 52 is 64.

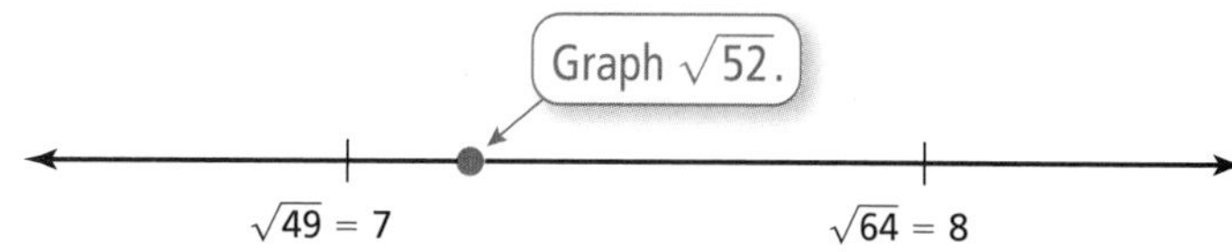

Because 52 is closer to 49 than to 64, $\sqrt{52}$ is closer to 7 than to 8.

∴ So, $\sqrt{52} \approx 7$.

On Your Own

Now You're Ready
Exercises 18–23

Estimate to the nearest integer.

4. $\sqrt{33}$ **5.** $\sqrt{85}$ **6.** $\sqrt{190}$ **7.** $-\sqrt{7}$

EXAMPLE 3 Comparing Real Numbers

a. Which is greater, $\sqrt{5}$ or $2\frac{3}{4}$?

Graph the numbers on a number line.

$\sqrt{5}$ $2\frac{3}{4} = 2.75$

$\sqrt{4} = 2$ $\sqrt{9} = 3$

∴ $2\frac{3}{4}$ is to the right of $\sqrt{5}$. So, $2\frac{3}{4}$ is greater.

b. Which is greater, $0.\overline{6}$ or $\sqrt{0.36}$?

Graph the numbers on a number line.

$\sqrt{0.36} = 0.6$ $0.\overline{6}$

0.6 0.7

∴ $0.\overline{6}$ is to the right of $\sqrt{0.36}$. So, $0.\overline{6}$ is greater.

On Your Own

Now You're Ready
Exercises 25–30

Which number is greater? Explain.

8. $4\frac{1}{5}, \sqrt{23}$ **9.** $\sqrt{10}, -\sqrt{5}$ **10.** $-\sqrt{2}, -2$

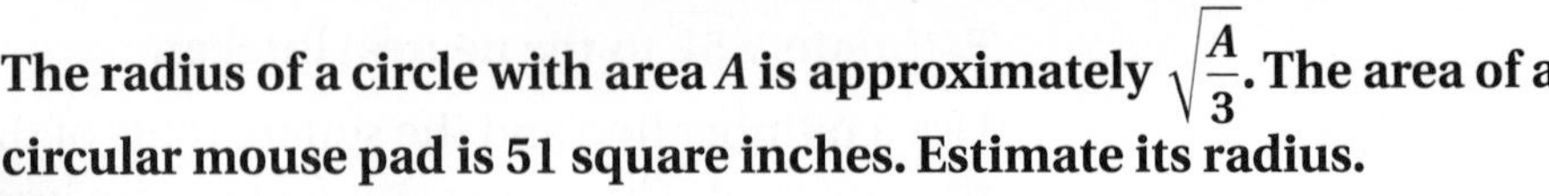

EXAMPLE 4 Approximating an Expression

The radius of a circle with area A is approximately $\sqrt{\frac{A}{3}}$. The area of a circular mouse pad is 51 square inches. Estimate its radius.

$$\sqrt{\frac{A}{3}} = \sqrt{\frac{51}{3}} \qquad \text{Substitute 51 for } A.$$

$$= \sqrt{17} \qquad \text{Divide.}$$

The nearest perfect square less than 17 is 16. The nearest perfect square greater than 17 is 25.

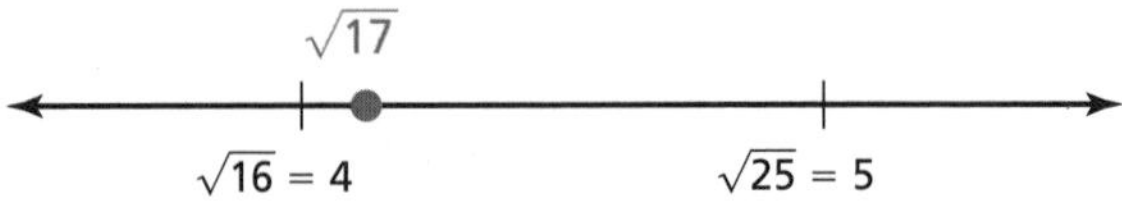

Because 17 is closer to 16 than to 25, $\sqrt{17}$ is closer to 4 than to 5.

∴ The radius is about 4 inches.

On Your Own

11. **WHAT IF?** The area of a circular mouse pad is 64 square inches. Estimate its radius.

EXAMPLE 5 Real-Life Application

The distance (in nautical miles) you can see with a periscope is $1.17\sqrt{h}$, where h is the height of the periscope above the water. Can a periscope that is 6 feet above the water see twice as far as a periscope that is 3 feet above the water? Explain.

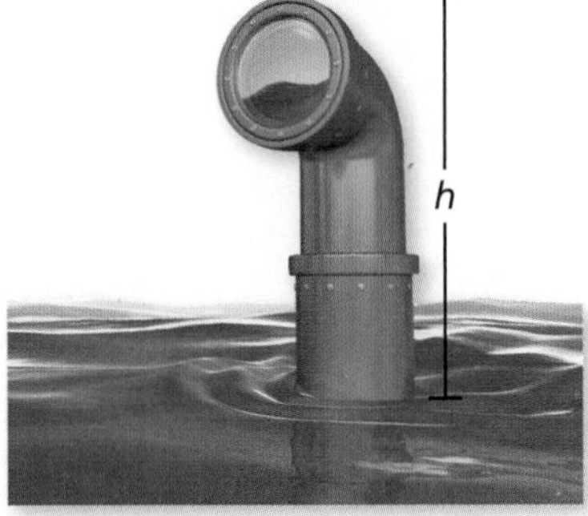

Use a calculator to find the distances.

3 feet above water		*6 feet above water*
$1.17\sqrt{h} = 1.17\sqrt{3}$	Substitute for h.	$1.17\sqrt{h} = 1.17\sqrt{6}$
≈ 2.03	Use a calculator.	≈ 2.87

You can see $\frac{2.87}{2.03} \approx 1.41$ times farther with the periscope that is 6 feet above the water than with the periscope that is 3 feet above the water.

∴ No, the periscope that is 6 feet above the water cannot see twice as far.

On Your Own

12. You use a periscope that is 10 feet above the water. Can you see farther than 4 nautical miles? Explain.

8.3 Exercises

Vocabulary and Concept Check

1. **VOCABULARY** How are rational numbers and irrational numbers different?
2. **WRITING** Describe a method of approximating $\sqrt{32}$.
3. **VOCABULARY** What are real numbers? Give three examples.
4. **WHICH ONE DOESN'T BELONG?** Which number does *not* belong with the other three? Explain your reasoning.

$-\frac{11}{12}$ 25.075 $\sqrt{8}$ 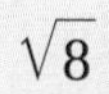 $-3.\overline{3}$

Practice and Problem Solving

Tell whether the rational number is a reasonable approximation of the square root.

5. $\frac{559}{250}, \sqrt{5}$
6. $\frac{3021}{250}, \sqrt{11}$
7. $\frac{678}{250}, \sqrt{28}$
8. $\frac{1677}{250}, \sqrt{45}$

Classify the real number.

1 9. 0
10. $\frac{\pi}{6}$
11. $-\sqrt{81}$
12. -1.125
13. $\frac{52}{13}$
14. $\sqrt{15}$

15. **ERROR ANALYSIS** Describe and correct the error in classifying the number.

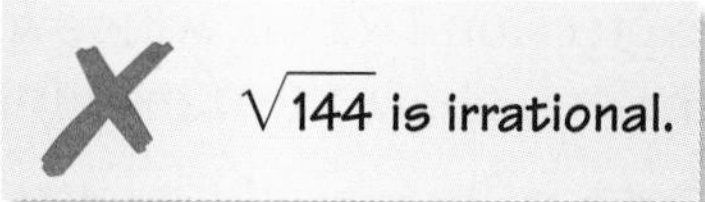

16. **SCRAPBOOKING** You cut a picture into a right triangle for your scrapbook. The lengths of the legs of the triangle are 4 inches and 6 inches. Is the length of the hypotenuse a rational number? Explain.

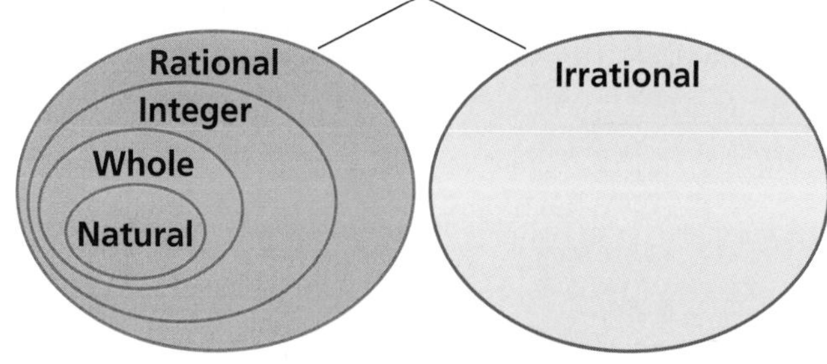

17. **VENN DIAGRAM** Place each number in the correct area of the Venn Diagram.
    a. The last digit of your phone number
    b. The square root of any prime number
    c. The ratio of the circumference of a circle to its diameter

Estimate to the nearest integer.

2 **18.** $\sqrt{24}$ **19.** $\sqrt{685}$ **20.** $-\sqrt{61}$

21. $-\sqrt{105}$ **22.** $\sqrt{\frac{27}{4}}$ **23.** $-\sqrt{\frac{335}{2}}$

24. **CHECKERS** A checkerboard is 8 squares long and 8 squares wide. The area of each square is 14 square centimeters. Estimate the perimeter of the checkerboard.

Which number is greater? Explain.

3 **25.** $\sqrt{20}$, 10 **26.** $\sqrt{15}$, -3.5 **27.** $\sqrt{133}$, $10\frac{3}{4}$

28. $\frac{2}{3}$, $\sqrt{\frac{16}{81}}$ **29.** $-\sqrt{0.25}$, -0.25 **30.** $-\sqrt{182}$, $-\sqrt{192}$

31. **FOUR SQUARE** The area of a four square court is 66 square feet. Estimate the length s of one of the sides of the court.

32. **RADIO SIGNAL** The maximum distance (in nautical miles) that a radio transmitter signal can be sent is represented by the expression $1.23\sqrt{h}$, where h is the height (in feet) above the transmitter.

Estimate the maximum distance x (in nautical miles) between the plane that is receiving the signal and the transmitter. Round your answer to the nearest tenth.

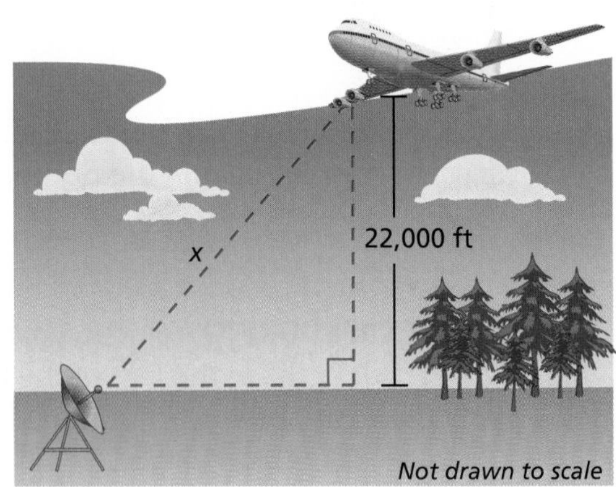

33. **OPEN-ENDED** Find two numbers a and b that satisfy the diagram.

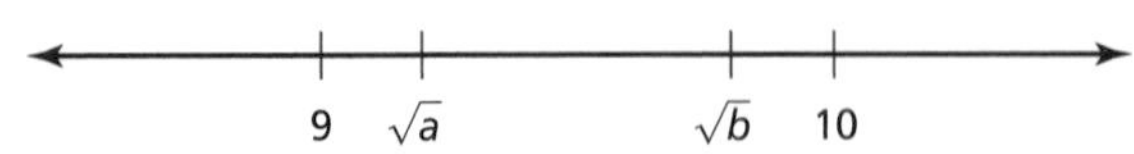

Estimate to the nearest tenth.

34. $\sqrt{0.39}$ **35.** $\sqrt{1.19}$ **36.** $\sqrt{1.52}$

37. ROLLER COASTER The velocity v (in meters per second) of a roller coaster is represented by the equation $v = 3\sqrt{6r}$, where r is the radius of the loop. Estimate the velocity of a car going around the loop. Round your answer to the nearest tenth.

38. Is $\sqrt{\frac{1}{4}}$ a rational number? Is $\sqrt{\frac{3}{16}}$ a rational number? Explain.

39. WATER BALLOON The time t (in seconds) it takes a water balloon to fall d meters is represented by the equation $t = \sqrt{\frac{d}{4.9}}$. Estimate the time it takes the balloon to fall to the ground from a window that is 14 meters above the ground. Round your answer to the nearest tenth.

40. Number Sense Determine if the statement is *sometimes, always,* or *never* true. Explain your reasoning and give an example of each.

a. A rational number multiplied by a rational number is rational.

b. A rational number multiplied by an irrational number is rational.

c. An irrational number multiplied by an irrational number is rational.

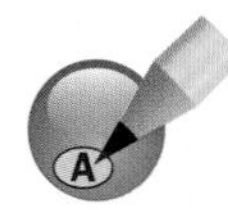

Fair Game Review What you learned in previous grades & lessons

Simplify the expression. *(Skills Review Handbook)*

41. $2x + 3y - 5x$ **42.** $3\pi + 8(t - \pi) - 4t$ **43.** $17k - 9 + 23k$

44. MULTIPLE CHOICE What is the ratio (red to blue) of the corresponding side lengths of the similar triangles? *(Skills Review Handbook)*

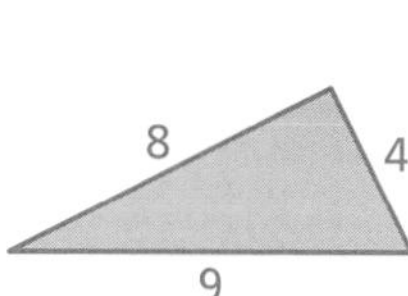

20 10 22.5

Ⓐ 1:3 Ⓑ 5:2 Ⓒ 3:4 Ⓓ 2:5

8.4 Simplifying Square Roots

STANDARDS OF LEARNING
8.1

Essential Question How can you use a square root to describe the golden ratio?

Two quantities are in the *golden ratio* if the ratio between the sum of the quantities and the greater quantity is the same as the ratio between the greater quantity and the lesser quantity.

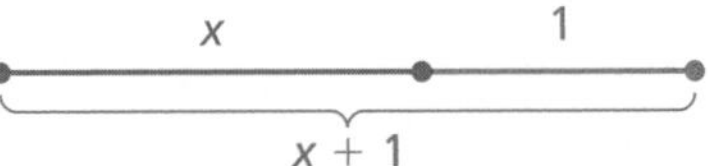

$$\frac{x+1}{x} = \frac{x}{1}$$

In a future algebra course, you will be able to prove that the golden ratio is

$$\frac{1+\sqrt{5}}{2}$$ Golden ratio.

1 ACTIVITY: Constructing a Golden Rectangle

Work with a partner.

a. Use grid paper and the given scale to draw a square that is 1 unit by 1 unit (blue).

b. Draw a line from midpoint *C* of one side of the square to the opposite corner *D*, as shown.

c. Use the Pythagorean Theorem to find the length of segment *CD*.

d. Set the point of a compass on *C*. Set the compass radius to the length of segment *CD*. Swing the compass to intersect line *BC* at point *E*.

e. The rectangle *ABEF* is called a *golden rectangle* because the ratio of its side lengths is the golden ratio.

f. Use a calculator to find a decimal approximation of the golden ratio. Round your answer to two decimal places.

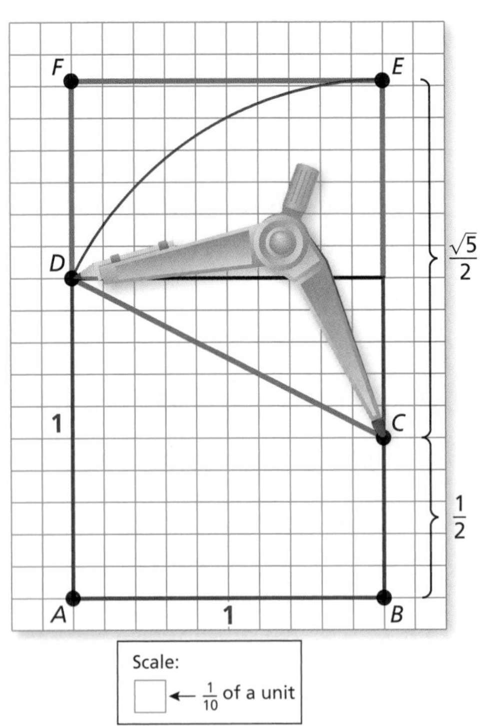

Scale: ← $\frac{1}{10}$ of a unit

2 ACTIVITY: The Golden Ratio and the Human Body

Work with a partner.

Leonardo da Vinci was one of the first to notice that there are several ratios in the human body that approximate the golden ratio.

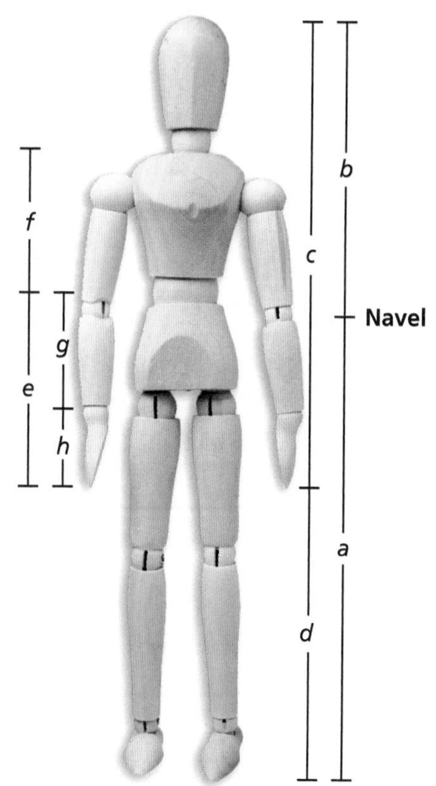

a. Use a tape measure or two yardsticks to measure the lengths shown in the diagram for both you and your partner. (Take your shoes off before measuring.)

b. Copy the tables below. Record your results in the first two columns.

c. Calculate the ratios shown in the tables.

d. Leonardo da Vinci stated that for many people, the ratios are close to the golden ratio. How close are your ratios?

You		
$a =$	$b =$	$\frac{a}{b} =$
$c =$	$d =$	$\frac{c}{d} =$
$e =$	$f =$	$\frac{e}{f} =$
$g =$	$h =$	$\frac{g}{h} =$

Partner		
$a =$	$b =$	$\frac{a}{b} =$
$c =$	$d =$	$\frac{c}{d} =$
$e =$	$f =$	$\frac{e}{f} =$
$g =$	$h =$	$\frac{g}{h} =$

What Is Your Answer?

3. **IN YOUR OWN WORDS** How can you use a square root to describe the golden ratio? Use the Internet or some other reference to find examples of the golden ratio in art and architecture.

Practice Use what you learned about square roots to complete Exercises 3–5 on page 382.

8.4 Lesson

You can add or subtract radical expressions the same way you combine like terms, such as $5x + 4x = 9x$.

EXAMPLE 1 Adding and Subtracting Square Roots

Reading

Do not assume that radicals that have different radicands cannot be simplified.

An expression such as $2\sqrt{4} + \sqrt{1}$ can easily be simplified.

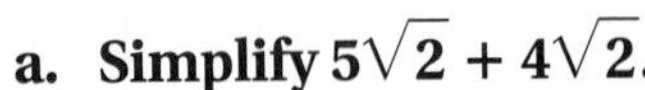

a. Simplify $5\sqrt{2} + 4\sqrt{2}$.

$5\sqrt{2} + 4\sqrt{2} = (5 + 4)\sqrt{2}$ — Use the Distributive Property.

$= 9\sqrt{2}$ — Simplify.

b. Simplify $2\sqrt{3} - 7\sqrt{3}$.

$2\sqrt{3} - 7\sqrt{3} = (2 - 7)\sqrt{3}$ — Use the Distributive Property.

$= -5\sqrt{3}$ — Simplify.

On Your Own

Now You're Ready
Exercises 6–14

Simplify the expression.

1. $\sqrt{5} + \sqrt{5}$
2. $6\sqrt{10} + 4\sqrt{10}$
3. $2\sqrt{7} - \sqrt{7}$

To simplify square roots that are not perfect squares, use the following property.

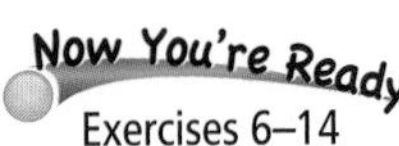

Key Idea

Product Property of Square Roots

Algebra $\sqrt{xy} = \sqrt{x} \cdot \sqrt{y}$, where $x, y \geq 0$

Numbers $\sqrt{4 \cdot 3} = \sqrt{4} \cdot \sqrt{3} = 2\sqrt{3}$

EXAMPLE 2 Simplifying Square Roots

Study Tip

A square root is simplified when the radicand has no perfect square factors other than 1.

Simplify $\sqrt{50}$.

$\sqrt{50} = \sqrt{25 \cdot 2}$ — Factor using the greatest perfect square factor.

$= \sqrt{25} \cdot \sqrt{2}$ — Use the Product Property of Square Roots.

$= 5\sqrt{2}$ — Simplify.

On Your Own

Now You're Ready
Exercises 16–20

Simplify the expression.

4. $\sqrt{24}$
5. $\sqrt{45}$
6. $\sqrt{98}$

Quotient Property of Square Roots

Algebra $\sqrt{\frac{x}{y}} = \frac{\sqrt{x}}{\sqrt{y}}$, where $x \geq 0$ and $y > 0$

Numbers $\sqrt{\frac{7}{9}} = \frac{\sqrt{7}}{\sqrt{9}} = \frac{\sqrt{7}}{3}$

EXAMPLE 3 Simplifying Square Roots

Simplify $\sqrt{\frac{11}{16}}$.

$\sqrt{\frac{11}{16}} = \frac{\sqrt{11}}{\sqrt{16}}$ Use the Quotient Property of Square Roots.

$= \frac{\sqrt{11}}{4}$ Simplify.

EXAMPLE 4 Finding a Volume

Remember

The volume V of a rectangular prism is the product of the area of its base B and its height h.

$V = Bh$

Find the volume of the rectangular prism.

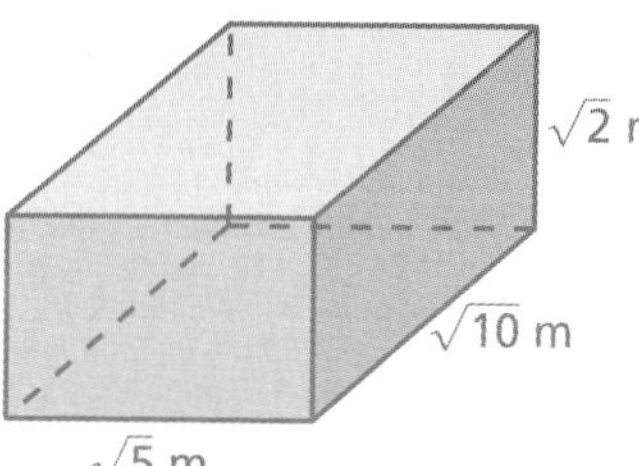

$V = Bh$ Write formula for volume.

$= (\sqrt{5})(\sqrt{10})(\sqrt{2})$ Substitute.

$= \sqrt{5 \cdot 10 \cdot 2}$ Use the Product Property of Square Roots.

$= \sqrt{100}$ Multiply.

$= 10$ Simplify.

∴ The volume is 10 cubic meters.

On Your Own

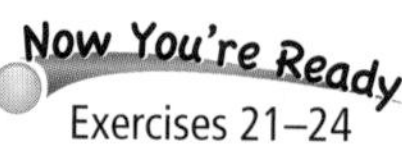

Simplify the expression.

7. $\sqrt{\frac{35}{36}}$ 8. $\sqrt{\frac{13}{4}}$ 9. $\sqrt{\frac{5}{b^2}}$

10. **WHAT IF?** In Example 4, the height of the rectangular prism is $\sqrt{8}$ meters. Find the volume of the prism.

8.4 Exercises

Vocabulary and Concept Check

1. **WRITING** Describe how combining like terms is similar to adding and subtracting square roots.
2. **WRITING** How are the Product Property of Square Roots and the Quotient Property of Square Roots similar?

Practice and Problem Solving

Find the ratio of the side lengths. Is the ratio close to the golden ratio?

3. 

4. 

5. 

Simplify the expression.

1 6. $\frac{\sqrt{2}}{9} + \frac{1}{9}$

7. $\frac{\sqrt{7}}{3} + \frac{1}{3}$

8. $\frac{1}{4} + \frac{\sqrt{13}}{4}$

9. $2\sqrt{3} + 4\sqrt{3}$

10. $6\sqrt{7} - 2\sqrt{7}$

11. $\frac{3}{4}\sqrt{5} + \frac{5}{4}\sqrt{5}$

12. $\sqrt{6} - 4\sqrt{6}$

13. $1.5\sqrt{15} - 9.2\sqrt{15}$

14. $\frac{7}{8}\sqrt{11} + \frac{3}{8}\sqrt{11}$

15. **ERROR ANALYSIS** Describe and correct the error in simplifying the expression.

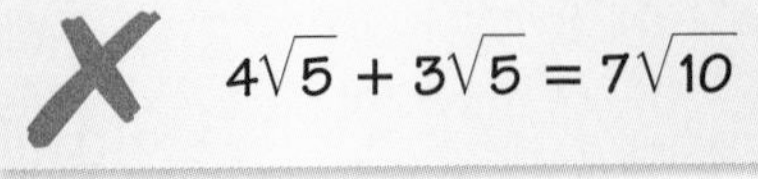

Simplify the expression.

2 3 16. $\sqrt{18}$

17. $\sqrt{200}$

18. $\sqrt{12}$

19. $\sqrt{48}$

20. $\sqrt{125}$

21. $\sqrt{\frac{23}{64}}$

22. $\sqrt{\frac{65}{121}}$

23. $\sqrt{\frac{17}{49}}$

24. $\sqrt{\frac{22}{c^2}}$

25. **RAIN GUTTER** A rain gutter is made from a single sheet of metal. What is the length of the red cross-section?

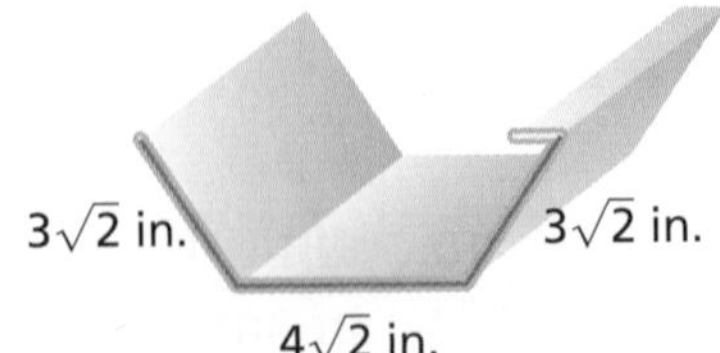

Simplify the expression.

26. $3\sqrt{5} - \sqrt{45}$

27. $\sqrt{24} + 4\sqrt{6}$

28. $\frac{4}{3}\sqrt{7} + \sqrt{28}$

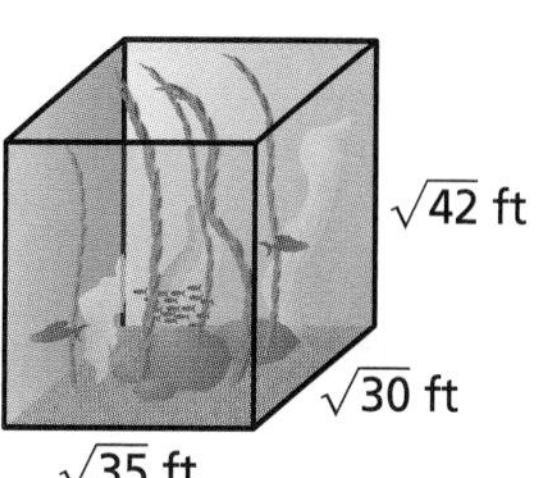

29. VOLUME What is the volume of the aquarium (in cubic feet)?

30. RATIO The ratio $3:x$ is equivalent to the ratio $x:5$. What are the possible values of x?

31. BILLBOARD The billboard has the shape of a rectangle.

a. What is the perimeter of the billboard?

b. What is the area of the billboard?

The height of Mt. Fuji is 3.8 kilometers.

32. MT. FUJI Mt. Fuji is in the shape of a cone with a volume of about 475π cubic kilometers. What is the radius of the base of Mt. Fuji?

33. Geometry A block of ice is in the shape of a square prism. You want to put the block of ice in a cylindrical cooler. The equation $s^2 = 2r^2$ represents the minimum radius r needed for the block of ice with side length s to fit in the cooler.

a. Solve the equation for r.

b. Use the equation in part (a) to find the minimum radius needed when the side length of the block of ice is $\sqrt{98}$ inches.

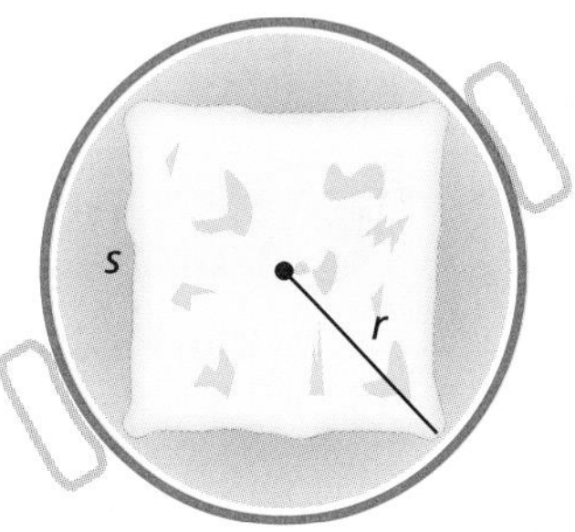

Fair Game Review What you learned in previous grades & lessons

Find the missing length of the triangle. *(Section 8.2)*

34.

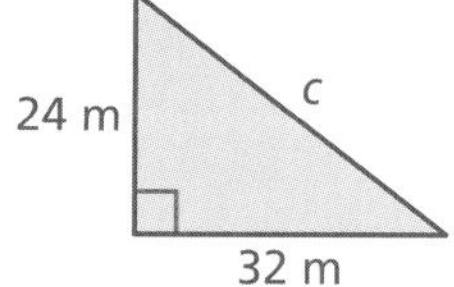

35.

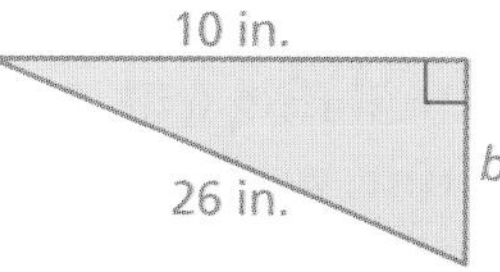

36.

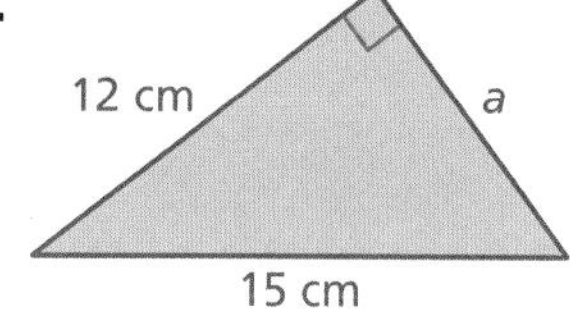

37. MULTIPLE CHOICE Where is $-\sqrt{110}$ on a number line? *(Section 8.3)*

Ⓐ Between -9 and -10

Ⓑ Between 9 and 10

Ⓒ Between -10 and -11

Ⓓ Between 10 and 11

8.5 Using the Pythagorean Theorem

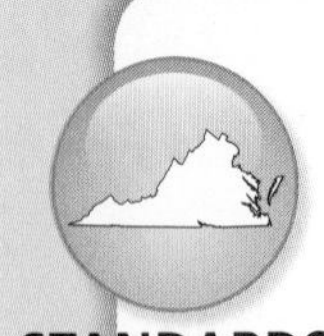

STANDARDS OF LEARNING
8.10

Essential Question How can you use the Pythagorean Theorem to solve real-life problems?

1 ACTIVITY: Using the Pythagorean Theorem

Work with a partner.

a. A baseball player throws a ball from second base to home plate. How far does the player throw the ball? Include a diagram showing how you got your answer. Decide how many decimal points of accuracy are reasonable. Explain your reasoning.

b. The distance from the pitcher's mound to home plate is 60.5 feet. Does this form a right triangle with first base? Explain your reasoning.

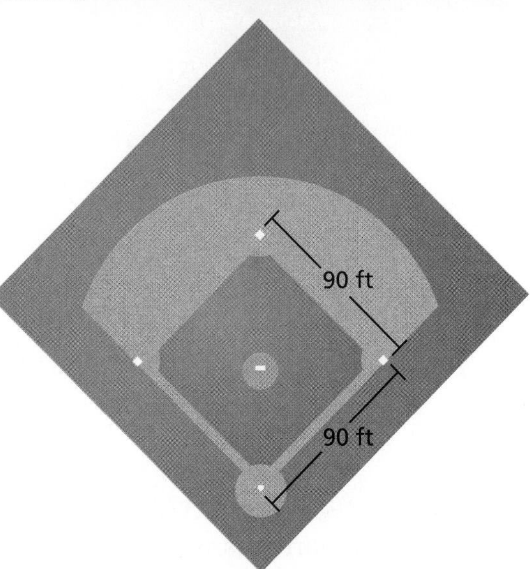

2 ACTIVITY: Firefighting and Ladders

Work with a partner.

The recommended angle for a firefighting ladder is 75°.

When a 110-foot ladder is put up against a building at this angle, the base of the ladder is about 28 feet from the building.

The base of the ladder is 8 feet above the ground.

How high on the building will the ladder reach? Round your answer to the nearest tenth.

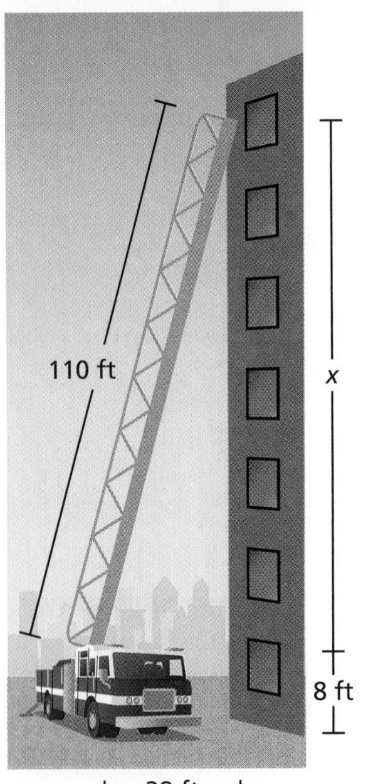

3 ACTIVITY: Finding Perimeters

Work with a partner.

Find the perimeter of each figure. Round your answer to the nearest tenth. Did you use the Pythagorean Theorem? If so, explain.

a. Right triangle

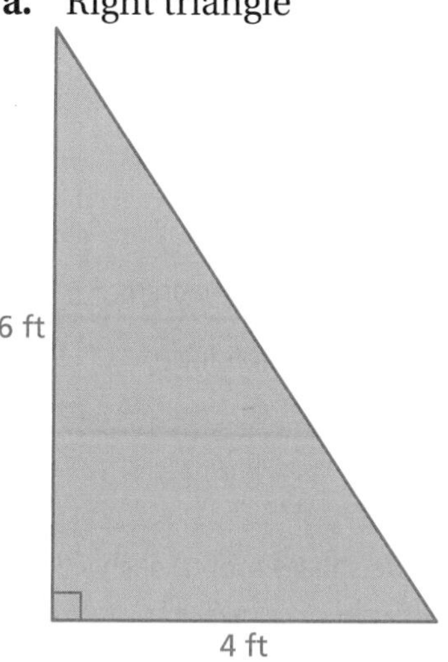

b. Trapezoid

c. Parallelogram

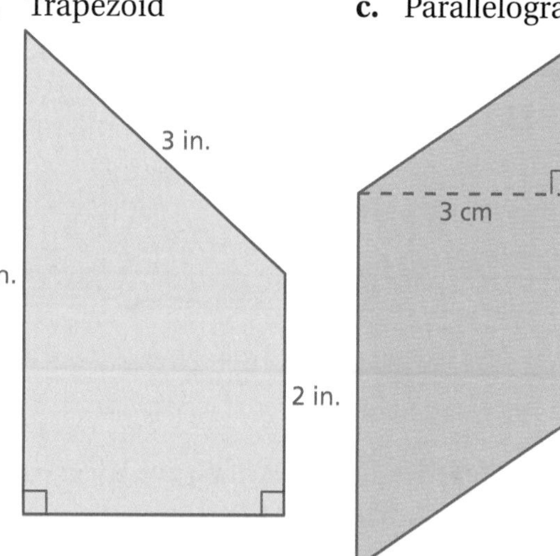

4 ACTIVITY: Writing a Formula

Work with a partner.

a. Write a formula for the area of an equilateral triangle with side length s.

b. Use your formula to find the area of an equilateral triangle with a side length of 10 inches.

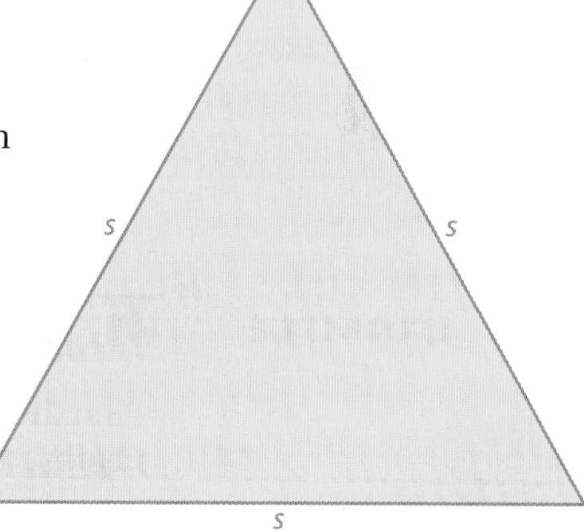

What Is Your Answer?

5. **IN YOUR OWN WORDS** How can you use the Pythagorean Theorem to solve real-life problems?

6. Describe a situation in which you could use the Pythagorean Theorem to help make decisions. Give an example of a real-life problem.

Practice Use what you learned about using the Pythagorean Theorem to complete Exercises 3–5 on page 388.

8.5 Lesson

EXAMPLE 1 Finding a Distance in a Coordinate Plane

Key Vocabulary
Pythagorean triple, *p. 387*

The park is 5 miles east of your home. The library is 4 miles north of the park. How far is your home from the library? Round your answer to the nearest tenth.

Plot a point for your home at the origin in a coordinate plane. Then plot points for the locations of the park and the library to form a right triangle.

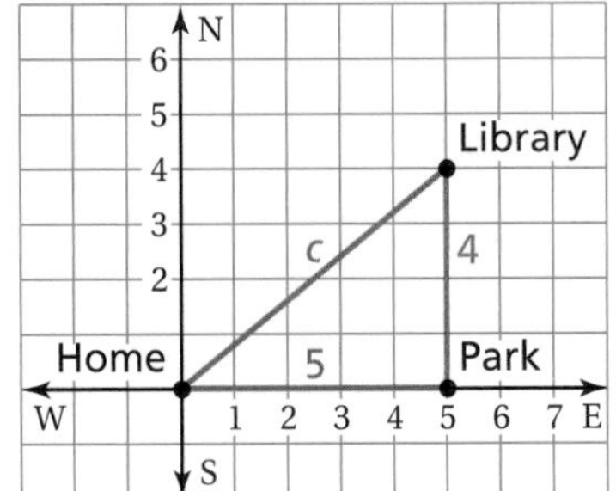

$a^2 + b^2 = c^2$	Write the Pythagorean Theorem.
$4^2 + 5^2 = c^2$	Substitute 4 for *a* and 5 for *b*.
$16 + 25 = c^2$	Evaluate powers.
$41 = c^2$	Add.
$\sqrt{41} = \sqrt{c^2}$	Take positive square root of each side.
$6.4 \approx c$	Use a calculator.

Your home is about 6.4 miles from the library.

On Your Own

1. The post office is 3 miles west of your home. Your school is 2 miles north of the post office. How far is your home from your school? Round your answer to the nearest tenth.

EXAMPLE 2 Real-Life Application

Find the height of the firework. Round your answer to the nearest tenth.

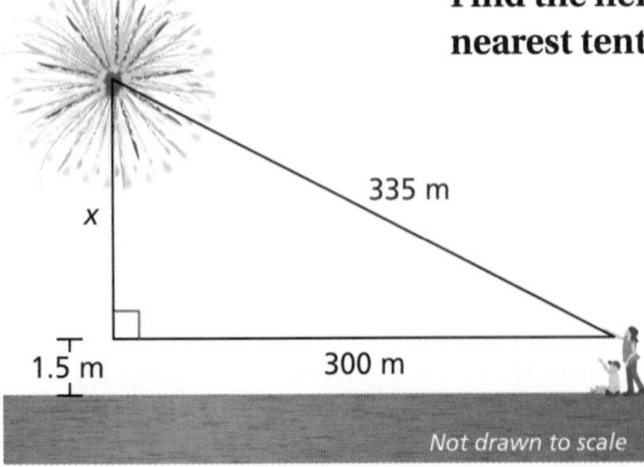

$a^2 + b^2 = c^2$	Write the Pythagorean Theorem.
$x^2 + 300^2 = 335^2$	Substitute.
$x^2 + 90{,}000 = 112{,}225$	Evaluate powers.
$x^2 = 22{,}225$	Subtract 90,000 from each side.
$\sqrt{x^2} = \sqrt{22{,}225}$	Take positive square root of each side.
$x \approx 149.1$	Use a calculator.

The height of the firework is about $149.1 + 1.5 = 150.6$ meters.

2. WHAT IF? In Example 2, the distance between you and the firework is 350 meters. Find the height of the firework. Round your answer to the nearest tenth.

A **Pythagorean triple** is a set of three positive integers a, b, and c where $a^2 + b^2 = c^2$.

Converse of the Pythagorean Theorem

If the equation $a^2 + b^2 = c^2$ is true for the side lengths of a triangle, then the triangle is a right triangle.

When using the converse of the Pythagorean Theorem, always substitute the length of the longest side for c.

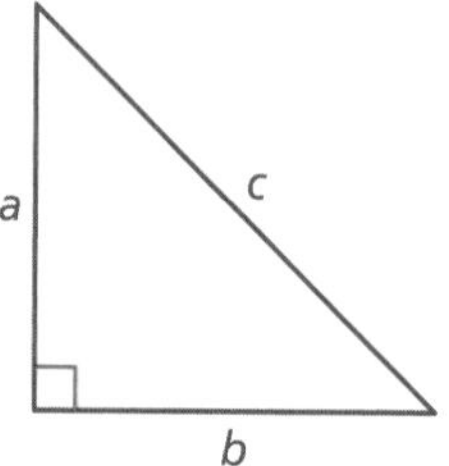

EXAMPLE 3 Identifying a Right Triangle

Tell whether the given triangle is a right triangle.

a. 9 cm, 41 cm, 40 cm

$$a^2 + b^2 = c^2$$
$$9^2 + 40^2 \stackrel{?}{=} 41^2$$
$$81 + 1600 \stackrel{?}{=} 1681$$
$$1681 = 1681 \checkmark$$

It *is* a right triangle.

b. 18 ft, 12 ft, 24 ft

$$a^2 + b^2 = c^2$$
$$12^2 + 18^2 \stackrel{?}{=} 24^2$$
$$144 + 324 \stackrel{?}{=} 576$$
$$468 \neq 576 \times$$

It is *not* a right triangle.

Tell whether the triangle with the given side lengths is a right triangle.

3.

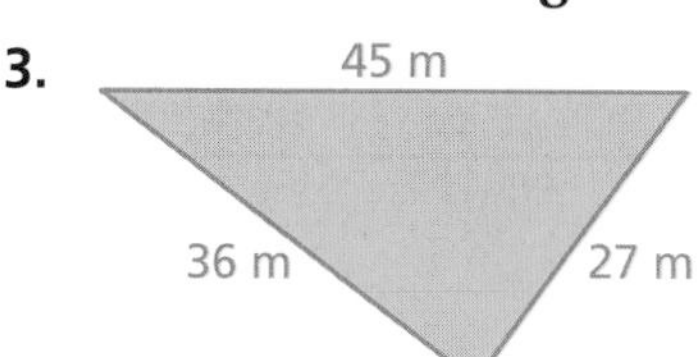

4.

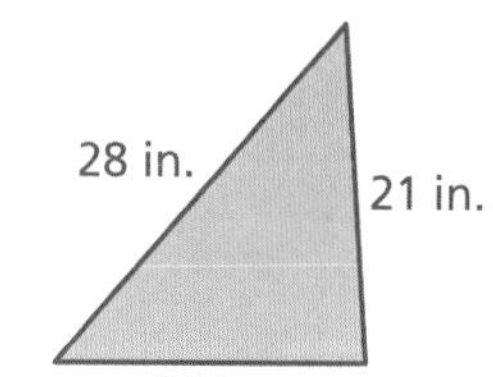

5. $1\frac{1}{2}$ yd, $2\frac{1}{2}$ yd, $3\frac{1}{2}$ yd

6. 1.25 mm, 1 mm, 0.75 mm

8.5 Exercises

Vocabulary and Concept Check

1. **WRITING** How can the Pythagorean Theorem be used to find distances in a coordinate plane?
2. **WHICH ONE DOESN'T BELONG?** Which set of numbers does *not* belong with the other three? Explain your reasoning.

3, 6, 8	6, 8, 10	5, 12, 13	7, 24, 25

Practice and Problem Solving

Find the perimeter of the figure. Round your answer to the nearest tenth.

3. Right triangle

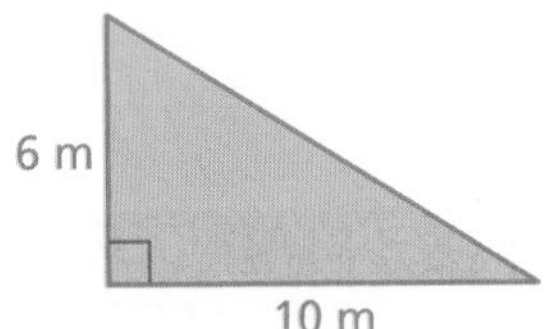

4. Parallelogram

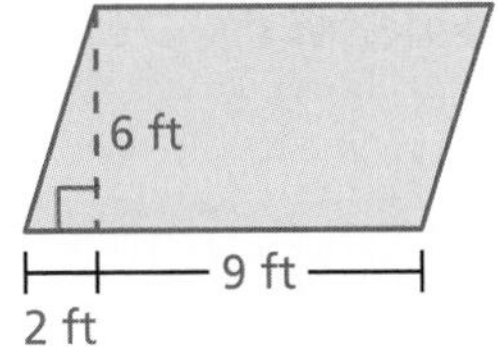

5. Square

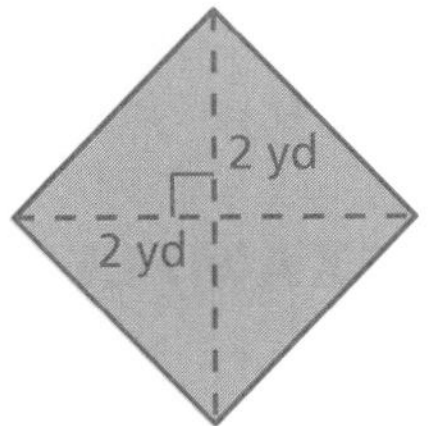

Find the distance *d*. Round your answer to the nearest tenth.

1 6.

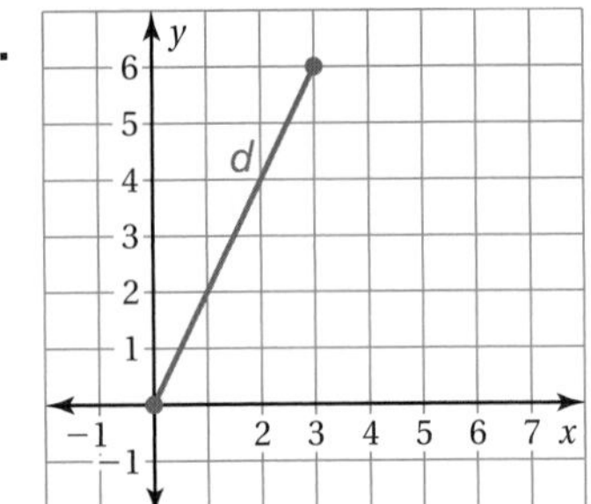

7.

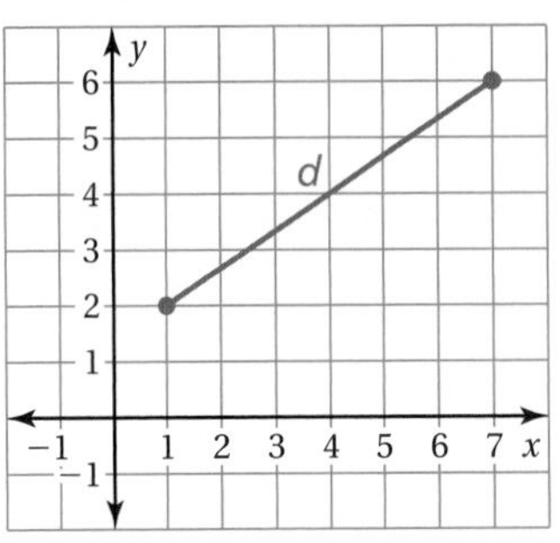

8.

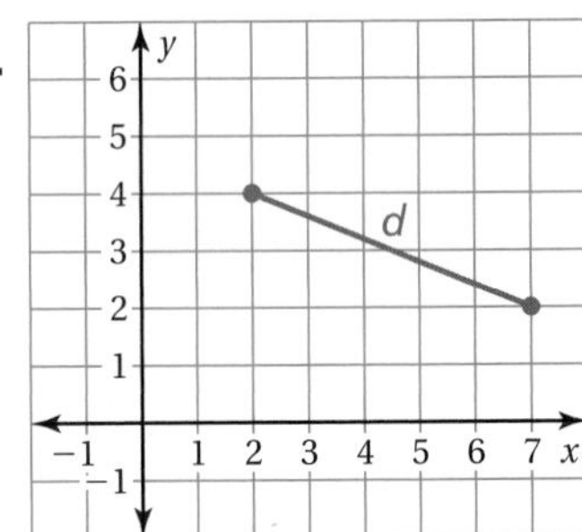

Find the height *x*. Round your answer to the nearest tenth.

2 9.

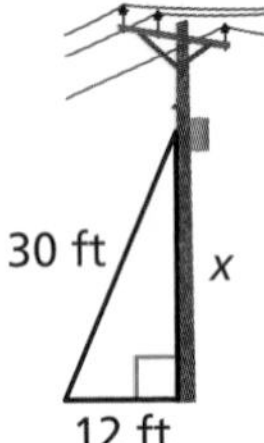

10.

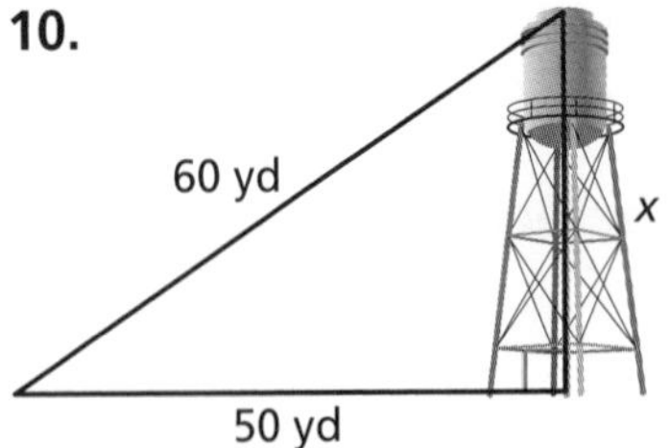

11.

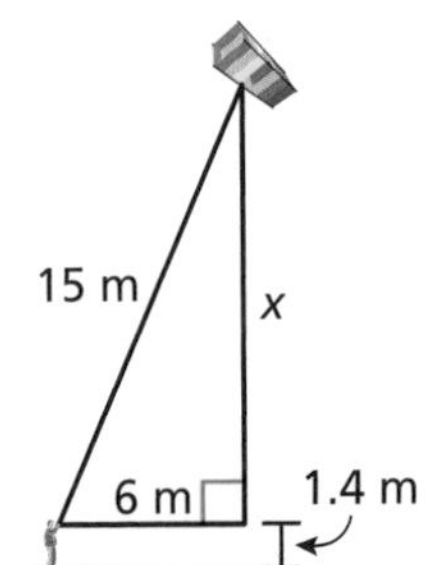

12. **BICYCLE** You ride your bicycle along the outer edge of a park. Then you take a shortcut back to where you started. Find the length of the shortcut. Round your answer to the nearest tenth.

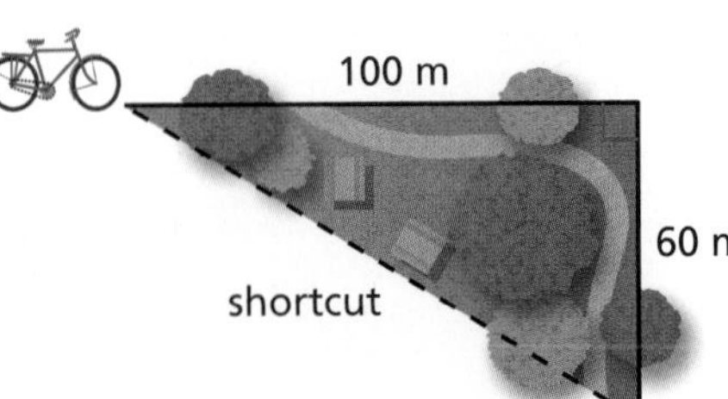

Tell whether the triangle with the given side lengths is a right triangle.

3 **13.**

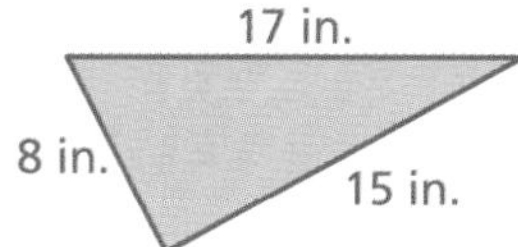

14.

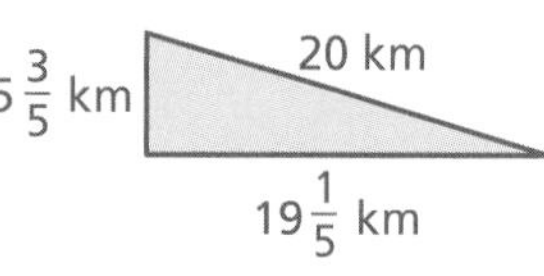

15.

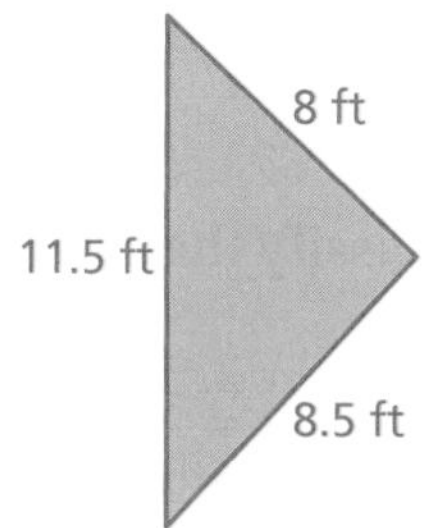

16. 14 mm, 19 mm, 23 mm

17. $\frac{9}{10}$ mi, $1\frac{1}{5}$ mi, $1\frac{1}{2}$ mi

18. 1.4 m, 4.8 m, 5 m

19. STAIRS There are 12 steps in the staircase. Find the distance from point A to point B (in feet). Round your answer to the nearest tenth.

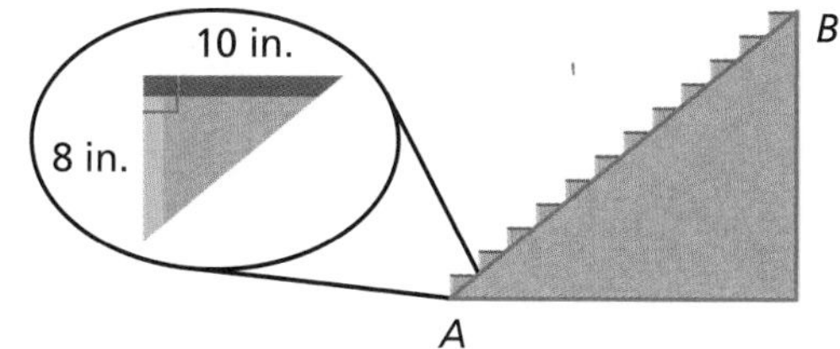

20. AIRPORT Which plane is closer to the tower? Explain.

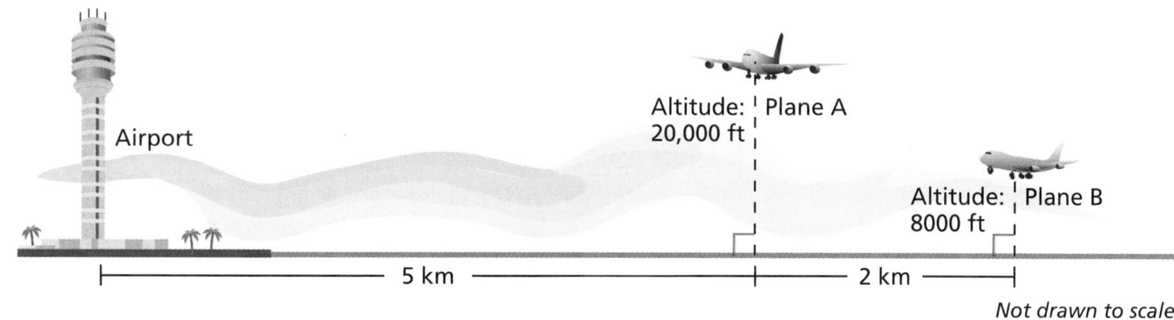

21. PROJECT Find a shoebox or some other small box.

a. Measure the dimensions of the box.

b. Without measuring, find length BC and length AB.

c. Use a piece of string and a ruler to check the lengths you found in part (b).

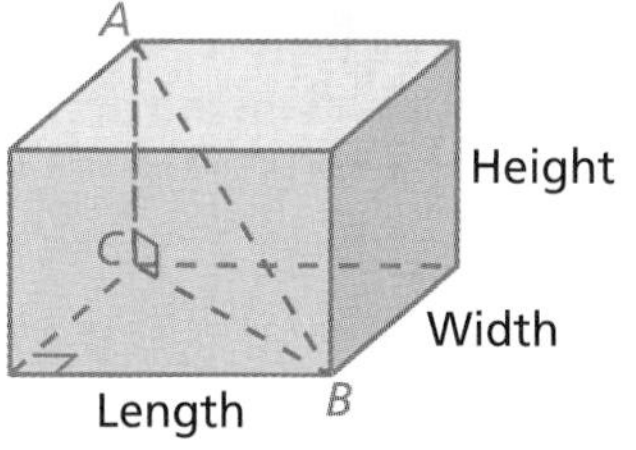

22. Critical Thinking Plot the points $(-1, -2)$, $(2, 1)$, and $(-3, 6)$ in a coordinate plane. Are the points the vertices of a right triangle? Explain.

Fair Game Review What you learned in previous grades & lessons

Find the mean, median, and mode of the data. *(Skills Review Handbook)*

23. 12, 9, 17, 15, 12, 13

24. 21, 32, 16, 27, 22, 19, 10

25. 67, 59, 34, 71, 59

26. MULTIPLE CHOICE What is the sum of the angle measures of an octagon? *(Section 5.3)*

Ⓐ 720° Ⓑ 1080° Ⓒ 1440° Ⓓ 1800°

8.3–8.5 Quiz

Classify the real number. *(Section 8.3)*

1. $-\sqrt{225}$
2. $-1\frac{1}{9}$
3. $\sqrt{41}$

Estimate to the nearest integer. *(Section 8.3)*

4. $\sqrt{38}$
5. $-\sqrt{99}$
6. $\sqrt{172}$

Which number is greater? Explain. *(Section 8.3)*

7. $\sqrt{11}, 3\frac{3}{5}$
8. $\sqrt{1.44}, 1.1\overline{8}$

Simplify the expression. *(Section 8.4)*

9. $\sqrt{2} + 2\sqrt{2}$
10. $3\sqrt{15} - 7\sqrt{15}$
11. $\sqrt{\frac{6}{25}}$

Find the volume of the rectangular prism. *(Section 8.4)*

12.

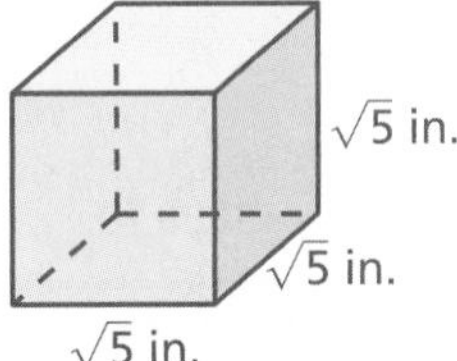

13.

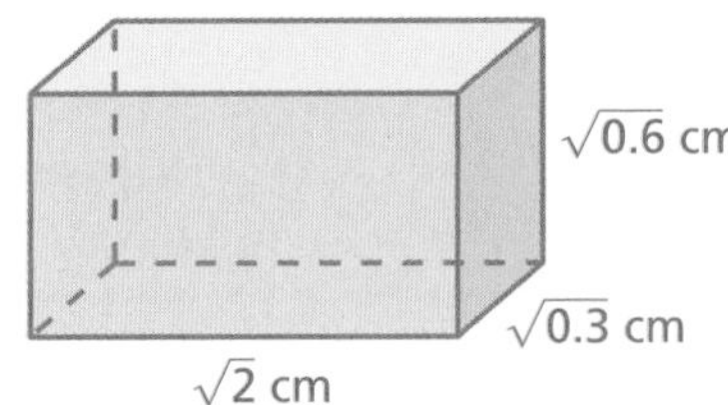

Use the figure to answer Exercises 14–17. Round your answer to the nearest tenth. *(Section 8.5)*

14. How far is the cabin from the peak?
15. How far is the fire tower from the lake?
16. How far is the lake from the peak?
17. You are standing at $(-5, -6)$. How far are you from the lake?

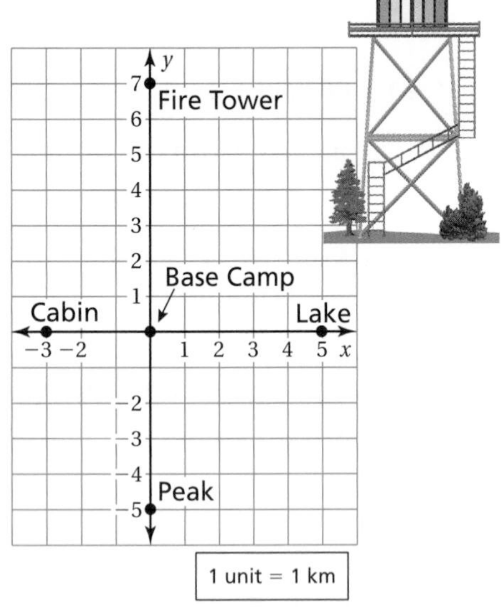

Tell whether the triangle with the given side lengths is a right triangle. *(Section 8.5)*

18.

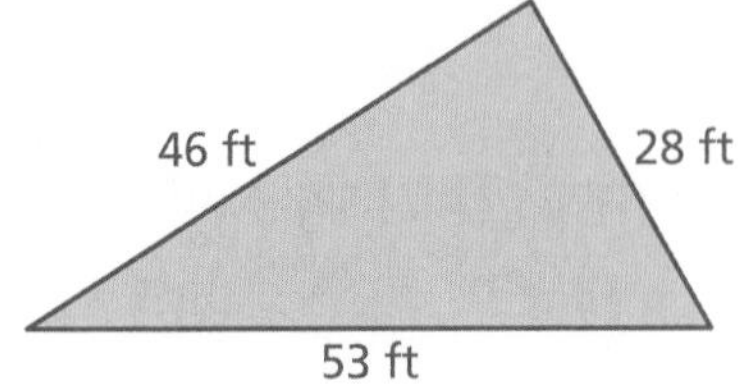

19.

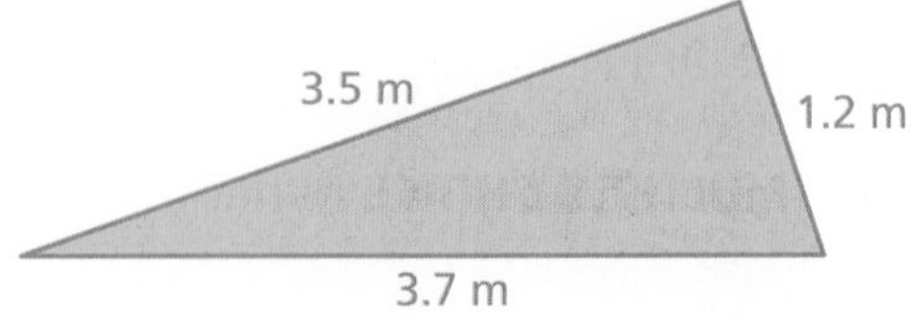

8 Chapter Review

Check It Out
Vocabulary Help
BigIdeasMath.com

Review Key Vocabulary

square root, *p. 358*
perfect square, *p. 358*
radical sign, *p. 358*
radicand, *p. 358*
theorem, *p. 362*
legs, *p. 364*
hypotenuse, *p. 364*
Pythagorean Theorem, *p. 364*
irrational number, *p. 372*
real numbers, *p. 372*
Pythagorean triple, *p. 387*

Review Examples and Exercises

8.1 Finding Square Roots *(pp. 356–361)*

Find the square root(s).

a. $-\sqrt{36}$

$-\sqrt{36}$ represents the *negative* square root.

Because $6^2 = 36$, $-\sqrt{36} = -\sqrt{6^2} = -6$.

b. $\sqrt{1.96}$

$\sqrt{1.96}$ represents the *positive* square root.

Because $1.4^2 = 1.96$, $\sqrt{1.96} = \sqrt{1.4^2} = 1.4$.

c. $\pm\sqrt{\frac{16}{81}}$

$\pm\sqrt{\frac{16}{81}}$ represents both the *positive and negative* square roots.

Because $\left(\frac{4}{9}\right)^2 = \frac{16}{81}$, $\pm\sqrt{\frac{16}{81}} = \pm\sqrt{\left(\frac{4}{9}\right)^2} = \frac{4}{9}$ and $-\frac{4}{9}$.

Exercises

Find the two square roots of the number.

1. 16
2. 900
3. 2500

Find the square root(s).

4. $\sqrt{1}$
5. $-\sqrt{\frac{9}{25}}$
6. $\pm\sqrt{1.69}$

Evaluate the expression.

7. $15 - 4\sqrt{16}$
8. $\sqrt{\frac{54}{6}} + \frac{2}{3}$
9. $10\left(\sqrt{81} - 12\right)$

8.2 The Pythagorean Theorem (pp. 362–367)

Find the length of the hypotenuse of the triangle.

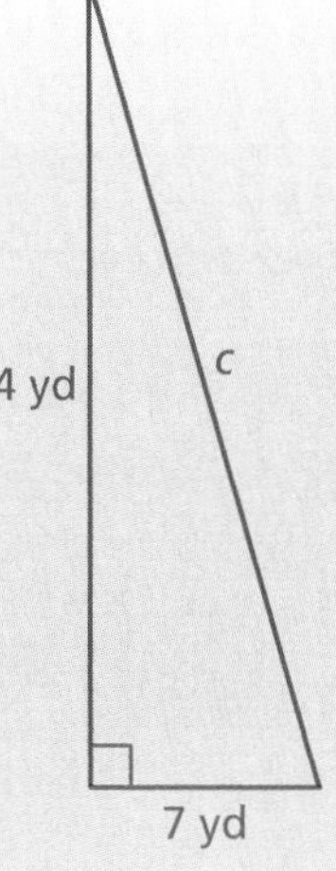

$a^2 + b^2 = c^2$	Write the Pythagorean Theorem.
$7^2 + 24^2 = c^2$	Substitute.
$49 + 576 = c^2$	Evaluate powers.
$625 = c^2$	Add.
$\sqrt{625} = \sqrt{c^2}$	Take positive square root of each side.
$25 = c$	Simplify.

The length of the hypotenuse is 25 yards.

Exercises

Find the missing length of the triangle.

10.

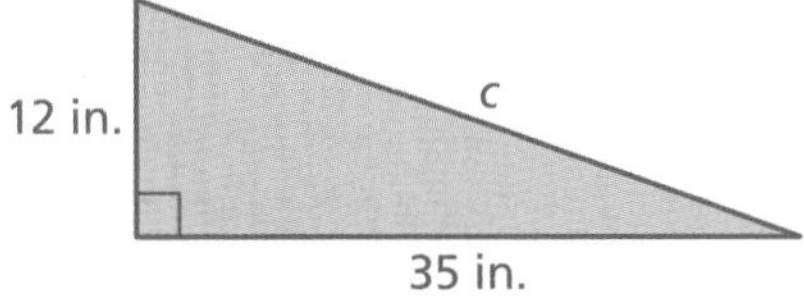

11.

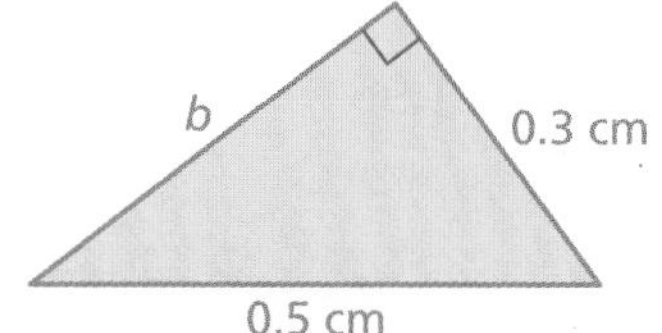

8.3 Approximating Square Roots (pp. 370–377)

Estimate $\sqrt{34}$ to the nearest integer.

Use a number line and the square roots of the perfect squares nearest to the radicand. The nearest perfect square less than 34 is 25. The nearest perfect square greater than 34 is 36.

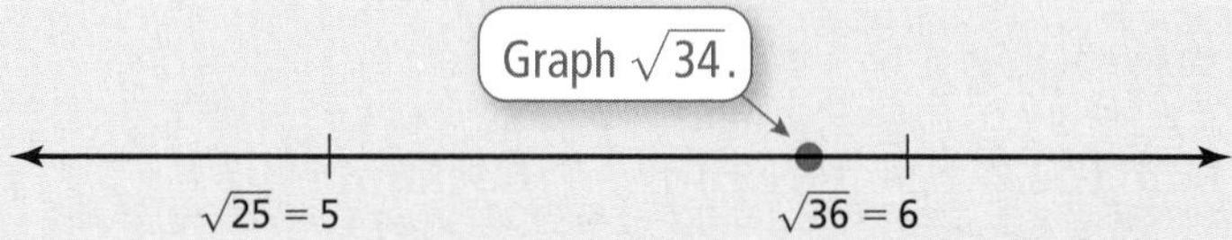

Because 34 is closer to 36 than to 25, $\sqrt{34}$ is closer to 6 than to 5.

So, $\sqrt{34} \approx 6$.

Exercises

Estimate to the nearest integer.

12. $\sqrt{14}$ **13.** $\sqrt{90}$ **14.** $\sqrt{175}$

8.4 Simplifying Square Roots (pp. 378–383)

Simplify $\sqrt{28}$.

$\sqrt{28} = \sqrt{4 \cdot 7}$ Factor using the greatest perfect square factor.

$= \sqrt{4} \cdot \sqrt{7}$ Use the Product Property of Square Roots.

$= 2\sqrt{7}$ Simplify.

Simplify $\sqrt{\frac{13}{64}}$.

$\sqrt{\frac{13}{64}} = \frac{\sqrt{13}}{\sqrt{64}}$ Use the Quotient Property of Square Roots.

$= \frac{\sqrt{13}}{8}$ Simplify.

Exercises

Simplify the expression.

15. $\sqrt{\frac{99}{100}}$

16. $\sqrt{96}$

17. $\sqrt{75}$

8.5 Using the Pythagorean Theorem (pp. 384–389)

Find the height of the stilt walker. Round your answer to the nearest tenth.

$a^2 + b^2 = c^2$ Write the Pythagorean Theorem.

$6^2 + x^2 = 13^2$ Substitute.

$36 + x^2 = 169$ Evaluate powers.

$x^2 = 133$ Subtract 36 from each side.

$\sqrt{x^2} = \sqrt{133}$ Take positive square root of each side.

$x \approx 11.5$ Use a calculator.

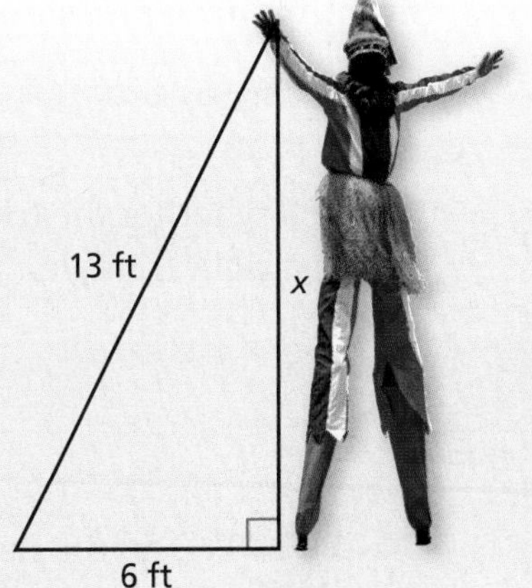

∴ The height of the stilt walker is about 11.5 feet.

Exercises

Find the height x. Round your answer to the nearest tenth, if necessary.

18.

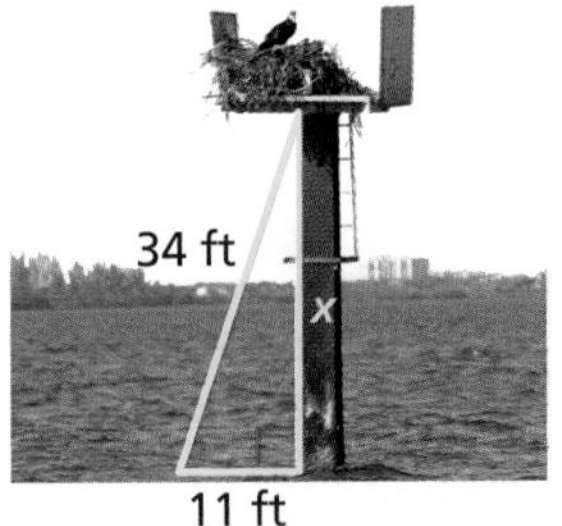

19.

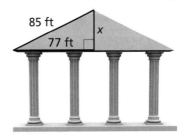

85 ft

77 ft

x

8 Chapter Test

Find the square root(s).

1. $-\sqrt{1600}$

2. $\sqrt{\frac{25}{49}}$

3. $\pm\sqrt{\frac{100}{9}}$

Evaluate the expression.

4. $12 + 8\sqrt{16}$

5. $\frac{1}{2} + \sqrt{\frac{72}{2}}$

6. Find the missing length of the triangle.

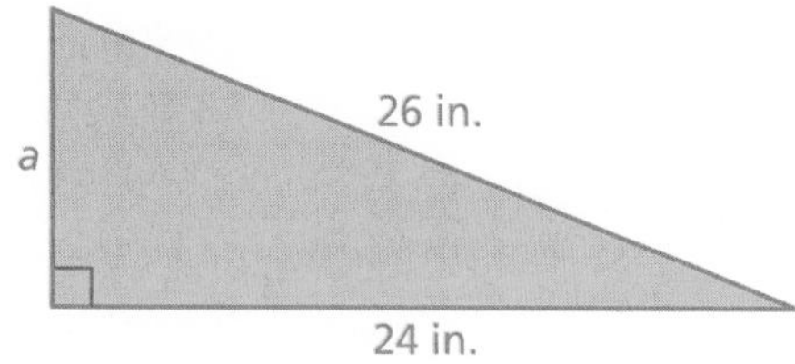

Classify the real number.

7. 16π

8. $-\sqrt{49}$

Which number is greater? Explain.

9. $\sqrt{0.16}, \frac{1}{2}$

10. $\sqrt{45}, 6.\overline{3}$

Simplify the expression.

11. $6\sqrt{5} + 5\sqrt{5}$

12. $\sqrt{250}$

13. Tell whether the triangle is a right triangle.

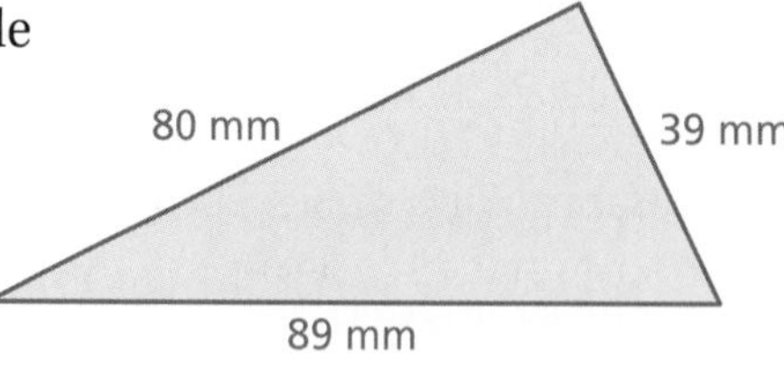

14. ROBOT Find the height of the dinosaur robot.

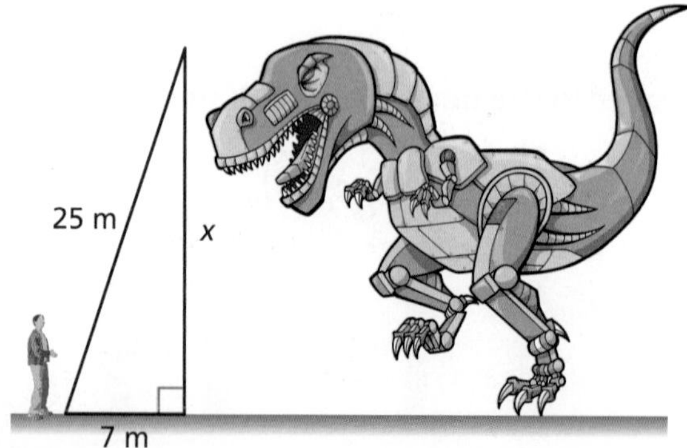

15. SUPERHERO Find the altitude of the superhero balloon.

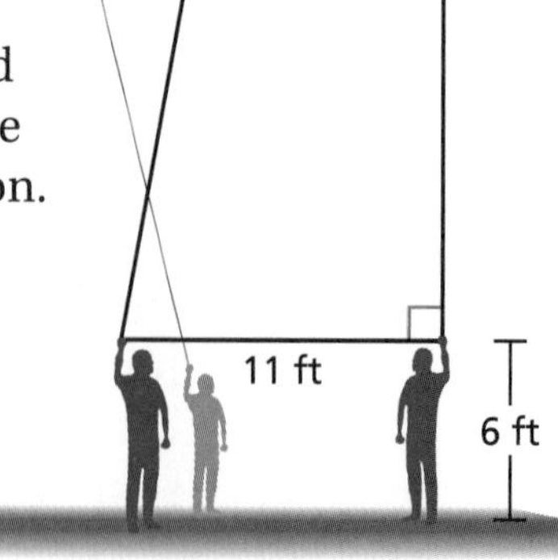

8 Standardized Test Practice

Test-Taking Strategy
Answer Easy Questions First
Was Fluffy in our kitchen?
There's √4 different tongue prints on the butter. How many cats licked the butter?
A 1
B 2
C -2
D 4
"Scan the test and answer the easy questions first. You know the square root of 4 is 2."

1. The period T of a pendulum is the time, in seconds, it takes the pendulum to swing back and forth. The period can be found using the formula $T = 1.1\sqrt{L}$, where L is the length, in feet, of the pendulum. A pendulum has a length of 4 feet. Find its period.

   A. 5.1 sec **C.** 3.1 sec

   B. 4.4 sec **D.** 2.2 sec

2. The steps Pat took to write the equation in slope-intercept form are shown below. What should Pat change in order to correctly rewrite the equation in slope-intercept form?

$$3x - 6y = 1$$
$$3x = 6y + 1$$
$$x = 2y + \frac{1}{3}$$

   F. Use the formula $m = \frac{\text{rise}}{\text{run}}$.

   G. Use the formula $m = \frac{\text{run}}{\text{rise}}$.

   H. Subtract $3x$ from both sides of the equation and divide every term by -6.

   I. Subtract 1 from both sides of the equation and divide every term by 3.

3. A housing community started with 60 homes. In each of the following years, 8 more homes were built. Let y represent the number of years that have passed since the first year and let n represent the number of homes. Which equation describes the relationship between n and y?

   A. $n = 8y + 60$ **C.** $n = 60y + 8$

   B. $n = 68y$ **D.** $n = 60 + 8 + y$

4. The domain of a function is 0, 1, 2, 3, 4, 5. What can you conclude?

   F. The domain is continuous. **H.** The function is linear.

   G. The domain is discrete. **I.** The range is 0, 1, 2, 3, 4, 5.

5. A football field is 40 yards wide and 120 yards long. Find the distance between opposite corners of the football field. Show your work and explain your reasoning.

6. A computer consultant charges $50 plus $40 for each hour she works. The consultant charged $650 for one job. This can be represented by the equation below, where h represents the number of hours worked.

$$40h + 50 = 650$$

How many hours did the consultant work?

7. The formula below can be used to find the number S of degrees in a polygon with n sides. Solve the formula for n.

$$S = 180(n - 2)$$

A. $n = 180(S - 2)$

B. $n = \dfrac{S}{180} + 2$

C. $n = \dfrac{S}{180} - 2$

D. $n = \dfrac{S}{180} + \dfrac{1}{90}$

8. The table below shows a linear pattern. Which linear function relates y to x?

x	1	2	3	4	5
y	4	2	0	−2	−4

F. $y = 2x + 2$

G. $y = 4x$

H. $y = -2x + 2$

I. $y = -2x + 6$

9. What is the value of x in the right triangle shown?

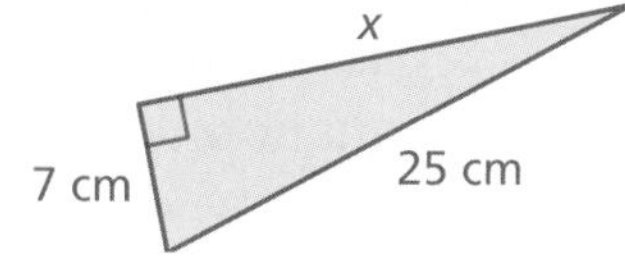

A. 16 cm

B. 18 cm

C. 24 cm

D. $\sqrt{674}$ cm

10. Find the height of the tree in the diagram.

F. 22.5 ft

G. 31.5 ft

H. 35 ft

I. 40 ft

11. Which expression is equivalent to $12\sqrt{24}$?

A. $48\sqrt{6}$

B. $24\sqrt{12}$

C. $24\sqrt{6}$

D. 6

12. The measure of an angle is x degrees. What is the measure of its complement?

F. $(90 - x)°$

G. $(180 - x)°$

H. $(x - 90)°$

I. $(x - 180)°$

13. You fill up the gas tank of your car and begin driving on the interstate. You drive at an average speed of 60 miles per hour. The amount g, in gallons, of gas left in your car can be estimated. Use the formula shown below, where h is the number of hours you have been driving.

$$g = 18 - 2.5h$$

You will fill up when you have 3 gallons of gas left in the gas tank. How long after you start driving will you fill up again?

A. about 36 min

B. about 6.0 h

C. about 7.2 h

D. about 8.4 h

14. An airplane flies 56 miles due north and then 33 miles due east. How many miles is the plane from its starting point?

15. Which graph represents the linear equation $y = -2x - 2$?

F.

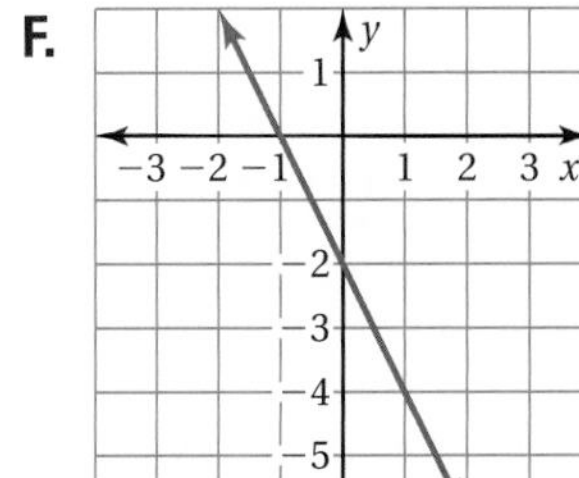

H.

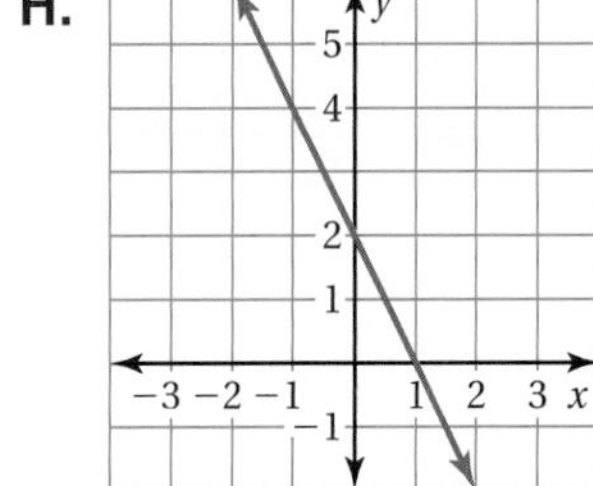

G.

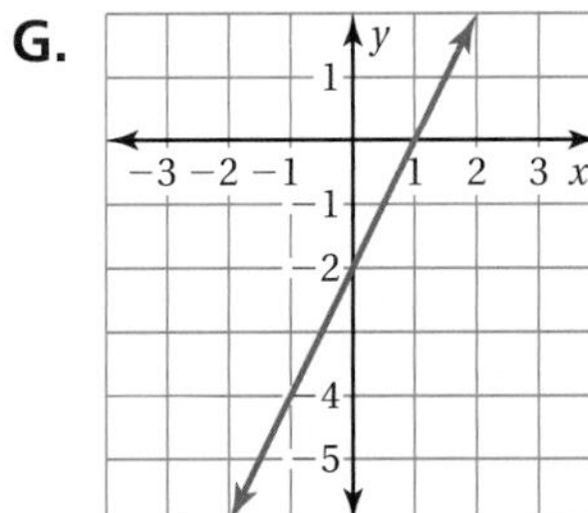

I.

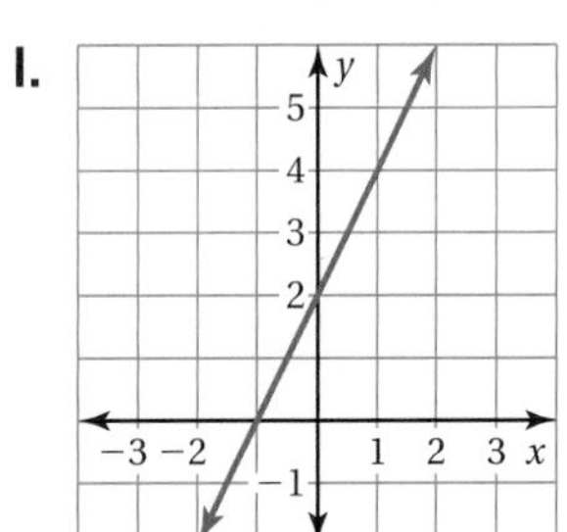

9 Data Displays and Probability

"Wow. The number of minutes I can dog paddle is growing like crazy!"

"Please hold still. I am trying to find the mean of 6, 8, and 10 by dividing their sum into three equal piles."

What You Learned Before

The one with the mouse, of course!
"Behind two of the doors is a doggy biscuit. Behind the other door is a mouse. Which door do you choose?"

Displaying Data

Example 1 **The table shows the results of a survey. Display the data in a circle graph.**

Class Trip Location	Water Park	Museum	Zoo	Other
Students	25	11	5	4

A total of 45 students took the survey.

Water park:

$$\frac{25}{45} \cdot 360^\circ = 200^\circ$$

Museum:

$$\frac{11}{45} \cdot 360^\circ = 88^\circ$$

Zoo:

$$\frac{5}{45} \cdot 360^\circ = 40^\circ$$

Other:

$$\frac{4}{45} \cdot 360^\circ = 32^\circ$$

Class Trip Locations

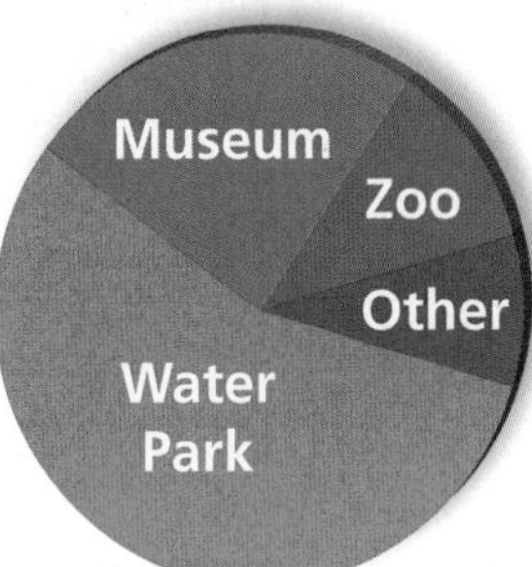

Example 2 **The frequency table shows the number of books that 12 people read last month. Display the data in a histogram.**

Books Read Last Month	Frequency
0–1	6
2–3	4
4–5	0
6–7	2

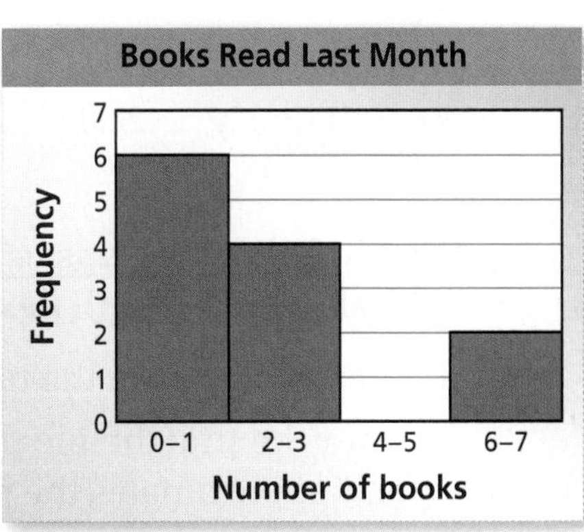

Try It Yourself

1. Conduct a survey to determine the after-school activities of students in your class. Display the results in a circle graph.
2. Conduct a survey to determine the number of pets owned by students in your class. Display the results in a histogram.

9.1 Scatter Plots and Lines of Best Fit

STANDARDS OF LEARNING

8.13

Essential Question How can you use data to predict an event?

1 ACTIVITY: Representing Data by a Linear Equation

Work with a partner. You have been working on a science project for 8 months. Each month, you have measured the length of a baby alligator.

The table shows your measurements.

Month, x	0 (September)	1	2	3	4	5	6	7 (April)
Length (in.), y	22.0	22.5	23.5	25.0	26.0	27.5	28.5	29.5

Use the following steps to predict the baby alligator's length next September.

a. Graph the data in the table.

b. Draw the straight line that you think best approximates the points.

c. Write an equation of the line you drew.

d. Use the equation to predict the baby alligator's length next September.

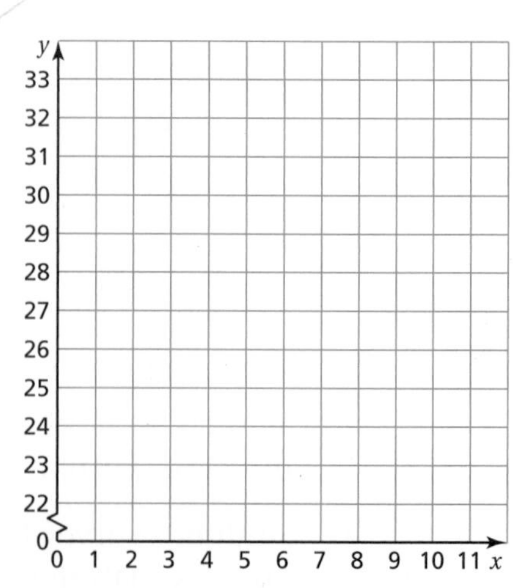

2 ACTIVITY: Representing Data by a Linear Equation

Work with a partner. You are a biologist and are studying bat populations.

You are asked to predict the number of bats that will be living in an abandoned mine in 3 years.

To start, you find the number of bats that have been living in the mine during the past 8 years.

The table shows the results of your research.

7 years ago → Year 0; this year → Year 7

Year, x	0	1	2	3	4	5	6	7
Bats (thousands), y	327	306	299	270	254	232	215	197

Use the following steps to predict the number of bats that will be living in the mine after 3 years.

a. Graph the data in the table.

b. Draw the straight line that you think best approximates the points.

c. Write an equation of the line you drew.

d. Use the equation to predict the number of bats in 3 years.

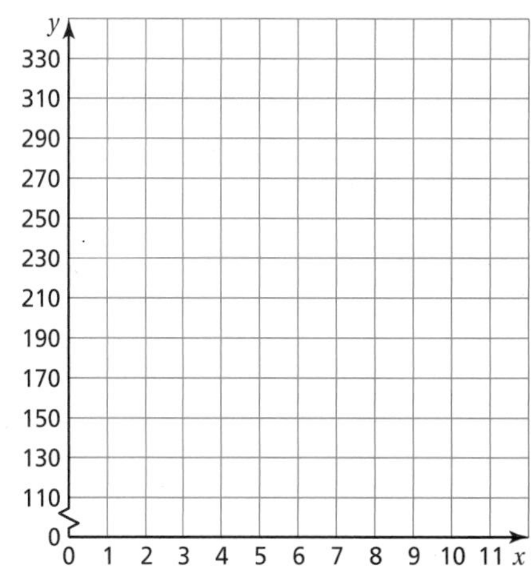

What Is Your Answer?

3. IN YOUR OWN WORDS How can you use data to predict an event?

4. Use the Internet or some other reference to find data that appear to have a linear pattern. List the data in a table and graph the data. Use an equation that is based on the data to predict a future event.

Practice Use what you learned about scatter plots and lines of best fit to complete Exercise 3 on page 405.

Key Vocabulary
scatter plot, *p. 402*
line of best fit, *p. 404*

Scatter Plot

A **scatter plot** is a graph that shows the relationship between two data sets. The two sets of data are graphed as ordered pairs in a coordinate plane.

EXAMPLE 

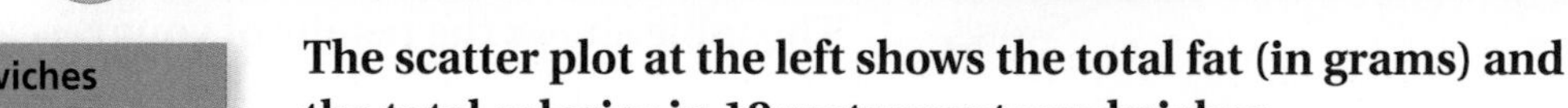

Restaurant Sandwiches

The scatter plot at the left shows the total fat (in grams) and the total calories in 12 restaurant sandwiches.

a. How many calories are in the sandwich that contains 17 grams of fat?

Draw a horizontal line from the point that has an x-value of 17. It crosses the y-axis at 400.

So, the sandwich has 400 calories.

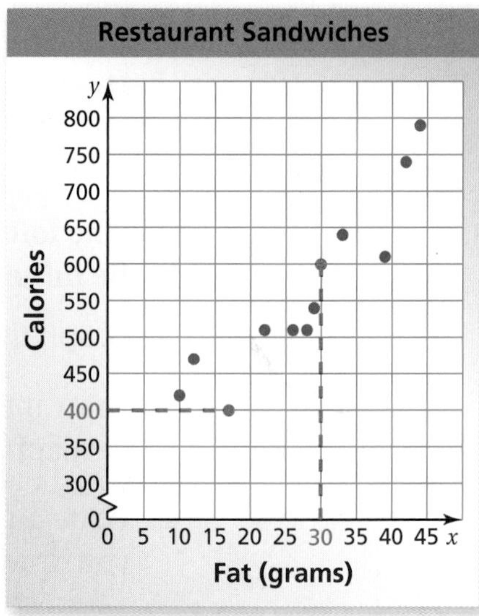

b. How many grams of fat are in the sandwich that contains 600 calories?

Draw a vertical line from the point that has a y-value of 600. It crosses the x-axis at 30.

So, the sandwich has 30 grams of fat.

c. What tends to happen to the number of calories as the number of grams of fat increases?

Looking at the graph, the plotted points go up from left to right.

So, as the number of grams of fat increases, the number of calories increases.

On Your Own

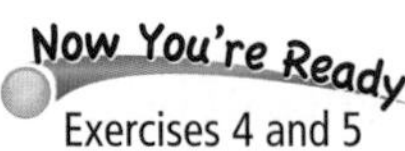

1. **WHAT IF?** A sandwich has 650 calories. Based on the scatter plot in Example 1, how many grams of fat would you expect the sandwich to have? Explain your reasoning.

A scatter plot can show that a relationship exists between two data sets.

Positive Relationship

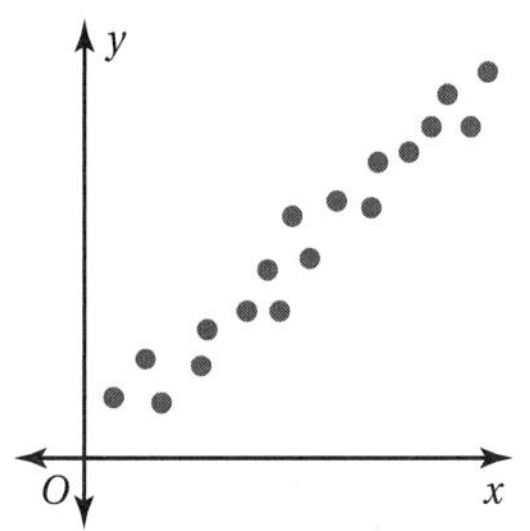

As x increases, y increases.

Negative Relationship

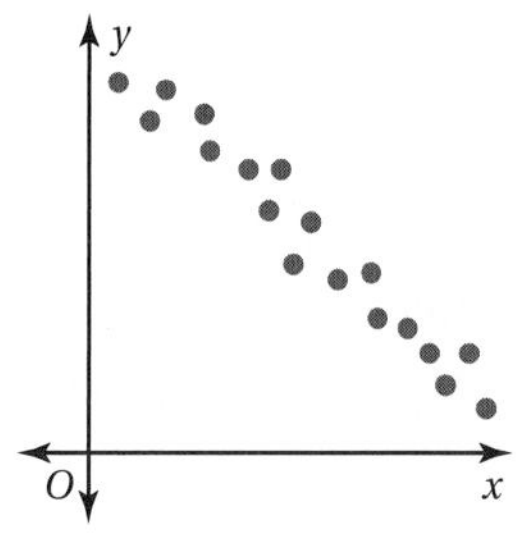

As x increases, y decreases.

No Relationship

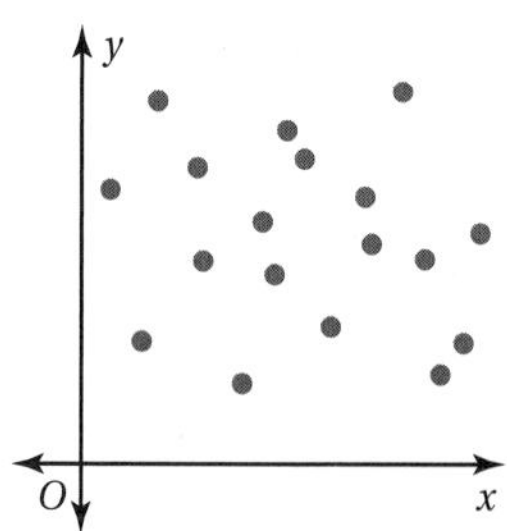

The points show no pattern.

EXAMPLE 2 Identifying a Relationship

Tell whether the data show a *positive*, a *negative*, or *no* relationship.

a. Television size and price

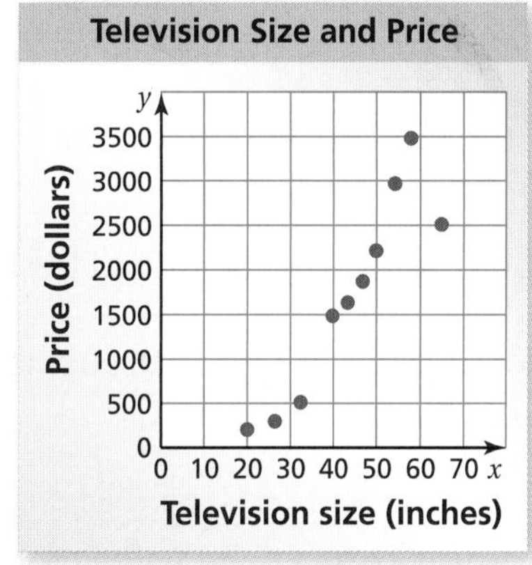
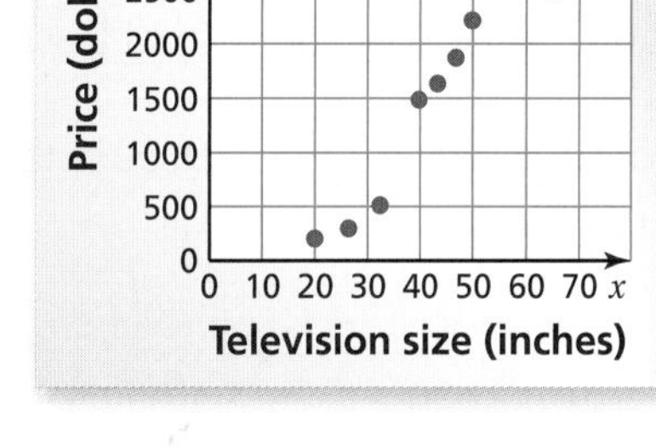

As the size of the television increases, the price increases.

So, the scatter plot shows a positive relationship.

b. Age and number of pets owned

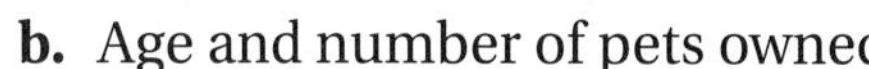

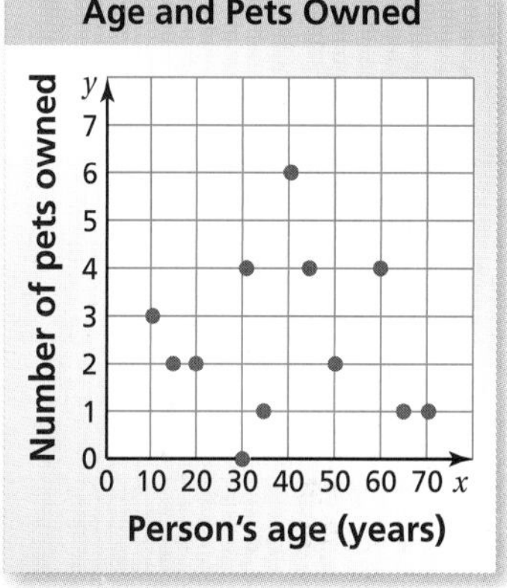

The number of pets owned does not depend on a person's age.

So, the scatter plot shows no relationship.

On Your Own

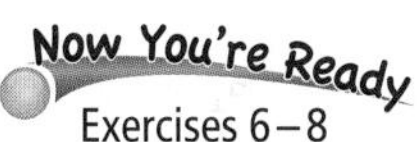

Make a scatter plot of the data. Tell whether the data show a *positive*, a *negative*, or *no* relationship.

2.

Study Time (min), x	30	20	60	90	45	10	30	75	120	80
Test Score, y	87	74	92	97	85	62	83	90	95	91

3.

Age of a Car (years), x	1	2	3	4	5	6	7	8
Value (thousands), y	\$24	\$21	\$19	\$18	\$15	\$12	\$8	\$7

A **line of best fit** is a line drawn on a scatter plot that is close to most of the data points. It can be used to estimate data on a graph.

EXAMPLE 3 Finding a Line of Best Fit

Week, x	Sales (millions), y
1	\$19
2	\$15
3	\$13
4	\$11
5	\$10
6	\$8
7	\$7
8	\$5

The table shows the weekly sales of a DVD and the number of weeks since its release. (a) Make a scatter plot of the data. (b) Draw a line of best fit. (c) Write an equation of the line of best fit. (d) Predict the sales in week 9.

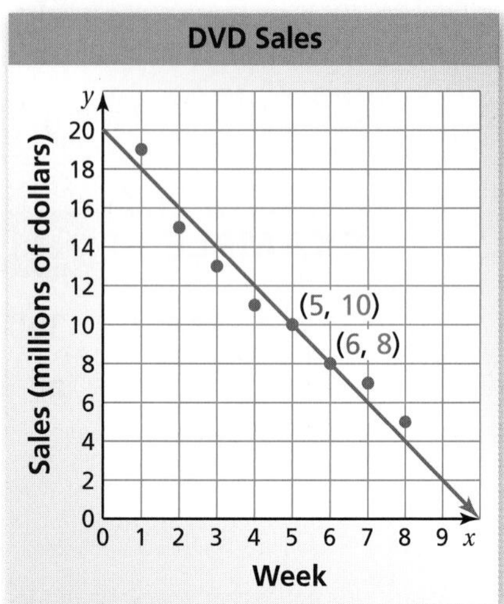

a. Plot the points in a coordinate plane. The scatter plot shows a negative relationship.

b. Draw a line that is close to the data points. Try to have as many points above the line as below it.

c. The line passes through (5, 10) and (6, 8).

$$\text{slope} = \frac{\text{rise}}{\text{run}} = \frac{-2}{1} = -2$$

Because the line crosses the y-axis at (0, 20), the y-intercept is 20.

So, the equation of the line of best fit is $y = -2x + 20$.

d. To predict the sales for week 9, substitute 9 for x in the equation of the line of best fit.

$y = -2x + 20$ Line of best fit

$= -2(9) + 20$ Substitute 9 for x.

$= 2$ Evaluate.

The sales in week 9 should be about \$2 million.

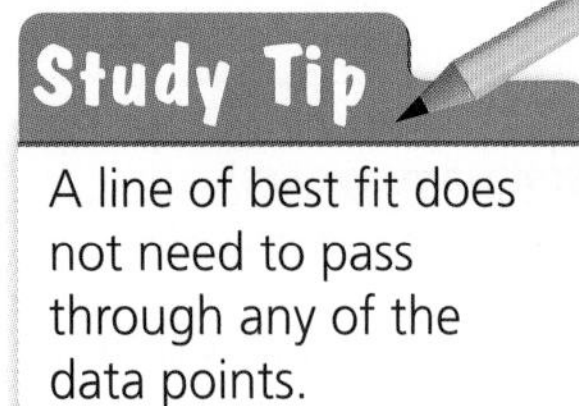

A line of best fit does not need to pass through any of the data points.

On Your Own

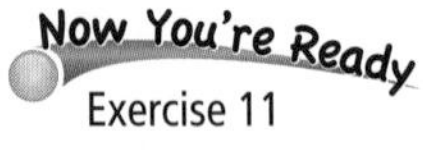

4. The table shows the number of people who have attended a neighborhood festival over an 8-year period.

Year, x	1	2	3	4	5	6	7	8
Attendance, y	420	500	650	900	1100	1500	1750	2400

a. Make a scatter plot of the data.

b. Draw a line of best fit.

c. Write an equation of the line of best fit.

d. Predict the number of people who will attend the festival in year 10.

9.1 Exercises

Vocabulary and Concept Check

1. **VOCABULARY** What type of data is needed to make a scatter plot? Explain.
2. **WRITING** Explain why a line of best fit is helpful when analyzing data.

Practice and Problem Solving

3. **BLUEBERRIES** The table shows the weight y of x pints of blueberries.

Number of Pints, x	0	1	2	3	4	5
Weight (pounds), y	0	0.8	1.50	2.20	3.0	3.75

   a. Graph the data in the table.
   b. Draw the straight line that you think best approximates the points.
   c. Write an equation of the line you drew.
   d. Use the equation to predict the weight of 10 pints of blueberries.
   e. Blueberries cost $2.25 per pound. How much do 10 pints of blueberries cost?

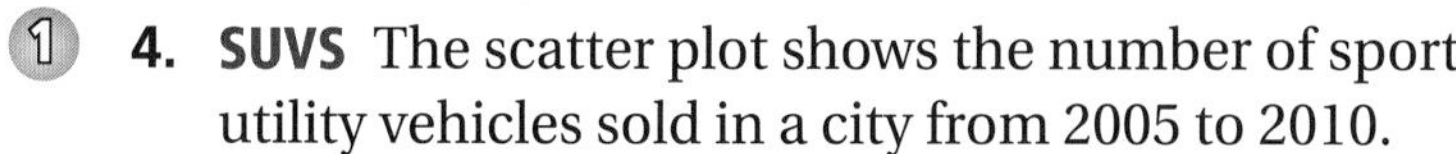

1 4. **SUVS** The scatter plot shows the number of sport utility vehicles sold in a city from 2005 to 2010.

   a. In what year were 1000 SUVs sold?
   b. About how many SUVs were sold in 2009?
   c. Describe the relationship shown by the data.

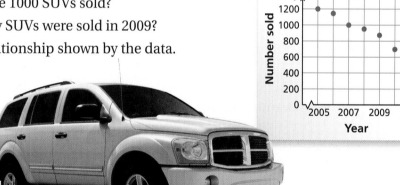

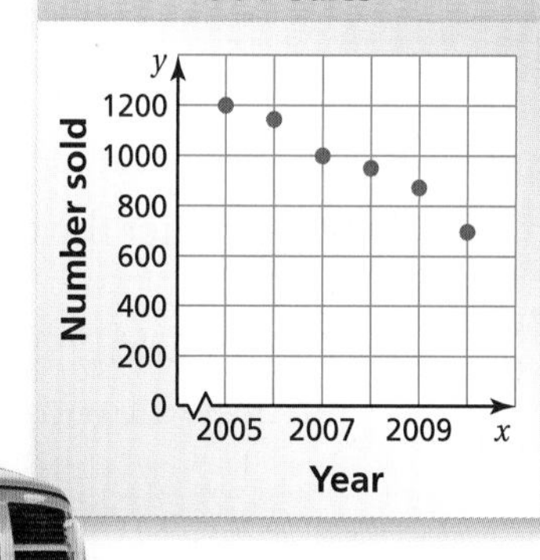

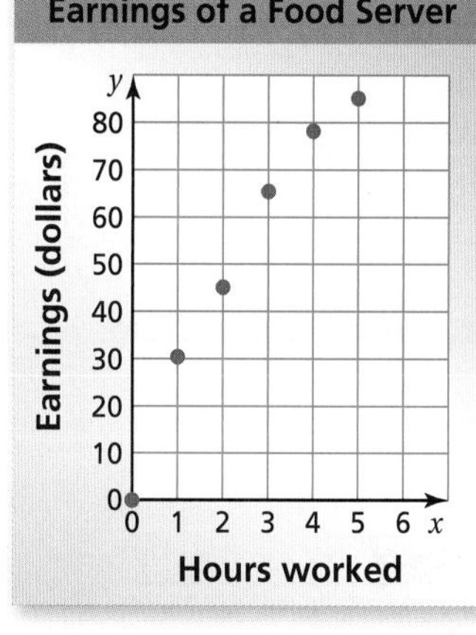

5. **EARNINGS** The scatter plot shows the total earnings (wages and tips) of a food server during 1 day.
   a. About how many hours must the server work to earn $70?
   b. About how much did the server earn for 5 hours of work?
   c. Describe the relationship shown by the data.

Tell whether the data show a *positive*, a *negative*, or *no* relationship.

2 **6.**

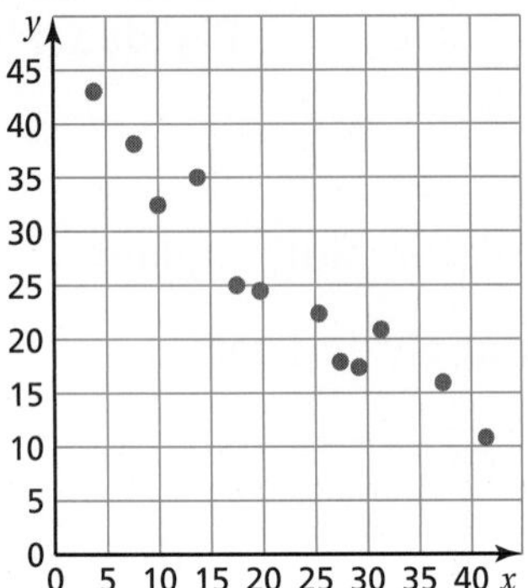

7.

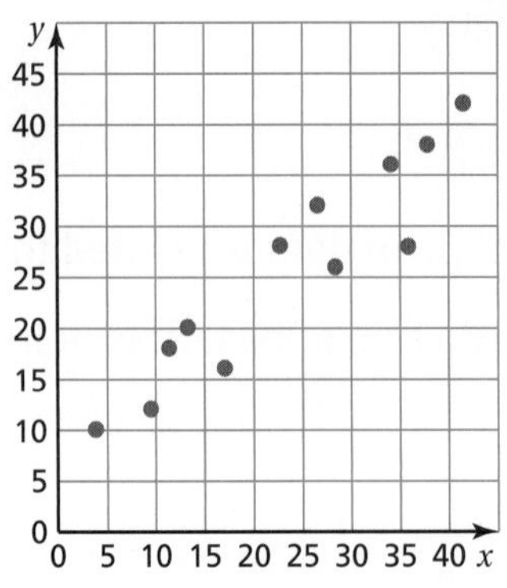

8.

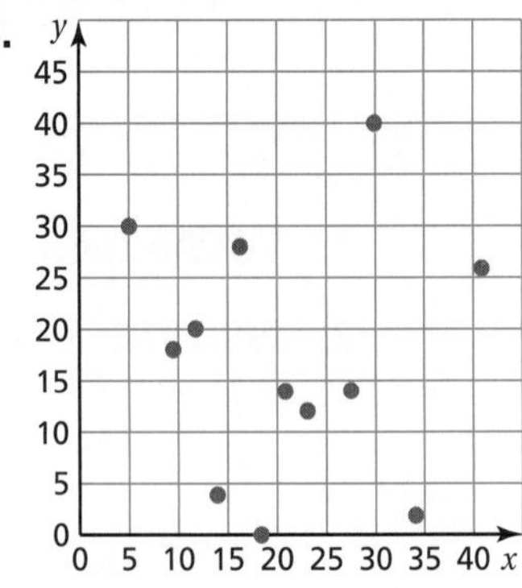

9. HONEYBEES The table shows the number of honeybee colonies in the United States from 2003 to 2006. What type of relationship does the data show?

Year, x	2003	2004	2005	2006
Honeybee Colonies (millions), y	2.599	2.556	2.413	2.392

10. OPEN-ENDED Describe a set of real-life data that has a positive relationship.

3 **11. VACATION** The table shows the distance you travel over a 6-hour period.

a. Make a scatter plot of the data.

b. Draw a line of best fit.

c. Write an equation of the line of best fit.

d. Predict the distance you will travel in 7 hours.

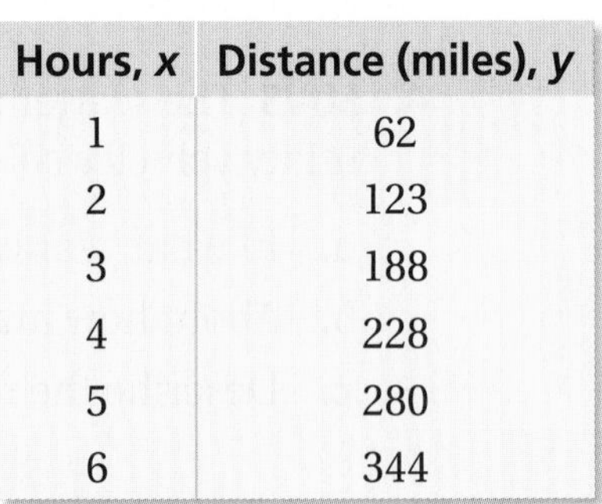

Hours, x	Distance (miles), y
1	62
2	123
3	188
4	228
5	280
6	344

12. ERROR ANALYSIS Describe and correct the error in drawing the line of best fit.

13. TEST SCORES The scatter plot shows the relationship between the number of minutes spent studying and the test scores for a science class.

a. What type of relationship does the data show?

b. Interpret the relationship.

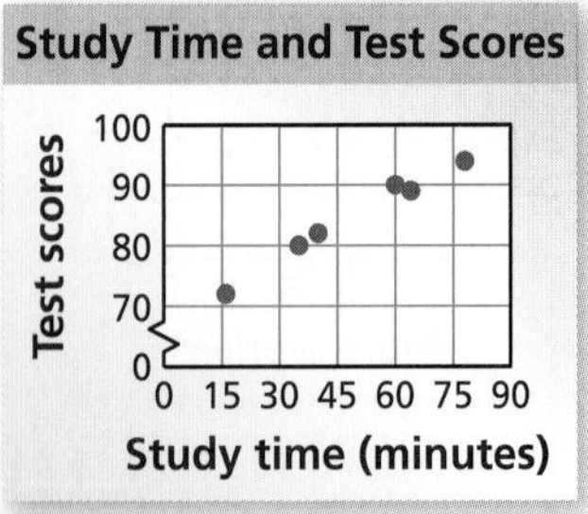

14. **REASONING** A data set has no relationship. Is it possible to find a line of best fit for the data? Explain.

15. **PROJECT** Use a ruler or a yardstick to find the height and arm span of three people.

  a. Make a scatter plot using the data you collected. Then draw a line of best fit for the data.
  b. Use your height and the line of best fit to predict your arm span.
  c. Measure your arm span. Compare the result with your prediction in part (b).
  d. Is there a relationship between a person's height x and arm span y? Explain.

16. 

The table shows the price of admission to a local theater and the yearly attendance for several years.

Price of Admission (dollars), x	Yearly Attendance, y
19.50	50,000
21.95	48,000
23.95	47,500
24.00	40,000
24.50	45,000
25.00	43,500

  a. Identify the outlier.
  b. How does the outlier affect a line of best fit? Explain.
  c. Make a scatter plot of the data and draw a line of best fit.
  d. Use the line of best fit to predict the attendance when the admission cost is $27.

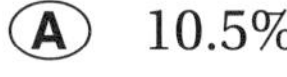

Fair Game Review What you learned in previous grades & lessons

Write the next three terms of the geometric sequence. *(Skills Review Handbook)*

17. $-2, 4, -8, 16, \ldots$

18. $96, 48, 24, 12, \ldots$

19. **MULTIPLE CHOICE** The circle graph shows the super powers chosen by a class. What percent of the students want strength as their super power? *(Skills Review Handbook)*

Ⓐ 10.5% Ⓑ 12.5%

Ⓒ 15% Ⓓ 25%

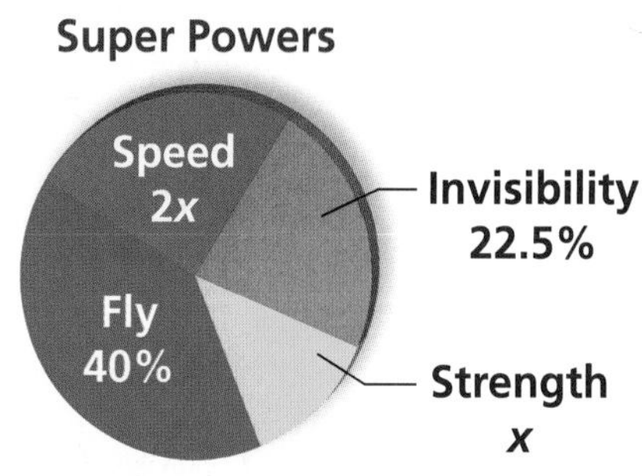

9.2 Choosing a Data Display

STANDARDS OF LEARNING
8.13

Essential Question How can you display data in a way that helps you make decisions?

1 ACTIVITY: Displaying Data

Work with a partner. Analyze and display each data set in a way that best describes the data. Explain your choice of display.

a. ROAD KILL A group of schools in New England participated in a 2-month study and reported 3962 dead animals.

Birds 307	Mammals 2746
Amphibians 145	Reptiles 75
Unknown 689	

b. BLACK BEAR ROAD KILL The data below show the number of black bears killed on Florida roads from 1987 to 2006.

1987	30	1994	47	2001	99
1988	37	1995	49	2002	129
1989	46	1996	61	2003	111
1990	33	1997	74	2004	127
1991	43	1998	88	2005	141
1992	35	1999	82	2006	135
1993	43	2000	109		

c. RACCOON ROAD KILL A 1-week study along a 4-mile section of road found the following weights (in pounds) of raccoons that had been killed by vehicles.

13.4	14.8	17.0	12.9
21.3	21.5	16.8	14.8
15.2	18.7	18.6	17.2
18.5	9.4	19.4	15.7
14.5	9.5	25.4	21.5
17.3	19.1	11.0	12.4
20.4	13.6	17.5	18.5
21.5	14.0	13.9	19.0

d. What do you think can be done to minimize the number of animals killed by vehicles?

2 ACTIVITY: Statistics Project

ENDANGERED SPECIES PROJECT Use the Internet or some other reference to write a report about an animal species that is (or has been) endangered. Include graphical displays of the data you have gathered.

Sample: Florida Key Deer

In 1939, Florida banned the hunting of Key deer. The numbers of Key deer fell to about 100 in the 1940s.

In 1947, public sentiment was stirred by 11-year-old Glenn Allen from Miami. Allen organized Boy Scouts and others in a letter-writing campaign that led to the establishment of the National Key Deer Refuge in 1957. The approximately 8600-acre refuge includes 2280 acres of designated wilderness.

Key Deer Refuge has increased the population of Key deer. A recent study estimated the total Key deer population to be between 700 and 800.

About half of Key deer deaths are due to vehicles.

One of two Key deer wildlife underpasses on Big Pine Key

What Is Your Answer?

3. **IN YOUR OWN WORDS** How can you display data in a way that helps you make decisions? Use the Internet or some other reference to find examples of the following types of data displays.

- Bar graph
- Circle graph
- Stem-and-leaf plot
- Scatter plot

Practice

Use what you learned about choosing data displays to complete Exercise 3 on page 413.

Data Display	What does it do?
Pictograph	shows data using pictures
Bar Graph	shows data in specific categories
Circle Graph	shows data as parts of a whole
Line Graph	shows how data change over time
Histogram	shows frequencies of data values in intervals of the same size
Stem-and-Leaf Plot	orders numerical data and shows how they are distributed
Line Plot	shows the number of times each value occurs in a data set
Scatter Plot	shows the relationship between two data sets using ordered pairs in a coordinate plane

EXAMPLE 1 Choosing an Appropriate Data Display

Choose an appropriate data display for the situation. Explain your reasoning.

a. the number of students in a marching band each year

∴ A line graph shows change over time. So, a line graph is an appropriate data display.

b. comparison of people's shoe sizes and their heights

∴ You want to compare two different data sets. So, a scatter plot is an appropriate data display.

On Your Own

Now You're Ready
Exercises 4–7

Choose an appropriate data display for the situation. Explain your reasoning.

1. the population of the United States divided into age groups
2. the percents of students in your school who play basketball, football, soccer, or lacrosse

EXAMPLE 2 Identifying an Appropriate Data Display

You record the number of hits for your school's new website for 5 months. Tell whether the data display is appropriate for representing how the number of hits changed during the 5 months. Explain your reasoning.

Month	Hits
August	250
September	320
October	485
November	650
December	925

a.

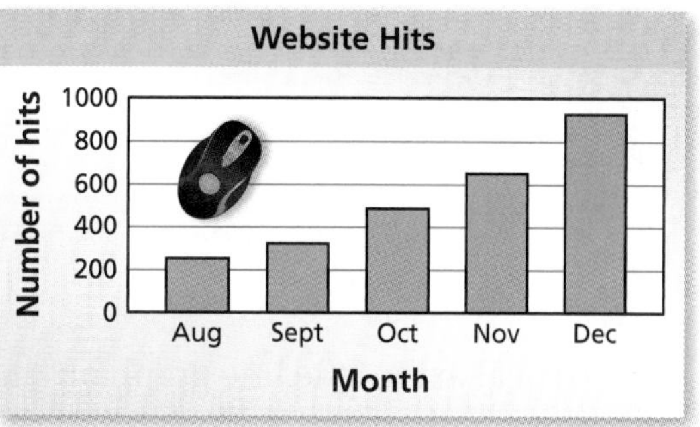

The bar graph shows the number of hits for each month. So, it is an appropriate data display.

b.

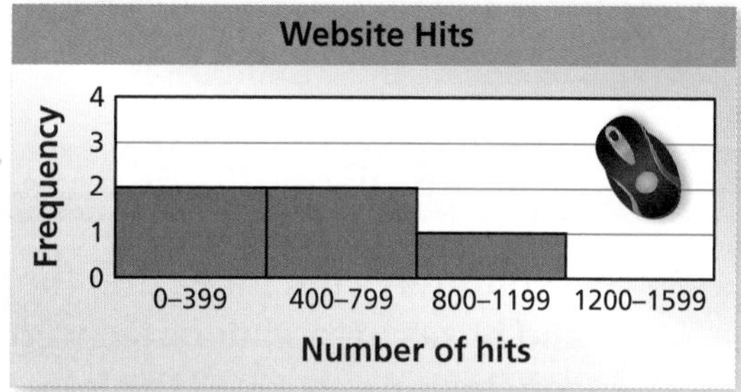

The histogram does not show the number of hits for each month or how the number of hits changes over time. So, it is *not* an appropriate data display.

c.

The line graph shows how the number of hits changes over time. So, it is an appropriate data display.

On Your Own

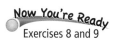

Now You're Ready
Exercises 8 and 9

Tell whether the data display is appropriate for representing the data in Example 2. Explain your reasoning.

3. line plot **4.** circle graph **5.** stem-and-leaf plot

EXAMPLE 3 Identifying a Misleading Data Display

Which line graph is misleading? Explain.

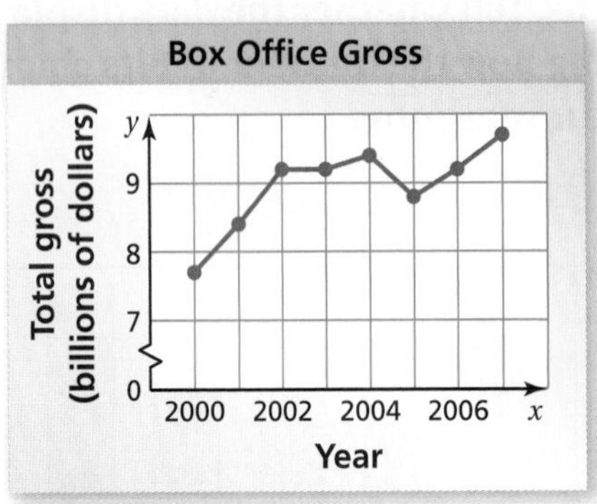

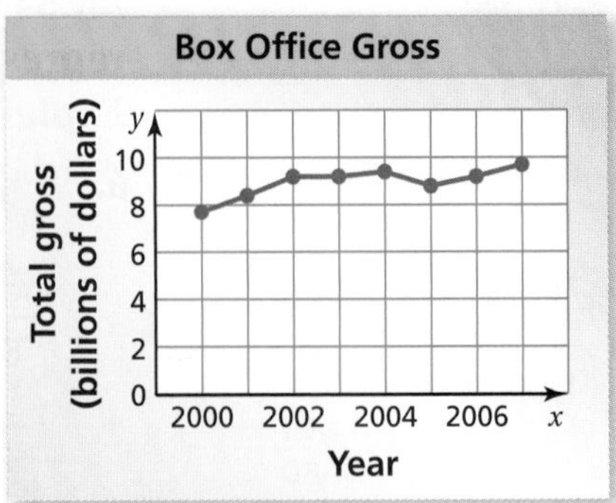

The vertical axis of the line graph on the left has a break (⚡) and begins at 7. This graph makes it appear that the total gross increased rapidly from 2000 to 2004. The graph on the right has an unbroken axis. It is more honest and shows that the total gross increased slowly.

So, the graph on the left is misleading.

EXAMPLE 4 Analyzing a Misleading Data Display

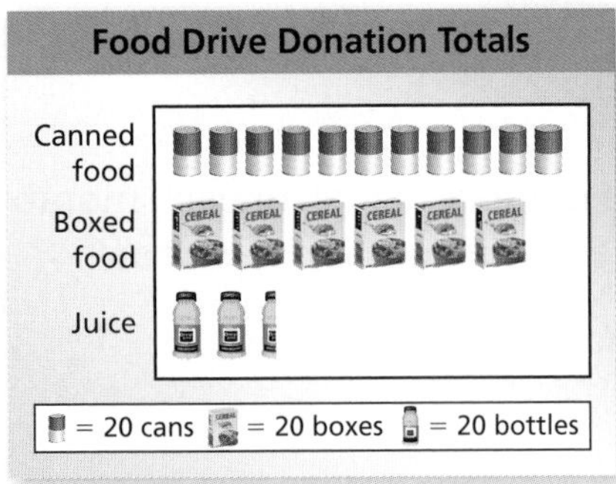

A volunteer concludes that the number of cans of food and boxes of food donated were about the same. Is this conclusion accurate? Explain.

Each icon represents the same number of items. Because the box icon is larger than the can icon, it looks like the number of boxes is about the same as the number of cans, but the number of boxes is actually about half of the number of cans.

So, the conclusion is not accurate.

On Your Own

Now You're Ready
Exercises 11–14

Explain why the data display is misleading.

6.

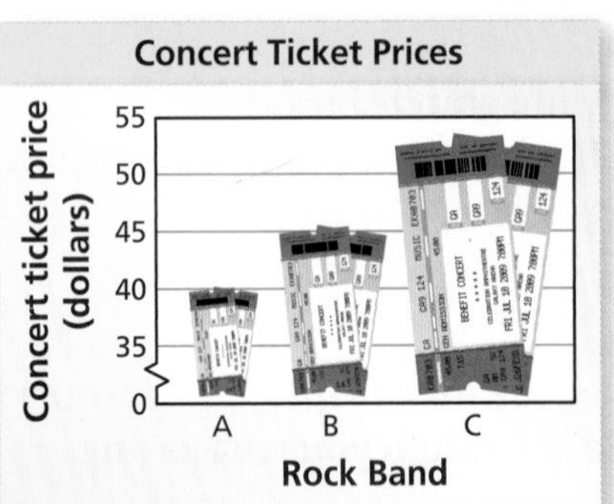

7.

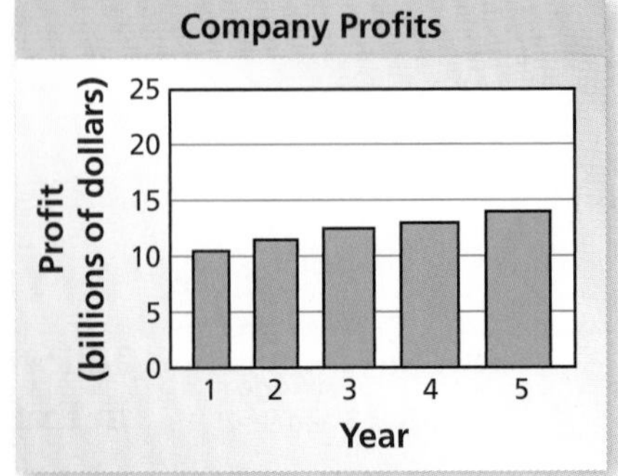

9.2 Exercises

Vocabulary and Concept Check

1. **REASONING** Can more than one display be appropriate for a data set? Explain.
2. **OPEN-ENDED** Describe how a histogram can be misleading.

Practice and Problem Solving

3. Analyze and display the data in a way that best describes the data. Explain your choice of display.

Notebooks Sold in One Week				
192 red	170 green	203 black	183 pink	230 blue
165 yellow	210 purple	250 orange	179 white	218 other

Choose an appropriate data display for the situation. Explain your reasoning.

① 4. a student's test scores and how the scores are spread out

5. the distance a person drives each month
6. the outcome of rolling a number cube
7. number of homework problems assigned each day

② 8. The table shows how many hours you worked as a lifeguard from May to August. Tell whether the data display is appropriate for representing how the number of hours worked changed during the 4 months. Explain your reasoning.

Lifeguard Schedule	
Month	**Hours Worked**
May	40
June	80
July	160
August	120

a.

May

June

July

August

Key: = 20 hours

b.

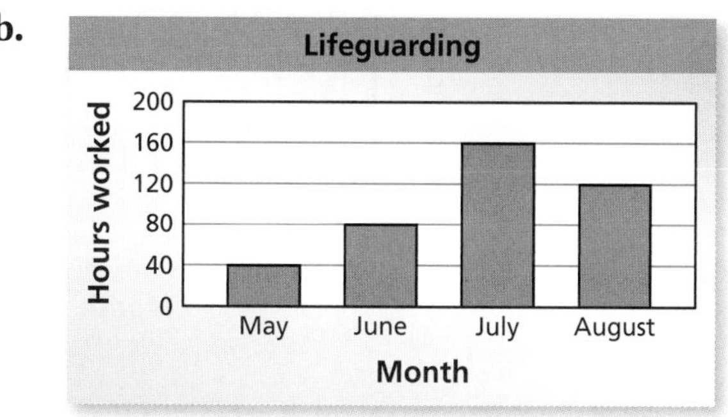

9. A survey asked 800 students to choose their favorite subject. The results are shown in the table. Tell whether the data display is appropriate for representing the portion of students who prefer math. Explain your reasoning.

Favorite School Subject	
Subject	**Number of Students**
Science	200
Math	160
Literature	240
Social Studies	120
Other	80

a.

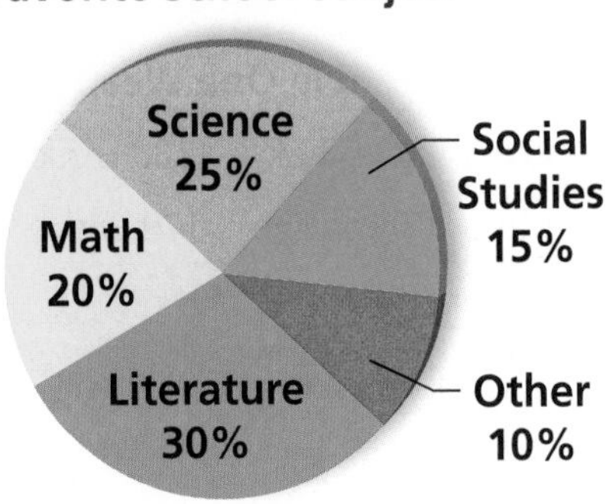

b.

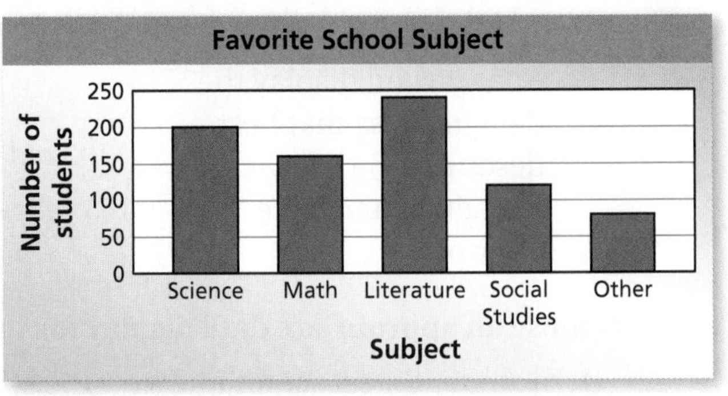

10. **WRITING** When should you use a histogram instead of a bar graph to display data? Use an example to support your answer.

Explain why the data display is misleading.

3 4 11.

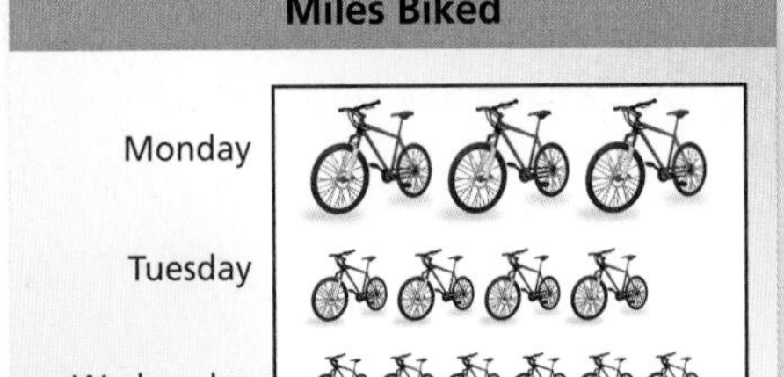

12.

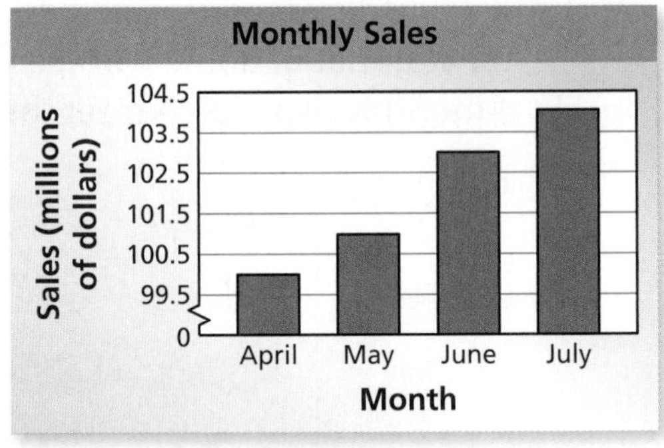

13.

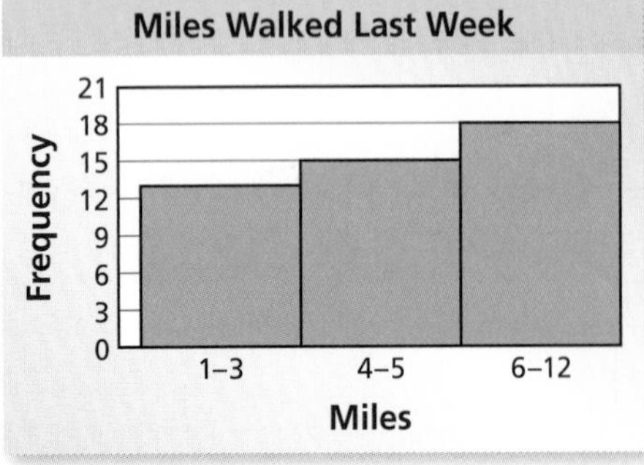

14.

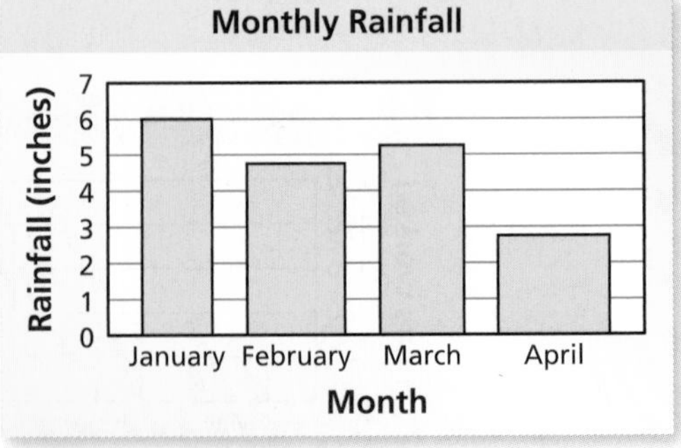

15. VEGETABLES A nutritionist wants to use a data display to show the favorite vegetables of the students at a school. Choose an appropriate data display for the situation. Explain your reasoning.

16. CHEMICALS A scientist gathers data about a decaying chemical compound. The results are shown in the scatter plot. Is the data display misleading? Explain.

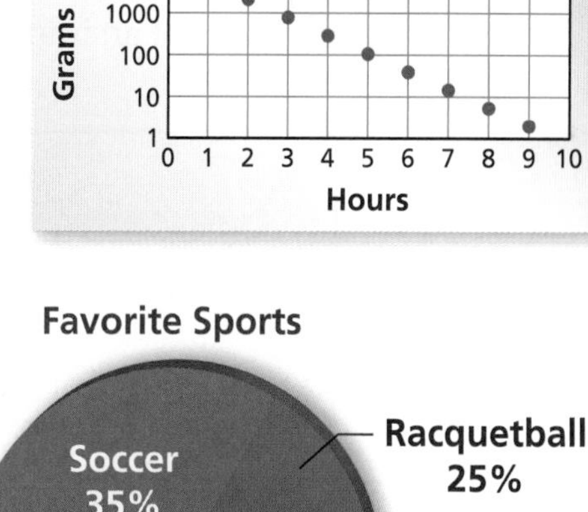

17. REASONING What type of data display is appropriate for showing the mode of a data set?

18. SPORTS A survey asked 100 students to choose their favorite sports. The results are shown in the circle graph.

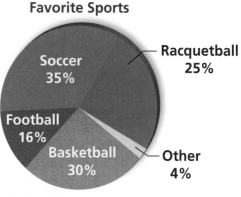

a. Explain why the graph is misleading.

b. What type of data display would be more appropriate for the data? Explain.

Favorite Sports

Soccer 35%
Racquetball 25%
Football 16%
Basketball 30%
Other 4%

19. Critical Thinking With the help of computers, mathematicians have computed and analyzed billions of digits of the irrational number π. One of the things they analyze is the frequency of each of the numbers 0 through 9. The table shows the frequency of each number in the first 100,000 digits of π.

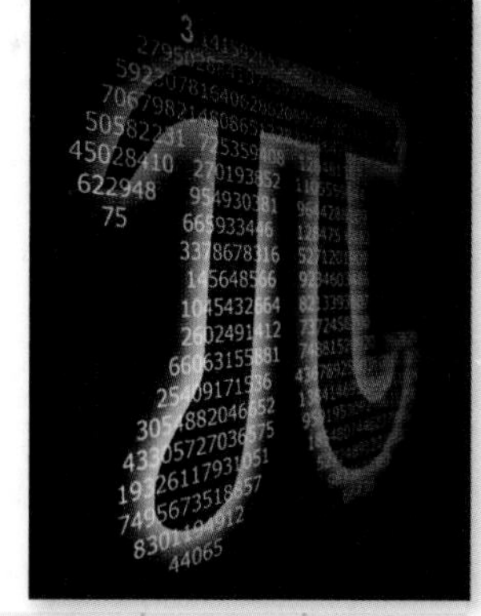

a. Display the data in a bar graph.

b. Display the data in a circle graph.

c. Which data display is more appropriate? Explain.

d. Describe the distribution.

Number	0	1	2	3	4	5	6	7	8	9
Frequency	9999	10,137	9908	10,025	9971	10,026	10,029	10,025	9978	9902

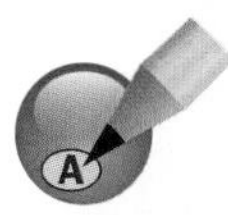

Fair Game Review What you learned in previous grades & lessons

Write the sentence as an equation. *(Skills Review Handbook)*

20. A number plus 3 is 5.

21. 8 times a number is 24.

22. MULTIPLE CHOICE What is 20% of 25% of 400? *(Skills Review Handbook)*

Ⓐ 20 Ⓑ 200 Ⓒ 240 Ⓓ 380

9 Study Help

You can use an **information frame** to help you organize and remember concepts. Here is an example of an information frame for scatter plots.

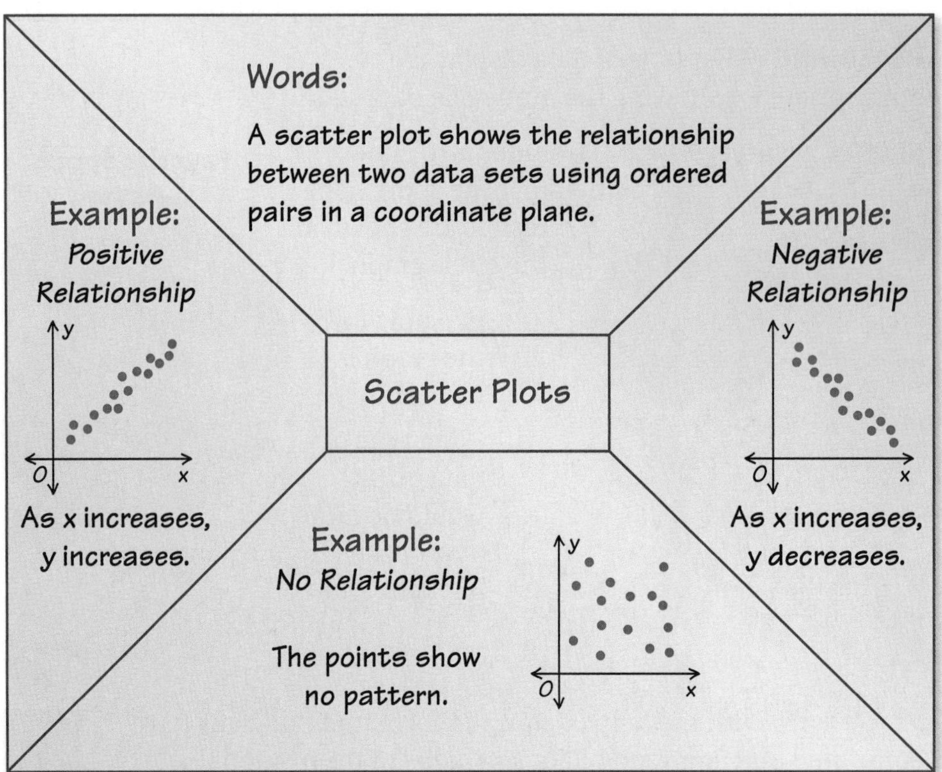

Words:
A scatter plot shows the relationship between two data sets using ordered pairs in a coordinate plane.
Example:
Positive Relationship
As x increases, y increases.
Scatter Plots
Example:
Negative Relationship
As x increases, y decreases.
Example:
No Relationship
The points show no pattern.
y
x
O

On Your Own

Make an information frame to help you study these topics.

1. lines of best fit
2. data displays

After you complete this chapter, make information frames for the following topics.

3. probability
4. independent events
5. dependent events

"Dear Teacher, I am emailing my information frame showing the characteristics of circles."

9.1–9.2 Quiz

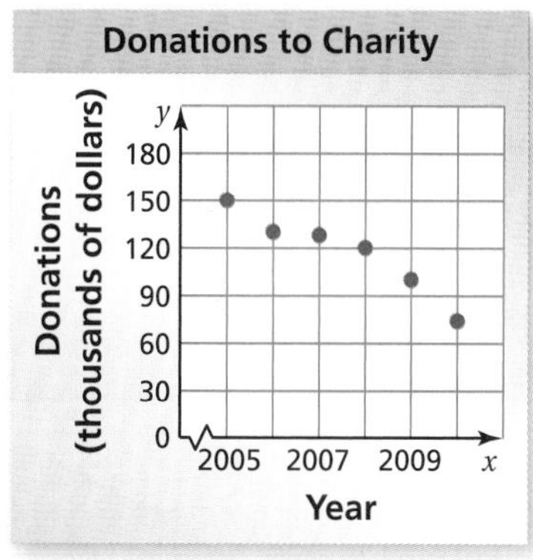

1. The scatter plot shows the amount of money donated to a charity from 2005 to 2010. *(Section 9.1)*

   a. In what year did the charity receive $150,000?

   b. How much did the charity receive in 2008?

   c. Describe the relationship shown by the data.

Tell whether the data show a *positive*, a *negative*, or *no* relationship. *(Section 9.1)*

2.

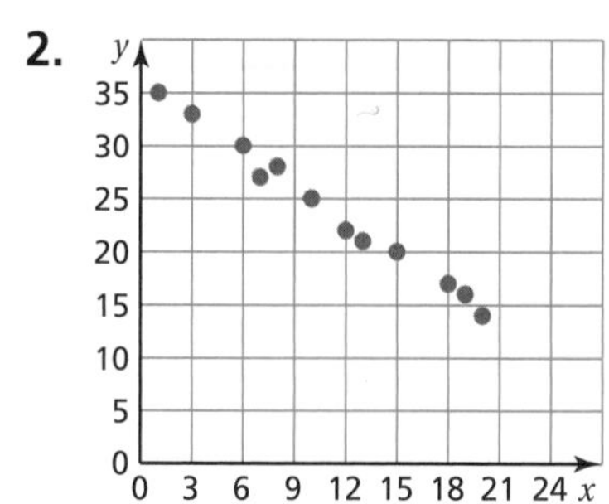

3.

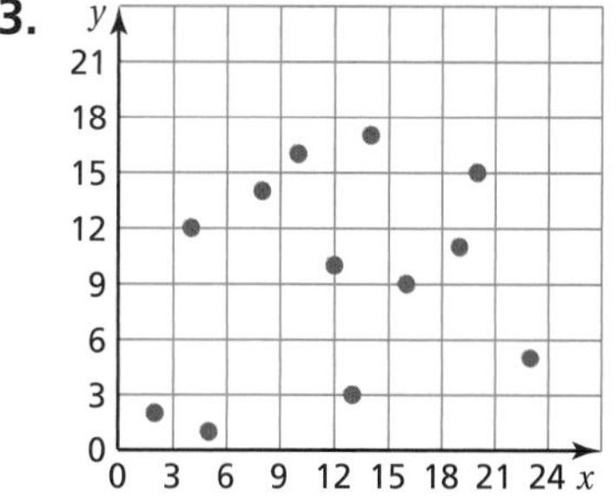

4.

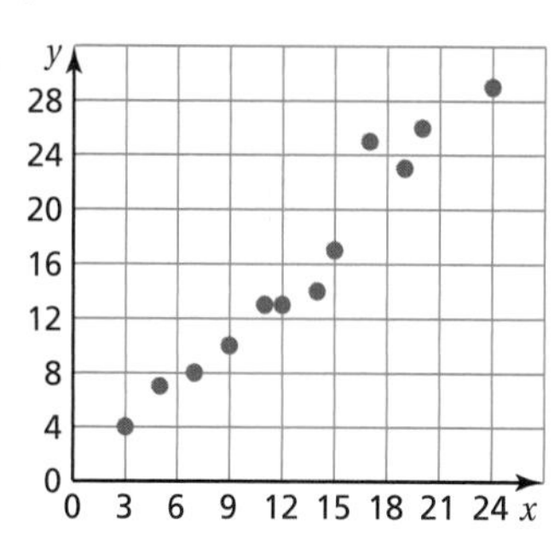

Choose an appropriate data display for the situation. Explain your reasoning. *(Section 9.2)*

5. percent of band students in each section

6. company's profit for each week

7. **FUNDRAISER** The graph shows the amount of money that the eighth-grade students at a school raised each month to pay for the class trip. Is the data display misleading? Explain. *(Section 9.2)*

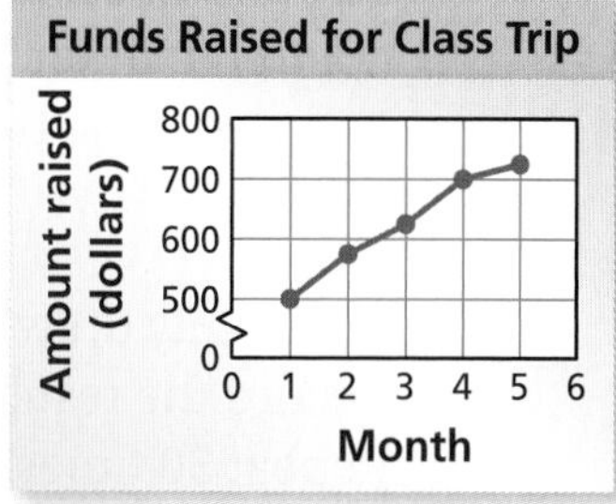

8. **CATS** The table shows the number of cats adopted from an animal shelter each month. *(Section 9.1)*

   a. Make a scatter plot of the data.

   b. Draw a line of best fit.

   c. Write an equation of the line of best fit.

   d. Predict how many cats will be adopted in month 10.

Month	1	2	3	4	5	6	7	8	9
Cats	3	6	7	11	13	14	15	18	19

9.3 Probability

STANDARDS OF LEARNING
8.12

Essential Question How is probability used in the "mark-recapture" method?

1 ACTIVITY: The Mark-Recapture Method

Work with a partner. One method used by marine biologists to determine the number of whales in a population is the "mark-recapture" method. Using this method, whales are captured, marked, and released back into the environment. The population is estimated from the number of marked whales that are recaptured.

a. Fill a paper bag with several dozen packing peanuts. Don't count them. Your goal is to estimate the total number of peanuts in the bag.

b. Remove 20 peanuts from the bag and mark them with a colored marker. Put them back and shake the bag to mix the peanuts.

c. Randomly draw 1 peanut from the bag. Record the result and replace the peanut. Repeat 30 times.

d. From your results, estimate how many peanuts are in the bag. Explain your reasoning.

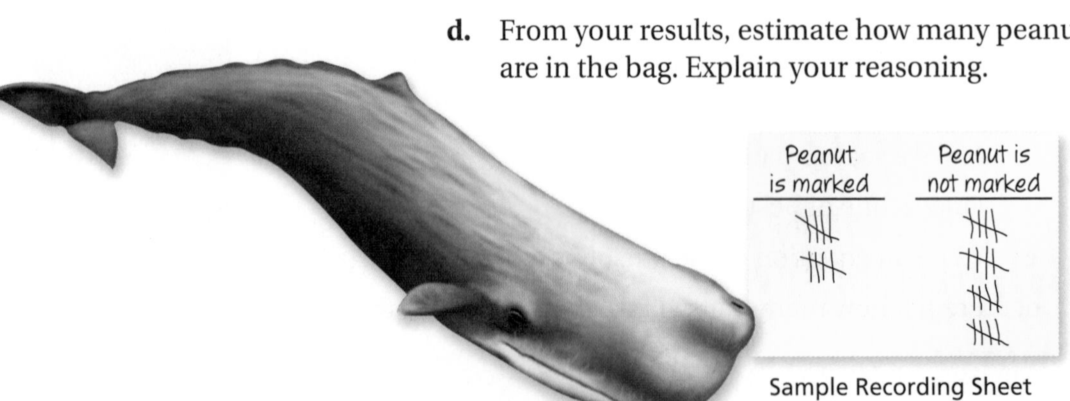

Sample Recording Sheet

2 ACTIVITY: The Mark-Recapture Method

Work with a partner. Estimate each wildlife population.

	Number Marked	Number Sampled	Number of Marked Animals in Sample
a. Large mouth bass in a lake	120	500	30
b. Lynx in a national park	40	120	20
c. Snowshoe hare in a national park	150	250	25
d. Gray squirrels in a national park	255	175	5

What Is Your Answer?

3. **IN YOUR OWN WORDS** How is probability used in the "mark-recapture" method?
4. **BIG IDEAS SCIENCE** Use the Internet or some other reference to write a report about a wildlife population that has been estimated using the "mark-recapture" method.

Practice Use what you learned about the "mark-recapture" method to complete Exercises 4–6 on page 423.

Key Vocabulary
theoretical probability, *p. 420*
experimental probability, *p. 421*

Theoretical Probability

When all possible outcomes are equally likely, the **theoretical probability** of an event is the ratio of the number of favorable outcomes to the number of possible outcomes. The probability of an event is written as $P(\text{event})$.

$$P(\text{event}) = \frac{\text{number of favorable outcomes}}{\text{number of possible outcomes}}$$

EXAMPLE 1 Finding a Theoretical Probability

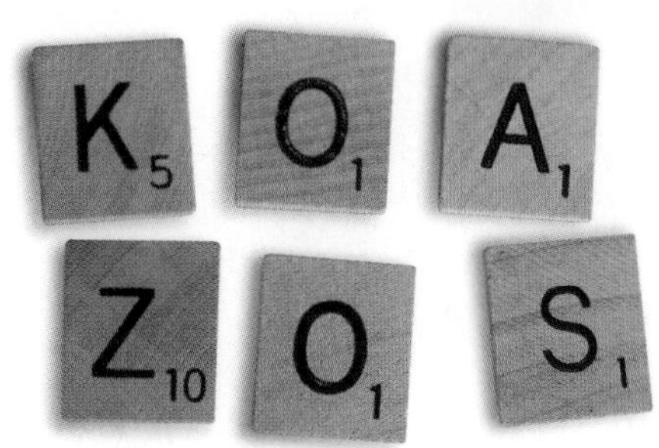

You randomly choose one of the SCRABBLE tiles shown. What is the theoretical probability of choosing a tile worth more than 1 point?

$$P(\text{event}) = \frac{\text{number of favorable outcomes}}{\text{number of possible outcomes}}$$

$$P(\text{more than 1 point}) = \frac{2}{6} = \frac{1}{3}$$

There are 2 tiles worth more than 1 point.

There is a total of 6 tiles.

∴ The probability of choosing a tile worth more than 1 point is $\frac{1}{3}$, or about 33%.

EXAMPLE 2 Using a Theoretical Probability

There are 100 tiles in a bag. The theoretical probability of randomly drawing an E from the bag is $\frac{3}{25}$. How many E's are in the bag?

$$P(\text{E}) = \frac{\text{number of E's}}{\text{total number of tiles}}$$

$\frac{3}{25} = \frac{n}{100}$ Substitute. Let n be the number of E's.

$12 = n$ Multiply each side by 100.

∴ There are 12 E's in the bag.

On Your Own

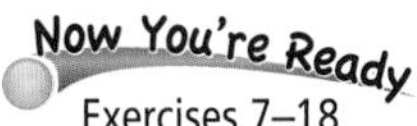

1. **WHAT IF?** In Example 1, what is the theoretical probability of choosing a consonant?
2. **WHAT IF?** In Example 2, the theoretical probability of randomly drawing an O is $\frac{2}{25}$. How many O's are in the bag?

Experimental Probability

Probability that is based on repeated trials of an experiment is called **experimental probability**.

$$P(\text{event}) = \frac{\text{number of times the event occurs}}{\text{total number of trials}}$$

EXAMPLE 3 Finding an Experimental Probability

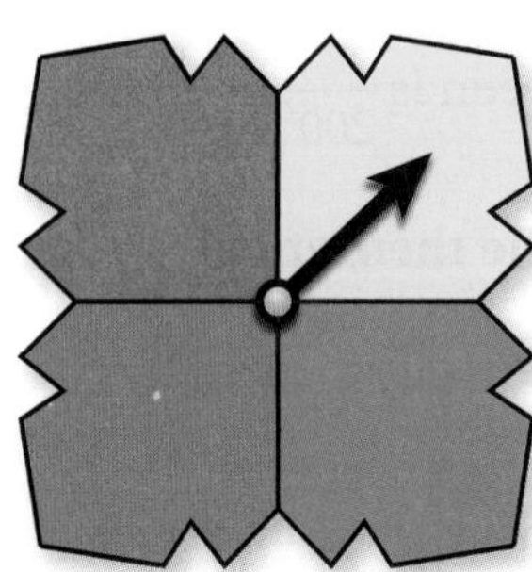

The bar graph shows the results of spinning the spinner 40 times. What is the experimental probability of spinning green?

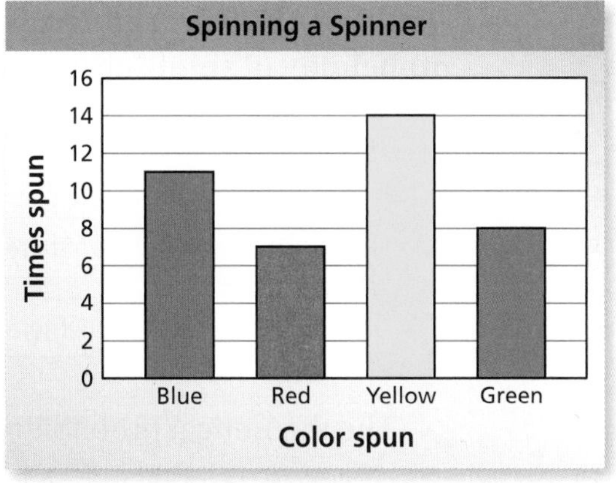

$$P(\text{event}) = \frac{\text{number of times the event occurs}}{\text{total number of trials}}$$

Green was spun 8 times.

$$P(\text{green}) = \frac{8}{40} = \frac{1}{5}$$

There was a total of 40 spins.

∴ The experimental probability of spinning green is $\frac{1}{5}$, or 20%.

On Your Own

3. What is the experimental probability of spinning red?

EXAMPLE 4 Comparing Theoretical and Experimental Probabilities

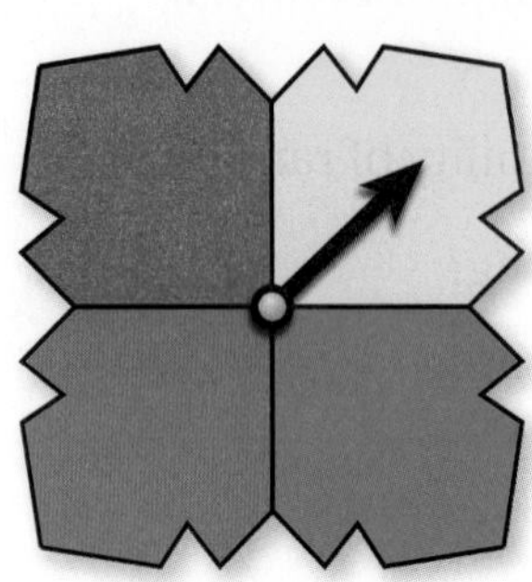

The bar graph shows the results of spinning the spinner 200 times.

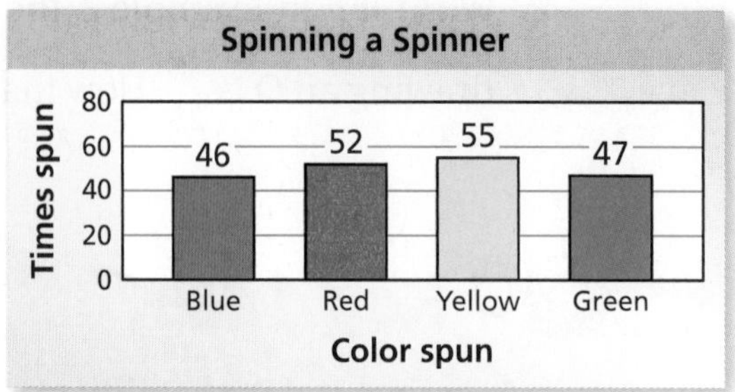

a. What is the experimental probability of spinning green?

$$P(\text{event}) = \frac{\text{number of times the event occurs}}{\text{total number of trials}}$$

$$P(\text{green}) = \frac{47}{200}$$

Green was spun 47 times.

There was a total of 200 spins.

The experimental probability of spinning green is $\frac{47}{200}$, or 23.5%.

b. How does the result of part (a) compare with the theoretical probability of spinning green?

$$P(\text{event}) = \frac{\text{number of favorable outcomes}}{\text{number of possible outcomes}}$$

$$P(\text{green}) = \frac{1}{4}$$

There is 1 green section.

There is a total of 4 sections.

The theoretical probability of spinning green is $\frac{1}{4}$, or 25%.

The experimental probability is close to the theoretical probability.

c. Compare the experimental probabilities in Example 3 and Example 4 part (a).

As the number of trials increased, the experimental probability increased from 20% to 23.5%. So, it became closer to the theoretical probability of 25%.

On Your Own

Now You're Ready
Exercises 28–30

4. What is the experimental probability of spinning red? How does this compare with the theoretical probability of spinning red?

9.3 Exercises

Vocabulary and Concept Check

1. **VOCABULARY** Describe how to find the experimental probability of an event.
2. **OPEN-ENDED** Describe an event that has a theoretical probability of 0.5.
3. **WRITING** Explain why the theoretical probability and the experimental probability of the same event are *not* always equal.

Practice and Problem Solving

Estimate the wildlife population.

	Number Marked	*Number Sampled*	*Number of Marked Animals in Sample*
4.	50	200	10
5.	75	650	25
6.	180	725	15

You roll a number cube. Determine the theoretical probability of the event.

1 **7.** Rolling a 2

8. Rolling an odd number

9. Rolling a multiple of 3

10. Rolling a prime number

11. Rolling an 8

12. Rolling a number less than 6

A bag contains 120 marbles. The theoretical probability of randomly drawing a blue marble is given. Find the number of blue marbles in the bag.

2 **13.** $\frac{1}{4}$

14. $\frac{1}{6}$

15. $\frac{1}{5}$

16. $\frac{1}{12}$

17. 0

18. $\frac{3}{10}$

19. VENDING MACHINE You randomly choose a button on the vending machine. What is the theoretical probability of choosing water?

20. GUESS 1 TO 10 Your friend is holding up fingers behind his back. What is the theoretical probability that the number of fingers is even if he is using one hand? both hands?

The bar graph shows the results of spinning the spinner 40 times. Find the experimental probability of the event.

③ **21.** Spinning a 4

22. Spinning a 3

23. Spinning a number greater than 4

24. Spinning a 1 or a 2

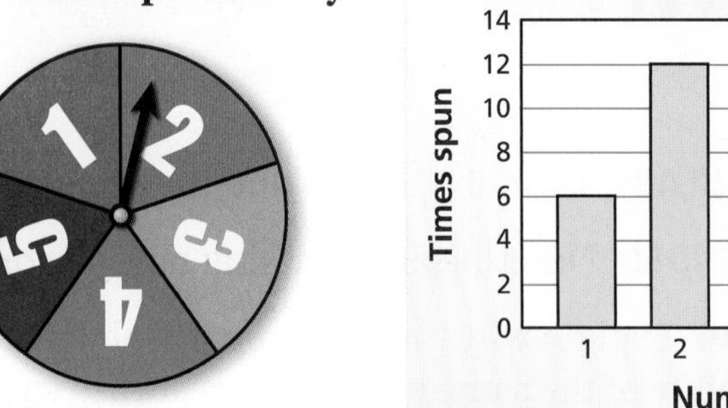

Spinning a Spinner

Number spun	1	2	3	4	5
Times spun	6	12	6	7	9

25. **ERROR ANALYSIS** Describe and correct the error in finding $P(2)$ using the bar graph shown above.

$$P(2) = \frac{\text{number of times the event occurs}}{\text{total number of trials}} = \frac{12}{28} = \frac{3}{7}$$

26. **DONATIONS** You randomly remove 10 bills from a donation box. Eight of them are \$1 bills. How many of the next 25 bills can you expect to be \$1 bills?

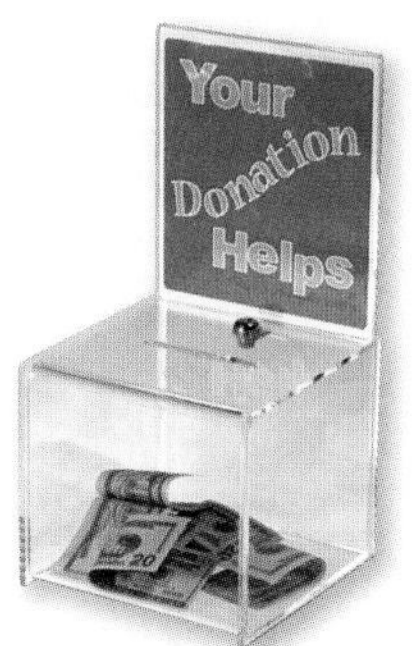

27. **MUSIC** You have 80 songs on your MP3 player. Seven of the last 16 songs played were pop songs. How many of the 80 songs can you expect to be pop songs?

The bar graph shows the results of spinning the spinner 200 times. Compare the theoretical and experimental probabilities of the event.

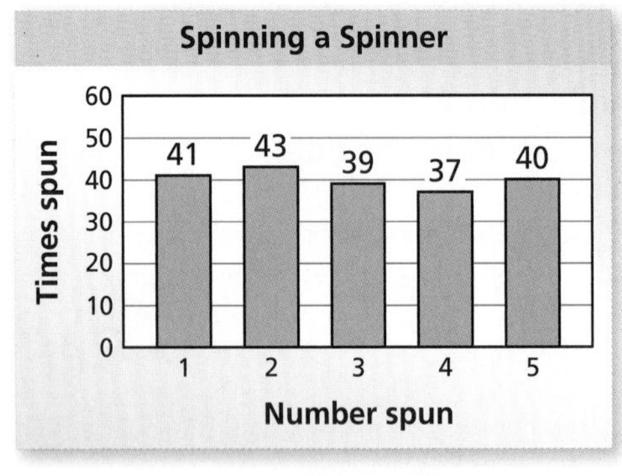

④ **28.** Spinning a 4

29. Spinning a 3

30. Spinning a number greater than 4

31. You spin the spinner 10,000 times. How many 3's can you expect to spin?

32. The table shows the results of flipping 2 coins 12 times each.

HH	HT	TH	TT
2	6	3	1

a. What is the experimental probability of flipping two tails?

b. Using your answer to part (a), how many times can you expect to flip two tails in 600 trials?

c. Use a tree diagram to find the theoretical probability of flipping two tails.

d. Using your answer to part (c), how many times can you expect to flip two tails in 600 trials?

e. Why is it important to use a large number of trials when using experimental probability to predict results?

33. FISHING You go on a fishing trip. The ratio of the number of bass you catch to the number of other fish you catch is 5 : 3.

a. What is the experimental probability that you catch a bass?

b. How many of the next 24 fish you catch can you expect to be bass?

34. REASONING A pollster surveys randomly selected individuals about an upcoming election. Do you think the pollster will use experimental probability or theoretical probability to make predictions? Explain.

35. MAGICIAN There are 102 cards in a magician's deck. The table shows the distribution of the cards among the colors.

Card Rank	Red	Brown	Purple	Yellow	Black
0	1	1	1	1	1
1, 2, 3, 4, 5, 6, 7, 8, 9	2	2	2	2	1
Joker	1	1	1	1	0
Wild	2	2	2	2	4

a. How many yellow cards are in the deck?

b. The magician deals the cards shown. What is the experimental probability of dealing a yellow card? What is the theoretical probability of dealing a yellow card?

c. What color is most likely to be dealt next? Explain.

36. Critical Thinking Describe how the theoretical probability of randomly choosing a red apple changes when a green apple is removed from the plate.

Fair Game Review What you learned in previous grades & lessons

Find the perimeter of the figure. *(Section 5.6)*

37.

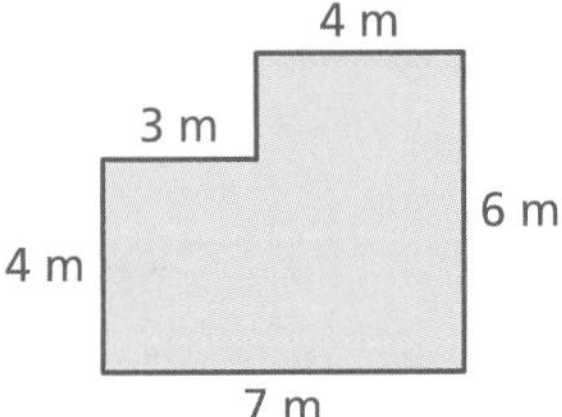

38.

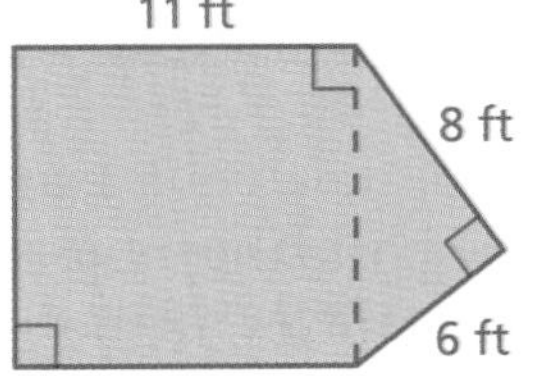

39.

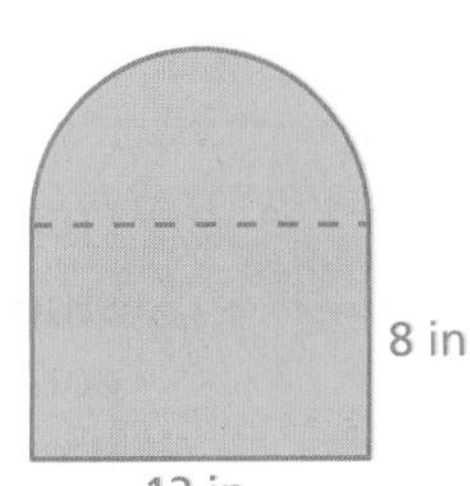

40. MULTIPLE CHOICE What is the surface area of the cone? *(Section 6.5)*

Ⓐ $14\pi\text{ cm}^2$ Ⓑ $18\pi\text{ cm}^2$

Ⓒ $28\pi\text{ cm}^2$ Ⓓ $44\pi\text{ cm}^2$

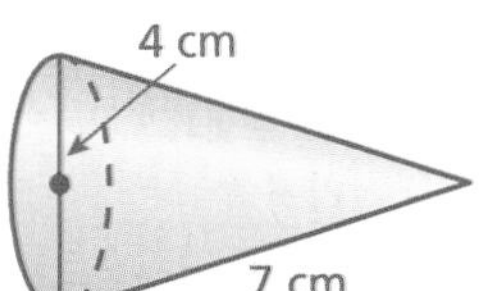

9.4 Independent and Dependent Events

STANDARDS OF LEARNING 8.12

Essential Question How can you use probability to help you win a game show?

1 ACTIVITY: Analyzing a Game

Work with a partner. You are a contestant on a television game show. You are asked to pick one of three doors. Behind two of the doors are goats. Behind the other door is a luxury car.

Use three cards to simulate this game. One student acts as the host. The other acts as the contestant. The host mixes up the cards and lays them face down. The contestant chooses a card and wins the prize on the card.

Play the game 30 times as the host and 30 times as the contestant. Record your results.

Write a summary of your results. Include a discussion of experimental probability and theoretical probability.

2 ACTIVITY: Analyzing "Let's Make a Deal®"

A version of the television program called *Let's Make a Deal®* was similar to the game in Activity 1. However, after the contestant chose a door, the host (who knew the location of the car) revealed the goat behind one of the remaining doors. Then, the host asked the contestant whether he or she wanted to switch.

Work with a partner. Use your three cards to simulate this version of the game. Play the game 30 times as the host and 30 times as the contestant.

- The host deals 3 cards face down.
- The contestant points to one of the cards.
- The host looks at the other two cards, but does not show the contestant.
- The host turns over one of the other cards that is a goat. Then, the host asks the contestant whether he or she wants to switch. For this game, the contestant should always switch.

Write a summary of your results. Include a discussion of experimental probability and theoretical probability. Should contestants stay with their first choice or switch?

What Is Your Answer?

3. **IN YOUR OWN WORDS** How can you use probability to help you win a game show?
4. **CONCLUSION** Compare your results from Activities 1 and 2. In which activity did the contestant win more? Explain your reasoning.

Use what you learned about independent and dependent events to complete Exercises 3–7 on page 430.

9.4 Lesson

Key Vocabulary
independent events, p. 428
dependent events, p. 429

Events are **independent events** if the occurrence of one event *does not* affect the likelihood that the other event(s) will occur.

Probability of Independent Events

Words The probability of two or more independent events is the product of the probabilities of the events.

Symbols $P(A \text{ and } B) = P(A) \cdot P(B)$

$P(A \text{ and } B \text{ and } C) = P(A) \cdot P(B) \cdot P(C)$

EXAMPLE 1 Finding the Probability of Independent Events

You flip three quarters. What is the probability that you flip three tails?

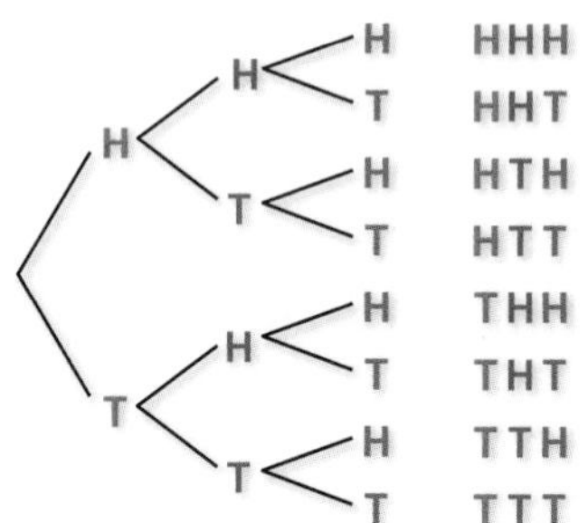

The outcome of flipping one quarter does not affect the outcome of flipping the other quarters. So, the events are independent.

Method 1: Use a tree diagram to find the probability.

Let H = Heads and T = Tails.

$$P(\text{three tails}) = \frac{\text{number of times three tails occur}}{\text{total number of outcomes}} = \frac{1}{8}$$

The probability that you flip three tails is $\frac{1}{8}$, or 12.5%.

Method 2: Use the formula for the probability of independent events.

$$P(A \text{ and } B \text{ and } C) = P(A) \cdot P(B) \cdot P(C)$$

$$P(\text{three tails}) = P(\text{tails}) \cdot P(\text{tails}) \cdot P(\text{tails})$$

$$= \frac{1}{2} \cdot \frac{1}{2} \cdot \frac{1}{2} \qquad \text{Substitute.}$$

$$= \frac{1}{8} \qquad \text{Multiply.}$$

The probability that you flip three tails is $\frac{1}{8}$, or 12.5%.

On Your Own

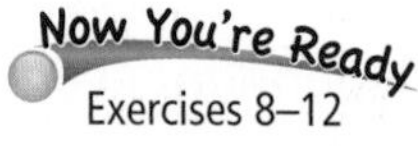

1. You flip two coins and roll a number cube. What is the probability of flipping heads, flipping tails, then rolling a 3?

Multi-Language Glossary at BigIdeasMath.com.

Events are **dependent events** if the occurrence of one event *does* affect the likelihood that the other event(s) will occur.

Probability of Dependent Events

Words The probability of two dependent events A and B is the probability of A times the probability of B after A occurs.

Symbols $P(A \text{ and } B) = P(A) \cdot P(B \text{ after } A)$

EXAMPLE 2 Finding the Probability of Dependent Events

People are randomly chosen to be game show contestants from an audience of 100 people. You are with 5 of your relatives and 6 other friends. What is the probability that one of your relatives is chosen first, and then one of your friends is chosen second?

Choosing an audience member changes the number of audience members left. So, the events are dependent.

$$P(\text{relative}) = \frac{5}{100} = \frac{1}{20}$$

There are 5 relatives.

There is a total of 100 audience members.

$$P(\text{friend}) = \frac{6}{99} = \frac{2}{33}$$

There are 6 friends.

There is a total of 99 audience members left.

Use the formula for the probability of dependent events.

$$P(A \text{ and } B) = P(A) \cdot P(B \text{ after } A)$$

$$P(\text{relative and friend}) = P(\text{relative}) \cdot P(\text{friend after relative})$$

$$= \frac{1}{20} \cdot \frac{2}{33} \quad \text{Substitute.}$$

$$= \frac{1}{330} \quad \text{Simplify.}$$

∴ The probability is $\frac{1}{330}$, or about 0.3%.

On Your Own

Now You're Ready
Exercises 13–18

2. What is the probability that you, your relatives, and your friends are *not* chosen to be either of the first two contestants?

9.4 Exercises

Vocabulary and Concept Check

1. **VOCABULARY** Events *A*, *B*, and *C* are independent. Describe two ways to find *P*(*A* and *B* and *C*).
2. **OPEN-ENDED** Describe a real-life example of three independent events. Describe a real-life example of two dependent events.

Practice and Problem Solving

Tell whether the events are *independent* or *dependent*. Explain.

3. You randomly draw a marble from a bag containing 5 yellow marbles and 7 blue marbles. You replace the marble and then draw a second marble.

   First Draw: Yellow   Second Draw: Yellow

4. You and two friends are in a drawing for five door prizes. You can only win one prize.

   First Draw: Your first friend's name is drawn.
   Second Draw: Your name is drawn.
   Third Draw: Your second friend's name is drawn.

5. You randomly draw a marble from a bag containing 10 black marbles, 5 gold marbles, and 4 white marbles. You keep the first marble, draw and keep a second marble, and then draw a third marble.

   First Draw: White   Second Draw: Black   Third Draw: Black

6. You flip a coin three times.

   First Flip: Heads
   Second Flip: Tails
   Third Flip: Tails

7. You roll a number cube three times.

   First Roll: You roll a 4.
   Second Roll: You roll an odd number.
   Third Roll: You roll an even number.

You spin the spinner, flip a coin, then spin the spinner again. Find the probability of the events.

1 8. Spinning a 4, flipping heads, then spinning a 7
9. Spinning an odd number, flipping heads, then spinning a 3
10. Spinning an even number, flipping tails, then spinning an odd number
11. *Not* spinning a 5, flipping heads, then spinning a 1
12. Spinning an odd number, *not* flipping heads, then *not* spinning a 6

You randomly choose one of the coins. Without replacing the first coin, you choose a second coin. Find the probability of choosing the first coin, then the second coin.

2 **13.** Nickel and dime

14. Quarter and nickel

15. Quarter and penny

16. Penny and dime

17. Nickel and *not* a penny

18. Dime and *not* a quarter

19. ERROR ANALYSIS Describe and correct the error in finding the probability.

You have 5 pairs of white socks and 10 pairs of black socks in a drawer. You randomly choose two pairs. What is the probability that both pairs are black?

✗

$$P(\text{black and black}) = P(\text{black}) \cdot P(\text{black})$$
$$= \frac{10}{15} \cdot \frac{10}{15}$$
$$= \frac{2}{3} \cdot \frac{2}{3} = \frac{4}{9}$$

20. WRITING A jar contains 12 purple straws and 12 blue straws. You randomly choose two straws. Is the probability of choosing two purple straws greater if you replace the first straw after you choose it, or if you keep the first straw after you choose it? Explain.

21. Critical Thinking If you randomly choose all seven tiles in order, what is the probability that you will spell the name of a city in Virginia?

Fair Game Review What you learned in previous grades & lessons

Simplify the expression. *(Section 8.4)*

22. $4\sqrt{2} - 7\sqrt{2}$

23. $-2.7\sqrt{11} + 1.2\sqrt{11}$

24. $2\sqrt{5} - \sqrt{20}$

25. MULTIPLE CHOICE What is the surface area of the prism? *(Section 6.2)*

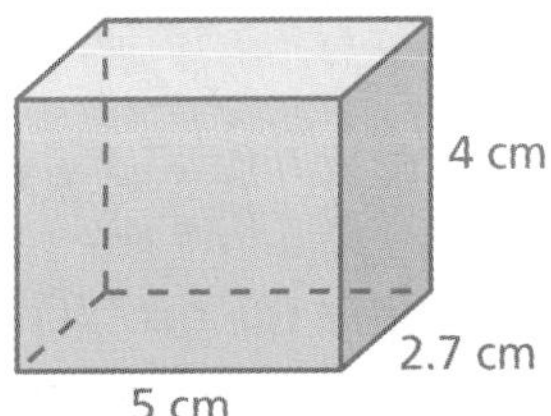

Ⓐ 48.6 cm^2 Ⓑ 54 cm^2

Ⓒ 61.6 cm^2 Ⓓ 88.6 cm^2

9.3–9.4 Quiz

You randomly choose a marble. Determine the theoretical probability of the event. *(Section 9.3)*

1. Choosing red
2. Choosing blue
3. *Not* choosing yellow
4. Choosing green

Color	Times Chosen
Red	50
Green	52
Yellow	45
Blue	53

The table shows the results of randomly choosing one of the marbles shown above 200 times. Find the experimental probability of the event. *(Section 9.3)*

5. Choosing green
6. Choosing yellow
7. Choosing red or blue
8. Choosing red or green

9. Use the marbles and the table shown above. Compare the experimental and theoretical probabilities of randomly choosing a red marble. *(Section 9.3)*

You flip a coin, spin the spinner, then flip a coin again. Find the probability of the events. *(Section 9.4)*

10. Flipping tails, spinning a 6, then flipping heads
11. Flipping heads, spinning an even number, then *not* flipping heads

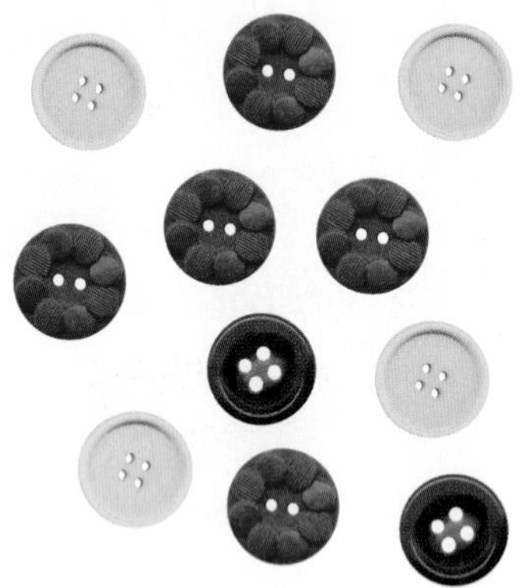

You randomly choose one of the buttons. Without replacing the first button, you choose a second button. Find the probability of choosing the first button, then the second button. *(Section 9.4)*

12. Green and yellow
13. Yellow and black
14. Black and *not* green
15. Green and *not* black

16. **MONEY** You randomly remove 150 coins from a jar. Thirty of them are quarters. How many of the next 200 coins can you expect to be quarters? *(Section 9.3)*

17. **STICKERS** You randomly choose one of the stickers. Without replacing the first sticker, you choose a second sticker. Find the probability of choosing two hearts. *(Section 9.4)*

9 Chapter Review

Check It Out
Vocabulary Help
BigIdeasMath.com

Review Key Vocabulary

scatter plot, *p. 402*
line of best fit, *p. 404*
theoretical probability, *p. 420*
experimental probability, *p. 421*
independent events, *p. 428*
dependent events, *p. 429*

Review Examples and Exercises

9.1 Scatter Plots and Lines of Best Fit *(pp. 400–407)*

Your school is ordering custom T-shirts. The scatter plot shows the number of T-shirts ordered and the cost per shirt. What tends to happen to the cost per shirt as the number of T-shirts ordered increases?

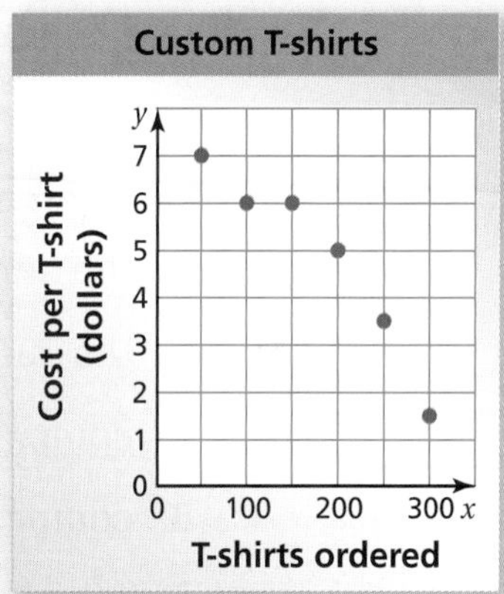

Looking at the graph, the plotted points go down from left to right.

So, as the number of T-shirts ordered increases, the cost per shirt decreases.

Exercises

1. The scatter plot shows the number of geese that migrated to a park each season.
   a. In what year did 270 geese migrate?
   b. How many geese migrated in 2007?
   c. Describe the relationship shown by the data.

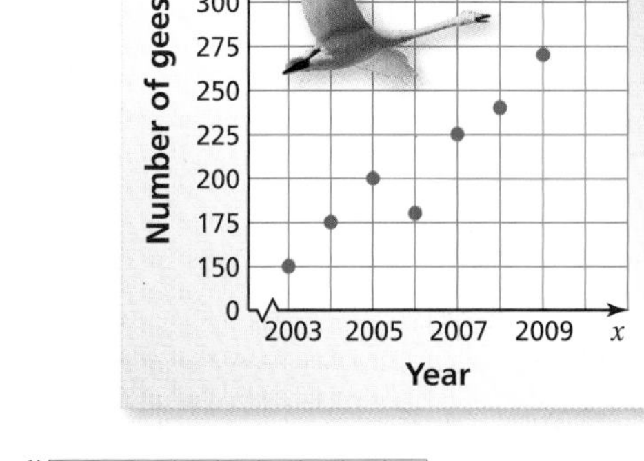

Tell whether the data show a *positive*, a *negative*, or *no* relationship.

2.

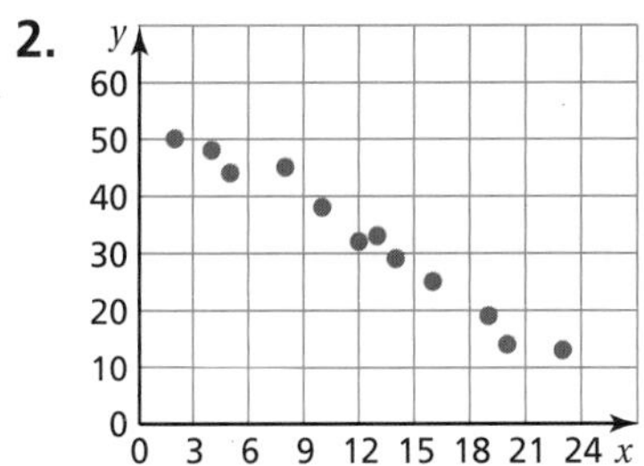

3.

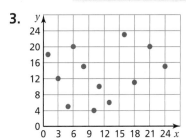

4. Consider the scatter plot in Exercise 2.
   a. Draw a line of best fit.
   b. Write an equation of the line of best fit.

9.2 Choosing a Data Display (pp. 408–415)

Choose an appropriate data display for each situation. Explain your reasoning.

a. the percent of votes that each candidate received in an election

∴ A circle graph shows data as parts of a whole. So, a circle graph is an appropriate data display.

b. the distribution of the ages of U.S. presidents

∴ A stem-and-leaf plot orders numerical data and shows how they are distributed. So, a stem-and-leaf plot is an appropriate data display.

Exercises

Choose an appropriate data display for the situation. Explain your reasoning.

5. the number of pairs of shoes sold by a store each week
6. the outcomes of spinning a spinner with 3 equal sections numbered 1, 2, and 3
7. comparison of the number of cans of food donated by each eighth-grade class
8. comparison of the heights of brothers and sisters

9.3 Probability (pp. 418–425)

The bar graph shows the results of spinning the spinner 40 times.

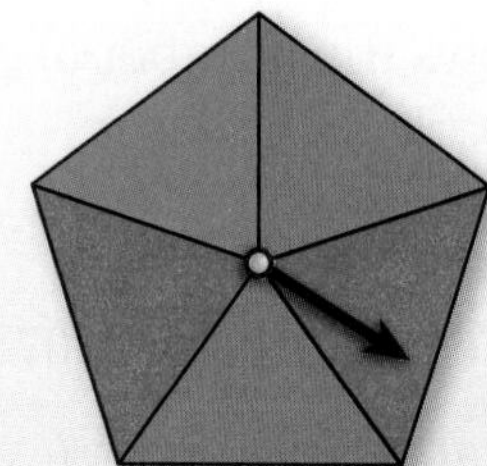

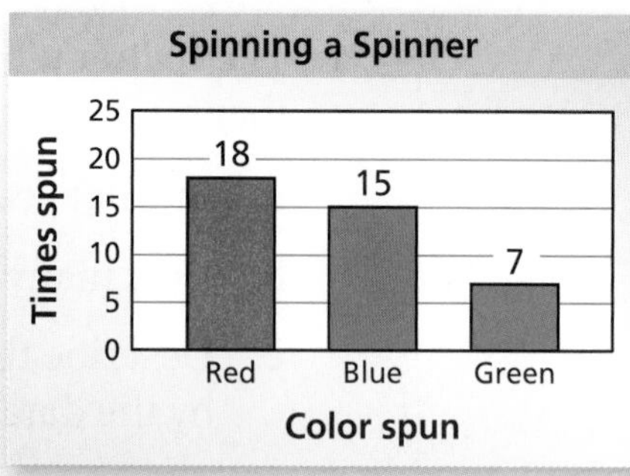

a. What is the experimental probability of spinning red?

$$P(\text{red}) = \frac{\text{number of times the event occurs}}{\text{total number of trials}} = \frac{18}{40} = \frac{9}{20}$$

∴ The experimental probability of spinning red is $\frac{9}{20}$, or 45%.

b. What is the theoretical probability of spinning red?

$$P(\text{red}) = \frac{\text{number of favorable outcomes}}{\text{number of possible outcomes}} = \frac{2}{5}$$

∴ The theoretical probability of spinning red is $\frac{2}{5}$, or 40%.

Exercises

9. You spin the spinner 500 times. How many times can you expect to spin blue?

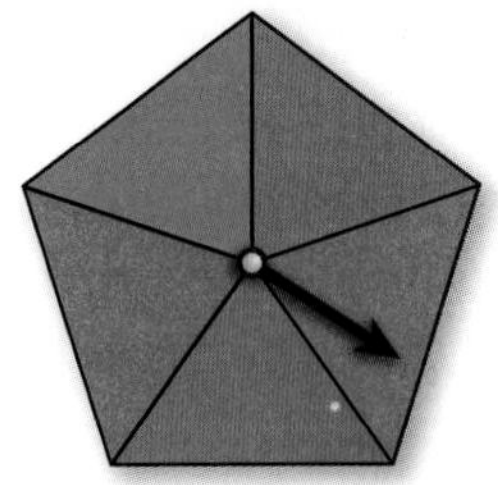

9.4 Independent and Dependent Events (pp. 426–431)

You randomly choose a marble without replacing it. Your friend then chooses another marble. What is the probability that you choose a red marble and your friend chooses a green marble?

Choosing a marble without replacement changes the number of marbles left. So, the events are dependent.

$$P(\text{first is red}) = \frac{5}{12}$$

There are 5 red marbles.

There is a total of 12 marbles.

$$P(\text{second is green}) = \frac{2}{11}$$

There are 2 green marbles.

There is a total of 11 marbles left.

Use the formula for the probability of dependent events.

$$P(\text{red and green}) = P(\text{red}) \cdot P(\text{green after red})$$

$$= \frac{5}{12} \cdot \frac{2}{11} \quad \text{Substitute.}$$

$$= \frac{10}{132} = \frac{5}{66} \quad \text{Simplify.}$$

The probability of choosing a red marble followed by a green marble is $\frac{5}{66}$, or about 7.6%.

Exercises

You randomly choose one of the lettered tiles. Without replacing the first tile, you choose a second tile. Find the probability of choosing the first tile, then the second tile.

10. C and I
11. I and I
12. V and *not* L

13. You choose one of the lettered tiles and flip two coins. What is the probability of choosing an I, flipping heads, then flipping tails?

9 Chapter Test

Check It Out
Test Practice
BigIdeasMath.com

The bar graph shows the results of spinning the spinner 50 times. Find the experimental probability of the event.

1. Spinning a 3
2. Spinning a 2 or a 5

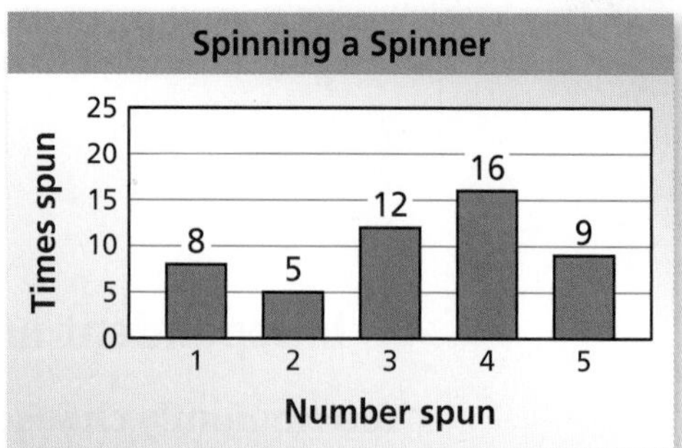

There are 10 skateboarders and 15 bikers at a skate park. You randomly choose two of them to judge a tournament. Find the probability of the event.

3. Choosing a biker, then choosing a skateboarder
4. Choosing a skateboarder, then choosing another skateboarder

5. **NUMBER CUBE** You roll a number cube three times. What is the probability that you roll an even number all three times?

6. **POPULATION** The graph shows the population (in millions) of the United States from 1960 to 2000.
   a. In what year was the population of the United States about 180 million?
   b. What was the approximate population of the United States in 1990?
   c. Describe the trend shown by the data.

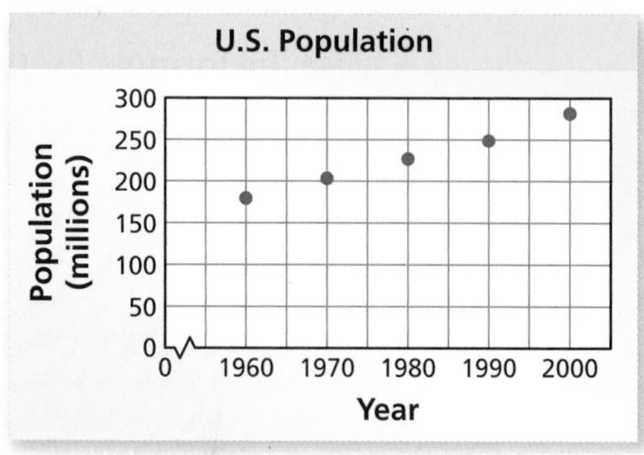

Choose an appropriate data display for the situation. Explain your reasoning.

7. magazine sales grouped by price
8. distance a person hikes each week

9. **NEWBORNS** The table shows the lengths and weights of several newborn babies.
   a. Make a scatter plot of the data.
   b. Draw a line of best fit.
   c. Write an equation of the line of best fit.
   d. Use the equation to predict the weight of a newborn that is 21.75 inches long.

Length (inches)	Weight (pounds)
19	6
19.5	7
20	7.75
20.25	8.5
20.5	8.5
22.5	11

9 Standardized Test Practice

1. Which graph represents the inequality below?

$$-2x + 3 < 1$$

A. 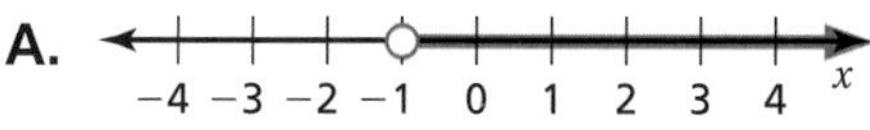

B. −4 −3 −2 −1 0 1 2 3 4 x

C. −4 −3 −2 −1 0 1 2 3 4 x

D. 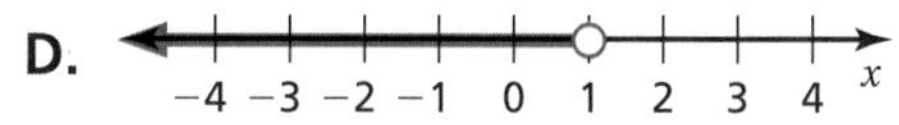

2. An object dropped from a height will fall under the force of gravity. The time t, in seconds, it takes to fall a distance d, in feet, can be found using the formula below.

$$t = \frac{\sqrt{d}}{4}$$

A ball is dropped from the top of a building that is 40 feet tall. Approximately how many seconds will it take for the ball to reach the ground?

F. 1.6 sec

G. 3.2 sec

H. 5 sec

I. 6.3 sec

3. You flip three nickels. What is the probability that you flip tails, tails, then heads?

A. $\frac{1}{8}$

B. $\frac{3}{8}$

C. $\frac{1}{2}$

D. $\frac{3}{4}$

4. The director of a research lab wants to present data to donors, showing how a great deal of donated money is used for research and how only a small amount of donated money is used for other expenses. Which type of display is best suited for showing these data?

F. histogram

G. circle graph

H. line graph

I. scatter plot

5. Which value of x makes the equation below true?

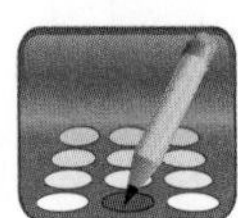

$$3x - 9 = 2(x + 4)$$

6. As part of a probability experiment, students were asked to roll two number cubes and find the sum of the numbers obtained. One group of students did this 600 times and obtained the results shown in the table. What was the experimental probability of rolling a sum of 3?

Sum	2	3	4	5	6	7	8	9	10	11	12
Number of Rolls	16	30	51	66	83	98	93	64	47	35	17

A. $\frac{2}{75}$

B. $\frac{1}{20}$

C. $\frac{8}{75}$

D. $\frac{11}{100}$

7. Which expression is equivalent to $\frac{\sqrt{32}}{\sqrt{18}}$?

F. $\sqrt{14}$

G. $\frac{4}{3}$

H. $\frac{8}{3}$

I. $\frac{16}{9}$

8. Which point lies on the graph of the line given by $y = -\frac{1}{2}x + 7$?

A. (5, 4)

B. (−4, 5)

C. (20, 3)

D. (40, −13)

9. Which scatter plot shows a negative relationship between x and y?

F. 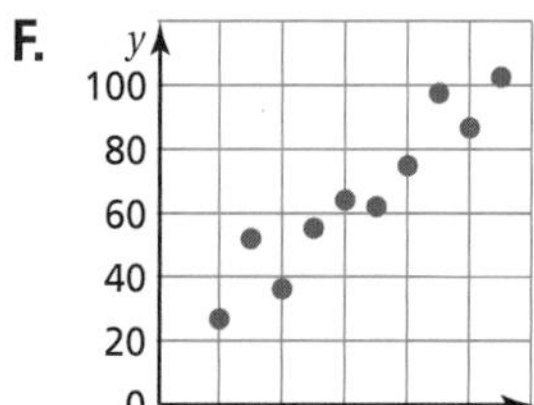

H. 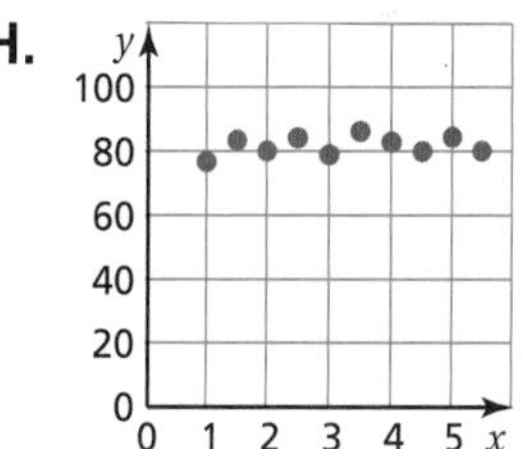

G. 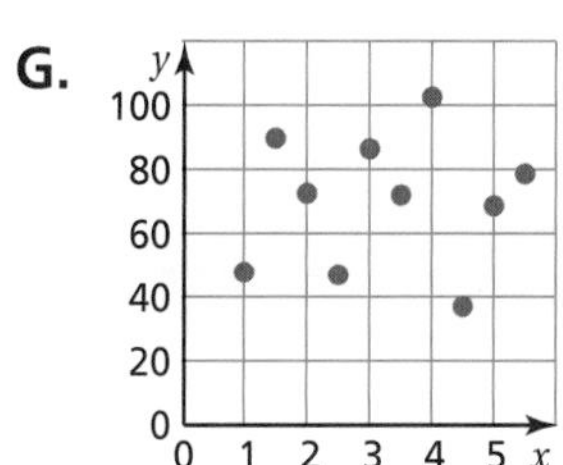

I. 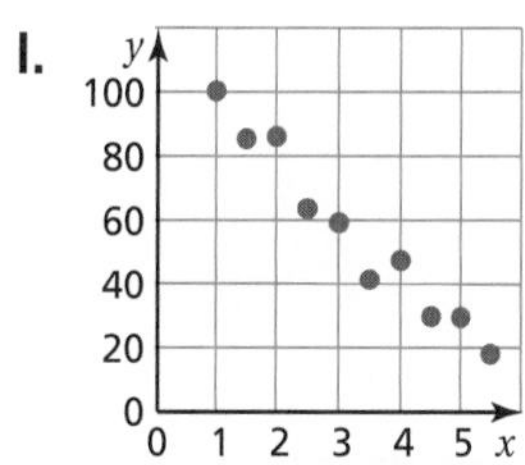

10. The legs of a right triangle have the lengths of 8 centimeters and 15 centimeters. What is the length of the hypotenuse, in centimeters?

11. A store has recorded total dollar sales each month for the past three years. Which type of graph would best show how sales have increased over this time period?

A. circle graph

B. line graph

C. histogram

D. stem-and-leaf plot

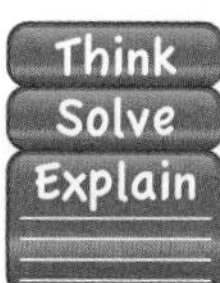

12. Does squaring a number always make it greater? Is the inequality shown below true for all numbers?

$$x^2 > x$$

Show your work and explain your reasoning.

10 Exponents and Scientific Notation

"Descartes, do you prefer the original *binary* definition that 1 kilobyte = 2^{10} bytes?"

"Or do you prefer the newer decimal definition that 1 kilobyte = 10^3 bytes?"

"The Mayans used base 20 for their number system."

"And the Babylonians used base 60 for their number system."

"Can you name an ancient culture that used base 10 for its number system?"

What You Learned Before

You mean bankruptcy, right?

"For my dog biscuit order, my calculator switched to scientific notation. I'm in ecstasy!"

Adding Integers

Example 1 Find each sum.

a. $-3 + (-6)$

The integers have the *same* sign.

$-3 + (-6) = -9$

1. Add the absolute values: $|-3| + |-6| = 9$
2. Use the common sign: negative

b. $4 + (-12)$

The integers have *different* signs.

$4 + (-12) = -8$

1. Subtract the lesser absolute value from the greater absolute value: $|-12| - |4| = 8$
2. Use the sign of the greater absolute value: negative

Subtracting Integers

Example 2 Find each difference.

a. $5 - 9$

$5 - 9 = 5 + (-9)$	Add the opposite of 9.
$= -4$	Add.

b. $6 - (-2)$

$6 - (-2) = 6 + 2$	Add the opposite of -2.
$= 8$	Add.

c. $-7 - (-13)$

$-7 - (-13) = -7 + 13$	Add the opposite of -13.
$= 6$	Add.

Try It Yourself

Find the sum or difference.

1. $-2 + 10$ **2.** $11 + (-9)$ **3.** $-8 + (-5)$

4. $7 - 11$ **5.** $-2 - (-8)$ **6.** $9 - (-10)$

10.1 Properties of Exponents

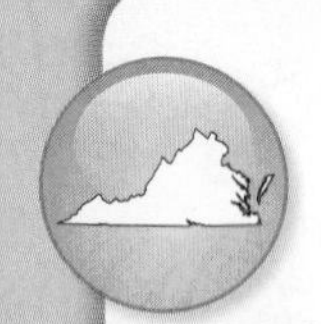

STANDARDS OF LEARNING
8.1

Essential Question How can you use carbon dating to estimate the age of an object?

1 ACTIVITY: Carbon Dating

When a living thing dies, its carbon-14 content begins to decay with a half-life of about 5700 years. This means that after 5700 years, half of the carbon-14 will have decayed.

Work with a partner. The fraction of remaining carbon-14 is given for each object. Use the fraction to estimate the age of each object. Explain your reasoning.

Sample: $\frac{1}{8}$ means that $\frac{7}{8}$ of the carbon-14 has decayed and only $\frac{1}{8}$ remains.

$\frac{1}{8}$ represents 3 half-lives because $\frac{1}{8} = \frac{1}{2} \cdot \frac{1}{2} \cdot \frac{1}{2}$.

So, the object is about $3 \cdot 5700 = 17{,}100$ years old.

a. Carbon-14 remaining: $\left(\frac{1}{2}\right)^2$

Sea Shell

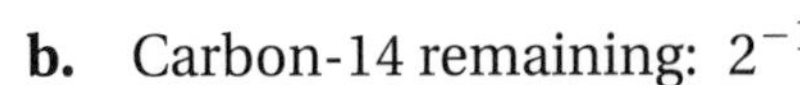

b. Carbon-14 remaining: 2^{-1}

Chinese Ivory Carving

c. Carbon-14 remaining: 2^0

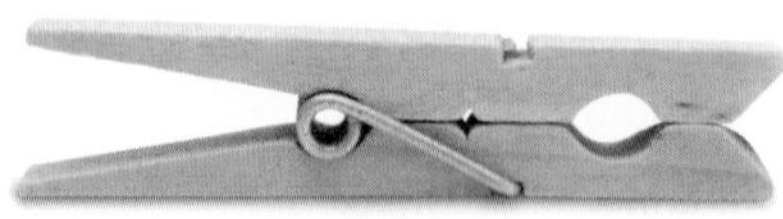

Clothes Pin

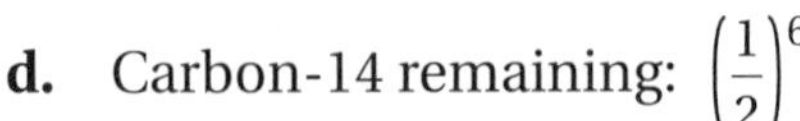

d. Carbon-14 remaining: $\left(\frac{1}{2}\right)^6$

Petrified Wood

2 ACTIVITY: Carbon Dating

Work with a partner.

a. Explain how to draw a graph that shows the percent of carbon-14 that remains in an object after it has died. Then draw the graph.

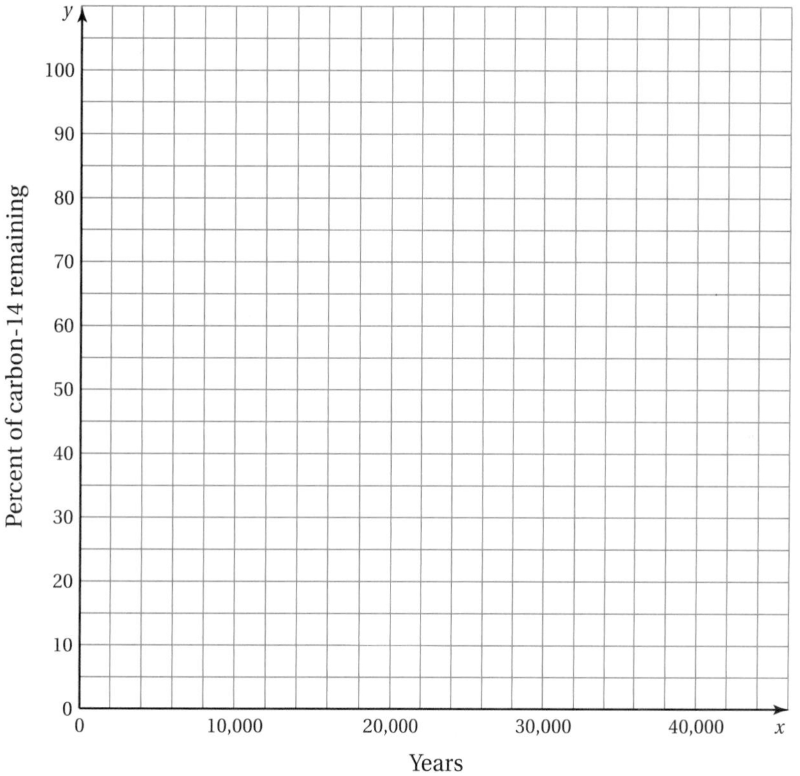

b. Use your graph to estimate the age of an object that has 80% of its carbon-14 remaining.

c. Use your graph to estimate the age of an object that has 40% of its carbon-14 remaining.

What Is Your Answer?

3. **IN YOUR OWN WORDS** How can you use carbon dating to estimate the age of an object?

4. **RESEARCH** Use the Internet or some other reference to write a report about other methods that are used to estimate the age of an object.

Practice Use what you learned about carbon dating to complete Exercises 5 and 6 on page 446.

10.1 Lesson

Key Vocabulary
power, *p. 444*
base, *p. 444*
exponent, *p. 444*

A **power** is a product of repeated factors. The **base** of a power is the common factor. The **exponent** of a power indicates the number of times the base is used as a factor.

base → exponent

$$5^6 = 5 \cdot 5 \cdot 5 \cdot 5 \cdot 5 \cdot 5$$

power — 5 is used as a factor 6 times.

EXAMPLE 1 Evaluating Expressions

Evaluate each expression.

a. $\left(-\frac{1}{2}\right)^4$

$$\left(-\frac{1}{2}\right)^4 = \left(-\frac{1}{2}\right) \cdot \left(-\frac{1}{2}\right) \cdot \left(-\frac{1}{2}\right) \cdot \left(-\frac{1}{2}\right)$$ Write as repeated multiplication.

The base is $-\frac{1}{2}$.

$$= \frac{1}{16}$$ Simplify.

b. -8^3

$$-8^3 = -(8 \cdot 8 \cdot 8)$$ Write as repeated multiplication.

The base is 8.

$$= -512$$ Simplify.

On Your Own

Now You're Ready
Exercises 7–11

Evaluate the expression.

1. $\left(-\frac{1}{3}\right)^2$ **2.** $(-4)^3$ **3.** -5^4 **4.** 2.5^2

Key Ideas

Zero Exponents

Words For any nonzero number a, $a^0 = 1$. The power 0^0 is *undefined.*

Numbers $7^0 = 1$ **Algebra** $a^0 = 1$, where $a \neq 0$

Negative Exponents

Words For any integer n and any nonzero number a, a^{-n} is the reciprocal of a^n.

Numbers $5^{-3} = \frac{1}{5^3}$ **Algebra** $a^{-n} = \frac{1}{a^n}$, where $a \neq 0$

 Multi-Language Glossary at BigIdeasMath.com.

EXAMPLE 2 Evaluating Expressions

a. $(-0.5)^{-3} = \frac{1}{(-0.5)^3}$ — Definition of negative exponent

$= \frac{1}{-0.125} = -8$ — Simplify.

b. $4^0 - 2^{-4} + \left(\frac{1}{4}\right)^2 = 4^0 - \frac{1}{2^4} + \left(\frac{1}{4}\right)^2$ — Definition of negative exponent

$= 1 - \frac{1}{16} + \frac{1}{16}$ — Evaluate the powers.

$= 1$ — Simplify.

On Your Own

Now You're Ready
Exercises 12–18

Evaluate the expression.

5. 2^{-5} **6.** $(-0.2)^{-3}$ **7.** $4^{-2} + \left(\frac{1}{2}\right)^3 - 8^0$

EXAMPLE 3 Real-Life Application

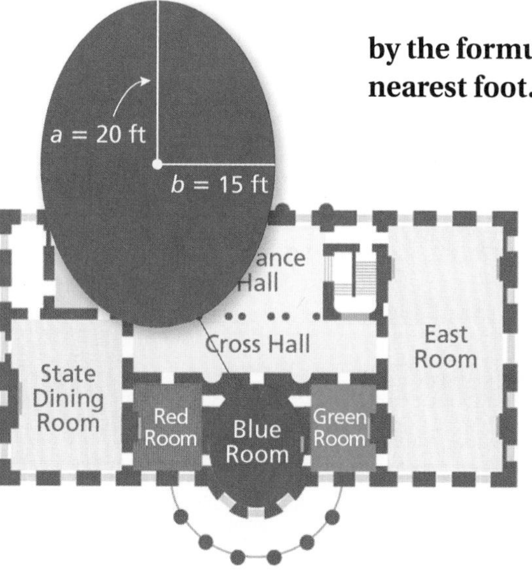

The circumference C of the Blue Room in the White House is given by the formula $C = 2\pi\sqrt{\frac{a^2 + b^2}{2}}$. Estimate the circumference to the nearest foot.

$C = 2\pi\sqrt{\frac{a^2 + b^2}{2}}$ — Write formula.

$= 2\pi\sqrt{\frac{20^2 + 15^2}{2}}$ — Substitute.

$= 2\pi\sqrt{\frac{400 + 225}{2}}$ — Evaluate the powers.

$= 2\pi\sqrt{312.5}$ — Simplify.

≈ 111 — Use a calculator.

The circumference of the room is about 111 feet.

On Your Own

8. Use the formula in Example 3 to estimate the circumference of the figure to the nearest foot.

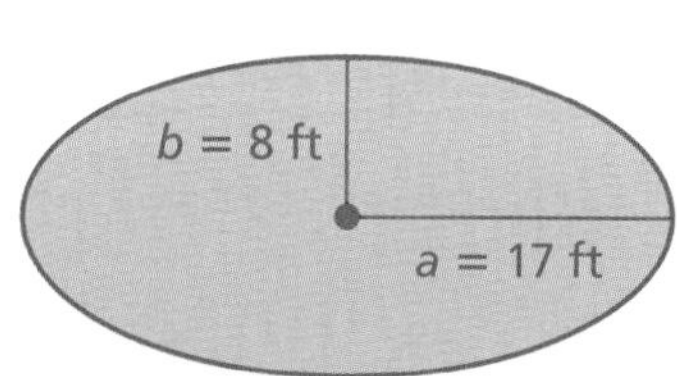

10.1 Exercises

Vocabulary and Concept Check

1. **VOCABULARY** Identify the base and exponent of each power in the expression below.

$$5^0 + 2^{-8}$$

Copy and complete the statement using < or >.

2. $3.2^2 \;\square\; 6^{-3}$ 3. $\left(-\frac{1}{4}\right)^0 \;\square\; 5^4$ 4. $7^0 \;\square\; 8^{-1}$

Practice and Problem Solving

The fraction of remaining carbon-14 is given for an object. Use the fraction to estimate the age of the object. Explain your reasoning.

5. Carbon-14 remaining: $\left(\frac{1}{2}\right)^5$ 6. Carbon-14 remaining: 2^{-4}

Evaluate the expression.

1 2 7. 4^3 8. $(-3)^4$ 9. -2^3

10. $\left(-\frac{1}{5}\right)^2$ 11. 2.8^2 12. 3^{-3}

13. $(-7)^{-2}$ 14. $\left(-\frac{1}{6}\right)^0$ 15. 9.8^0

16. $2^{-3} - 8^{-1} + \left(\frac{1}{2}\right)^0$ 17. $(-2.5)^0 - 5^0 - 10^{-3}$ 18. $10^{-2} - \left(\frac{2}{5}\right)^2 + 2^{-2}$

19. **ERROR ANALYSIS** Describe and correct the error in evaluating the expression.

✗ $5^{-2} = (5)(-2) = -10$

20. **BINOCULARS** You are 600 meters from a boat. When you look through the binoculars, the boat appears to be $600 \cdot 10^{-1}$ meters away. Evaluate this expression.

10x magnification: objects will appear 10 times closer

21. YOU BE THE TEACHER A classmate's work is shown. Is your classmate's final answer correct? Is the work shown correct? Explain.

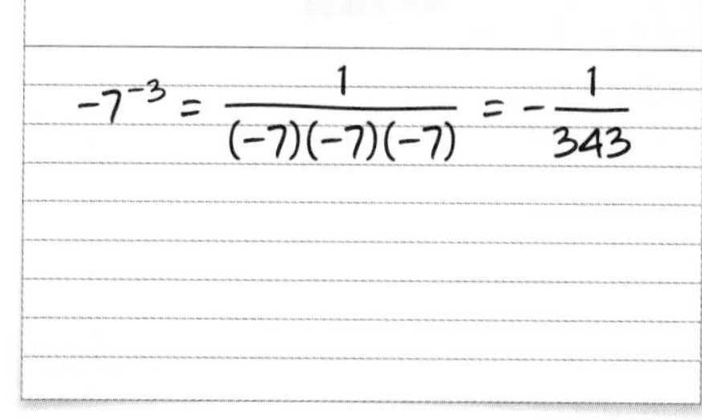

22. NUMBER SENSE Write $-\left(\frac{1}{8} \cdot \frac{1}{8} \cdot \frac{1}{8} \cdot \frac{1}{8} \cdot \frac{1}{8}\right)$ using negative exponents.

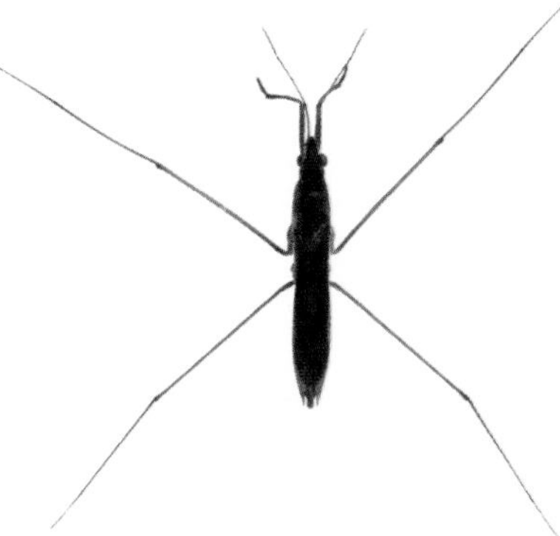

23. WATER STRIDER A water strider has thousands of microscopic hairs on its legs which give it the ability to walk on water. The length of each hair is about 50 micrometers. What is the length of one hair in *meters*? (A micrometer is 10^{-6} meter.)

24. INK CARTRIDGE The black ink cartridge contains 5^{-3} liter of ink. The ink in the cartridge costs \$10. About how much does a *gallon* of black ink cost? (1 gal ≈ 3.79 L)

25. CRITICAL THINKING Given that $3^{-6} = \frac{1}{729}$, how do you evaluate 3^{-7} without multiplying seven 3's?

26. Reasoning Copy and complete the table. Describe the pattern in the exponents. Use the pattern to simplify the expression $x^2 \cdot x^{-5}$.

Expression	Evaluate	Write as a power whose base is 4
$4^2 \cdot 4^1$		
$4^3 \cdot 4^{-2}$		
$4^1 \cdot 4^{-2}$		
$4^{-1} \cdot 4^{-2}$		

Fair Game Review What you learned in previous grades & lessons

Tell whether the triangle with the given side lengths is a right triangle. *(Section 8.5)*

27. 5 ft, 12 ft, 13 ft **28.** 9 mm, 14 mm, 17 mm **29.** 7 m, 24 m, 25 m

30. MULTIPLE CHOICE Which data display best orders numerical data and shows how they are distributed? *(Section 9.2)*

Ⓐ bar graph Ⓑ line graph

Ⓒ scatter plot Ⓓ stem-and-leaf plot

10.2 Product of Powers Property

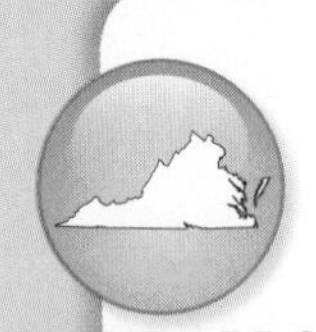

STANDARDS OF LEARNING
8.1

Essential Question How can you multiply two powers that have the same base?

1 ACTIVITY: Finding Products of Powers

Work with a partner.

a. Copy and complete the table.

Product	Repeated Multiplication Form	Power
$2^2 \cdot 2^4$	$2 \cdot 2 \cdot 2 \cdot 2 \cdot 2 \cdot 2$	2^6
$(-3)^2 \cdot (-3)^4$	$(-3) \cdot (-3) \cdot (-3) \cdot (-3) \cdot (-3) \cdot (-3)$	$(-3)^6$
$7^3 \cdot 7^2$		
$5.1^1 \cdot 5.1^6$		
$(-4)^2 \cdot (-4)^2$		
$10^3 \cdot 10^5$		
$\left(\frac{1}{2}\right)^5 \cdot \left(\frac{1}{2}\right)^5$		

b. **INDUCTIVE REASONING** Describe the pattern in the table. Then write a rule for multiplying two powers that have the same base.

$$a^m \cdot a^n = a^{\square}$$

c. Use your rule to simplify the products in the first column of the table above. Does your rule give the results in the third column?

2 ACTIVITY: Using a Calculator

Work with a partner.

Some calculators have *exponent keys* that are used to evaluate powers.

Use a calculator with an exponent key to evaluate the products in Activity 1.

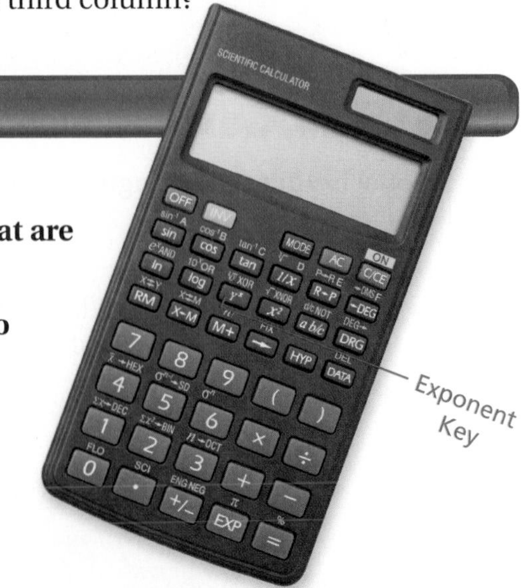

3 ACTIVITY: The Penny Puzzle

Work with a partner.

- The rows y and columns x of a chess board are numbered as shown.
- Each position on the chess board has a stack of pennies. (Only the first row is shown.)
- The number of pennies in each stack is

  $2^x \cdot 2^y$.

a. How many pennies are in the stack in location (3, 5)?

b. Which locations have 32 pennies in their stacks?

c. How much money (in dollars) is in the location with the tallest stack?

d. A penny is about 0.06 inch thick. About how tall (in inches) is the tallest stack?

What Is Your Answer?

4. IN YOUR OWN WORDS How can you multiply two powers that have the same base? Give two examples of your rule.

Practice Use what you learned about the Product of Powers Property to complete Exercises 3–5 on page 452.

Product of Powers Property

Words To multiply powers with the same base, add their exponents.

Numbers $4^2 \cdot 4^3 = 4^{2+3} = 4^5$ **Algebra** $a^m \cdot a^n = a^{m+n}$

EXAMPLE 1 Multiplying Powers with the Same Base

a. $2^4 \cdot 2^5 = 2^{4+5}$ The base is 2. Add the exponents.

$= 2^9$ Simplify.

b. $(-5.1)^{-3} \cdot (-5.1)^3 = (-5.1)^{-3+3}$ The base is −5.1. Add the exponents.

$= (-5.1)^0$ Simplify.

$= 1$ Definition of zero exponent

c. $x^3 \cdot x^7 = x^{3+7}$ The base is *x*. Add the exponents.

$= x^{10}$ Simplify.

EXAMPLE 2 Finding a Power of a Power

a. $(3^4)^3 = 3^4 \cdot 3^4 \cdot 3^4$ Write as repeated multiplication.

$= 3^{4+4+4}$ The base is 3. Add the exponents.

$= 3^{12}$ Simplify.

b. $(w^{-5})^4 = w^{-5} \cdot w^{-5} \cdot w^{-5} \cdot w^{-5}$ Write as repeated multiplication.

$= w^{-5+(-5)+(-5)+(-5)}$ The base is *w*. Add the exponents.

$= w^{-20}$ Simplify.

$= \dfrac{1}{w^{20}}$ Definition of negative exponent

On Your Own

Now You're Ready
Exercises 3–14

Simplify. Write your answer using only positive exponents.

1. $6^2 \cdot 6^4$
2. $\left(-\frac{1}{2}\right)^3 \cdot \left(-\frac{1}{2}\right)^6$
3. $z \cdot z^{-12}$
4. $(4^{-4})^3$
5. $(y^2)^4$
6. $\left((-4)^3\right)^2$

EXAMPLE 3 Finding a Power of a Product

a. $(2x)^3 = 2x \cdot 2x \cdot 2x$ — Write as repeated multiplication.

$= (2 \cdot 2 \cdot 2) \cdot (x \cdot x \cdot x)$ — Group like bases using properties of multiplication.

$= 2^{1+1+1} \cdot x^{1+1+1}$ — The bases are 2 and x. Add the exponents.

$= 2^3 \cdot x^3 = 8x^3$ — Simplify.

b. $(xy)^2 = xy \cdot xy$ — Write as repeated multiplication.

$= (x \cdot x) \cdot (y \cdot y)$ — Group like bases using properties of multiplication.

$= x^{1+1} \cdot y^{1+1}$ — The bases are x and y. Add the exponents.

$= x^2y^2$ — Simplify.

On Your Own

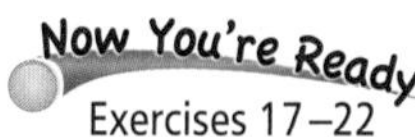

Exercises 17–22

Simplify. Write your answer using only positive exponents.

7. $(-5y)^4$ **8.** $(0.5n)^{-2}$ **9.** $(ab)^5$

EXAMPLE 4 Standardized Test Practice

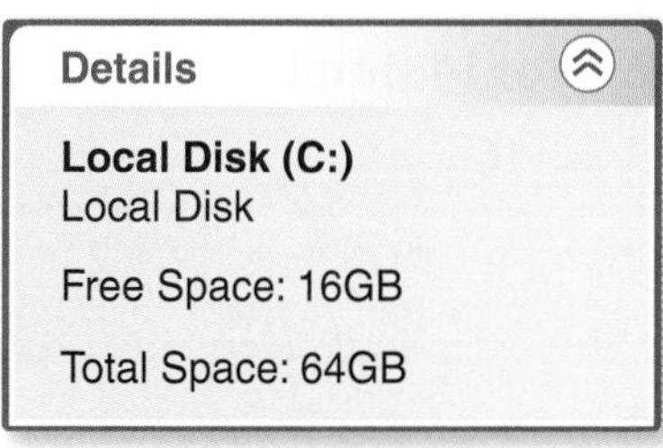

A gigabyte (GB) of computer storage space is 2^{30} bytes. The details of a computer are shown. How many bytes of total storage space does the computer have?

Ⓐ 2^{34} Ⓑ 2^{36} Ⓒ 2^{180} Ⓓ 128^{30}

The computer has 64 gigabytes of total storage space. Notice that 64 can be written as a power, 2^6. Use a model to solve the problem.

Total number of bytes = Number of bytes in a gigabyte • Number of gigabytes

$= 2^{30} \cdot 2^6$ — Substitute.

$= 2^{30+6}$ — Add exponents.

$= 2^{36}$ — Simplify.

The computer has 2^{36} bytes of total storage space. The correct answer is Ⓑ.

On Your Own

10. How many bytes of free storage space does the computer have?

10.2 Exercises

Vocabulary and Concept Check

1. **REASONING** When should you use the Product of Powers Property?
2. **CRITICAL THINKING** Can you use the Product of Powers Property to multiply powers with different bases? Explain.

Practice and Problem Solving

Simplify. Write your answer using only positive exponents.

(1) (2) 3. $3^2 \cdot 3^2$ 4. $8^{10} \cdot 8^{-4}$ 5. $(-4)^5 \cdot (-4)^7$

6. $a^{-3} \cdot a^3$ 7. $h^6 \cdot h$ 8. $\left(\frac{2}{3}\right)^{-2} \cdot \left(\frac{2}{3}\right)^6$

9. $\left(-\frac{5}{7}\right)^8 \cdot \left(-\frac{5}{7}\right)^9$ 10. $(-2.9) \cdot (-2.9)^7$ 11. $(5^4)^3$

12. $(b^{12})^{-3}$ 13. $(3.8^{-3})^{-4}$ 14. $\left(\left(-\frac{3}{4}\right)^5\right)^2$

ERROR ANALYSIS Describe and correct the error in simplifying the expression.

15.

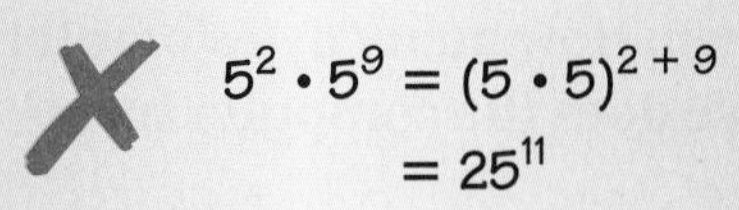

16.

✗ $(r^6)^4 = r^{6+4}$
$= r^{10}$

Simplify. Write your answer using only positive exponents.

(3) 17. $(6g)^3$ 18. $(2v)^{-5}$ 19. $\left(\frac{1}{5}k\right)^2$

20. $(1.2m)^4$ 21. $(rt)^{-6}$ 22. $\left(-\frac{3}{4}p\right)^3$

23. **CRITICAL THINKING** Is $3^2 + 3^3$ equal to 3^5? Explain.

24. **ARTIFACT** A display case for the artifact is in the shape of a cube. Each side of the display case is three times longer than the width of the artifact.

    a. Write an expression for the volume of the case. Write your answer as a power.

    b. Simplify the expression.

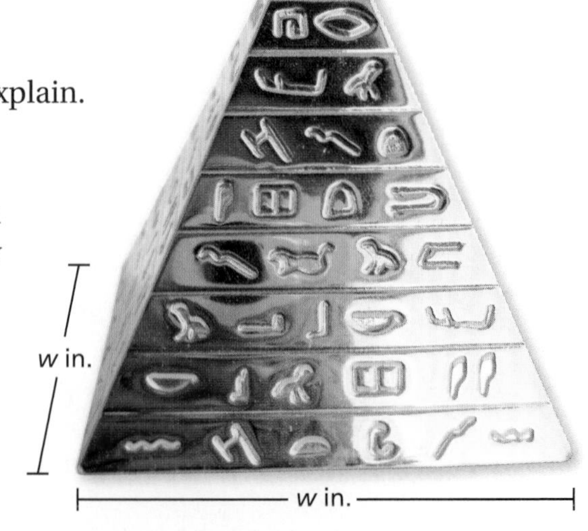

Simplify the expression.

25. $2^4 \cdot 2^5 - (2^2)^2$ **26.** $16\left(\frac{1}{2}x\right)^4$ **27.** $5^{-2}(5^3 \cdot 5^2)$

28. CLOUDS The lowest altitude of an altocumulus cloud is about 3^8 feet. The highest altitude of an altocumulus cloud is about 3 times the lowest altitude. What is the highest altitude of an altocumulus cloud? Write your answer as a power.

29. PYTHON EGG The volume V of a python egg is given by the formula $V = \frac{4}{3}\pi abc$. For the python egg shown, $a = 2$ inches, $b = 2$ inches, and $c = 3$ inches.

a. Find the volume of the python egg.

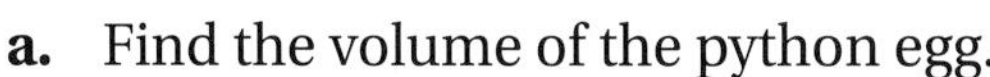

b. Square the dimensions of the python egg. Then evaluate the formula. How does this volume compare to your answer in part (a)?

30. PYRAMID The volume of a square pyramid is $V = \frac{1}{3}b^2h$, where b is the length of one side of the base and h is the height of the pyramid. The length of each side of the base increases by 50%. Write a formula for the volume of the new pyramid.

31. MAIL The United States Postal Service delivers about $2^6 \cdot 5^3$ pieces of mail each second. There are $2^8 \cdot 3^4 \cdot 5^2$ seconds in 6 days. How many pieces of mail does the United States Postal Service deliver in 6 days? Write your answer as a power.

32. Critical Thinking Find the value of x in the equation without evaluating the power.

a. $2^5 \cdot 2^x = 256$ **b.** $\left(\frac{1}{3}\right)^2 \cdot \left(\frac{1}{3}\right)^x = \frac{1}{729}$

Fair Game Review What you learned in previous grades & lessons

Simplify. *(Skills Review Handbook)*

33. $\frac{4 \cdot 4}{4}$ **34.** $\frac{5 \cdot 5 \cdot 5}{5}$ **35.** $\frac{2 \cdot 3}{2}$ **36.** $\frac{8 \cdot 6 \cdot 6}{6 \cdot 8}$

37. MULTIPLE CHOICE What is the measure of each angle of the regular polygon? *(Section 5.3)*

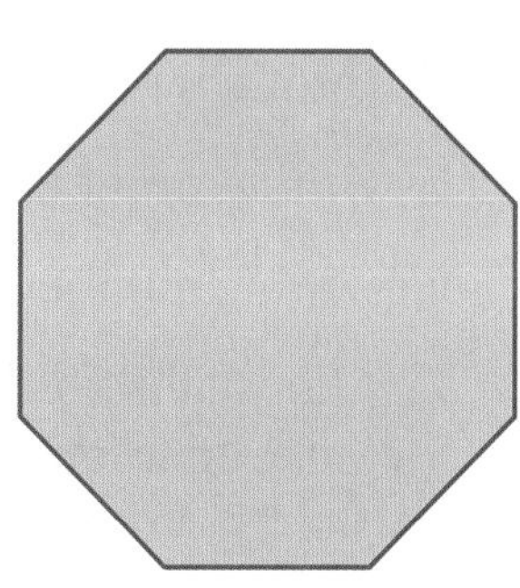

Ⓐ 45° Ⓑ 135°

Ⓒ 1080° Ⓓ 1440°

10 Study Help

Check It Out
Graphic Organizer
BigIdeasMath.com

You can use an **information wheel** to organize information about a topic. Here is an example of an information wheel for exponents.

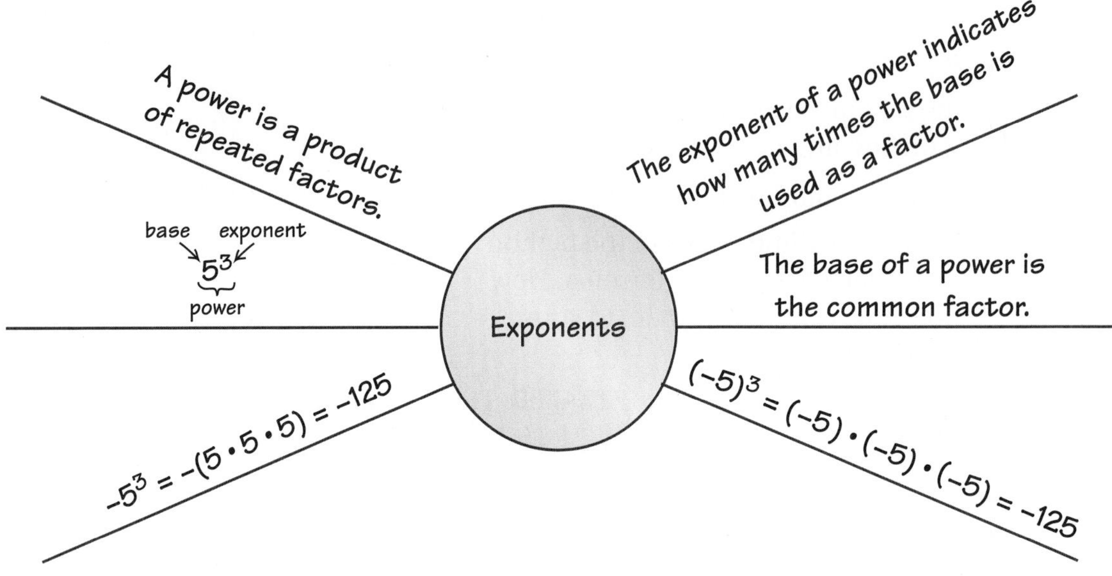

Exponents
A power is a product of repeated factors.
The exponent of a power indicates how many times the base is used as a factor.
base exponent
5^3
power
The base of a power is the common factor.
$-5^3 = -(5 \cdot 5 \cdot 5) = -125$
$(-5)^3 = (-5) \cdot (-5) \cdot (-5) = -125$

On Your Own

Make an information wheel to help you study these topics.

1. zero exponents
2. negative exponents
3. Product of Powers Property

After you complete this chapter, make information wheels for the following topics.

4. Quotient of Powers Property
5. writing numbers in standard form
6. writing numbers in scientific notation
7. Choose three other topics you studied earlier in this course. Make an information wheel for each topic.

Purring
Persian
Fluffy
Fancy
Feline
Why can't I be on the wheel? I'm calling Vanna.

"My information wheel for Fluffy has matching adjectives and nouns."

10.1–10.2 Quiz

Check It Out
Progress Check
BigIdeasMath.com

Evaluate the expression. *(Section 10.1)*

1. 4^{-3}

2. $\left(-\frac{1}{2}\right)^2$

3. $\left(-\frac{2}{3}\right)^0$

4. -2^{-4}

Simplify. Write your answer using only positive exponents. *(Section 10.2)*

5. $(-6)^2 \cdot (-6)^3$

6. $\left(\frac{6}{7}\right)^{-4} \cdot \left(\frac{6}{7}\right)^4$

7. $(-2.3)^{-1} \cdot (-2.3)^2$

8. $(8^2)^{-3}$

9. $(0.6f)^2$

10. $\left(\frac{1}{4}t\right)^3$

11. $(4z)^{-4}$

12. $(3m)^{-2}$

13. SHOPPING Apricot jelly costs 2^{-2} dollar per ounce. How much does the jar of jelly cost? *(Section 10.1)*

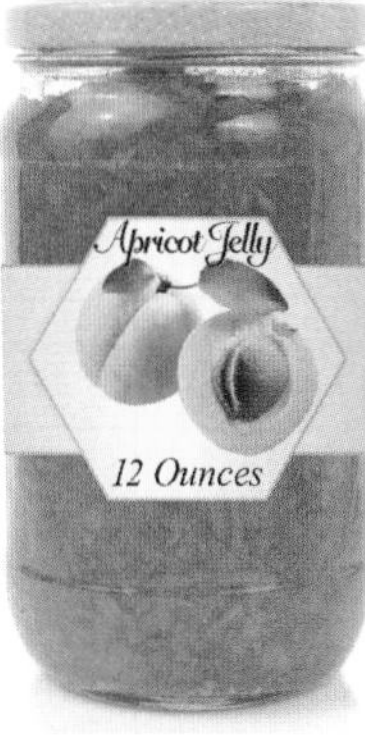

14. VOLUME The volume of a cube is s^3, where s is the length of one side of the cube. A cube has a side length of 1.2 centimeters. What is the volume of the cube in cubic centimeters? *(Section 10.1)*

100 mm

15. GECKO Find the length of the gecko in *meters*. ($1 \text{ mm} = 10^{-3} \text{ m}$) *(Section 10.2)*

16. CRITICAL THINKING Is $(ab)^2$ equivalent to ab^2? Explain. *(Section 10.2)*

17. WEIGHT The weight of a lion is 10^3 times greater than the weight of a bird. The weight of a whale is 10^3 times greater than the weight of the lion. How many times greater is the weight of the whale than the weight of the bird? *(Section 10.2)*

10.3 Quotient of Powers Property

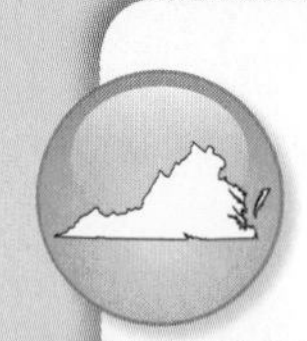

STANDARDS OF LEARNING
8.1

Essential Question How can you divide two powers that have the same base?

1 ACTIVITY: Finding Quotients of Powers

Work with a partner.

a. Copy and complete the table.

Quotient	Repeated Multiplication Form	Power
$\frac{2^4}{2^2}$	$\frac{\cancel{2} \cdot \cancel{2} \cdot 2 \cdot 2}{\cancel{2} \cdot \cancel{2}}$	2^2
$\frac{(-4)^5}{(-4)^2}$	$\frac{\cancel{(-4)} \cdot \cancel{(-4)} \cdot (-4) \cdot (-4) \cdot (-4)}{\cancel{(-4)} \cdot \cancel{(-4)}}$	$(-4)^3$
$\frac{7^7}{7^3}$		
$\frac{8.5^9}{8.5^6}$		
$\frac{10^8}{10^5}$		
$\frac{3^{12}}{3^4}$		
$\frac{(-5)^7}{(-5)^5}$		
$\frac{11^4}{11^1}$		

b. **INDUCTIVE REASONING** Describe the pattern in the table. Then write a rule for dividing two powers that have the same base.

$$\frac{a^m}{a^n} = a^{\square}$$

c. Use your rule to simplify the quotients in the first column of the table above. Does your rule give the results in the third column?

2 ACTIVITY: Comparing Volumes

Work with a partner.

How many of the smaller cubes will fit inside the larger cube? Record your results in the table. Describe the pattern in the table.

a. Sample:

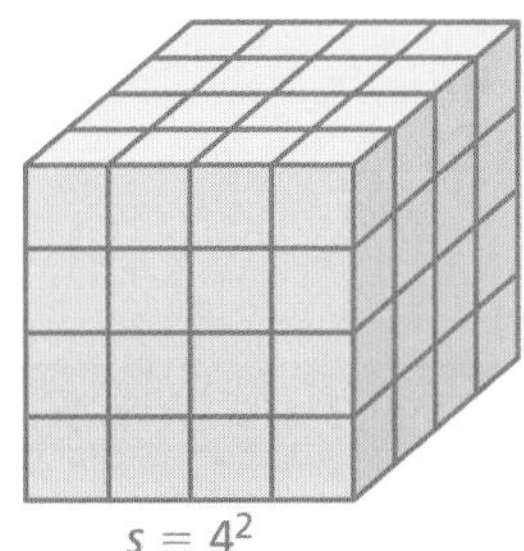

b.

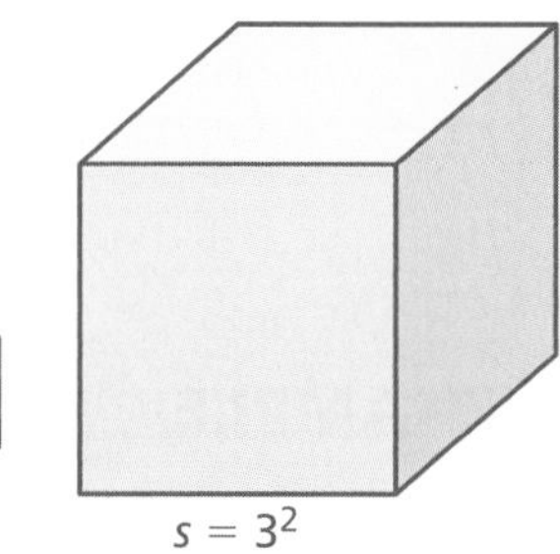

c.

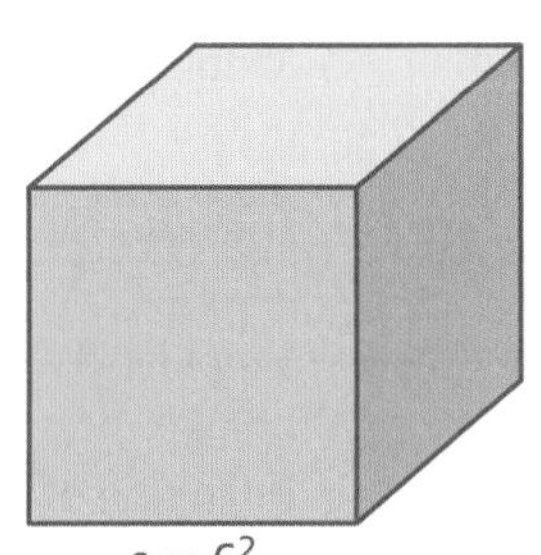

d.

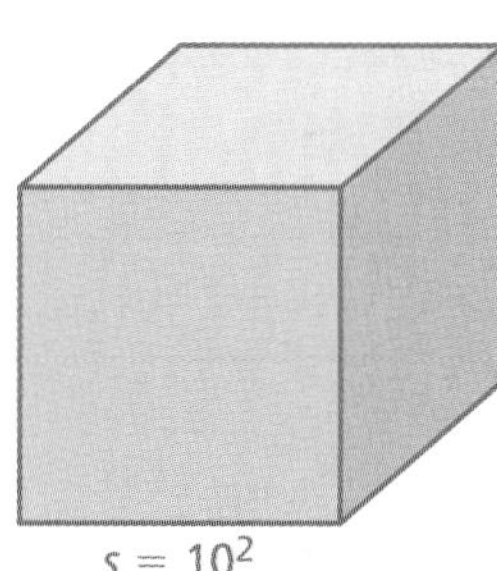

	Volume of Smaller Cube	Volume of Larger Cube	$\frac{\text{Larger Volume}}{\text{Smaller Volume}}$	Answer
a.	4^3	$(4^2)^3 = 4^6$	$\frac{4^6}{4^3}$	4^3
b.				
c.				
d.				

What Is Your Answer?

3. **IN YOUR OWN WORDS** How can you divide two powers that have the same base? Give two examples of your rule.

Practice Use what you learned about the Quotient of Powers Property to complete Exercises 3–6 on page 460.

10.3 Lesson

Quotient of Powers Property

Words To divide powers with the same base, subtract their exponents.

Numbers $\frac{4^5}{4^2} = 4^{5-2} = 4^3$ **Algebra** $\frac{a^m}{a^n} = a^{m-n}$, where $a \neq 0$

EXAMPLE 1 Dividing Powers with the Same Base

a. $\frac{2^6}{2^4} = 2^{6-4}$ The base is 2. Subtract the exponents.

$= 2^2$ Simplify.

Common Error

When dividing powers, do not divide the bases.

$\frac{2^6}{2^4} = 2^2$, not 1^2.

b. $\frac{(-7)^3}{(-7)^9} = (-7)^{3-9}$ The base is −7. Subtract the exponents.

$= (-7)^{-6}$ Simplify.

$= \frac{1}{(-7)^6}$ Definition of negative exponent

c. $\frac{h^7}{h^6} = h^{7-6}$ The base is h. Subtract the exponents.

$= h^1 = h$ Simplify.

On Your Own

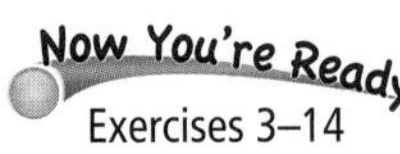

Exercises 3–14

Simplify. Write your answer using only positive exponents.

1. $\frac{9^4}{9^7}$
2. $\frac{4.2^6}{4.2^5}$
3. $\frac{(-8)^8}{(-8)^4}$
4. $\frac{x^3}{x^{-8}}$

EXAMPLE 2 Simplifying an Expression

Simplify $\frac{3^4 \cdot 3^2}{3^3}$. Write your answer using only positive exponents.

The numerator is a product of powers.

$\frac{3^4 \cdot 3^2}{3^3} = \frac{3^{4+2}}{3^3}$ The base is 3. Add the exponents in the numerator.

$= \frac{3^6}{3^3}$ Simplify.

$= 3^{6-3}$ The base is 3. Subtract the exponents.

$= 3^3$ Simplify.

EXAMPLE 3 Simplifying an Expression

Simplify $\frac{a^{10}}{a^6} \cdot \frac{a^7}{a^4}$. Write your answer using only positive exponents.

$$\frac{a^{10}}{a^6} \cdot \frac{a^7}{a^4} = a^{10-6} \cdot a^{7-4}$$ Subtract the exponents.

$$= a^4 \cdot a^3$$ Simplify.

$$= a^{4+3}$$ Add the exponents.

$$= a^7$$ Simplify.

Study Tip

You can also simplify the expression in Example 3 as follows.

$$\frac{a^{10}}{a^6} \cdot \frac{a^7}{a^4} = \frac{a^{10} \cdot a^7}{a^6 \cdot a^4}$$
$$= \frac{a^{17}}{a^{10}}$$
$$= a^{17-10}$$
$$= a^7$$

On Your Own

Now You're Ready
Exercises 16–21

Simplify. Write your answer using only positive exponents.

5. $\frac{2^{15}}{2^3 \cdot 2^5}$

6. $\frac{d^5}{d} \cdot \frac{d^8}{d^9}$

EXAMPLE 4 Real-Life Application

The projected population of Tennessee in 2030 is about $5 \cdot 5.9^8$. Predict the average number of people per square mile in 2030.

Use a model to solve the problem.

$$\text{People per square mile} = \frac{\text{Population in 2030}}{\text{Land area}}$$

Land Area: about 5.9^6 mi^2

$$= \frac{5 \cdot 5.9^8}{5.9^6}$$ Substitute.

$$= 5 \cdot \frac{5.9^8}{5.9^6}$$ Rewrite.

$$= 5 \cdot 5.9^2$$ Subtract the exponents.

$$= 174.05$$ Evaluate.

There will be about 174 people per square mile in Tennessee in 2030.

On Your Own

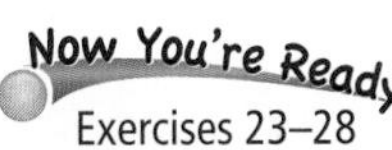

Exercises 23–28

7. The projected population of Alabama in 2020 is about $2.25 \cdot 2^{21}$. The land area of Alabama is about 2^{17} square kilometers. Predict the average number of people per square kilometer in 2020.

10.3 Exercises

Vocabulary and Concept Check

1. **WRITING** Explain what it means to divide powers.

2. **WHICH ONE DOESN'T BELONG?** Which quotient does *not* belong with the other three? Explain your reasoning.

$\frac{(-10)^7}{(-10)^2}$ $\frac{6^3}{6^2}$ $\frac{(-4)^8}{(-3)^4}$ $\frac{5^6}{5^3}$

Practice and Problem Solving

Simplify. Write your answer using only positive exponents.

1 3. $\frac{6^{10}}{6^4}$ 4. $\frac{8^7}{8^9}$ 5. $\frac{(-3)^4}{(-3)^1}$ 6. $\frac{4.5^{-5}}{4.5^{-5}}$

7. $\frac{5^9}{5^3}$ 8. $\frac{64^4}{64^3}$ 9. $\frac{(-17)^{-5}}{(-17)^{-2}}$ 10. $\frac{(-7.9)^{10}}{(-7.9)^4}$

11. $\frac{(-6.4)^8}{(-6.4)^{-6}}$ 12. $\frac{\pi^{11}}{\pi^7}$ 13. $\frac{b^{11}}{b^{24}}$ 14. $\frac{n^{18}}{n^7}$

15. **ERROR ANALYSIS** Describe and correct the error in simplifying the quotient.

✗ $\frac{6^{15}}{6^5} = 6^{\frac{15}{5}}$
$= 6^3$

Simplify. Write your answer using only positive exponents.

 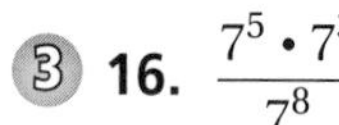

16. $\frac{7^5 \cdot 7^3}{7^8}$ 17. $\frac{2^{19} \cdot 2^5}{2^{12} \cdot 2^3}$ 18. $\frac{(-8.3)^8}{(-8.3)^7} \cdot \frac{(-8.3)^4}{(-8.3)^3}$

19. $\frac{\pi^{30}}{\pi^{18} \cdot \pi^{24}}$ 20. $\frac{c^{22}}{c^8 \cdot c^9}$ 21. $\frac{k^{13}}{k^5} \cdot \frac{k^{11}}{k^{20}}$

22. **SOUND INTENSITY** The sound intensity of a normal conversation is 10^6 times greater than the quietest noise a person can hear. The sound intensity of a jet at takeoff is 10^{14} times greater than the quietest noise a person can hear. How many times more intense is the sound of a jet at takeoff than the sound of a normal conversation?

Simplify. Write your answer using only positive exponents.

④ **23.** $\dfrac{x \cdot 4^8}{4^5}$ **24.** $\dfrac{6^3 \cdot w}{6^2}$ **25.** $\dfrac{a^3 \cdot b^4 \cdot 5^4}{b^2 \cdot 5}$

26. $\dfrac{5^{12} \cdot c^{10} \cdot d^2}{5^9 \cdot c^9}$ **27.** $\dfrac{x^{15}y^3}{x^8y^9}$ **28.** $\dfrac{m^{10}n^7}{m^1n^7}$

29. MEMORY The memory capacities and prices of five MP3 players are shown in the table.

MP3 Player	Memory (GB)	Price
A	2^1	\$70
B	2^2	\$120
C	2^3	\$170
D	2^4	\$220
E	2^5	\$270

a. How many times more memory does MP3 Player D have than MP3 Player B?

b. Do the differences in price between consecutive sizes reflect a constant rate of change?

30. CRITICAL THINKING Consider the equation $\dfrac{9^m}{9^n} = 9^2$.

a. Find two numbers m and n that satisfy the equation.

b. Are there any other pairs of numbers that satisfy the equation? Explain.

Milky Way Galaxy
$10 \cdot 10^{10}$ stars

31. STARS There are about 10^{24} stars in the Universe. Each galaxy has approximately the same number of stars as the Milky Way Galaxy. About how many galaxies are in the Universe?

32. Number Sense Find the value of x that makes $\dfrac{8^{3x}}{8^{2x+1}} = 8^9$ true. Explain how you found your answer.

Fair Game Review What you learned in previous grades & lessons

Subtract. *(Skills Review Handbook)*

33. $-4 - 5$ **34.** $-23 - (-15)$ **35.** $33 - (-28)$ **36.** $18 - 22$

37. MULTIPLE CHOICE What is the value of x? *(Section 5.1)*

Ⓐ 20 Ⓑ 30

Ⓒ 45 Ⓓ 60

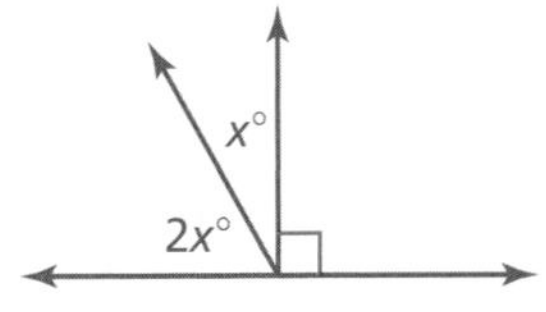

10.4 Scientific Notation

STANDARDS OF LEARNING
8.1

Essential Question How did people in ancient cultures represent large numbers?

1 ACTIVITY: Hieroglyphics

Ancient Egyptians used hieroglyphics to represent numbers.

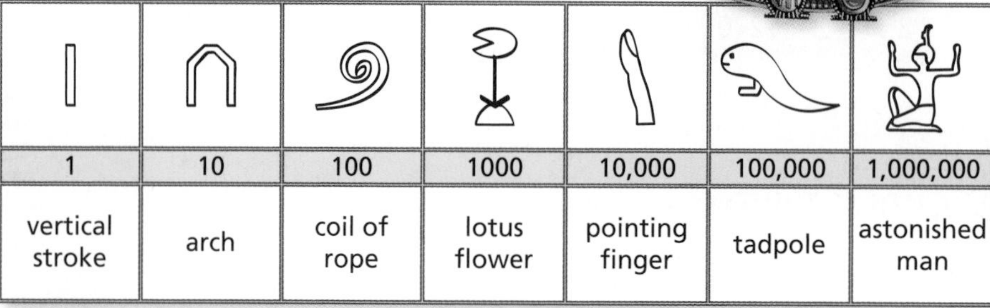

1	10	100	1000	10,000	100,000	1,000,000
vertical stroke	arch	coil of rope	lotus flower	pointing finger	tadpole	astonished man

Work with a partner. Write each Egyptian number in standard form.

a.

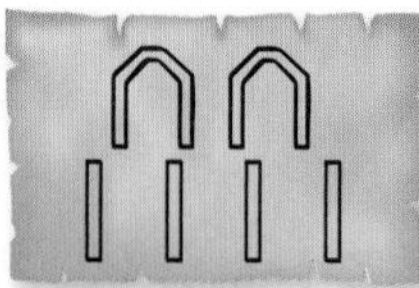

b.

c.

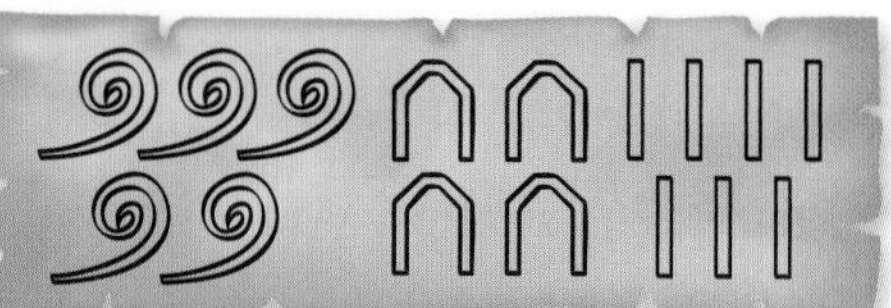

d.

e.

f.

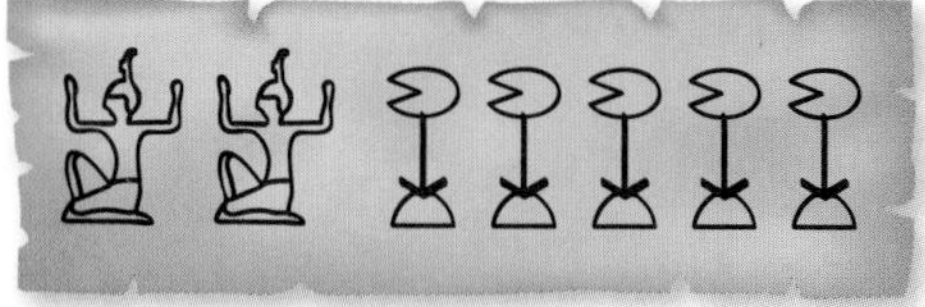

Write each number using hieroglyphics.

g. 58 **h.** 608 **i.** 1501

j. 27,900 **k.** 404,000 **l.** 2,500,000

2 ACTIVITY: Roman Numerals

Ancient Romans used Roman numerals to represent numbers.

I	V	X	L	C
1	5	10	50	100

D	M	$\overline{V}$	$\overline{X}$
500	1000	5000	10,000
$\overline{L}$	$\overline{C}$	$\overline{D}$	$\overline{M}$
50,000	100,000	500,000	1,000,000

Work with a partner. Write each Roman numeral in standard form.

a.

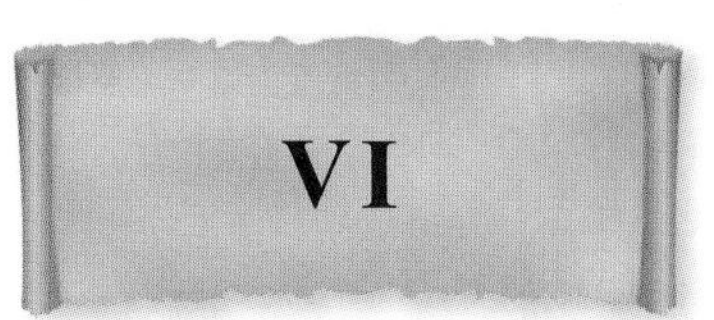

b.

c.

d.

e.

f.

Write each number using Roman numerals.

g. 58 **h.** 608 **i.** 1501

j. 27,900 **k.** 404,000 **l.** 2,500,000

What Is Your Answer?

3. **IN YOUR OWN WORDS** How did people in ancient cultures represent large numbers?

4. **RESEARCH** Use the Internet or some other reference to find information about how other ancient cultures represented numbers.

10.4 Lesson

Key Vocabulary
scientific notation, *p. 464*

A number is written in **scientific notation** when it is represented as the product of a factor and a power of 10. The factor must be greater than or equal to 1 and less than 10.

The factor is greater than or equal to 1 and less than 10. → 1.5×10^6 ← The power of 10 has an integer exponent.

EXAMPLE 1 Identifying Numbers Written in Scientific Notation

Tell whether the number is written in scientific notation. Explain.

a. 8.4×10^{-4}

The factor is greater than or equal to 1 and less than 10. The power of 10 has an integer exponent. So, the number is written in scientific notation.

b. 10.7×10^2

The factor is greater than 10. So, the number is not written in scientific notation.

On Your Own

Now You're Ready
Exercises 3–8

Tell whether the number is written in scientific notation. Explain.

1. 0.9×10^{-2} **2.** 12×10^{-3} **3.** 7.25×10^8

Key Idea

Writing Numbers in Standard Form

The absolute value of the exponent indicates how many places to move the decimal point.

- If the exponent is negative, move the decimal point to the left.
- If the exponent is positive, move the decimal point to the right.

EXAMPLE 2 Writing Numbers in Standard Form

a. Write 4.17×10^{-3} in standard form.

$4.17 \times 10^{-3} = 0.00417$ (3) Move decimal point $|-3| = 3$ places to the left.

b. Write 2.2×10^6 in standard form.

$2.2 \times 10^6 = 2{,}200{,}000$ (6) Move decimal point $|6| = 6$ places to the right.

Multi-Language Glossary at BigIdeasMath.com.

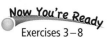

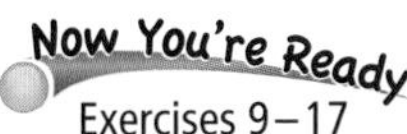

Write the number in standard form.

4. 5.1×10^5 **5.** 2×10^{-4} **6.** 3.57×10^{-7}

Key Idea

Writing Numbers in Scientific Notation

Step 1: Move the decimal point to the right of the leading nonzero digit.

Step 2: Count the number of places you moved the decimal point. This indicates the exponent of the power of 10, as shown below.

Number greater than or equal to 10

Use a positive exponent when you move the decimal point to the left.

$$8600 = 8.6 \times 10^3$$

3

Number between 0 and 1

Use a negative exponent when you move the decimal point to the right.

$$0.0024 = 2.4 \times 10^{-3}$$

3

Study Tip

When you write a number greater than or equal to 1 and less than 10 in scientific notation, use zero as the exponent.

$7 = 7 \times 10^0$

EXAMPLE 3 Writing Numbers in Scientific Notation

A jellyfish emits about 125,000,000 particles of light, or photons, in 0.000625 second.

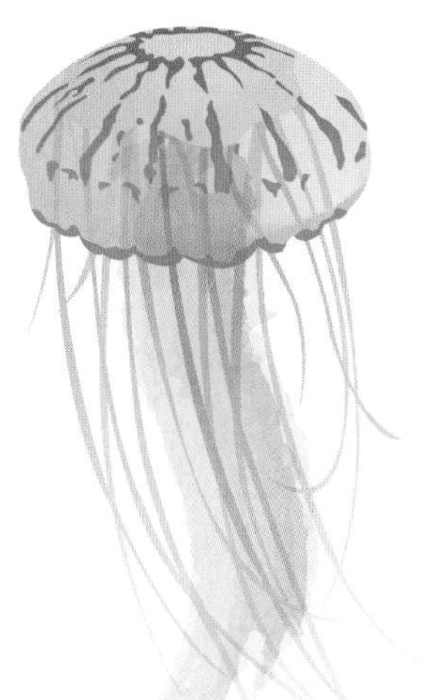

a. Write the number of photons in scientific notation.

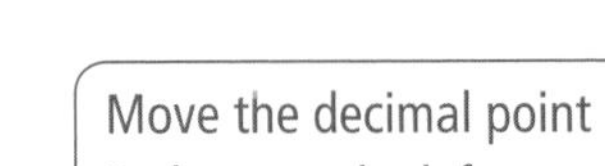

Move the decimal point
8 places to the left.

$$125{,}000{,}000 = 1.25 \times 10^8$$

8

The number is greater than 10. So, the exponent is positive.

b. Write the number of seconds in scientific notation.

Move the decimal point 4 places to the right.

$$0.000625 = 6.25 \times 10^{-4}$$

4

The number is between 0 and 1. So, the exponent is negative.

On Your Own

Now You're Ready
Exercises 19–27

Write the number in scientific notation.

7. 300,000 **8.** 72,500,000 **9.** 0.000901

EXAMPLE 4 Ordering Numbers in Scientific Notation

The table shows the final sale price of three items at an auction. Order the items from least expensive to most expensive.

Item	Roman Sculpture	24.4-carat Diamond Ring	Magna Carta
Final Price (in dollars)	2.86×10^7	3.625×10^6	2.13×10^7

Step 1: Compare the powers of 10.

Because $10^6 < 10^7$,

$3.625 \times 10^6 < 2.86 \times 10^7$ and $3.625 \times 10^6 < 2.13 \times 10^7$.

Step 2: Compare the factors when the powers of 10 are the same.

Because $2.13 < 2.86$,

$2.13 \times 10^7 < 2.86 \times 10^7$.

From least to greatest, the order is 3.625×10^6, 2.13×10^7, and 2.86×10^7.

So, the items in order from least expensive to most expensive are the diamond ring, the Magna Carta, and the Roman sculpture.

On Your Own

Now You're Ready
Exercises 32–35

10. **WHAT IF?** The final sale price of a 1933 Double Eagle coin is 7.59×10^6 dollars. Order the four items from least expensive to most expensive.

EXAMPLE 5 Multiplying Numbers in Scientific Notation

Find $(3 \times 10^{-5}) \times (5 \times 10^{-2})$. Write your answer in scientific notation.

$(3 \times 10^{-5}) \times (5 \times 10^{-2})$

$= 3 \times 5 \times 10^{-5} \times 10^{-2}$ — Commutative Property of Multiplication

$= (3 \times 5) \times (10^{-5} \times 10^{-2})$ — Associative Property of Multiplication

$= 15 \times 10^{-7}$ — Simplify.

$= 1.5 \times 10^1 \times 10^{-7}$ — Write 15 in scientific notation.

$= 1.5 \times 10^{-6}$ — Simplify.

Study Tip

You can check your answer using standard form.

$(3 \times 10^{-5}) \times (5 \times 10^{-2})$
$= 0.00003 \times 0.05$
$= 0.0000015$
$= 1.5 \times 10^{-6}$

On Your Own

Now You're Ready
Exercises 37–42

Multiply. Write your answer in scientific notation.

11. $(2.5 \times 10^8) \times (2 \times 10^3)$
12. $(2 \times 10^{-4}) \times (1 \times 10^{-4})$
13. $(5 \times 10^{-4}) \times (5.4 \times 10^{-9})$
14. $(7 \times 10^2) \times (3 \times 10^5)$

10.4 Exercises

Vocabulary and Concept Check

1. **REASONING** When writing a number in standard form, which way do you move the decimal point when the exponent is positive? negative?

2. **WHICH ONE DOESN'T BELONG?** Which number does *not* belong with the other three? Explain your reasoning.

4.7×10^3	7.89×10^{-6}	11.5×10^8	6.025×10^{-9}

Practice and Problem Solving

Tell whether the number is written in scientific notation. Explain.

1 3. 0.4×10^{-5}
4. 5.3×10^7
5. 2.65×10^{12}
6. 0.88×10^{-3}
7. 2.0×10^{-11}
8. 11.2×10^{-6}

Write the number in standard form.

2 9. 7.5×10^3
10. 5.77×10^2
11. 3.89×10^{-7}
12. 1.16×10^{-4}
13. 4.3×10^5
14. 2.04×10^6
15. 8.09×10^{-10}
16. 6.332×10^{-8}
17. 9.654×10^1

18. **ERROR ANALYSIS** Describe and correct the error in writing the number in standard form.

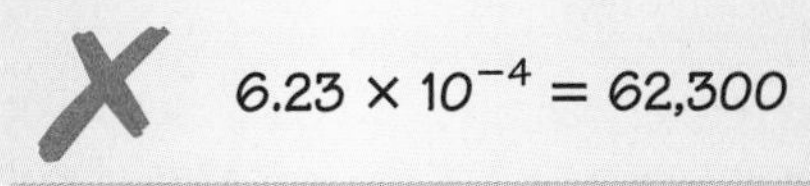

Write the number in scientific notation.

3 19. 12,000
20. 789
21. 0.27
22. 0.0035
23. 0.002
24. 135,000
25. 1,750,000
26. 0.000355
27. 800,200

28. **REASONING** When is it convenient to write a number in scientific notation?

29. **DUST MITE** The length of a dust mite is 2.75×10^{-7} kilometer. Write this number in standard form.

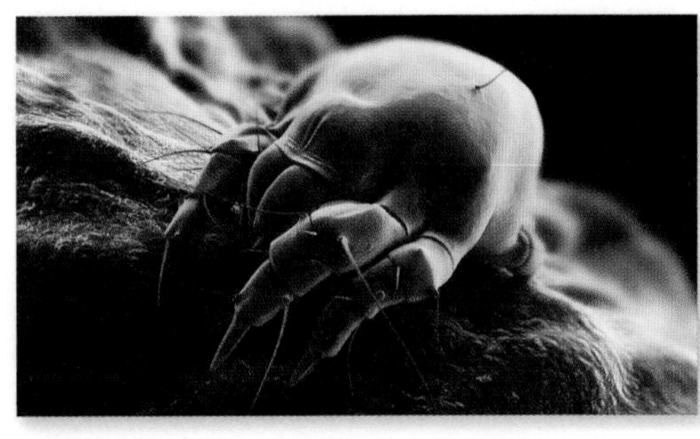

30. **LCD TVS** An LCD flat panel television has 921,600 pixels. Write this number in scientific notation.

31. **ERROR ANALYSIS** Describe and correct the error in writing the number in scientific notation.

Order the numbers from greatest to least.

4 32. $9.7 \times 10^5, 7.45 \times 10^6, 8.4 \times 10^5$

33. $1.49 \times 10^4, 2.11 \times 10^{-3}, 1.09 \times 10^4$

34. $5.27 \times 10^{-3}, 4.02 \times 10^2, 6.0 \times 10^{-3}$

35. $2.78 \times 10^{-7}, 3.49 \times 10^{-8}, 3.611 \times 10^{-7}$

36. **SALARY** The table shows the annual salary of four jobs. Order the salaries from least to greatest.

Job Title	Nurse	Dentist	Psychologist	Pharmacist
Annual Salary (in dollars)	6.2×10^4	1.4×10^5	7.8×10^4	1.1×10^5

Multiply. Write your answer in scientific notation.

5 37. $(4 \times 10^4) \times (2 \times 10^6)$

38. $(3 \times 10^{-8}) \times (3 \times 10^{-2})$

39. $(5 \times 10^{-7}) \times (3 \times 10^6)$

40. $(8 \times 10^3) \times (2 \times 10^4)$

41. $(6 \times 10^8) \times (1.4 \times 10^{-5})$

42. $(7.2 \times 10^{-1}) \times (4 \times 10^{-7})$

Find the area of the figure. Write your answer in scientific notation.

43.

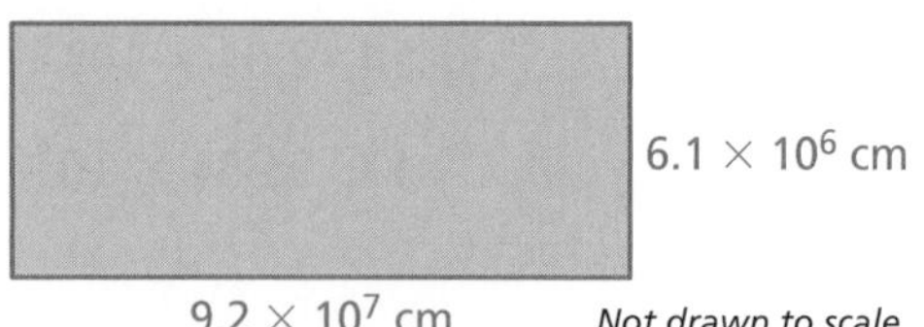

44.

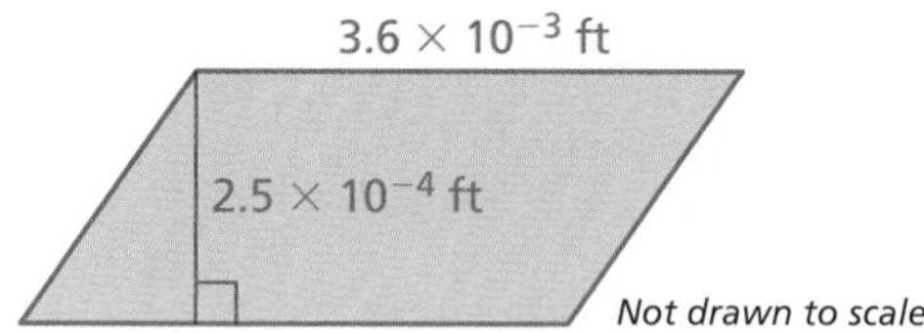

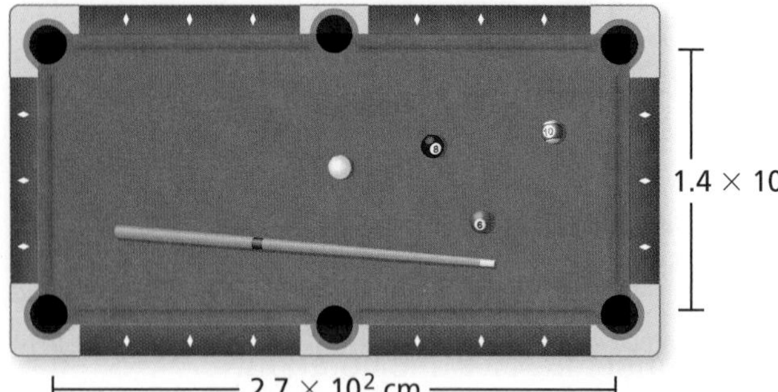

45. **POOL TABLE** Find the playing area of the pool table in square centimeters. Write your answer in scientific notation. How many square *meters* is the playing area?

46. **LIGHT BULB** A 100-watt light bulb emits about 800,000,000 photons in 0.0000000008 second.

a. Write the number of photons in scientific notation.

b. Write the number of seconds in scientific notation.

c. Which emits photons at a greater rate, a 100-watt light bulb or the jellyfish in Example 3? Explain.

47. **CONVERSIONS** The length of a bridge is 1.5×10^{-2} kilometer. Write the length in *meters* and in *centimeters* using scientific notation.

Order the numbers from greatest to least.

48. $\frac{79{,}500}{10}$, 790, 7.9×10^3

49. $\frac{6}{205}$, 0.03, 3.1×10^{-2}

50. 2.3%, 2.35×10^{-3}, $\frac{1}{4}$, 0.235

51. 8922.1, 892%, $\frac{2650}{3}$, 8.9×10^2

52. **PROJECT** Use the Internet or some other reference to find the populations and population densities of India, China, Argentina, the United States, and Egypt. Round each population to the nearest million.

   a. Write each population in scientific notation.

   b. Find the area of each country.

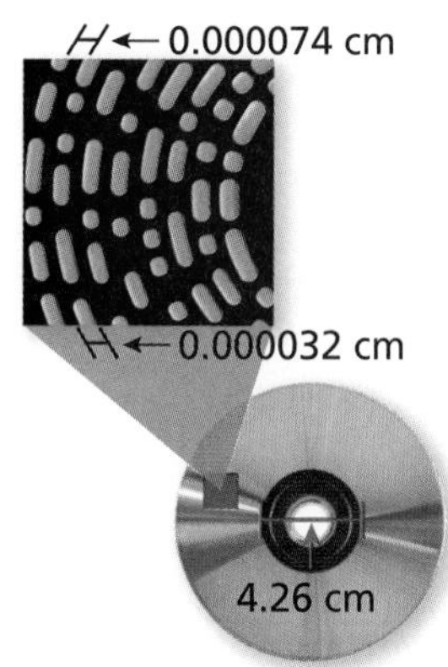

53. **DVDS** On a DVD, information is stored on bumps that spiral around the disk. There are 73,000 ridges (with bumps) and 73,000 valleys (without bumps) across the diameter of the DVD. What is the diameter of the DVD in centimeters?

54. Number Sense Simplify. Write your answer in scientific notation.

   a. $\frac{(53{,}000{,}000)(0.002)}{(0.0004)}$

   b. $\frac{(0.33)(60{,}000)}{(90{,}000{,}000)}$

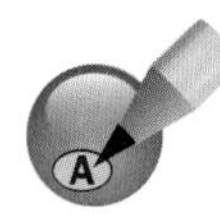

Fair Game Review What you learned in previous grades & lessons

Graph the function. Is the domain of the graph discrete or continuous? *(Section 3.2)*

55.

Input Jars of Jelly, x	Output Cost, y (dollars)
0	0
1	3.99
2	7.98
3	11.97

56.

Input Years, x	Output Height of a Shrub, y (inches)
0	4.5
1	7.5
2	10.5
3	13.5

57. **MULTIPLE CHOICE** The triangles are similar. What is the value of x? *(Section 5.4)*

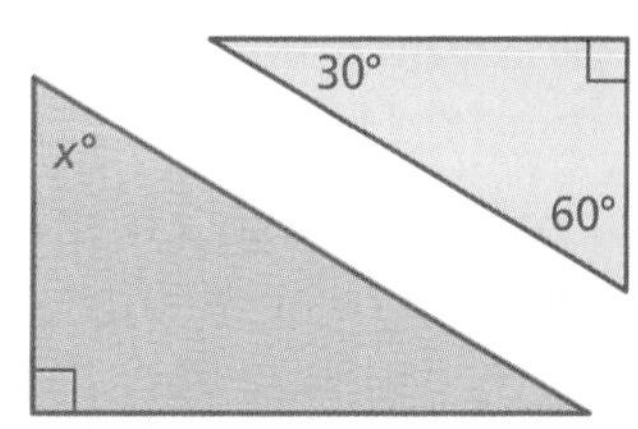

Ⓐ 30 Ⓑ 60 Ⓒ 90 Ⓓ 120

10.3 – 10.4 Quiz

Simplify. Write your answer using only positive exponents. *(Section 10.3)*

1. $\dfrac{8^{-7}}{8^{-4}}$
2. $\dfrac{6^3 \cdot 6^7}{6^{12}}$
3. $\dfrac{\pi^{15}}{\pi^3 \cdot \pi^9}$
4. $\dfrac{t^{13}}{t^5} \cdot \dfrac{t^8}{t^6}$

Tell whether the number is written in scientific notation. Explain. *(Section 10.4)*

5. 11×10^{-8}
6. 0.1×10^3

Write the number in standard form. *(Section 10.4)*

7. 5.2×10^4
8. 4.6×10^{-2}

Write the number in scientific notation. *(Section 10.4)*

9. 45,900,000
10. 0.0000683

Order the numbers from greatest to least. *(Section 10.4)*

11. $9.2 \times 10^5,\ 9.9 \times 10^4,\ 9.6 \times 10^5$
12. $5.4 \times 10^{-6},\ 8.3 \times 10^{-6},\ 6.05 \times 10^{-7}$

Multiply. Write your answer in scientific notation. *(Section 10.4)*

13. $(3 \times 10^2) \times (8 \times 10^6)$
14. $(2.5 \times 10^{-4}) \times (4 \times 10^{-2})$

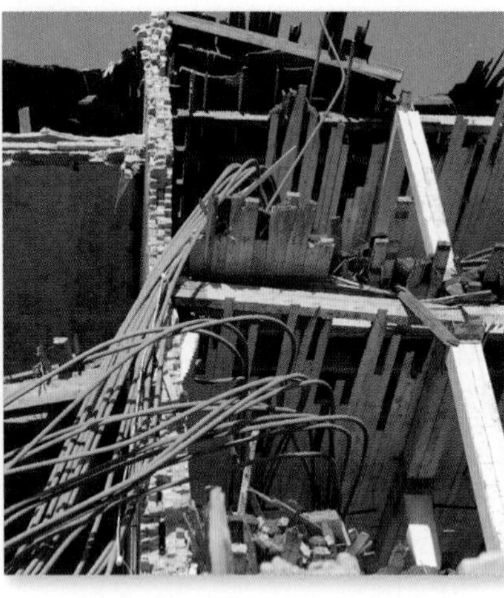

15. **EARTHQUAKES** An earthquake of magnitude 3.0 is 10^2 times stronger than an earthquake of magnitude 1.0. An earthquake of magnitude 8.0 is 10^7 times stronger than an earthquake of magnitude 1.0. How many times stronger is an earthquake of magnitude 8.0 than an earthquake of magnitude 3.0? *(Section 10.3)*

16. **HAIR** The human scalp contains about 100,000 hairs. Write this number in scientific notation. *(Section 10.4)*

17. **CAMERA** A retailer sold 3.5×10^5 digital cameras last year. *(Section 10.4)*

    a. Write the number of digital cameras in standard form.

    b. The retailer expects the number of cameras sold this year to be 10 times greater than last year. How many cameras does the retailer expect to sell this year? Write your answer in scientific notation.

10 Chapter Review

Review Key Vocabulary

power, *p. 444*
base, *p. 444*
exponent, *p. 444*
scientific notation, *p. 464*

Review Examples and Exercises

10.1 Properties of Exponents (*pp. 442–447*)

a. $-5^{-3} = -\frac{1}{5^3}$ Definition of negative exponent

$= -\frac{1}{125}$ Simplify.

b. $8^0 - 3^{-2} + \left(\frac{1}{3}\right)^2 = 8^0 - \frac{1}{3^2} + \left(\frac{1}{3}\right)^2$ Definition of negative exponent

$= 1 - \frac{1}{9} + \frac{1}{9}$ Evaluate the powers.

$= 1$ Simplify.

Exercises

Evaluate the expression.

1. $(-6)^{-3}$
2. -1.9^0
3. $\left(-\frac{1}{2}\right)^5$
4. -1.5^{-2}
5. $\left(\frac{1}{4}\right)^2 - 2^{-3} + 4^0$
6. $5^{-2} + \left(\frac{1}{10}\right)^2 - \left(\frac{2}{3}\right)^0$

10.2 Product of Powers Property (*pp. 448–453*)

a. $\left(-\frac{1}{8}\right)^7 \cdot \left(-\frac{1}{8}\right)^{-4} = \left(-\frac{1}{8}\right)^{7+(-4)}$ The base is $-\frac{1}{8}$. Add the exponents.

$= \left(-\frac{1}{8}\right)^3$ Simplify.

b. $(3m)^2 = 3m \cdot 3m$ Write as repeated multiplication.

$= (3 \cdot 3) \cdot (m \cdot m)$ Group like bases using properties of multiplication.

$= 3^{1+1} \cdot m^{1+1}$ The bases are 3 and m. Add the exponents.

$= 3^2 \cdot m^2 = 9m^2$ Simplify.

Exercises

Simplify. Write your answer using only positive exponents.

7. $7^8 \cdot 7^{-5}$

8. $(-3)^4 \cdot (-3)$

9. $\left(-\frac{1}{4}\right)^{-4} \cdot \left(-\frac{1}{4}\right)^{12}$

10. $(5^3)^2$

11. $(m^4)^5$

12. $(w^6)^{-3}$

13. $(5y)^2$

14. $(2x)^{-3}$

15. $\left(-\frac{1}{3}k\right)^4$

10.3 Quotient of Powers Property *(pp. 456–461)*

a. $\frac{(-4)^6}{(-4)^9} = (-4)^{6-9}$ — The base is −4. Subtract the exponents.

$= (-4)^{-3}$ — Simplify.

$= \frac{1}{(-4)^3}$ — Definition of negative exponent

b. $\frac{5^5 \cdot 5^2}{5^3} = \frac{5^{5+2}}{5^3}$ — The base is 5. Add the exponents in the numerator.

$= \frac{5^7}{5^3}$ — Simplify.

$= 5^{7-3}$ — The base is 5. Subtract the exponents.

$= 5^4$ — Simplify.

c. $\frac{a^6}{a^3} \cdot \frac{a^4}{a^5} = a^{6-3} \cdot a^{4-5}$ — Subtract the exponents.

$= a^3 \cdot a^{-1}$ — Simplify.

$= a^{3+(-1)}$ — Add the exponents.

$= a^2$ — Simplify.

Exercises

Simplify. Write your answer using only positive exponents.

16. $\frac{(-8)^3}{(-8)^8}$

17. $\frac{2^2 \cdot 2^5}{2^3}$

18. $\frac{w^8}{w^7} \cdot \frac{w^5}{w^2}$

19. $\frac{3^2 \cdot 3^4}{3^9}$

20. $\frac{c^0}{c^5}$

21. $\frac{m^0}{m^6} \cdot \frac{m^{10}}{m^5}$

10.4 Scientific Notation *(pp. 462–469)*

a. Write 2.9×10^4 in standard form.

$2.9 \times 10^4 = 29{,}000$ (4) Move decimal point $|4| = 4$ places to the right.

b. Write 3.08×10^{-6} in standard form.

$3.08 \times 10^{-6} = 0.00000308$ (6) Move decimal point $|-6| = 6$ places to the left.

c. There are 1860 steps from the ground to the observatory on the 102nd floor of the Empire State Building. Write this number in scientific notation.

Move the decimal point 3 places to the left.

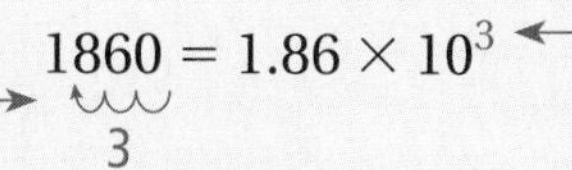

$1860 = 1.86 \times 10^3$ (3)

The number is greater than 10. So, the exponent is positive.

d. The outer layer of skin is called the epidermis. On the palm of your hand, the epidermis is 0.0015 meter thick. Write this number in scientific notation.

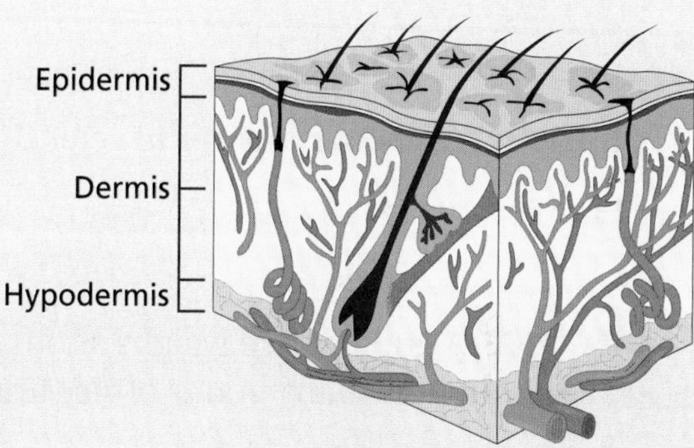

Move the decimal point 3 places to the right.

$0.0015 = 1.5 \times 10^{-3}$ (3)

The number is between 0 and 1. So, the exponent is negative.

Exercises

Write the number in standard form.

22. 4×10^4

23. 9.6×10^{-5}

Write the number in scientific notation.

24. 8,260,000

25. 0.0000507

Order the numbers from least to greatest.

26. $4.5 \times 10^6,\ 8.2 \times 10^5,\ 4.8 \times 10^6$

27. $1.6 \times 10^{-8},\ 1.06 \times 10^{-8},\ 3.4 \times 10^{-7}$

Multiply. Write your answer in scientific notation.

28. $(6.2 \times 10^5) \times (3 \times 10^4)$

29. $(4 \times 10^{-7}) \times (5.5 \times 10^{-6})$

10 Chapter Test

Write the number in scientific notation.

1. 0.000258
2. 456,000

Evaluate the expression.

3. $(-5)^{-3}$
4. $\left(-\frac{9}{11}\right)^0$

Write the number in standard form.

5. 4.9×10^{-7}
6. 7.256×10^5

Simplify. Write your answer using only positive exponents.

7. $9^{10} \cdot 9$
8. $(2^{-3})^2$
9. $\frac{(-3.5)^{-13}}{(-3.5)^9}$
10. $\frac{j^3}{j^5} \cdot \frac{j^{-5}}{j^{-2}}$
11. $(2s)^{-4}$
12. $\left(-\frac{1}{4}w\right)^3$

Multiply. Write your answer in scientific notation.

13. $(7 \times 10^3) \times (5 \times 10^2)$
14. $(3 \times 10^{-5}) \times (2 \times 10^{-3})$

15. **RICE** A grain of rice weighs about 3^3 milligrams. About how many grains of rice are in one scoop?

16. **CRITICAL THINKING** Is $(xy^2)^3$ the same as $(xy^3)^2$? Explain.

One scoop of rice weighs about 3^9 milligrams.

17. **LEAD** From 1978 to 2008, the amount of lead allowed in the air in the United States was 1.5×10^{-6} gram per cubic meter. In 2008, the amount allowed decreased by a factor of 9×10^{-1}. What is the new amount of lead allowed in the air?

10 Standarized Test Practice

Test-Taking Strategy
Use Intelligent Guessing
Cats were first tamed 3·2¹⁰ years ago in Egypt. How long ago was that?
Ⓐ 3000 Ⓑ 3072 Ⓒ 5000 Ⓓ 40
Who says I am tame? Growl. Hiss.
"It can't be 40 or 5000 because they aren't divisible by 3. So, you can intelligently guess between 3000 and 3072."

1. Mercury's distance to the Sun is approximately 5.79×10^7 kilometers. What is this distance in standard form?

   A. 5,790,000,000 km **C.** 57,900,000 km

   B. 579,000,000 km **D.** 5,790,000 km

2. The steps Jim took to answer the question are shown below. What should Jim change to correctly answer the question?

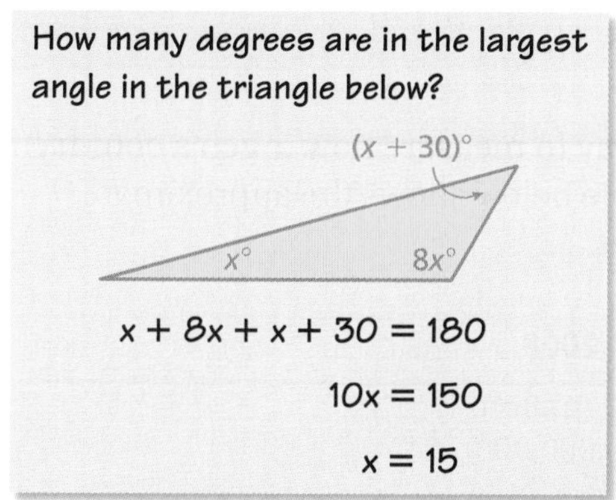

How many degrees are in the largest angle in the triangle below?
(x + 30)°
x°
8x°
x + 8x + x + 30 = 180
10x = 150
x = 15

   F. The left side of the equation should equal 360° instead of 180°.

   G. The sum of the acute angles should equal 90°.

   H. Evaluate the smallest angle when $x = 15$.

   I. Evaluate the largest angle when $x = 15$.

3. Which expression is equivalent to the expression below?

$$2^4 2^3$$

   A. 2^{12} **C.** 48

   B. 4^7 **D.** 128

4. The volume of a rectangular prism is 336 cubic inches. The length of the base is 8 inches and the width of the base is 6 inches. What is the height, in inches, of the rectangular prism?

5. The temperature in Frostbite Falls has never been above 38 degrees Fahrenheit. Let t represent the temperature, in degrees Fahrenheit. Write this as an inequality.

   F. $t < 38$ **H.** $t > 38$

   G. $t \leq 38$ **I.** $t \geq 38$

6. A bank account pays interest so that the amount in the account doubles every 10 years. The account started with $5,000 in 1940. How much would be in the account in the year 2010?

A. $40,000

B. $320,000

C. $640,000

D. $1,280,000

7. Which expression is equivalent to $5\sqrt{5} + 2\sqrt{5}$?

F. $7\sqrt{5}$

G. $10\sqrt{5}$

H. $7\sqrt{10}$

I. $10\sqrt{10}$

8. The gross domestic product (GDP) is a way to measure how much a country produces economically in a year. The table below shows the approximate population and GDP for the United States.

United States 2008	
Population	300 million (300,000,000)
GDP	14.4 trillion dollars ($14,400,000,000,000)

Part A Find the GDP per person for the United States. Show your work and explain your reasoning.

Part B Write the population and GDP using scientific notation.

Part C Find the GDP per person for the United States using your answers from Part B. Write your answer in scientific notation. Show your work and explain your reasoning.

9. What is the equation of the line shown in the graph?

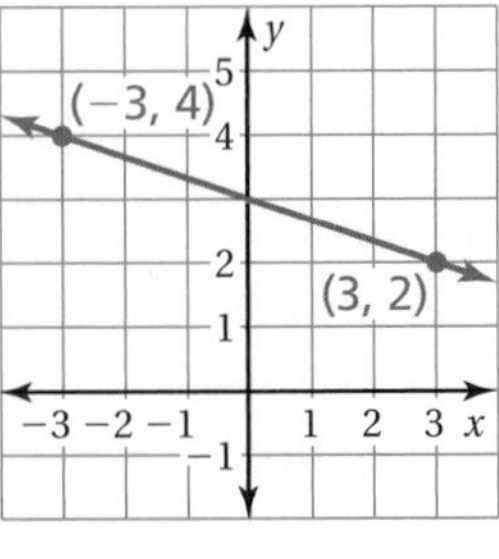

A. $y = -\frac{1}{3}x + 3$

B. $y = \frac{1}{3}x + 1$

C. $y = -3x + 3$

D. $y = 3x - \frac{1}{3}$

10. Which graph represents the inequality shown below?

$$x - 1.5 \leq -1$$

F. 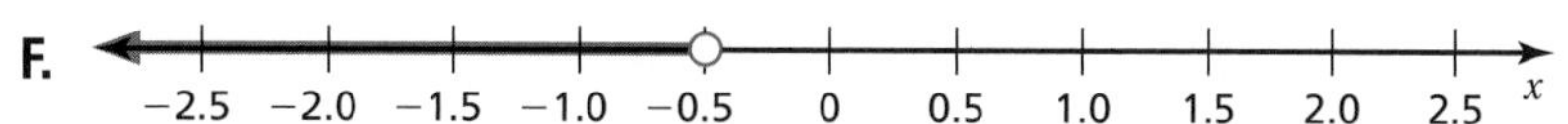

G. −2.5 −2.0 −1.5 −1.0 −0.5 0 0.5 1.0 1.5 2.0 2.5 x

H. −2.5 −2.0 −1.5 −1.0 −0.5 0 0.5 1.0 1.5 2.0 2.5 x

I. −2.5 −2.0 −1.5 −1.0 −0.5 0 0.5 1.0 1.5 2.0 2.5 x

11. Find $(-2.5)^{-2}$.

12. The director of a research lab wants to present data to donors, showing how a great deal of donated money is used for research and only a small amount of money is used for other expenses. Which type of display is best suited for showing these data?

A. histogram

B. circle graph

C. line graph

D. scatter plot

13. You earn \$14.75 per hour at your job. Your goal is to earn more than \$2000 next month. If you work h hours next month, which inequality represents this situation algebraically?

F. $14.75 + h > 2000$

G. $14.75 + h \geq 2000$

H. $14.75h > 2000$

I. $14.75h \geq 2000$

Appendix A
My Big Ideas Projects

A.1 Literature Project
Swiss Family Robinson

A.2 History Project
Mathematics in Ancient China

My Big Ideas Projects

A.3 Art Project
Polyhedra in Art

A.4 Science Project
Our Solar System

A.1 Literature Project

STANDARDS OF LEARNING
8.1–17

1 Getting Started

Swiss Family Robinson is a novel about a Swiss family who was shipwrecked in the East Indies. The story was written by Johann David Wyss, and was first published in 1812.

Essential Question How does the knowledge of mathematics provide you and your family with survival tools?

Read *Swiss Family Robinson*. As you read the exciting adventures, think about the mathematics the family knew and used to survive.

Sample: The tree house built by the family was accessed by a long rope ladder. The ladder was about 30 feet long with a rung every 10 inches. To make the ladder, the family had to plan how many rungs were needed. They decided the number was $1 + 12(30) \div 10$. Why?

2 Things to Include

- Suppose you lived in the 18th century. Plan a trip from Switzerland to Australia. Describe your route. Estimate the length of the route and the number of miles you will travel each day. About how many days will the entire trip take?
- Suppose that your family is shipwrecked on an island that has no other people. What do you need to do to survive? What types of tools do you hope to salvage from the ship? Describe how mathematics could help you survive.
- Suppose that you are the oldest of four children in a shipwrecked family. Your parents have made you responsible for the education of your younger siblings. What type of mathematics would you teach them? Explain your reasoning.

3 Things to Remember

- You can download each part of the book at *BigIdeasMath.com*.
- Add your own illustrations to your project.
- Organize your math stories in a folder, and think of a title for your report.

A.2 History Project

STANDARDS OF LEARNING
8.1–17

Mathematics in Ancient China

1 Getting Started

Mathematics was developed in China independently of the mathematics that was developed in Europe and the Middle East. For example, the Pythagorean Theorem and the computation of pi were used in China prior to the time when China and Europe began communicating with each other.

Essential Question How have tools and knowledge from the past influenced modern day mathematics?

Sample: Here are the names and symbols that were used in ancient China to represent the digits from 1 through 10.

1	yi	一
2	er	二
3	san	三
4	si	四
5	wu	五
6	liu	六
7	qi	七
8	ba	八
9	jiu	九
10	shi	十

Life-size Terra-cotta Warriors

A Chinese Abacus

2 Things to Include

- Describe the ancient Chinese book *The Nine Chapters on the Mathematical Art* (c. 100 B.C.). What types of mathematics are contained in this book?
- How did the ancient Chinese use the abacus to add and subtract numbers? How is the abacus related to base 10?
- How did the ancient Chinese use mathematics to build large structures, such as the Great Wall and the Forbidden City?
- How did the ancient Chinese write numbers that are greater than 10?

Ancient Chinese Teapot

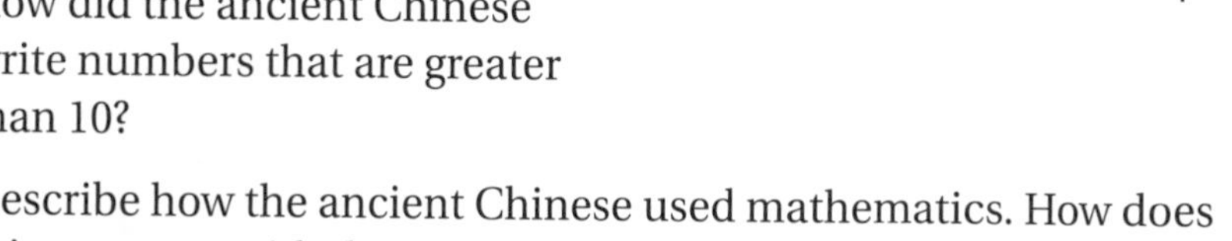

- Describe how the ancient Chinese used mathematics. How does this compare with the ways in which mathematics is used today?

The Great Wall of China

3 Things to Remember

- Add your own illustrations to your project.
- Organize your math stories in a folder, and think of a title for your report.

Chinese Guardian Fu Lions

A.3 Art Project

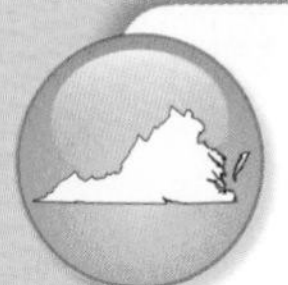

STANDARDS OF LEARNING
8.1–17

Polyhedra in Art

1 Getting Started

Polyhedra is the plural of *polyhedron*. Polyhedra have been used in art for many centuries, in cultures all over the world.

Essential Question Do polyhedra influence the design of games and architecture?

Some of the most famous polyhedra are the five Platonic solids. They have faces that are congruent, regular, convex polygons.

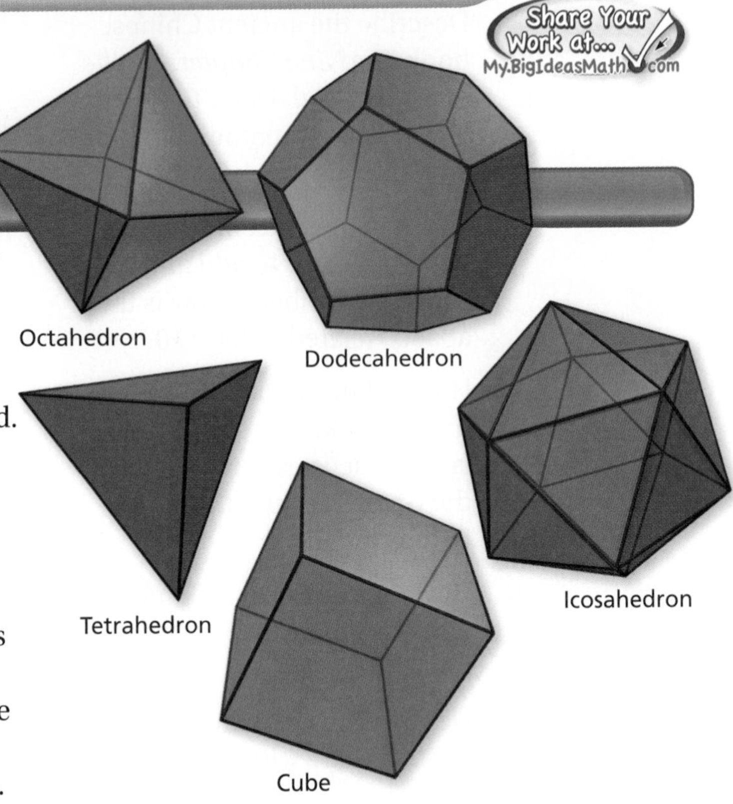

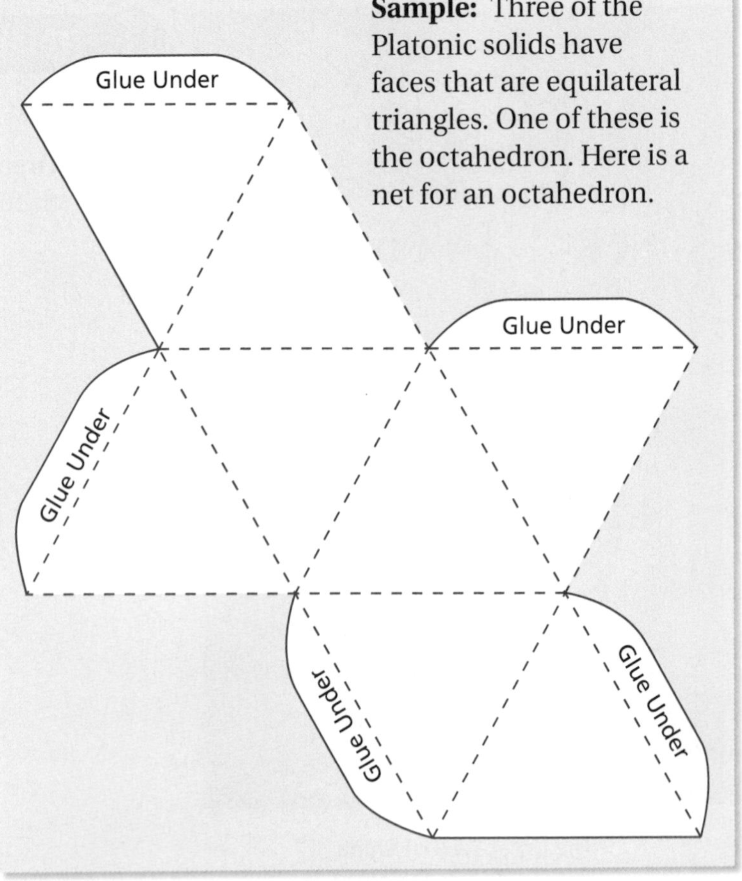

Sample: Three of the Platonic solids have faces that are equilateral triangles. One of these is the octahedron. Here is a net for an octahedron.

Mosaic by Paolo Uccello, 1430 A.D.

2 Things to Include

Faceted Cut Gem

- Explain why the platonic solids are sometimes referred to as the cosmic figures.
- Draw a net for an icosahedron or a dodecahedron. Cut out the net and fold it to form the polyhedron.
- Describe the 13 polyhedra that are called Archimedean solids. What is the definition of this category of polyhedra? Draw a net for one of them. Then cut out the net and fold it to form the polyhedron.
- Find examples of polyhedra in games and architecture.

Origami Polyhedron

3 Things to Remember

- Add your own illustrations or paper creations to your project.
- Organize your report in a folder, and think of a title for your report.

Concrete Tetrahedrons by Ocean

Bulatov Sculpture

A.4 Science Project

STANDARDS OF LEARNING
8.1–17

Share Your Work at... My.BigIdeasMath.com

Our Solar System

1 Getting Started

Our solar system consists of four inner planets, four outer planets, dwarf planets such as Pluto, several moons, and many asteroids and comets.

Essential Question How do the characteristics of a planet influence whether or not it can sustain life?

Sample: The average temperatures of the eight planets in our solar system are shown in the graph.

The average temperature tends to drop as the distance between the Sun and the planet increases.

An exception to this rule is Venus. It has a higher average temperature than Mercury, even though Mercury is closer to the Sun.

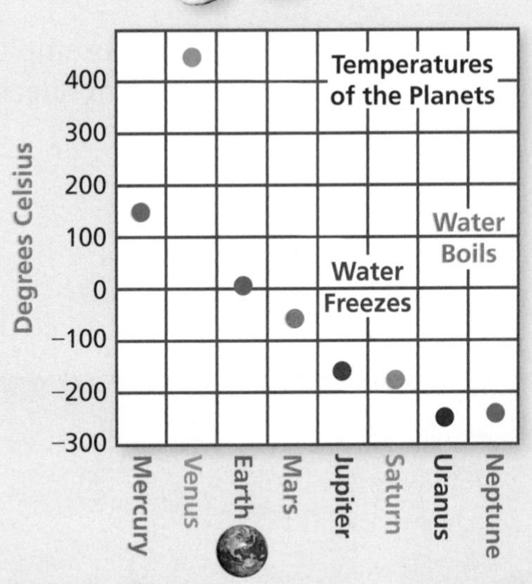

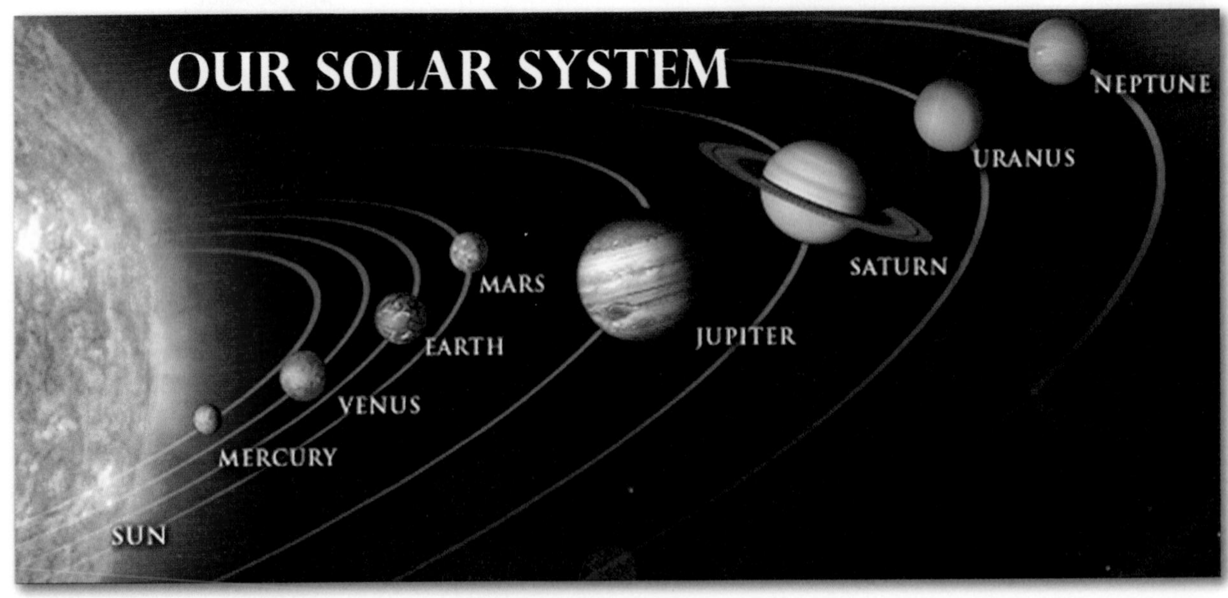

2 Things to Include

- Compare the masses of the planets.
- Compare the gravitational forces of the planets.
- How long is a “day” on each planet? Why?
- How long is a “year” on each planet? Why?
- Which planets or moons have humans explored?
- Which planets or moons could support human life? Explain your reasoning.

Mars Rover

3 Things to Remember

- Add your own drawings or photographs to your report. You can download photographs of the solar system and space travel at *NASA.gov*.
- Organize your report in a folder, and think of a title for your report.

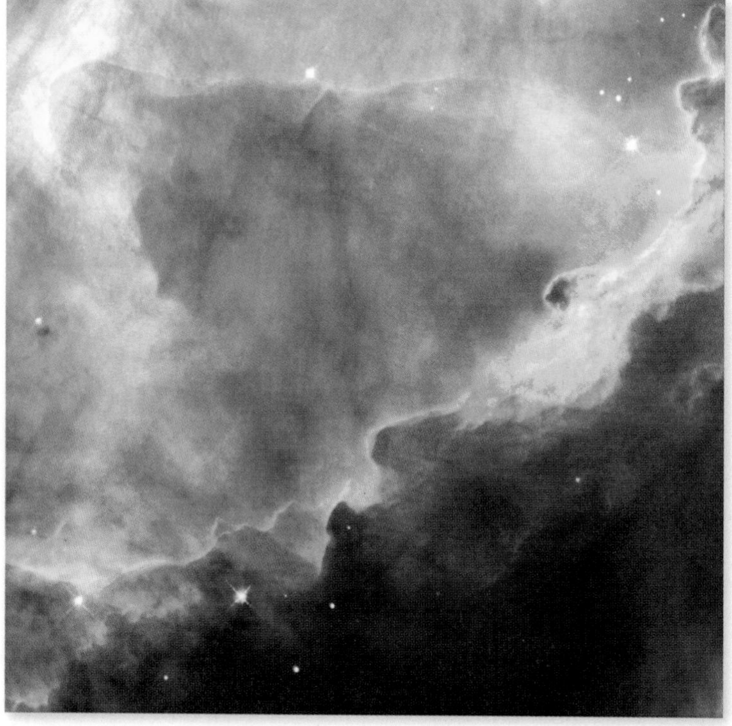

Hubble Image of Space

Hubble Spacecraft

Photo Credits

iv Big Ideas Learning, LLC; **viii** *top* ©iStockphoto.com/Angel Rodriguez, ©iStockphoto.com/Ann Marie Kurtz; *bottom* Evok20; **ix** *top* ©iStockphoto.com/Jonathan Larsen; *bottom* Peter Close; **x** *top* ©iStockphoto.com/Ron Sumners, ©iStockphoto.com/Ann Marie Kurtz; *bottom* Apollofoto; **xi** *top* ©iStockphoto.com/Michael Flippo, ©iStockphoto.com/Ann Marie Kurtz; *bottom* ©iStockphoto.com/ronen; **xii** *top* Chiyacat, Zoom Team; *bottom* Apollofoto; **xiii** *top* ©iStockphoto.com/Lisa Thornberg, ©iStockphoto.com/Ann Marie Kurtz; *bottom* Jane Norton; **xiv** *top* Cigdem Cooper, ©iStockphoto.com/Andreas Gradin, stephan kerkhofs; *bottom* ©iStockphoto.com/ranplett; **xv** *top* ©iStockphoto.com/Angel Rodriguez, ©iStockphoto.com/Ann Marie Kurtz; *bottom* ©iStockphoto.com/daaronj; **xvi** *top* ©iStockphoto.com/Alistair Cotton; *bottom* Heather Prosch-Jensen; **xvi** *top* Varina and Jay Patel, ©iStockphoto.com/Ann Marie Kurtz; *bottom* ©iStockphoto.com/Thomas Perkins; **xviii** ©iStockphoto.com/Ekaterina Monakhova; **1** ©iStockphoto.com/Angel Rodriguez, ©iStockphoto.com/Ann Marie Kurtz; **6** ©iStockphoto.com/David Freund; **7** ©iStockphoto.com/shapecharge; **8** NASA; **9** ©iStockphoto.com/Judson Lane; **12** ©iStockphoto.com/harley_mccabe; **13** ©iStockphoto.com/Jacom Stephens; **14** ©iStockphoto.com/Harry Hu; **15** ©Paul Slaughter; **20** ©iStockphoto.com/Andrey Krasnov; **27** *top right* ©iStockphoto.com/Alan Crawford; *center left* ©iStockphoto.com/Julio Yeste; *center right* ©iStockphoto.com/Mark Stay; **31** ©iStockphoto.com/Floortje; **35** *top* The ESRB rating icons are registered trademarks of the Entertainment Software Association; *center right* ©iStockphoto.com/Richard Goerg; **36** ©iStockphoto.com/George Peters; **37** ©iStockphoto.com/George Peters; **43** *center right* Norman Chan; *center left* Rick Harpenau; **44** ©iStockphoto.com/Lisa Fletcher; **45** NASA; **49** *top right* ©Lars Christenen/123RF; *Exercise 26* ©iStockphoto.com/Jill Chen; *Exercise 27* ©iStockphoto.com/7unit; *Exercise 28* ©iStockphoto.com/George Clerk; **54** ©iStockphoto.com/Jack Puccio; **56** *center right* Jaimie Duplass; *bottom left* ©iStockphoto.com/Heather Shimmin, ©iStockphoto.com/itographer; **60** ©iStockphoto.com/Jonathan Larsen; **65** NASA; **66** ©iStockphoto.com/David Morgan; **67** *top right* NASA; *center left* ©iStockphoto.com/Jakub Semeniuk; **74** ©iStockphoto.com/Amanda Rohde; **75** Julián Rovagnati; **80** ©iStockphoto.com/whitechild; **81** *top right* Jerry Horbert; *bottom left* ©iStockphoto.com/Chris Schmidt; **83** ©iStockphoto.com/Peter Finnie; **86** ©iStockphoto.com/Stephen Pothier; **87** *top* Gina Smith; *bottom* Dewayne Flowers; **89** Philip Lange; **93** Photo courtesy of Herrenknecht AG; **94** ©iStockphoto.com/Adam Mattel; **95** *top left* ©iStockphoto.com/Gene Chutka; *center right* ©iStockphoto.com/Pawel Liprec, ©iStockphoto.com/beetle8; **97** ©iStockphoto.com/Kirsty Pargeter; **99** ©iStockphoto.com/Connie Maher; **100** ©iStockphoto.com/Jacom Stephens; **101** *top right* ©iStockphoto.com/Petr Podzemny; *center left* ©iStockphoto.com/Andrea Krause; **105** ©iStockphoto.com/Michael Chen; **107** *top* ©iStockphoto.com/Brian McEntire; *bottom* ©iStockphoto.com/adrian beesley; **110** ©iStockphoto.com/Ryan Putnam; **111** ©iStockphoto.com/iLexx; **112** ©iStockphoto.com/Jeremy Edwards; **113** ©iStockphoto.com/Robert Kohlhuber; **114** ©iStockphoto.com/Rich Yasick; **119** ©iStockphoto.com/Marcio Silva; **124** ©iStockphoto.com/Ron Sumners, ©iStockphoto.com/Ann Marie Kurtz; **127** *left* ©iStockphoto.com/Andrew Johnson; *right* ©2010 Zappos.com, Inc.; **129** ©iStockphoto.com/alohaspirit; **130** ©iStockphoto.com/Timur Kulgarin; **131** *center left* ©iStockphoto.com/Wayne Johnson; *center right* Primo Ponies Photography; **133** Digital Vision Royalty Free Photograph/Getty Images; **136** ©iStockphoto.com/Hannu Liivaar; **137** *center left* ©iStockphoto.com/LoopAll; *center right* ©iStockphoto.com/Justin Horrocks, ©iStockphoto.com/Ana Abejon, ©iStockphoto.com/Huchen Lu; **139** ©iStockphoto.com/Lisa F. Young; **143** ©iStockphoto.com/technotr; **145** *top* ©iStockphoto.com/Alexander Hafemann; *bottom* ©iStockphoto.com/medobear; **147** *left* ©iStockphoto.com/PeskyMonkey; *right* ©iStockphoto.com/shapecharge; **151** *top right* ©iStockphoto.com/Dean Turner; *center* ©iStockphoto.com/Tom Buttle; *bottom* ©iStockphoto.com/Mladen Mladenov; **154** Junial Enterprises; **156** ©iStockphoto.com/Louis Aguinaldo; **160** ©iStockphoto.com/Michael Flippo, ©iStockphoto.com/Ann Marie Kurtz; **170** ©iStockphoto.com/Robert Hadfield; **172** ©iStockphoto.com/TheSupe87; **179** ©iStockphoto.com/Wolfgang Amri; **180** ©iStockphoto.com/Albert Smirnov; **181** ©iStockphoto.com/Lori Sparkia; **185** ©iStockphoto.com/Anne de Haas; **187** *top right* Big Ideas Learning, LLC; *center left* ©iStockphoto.com/Rui Matos; **188** ©iStockphoto.com/Michael Fernahl; **190** ©iStockphoto.com/Ted Johns; **196** Chiyacat, Zoom Team; **203** ©iStockphoto.com/Jorgen Jacobsen; **205** Abstract II by Linda Bahner; **208** *Exercise 9* ©iStockphoto.com/Chih-Feng Chen; *Exercise 10* ©iStockphoto.com/Andreas Gradin; *Exercise 11* ©iStockphoto.com/Jim Lopes; **209** ©iStockphoto.com/Zoran Kolundzija; **212** *bottom left* ©iStockphoto.com/Black Jack 3D; *bottom right* ©iStockphoto.com/Vadym Volodin; **213** NASA; **216** ©iStockphoto.com/Evelyn Peyton; **217** *top left* ©iStockphoto.com/Lora Clark; *top right* ©iStockphoto.com/Terraxplorer; **234** ©iStockphoto.com/Jerry Koch, ©iStockphoto.com/Chad Anderson; **239** ©iStockphoto.com/Scott Slattery; **244** Big Ideas Learning, LLC; **246** Kalamazoo (Michigan) Public Library; **256** ©iStockphoto.com/Lisa Thornberg, ©iStockphoto.com/Ann Marie Kurtz; **259** *bottom left* www.cartoonstock.com; *bottom right* M.C. Escher's, Ascending and Descending ©2009 The M.C. Escher Company-Holland. All rights reserved. www.mcescher.com; **262** *bottom left* ©iStockphoto.com/Rich Koele; *bottom center* ©iStockphoto.com/titelio; *bottom right* ©iStockphoto.com/David Spieth; **263** *top right* ©iStockphoto.com/Hedda Gjerpen; *center* ©iStockphoto.com/Rafal Zdeb; **274** *Exercise 8* sevenke; *Exercise 11* E.G.Pors; **275** *top right* Stefan Petru Andronache; *center left* Arne Bonde; **278** *Activity 1a* ©iStockphoto.com/Luke Daniek; *Activity 1b* ©iStockphoto.com/Jeff Whyte; *Activity 1c* ©Michael Mattox/BigStockPhoto.com; *Activity 1d* ©iStockphoto.com/Hedda Gjerpen; **279** ©iStockphoto.com/Josh Webb; **283** ©iStockphoto.com/Robert Simon; **287** ©iStockphoto.com/Elena Schweitzer; **288** ©iStockphoto.com/Gordon Warlow; **290** ©iStockphoto.com/AVTG; **292** NPS photo by Linda Chandler; **304** Cigdem Cooper, ©iStockphoto.com/Andreas Gradin, stephan kerkhofs; **306** *bottom* ©iStockphoto.com/Ivan Ponomarev; **311** *top left* ©iStockphoto.com/David Franklin; *top right* ©Ruslan Kokarev. Image from BigStockPhoto.com; *center right* ©iStockphoto.com/Ebru Baraz, ©iStockphoto.com/Lev Mel; **312** *top right* janprchal; *bottom* Joao Virissimo; **316** *Exercise 4* Kokhanchikov; *Exercise 8* titelio; *Exercise 10* ©iStockphoto.com/Valerii Kaliuzhnyi; **318** *bottom left* ©iStockphoto.com/Jiri Vatka; *bottom right* ©iStockphoto.com/BostjanT; **322** Image ® Courtesy of the Museum of Science, Boston, ©iStockphoto.com/ranplett; **323** *top left* ©iStockphoto.com/James Kingman; *top right* ©iStockphoto.com/Yails; **329** ©iStockphoto.com/Stefano Tiraboschi; **336** ©iStockphoto.com/Gary Alvis; **337** *top left* ©iStockphoto.com/Jan Tyler; *center left* ©iStockphoto.com/Ben Greer; *center right* ©iStockphoto.com/Roberta Casaliggi; **344** GreenLight Collectibles; **345** *top left* ©iStockphoto.com/Daniel Cardiff; *center right* ©iStockphoto.com/pomortzeff; *bottom left* ©iStockphoto.com/Ivana Starcevic; **354** ©iStockphoto.com/Angel Rodriguez, ©iStockphoto.com/Ann Marie Kurtz; **359** Perfectblue97; **360** ©iStockphoto.com/Benjamin Lazare; **361** *top right* ©iStockphoto.com/Sheldon Kralstein; *center* ©iStockphoto.com/Jill Chen; **362** ©ImageState; **366** ©iStockphoto.com/Melissa Carroll; **367** *center left* ©iStockphoto.com/Alex Slobodkin, ©iStockphoto.com/Sebastian Duda; *center right* ©iStockphoto.com/Cathy Keifer; **369** *center left* ©iStockphoto.com/Yvan Dubé; *bottom right* ©iStockphoto.com/MACIEJ NOSKOWSKI; **370** *bottom* ©iStockphoto.com/Kais Tolmats; **374** *top left* ©iStockphoto.com/Don Bayley; *bottom right* ©iStockphoto.com/iLexx; **377** ©iStockphoto.com/Marcio Silva; **379** Luminis; **382** *Exercise 3* Joshua Haviv; *Exercise 4* ©iStockphoto.com/William D Fergus McNeill; *Exercise 5* ©iStockphoto.com/Klaas Jan Schraa; **383** *left* ©iStockphoto.com/Parema; *right* ©iStockphoto.com/Nikontiger; **393** *center right* Hasan Shaheed; *bottom left* ©iStockphoto.com/JenDen2005; *bottom right* Orla; **394** *center right* CD Lenzen; *bottom left* red06; **398** ©iStockphoto.com/Alistair Cotton; **400** Gina Brockett; **401** ©iStockphoto.com/CraigRJD; **405** ©iStockphoto.com/Jill Fromer; **406** ©iStockphoto.com/Janis Litavnieks; **407** DLD; **408** *center left* ©iStockphoto.com/Tony Campbell; *bottom right* ©iStockphoto.com/Eric Isselée; **409** *top right* Larry Korhnak; *center right* Photo by Andy Newman; **415** *center left* ©iStockphoto.com/Jane norton; *center right* ©iStockphoto.com/Krzysztof Zmij; **417** Dwight Smith; **418** *top left and bottom right* Andrea Danti; *center* Feng Yu; **419** *Activity 2a* Milos Luzanin; *Activity 2b* Eric Isselée; *Activity 2c* nialat; *Activity 2d* Jeff Kubina; **420** SCRABBLE, the distinctive game board and letter tiles, and all associated logos are trademarks of Hasbro in the United States and Canada and are used with permission. © 2010 Hasbro. All Rights Reserved.; **423** Tischenko Irina, cloki, Gaby Kooijman, ©iStockphoto.com/Pali Rao; **425** NatUlrich, Yuryev Pavel; **429** Univega; **432** marymary; **433** WizData, inc.; **436** *Exercise 3* Brooke Whatnall, Galina Barskaya; *Exercise 4* goldenangel; **440** Varina and Jay Patel, ©iStockphoto.com/Ann Marie Kurtz; **442** *Activity 1a* Angarato; *Activity 1b* Patricia Hofmeester; *Activity 1c* easyshoot; *Activity 1d* Sascha Burkard; **445** Jim Hood; **446** kosam; **447** *center left* Knorre; *center right* ericlefrancais; **448** ©iStockphoto.com/John Tomaselli; **452** ©iStockphoto.com/Viktoriia Kulish; **453** *top right* ©iStockphoto.com/Paul Tessier; *center left* ©iStockphoto.com/Marie-france Bélanger, ©iStockphoto.com/Valerie Loiseleux, ©iStockphoto.com/Linda Steward; **455** Petar Tasevski; **460** ©iStockphoto.com/Andrey Volodin; **461** *top right* Dash; *center left* NASA/JPL-Caltech/L. Cieza (UT Austin); **462** Maugli; **463** Linda Bucklin; **466** *top left* Danilo Ascione; *top center* Rago Arts; **467** Sebastian Kaulitzki; **469** BORTEL Pavel; **470** *center left* ©iStockphoto.com/Dan Moore; *bottom right* ©iStockphoto.com/Murat Koc; **473** mmutlu; **474** *bottom left* TranceDrumer; *bottom right* ©iStockphoto.com/Eric Holsinger; **A0** ©iStockphoto.com/Björn Kindler; *center left* ©iStockphoto.com/Mika Makkonen; *center right* ©iStockphoto.com/Hsing-WenHsu; **A1** *top right* Emmer, Michele, ed., The Visual Mind: Art and Mathematics, Plate 2, ©1993 Massachusetts Institute of Technology, by permission of The MIT Press.; *bottom left* ©iStockphoto.com/Andrew Cribb; *bottom right* NASA; **A4** *top right* ©iStockphoto.com/Hsing-WenHsu; *center right* ©iStockphoto.com/blackred; *bottom left* ©iStockphoto.com/Thomas Kuest; *bottom right* ©iStockphoto.com/Lim ChewHow; **A5** *top right* ©iStockphoto.com/Richard Cano; *bottom left* ©iStockphoto.com/best-photo; *bottom right* ©iStockphoto.com/Mika Makkonen; **A6** Emmer, Michele, ed., The Visual Mind: Art and Mathematics, Plate 2, ©1993 Massachusetts Institute of Technology, by permission of The MIT Press.; **A7** *top right* Elena Borodynkina; *center right* ©iStockphoto.com/Andrew Cribb; *bottom left* ©iStockphoto.com/Matthew Okimi; *bottom right* Vladimir Bulatov; **A8** NASA; **A9** NASA

Cartoon illustrations Tyler Stout
Cover image Lechner & Benson Design

Selected Answers

Section 1.1 Solving Simple Equations
(pages 7–9)

1. + and − are inverses. × and ÷ are inverses.

3. $x - 3 = 6$; It is the only equation that does not have $x = 6$ as a solution.

5. $x = 57$ 7. $x = -5$ 9. $p = 21$ 11. $x = 9\pi$ 13. $d = \frac{1}{2}$ 15. $n = -4.9$

17. **a.** $105 = x + 14; x = 91$

 b. no; Because $82 + 9 = 91$, you did not knock down the last pin with the second ball of the frame.

19. $n = -5$ 21. $m = 7.3\pi$ 23. $k = 1\frac{2}{3}$ 25. $p = -2\frac{1}{3}$

27. They should have added 1.5 to each side.

$$-1.5 + k = 8.2$$
$$k = 8.2 + 1.5$$
$$k = 9.7$$

29. $6.5x = 42.25$; \$6.50 per hour

31. $420 = \frac{7}{6}b, b = 360$; \$60

33. $h = -7$ 35. $q = 3.2$ 37. $x = -1\frac{4}{9}$

39. greater than; Because a negative number divided by a negative number is a positive number.

41. 3 mg 43. 8 in. 45. $7x - 4$ 47. $\frac{25}{4}g - \frac{2}{3}$

Section 1.2 Solving Multi-Step Equations
(pages 14 and 15)

1. $2 + 3x = 17; x = 5$ 3. $k = 45$; 45°, 45°, 90° 5. $b = 90$; 90°, 135°, 90°, 90°, 135°

7. $c = 0.5$ 9. $h = -9$ 11. $x = -\frac{2}{9}$ 13. 20 watches

15. $4(b + 3) = 24$; 3 in. 17. $\frac{2580 + 2920 + x}{3} = 3000$; 3500 people

19. $<$ 21. $>$

Section 1.3 Solving Equations with Variables on Both Sides
(pages 20 and 21)

1. no; When 3 is substituted for x, the left side simplifies to 4 and the right side simplifies to 3.

3. $x = 13.2$ in. 5. $x = 7.5$ in. 7. $k = -0.75$

9. $p = -48$ 11. $n = -3.5$ 13. $x = -4$

15. The 4 should have been added to the right side.

$$3x - 4 = 2x + 1$$
$$3x - 2x - 4 = 2x + 1 - 2x$$
$$x - 4 = 1$$
$$x - 4 + 4 = 1 + 4$$
$$x = 5$$

17. $15 + 0.5m = 25 + 0.25m$; 40 mi

19. 7.5 units

21. Remember that the box is with priority mail and the envelope is with express mail.

23. 10 mL

25. square: 12 units; triangle: 10 units, 19 units, 19 units

27. 54.6 in.^{3}

29. C

Hint

Section 1.4 Rewriting Equations and Formulas

(pages 26 and 27)

1. no; The equation only contains one variable.

3. **a.** $A = \frac{1}{2}bh$ **b.** $b = \frac{2A}{h}$ **c.** $b = 12$ mm

5. $y = 4 - \frac{1}{3}x$

7. $y = \frac{2}{3} - \frac{4}{9}x$

9. $y = 3x - 1.5$

11. The y should have a negative sign in front of it.

$$2x - y = 5$$
$$-y = -2x + 5$$
$$y = 2x - 5$$

13. **a.** $t = \frac{I}{Pr}$

b. $t = 3$ yr

15. $m = \frac{e}{c^2}$

17. $\ell = \frac{A - \frac{1}{2}\pi w^2}{2w}$

19. $w = 6g - 40$

21. **a.** $F = 32 + \frac{9}{5}(K - 273.15)$

b. 32°F

c. liquid nitrogen

23. $r^3 = \frac{3V}{4\pi}$; $r = 4.5$ in.

25. $6\frac{2}{5}$

27. $1\frac{1}{4}$

Section 1.5 Writing and Graphing Inequalities

(pages 34 and 35)

1. An open circle would be used because 250 is not a solution.

3. no; $x \geq -9$ is all values of x greater than or equal to -9. $-9 \geq x$ is all values of x less than or equal to -9.

5. $x < -3$; all values of x less than -3

7. $y + 5.2 < 23$

9. $k - 8.3 > 48$

11. yes

13. yes

15. no

17. 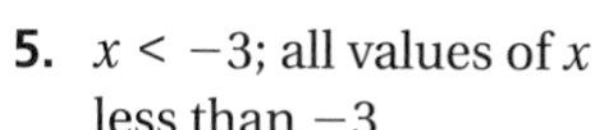

19. 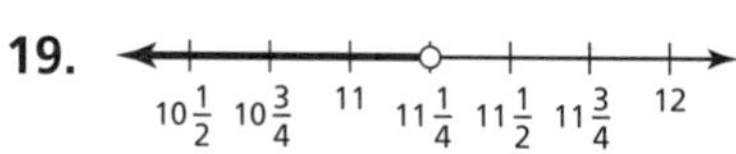

21. $x \geq 21$

23. yes

Section 1.5 Writing and Graphing Inequalities *(continued)* *(pages 34 and 35)*

25. **a.** $a \geq 10$; 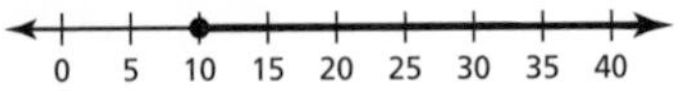 0 5 10 15 20 25 30 35 40

$s \geq 200$;  0 50 100 150 200 250 300 350 400

$t \geq 10$; 0 2 4 6 8 10 12 14 16

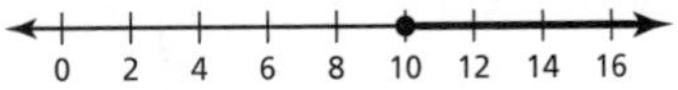

b. yes; You satisfy the swimming requirement of the course because $10(25) = 250$ and $250 \geq 200$.

27. **a.** $m < n$; $n \leq p$ **b.** $m < p$

c. no; Because n is no more than p and m is less than n, m cannot be equal to p.

29. $p = -1.7$

31. B

Section 1.6 Solving One-Step Inequalities *(pages 41–43)*

1. *Sample answer:* Inequalities and equations represent a relationship between two expressions. In an equation, both expressions are equal. In an inequality, one expression is less than the other expression.

3. *Sample answer:* $x + 5 < -3$

5. *Sample answer:* $A = 350$, $C = 275$, $Y = 3105$, $T = 50$, $N = 2$

7. *Sample answer:* $A = 400$, $C = 380$, $Y = 6510$, $T = 83$, $N = 0$

9. $m < 10$; 7 8 9 10 11 12 13

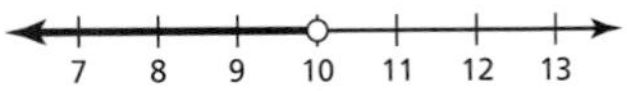

11. $k \geq 4.4$; 4.4 1 2 3 4 5 6 7

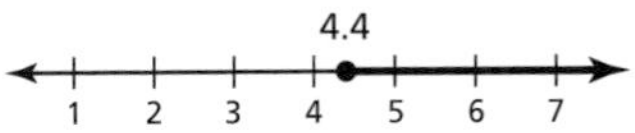

13. $c > -\frac{1}{2}$; -2 $-\frac{3}{2}$ -1 $-\frac{1}{2}$ 0 $\frac{1}{2}$ 1

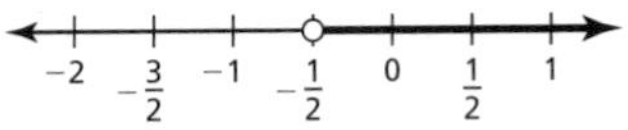

15. $m < -7.6$; -7.6 -10 -9 -8 -7 -6 -5 -4

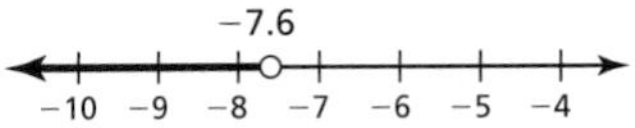

17. When the solution was rewritten with the variable on the left side, the inequality symbol was not reversed. $x < -3.7$

19. $x + 12 \leq 22$; $x \leq 10$

21. $m > -9$; -12 -11 -10 -9 -8 -7 -6

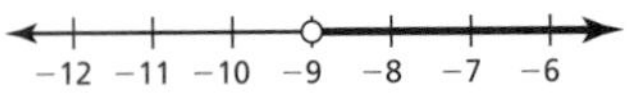

23. $v \leq -30$; -60 -50 -40 -30 -20 -10 0

25. $x < -\frac{6}{7}$; $-1\frac{2}{7}$ $-1\frac{1}{7}$ -1 $-\frac{6}{7}$ $-\frac{5}{7}$ $-\frac{4}{7}$ $-\frac{3}{7}$

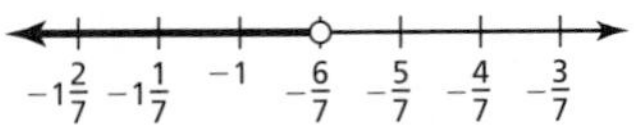

27. $g > -20.4$; -20.4 -35 -30 -25 -20 -15 -10 -5

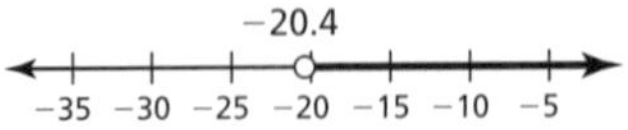

29. $b \geq -3$; -6 -5 -4 -3 -2 -1 0

31. $n > -20$; -23 -22 -21 -20 -19 -18 -17

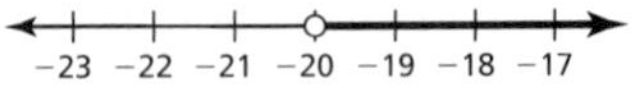

33. $b > -18$; -21 -20 -19 -18 -17 -16 -15

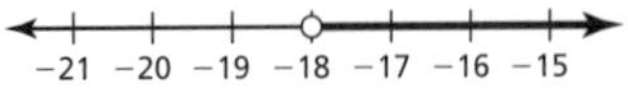

35. $a \leq 5$; 2 3 4 5 6 7 8

37. $d \leq 6.8$; 6.8 3 4 5 6 7 8 9

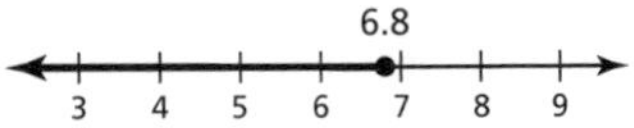

39. $x \leq -3$; -6 -5 -4 -3 -2 -1 0

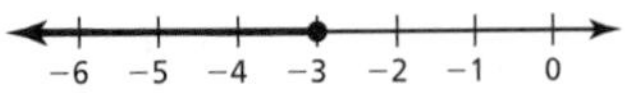

41. **a.** $4.5x \geq 225$; $x \geq 50$; at least 50 sandwiches

b. If the price decreases, you will need to sell more than 50 to meet your goal. If the price increases, you can sell less than 50 to meet your goal.

43. $9x \geq 108$; $x \geq 12$ mm

45. always; The product of two positive numbers is positive.

47. never; The product of a negative number and a positive number is negative.

49. at least \$1.25

51. no; *Sample answer:* $a = 3$, $b = 2$, $x = 8$, and $y = 1$; $a - x = -5$, $b - y = 1$; So, $a - x \not> b - y$.

53. no; *Sample answer:* $a = 4$, $b = 2$, $x = -2$, and $y = -4$; $\frac{a}{x} = -2$, $\frac{y}{b} = -2$; So $\frac{a}{x} \not> \frac{y}{b}$.

55. $m = 13$

57. B

Section 1.7 Solving Two-Step Inequalities

(pages 48 and 49)

1. *Sample answer:* They use the same techniques, but when solving an inequality, you must be careful to reverse the inequality symbol when you multiply or divide by a negative number.

3. C

5. $b \geq 1$;

7. $m \geq -15$;

9. $p < -1$;

11. They did not perform the operations in proper order.

$$\frac{x}{4} + 6 \geq 3$$
$$\frac{x}{4} \geq -3$$
$$x \geq -12$$

13. $y \leq 13$;

15. $u < -17$;

17. $z > -0.9$;

19. $x \leq 6$;

21. $\frac{3}{16}x + 2 \leq 11$; $x \leq 48$; at most 48 lines

23. Remember that the whale needs to eat 140 pounds or more of fish each day.

25. $r \geq 8$ units

27. 625π in.^{2}

29. A

Section 2.1 Graphing Linear Equations

(pages 66 and 67)

1. a line

3. *Sample answer:*

x	0	1
$y = 3x - 1$	−1	2

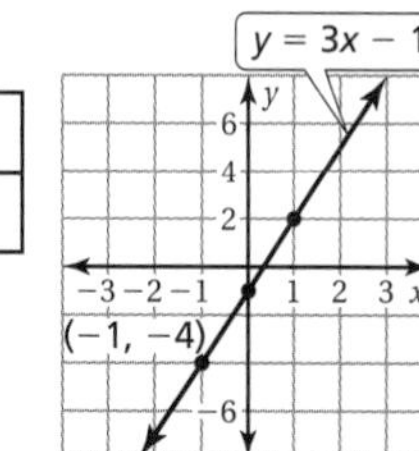

Section 2.1 Graphing Linear Equations *(continued)*

(pages 66 and 67)

5.

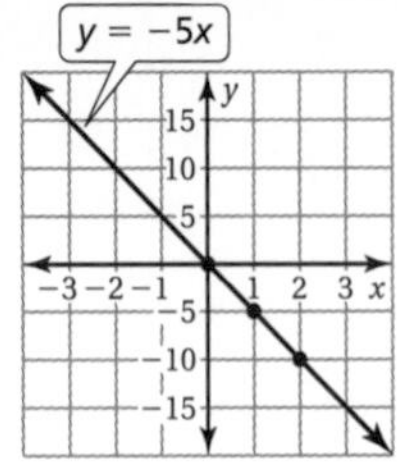

7.

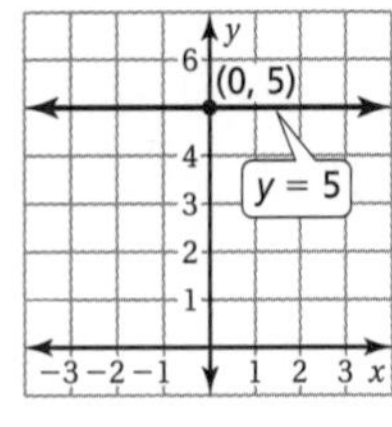

9.

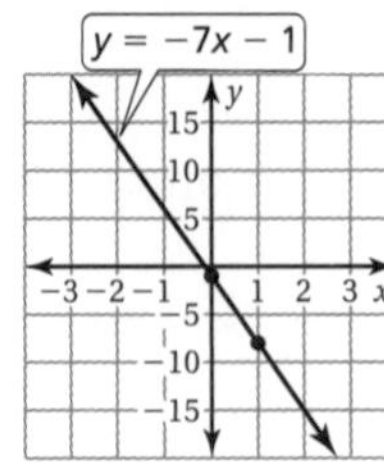

11.

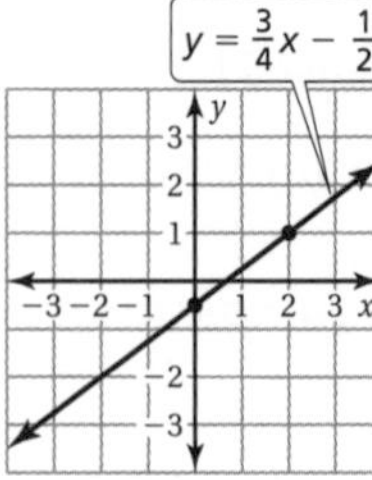

13.

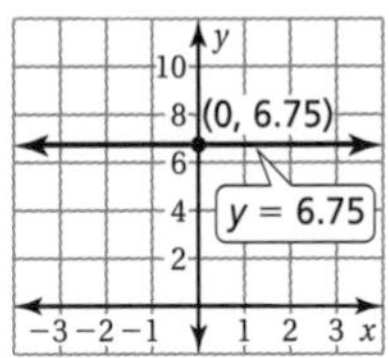

15.

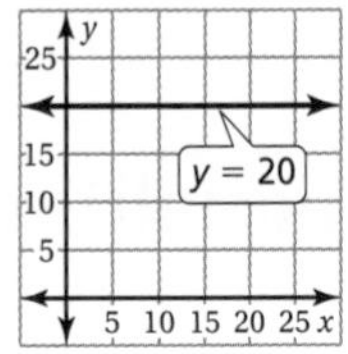

17. $y = 3x + 1$

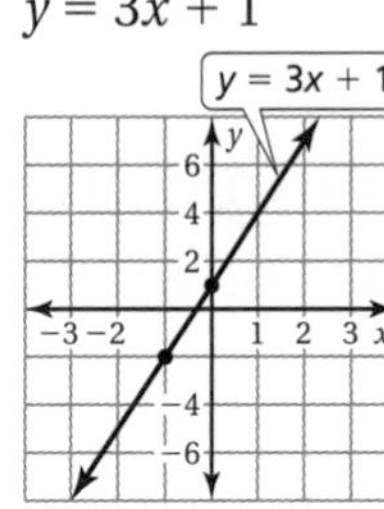

19. $y = 12x - 9$

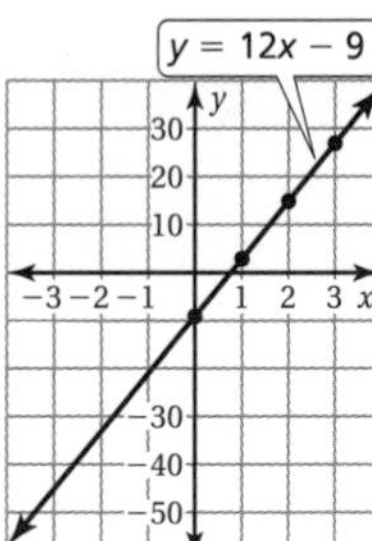

21. a. $y = 100 + 12.5x$

b. 6 mo

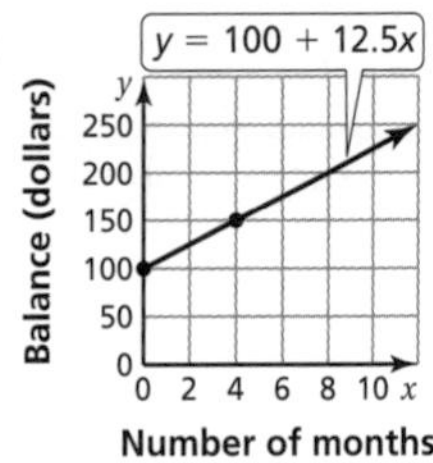

23. a. $y = 2x$

b. *Sample answer:* If you are 13 years old, the sea level has risen 26 millimeters since you were born.

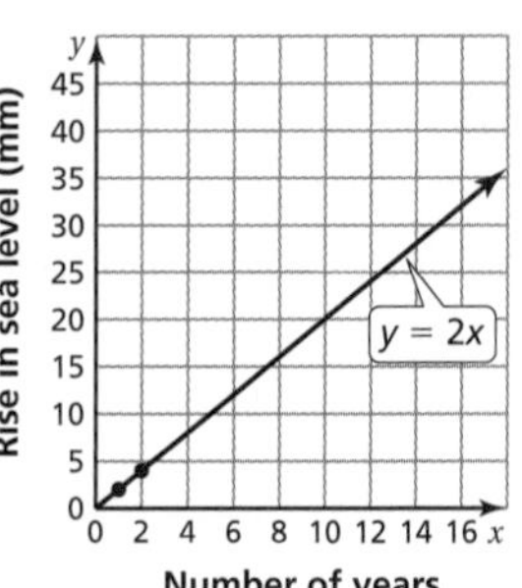

25. (5, 3)

27. (2, −2)

29. B

Section 2.2 Slope of a Line

(pages 73–75)

1. a. B and C

b. A

c. no; All of the slopes are different.

3. The line is horizontal.

5.

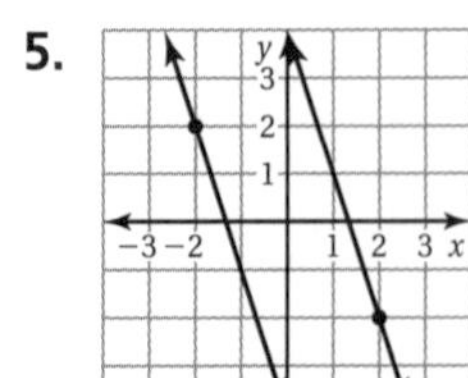

The lines are parallel.

7. $\frac{3}{4}$

9. $-\frac{3}{5}$

11. 0

13. The 2 should be −2 because it goes down.

Slope $= -\frac{2}{3}$

15. 4

17. $-\frac{3}{4}$

19. $\frac{1}{3}$

21. red and green; They both have a slope of $\frac{4}{3}$.

23. no; Opposite sides have different slopes.

25. **a.** $\frac{3}{40}$

b. The cost increases by \$3 for every 40 miles you drive, or the cost increases by \$0.075 for every mile you drive.

27. You can draw the slide in a coordinate plane and let the x-axis be the ground to find the slope.

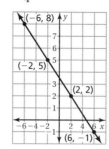

Hint

29.

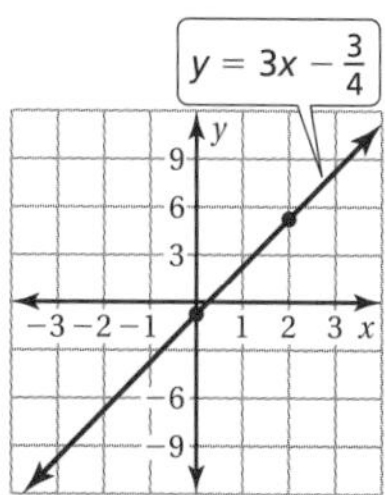

31. B

Section 2.3 Graphing Linear Equations in Slope-Intercept Form *(pages 80 and 81)*

1. Find the x-coordinate of the point where the graph crosses the x-axis.

3. *Sample answer:* The amount of gasoline y (in gallons) left in your tank after you travel x miles is $y = -\frac{1}{20}x + 20$. The slope of $-\frac{1}{20}$ means the car uses 1 gallon of gas for every 20 miles driven. The y-intercept of 20 means there is originally 20 gallons of gas in the tank.

5. A; slope: $\frac{1}{3}$; y-intercept: -2

7. slope: 4; y-intercept: -5

9. slope: $-\frac{4}{5}$; y-intercept: -2

11. slope: $\frac{4}{3}$; y-intercept: -1

13. slope: -2; y-intercept: 3.5

15. slope: 1.5; y-intercept: 11

17. **a.**

b. The x-intercept of 300 means the skydiver lands on the ground after 300 seconds. The slope of -10 means that the skydiver falls to the ground at a rate of 10 feet per second.

Selected Answers

Section 2.3 Graphing Linear Equations in Slope-Intercept Form *(continued)* *(pages 80 and 81)*

19.

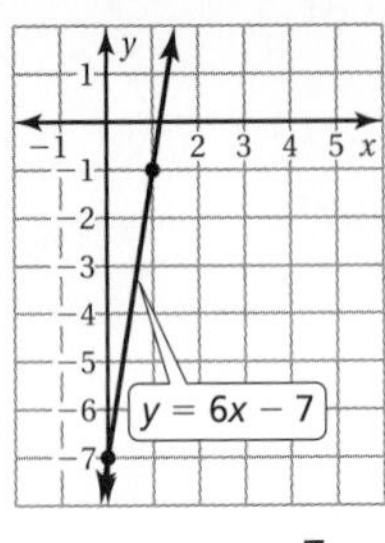

x-intercept: $\frac{7}{6}$

21.

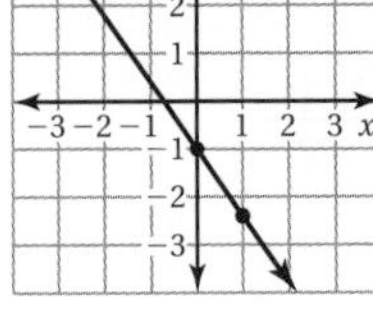

x-intercept: $-\frac{5}{7}$

23.

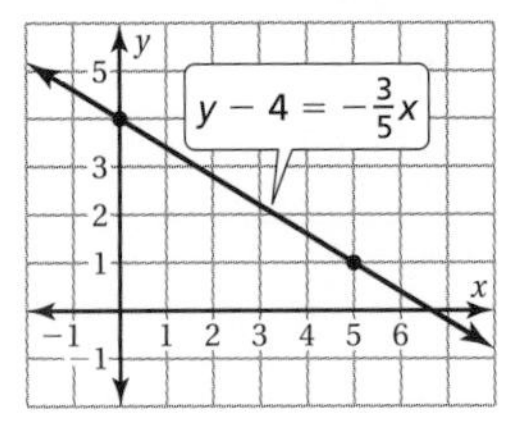

x-intercept: $\frac{20}{3}$

25. $y = 0.75x + 5$

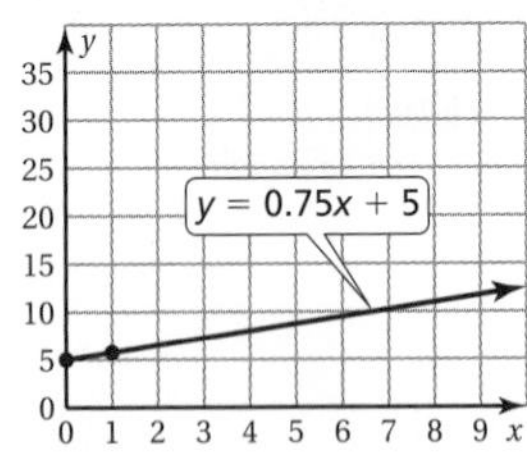

27. $y = 0.15x + 35$

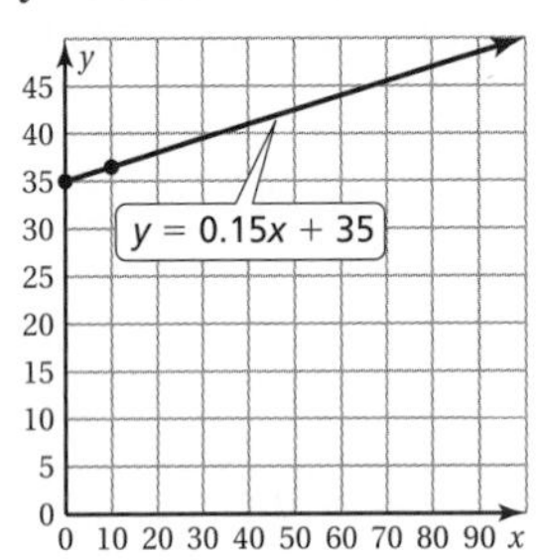

29. $y = 2x + 3$

31. $y = \frac{2}{3}x - 2$

33. B

Section 2.4 Graphing Linear Equations in Standard Form *(pages 86 and 87)*

1. no; The equation is in slope-intercept form.

3. x = pounds of peaches

y = pounds of apples

$y = -\frac{4}{3}x + 10$

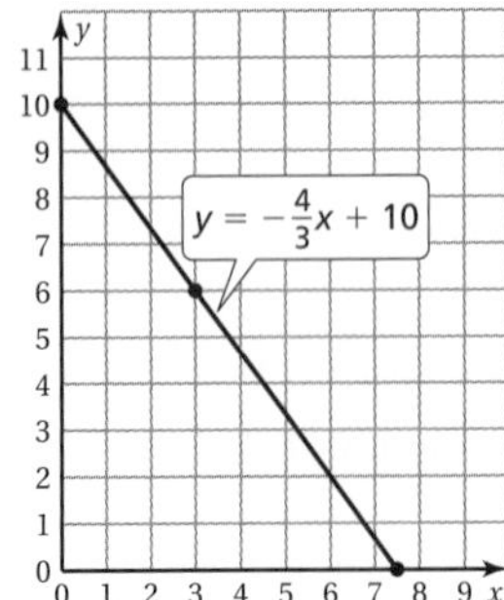

5. $y = -2x + 17$

7. $y = \frac{1}{2}x + 10$

9.

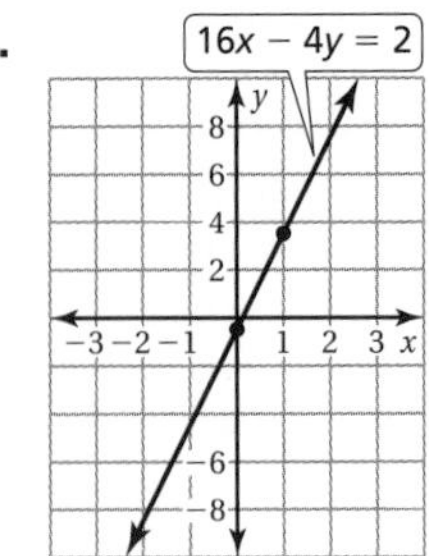

11. x-intercept: -6

y-intercept: 3

13. x-intercept: none

y-intercept: -3

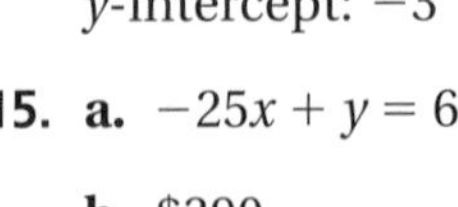

15. **a.** $-25x + y = 65$

b. $390

17. 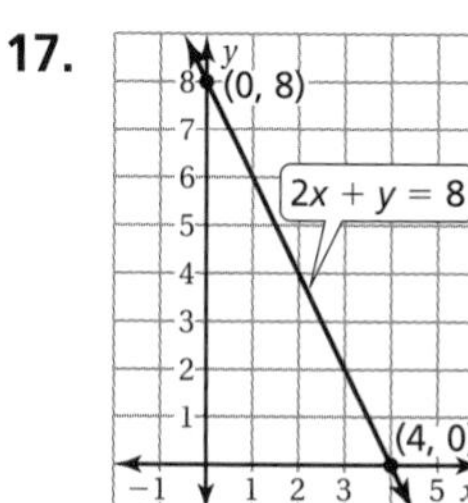

19. x-intercept: 9

y-intercept: 7

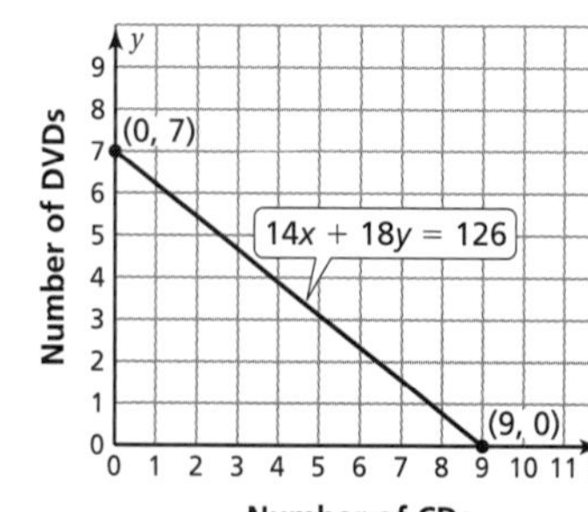

21. **a.** $9.45x + 7.65y = 160.65$

b. 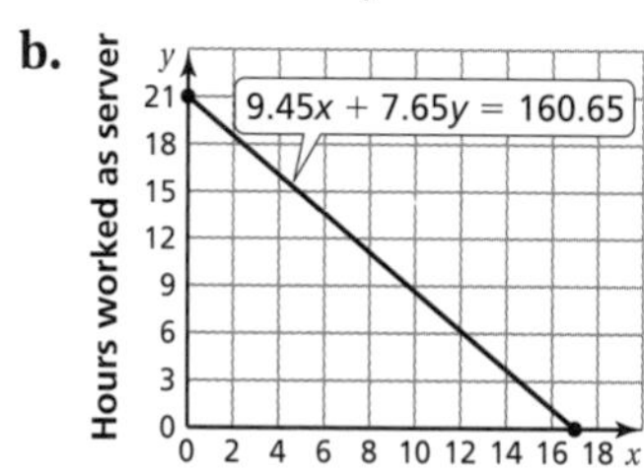

23. **a.** $y = 40x + 70$

b. x-intercept: $-\frac{7}{4}$; It will not be on the graph because you cannot have a negative time.

c. 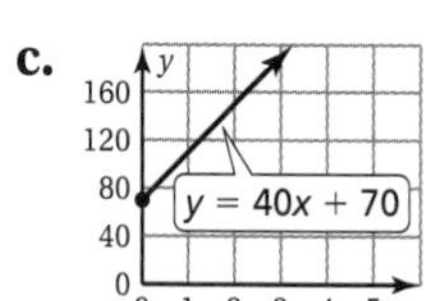

25.

x	-2	-1	0	1	2
$-5 - 3x$	1	-2	-5	-8	-11

Section 2.5 Writing Equations in Slope-Intercept Form
(pages 94 and 95)

1. *Sample answer:* Find the ratio of the rise to the run between the intercepts.

3. $y = 3x + 2$; $y = 3x - 10$; $y = 5$; $y = -1$

5. $y = x + 4$

7. $y = \frac{1}{4}x + 1$

9. $y = \frac{1}{3}x - 3$

11. The x-intercept was used instead of the y-intercept. $y = \frac{1}{2}x - 2$

13. $y = 5$

15. $y = -2$

17. **a–b.** (0, 60); (6, 0); Speed (mi/h); Braking time (seconds)

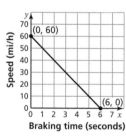

(0, 60) represents the speed of the automobile before braking. (6, 0) represents the amount of time it takes to stop. The line represents the speed y of the automobile after x seconds of braking.

c. $y = -10x + 60$

19. Be sure to check that your rate of growth will not lead to a 0-year-old tree with a negative height.

21 and 23. 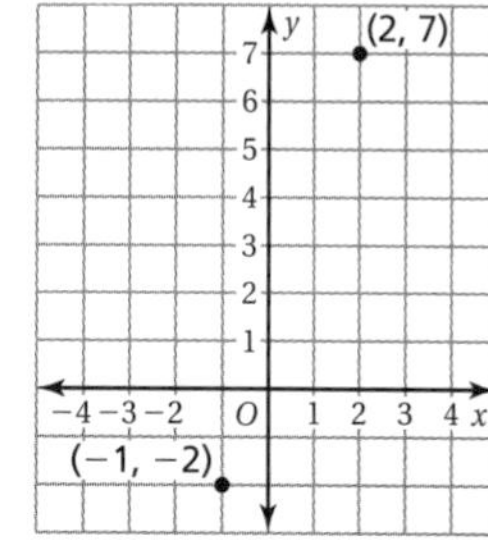

Section 2.6 Writing Equations Using a Slope and a Point
(pages 100 and 101)

1. *Sample answer:* slope and a point

3. $y = \frac{1}{2}x + 1$ **5.** $y = -3x + 8$ **7.** $y = \frac{3}{4}x + 5$

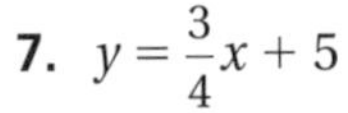

9. $y = -\frac{1}{7}x - 4$ **11.** $y = -2x - 6$ **13.** $V = \frac{2}{25}T + 22$

15. The rate of change is 0.25 degree per chirp.

17. **a.** $y = -0.03x + 2.9$

b. 2 g/cm^2

c. *Sample answer:* Eventually $y = 0$, which means the astronaut's bones will be very weak.

19. B

Section 2.7 Writing Equations Using Two Points
(pages 106 and 107)

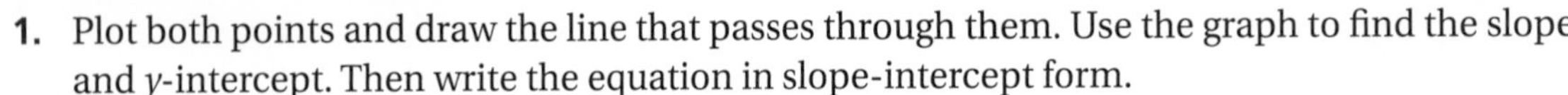

1. Plot both points and draw the line that passes through them. Use the graph to find the slope and y-intercept. Then write the equation in slope-intercept form.

3. slope $= -1$; y-intercept: 0; $y = -x$

5. slope $= \frac{1}{3}$; y-intercept: -2; $y = \frac{1}{3}x - 2$

7. $y = 2x$ **9.** $y = \frac{1}{4}x$ **11.** $y = x + 1$ **13.** $y = \frac{3}{2}x - 10$

15. They switched the slope and y-intercept in the equation. $y = 2x - 4$

17. **a.**

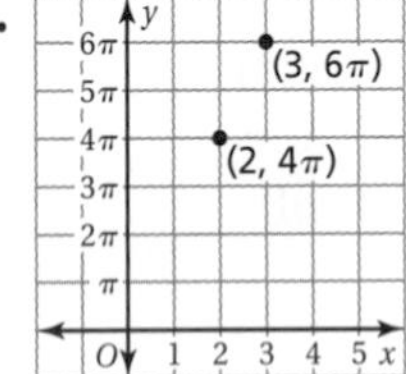

b. $y = 2\pi x$; The equation is the formula for the circumference of a circle given the radius.

19. **a.** $y = -2000x + 21{,}000$

b.

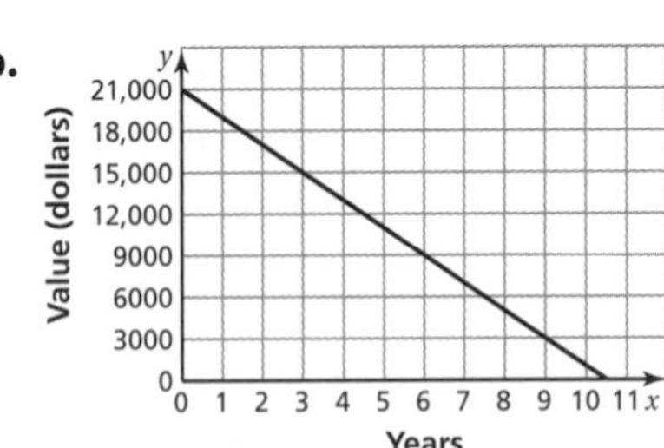

c. \$21,000; the original price of the car

21. **a.** $y = 14x - 108.5$

b. 4 m

23. 175 **25.** D

Section 2.8 Solving Real-Life Problems
(pages 112 and 113)

1. The y-intercept is -6 because the line crosses the y-axis at the point $(0, -6)$. The x-intercept is 2 because the line crosses the x-axis at the point $(2, 0)$. You can use these two points to find the slope.

   $\text{Slope} = \dfrac{\text{change in } y}{\text{change in } x} = \dfrac{6}{2} = 3$

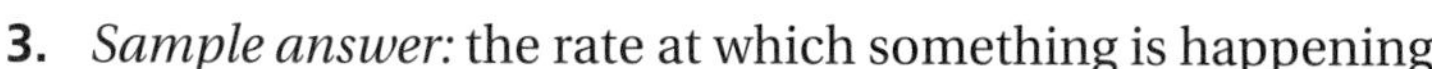

3. *Sample answer:* the rate at which something is happening

5. *Sample answer:* On a visit to Mexico, you spend 45 pesos every week. After 4 weeks, you have no pesos left.

7. **a.** slope: -3.6; y-intercept: 59 **b.** $y = -3.6x + 59$

   c. 59°F

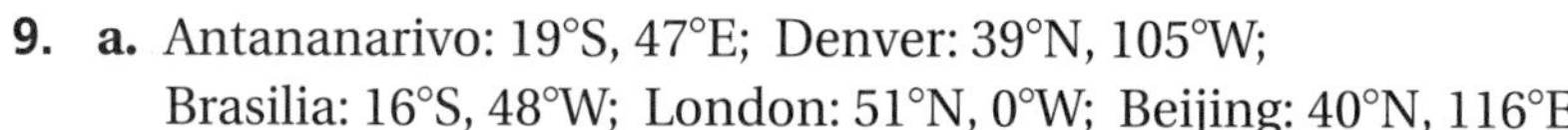

9. **a.** Antananarivo: 19°S, 47°E; Denver: 39°N, 105°W; Brasilia: 16°S, 48°W; London: 51°N, 0°W; Beijing: 40°N, 116°E

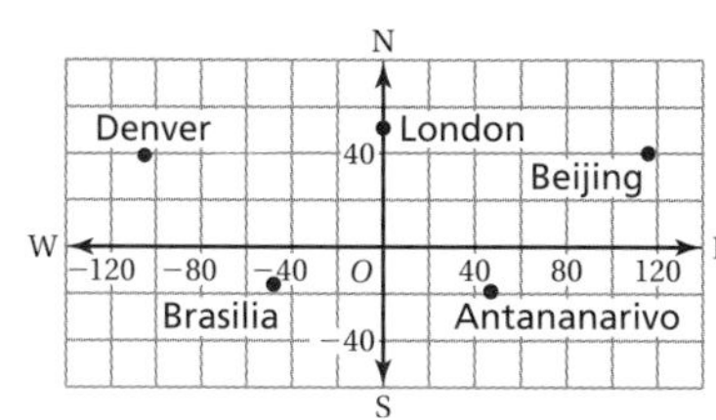

   b. $y = \dfrac{1}{221}x + \dfrac{8724}{221}$

   c. a place that is on the prime meridian

11. $x \leq -1.3$

13. $m \leq -7.2$

15. B

Section 3.1 Domain and Range of a Function
(pages 130 and 131)

1. *Sample answer:* An independent variable represents an input value, and a dependent variable represents an output value.

3. **a.** $y = 6 - 2x$ **b.** domain: 0, 1, 2, 3; range: 6, 4, 2, 0

   c. $x = 6$ is not in the domain because it would make y negative, and it is not possible to buy a negative number of headbands.

5. domain: $-2, -1, 0, 1, 2$; range: $-2, 0, 2$

7. The domain and range are switched. The domain is $-3, -1, 1$, and 3. The range is $-2, 0, 2$, and 4.

Selected Answers

Section 3.1 Domain and Range of a Function *(continued)*

(pages 130 and 131)

9.

x	-1	0	1	2
y	-4	2	8	14

domain: $-1, 0, 1, 2$

range: $-4, 2, 8, 14$

11.

x	-1	0	1	2
y	1.5	3	4.5	6

domain: $-1, 0, 1, 2$

range: 1.5, 3, 4.5, 6

Hint

13. Rewrite the percent as a fraction or decimal before writing an equation.

15.

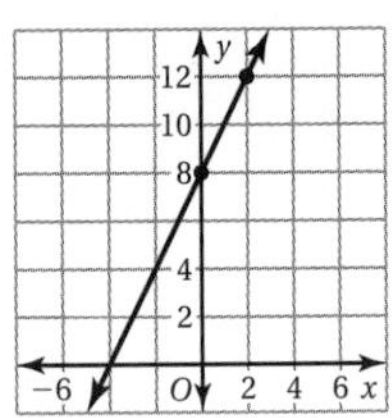

17.

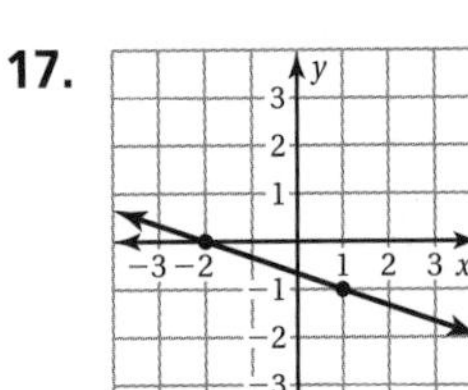

19. D

Section 3.2 Discrete and Continuous Domains

(pages 136 and 137)

1. A discrete domain consists of only certain numbers in an interval, whereas a continuous domain consists of all numbers in an interval.

3. domain: $x \geq 0$ and $x \leq 6$

range: $y \geq 0$ and $y \leq 6$;

continuous

5.

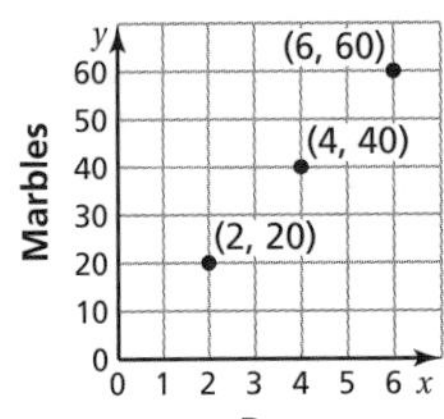

discrete

7.

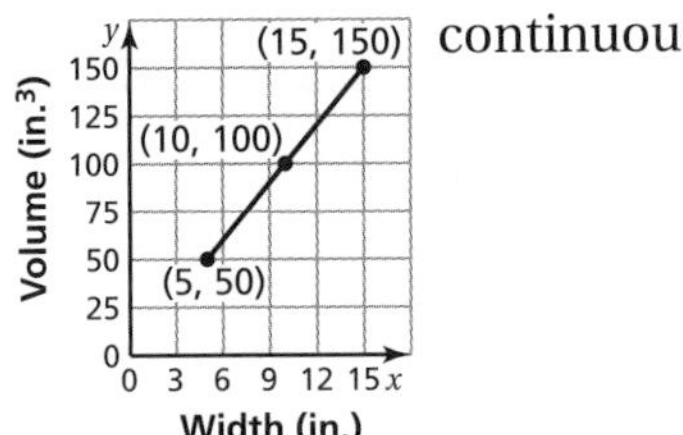

continuous

9. 2.5 is not in the domain because the domain is discrete, consisting only of 1, 2, 3, and 4.

11. The function with an input of length has a continuous domain because you can use any length, but you cannot have half a shirt.

Hint

13.

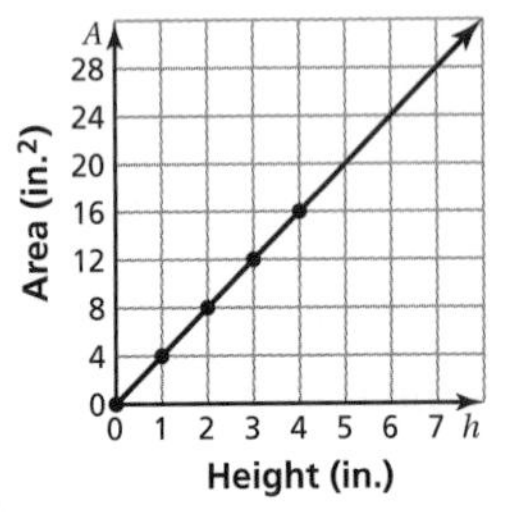

continuous

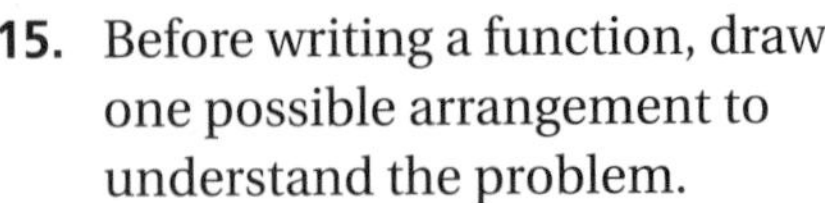

15. Before writing a function, draw one possible arrangement to understand the problem.

17. 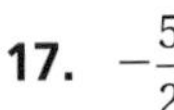 $-\frac{5}{2}$

19. C

Section 3.3 Linear Function Patterns
(pages 144 and 145)

1. words, equation, table, graph

3. $y = \pi x$; x is the diameter; y is the circumference.

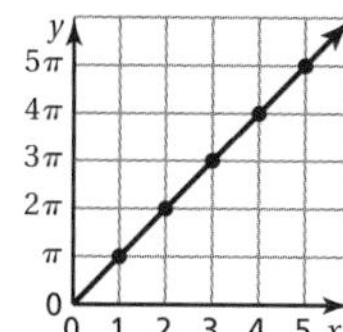

5. $y = \frac{4}{3}x + 2$

7. $y = 3$

9. $y = -\frac{1}{4}x$

11. a.
Cost (dollars)
(0, 0) (4, 12) (2, 6) (1, 3)
Number of Movies
discrete

b. $y = 3x$

c. $9

13. Substitute 8 for t in the equation.

15. $y = x$

17. $y = 1$

Section 3.4 Comparing Linear and Nonlinear Functions
(pages 150 and 151)

1. A linear function has a constant rate of change. A nonlinear function does not have a constant rate of change.

3. 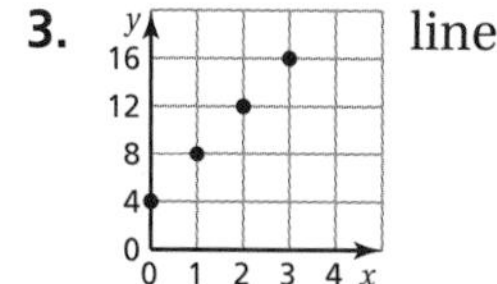

linear

5. nonlinear

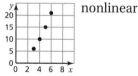

7. linear; The graph is a line.

9. linear; As x increases by 6, y increases by 4.

11. nonlinear; As x increases by 1, V increases by different amounts.

13. linear; The equation can be written in slope-intercept form.

15. Because you want the table to represent a linear function and 3 is half-way between 2 and 4, the missing value is half-way between 2.80 and 5.60.

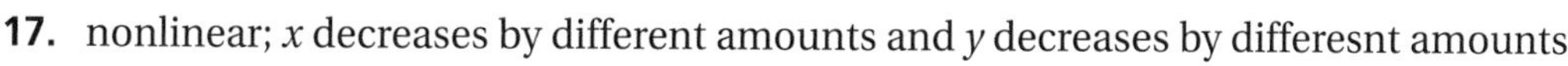

17. nonlinear; x decreases by different amounts and y decreases by differesnt amounts.

19. linear; As the height increases by 1, the volume increases by 9π.

21. straight

23. right

Section 4.1 The Percent Equation
(pages 166 and 167)

1. A part of the whole is equal to a percent times the whole.

3. 55 is 20% of what number?; 275; 11

5. 37.5% 7. 84 9. 64

11. $45 = p \cdot 60$; 75% 13. $a = 0.32 \cdot 25$; 8 15. $12 = 0.005 \cdot w$; 2400 17. $102 = 1.2 \cdot w$; 85

19. 30 represents the part of the whole.

$30 = 0.6 \cdot w$

$50 = w$

21. \$5400 23. 26 years old 25. 56 signers

27. If the percent is less than 100%, the percent of a number is less than the number. If the percent is equal to 100%, the percent of a number will equal the number. If the percent is greater than 100%, the percent of a number is greater than the number.

Hint

29. Remember when writing a proportion that either the units are the same on each side of the proportion, or the numerators have the same units and the denominators have the same units.

31. 92% 33. 0.88 35. 0.36

Section 4.2 Percents of Increase and Decrease
(pages 172 and 173)

1. If the original amount decreases, the percent of change is a percent of decrease. If the original amount increases, the percent of change is a percent of increase.

3. The new amount is now 0.

5. decrease; 66.7% 7. increase; 225% 9. decrease; 12.5% 11. decrease; 37.5%

13. 10 m 15. 37 points 17. 153 students 19. 42.16 kg

21. They should have subtracted 10 in the last step because 25 is decreased by 40%.

40% of $25 = 0.4 \cdot 25 = 10$

So, $25 - 10 = 15$.

23. increase; 100% 25. increase; 133.3%

27. Increasing 20 to 40 is the same as increasing 20 by 20. So, it is a 100% increase. Decreasing 40 to 20 is the same as decreasing 40 by one-half of 40. So, it is a 50% decrease.

29. **a.** 100% increase **b.** 300% increase

31. less than; *Sample answer:* Let x represent the number. A 10% increase is equal to $x + 0.1x$, or $1.1x$. A 10% decrease of this new number is equal to $1.1x - 0.1(1.1x)$, or $0.99x$. Because $0.99x < x$, the result is less than the original number.

33. 10 girls 35. $39.2 = p \cdot 112$; 35% 37. $18 = 0.32 \cdot w$; 56.25

Section 4.3 Discounts and Markups
(pages 180 and 181)

1. *Sample answer:* Multiply the original price by 100% − 25% = 75% to find the sale price.

3. **a.** 6% tax on a discounted price; The discounted price is less, so the tax is less.

   b. 30% markup on a $30 shirt; 30% of $30 is less than $30.

5. $35.70 7. $76.16 9. $53.33 11. $450 13. $172.40 15. 20%

17. no; Only the amount of markup should be in the numerator, $\frac{105 - 60}{60} = 0.75$. So, the markup is 75%.

19. $36

21. "Multiply $45.85 by 0.1" and "Multiply $45.85 by 0.9, then subtract from $45.85." Both will give the sale price of $4.59. The first method is easier because it is only one step.

23. no; $31.08 25. $30 27. 180 29. C

Section 4.4 Simple Interest
(pages 186 and 187)

1. I = simple interest, P = principal, r = annual interest rate (in decimal form), t = time (in years)

3. You have to change 6% to a decimal and 8 months to a fraction of a year.

5. **a.** $300 **b.** $1800 7. **a.** $292.50 **b.** $2092.50

9. **a.** $308.20 **b.** $1983.20 11. **a.** $1722.24 **b.** $6922.24

13. 3% 15. 4% 17. 2 yr 19. 1.5 yr 21. $1440 23. 2 yr

25. $2720 27. $6700.80 29. $8500 31. 5.25% 33. 4 yr

35. 12.5 yr; Substitute $2000 for P and I, 0.08 for r, and solve for t.

37. Year 1 = $520; Year 2 = $540.80; Year 3 = $562.43

39. 40, 25, 10

Section 5.1 Classifying Angles
(pages 202 and 203)

1. The sum of the measures of two complementary angles is 90°. The sum of the measures of two supplementary angles is 180°.

3. sometimes; Either x or y may be obtuse.

5. never; Because x and y must both be less than 90° and greater than 0°.

7. complementary 9. supplementary 11. neither 13. vertical; 128

15. Vertical angles are congruent. The value of x is 35.

Section 5.1 Classifying Angles *(continued)*

(pages 202 and 203)

17. vertical; 75°, 75°

19. adjacent; 140°, 40°

21. **a.** $\angle CBD$ and $\angle DBE$; $\angle ABF$ and $\angle FBE$

b. $\angle ABE$ and $\angle CBE$; $\angle ABD$ and $\angle CBD$; $\angle CBF$ and $\angle ABF$

23. Adjacent angles are not defined by their measure, so they can be complementary, supplementary, or neither.

25. Begin by drawing two intersecting lines and identifying the vertical angles.

27. 75

29. 35

Section 5.2 Angles and Sides of Triangles

(pages 208 and 209)

1. An equilateral triangle has three congruent sides. An isosceles triangle has at least two congruent sides. So, an equilateral triangle is a specific type of isosceles triangle.

3. right isosceles triangle

5. obtuse isosceles triangle

7. 94; obtuse scalene triangle

9. 67.5; acute isosceles triangle

11. 24; obtuse isosceles triangle

13. **a.** 70 **b.** acute isosceles triangle

15. no; 39.5°

17. yes

19. If two angle measures of a triangle were each greater than or equal to 90°, the sum of those two angle measures would be greater than or equal to 180°. The sum of the three angle measures would be greater than 180°, which is not possible.

21. $x + 9 + 12 = 28$; 7

23. $6x = 30$; 5

Section 5.3 Angles of Polygons

(pages 215–217)

1. *Sample answer:*

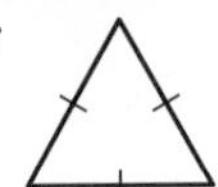

3. What is the measure of an angle of a regular pentagon?; 108°; 540°

5. 1260°

7. 1080°

9. 1800°

11. no; The angle measures given add up to 535°, but the sum of the angle measures of a pentagon is 540°.

13. 135 15. 140° 17. 140°

19. The sum of the angle measures should have been divided by the number of angles, 20. $3240° \div 20 = 162°$; The measure of each angle is 162°.

21. 24 sides

23. convex; No line segment connecting two vertices lies outside the polygon.

25. no; All of the angles would not be congruent.

27. 135° 29. 120°

31. You can determine if it is a linear function by writing an equation or by graphing the points.

33. 9 35. 3 37. D

Section 5.4 Using Similar Triangles
(pages 224 and 225)

1. Write a proportion that uses the missing measurement because the ratios of corresponding side lengths are equal.

3. Student should draw a triangle with the same angle measures as the textbook. The ratio of the corresponding side lengths, $\frac{\text{student's triangle length}}{\text{book's triangle length}}$, should be greater than one.

5. yes; The triangles have the same angle measures, 107°, 39°, and 34°.

7. no; The triangles do not have the same angle measures.

9. The numerators of the fractions should be from the same triangle.

$$\frac{18}{16} = \frac{x}{8}$$
$$16x = 144$$
$$x = 9$$

11. 65

13. no; Each side increases by 50%, so each side is multiplied by a factor of $\frac{3}{2}$. The area is $\frac{3}{2}\left(\frac{3}{2}\right) = \frac{9}{4}$ or 225% of the original area, which is a 125% increase.

15. When two triangles are similar, the ratios of corresponding sides are equal.

17. linear; The equation can be rewritten in slope-intercept form.

19. nonlinear; The equation cannot be rewritten in slope-intercept form.

Section 5.5 Polygons and Transformations
(pages 231–233)

1. **a.** rotation **b.** translation

 c. reflection **d.** dilation

3. Anthony; yes; It is the same when rotated 180°.

5. $A'(-2, 9), B'(2, 9), C'(2, 2), D'(-1, 2)$

7. $A'(0, 8), B'(-4, 8), C'(-4, 1), D'(-1, 1)$

9. $A'(8, 0), B'(8, -4), C'(1, -4), D'(1, -1)$

11. $A'(0, 24), B'(12, 24), C'(12, 3), D'(3, 3)$

13. enlargement; reduction

15. *Sample answer:*

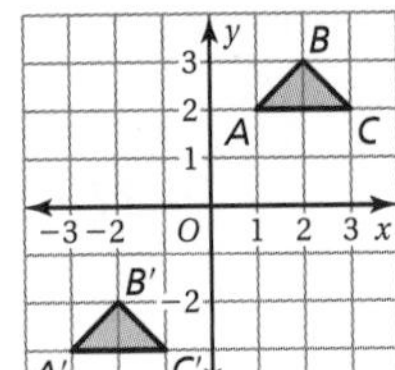

17. The vertices do not correspond for a translation. $A'B'C'D'$ is a 180° rotation of $ABCD$.

19. yes; The polygon and its image have the same size and shape.

21. no; The polygon and its image have the same shape but not the same size.

23. Quadrant II

25. Quadrant I

27. 2

29. Look at the center of the kaleidoscope pattern to identify possible lines of symmetry.

31. 270° counterclockwise; 270° clockwise

33. domain: −1, 1, 3, 5
 range: 0, 1, 2, 3

35. domain: −5, −4, −3, −2
 range: −5, −3, −1, 1

Section 5.6 Perimeters of Composite Figures
(pages 238 and 239)

1. less than and equal to; The perimeter is *less than* when figures making up a composite figure share a common side (dashed line).

 The perimeter is *equal to* when the figures making up a composite figure share a common vertex.

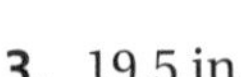

3. 19.5 in.

5. 25.5 in.

7. 19 in.

9. 56 m

11. 30 cm

13. about 26.85 in.

15. about 36.84 ft

17. Remember to subtract the original garden side that you now cover up with the new portion of the flower garden when trying to add 15 feet to the perimeter.

19. Yes; *Sample answer:* By adding the triangle shown by the dashed line to the L-shaped figure, you *reduce* the perimeter.

21. 279.68

23. 205

Section 5.7 Areas of Composite Figures
(pages 244 and 245)

1. *Sample answer:* You could add the areas of an 8-inch × 4-inch rectangle and a triangle with a base of 6 inches and a height of 6 inches. Also you could add the area of a 2-inch × 4-inch rectangle to the area of a trapezoid with a height of 6 inches, and base lengths of 4 inches and 10 inches.

3. 28.5 in.^{2} 5. 25 in.^{2} 7. 25 in.^{2} 9. 132 cm^2

11. *Answer will include but is not limited to:* Tracings of a hand and foot on grid paper, estimates of the areas, and a statement of which is greater.

13. 23.5 in.^{2} 15. 24 m^2

17. Each envelope can be broken up into 5 smaller figures to find the area.

19. $y \div 6$ 21. $7w$

Hint

Section 6.1 Drawing 3-Dimensional Figures
(pages 262 and 263)

1. Prisms and cylinders both have two parallel, identical bases. The bases of a cylinder are circles. The bases of a prism are polygons. A prism has lateral faces that are parallelograms or rectangles. A cylinder has one smooth, round lateral surface.

3. *Sample answer:* Prisms: A cereal box is a rectangular prism. A pup tent with parallel triangular bases at the front and back is a triangular prism.

   Pyramids: The Egyptian pyramids are rectangular pyramids. A house roof forms a pyramid if it has lateral faces that are triangles that meet at a common vertex.

   Cylinders: Some examples of cylinders are a soup can, a tuna fish can, and a new, unsharpened, round pencil.

   Cones: Some examples of cones are a traffic cone, an ice cream sugar cone, a party hat, and the sharpened end of a pencil.

5. base: circle; solid: cylinder

7. front:  side:  top:

   surface area: 34 units^2; volume: 10 units^3

9. front: 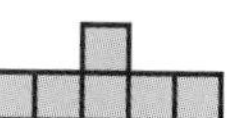 side: 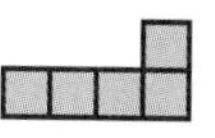 top: 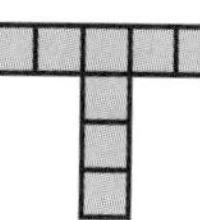

   surface area: 38 units^2; volume: 9 units^3

11. 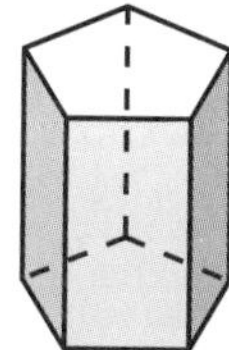

13. 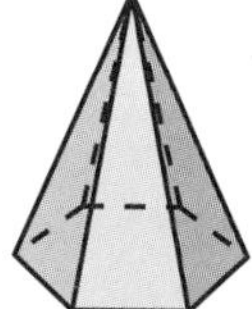

15. 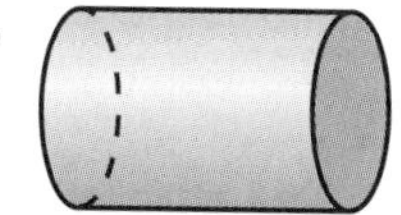

Section 6.1 Drawing 3-Dimensional Figures *(continued)*
(pages 262 and 263)

17. front: 

side: 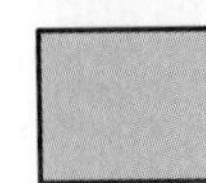

top: 

19. front: 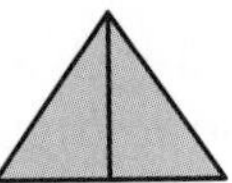

side: 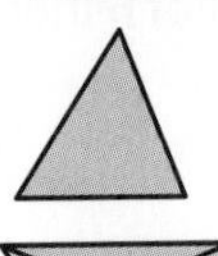

top: 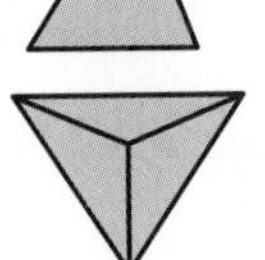

21. front: 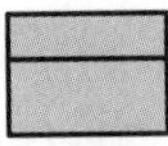

side: 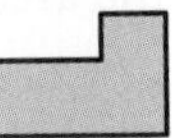

top: 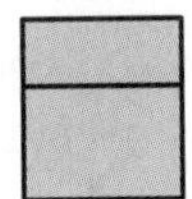

23. The Washington Monument is an *obelisk*. It consists of a pyramid sitting on top of a solid that tapers as it rises.

25. 

27. Use cubes to create solids that are possible.

29. 28 m^2

31. 15 ft^2

Section 6.2 Surface Areas of Prisms
(pages 268 and 269)

1. *Sample answer:* You want to paint a large toy chest in the form of a rectangular prism, and in order to know how much paint to buy, you need to know the surface area.

3. 18 cm^2

5. 108 cm^2

7. 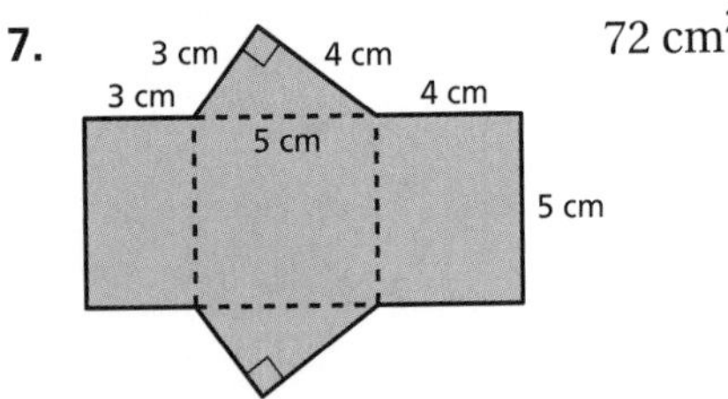

72 cm^2

9. 130 ft^2

11. 76 yd^2

13. 740 m^2

15. 448 in.^2; The surface area of the box is 448 square inches, so that is the least amount of paper needed to cover the box.

17. 156 in.^2

19. **a.** 83 ft^2

b. 332 ft^2

c. The amount of glass is 4 times greater.

21. $x = 4$ in.

23. 25 units

25. 54 units

Section 6.3 Surface Areas of Cylinders
(pages 274 and 275)

1. true
3. false; The area of the bases of a cylinder can be less than, equal to, or greater than its lateral surface area.
5. $44\pi \approx 138.2$ yd^2
7. $52.5\pi \approx 164.9$ m^2
9. $0.96\pi \approx 3.0$ mm^2
11. $306\pi \approx 960.8$ cm^2
13. The dimensions of the red cylinder are 4 times greater than the dimensions of the blue cylinder. The surface area is 16 times greater.
15. **a.** $16\pi \approx 50.2$ in.^{2}

    b. The lateral surface area triples.
17. **a.** 4 times greater; 9 times greater; 25 times greater; 100 times greater

    b. When both dimensions are increased by a factor of k, the surface area increases by a factor of k^2; 400 times greater
19. $y = 2x - 1$

Section 6.4 Surface Areas of Pyramids
(pages 282 and 283)

1. the triangle and the hexagon
3. Knowing the slant height helps because it represents the height of the triangle that makes up each lateral face. So, the slant height helps you to find the area of each lateral face.
5. 178.3 mm^2
7. 144 ft^2
9. 170.1 yd^2
11. 1240.4 mm^2
13. 6 m
15. Determine how long the fabric needs to be so you can cut the fabric most efficiently.

17. 124 cm^2
19. $A \approx 452.16$ units^2; $C \approx 75.36$ units
21. $A \approx 572.265$ units^2; $C \approx 84.78$ units

Section 6.5 Surface Areas of Cones
(pages 288 and 289)

1. no; The base of a cone is a circle. A circle is not a polygon.
3. $\ell > r$
5. $36\pi \approx 113.0$ m^2
7. $119\pi \approx 373.7$ ft^2
9. $64\pi \approx 201.0$ yd^2
11. 15 cm
13. $130\pi \approx 408.2$ in.^{2}
15. $360\pi \approx 1130.4$ in.^{2}; $2.5\pi \approx 7.85$ ft^2
17. $96\pi \approx 301.44$ ft^2; $\frac{32}{3}\pi \approx 33.49\overline{3}$ yd^2
19. 12%
21. the lateral surface area
23. 45 in.^{2}
25. 16 ft^2

Section 6.6 Surface Areas of Composite Solids
(pages 294 and 295)

1. *Sample answer:*

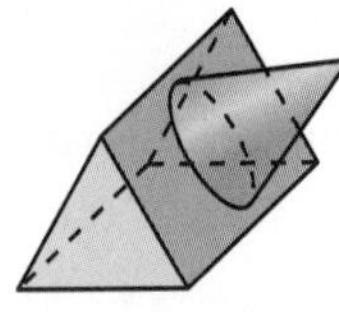

3. three cylinders

5. rectangular prism, half of a cylinder

7. cones; $104\pi \approx 326.6$ m^2

9. trapezoidal prism, rectangular prism; 152 cm^2

11. two rectangular prisms; 308 ft^2

13. 63.4%

15. $144\pi \approx 452.2$ in.^{2}

17. $806\pi \approx 2530.84$ mm^2

19. 10 ft^2

21. 47.5 in.^{2}

Section 7.1 Volumes of Prisms
(pages 310 and 311)

1. cubic units

3. *Sample answers:* Volume because you want to make sure the product will fit inside the package. Surface area because of the cost of packaging.

5. 288 cm^3

7. 160 yd^3

9. 420 mm^3

11. 645 mm^3

13. The area of the base is wrong.

$$V = \frac{1}{2}(7)(5) \cdot 10$$
$$= 175 \text{ cm}^3$$

15. 225 in.^{3}

17. 7200 ft^3

19. 1728 in.^{3}

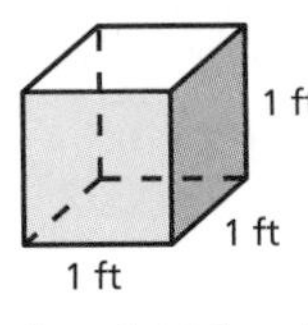

$1 \times 1 \times 1 = 1$ ft^3

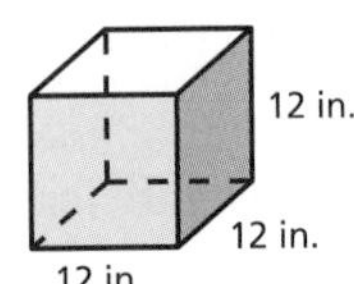

$12 \times 12 \times 12 = 1728$ in.^{3}

21. 20 cm

23. You can write the volume in cubic inches and use prime factorization to find the dimensions.

25. reflection

27. rotation

Section 7.2 Volumes of Cylinders
(pages 316 and 317)

1. Both formulas use the cylinder height and area of the base; In the formula for volume, the area of the base is multiplied by the height, but in the formula for surface area, the area of the base is doubled and added to the lateral surface area.

3. $50\pi \approx 157.0$ m^3

5. $\pi \approx 3.1$ mm^3

7. $112\pi \approx 351.7$ yd^3

9. The area of the base should have a factor of π.

$$V = Bh$$
$$= \pi(3.5)^2(4)$$
$$= 49\pi \approx 153.9 \text{ yd}^3$$

11. The volume is 4 times greater.

13. Yes, the ratio of the volumes is a constant. No, depending on the values of r and h, the ratio of the surface areas may *not* be a constant.

15. One cup of water is equal to 8 fluid ounces. Use unit analysis when converting units of measure.

17. $x \geq 3$;

0 1 2 3 4 5 6

19. $y \leq -6\frac{1}{3}$;

$-7\frac{1}{3}$ -7 $-6\frac{2}{3}$ $-6\frac{1}{3}$ -6 $-5\frac{2}{3}$ $-5\frac{1}{3}$

Section 7.3 Volumes of Pyramids
(pages 322 and 323)

1. The volume of a pyramid is $\frac{1}{3}$ times the area of the base times the height. The volume of a prism is the area of the base times the height.

3. 3 times

5. 20 mm^3

7. 80 in.^{3}

9. 252 mm^3

11. 700 mm^3

13. 30 in.^{2}

15. 7.5 ft

17. 12,000 in.^{3}; The volume of one paperweight is 12 cubic inches. So, 12 cubic inches of glass is needed to make one paperweight. So, it takes $12 \times 1000 = 12{,}000$ cubic inches to make 1000 paperweights.

19. *Sample answer:* 5 ft by 4 ft

21. 28

23. 60

25. B

Section 7.4 Volumes of Cones
(pages 328 and 329)

1. The height of a cone is the distance from the vertex to the center of the base.

3. Divide by 3.

5. $9\pi \approx 28.3$ m^3

7. $\frac{2\pi}{3} \approx 2.1$ ft^3

9. $27\pi \approx 84.8$ yd^3

11. $\frac{125\pi}{6} \approx 65.4$ in.^{3}

13. The diameter was used instead of the radius.

$$V = \frac{1}{3}(\pi)(3)^2(8)$$
$$= 24\pi \text{ m}^3$$

15. 1.5 ft

17. $\frac{40}{3\pi} \approx 4.2$ in.

19. 24.1 min

21. $3y$

23. 315 m^3

25. $152\pi \approx 477.28$ ft^3

Selected Answers

Section 7.5 Volumes of Composite Solids
(pages 336 and 337)

1. A composite solid is a solid that is made up of more than one solid.

3. In Example 2, you had to subtract the volume of the cylinder-shaped hole from the volume of the entire cylinder. In Example 1, you had to find the volumes of the square prism and the square pyramid and add them together.

5. $125 + 16\pi \approx 175.2$ in.^{3}

7. 220 cm^3

9. 173.3 ft^3

11. $216 - 24\pi \approx 140.6$ m^3

13. **a.** *Sample answer:* 80%

    b. *Sample answer:* $100\pi \approx 314$ in.^{3}

15. 13.875 in.^{3}; The volume of the hexagonal prism is 10.5(0.75) and the volume of the hexagonal pyramid is $\frac{1}{3}(6)(3)$.

17. $\frac{25}{9}$

19. B

Section 7.6 Surface Areas and Volumes of Similar Solids
(pages 343–345)

1. Similar solids are solids of the same type that have proportional corresponding linear measures.

3. **a.** $\frac{4}{9}$ **b.** $\frac{8}{27}$

5. no

7. no

9. $b = 18$ m; $c = 19.5$ m; $h = 9$ m

11. 1012.5 in.^{2}

13. 13,564.8 ft^3

15. 673.75 cm^2

17. **a.** yes; Because all circles are similar, the slant height and the circumference of the base of the cones are proportional.

    b. no; because the ratio of the volumes of similar solids is equal to the cube of the ratio of their corresponding linear measures

19. Choose two variables, one to represent the surface area of the smallest doll and one to represent the volume of the smallest doll. Use these variables to find the surface areas and volumes of the other dolls.

21. 1

23. C

Section 8.1 Finding Square Roots
(pages 360 and 361)

1. no; There is no integer whose square is 26.

3. $\sqrt{256}$ represents the positive square root because there is not a – or a ± in front.

5. $s = 1.3$ km

7. 3 and -3

9. 2 and -2

11. 25

13. $\frac{1}{31}$ and $-\frac{1}{31}$

15. 2.2 and -2.2

17. The positive and negative square roots should have been given.
$\pm\sqrt{\frac{1}{4}} = \frac{1}{2}$ and $-\frac{1}{2}$

19. 9

21. 25

23. 40

25. because a negative radius does not make sense

27. =

29. 9 ft

31. 8 m/sec

33. 2.5 ft

35. 25

37. 144

39. B

Section 8.2 The Pythagorean Theorem
(pages 366 and 367)

1. The hypotenuse is the longest side and the legs are the other two sides.

3. 24 cm

5. 9 in.

7. 12 ft

9. The length of the hypotenuse was substituted for the wrong variable.

$$\begin{aligned} a^2 + b^2 &= c^2 \\ 7^2 + b^2 &= 25^2 \\ 49 + b^2 &= 625 \\ b^2 &= 576 \\ b &= 24 \end{aligned}$$

11. 16 cm

13. 10 ft

15. 8.4 cm

17. **a.** *Sample answer:*

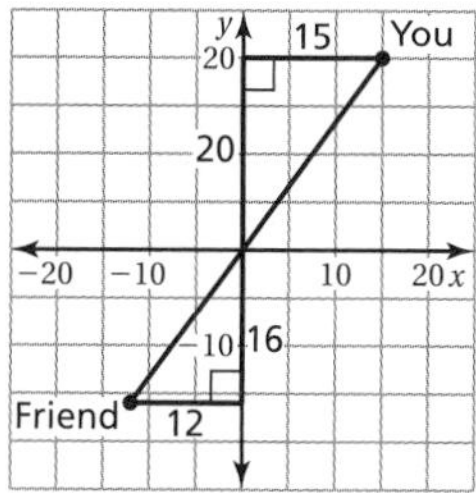

b. 45 ft

19. 6 and -6

21. 13

23. C

Section 8.3 Approximating Square Roots
(pages 375–377)

1. A rational number can be written as the ratio of two integers. An irrational number cannot be written as the ratio of two integers.
3. all rational and irrational numbers; *Sample answer:* $-2, \frac{1}{8}, \sqrt{7}$
5. yes
7. no
9. whole, integer, rational
11. integer, rational
13. natural, whole, integer, rational
15. 144 is a perfect square. So, $\sqrt{144}$ is rational.
17. **a.** If the last digit is 0, it is a whole number. Otherwise, it is a natural number.

    b. irrational number **c.** irrational number
19. 26
21. -10
23. -13
25. 10; 10 is to the right of $\sqrt{20}$.
27. $\sqrt{133}$; $\sqrt{133}$ is to the right of $10\frac{3}{4}$.
29. -0.25; -0.25 is to the right of $-\sqrt{0.25}$.
31. 8 ft
33. *Sample answer:* $a = 82$, $b = 97$
35. 1.1
37. 30.1 m/sec

39. Falling objects do not fall at a linear rate. Their speed increases with each second they are falling.
41. $-3x + 3y$

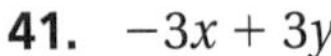

43. $40k - 9$

Section 8.4 Simplifying Square Roots
(pages 382 and 383)

1. *Sample answer:* The square root is like a variable. So, you add or subtract the number in front to simplify.
3. about 1.62; yes
5. about 1.11; no
7. $\frac{\sqrt{7}+1}{3}$
9. $6\sqrt{3}$
11. $2\sqrt{5}$
13. $-7.7\sqrt{15}$
15. You do not add the radicands. $4\sqrt{5} + 3\sqrt{5} = 7\sqrt{5}$
17. $10\sqrt{2}$
19. $4\sqrt{3}$
21. $\frac{\sqrt{23}}{8}$
23. $\frac{\sqrt{17}}{7}$
25. $10\sqrt{2}$ in.
27. $6\sqrt{6}$
29. 210 ft^3
31. **a.** $88\sqrt{2}$ ft **b.** 680 ft^2
33. Remember to take the square root of each side when solving for r.
35. 24 in.
37. C

Section 8.5 Using the Pythagorean Theorem (pages 388 and 389)

1. *Sample answer:* You can plot a point at the origin and then draw lengths that represent the legs. Then, you can use the Pythagorean Theorem to find the hypotenuse of the triangle.

3. 27.7 m
5. 11.3 yd
7. 7.2 units
9. 27.5 ft
11. 15.1 m
13. yes
15. no
17. yes
19. 12.8 ft
21. **a.** *Sample answer:* 5 in., 7 in., 3 in.

    b. *Sample answer:* $BC \approx 8.6$ in.; $AB \approx 9.1$ in.

    c. Check students' work.
23. mean: 13; median: 12.5; mode: 12
25. mean: 58; median: 59; mode: 59

Section 9.1 Scatter Plots and Lines of Best Fit (pages 405–407)

1. They must be ordered pairs so there are equal amounts of x- and y-values.
3. **a–b.**

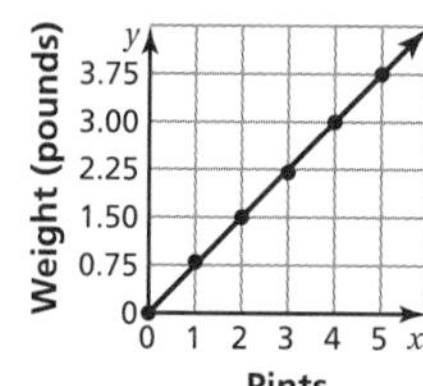

   c. *Sample answer:* $y = 0.75x$

   d. *Sample answer:* 7.5 lb

   e. *Sample answer:* \$16.88
5. **a.** 3.5 h **b.** \$85

   c. There is a positive relationship between hours worked and earnings.
7. positive relationship
9. negative relationship
11. **a–b.**

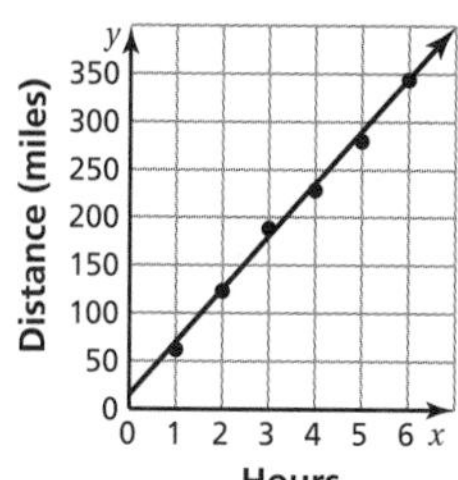

   c. *Sample answer:* $y = 55x + 15$

   d. *Sample answer:* 400 mi
13. **a.** positive relationship

    b. The more time spent studying, the better the test score.
15. The slope of the line of best fit should be close to 1.
17. $-32,\ 64,\ -128$
19. B

Selected Answers

Section 9.2 Choosing a Data Display

(pages 413–415)

1. yes; Different displays may show different aspects of the data.

3. *Sample answer:*

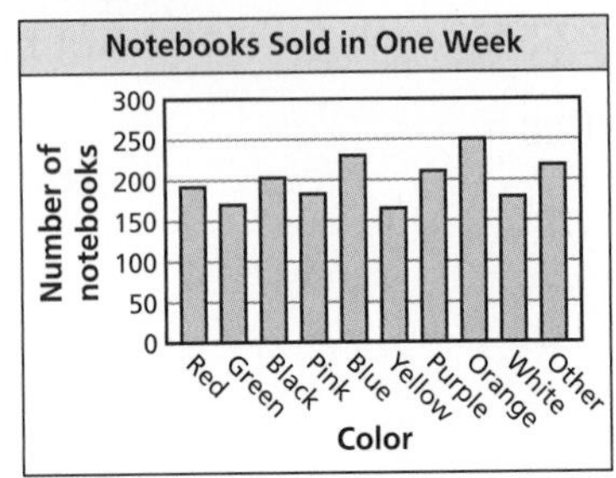

A bar graph shows the data in different color categories.

5. *Sample answer:* Line graph; shows changes over time.

7. *Sample answer:* Line graph; shows changes changes over time.

9. **a.** yes; The circle graph shows the data as parts of the whole.
   b. no; The bar graph shows the number of students, not the portion of students.

11. The pictures of the bikes are the largest on Monday and the smallest on Wednesday, which makes it seem like the distance is the same each day.

13. The intervals are not the same size.

15. *Sample answer:* bar graph; Each bar can represent a different vegetable.

17. *Sample answer:* line plot

19. Does one display better show the differences in digits?

21. $8x = 24$

Section 9.3 Probability

(pages 423–425)

1. Perform an experiment several times. Count how often the event occurs and divide by the number of trials.

3. Experimental probability is based on actual results of an experiment, so it will not always equal the theoretical probability.

5. 1950

7. $\frac{1}{6}$, or about 16.7%

9. $\frac{1}{3}$, or about 33.3%

11. 0, or 0%

13. 30

15. 24

17. 0

19. $\frac{1}{6}$, or about 16.7%

21. $\frac{7}{40}$, or 17.5%

23. $\frac{9}{40}$, or 22.5%

25. The total number of trials, 40, should be in the denominator, not 28.

$$P(2) = \frac{12}{40} = \frac{3}{10}$$

27. 35

29. theoretical: $\frac{1}{5}$, or 20%; experimental: $\frac{39}{200}$, or 19.5%;

The experimental probability is close to the theoretical probability.

31. 2000

33. **a.** $\frac{5}{8}$, or 62.5%

b. 15

35. Rewrite the table listing the cards of each rank in a separate row.

37. 26 m

39. about 46.84 in.

Section 9.4 Independent and Dependent Events
(pages 430 and 431)

1. Draw a tree diagram or multiply $P(A)$, $P(B)$, and $P(C)$.

3. independent; The marble from the first draw is replaced so it does not affect the outcome of the second draw.

5. dependent; There is one less marble to choose from on the second draw and two less marbles to choose from on the third draw.

7. independent; The outcome of one roll does not affect the outcome of the other rolls.

9. $\frac{5}{162}$, or about 3.1%

11. $\frac{4}{81}$, or about 4.9%

13. $\frac{2}{15}$, or about 13.3%

15. $\frac{1}{45}$, or about 2.2%

17. $\frac{4}{15}$, or about 26.7%

19. The two events are dependent, so the probability of the second event is $\frac{9}{14}$.

$$P(\text{black and black}) = P(\text{black}) \cdot P(\text{black after black})$$
$$= \frac{10}{15} \cdot \frac{9}{14}$$
$$= \frac{2}{3} \cdot \frac{9}{14} = \frac{3}{7}$$

21. The letters spell the city "Norfolk."

23. $-1.5\sqrt{11}$

25. D

Section 10.1 Properties of Exponents
(pages 446 and 447)

1. power: 5^0, base: 5, exponent: 0; power: 2^{-8}, base: 2, exponent: -8

3. $\left(-\frac{1}{4}\right)^0 < 5^4$ 5. 28,500 years old 7. 64 9. -8

11. 7.84 13. $\frac{1}{49}$ 15. 1 17. $-\frac{1}{1000}$

19. The exponent should not be used as a factor.
$5^{-2} = \frac{1}{5^2} = \frac{1}{25}$

21. yes; no; The base is 7, not -7, so the middle step should be $-\frac{1}{(7)(7)(7)}$.

23. Use unit analysis when converting units of measures.

25. Multiply the denominator of $\frac{1}{729}$ by 3 to get $\frac{1}{2187}$.

27. yes

29. yes

Section 10.2 Product of Powers Property
(pages 452 and 453)

1. when multiplying powers with the same base

3. 3^4 5. $(-4)^{12}$ 7. h^7

9. $\left(-\frac{5}{7}\right)^{17}$ 11. 5^{12} 13. 3.8^{12}

15. The bases should not be multiplied. $5^2 \cdot 5^9 = 5^{2+9} = 5^{11}$

17. $216g^3$ 19. $\frac{1}{25}k^2$ 21. $\frac{1}{r^6 t^6}$

23. no; $3^2 + 3^3 = 9 + 27 = 36$ and $3^5 = 243$

25. 496 27. 125

29. **a.** $16\pi \approx 50.24$ in.^{3}

b. $192\pi \approx 602.88$ in.^{3} Squaring each of the dimensions causes the volume to be 12 times larger.

31. Use the Commutative and Associative Properties of Multiplication to group the powers.

33. 4 35. 3 37. B

Section 10.3 Quotient of Powers Property
(pages 460 and 461)

1. *Sample answer:* To divide powers with the same base, write the power with the common base and the exponent found by subtracting the exponent in the denominator from the exponent in the numerator.

3. 6^6 5. $(-3)^3$ 7. 5^6 9. $\frac{1}{(-17)^3}$ 11. $(-6.4)^{14}$ 13. $\frac{1}{b^{13}}$

15. You should subtract the exponents instead of dividing them. $\frac{6^{15}}{6^5} = 6^{15-5} = 6^{10}$

17. 2^9 19. $\frac{1}{\pi^{12}}$ 21. $\frac{1}{k}$ 23. $64x$ 25. $125a^3b^2$ 27. $\frac{x^7}{y^6}$

29. You are checking to see if there is a constant rate of change in the prices, not if it is a linear function.

31. 10^{13} galaxies 33. -9

35. 61 37. B

Section 10.4 Scientific Notation
(pages 467–469)

1. right; left 3. no; The factor is less than 1.

5. yes; The factor is greater than or equal to 1 and less than 10. The power of 10 has an integer exponent.

7. yes; The factor is greater than or equal to 1 and less than 10. The power of 10 has an integer exponent.

9. 7500 11. 0.000000389 13. 430,000 15. 0.000000000809

17. 96.54 19. 1.2×10^4 21. 2.7×10^{-1} 23. 2×10^{-3}

25. 1.75×10^6 27. 8.002×10^5 29. 0.000000275

31. The decimal point moved 7 places to the right, so the exponent should be negative.
$0.000000489 = 4.89 \times 10^{-7}$

33. 1.49×10^4, 1.09×10^4, 2.11×10^{-3} 35. 3.611×10^{-7}, 2.78×10^{-7}, 3.49×10^{-8}

37. 8×10^{10} 39. 1.5×10^0 41. 8.4×10^3 43. 5.612×10^{14} cm^2

45. 3.78×10^4 cm^2; 3.78 m^2 47. 1.5×10^1 m; 1.5×10^3 cm

49. 3.1×10^{-2}, 0.03, $\frac{6}{205}$ 51. 8922.1, 89×10^2, $\frac{2650}{3}$, 892%

53. Begin by summarizing the information and writing the numbers in scientific notation.

55. discrete

Cost (dollars)
y
16
12
8
4
0
(3, 11.97)
(2, 7.98)
(1, 3.99)
(0, 0)
0 1 2 3 4 x
Jars

57. B

Key Vocabulary Index

Mathematical terms are best understood when you see them used and defined *in context*. This index lists where you will find key vocabulary. A full glossary is available in your Record and Practice Journal and at *BigIdeasMath.com*.

Student Index

This student-friendly index will help you find vocabulary, key ideas, and concepts. It is easily accessible and designed to be a reference for you whether you are looking for a definition, a real-life application, or help with avoiding common errors.

D

E

Student Index

F

G

Student Index

M

N

O

P

Q

R

S

K

Number and Number Sense	–	Whole Number Concepts
Computation and Estimation	–	Whole Number Operations
Measurement	–	Instruments and Attributes
Geometry	–	Plane Figures
Probability and Statistics	–	Data Collection and Display
Patterns, Functions, and Algebra	–	Attributes and Patterning

1

Number and Number Sense	–	Place Value and Fraction Concepts
Computation and Estimation	–	Whole Number Operations
Measurement	–	Time and Nonstandard Measurement
Geometry	–	Characteristics of Plane Figures
Probability and Statistics	–	Data Collection and Interpretation
Patterns, Functions, and Algebra	–	Patterning and Equivalence

2

Number and Number Sense	–	Place Value, Number Patterns, and Fraction Concepts
Computation and Estimation	–	Number Relationships and Operations
Measurement	–	Money, Linear Measurement, Weight/Mass, and Volume
Geometry	–	Symmetry and Plane and Solid Figures
Probability and Statistics	–	Applications of Data
Patterns, Functions, and Algebra	–	Patterning and Numerical Sentences

3

Number and Number Sense	–	Place Value and Fractions
Computation and Estimation	–	Computation and Fraction Operations
Measurement	–	U.S. Customary and Metric Units, Area and Perimeter, and Time
Geometry	–	Properties and Congruence Characteristics of Plane and Solid Figures
Probability and Statistics	–	Applications of Data and Chance
Patterns, Functions, and Algebra	–	Patterns and Property Concepts

4

Number and Number Sense	–	Place Value, Fractions, and Decimals
Computation and Estimation	–	Factors and Multiples, and Fraction and Decimal Operations
Measurement	–	Equivalence within U.S. Customary and Metric Systems
Geometry	–	Representations and Polygons
Probability and Statistics	–	Outcomes and Data
Patterns, Functions, and Algebra	–	Geometric Patterns, Equality, and Properties

5

Number and Number Sense	–	Prime and Composite Numbers and Rounding Decimals
Computation and Estimation	–	Multistep Applications and Order of Operations
Measurement	–	Perimeter, Area, Volume, and Equivalent Measures
Geometry	–	Classification and Subdividing
Probability and Statistics	–	Outcomes and Measures of Center
Patterns, Functions, and Algebra	–	Equations and Properties

Mathematics Reference Sheet

Conversions

U.S. Customary
1 foot = 12 inches
1 yard = 3 feet
1 mile = 5280 feet
1 acre ≈ 43,560 square feet
1 cup = 8 fluid ounces
1 pint = 2 cups
1 quart = 2 pints
1 gallon = 4 quarts
1 gallon = 231 cubic inches
1 pound = 16 ounces
1 ton = 2000 pounds
1 cubic foot ≈ 7.5 gallons

U.S. Customary to Metric
1 inch ≈ 2.54 centimeters
1 foot ≈ 0.3 meter
1 mile ≈ 1.6 kilometers
1 quart ≈ 0.95 liter
1 gallon ≈ 3.79 liters
1 cup ≈ 237 milliliters
1 pound ≈ 0.45 kilogram
1 ounce ≈ 28.3 grams
1 gallon ≈ 3785 cubic centimeters

Time
1 minute = 60 seconds
1 hour = 60 minutes
1 hour = 3600 seconds
1 year = 52 weeks

Temperature

$C = \frac{5}{9}(F - 32)$

$F = \frac{9}{5}C + 32$

Metric
1 centimeter = 10 millimeters
1 meter = 100 centimeters
1 kilometer = 1000 meters
1 liter = 1000 milliliters
1 kiloliter = 1000 liters
1 milliliter = 1 cubic centimeter
1 liter = 1000 cubic centimeters
1 cubic millimeter = 0.001 milliliter
1 gram = 1000 milligrams
1 kilogram = 1000 grams

Metric to U.S. Customary
1 centimeter ≈ 0.39 inch
1 meter ≈ 3.28 feet
1 kilometer ≈ 0.6 mile
1 liter ≈ 1.06 quarts
1 liter ≈ 0.26 gallon
1 kilogram ≈ 2.2 pounds
1 gram ≈ 0.035 ounce
1 cubic meter ≈ 264 gallon

Equations of Lines

Slope-intercept form

$$y = mx + b$$

Standard form

$$ax + by = c,\ a, b \neq 0$$

Pythagorean Theorem

$a^2 + b^2 = c^2$

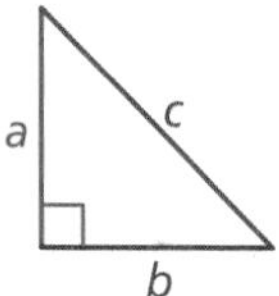

Rules of Exponents

Product of Powers Property

$$a^m \cdot a^n = a^{m+n}$$

Quotient of Powers Property

$$\frac{a^m}{a^n} = a^{m-n}, \text{ where } a \neq 0$$

Surface Area and Volume

Prism

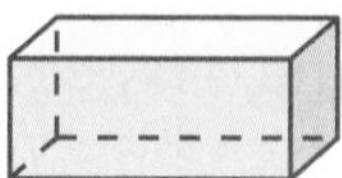

S = areas of bases + areas of lateral faces

$V = Bh$

Cylinder

$S = 2\pi r^2 + 2\pi rh$

$V = Bh$

Pyramid

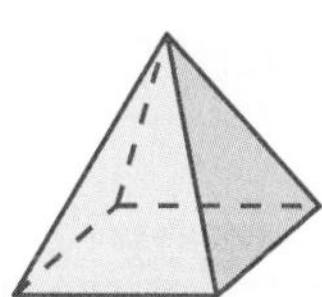

S = area of base + areas of lateral faces

$V = \frac{1}{3}Bh$

Cone

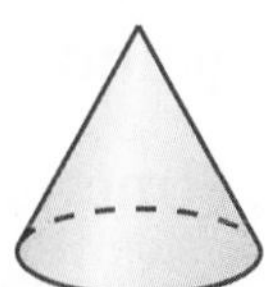

$S = \pi r^2 + \pi r\ell$

$V = \frac{1}{3}Bh$